Elementary Statistics

A STEP BY STEP APPROACH

Ninth Edition

D1283279

McGraw Hill Education

ALLAN G. BLUMAN
PROFESSOR EMERITUS
COMMUNITY COLLEGE OF ALLEGHENY COUNTY

ELEMENTARY STATISTICS: A STEP BY STEP APPROACH, NINTH EDITION

Published by McGraw-Hill Education, 2 Penn Plaza, New York, NY 10121. Copyright © 2014 by McGraw-Hill Education. All rights reserved. Printed in the United States of America. Previous editions © 2012, 2009, and 2007. No part of this publication may be reproduced or distributed in any form or by any means, or stored in a database or retrieval system, without the prior written consent of McGraw-Hill Education, including, but not limited to, in any network or other electronic storage or transmission, or broadcast for distance learning.

Some ancillaries, including electronic and print components, may not be available to customers outside the United States.

This book is printed on acid-free paper.

8 9 LWI 21 20 19 18 17

ISBN 978–0–07–353498–5
MHID 0–07–353498–6

ISBN 978–0–07–766572–2 (Annotated Instructor's Edition)
MHID 0–07–766572–4

Senior Vice President, Products & Markets: *Kurt L. Strand*
Vice President, General Manager, Products & Markets: *Marty Lange*
Vice President, Content Production & Technology Services: *Kimberly Meriwether David*
Managing Director: *Ryan Blankenship*
Brand Manager: *Holly Rhodes*
Director of Development: *Rose Koos*
Development Editor: *Ashley Zellmer McFadden*
Director of Digital Content: *Rob Brieler, Ph.D.*
Digital Development Editor: *Adam Fischer*
Digital Product Analyst: *Michael Lemke*
Director of Marketing: *Alex Gay*
Director, Content Production: *Terri Schiesl*
Content Project Manager: *Vicki Krug*
Senior Buyer: *Sandy Ludovissy*
Design: *Matthew Backhaus*
Cover Photo: *Image 1: Lonely Planet Images/Bob Charlton/Getty Images; Image 2: Stuart Dee/Getty Images*
Senior Content Licensing Specialist: *Lori Hancock*
Compositor: *MPS Limited*
Typeface: *10.5/12 Times Roman*
Printer: *LSC Communications*

All credits appearing on page or at the end of the book are considered to be an extension of the copyright page.

Library of Congress Cataloging-in-Publication Data

Bluman, Allan G., author.
  Elementary statistics : a step by step approach / Allan G. Bluman, professor emeritus, Community College of Allegheny County. – Ninth edition.
     pages cm
  Includes index.
  ISBN 978–0–07–353498–5 — ISBN 0–07–353498–6 (hard copy : alk. paper) — ISBN 978–0–07–766572–2 — ISBN 0–07–766572–4 (annotated instructor's edition : hard copy) 1. Statistics–Textbooks. I. Title.
  QA276.12.B59 2014
  519.5–dc23

                                    2013031502

The Internet addresses listed in the text were accurate at the time of publication. The inclusion of a website does not indicate an endorsement by the authors or McGraw-Hill Education, and McGraw-Hill Education does not guarantee the accuracy of the information presented at these sites.

www.mhhe.com

ABOUT THE AUTHOR

Allan G. Bluman

Allan G. Bluman is a professor emeritus at the Community College of Allegheny County, South Campus, near Pittsburgh, Pennsylvania. He has taught mathematics and statistics for over 35 years. He received an Apple for the Teacher award in recognition of his bringing excellence to the learning environment at South Campus. He has also taught statistics for Penn State University at the Greater Allegheny (McKeesport) Campus and at the Monroeville Center. He received his master's and doctor's degrees from the University of Pittsburgh.

He is also author of *Elementary Statistics: A Brief Version* and coauthor of *Math in Our World.* In addition, he is the author of four mathematics books in the McGraw-Hill DeMystified Series. They are *Pre-Algebra, Math Word Problems, Business Math,* and *Probability.*

He is married and has two sons, a granddaughter, and a grandson.

Dedication: *To Betty Bluman, Earl McPeek, and Dr. G. Bradley Seager, Jr.*

CONTENTS

Preface *ix*

CHAPTER 1

The Nature of Probability and Statistics *1*

Introduction *2*
1–1 Descriptive and Inferential Statistics *3*
1–2 Variables and Types of Data *6*
1–3 Data Collection and Sampling Techniques *11*
   Random Sampling 12
   Systematic Sampling 12
   Stratified Sampling 13
   Cluster Sampling 14
   Other Sampling Methods 14
1–4 Experimental Design *18*
   Observational and Experimental Studies 18
   Uses and Misuses of Statistics 21
1–5 Computers and Calculators *26*
   Summary *33*

CHAPTER 2

Frequency Distributions and Graphs *41*

Introduction *42*
2–1 Organizing Data *42*
   Categorical Frequency Distributions 43
   Grouped Frequency Distributions 44
2–2 Histograms, Frequency Polygons, and Ogives *57*
   The Histogram 57
   The Frequency Polygon 58
   The Ogive 59
   Relative Frequency Graphs 61
   Distribution Shapes 63
2–3 Other Types of Graphs *74*
   Bar Graphs 75
   Pareto Charts 77
   The Time Series Graph 78
   The Pie Graph 80
   Dotplots 83
   Stem and Leaf Plots 83
   Misleading Graphs 86
   Summary *100*

CHAPTER 3

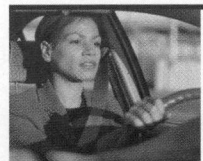

Data Description *109*

Introduction *110*
3–1 Measures of Central Tendency *111*
   The Mean 111
   The Median 115
   The Mode 116
   The Midrange 118
   The Weighted Mean 119
   Distribution Shapes 121
3–2 Measures of Variation *128*
   Range 129
   Population Variance and Standard Deviation 130
   Sample Variance and Standard Deviation 133
   Variance and Standard Deviation for Grouped Data 135
   Coefficient of Variation 138
   Range Rule of Thumb 139
   Chebyshev's Theorem 139
   The Empirical (Normal) Rule 142
3–3 Measures of Position *148*
   Standard Scores 148

vi   **Contents**

Percentiles 149
Quartiles and Deciles 155
Outliers 157
3–4   Exploratory Data Analysis *168*
The Five-Number Summary and Boxplots 168
Summary *177*

CHAPTER **4**

Probability and Counting Rules *185*

Introduction *186*
4–1   Sample Spaces and Probability *186*
Basic Concepts 186
Classical Probability 189
Complementary Events 192
Empirical Probability 194
Law of Large Numbers 196
Subjective Probability 196
Probability and Risk Taking 196
4–2   The Addition Rules for Probability *201*
4–3   The Multiplication Rules and Conditional Probability *213*
The Multiplication Rules 213
Conditional Probability 217
Probabilities for "At Least" 220
4–4   Counting Rules *226*
The Fundamental Counting Rule 227
Factorial Notation 229
Permutations 229
Combinations 232
4–5   Probability and Counting Rules *242*
Summary *246*

CHAPTER **5**

Discrete Probability Distributions *257*

Introduction *258*
5–1   Probability Distributions *258*
5–2   Mean, Variance, Standard Deviation, and Expectation *265*
Mean 265

Variance and Standard Deviation 267
Expectation 269
5–3   The Binomial Distribution *276*
5–4   Other Types of Distributions *290*
The Multinomial Distribution 290
The Poisson Distribution 291
The Hypergeometric Distribution 293
The Geometric Distribution 295
Summary *303*

CHAPTER **6**

The Normal Distribution *311*

Introduction *312*
6–1   Normal Distributions *312*
The Standard Normal Distribution 315
Finding Areas Under the Standard Normal Distribution Curve 316
A Normal Distribution Curve as a Probability Distribution Curve 318
6–2   Applications of the Normal Distribution *328*
Finding Data Values Given Specific Probabilities 332
Determining Normality 334
6–3   The Central Limit Theorem *344*
Distribution of Sample Means 344
Finite Population Correction Factor (Optional) 350
6–4   The Normal Approximation to the Binomial Distribution *354*
Summary *361*

CHAPTER **7**

Confidence Intervals and Sample Size *369*

Introduction *370*
7–1   Confidence Intervals for the Mean When σ Is Known *370*
Confidence Intervals 371
Sample Size 377
7–2   Confidence Intervals for the Mean When σ Is Unknown *383*

7–3 Confidence Intervals and Sample Size for Proportions *390*

Confidence Intervals *391*

Sample Size for Proportions *393*

7–4 Confidence Intervals for Variances and Standard Deviations *399*

Summary *406*

CHAPTER **8**

Hypothesis Testing *413*

Introduction *414*

8–1 Steps in Hypothesis Testing—Traditional Method *414*

8–2 *z* Test for a Mean *426*

P-Value Method for Hypothesis Testing *430*

8–3 *t* Test for a Mean *442*

8–4 *z* Test for a Proportion *453*

8–5 χ^2 Test for a Variance or Standard Deviation *461*

8–6 Additional Topics Regarding Hypothesis Testing *474*

Confidence Intervals and Hypothesis Testing *474*

Type II Error and the Power of a Test *476*

Summary *479*

CHAPTER **9**

Testing the Difference Between Two Means, Two Proportions, and Two Variances *487*

Introduction *488*

9–1 Testing the Difference Between Two Means: Using the *z* Test *488*

9–2 Testing the Difference Between Two Means of Independent Samples: Using the *t* Test *499*

9–3 Testing the Difference Between Two Means: Dependent Samples *507*

9–4 Testing the Difference Between Proportions *519*

9–5 Testing the Difference Between Two Variances *528*

Summary *539*

CHAPTER **10**

Correlation and Regression *549*

Introduction *550*

10–1 Scatter Plots and Correlation *550*

Correlation *554*

10–2 Regression *566*

Line of Best Fit *566*

Determination of the Regression Line Equation *567*

10–3 Coefficient of Determination and Standard Error of the Estimate *582*

Types of Variation for the Regression Model *582*

Residual Plots *584*

Coefficient of Determination *585*

Standard Error of the Estimate *586*

Prediction Interval *589*

10–4 Multiple Regression (Optional) *592*

The Multiple Regression Equation *594*

Testing the Significance of R *596*

Adjusted R^2 *597*

Summary *601*

CHAPTER **11**

Other Chi-Square Tests *609*

Introduction *610*

11–1 Test for Goodness of Fit *610*

Test of Normality (Optional) *616*

11–2 Tests Using Contingency Tables *624*

Test for Independence *624*

Test for Homogeneity of Proportions *630*

Summary *640*

CHAPTER **12**

Analysis of Variance *647*

Introduction *648*
12–1 One-Way Analysis of Variance *648*
12–2 The Scheffé Test and the Tukey Test *660*
     Scheffé Test *660*
     Tukey Test *662*
12–3 Two-Way Analysis of Variance *665*
     Summary *679*

CHAPTER **13**

Nonparametric Statistics *689*

Introduction *690*
13–1 Advantages and Disadvantages of Nonparametric Methods *690*
     Advantages *690*
     Disadvantages *690*
     Ranking *691*
13–2 The Sign Test *693*
     Single-Sample Sign Test *693*
     Paired-Sample Sign Test *695*
13–3 The Wilcoxon Rank Sum Test *702*
13–4 The Wilcoxon Signed-Rank Test *707*
13–5 The Kruskal-Wallis Test *712*
13–6 The Spearman Rank Correlation Coefficient and the Runs Test *719*
     Rank Correlation Coefficient *719*
     The Runs Test *722*
     Summary *733*

CHAPTER **14**

Sampling and Simulation *741*

Introduction *742*
14–1 Common Sampling Techniques *742*
     Random Sampling *743*
     Systematic Sampling *746*
     Stratified Sampling *748*
     Cluster Sampling *749*
     Other Types of Sampling Techniques *750*
14–2 Surveys and Questionnaire Design *757*
14–3 Simulation Techniques and the Monte Carlo Method *759*
     The Monte Carlo Method *760*
     Summary *766*

APPENDICES

A Tables *773*
B Data Bank *803*
C Glossary *810*
D Photo Credits *818*
E Selected Answers *SA–1*

Index *I–1*

ADDITIONAL TOPICS ONLINE
(www.mhhe.com/bluman)

Algebra Review

Writing the Research Report

Bayes' Theorem

Alternate Approach to the Standard Normal Distribution

Bibliography

PREFACE

Approach

Elementary Statistics: A Step by Step Approach was written as an aid in the beginning statistics course to students whose mathematical background is limited to basic algebra. The book follows a nontheoretical approach without formal proofs, explaining concepts intuitively and supporting them with abundant examples. The applications span a broad range of topics certain to appeal to the interests of students of diverse backgrounds, and they include problems in business, sports, health, architecture, education, entertainment, political science, psychology, history, criminal justice, the environment, transportation, physical sciences, demographics, eating habits, and travel and leisure.

About This Book

While a number of important changes have been made in the ninth edition, the learning system remains untouched and provides students with a useful framework in which to learn and apply concepts. Some of the retained features include the following:

- Over **1800 exercises** are located at the end of major sections within each chapter.
- **Hypothesis-Testing Summaries** are found at the end of Chapter 9 (z, t, χ^2, and F tests for testing means, proportions, and variances), Chapter 12 (correlation, chi-square, and ANOVA), and Chapter 13 (nonparametric tests) to show students the different types of hypotheses and the types of tests to use.
- A **Data Bank** listing various attributes (educational level, cholesterol level, gender, etc.) for 100 people and several additional data sets using real data are included and referenced in various exercises and projects throughout the book.
- An updated **reference card** containing the formulas and the z, t, χ^2, and PPMC tables is included with this textbook.
- End-of-chapter **Summaries, Important Terms,** and **Important Formulas** give students a concise summary of the chapter topics and provide a good source for quiz or test preparation.
- **Review Exercises** are found at the end of each chapter.

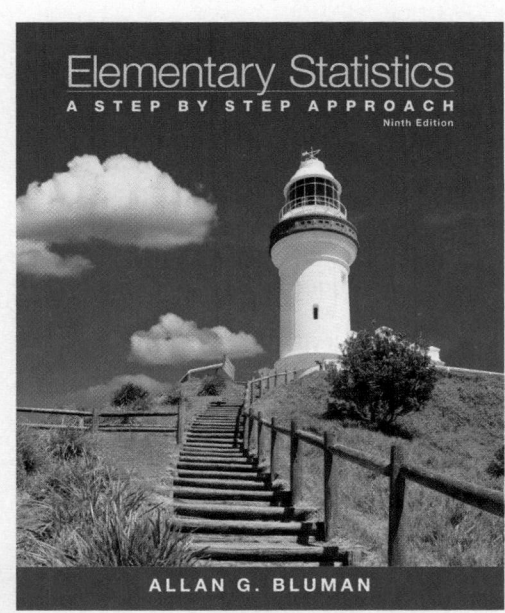

- Special sections called **Data Analysis** require students to work with a data set to perform various statistical tests or procedures and then summarize the results. The data are included in the Data Bank in Appendix B and can be downloaded from the book's website at **www.mhhe.com/bluman**.
- **Chapter Quizzes,** found at the end of each chapter, include multiple-choice, true/false, and completion questions along with exercises to test students' knowledge and comprehension of chapter content.
- The **Appendixes** provide students with extensive reference tables, a glossary, and answers to all quiz questions and odd-numbered exercises. New to this edition, the additional Online Appendixes include algebra review, an outline for report writing, Bayes' theorem, and an alternative method for using the standard normal distribution. These can be found at **www.mhhe.com/bluman**.
- The **Applying the Concepts** feature is included in all sections and gives students an opportunity to think about the new concepts and apply them to examples and scenarios similar to those found in newspapers, magazines, and radio and television news programs.

Changes in the Ninth Edition

Global Changes

- Updated and redesigned the Technology Boxes to reflect the latest technology updates
- Over 60 new examples and more than 400 new exercises have been added or revised throughout the book
- Design of graphs, photos and art has been revised for clarity
- New interior design was incorporated for ease of reading and flow
- Matched the odd and even exercises

Chapter 1   Nearly 100 new section exercises have been added
Statistics Today updated
Added new material on sampling and the three types of observational studies

Chapter 2   New subsection on dotplots added
More material on class boundaries added
Statistics Today updated

Chapter 3   New Procedure Table for median added
New Procedure Table for variance and standard deviation added
Summary for Chebyshev's Theorem added
New procedure Table for boxplots included

Chapter 4   New subsection for permutations with identical objects added

Chapter 5   New subsection on the geometric probability distribution added

Chapter 6   Improved flow with a shortened introduction
Added New Procedure Table for finding data values for specific probabilities

Chapter 7   Statistics Today updated
Included summary of the Characteristics of the Chi-Square Distribution

Chapter 8   Reorganized Section 8-1 for a better flow
Simplified diagram on stating the conclusion from a hypothesis test

Chapter 9   Expanded explanation of independent samples
Added 20 new exercises

Chapter 10   Statistics Today updated
Revised and Shortened Introduction
Added additional information on analyzing scatter plots
Included six new Procedure Tables

Chapter 11   Expanded explanation on finding expected frequencies

Chapter 12   Added additional material on the Computation of the F test
Added two new figures

Chapter 13   Boxed definitions and listed assumptions for the nonparametric tests
Added a new Procedure Table for finding and testing the significance of the Spearman's Rank Correlation Coefficient
Added a new Procedure Table for the runs test

Chapter 14   Added a formal definition for convenience sample
Improved definitions for systematic sampling and stratified sampling

Acknowledgments

It is important to acknowledge the many people whose contributions have gone into the Ninth Edition of *Elementary Statistics*. Very special thanks are due to Jackie Miller of the University of Michigan for her provision of the Index of Applications, her exhaustive accuracy check of the page proofs, and her general availability and advice concerning all matters statistical. The Technology Step by Step sections were provided by Gerry Moultine of Northwood University (MINITAB), John Thomas of College of Lake County (Excel), and William Vezko of Saint Johns River State College-Orange Park (TI-84 Plus).

I would also like to thank Diane P. Cope for providing the new exercises; Kelly Jackson for writing the new Data Projects; Lisa Collette, developmental copyeditor, for her thoughtful suggestions; Phyllis Barnidge for her error checking; and Sally Robinson for error checking, adding technology-accurate answers to Appendix E, and writing the Solutions Manuals.

Finally, at McGraw-Hill Education, thanks to Ryan Blankenship, Managing Director; Holly Rhodes, Brand Manager; Ashley Zellmer McFadden, Developmental Editor; Alex Gay, Marketing Director; Rob Brieler, Director of Digital Content; and Vicki Krug, Content Project Manager.

—**Allan G. Bluman**

Special thanks for their advice and recommendations for the Ninth Edition go to:

Wesley Anderson, *Northwest Vista College*
Elizabeth Betzel, *Columbus State Community College*
David Bosworth, *Hutchinson Community College*
Christine M. Brady, *Suffolk County Community College*
Gregory Cianflone, *Suffolk County Community College*
Lisa M. Crawford, *Piedmont Technical College*
Hemangini Deshmukh, *Mercyhurst College*
Angela Everett, *Chattanooga State Community College*
Robert Feinerman, *Lehman College (CUNY)*
Kathi Fields, *Blue Ridge Community College*
Maggie Flint, *Northeast State Community College*
Jesus Gutierrez, *Citrus College*
Jaffar Ali Shahul Hameed, *Florida Gulf Coast University*
Kelly Jackson, *Camden County College*
Mohammad Kazemi, *University of North Carolina Charlotte*

Brian Kelly, *Bryant University*
Patrick Kelly, *Mercyhurst College*
Jong Kim, *Portland State University*
James E. Martin, *Christopher Newport University*
Angie Schirck Matthews, *Broward College*
Carla Monticelli, *Camden County College*
Keith Oberlander, *Pasadena City College*
Dr. Elaine H. Olaoye, *Brookdale Community College*
Sherri Rankin, *Hutchinson Community College*
Fred Rispoli, *Dowling College*
Pam Stogsdill, *Bossier Parish Community College*
Fernando Rincon Tellez, *Piedmont Technical College*
Malissa Trent, *Northeast State Community College*
Barbara Villatoro, *Diablo Valley College*
Cassandra Vincent, *State University of New York College at Plattsburgh*
Henry Wakhungu, *Indiana University*
Jane West, *Trident Technical College*
Bashar Zogheib, *American University of Kuwait*

A STEP BY STEP APPROACH

Confidence Intervals and Sample Size

≡ STATISTICS TODAY
Stress and the College Student

A recent poll conducted by the mtvU/Associated Press found that 85% of college students reported that they experience stress daily. The study said, "It is clear that being stressed is a fact of life on college campuses today."

The study also reports that 74% of students' stress comes from school work, 71% from grades, and 62% from financial woes. The report stated that 2240 undergraduate students were selected and that the poll has a margin of error of ±3.0%.

In this chapter you will learn how to make a true estimate of a parameter, what is meant by the margin of error, and whether or not the sample size was large enough to represent all college students.

See Statistics Today—Revisited at the end of this chapter for more details.

OUTLINE

Introduction
7–1 Confidence Intervals for the Mean When σ Is Known
7–2 Confidence Intervals for the Mean When σ Is Unknown
7–3 Confidence Intervals and Sample Size for Proportions
7–4 Confidence Intervals for Variances and Standard Deviations
Summary

OBJECTIVES

After completing this chapter, you should be able to

1. Find the confidence interval for the mean when σ is known.
2. Determine the minimum sample size for finding a confidence interval for the mean.
3. Find the confidence interval for the mean when σ is unknown.
4. Find the confidence interval for a proportion.
5. Determine the minimum sample size for finding a confidence interval for a proportion.
6. Find a confidence interval for a variance and a standard deviation.

Each chapter begins with an **outline,** a **list of learning objectives,** and a feature titled **Statistics Today;** in which a real-life problem shows students the relevance of the material. This problem is solved near the end of the chapter using statistical techniques presented in the chapter.

EXAMPLE 8–6 Cost of College Tuition

A researcher wishes to test the claim that the average cost of tuition and fees at a four-year public college is greater than $5700. She selects a random sample of 36 four-year public colleges and finds the mean to be $5950. The population standard deviation is $659. Is there evidence to support the claim at $\alpha = 0.05$? Use the P-value method.

Source: Based on information from the College Board.

SOLUTION

Step 1 State the hypotheses and identify the claim.

$$H_0: \mu = \$5700 \quad \text{and} \quad H_1: \mu > \$5700 \text{ (claim)}.$$

Step 2 Compute the test value.

$$z = \frac{\overline{X} - \mu}{\sigma/\sqrt{n}} = \frac{5950 - 5700}{659/\sqrt{36}} = 2.28$$

Step 3 Find the P-value. Using Table E in Appendix A, find the corresponding area under the normal distribution for $z = 2.28$. It is 0.9887. Subtract this value for the area from 1.0000 to find the area in the right tail.

$$1.0000 - 0.9887 = 0.0113$$

Hence, the P-value is 0.0113.

Step 4 Make the decision. Since the P-value is less than 0.05, the decision is to reject the null hypothesis. See Figure 8–17.

Hundreds of examples with detailed solutions serve as models to help students solve problems on their own. Examples are solved by using a step by step explanation, and illustrations provide a clear display of results.

Procedure Table
Solving Hypothesis-Testing Problems (Traditional Method)

Step 1 State the hypotheses and identify the claim.

Step 2 Find the critical value(s) from the appropriate table in Appendix A.

Step 3 Compute the test value.

Step 4 Make the decision to reject or not reject the null hypothesis.

Step 5 Summarize the results.

Numerous **Procedure Tables** summarize processes for students' quick reference.

Critical Thinking sections at the end of each chapter challenge students to apply what they have learned to new situations while deepening conceptual understanding.

Technology Step by Step boxes instruct students how to use Excel, TI-84 Plus graphing calculators, and MINITAB to solve the types of problems covered in the section. Numerous computer or calculator screens are displayed as well as numbered steps.

Applying the Concepts are end-of-section exercises that reinforce the concepts explained in the section. They give students an opportunity to think about the concepts and apply them to hypothetical examples similar to real-life ones.

Data Projects, which appear at the end of each chapter, further challenge students' understanding and application of the material presented in the chapter. Many of these require the student to gather, analyze, and report on real data.

SUPPLEMENTS

McGraw-Hill conducted in-depth research to create a new learning experience that meets the needs of students and instructors today. The result is a reinvented learning experience rich in information, visually engaging, and easily accessible to both instructors and students.

- McGraw-Hill's Connect is a Web-based assignment and assessment platform that helps students connect to their coursework and prepares them to succeed in and beyond the course.
- Connect enables math and statistics instructors to create and share courses and assignments with colleagues and adjuncts with only a few clicks of the mouse. All exercises, learning objectives, and activities are vetted and developed by math instructors to ensure consistency between the textbook and the online tools.
- Connect also links students to an interactive eBook with access to a variety of media assets and a place to study, highlight, and keep track of class notes.

To learn more, contact your sales rep or visit **www.connectmath.com**.

ALEKS is a Web-based program that uses artificial intelligence to assess a student's knowledge and provide personalized instruction on the exact topics the student is most ready to learn. By providing individualized assessment and learning, ALEKS helps students to master course content quickly and easily. ALEKS allows students to easily move between explanations and practice, and it provides intuitive feedback to help students correct and analyze errors. ALEKS also includes a powerful instructor module that simplifies course management so instructors spend less time with administrative tasks and more time directing student learning.

ALEKS 360 is a new cost-effective total course solution: fully integrated, interactive eBook, including lecture and exercise videos tied to the textbook, combined with ALEKS personalized assessment and learning.

To learn more about ALEKS and ALEKS 360, contact your sales rep or visit **www.aleks.com**.

Give students the tools they need. Right when they need them. McGraw-Hill LearnSmart adaptively assesses students' skill levels to determine which topics students have mastered and which require further practice. Then it delivers customized learning content based on their strengths and weaknesses. The result: students learn faster and more efficiently because they get the help they need, right when they need it—instead of getting stuck on lessons or being continually frustrated with stalled progress.

SmartBook is the first and only adaptive reading experience available for the higher education market. Powered by the intelligent and adaptive LearnSmart engine, Smart-Book facilitates the reading process by identifying what content a student knows and doesn't know. As a student reads, the material continuously adapts to ensure the student is focused on the content he or she needs the most to close specific knowledge gaps.

With **McGraw-Hill Create™,** you can easily rearrange chapters, combine material from other content sources, and quickly upload content you have written such as your course syllabus or teaching notes. Find the content you need in Create by searching through thousands of leading McGraw-Hill textbooks. Arrange your book to fit your teaching style. Create even allows you to personalize your book's appearance by selecting the cover and adding your name, school, and course information. Assemble a Create book, and you'll receive a complimentary print review copy in 3–5 business days or a complimentary electronic review copy (eComp) via email in minutes. Go to **www.mcgrawhillcreate .com** today and experience how McGraw-Hill Create™ empowers you to teach your students your way.

Instructor's Testing and Resource Online

This computerized test bank, available online to adopting instructors, utilizes TestGen® cross-platform test generation software to quickly and easily create customized exams. Using hundreds of test items taken directly from the text, TestGen allows rapid test creation and flexibility for instructors to create their own questions from scratch with the ability to randomize number values. Powerful search and sort functions help quickly locate questions and arrange them in any order, and built-in mathematical templates let instructors insert stylized text, symbols, graphics, and equations directly into questions without need for a separate equation editor.

MegaStat®

MegaStat® is a statistical add-in for Microsoft Excel, handcrafted by J. B. Orris of Butler University. When MegaStat is installed, it appears as a menu item on the Excel menu bar and allows you to perform statistical analysis on data in an Excel workbook. The MegaStat plug-in can be purchased at **www.mhhe.com/megastat**.

MINITAB Student Release 14

The student version of MINITAB statistical software is available with copies of the text. Ask your McGraw-Hill representative for details.

SPSS Student Version for Windows

A student version of SPSS statistical software is available with copies of this text. Consult your McGraw-Hill representative for details.

MINITAB 14 Manual

This manual provides the student with how-to information on data and file management, conducting various statistical analyses, and creating presentation-style graphics while following each text chapter.

TI-84 Plus Graphing Calculator Manual

This friendly, practical manual teaches students to learn about statistics and solve problems by using these calculators while following each text chapter.

Excel Manual

This workbook, specially designed to accompany the text, provides additional practice in applying the chapter concepts while using Excel.

Instructor's Solutions Manual (instructors only)

By Sally Robinson of South Plains College, this manual includes worked-out solutions to all the exercises in the text and answers to all quiz questions. This manual can be found online at **www.mhhe.com/bluman**.

Student's Solutions Manual

By Sally Robinson of South Plains College, this manual contains detailed solutions to all odd-numbered text problems and answers to all quiz questions.

INDEX OF APPLICATIONS

CHAPTER 1
The Nature of Probability and Statistics

Education and Testing
Attendance and Grades, 5
Is Higher Education "Going Digital"?, 1, 35
Piano Lessons Improve Math Ability, 37

Medicine, Clinical Studies, and Experiments
Beneficial Bacteria, 25
Caffeine and Health, 25
Smoking and Criminal Behavior, 37
Thyme and Antioxidants, 35
The Worst Day for Weight Loss, 13

Psychology and Human Behavior
Anger and Snap Judgments, 37
Hostile Children Fight Unemployment, 38

Sports, Exercise, and Fitness
ACL Tears in Collegiate Soccer Players, 37

Surveys and Culture
American Culture and Drug Abuse, 17

Transportation
Fatal Transportation Injuries, 10
World's Busiest Airports, 37

CHAPTER 2
Frequency Distributions and Graphs

Buildings and Structures
Selling Real Estate, 65
Stories in Tall Buildings, 86
Stories in the World's Tallest Buildings, 52

Business, Management, and Work
Career Changes, 103
Charity Donations, 52
Commuting Times, 92
Elderly in the U.S. Labor Force, 79
Patents, 93
Trip Reimbursements, 93

Demographics and Population Characteristics
Counties, Divisions, or Parishes for 50 States, 66
Distribution of Blood Types, 43
Never Married Adults in the United States, 76
Percent of Cigarette Smokers in the United States, 78

U.S. Population by Age, 93
Wealthy People, 42

Education and Testing
Classroom Technology, 101
College Completions, 102
College Spending for First-Year Students, 76
Do Students Need Summer Development?, 65
Grading of Schools, 91
High School Dropout Rate, 102
Making the Grade, 67
Math and Reading Achievement Scores, 92
Math SAT Scores, 68
Number of College Faculty, 66
Percentage of People Who Completed 4 or More Years of College, 53
Teacher Strikes, 92, 107

Entertainment
Roller Coaster Mania, 91
Songs on CDs, 103
Unclaimed Expired Prizes, 53

Environmental Sciences, the Earth, and Space
Air Pollution, 66
Average Wind Speeds, 53
Coal Consumption, 106
Consumption of Natural Gas, 53
Cost of Utilities, 66
Energy Consumption, 91
Length of Major Rivers, 92
Named Storms, 83
Record High Temperatures, 47, 57, 58, 59
Recycled Trash, 106
Space Launches, 102
The Great Lakes, 107
Wind Speed, 101

Food and Dining
Cost of Milk, 93
Eating at Fast Food Restaurants, 52
Super Bowl Snack Foods, 80
Worldwide Sales of Fast Foods, 90

Government, Taxes, Politics, Public Policy, and Voting
How Much Paper Money is in Circulation Today?, 85
Salaries of Governors, 52

History
Ages of Declaration of Independence Signers, 52
Ages of Presidents at Inauguration, 51
Ages of the Vice Presidents at the Time of Their Death, 102
JFK Assassination, 53

Law and Order: Criminal Justice
Car Thefts in a Large City, 85
Causes of Accidental Deaths in the United States, 90
Concealed Weapons Licenses, 93
How Your Identity Can Be Stolen, 41, 104
Identity Thefts, 106
Murders in the United States, 81
Police Calls, 77, 82
Violent Crimes, 91

Marketing, Sales, and Consumer Behavior
Cost of a 30-second Super Bowl Commercial, 89
How People Get Their News, 101
Online Ad Spending, 91
Spending of College Freshmen, 103
Super Bowl Viewer's Expenditures, 91
Valentine's Day Spending, 91

Medicine, Clinical Studies, and Experiments
Blood Glucose Levels, 67
BUN Count, 101
Outpatient Cardiograms, 84
Pain Relief, 103
Patients at a Medical Care Facility, 92
Waiting Times, 67

Public Health and Nutrition
Calories in Salad Dressings, 92
Calories of Nuts, 102
Cereal Calories, 67
Protein Grams in Fast Food, 67
Needless Deaths of Children, 106
U.S. Health Dollar, 92

Sports, Exercise, and Fitness
50 Home Run Club, 92
Ages of Football Players, 91
Calories Burned While Exercising, 91
Favorite Sport, 52
Men's World Hockey Champions, 101
Miles Run per Week, 61
NFL Payrolls, 53
NFL Salaries, 66
Peyton Manning's Colts Career, 103
Super Bowl Scores, 66

Surveys and Culture
Ages of Dogs, 52
Pet Care, 102
Pet Population, 90

Technology
Energy Used by Plasma TVs, 52
Trust in Internet Information, 52

The Sciences
Bear Kills, 65
The Value of Pi, 53

Transportation
Activities While Driving, 102
Colors of Automobiles, 91
Fuel Economy for General Motors Vehicles, 88
MPGs for SUVs, 49
Railroad Crossing Accidents, 66

Travel and Leisure
Museum Visitors, 103
Public Libraries, 103
Reasons We Travel, 91

CHAPTER 3
Data Description

Buildings and Structures
Prices of Homes, 141
Suspension Bridges, 145
Tallest Buildings, 179

Business, Management, and Work
Average Earnings of Workers, 179
Average Weekly Earnings, 160
Bank Failures, 119
Commissions Earned, 124
Costs to Train Employees, 179
Employee Salaries, 129
Employee Years of Service, 182
Executive Bonuses, 124
Foreign Workers, 123
Hourly Compensation for Production Workers, 124
Hours Worked, 180
Labor Charges, 179
Missing Work, 145
Net Worth of Corporations, 124
Salaries of Personnel, 118
The Noisy Workplace, 171
Top-Paid CEOs, 123
Travel Allowances, 141
Unemployment Benefits, 143

Demographics and Population Characteristics
Ages of Accountants, 145
Ages of Consumers, 146
Ages of the Top 50 Wealthiest People, 114
Ages of U.S. Astronaut Candidates, 144
Ages of U.S. Residents, 183
Net Worth of Wealthy People, 178
Percentage of College-Educated Population over 25, 124
Percentage of Foreign-Born People, 124

Economics and Investment
Investment Earnings, 178

Education and Testing
Achievement Test Scores, 160
College and University Debt, 159
College Enrollments, 123
College Room and Board
    Costs, 160
Contest Spelling Words, 124
Driver's License Exam
    Scores, 159
Enrollments for Selected Independent Religiously Controlled
    4-Year Colleges, 125
Errors on a Typing Test, 182
Exam Completion Time, 179
Exam Grades, 179, 182
Graduation Rates, 173
SAT Scores, 146, 178, 182
Starting Teachers' Salaries, 143
Teacher Salaries, 122, 159
Teacher Strikes, 134, 135, 173
Test Scores, 148, 149, 153,
    161, 182
Textbooks in Professors'
    Offices, 179
Work Hours for College
    Faculty, 146

Entertainment
Earnings of Nonliving
    Celebrities, 123
FM Radio Stations, 145
Households of Four Television
    Networks, 178
Top Movie Sites, 180

**Environmental Sciences, the
Earth, and Space**
Annual Precipitation Days, 144
Distance of Stars, 123
Earthquakes, 161
Farm Sizes, 146
High Temperatures, 179
Hurricane Damage, 161
Licensed Nuclear Reactors, 117
Moons of Jupiter, 123
Natural Gas Drilling Sites, 123
Number of Meteorites
    Found, 169
Number of Tornadoes, 173
Observers in the Frogwatch
    Program, 123
Rise in Tides, 179
Shark Attacks, 178
Size of Dams, 173
Size of U.S. States, 143
Solid Waste Production, 146
Tornadoes in the United
    States, 115
Tornado Occurrences, 179
Unhealthy Smog Days, 173

Food and Dining
Citrus Fruit Consumption, 146
Specialty Coffee Shops, 124

**Government, Taxes, Politics,
Public Policy, and Voting**
Cigarette Taxes, 143
Gasoline Taxes, 161

History
Age of Senators, 159

Law and Order: Criminal Justice
Accidental Firearm Deaths, 117
Murder Rates, 145
Murders in Cities, 144
Police Calls in Schools, 161
Police Incidents, 112
Police Officers Killed, 115
Prison Executions, 144
Violent Crimes, 123

**Manufacturing and Product
Development**
Battery Lives, 145, 178
Comparison of Outdoor
    Paint, 128, 129, 131, 132
Copier Service Calls, 125
Printer Repairs, 180

**Marketing, Sales, and Consumer
Behavior**
Average Cost of Smoking, 183
Average Cost of Weddings, 182
Cost per Load of Laundry
    Detergents, 144
Delivery Charges, 182
Diet Cola Preference, 125
Magazines in Bookstores, 179
Newspapers for Sale, 182
Pages in Women's Fitness
    Magazines, 139
Sale Price of Homes, 146
Sales of Automobiles, 138

**Medicine, Clinical Studies,
and Experiments**
Blood Pressure, 142
Determining Dosages, 159
Hospital Emergency Waiting
    Times, 145
Hospital Infections, 112
Multiple Births, 143
Serum Cholesterol Levels, 146
Systolic Blood Pressure, 151

Psychology and Human Behavior
Reaction Times, 144
Trials to Learn a Maze, 146

Public Health and Nutrition
Calories in Bagels, 145
Calories in Salads, 122
Fat Grams, 125
Protein Grams of Energy
    Bars, 173
Sodium Content of Cheese, 170

Sports, Exercise, and Fitness
Baseball Team Batting
    Averages, 145
Basketball Scores, 160
Bowling Scores, 143
Earned Run Average, 172
Innings Pitched, 173
Miles Run per Week, 113, 117, 136
NFL Salaries, 180
NFL Signing Bonuses, 116, 119

Technology
Time Spent Online, 145

The Sciences
Sheep Population, 161

Transportation
Airplane Speeds, 160
Airport Parking, 123
Annual Miles Driven, 160
Automobile Fuel Efficiency,
    124, 144
Commuter Times, 179
Cost of Car Rentals, 179
Cost of Helicopters, 125
Fuel Capacity, 179
Gas Prices for Rental Cars, 182
How Long Are You Delayed by
    Road Congestion?, 109, 180
Miles per Gallon, 182
Passenger Vehicle Deaths, 144
Times Spent in Rush-Hour
    Traffic, 144

Travel and Leisure
Area Boat Registrations, 118
Vacation Days, 159
Visitors Who Travel to Foreign
    Countries, 173

CHAPTER 4
Probability and Counting Rules

Buildings and Structures
Building a New Home, 209

**Business, Management,
and Work**
Distribution of CEO Ages, 200
Overqualified Workers, 216
Research and Development
    Employees, 203
Working Women and Computer
    Use, 223

**Demographics and Population
Characteristics**
Blood Types and Rh Factors, 224
Distribution of Blood Types,
    194, 228
Education Level and
    Smoking, 249
Education of Factory
    Employees, 252
Foreign Adoptions, 225
Human Blood Types, 199
Living Arrangements for
    Children, 200
Male Color Blindness, 214
Marital Status of Women, 225
Names for Boys, 249
Population of Hawaii, 200
U.S. Population, 207
War Veterans, 249
Young Adult Residences, 207

Education and Testing
College Courses, 224
College Debt, 199
College Degrees Awarded, 206
College Enrollment, 226

Computers in Elementary
    Schools, 199
Doctoral Assistantships, 225
High School Grades of First-Year
    College Students, 226
Online Course Selection, 248
Reading to Children, 225
Required First-Year College
    Courses, 200
Student Financial Aid, 223

Entertainment
Cable Television, 223
Craps Game, 199
de Mere Dice Game, 252
Dominoes, 237
DVD Players, 249
Family and Children's Computer
    Games, 225
Getting a Full House, 245
Movie Releases, 248
Odds, 201
Poker Hands, 237
Quinto Lottery, 235
Selecting a Movie, 207, 236
State Lottery Number, 243
The Mathematics of
    Gambling, 244
Video and Computer Games, 222
Yahtzee, 250

**Environmental Sciences, the
Earth, and Space**
Corn Products, 209
Endangered Species, 207
Lightning Strikes, 224
Plant Selection, 246
Sources of Energy Uses in the
    United States, 199
Threatened Species of
    Reptiles, 235

Food and Dining
Breakfast Drink, 248
Coffee Shop Selection, 203
Family Dinner Combinations, 200
Favorite Ice Cream Flavors,
    193, 204
Pizzas and Salads, 224
Purchasing a Pizza, 209

**Government, Taxes, Politics,
Public Policy, and Voting**
Congressional Terms, 224
Federal Government
    Revenue, 200
Government Employees, 222
Health Insurance, 200
Senate Partisanship, 245

Law and Order: Criminal Justice
Arrests for Property Crimes, 200
Guilty or Innocent?, 221
Murder Victims, 199
Prison Populations, 222, 223

**Manufacturing and Product
Development**
Defective Items, 223
Defective Resistors, 245

Defective Transistors, 242
Flashlight Batteries, 223
Garage Door Openers, 234

Marketing, Sales, and Consumer Behavior
Commercials, 226
Customer Purchases, 225
Door-to-Door Sales, 208
Gift Baskets, 224
Shopping Mall Promotion, 198
Ties, 221

Medicine, Clinical Studies, and Experiments
Autism, 225
Chronic Sinusitis, 249
Doctor Specialties, 224
Effectiveness of a Vaccine, 248
Hospital Stays for Knee
    Replacements, 195
Heart Disease, 224
Medical Patients, 208
Medical Tests on Emergency
    Patients, 208
Medical Treatment, 200
Medication Effectiveness, 225
Multiple Births, 207
Which Pain Reliever Is Best?, 206

Psychology and Human Behavior
Would You Bet Your Life?,
    185, 250

Sports, Exercise, and Fitness
Fitness Center Members, 247
Health Club Membership, 248
Leisure Time Exercise, 225

Surveys and Culture
Student Survey, 208
Survey on Stress, 214
Survey on Women in the
    Military, 219

Technology
Software Selection, 247
Text Messages via Cell
    Phones, 223

Transportation
Automobile Insurance, 223
Automobile License Plate, 249
Automobile Sales, 222
Carry-on Items, 249
Driving While Intoxicated, 205
Fatal Accidents, 225
License Plates, 250
Licensed Drivers in the United
    States, 208
Motor Vehicle Producers, 247
On-Time Airplane Arrivals, 225
Railroad Memorial License
    Plates, 229
Rural Speed Limits, 199
Seat Belt Use, 222
Types of Vehicles, 226

Travel and Leisure
Bowling and Club
    Membership, 251

Country Club Activities, 224
Travel over the Thanksgiving
    Holiday, 194
World-Class Orchestras, 245

CHAPTER 5
Discrete Probability Distributions

Business, Management, and Work
Employed Women, 307
Job Applications, 299
Job Elimination, 285
Union Workers, 284
Work Versus Conscience, 300

Demographics and Population Characteristics
Alcohol Abstainers, 308
American and Foreign-Born
    Citizens, 284
Blood Types, 296, 300, 308
Left-Handed People, 293
Likelihood of Twins, 282
Today's Marriages, 283
Unmarried Women, 305

Economics and Investment
Benford's Law, 272
House Insurance, 295
Income Tax Errors, 307
Life Insurance, 273

Education and Testing
College Education and Business
    World Success, 284
Dropping College Courses, 263
High School Dropouts, 284
Lessons Outside of School, 300
Meeting Attendance, 307
People Who Have Some College
    Education, 284
Students Using the Math Lab, 273
Teachers and Summer
    Vacation, 300

Entertainment
Chuck-a-Luck, 308
Coins, Births, and Other
    Random (?) Events, 262
Gambler's Fallacy, 275
Lottery Numbers, 308
Lottery Prizes, 273
On Hold for Talk Radio, 269
Roulette, 273
Winning the Lottery, 273

Environmental Sciences, the Earth, and Space
Alternate Sources of Fuel, 285
Household Wood Burning, 305
Radiation Exposure, 271

Food and Dining
Coffee Shop Customers, 291
Hors d'Oeuvres Selection, 299
Items Donated to a Food
    Bank, 306
M&M's Color Distribution, 298

Pizza Deliveries, 273
Pizza for Breakfast, 305
Unsanitary Restaurants, 282

Government, Taxes, Politics, Public Policy, and Voting
Accuracy Count of Votes, 306
Federal Government Employee
    E-mail Use, 285
Poverty and the Federal
    Government, 285
Social Security Recipients, 284

History
Rockets and Targets, 297

Law and Order: Criminal Justice
Calls for a Fire Company, 307
Emergency Calls, 304
Study of Robberies, 298
U.S. Police Chiefs and the Death
    Penalty, 305

Manufacturing and Product Development
Defective Calculators, 299
Defective Compressor Tanks, 295
Defective Computer
    Keyboards, 299
Defective DVDs, 272, 306
Defective Electronics, 299
Quality Control Check, 307

Marketing, Sales, and Consumer Behavior
Car Sales, 306
CD Purchases, 307
Cellular Phone Sales, 272
Color of Raincoats, 308
Company Mailings, 299
Credit Cards, 304
Internet Purchases, 285
Mail Ordering, 299
Number of Credit Cards, 272
Reusable Grocery Bags, 298
Selling Carpet, 299
Suit Sales, 272
Tie Purchases, 304

Medicine, Clinical Studies, and Experiments
Flu Shots, 305
Pooling Blood Samples, 257, 306

Psychology and Human Behavior
Calls for a Crisis Hotline, 307

Sports, Exercise, and Fitness
Baseball World Series, 260
Shooting an Arrow, 299
Sports Score Hot Line Calls, 307

Surveys and Culture
Survey on Answering Machine
    Ownership, 285
Survey on Bathing Pets, 285
Survey on Concern for
    Criminals, 284
Survey on Doctor Visits, 279
Survey on Employment, 279
Survey on Fear of Being Home
    Alone at Night, 280

Survey of High School
    Seniors, 285
Survey on Internet Awareness, 285

Technology
Computer Assistance, 306
Computer Literacy Test, 305
Guidance Missile System, 284
Internet Access via Cell
    Phone, 305
Telephones per Household, 307

The Sciences
Colors of Flowers, 299
Elm Trees, 307
Mendel's Theory, 298

Transportation
Arrivals at an Airport, 305
Carpooling, 307
Driver's Exam, 307
Driving to Work Alone, 284
Driving While Intoxicated, 280
Emissions Inspection
    Failures, 299
Traffic Accidents, 272
Truck Inspection Violations, 298

Travel and Leisure
Amusement Park Game, 299
Boating Accidents, 306
Bowling Team Uniforms, 307
Christmas Lights, 306
Destination Weddings, 284
Leisure Activities, 290
Lost Luggage in Airlines, 306
Outdoor Regatta, 305
Watching Fireworks, 285

CHAPTER 6
The Normal Distribution

Buildings and Structures
New Home Prices, 339
New Home Sizes, 339
Parking Lot Construction, 361
Prices of Homes, 362

Business, Management, and Work
Health Insurance Through
    Work, 360
Jobs for Registered Nurses, 338
Multiple-Job Holders, 363
Retirement Income, 363
Salaries for Actuaries, 362
Working Weekends, 349
Unemployment, 365

Demographics and Population Characteristics
Ages of Proofreaders, 353
Amount of Laundry Washed Each
    Year, 353
Heights of People, 365
Life Expectancies, 353
Membership in an Organiza-
    tion, 365
Per Capita Income of Delaware
    Residents, 353

Population of College Cities, 360
Residences of U.S. Citizens, 360
U.S. Population, 363

Economics and Investment
Home Ownership, 360
Home Values, 353
Itemized Charitable
    Contributions, 339
Monthly Mortgage Payments, 338

Education and Testing
College Costs, 352
Doctoral Student Salaries, 338
Elementary School Teachers, 361
Enrollment in Personal Finance
    Course, 363
Exam Scores, 340
Female Americans Who Have
    Completed 4 Years of
    College, 360
GMAT Scores, 366
High School Competency Test, 339
Private Four-Year College
    Enrollment, 363
Professors' Salaries, 338, 339
Reading Improvement
    Program, 339
Salary of Full Professors, 338
SAT Scores, 338, 340, 352
School Enrollment, 360
Smart People, 337
Teachers' Salaries, 337
Teachers' Salaries in
    Connecticut, 352
Teachers' Salaries in North
    Dakota, 352
TIMSS Test, 353
Years to Complete a Graduate
    Program, 365

Entertainment
Admission Charge for
    Movies, 337
Box Office Revenues, 340
Drive-in Movies, 340
Hours That Children Watch
    Television, 347
Movie Ticket Prices, 352
Slot Machines, 363

**Environmental Sciences, the
Earth, and Space**
Amount of Rain in a City, 365
Annual Precipitation, 353
Average Precipitation, 363
Electric Bills, 365
Glass Garbage Generation, 352
Heights of Active Volcanoes, 363
Monthly Newspaper
    Recycling, 330
Paper Use, 338
Temperatures for Dallas, 340
Water Use, 352

Food and Dining
Bottled Drinking Water, 339
Lemonade Consumption, 365
Confectionary Products, 363

**Government, Taxes, Politics,
Public Policy, and Voting**
Cigarette Taxes, 340
Medicare Hospital Insurance, 353
Social Security Payments, 340
Unemployment Benefits, 352
Voter Preference, 360

Law and Order: Criminal Justice
Larceny Thefts, 363
Police Academy Acceptance
    Exams, 339
Police Academy
    Qualifications, 333
Population in U.S. Jails, 337

**Manufacturing and Product
Development**
Breaking Strength of Steel
    Cable, 353
Portable CD Player Lifetimes, 363
Repair Cost for Microwave
    Ovens, 365
Wristwatch Lifetimes, 339

**Marketing, Sales, and Consumer
Behavior**
Credit Card Debt, 338
Mail Order, 360
Product Marketing, 339
Technology Inventories, 335

**Medicine, Clinical Studies,
and Experiments**
Lengths of Hospital Stays, 339
Liters of Blood in Adults, 329
Normal Ranges for Vital
    Statistics, 311, 364
Per Capita Spending on Health
    Care, 362
Serum Cholesterol Levels, 352
Systolic Blood Pressure, 334, 353

Public Health and Nutrition
Calories in Fast-Food
    Sandwiches, 366
Chocolate Bar Calories, 338
Cholesterol Content, 353
People Who Smoke, 360
Sodium in Frozen Food, 363
Youth Smoking, 360

Sports, Exercise, and Fitness
Batting Averages, 358
Number of Baseball Games
    Played, 336
Number of Runs Made, 340

Surveys and Culture
Sleep Survey, 365

Technology
Amount of Electricity Used by a
    PC, 331
Cell Phone Lifetimes, 352
Computer Ownership, 365
Cost of iPod Repair, 362
Cost of Personal Computers, 339
Household Computers, 360
Household Online
    Connection, 365
Internet Users, 340

Monthly Spending for Paging and
    Messaging Services, 362
Telephone Answering
    Devices, 360

The Sciences
Newborn Elephant Weights, 338
Ragweed Allergies, 357

Transportation
Ages of Amtrak Passenger
    Cars, 339
Ages of Registered Vehicles, 348
Commute Time to Work, 338
Commuter Train Passengers, 362
Miles Driven Annually, 338
Passengers on a Bus, 365
Price of Gasoline, 338
Reading While Driving, 356
Used Car Prices, 339

Travel and Leisure
Cost of Overseas Trip, 352
Mountain Climbing Safety, 359
Number of Branches of the
    50 Top Libraries, 322
Thickness of Library Books, 365

CHAPTER 7
Confidence Intervals and Sample Size

Buildings and Structures
Home Fires Started by
    Candles, 385
Home Security Systems, 396

**Business, Management,
and Work**
Dog Bites to Postal Workers, 407
Number of Jobs, 379
Work Interruptions, 396

**Demographics and Population
Characteristics**
Ages of Insurance
    Representatives, 410
Marriages in the United
    States, 408
Number of Homeless
    Individuals, 404
Unmarried Americans, 396
Widows, 396

Economics and Investment
Credit Union Assets, 376
Home Ownership Rates, 405
NYSE Stock Prices, 388
Stock Prices, 404

Education and Testing
Adult Education Activities, 408
Age of College Students, 404
Child Care Programs, 408
Cost of Texts, 409
Covering College Costs, 392
Credit Card Use by College
    Students, 398
Day Care Tuition, 380
Educational Television, 396
Freshmen's GPA, 379

High School Graduates Who Take
    the SAT, 396
Hours Spent Studying, 410
National Accounting
    Examination, 380
Number of Faculty, 379
Private Schools, 395
SAT Scores, 405
Spending for Postage at a
    Community College, 407
Students per Teacher in U.S.
    Public Schools, 387
Students Who Major in
    Business, 396
Undergraduate GPAs, 380

Entertainment
Lengths of Children's Animated
    Films, 407, 408
Perry Como Fans, 395
Playing Video Games, 379
Television Viewing, 380

**Environmental Sciences,
the Earth, and Space**
Depth of a River, 377
High Temperatures for May, 387
Lawn Weeds, 392
Length of Growing Seasons, 380
Named Storms, 403
Number of Farms, 380
Thunderstorm Speeds, 387
Travel to Outer Space, 396
Unhealthy Days in Cities, 388

Food and Dining
Cost of Pizzas, 380
Fast-Food Bills for Drive-Thru
    Customers, 379

**Government, Taxes, Politics,
Public Policy, and Voting**
Money Spent on Road Repairs, 410
Parking Meter Revenues, 388
Presidential Travel, 408
State Gasoline Taxes, 387
Women Representatives in State
    Legislature, 387

History
Ages of Presidents at Time of
    Death, 403

Law and Order: Criminal Justice
Burglaries, 410
Gun Control, 397

**Manufacturing and Product
Development**
Baseball Diameters, 408
Calculator Battery Lifetimes, 405
How Many Kleenexes Should Be
    in a Box?, 378
Lifetimes of Snowmobiles, 408
Lifetimes of Wristwatches, 404
MPG for Lawn Mowers, 408
Nicotine Content, 402

**Marketing, Sales, and Consumer
Behavior**
Costs for a 30-Second Spot on
    Cable Television, 388

Days It Takes to Sell an Aveo, 373
Number of Customers, 374

Medicine, Clinical Studies, and Experiments
Birth Weights of Infants, 380
Contracting Influenza, 395
Cost of Knee Replacement
    Surgery, 404
Doctor Visit Costs, 409
Emergency Room Accidents, 410
Hospital Noise Levels, 380, 388
Infant Growth, 385
Patients Treated in Hospital
    Emergency Rooms, 410

Psychology and Human Behavior
Stress and the College Student,
    369, 408

Public Health and Nutrition
Calories in a Standard Size Candy
    Bar, 405
Calories in Candy Bars, 387
Carbohydrate Grams in Commer-
    cial Subs, 379
Carbohydrates in Yogurt, 404
Carbon Monoxide Deaths, 404
Daily Cholesterol Intake, 405
Diet Habits, 396
Fruit Consumption, 396
Obesity, 396
Skipping Lunch, 410
Sport Drink Decision, 386

Sports, Exercise, and Fitness
Dance Company Students, 387
Indy 500 Qualifier Speeds, 388

Surveys and Culture
Belief in Haunted Places, 395
Does Success Bring
    Happiness?, 394
Pet Owners, 408
Political Survey, 410
Shopping Survey, 407
Survey on Politics, 397

Technology
Digital Camera Prices, 387
Direct Satellite Television, 396
Home Broadband Internet
    Access, 396
Home Computers, 394
Social Networking Sites, 387
Television Set Ownership, 410

The Sciences
Isotopes, 407

Transportation
Automobile Pollution, 410
Chicago Commuters, 388
Distance Traveled to Work, 387
Driving to Work, 391
Fuel Efficiency of Cars and
    Trucks, 379
Manual Transmission
    Automobiles, 395
Monthly Gasoline Expendi-
    tures, 380

New Car Lease Fees, 404
Truck Safety Check, 410
Weights of Minivans, 409

Travel and Leisure
Novel Pages, 410
Overseas Travel, 396
Vacation Days, 407
Vacation Sites, 408

CHAPTER 8
Hypothesis Testing

Buildings and Structures
Cost of Building a Home, 435
Heights of Tall Buildings, 449
Home Security Systems, 481
Monthly Home Rent, 481

Business, Management, and Work
Copy Machine Use, 436
Hourly Wage, 437
Men Aged 65 and Over in the
    Labor Force, 481
Number of Jobs, 450
Revenue of Large Businesses, 435
Sick Days, 437
Starting Salary for Nurse
    Practitioners, 444
Working at Home, 479

Demographics and Population Characteristics
Ages of Professional Women, 483
Average Family Size, 450
First-Time Marriages, 484
Heights of 1-Year-Olds, 436
Heights of Models, 483

Economics and Investment
Home Closing Costs, 483
Stocks and Mutual Fund
    Ownership, 457

Education and Testing
College Room and Board
    Costs, 470
Cost of College Tuition, 432
Debt of College Graduates, 480
Doctoral Students' Salaries, 458
Exam Grades, 470
How Much Better is Better on the
    SAT?, 413, 482
Intelligence Tests, 427
Math SAT Test, 464
Nonparental Care, 435
SAT Tests, 429
Student Expenditures, 436
Teaching Assistants'
    Stipends, 450
Undergraduate Enrollment, 458

Entertainment
Cost of a Movie Ticket, 450
Cost of Making a Movie, 449
Movie Admission Prices, 481
Moviegoers, 435, 458
Television Set Ownership, 458
Television Viewing by Teens, 449

Times of Videos, 482
Trifecta Winnings, 481

Environmental Sciences, the Earth, and Space
Farm Sizes, 437
Heights of Volcanoes, 470
High Temperatures in
    January, 470
Natural Gas Heat, 458
Pollution By-Products, 484
Recycling, 458
Tornado Deaths, 470
Warming and Ice Melt, 435
Water Consumption, 450
Wind Speed, 432

Food and Dining
Chewing Gum Use, 483
Soft Drink Consumption, 436

Government, Taxes, Politics, Public Policy, and Voting
Ages of U.S. Senators, 436
Free School Lunches, 481
IRS Audits, 478
Replacing $1 Bills with $1
    Coins, 455
Salaries of Government
    Employees, 436

Law and Order: Criminal Justice
Ages of Robbery Victims, 484
Burglaries, 458
Car Thefts, 434
Federal Prison Populations, 481
Female Gun Owners, 454
Prison Sentences, 436
Prison Time, 479
Speeding Ticket Costs, 436
Speeding Tickets, 437
Stolen Aircraft, 469

Manufacturing and Product Development
Breaking Strength of Cable, 437
Manufactured Machine Parts, 470
Soda Bottle Content, 469
Strength of Wrapping Cord, 484
Sugar Packaging, 474
Weights on Men's Soccer
    Shoes, 481

Marketing, Sales, and Consumer Behavior
Attorney Advertisements, 456
Consumer Protection Agency
    Complaints, 478

Medicine, Clinical Studies, and Experiments
Cost of Braces, 449
Cost of Rehabilitation, 430
Doctor Visits, 450
Female Physicians, 458
First-Time Births, 478
Hospital Infections, 444
Outpatient Surgery, 465
Time Until Indigestion Relief, 481

Public Health and Nutrition
After-School Snacks, 458

Alcohol and Tobacco Use by High
    School Students, 481
Calories in Pancake Syrup, 470
Carbohydrates in Fast Foods, 469
Chocolate Chip Cookie
    Calories, 449
Eggs and Your Health, 425
High-Potassium Foods, 469
Nicotine Content of
    Cigarettes, 448, 466
Obese Young People, 454
Quitting Smoking, 457
Sodium Amounts in Food, 470
Vitamin C in Fruits and
    Vegetables, 470
Youth Smoking, 458

Sports, Exercise, and Fitness
Burning Calories by Playing
    Tennis, 437
Exercise to Reduce Stress, 458
Fans of Professional Baseball, 458
Football Injuries, 458
Games Played by NBA Scoring
    Leaders, 482
Golf Scores, 470
Heights of NBA Players, 436
Joggers' Oxygen Uptake, 447
Step to It with Pedometers, 428

Surveys and Culture
Breakfast Survey, 484
Caffeinated Beverage Survey, 484
Survey on Vitamin Usage, 484

Technology
Cell Phone Bills, 450
Cell Phone Call Lengths, 450
Facebook Friends, 435
Internet Visits, 450
MP3 Ownership, 481
Radio Ownership, 484
Time Online, 480
Transferring Phone Calls, 469

The Sciences
Hog Weights, 475
Plant Leaf Lengths, 482
Seed Germination Times, 484
Strawberry Seeds, 449
Whooping Crane Eggs, 481

Transportation
Car Inspection Times, 468
Commute Time to Work, 450
Experience of Taxi Drivers, 484
First-Class Airline
    Passengers, 459
Fuel Consumption, 481
Improper Driving, 457
Interstate Speeds, 470
One-Way Airfares, 478
Operating Costs of an
    Automobile, 436
Stopping Distances, 436
Testing Gas Mileage Claims, 468
Tire Inflation, 482
Transmission Service, 437
Travel Times to Work, 480

Travel and Leisure
Borrowing Library Books, 458
Hotel Rooms, 483
Newspaper Reading Times, 479
Number of Words in a Novel, 449
Pages in Romance Novels, 484

CHAPTER 9

Testing the Difference Between Two Means, Two Proportions, and Two Variances

Buildings and Structures
Ages of Homes, 504
Apartment Rental Fees, 543
Heights of Tall Buildings, 536
Heights of World Famous
    Cathedrals, 541
Home Prices, 495, 497

Business, Management, and Work
Animal Bites of Postal
    Workers, 525
Interview Errors, 526
Male and Female Workers, 522
Medical Supply Sales, 526
Senior Workers, 526
Too Long on the Telephone, 502

Demographics and Population Characteristics
Ages of Gamblers, 503
Ages of Hospital Patients, 537
County Size in Indiana and
    Iowa, 536
Family Incomes, 543
Heights of 9-Year-Olds, 495
Male Head of Household, 544
Married People, 526
Never Married People, 526
Per Capita Income, 495
Population and Area, 536
Salaries of Chemists, 543

Economics and Investment
Bank Deposits, 510
Daily Stock Prices, 537

Education and Testing
ACT Scores, 495
Ages of College Students, 496
Average Earnings for College
    Graduates, 497, 541
College Education, 526
Cyber School Enrollment, 504
Exam Scores at Private and Public
    Schools, 497
Factory Worker Literacy
    Rates, 543
High School Graduation
    Rates, 526
Improving Study Habits, 515
Lay Teachers in Religious
    Schools, 541
Lecture versus Computer-Assisted
    Instruction, 525

Literacy Scores, 496
Mathematical Skills, 543
Medical School Enrollments, 504
Out-of-State Tuitions, 504
Reading Program, 536
Reducing Errors in Grammar, 516
Retention Test Scores, 515
Teachers' Salaries, 495, 503,
    536, 541
Testing After Review, 541
Tuition Costs for Medical
    School, 536
Undergraduate Financial Aid, 526
Women Science Majors, 495

Entertainment
Hours Spent Watching
    Television, 503
Television Watching, 496

Environmental Sciences, the Earth, and Space
Air Quality, 515
Average Temperatures, 541
High and Low Temperatures, 541
Lengths of Major Rivers, 494
Winter Temperatures, 536

Food and Dining
Prices of Low-Calorie Foods, 543
Soft Drinks in School, 541

Government, Taxes, Politics, Public Policy, and Voting
Money Spent on Road Repair, 544
Monthly Social Security
    Benefits, 495
Partisan Support of Salary
    Increase Bill, 525
Tax-Exempt Properties, 503

Manufacturing and Product Development
Battery Voltage, 496
Noise Levels of Power
    Mowers, 532
Weights of Running Shoes,
    503, 536
Weights of Vacuum Cleaners, 503

Marketing, Sales, and Consumer Behavior
Coupon Use, 526
Credit Card Debt, 496
Paint Prices, 542
Store Sales, 497

Medicine, Clinical Studies, and Experiments
Can Video Games Save
    Lives?, 514
Hospital Stays for Maternity
    Patients, 504
Hospital Volunteers, 541
Is More Expensive Better?, 523
Length of Hospital Stays, 495
Noise Levels in Hospitals, 503,
    535, 541
Obstacle Course Times, 516
Only the Timid Die Young, 544
Overweight Dogs, 516

Pulse Rates of Identical
    Twins, 516
Sleeping Brain, Not at Rest, 545
Vaccination Rates in Nursing
    Homes, 487, 521, 542
Weights of Newborn
    Infants, 500

Psychology and Human Behavior
Bullying, 527
Mistakes in a Song, 516
Problem-Solving Ability, 496
Self-Esteem Scores, 496
Smoking and Education, 524
Toy Assembly Test, 516

Public Health and Nutrition
Calories in Ice Cream, 536
Carbohydrates in Candy, 503, 536
Cholesterol Levels, 512, 543
Heart Rates of Smokers, 532
Hypertension, 525

Sports, Exercise, and Fitness
Batting Averages, 505
College Sports Offerings, 492
Golf Scores, 516
Heights of Basketball Players, 544
Hockey's Highest Scorers, 504
Home Runs, 493
Miniature Golf Scores, 504
NFL Salaries, 504
PGA Golf Scores, 516

Surveys and Culture
Desire to Be Rich, 525
Dog Ownership, 525
Sleep Report, 516
Smoking Survey, 526
Survey on Inevitability of
    War, 525

Technology
Cell Phones, 541

The Sciences
Egg Production, 543
Wolf Pack Pups, 535

Transportation
Airline On-Time Arrivals, 526
Airport Passengers, 533
Automatic Transmissions, 534
Commuting Times, 495
Commuting Times for College
    Students, 496
Gasoline Prices, 504
Seat Belt Use, 525

Travel and Leisure
Bestseller Books, 503
Driving for Pleasure, 540
Jet Ski Accidents, 543
Leisure Time, 491, 525
Museum Attendance, 537

CHAPTER 10

Correlation and Regression

Buildings and Structures
Tall Buildings, 565, 573

Business, Management, and Work
Typing Speed and Word
    Processing, 603

Demographics and Population Characteristics
Age and Cavities, 605
Age and Net Worth, 574
Age and Wealth, 553, 558
Age, GPA, and Income, 598
Life Expectancies, 565, 573

Economics and Investment
Oil and Gas Prices, 564, 572

Education and Testing
Absences and Final Grades, 552,
    557, 569, 574
Alumni Contributions, 564, 573
Aspects of Students' Academic
    Behavior, 598
Class Size and Grades, 565, 573
Faculty and Students, 565, 573
Home Smart Home, 593
Literacy Rates, 565, 573
More Math Means More
    Money, 597
SAT Scores, 574
State Board Scores, 595, 596, 597

Entertainment
Commercial Movie Releases,
    564, 572
Television Viewers, 574

Environmental Sciences, the Earth, and Space
Coal Production, 574
Deaths from Lightning, 603
Energy Consumption, 565, 573
Farm Acreage, 574
Forest Fires and Acres Burned,
    564, 573

Food and Dining
Special Occasion Cakes, 598

Government, Taxes, Politics, Public Policy, and Voting
State Debt and Per Capita Tax,
    564, 573

Law and Order: Criminal Justice
Can Temperature Predict Crime?,
    549, 604
Crimes, 564, 572

Manufacturing and Product Development
Copy Machine Maintenance
    Costs, 587

Medicine, Clinical Studies, and Experiments
Coffee Not Disease Culprit, 563
Father's and Son's Weights, 574
Fireworks and Injuries, 574
Medical Specialties and
    Gender, 603
Prescription Drug Prices, 605

Public Health and Nutrition
Age, Cholesterol, and Sodium, 598

Carbohydrates and Kilocalories, 565, 573
Fat and Cholesterol, 605
Fruit Nutrients, 598
Protein and Diastolic Blood Pressure, 603
Water and Carbohydrates, 565, 573

Sports, Exercise, and Fitness
Bowling Scores, 565, 573
NHL Assists and Total Points, 565, 573
Touchdowns and QB Ratings, 603
Triples and Home Runs, 565, 573

Transportation
Car Rental Companies, 552, 556, 568
Driver's Age and Accidents, 603, 605
Stopping Distances, 562, 572

Travel and Leisure
Passengers and Airline Fares, 603

CHAPTER 11
Other Chi-Square Tests

Business, Management, and Work
Displaced Workers, 641
Employment of High School Females, 641
Employment Satisfaction, 644
Job Loss Reasons, 643
Mothers Working Outside the Home, 635
Workforce Distribution, 635

Demographics and Population Characteristics
Education Level and Health Insurance, 620
Ethnicity and Movie Admissions, 634
Health Insurance Coverage, 642
Population and Age, 634
Women in the Military, 634

Economics and Investment
Pension Investments, 641

Education and Testing
Ages of Head Start Program Students, 620
Assessment of Mathematics Students, 620
College Degree Recipients, 620
Education Level of Adults, 614
Student Majors at Colleges, 634
Study Groups and Professors, 635
Volunteer Practices of Students, 636

Entertainment
Record CDs Sold, 635
State Lottery Numbers, 621
Television Viewing, 643

Environmental Sciences, the Earth, and Space
Tornadoes, 641

Food and Dining
Consumption of Takeout Foods, 643
Favorite Ice Cream Flavor, 643
Fruit Soda Flavor Preference, 612
Genetically Modified Food, 619
Restaurants and Types of Meals Purchased, 633
Skittles Color Distribution, 618
Types of Pizza Purchased, 644

Government, Taxes, Politics, Public Policy, and Voting
Congressional Representatives, 634
Tax Credit Refunds, 644

Law and Order: Criminal Justice
Firearm Deaths, 615, 620
Gun Sale Denials, 641
Violent Crimes, 634

Marketing, Sales, and Consumer Behavior
Grocery Lists, 636
Music Sales, 619
Pennant Colors Purchased, 644
Types of Shopping Bags Used, 619

Medicine, Clinical Studies, and Experiments
Cardiovascular Procedures, 642
Effectiveness of a New Drug, 635
Fathers in the Delivery Room, 636
Hospitals and Infections, 627
Organ Transplantation, 634
Paying for Prescriptions, 620
Risk of Injury, 641

Psychology and Human Behavior
Combatting Midday Drowsiness, 619
Does Color Affect Your Appetite?, 637
Happiness and Income, 631

Sports, Exercise, and Fitness
Injuries on Monkey Bars, 636
Sports Preferences of Males and Females, 629
Types of Pitches Thrown, 641
Youth Physical Fitness, 635

Surveys and Culture
Participation in a Market Research Survey, 635

Technology
Internet Users, 620
Satellite Dishes in Restricted Areas, 633

The Sciences
Endangered or Threatened Species, 634
Statistics and Heredity, 609, 642

Transportation
On-Time Performance by Airlines, 619
Truck Colors, 620

Types of Automobiles Purchased, 620
Ways to Get to Work, 643

Travel and Leisure
Recreational Reading and Gender, 635
Thanksgiving Travel, 636
Travel Accident Fatalities, 641

CHAPTER 12
Analysis of Variance

Buildings and Structures
Home Building Times, 675
Lengths of Various Types of Bridges, 680

Business, Management, and Work
Weekly Unemployment Benefits, 665

Demographics and Population Characteristics
Ages of Late-Night TV Talk Show Viewers, 683

Education and Testing
Alumni Gift Solicitation, 684
Annual Child Care Costs, 657
Average Debt of College Graduates, 658
Expenditures per Pupil, 657, 665
Number of Pupils in a Class, 658
Review Preparation for Statistics, 681
Soap Bubble Experiments (and Math), 674
Student Loans, 656

Entertainment
Television Viewing Time, 657

Environmental Sciences, the Earth, and Space
Air Pollution, 683
Number of State Parks, 680
Temperatures in January, 681

Government, Taxes, Politics, Public Policy, and Voting
Voters in Presidential Elections, 683

Law and Order: Criminal Justice
Eyewitness Testimony, 647, 682
School Incidents Involving Police Calls, 681

Manufacturing and Product Development
Durability of Paint, 675
Environmentally Friendly Air Freshener, 675
Types of Outdoor Paint, 675

Marketing, Sales, and Consumer Behavior
Age and Sales, 676
Automobile Sales Techniques, 673
Microwave Oven Prices, 657

Prices of Body Soap, 683
Tire Prices, 656

Medicine, Clinical Studies, and Experiments
Diets and Exercise Programs, 684
Effects of Different Types of Diets, 681
Emergency Room Visits, 664
Tricking Knee Pain, 662

Psychology and Human Behavior
Adult Children of Alcoholics, 684
Colors That Make You Smarter, 655, 664

Public Health and Nutrition
Calories in Fast-Food Sandwiches, 658
Carbohydrates in Cereals, 681
Carbohydrates in Juices, 681
Fiber Content of Foods, 665
Grams of Fat per Serving of Pizza, 681
Healthy Eating, 656
Iron Content of Foods and Drinks, 681
Sodium Content of Foods, 656

Sports, Exercise, and Fitness
Weight Gain of Athletes, 656

Technology
Cell Phone Bills, 657
Weights of Digital Cameras, 665

The Sciences
Increasing Plant Growth, 674

Transportation
Employees at Toll Road Interchanges, 653
Gasoline Consumption, 669
Gasoline Prices, 683
Hybrid Vehicles, 656
Miles per Gallon, 652

CHAPTER 13
Nonparametric Statistics

Buildings and Structures
Home Prices, 737
Property Assessments, 711

Business, Management, and Work
Annual Incomes for Men, 698
Employee Absences, 730
Family Income, 699
Job Offers for Chemical Engineers, 716
Weekly Earnings of Women, 698

Demographics and Population Characteristics
Ages of Drug Program Participants, 725
Age of Foreign-Born Residents, 695
Ages at First Marriage for Women, 698

Birth Registry, 738
Gender of Train Passengers, 725

Economics and Investment
Bank Branches and Deposits, 720

Education and Testing
Class Size and Average
  Grade, 729
Cyber School Enrollments, 729
Exam Scores, 699, 736
Expenditures for Pupils, 716
Funding and Enrollment for Head
  Start Students, 738
Homework Exercises and Exam
  Scores, 735
Hours Worked by Student
  Employees, 735
Legal Costs for School
  Districts, 712
Manuscript Pages and
  References, 735
Mathematics Achievement Test
  Scores, 728
Mathematics Literacy Scores, 716
Medical School Enrollments, 706
Number of Faculty for Proprietary
  Schools, 699
Student Participation in a Blood
  Drive, 706
Students' Opinions on Lengthen-
  ing the School Year, 699
Technology Proficiency Test, 705

Entertainment
Concert Seating, 730
Daily Lottery Numbers,
  729, 738
Motion Picture Releases and
  Gross Revenue, 729
On-Demand Movie Rentals, 730
Television Viewers, 699, 700

**Environmental Sciences, the
Earth, and Space**
Clean Air, 698
Deaths Due to Severe
  Weather, 699
Heights of Waterfalls, 715
Record High Temperatures, 735
Tall Trees, 728

Food and Dining
Lunch Costs, 735
Price of Pizza, 734
Teaspoon Size, 699

**Government, Taxes, Politics,
Public Policy, and Voting**
Tolls for Bridge, 738
Unemployment Benefits, 716

Law and Order: Criminal Justice
Lengths of Prison Sentences, 705
Local Crimes, 716
Motor Vehicle Thefts and
  Burglaries, 729
Number of Crimes per Week, 717
Shoplifting Incidents, 709
Speeding Tickets, 730

**Manufacturing and Product
Development**
Breaking Strengths of Ropes, 735
Lifetime of Truck Tires, 734
Lifetimes of Batteries, 737
Lifetimes of Handheld Video
  Games, 705
Output of Motors, 738
Routine Maintenance and
  Defective Parts, 700
Too Much or Too Little?, 689, 736

**Marketing, Sales, and Consumer
Behavior**
Book Publishing, 729
Grocery Store Repricing, 734
Paper or Plastic Bags, 736
Printer Costs, 717
Textbook Costs, 737

**Medicine, Clinical Studies, and
Experiments**
Accidents or Illnesses, 730
Cavities in Fourth-Grade
  Students, 729
Diet Medication and Weight, 699
Drug Prices, 711, 712, 729, 738
Drug Side Effects, 692
Ear Infections in Swimmers, 696
Effects of a Pill on Appetite, 699
Hospital Infections, 714, 718
Hospitals and Nursing
  Homes, 729

Medication and Reaction
  Times, 737
Pain Medication, 711
Patients at a Medical
  Center, 694
Speed of Pain Relievers, 706
Weight Loss Through Diet, 711

Public Health and Nutrition
Amounts of Caffeine in
  Beverages, 717
Calories and Cholesterol in
  Fast-Food Sandwiches, 729
Calories in Cereals, 716
Prices of Vitamin/Mineral
  Supplements, 717
School Lunch, 704
Sodium Content of Fast-Food
  Sandwiches, 737
Sodium Content of Microwave
  Dinners, 716

Sports, Exercise, and Fitness
Bowling Scores, 712
Game Attendance, 698
Hunting Accidents, 706
Olympic Medals, 738
Skiing Conditions, 730
Speed Skating Times, 705
Times to Complete an Obstacle
  Course, 703
Winning Baseball Games, 705

The Sciences
Maximum Speeds of
  Animals, 717
Natural Gas Costs, 699
Weights of Turkeys, 737

Transportation
Fuel Efficiency of
  Automobiles, 735
Glasses or Contact Lenses for
  Driving, 730
Stopping Distances of
  Automobiles, 705
Subway and Commuter Rail
  Passengers, 728

Travel and Leisure
Amusement Park Admission
  Price, 729

Beach Temperatures for
  July, 735
Fiction or Nonfiction
  Books, 736

**CHAPTER 14
Sampling and Simulation**

**Demographics and Population
Characteristics**
Foreign-Born Residents, 765
Stay-at-Home Parents, 765

Education and Testing
Is That Your Final Answer?, 750
Overview of U.S. Public
  Schools, 752

Entertainment
Television Set Ownership, 765
Let's Make A Deal, 741, 769

**Environmental Sciences, the
Earth, and Space**
Record High Temperatures by
  State, 753
Should We Be Afraid of
  Lightning?, 747
Wind Speed of Hurricanes, 767

Food and Dining
Smoking Bans and Profits, 759

**Government, Taxes, Politics,
Public Policy, and Voting**
Electoral Votes, 753
Unemployment Rates and
  Benefits, 767

Law and Order: Criminal Justice
State Governors on Capital
  Punishment, 744

**Medicine, Clinical Studies,
and Experiments**
Snoring, 761

Public Health and Nutrition
The White or Wheat Bread
  Debate, 751

Sports, Exercise, and Fitness
Basketball Foul Shots, 765
Clay Pigeon Shooting, 765
Playing Basketball, 765

The Nature of Probability and Statistics

STATISTICS TODAY

Is Higher Education "Going Digital"?

Today many students take college courses online and use eBooks. Also, many students use a laptop, smartphone, or computer tablet in the classroom. With the increased use of technology, some questions about the effectiveness of this technology have been raised. For example,

> How many colleges and universities offer online courses?
>
> Do students feel that the online courses are equal in value to the traditional classroom presentations?
>
> Approximately how many students take online courses now?
>
> Will the number of students who take online courses increase in the future?
>
> Has plagiarism increased since the advent of computers and the Internet?
>
> Do laptops, smartphones, and tablets belong in the classroom?
>
> Have colleges established any guidelines for the use of laptops, smartphones, and tablets?

To answer these questions, Pew Research Center conducted a study of college graduates and college presidents in 2011. The procedures they used and the results of the study are explained in this chapter. See Statistics Today—Revisited at the end of the chapter.

OUTLINE

    Introduction
1–1 Descriptive and Inferential Statistics
1–2 Variables and Types of Data
1–3 Data Collection and Sampling Techniques
1–4 Experimental Design
1–5 Computers and Calculators
    Summary

OBJECTIVES

After completing this chapter, you should be able to

1 Demonstrate knowledge of statistical terms.

2 Differentiate between the two branches of statistics.

3 Identify types of data.

4 Identify the measurement level for each variable.

5 Identify the four basic sampling techniques.

6 Explain the difference between an observational and an experimental study.

7 Explain how statistics can be used and misused.

8 Explain the importance of computers and calculators in statistics.

Introduction

You may be familiar with probability and statistics through radio, television, newspapers, and magazines. For example, you may have read statements like the following found in newspapers.

- The FBI reported that violent crimes were down by 6.4% in 2011.
- *USA TODAY* reported that the average college graduate student loan debt was about $19,000.
- The College Stress and Mental Illness Poll reported that 85% of college and university students reported feeling stress daily; 77% reported stress from school work, and 74% experienced stress from grades.
- The *Occupational Outlook Handbook* reported that the median hourly wage for a registered nurse was $31.10 per hour.
- *Reader's Digest* reported that the average cost of using a plasma television is $0.1152 per hour.
- In 2013, the number of sales of smartphones is estimated to be 832.5 million units globally.

Statistics is used in almost all fields of human endeavor. In sports, for example, a statistician may keep records of the number of yards a running back gains during a football game, or the number of hits a baseball player gets in a season. In other areas, such as public health, an administrator might be concerned with the number of residents who contract a new strain of flu virus during a certain year. In education, a researcher might want to know if new methods of teaching are better than old ones. These are only a few examples of how statistics can be used in various occupations.

Furthermore, statistics is used to analyze the results of surveys and as a tool in scientific research to make decisions based on controlled experiments. Other uses of statistics include operations research, quality control, estimation, and prediction.

Statistics is the science of conducting studies to collect, organize, summarize, analyze, and draw conclusions from data.

Students study statistics for several reasons:

1. Like professional people, you must be able to read and understand the various statistical studies performed in your fields. To have this understanding, you must be knowledgeable about the vocabulary, symbols, concepts, and statistical procedures used in these studies.
2. You may be called on to conduct research in your field, since statistical procedures are basic to research. To accomplish this, you must be able to design experiments; collect, organize, analyze, and summarize data; and possibly make reliable predictions or forecasts for future use. You must also be able to communicate the results of the study in your own words.
3. You can also use the knowledge gained from studying statistics to become better consumers and citizens. For example, you can make intelligent decisions about what products to purchase based on consumer studies, about government spending based on utilization studies, and so on.

These reasons can be considered some of the goals for studying statistics.

It is the purpose of this chapter to introduce the goals for studying statistics by answering questions such as the following:

What are the branches of statistics?

What are data?

How are samples selected?

1–1   Descriptive and Inferential Statistics

OBJECTIVE

Demonstrate knowledge
of statistical terms.

To gain knowledge about seemingly haphazard situations, statisticians collect information for *variables,* which describe the situation.

> A **variable** is a characteristic or attribute that can assume different values.

Data are the values (measurements or observations) that the variables can assume. Variables whose values are determined by chance are called **random variables.**

Suppose that an insurance company studies its records over the past several years and determines that, on average, 3 out of every 100 automobiles the company insured were involved in accidents during a 1-year period. Although there is no way to predict the specific automobiles that will be involved in an accident (random occurrence), the company can adjust its rates accordingly, since the company knows the general pattern over the long run. (That is, on average, 3% of the insured automobiles will be involved in an accident each year.)

A collection of data values forms a **data set.** Each value in the data set is called a **data value** or a **datum.**

In statistics it is important to distinguish between a sample and a population.

> A **population** consists of all subjects (human or otherwise) that are being studied.

When data are collected from every subject in the population, it is called a *census*.

For example, every 10 years the United States conducts a census. The primary purpose of this census is to determine the apportionment of the seats in the House of Representatives.

The first census was conducted in 1790 and was mandated by Article 1, Section 2 of the Constitution. As the United States grew, the scope of the census also grew. Today the Census limits questions to populations, housing, manufacturing, agriculture, and mortality. The Census is conducted by the Bureau of the Census, which is part of the Department of Commerce.

Most of the time, due to the expense, time, size of population, medical concerns, etc., it is not possible to use the entire population for a statistical study; therefore, researchers use samples.

> A **sample** is a group of subjects selected from a population.

If the subjects of a sample are properly selected, most of the time they should possess the same or similar characteristics as the subjects in the population. See Figure 1–1.

However, the information obtained from a statistical sample is said to be *biased* if the results from the sample of a population are radically different from the results of a census of the population. Also, a sample is said to be biased if it does not represent the population from which it has been selected. The techniques used to properly select a sample are explained in Section 1–3.

The body of knowledge called statistics is sometimes divided into two main areas, depending on how data are used. The two areas are

1. Descriptive statistics

2. Inferential statistics

> **Descriptive statistics** consists of the collection, organization, summarization, and presentation of data.

In *descriptive statistics* the statistician tries to describe a situation. Consider the national census conducted by the U.S. government every 10 years. Results of this census give you the average age, income, and other characteristics of the U.S. population. To obtain this information, the Census Bureau must have some means to collect relevant data. Once data are collected, the bureau must organize and summarize them. Finally, the bureau needs a means of presenting the data in some meaningful form, such as charts, graphs, or tables.

OBJECTIVE

Differentiate between the
two branches of statistics.

FIGURE 1–1
Population and Sample

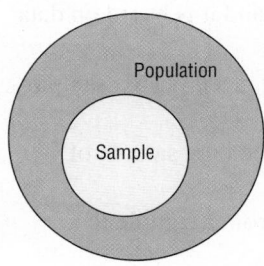

The second area of statistics is called *inferential statistics.*

> **Inferential statistics** consists of generalizing from samples to populations, performing estimations and hypothesis tests, determining relationships among variables, and making predictions.

Here, the statistician tries to make inferences from *samples* to *populations.* Inferential statistics uses **probability,** i.e., the chance of an event occurring. You may be familiar with the concepts of probability through various forms of gambling. If you play cards, dice, bingo, or lotteries, you win or lose according to the laws of probability. Probability theory is also used in the insurance industry and other areas.

The area of inferential statistics called **hypothesis testing** is a decision-making process for evaluating claims about a population, based on information obtained from samples. For example, a researcher may wish to know if a new drug will reduce the number of heart attacks in men over age 70 years of age. For this study, two groups of men over age 70 would be selected. One group would be given the drug, and the other would be given a placebo (a substance with no medical benefits or harm). Later, the number of heart attacks occurring in each group of men would be counted, a statistical test would be run, and a decision would be made about the effectiveness of the drug.

Statisticians also use statistics to determine *relationships* among variables. For example, relationships were the focus of the most noted study in the 20th century, "Smoking and Health," published by the Surgeon General of the United States in 1964. He stated that after reviewing and evaluating the data, his group found a definite relationship between smoking and lung cancer. He did not say that cigarette smoking actually causes lung cancer, but that there is a relationship between smoking and lung cancer. This conclusion was based on a study done in 1958 by Hammond and Horn. In this study, 187,783 men were observed over a period of 45 months. The death rate from lung cancer in this group of volunteers was 10 times as great for smokers as for nonsmokers.

Finally, by studying past and present data and conditions, statisticians try to make predictions based on this information. For example, a car dealer may look at past sales records for a specific month to decide what types of automobiles and how many of each type to order for that month next year.

EXAMPLE 1–1 Descriptive or Inferential Statistics

Determine whether descriptive or inferential statistics were used.

   a. The average jackpot for the top five lottery winners was $367.6 million.

   b. A study done by the American Academy of Neurology suggests that older people who had a high caloric diet more than doubled their risk of memory loss.

   c. Based on a survey of 9317 consumers done by the National Retail Federation, the average amount that consumers spent on Valentine's Day in 2011 was $116.

   d. Scientists at the University of Oxford in England found that a good laugh significantly raises a person's pain level tolerance.

SOLUTION

   a. Descriptive statistics were used because this is an average, and it is based on data obtained from the top five lottery winners at this time.

   b. Inferential statistics were used since this is a generalization made from a sample to a population.

   c. Descriptive statistics were used since this is an average based on a sample of 9317 respondents.

   d. Inferential statistics were used since an inference is made from a sample to a population.

≡ Applying the Concepts 1–1

Attendance and Grades

Read the following on attendance and grades, and answer the questions.

A study conducted at Manatee Community College revealed that students who attended class 95 to 100% of the time usually received an A in the class. Students who attended class 80 to 90% of the time usually received a B or C in the class. Students who attended class less than 80% of the time usually received a D or an F or eventually withdrew from the class.

Based on this information, attendance and grades are related. The more you attend class, the more likely it is you will receive a higher grade. If you improve your attendance, your grades will probably improve. Many factors affect your grade in a course. One factor that you have considerable control over is attendance. You can increase your opportunities for learning by attending class more often.

1. What are the variables under study?

2. What are the data in the study?

3. Are descriptive, inferential, or both types of statistics used?

4. What is the population under study?

5. Was a sample collected? If so, from where?

6. From the information given, comment on the relationship between the variables.

See page 39 for the answers.

> **Unusual Stat**
> Only one-third of crimes committed are reported to the police.

≡ Exercises 1–1

1. Define statistics.

2. What is a variable?

3. What is meant by a census?

4. How does a population differ from a sample?

5. Explain the difference between descriptive and inferential statistics.

6. Name two areas where probability is used.

7. Why is information obtained from samples used more often than information obtained from populations?

8. What is meant by a biased sample?

For Exercises 9–17, determine whether descriptive or inferential statistics were used.

9. Because of the current economy, 49% of 18 to 34 year-olds have taken a job to pay the bills. (Source: Pew Research Center)

10. In 2025, the world population is predicted to be 8 billion people. (Source: United Nations)

11. In 2011, there were 34 deaths from the avian flu. (Source: World Health Organization)

12. Based on a sample of 2739 respondents, it is estimated that pet owners spent a total of 14 billion dollars on veterinarian care for their pets. (Source: American Pet Products Association, Pet Owners Survey)

13. In 2011, 79% of U.S. adults used the Internet. (Source: Pew Research Center)

14. In 2010, a total of 68,905 people died from diabetes. (Source: Centers for Disease Control and Prevention)

15. In an online survey of 500 Virginia Tech students between spring 2010 and spring 2011, 31% said that they had missed class because of alcohol consumption. (Source: Center for Applied Behavior Systems at Virginia Tech)

16. In 2008–2009, a total of 260,327 U.S. students were studying abroad. (Source: Institute of International Education)

17. Forty-four percent of the people in the United States have type O blood. (Source: American Red Cross)

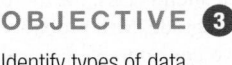 **Extending the Concepts**

18. Find three statistical studies and explain whether they used descriptive or inferential statistics.

19. Find a gambling game and explain how probability was used to determine the outcome.

1–2   Variables and Types of Data

OBJECTIVE ❸

Identify types of data.

As stated in Section 1–1, statisticians gain information about a particular situation by collecting data for random variables. This section will explore in greater detail the nature of variables and types of data.

Variables can be classified as qualitative or quantitative.

> **Qualitative variables** are variables that have distinct categories according to some characteristic or attribute.

For example, if subjects are classified according to gender (male or female), then the variable *gender* is qualitative. Other examples of qualitative variables are religious preference and geographic locations.

> **Quantitative variables** are variables that can be counted or measured.

For example, the variable *age* is numerical, and people can be ranked in order according to the value of their ages. Other examples of quantitative variables are heights, weights, and body temperatures.

Quantitative variables can be further classified into two groups: discrete and continuous. *Discrete variables* can be assigned values such as 0, 1, 2, 3 and are said to be *countable*. Examples of discrete variables are the number of children in a family, the number of students in a classroom, and the number of calls received by a switchboard operator each day for a month.

> **Discrete variables** assume values that can be counted.

Continuous variables, by comparison, can assume an infinite number of values in an interval between any two specific values. Temperature, for example, is a continuous variable, since the variable can assume an infinite number of values between any two given temperatures.

> **Continuous variables** can assume an infinite number of values between any two specific values. They are obtained by measuring. They often include fractions and decimals.

The classification of variables can be summarized as follows:

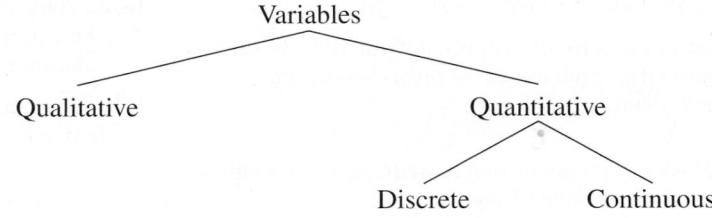

EXAMPLE 1–2   Discrete or Continuous Variables

Classify each variable as a discrete variable or a continuous variable.

    a. The highest wind speed of a hurricane

    b. The weight of baggage on an airplane

    c. The number of pages in a statistics book

    d. The amount of money a person spends per year for online purchases

SOLUTION

    a. Continuous, since wind speed must be measured

    b. Continuous, since weight is measured

    c. Discrete, since the number of pages is countable

    d. Discrete, since the smallest value that money can assume is in cents

Unusual Stat

Fifty-two percent of Americans live within 50 miles of a coastal shoreline.

Since continuous data must be measured, answers must be rounded because of the limits of the measuring device. Usually, answers are rounded to the nearest given unit. For example, heights might be rounded to the nearest inch, weights to the nearest ounce, etc. Hence, a recorded height of 73 inches could mean any measure from 72.5 inches up to but not including 73.5 inches. Thus, the boundary of this measure is given as 72.5–73.5 inches. The **boundary** of a number, then, is defined as a class in which a data value would be placed before the data value was rounded. *Boundaries are written for convenience as 72.5–73.5 but are understood to mean all values up to but not including 73.5.* Actual data values of 73.5 would be rounded to 74 and would be included in a class with boundaries of 73.5 up to but not including 74.5, written as 73.5–74.5. As another example, if a recorded weight is 86 pounds, the exact boundaries are 85.5 up to but not including 86.5, written as 85.5–86.5 pounds. Table 1–1 helps to clarify this concept. The boundaries of a continuous variable are given in one additional decimal place and always end with the digit 5.

TABLE 1–1 Recorded Values and Boundaries		
Variable	**Recorded value**	**Boundaries**
Length	15 centimeters (cm)	14.5–15.5 cm
Temperature	86 degrees Fahrenheit (°F)	85.5–86.5°F
Time	0.43 second (sec)	0.425–0.435 sec
Mass	1.6 grams (g)	1.55–1.65 g

EXAMPLE 1–3   Class Boundaries

Find the boundaries of each variable.

    a. 8.4 quarts

    b. 138 mmHg

    c. 137.63 mg/dL

SOLUTION

    a. 8.35–8.45 quarts

    b. 137.5–138.5 mmHg

    c. 137.625–137.635 mg/dL

In addition to being classified as qualitative or quantitative, variables can be classified by how they are categorized, counted, or measured. For example, can the data be organized into specific categories, such as area of residence (rural, suburban, or urban)? Can the data values be ranked, such as first place, second place, etc.? Or are the values obtained from measurement, such as heights, IQs, or temperature? This type of classification—i.e., how variables are categorized, counted, or measured—uses **measurement scales,** and four common types of scales are used: nominal, ordinal, interval, and ratio.

The first level of measurement is called the *nominal level* of measurement. A sample of college instructors classified according to subject taught (e.g., English, history, psychology, or mathematics) is an example of nominal-level measurement. Classifying survey subjects as male or female is another example of nominal-level measurement. No ranking or order can be placed on the data. Classifying residents according to zip codes is also an example of the nominal level of measurement. Even though numbers are assigned as zip codes, there is no meaningful order or ranking. Other examples of nominal-level data are political party (Democratic, Republican, Independent, etc.), religion (Christianity, Judaism, Islam, etc.), and marital status (single, married, divorced, widowed, separated).

> The **nominal level of measurement** classifies data into mutually exclusive (nonoverlapping) categories in which no order or ranking can be imposed on the data.

The next level of measurement is called the *ordinal level*. Data measured at this level can be placed into categories, and these categories can be ordered, or ranked. For example, from student evaluations, guest speakers might be ranked as superior, average, or poor. Floats in a homecoming parade might be ranked as first place, second place, etc. *Note that precise measurement of differences in the ordinal level of measurement* does not *exist.* For instance, when people are classified according to their build (small, medium, or large), a large variation exists among the individuals in each class.

Other examples of ordinal data are letter grades (A, B, C, D, F).

> The **ordinal level of measurement** classifies data into categories that can be ranked; however, precise differences between the ranks do not exist.

The third level of measurement is called the *interval level*. This level differs from the ordinal level in that precise differences do exist between units. For example, many standardized psychological tests yield values measured on an interval scale. IQ is an example of such a variable. There is a meaningful difference of 1 point between an IQ of 109 and an IQ of 110. Temperature is another example of interval measurement, since there is a meaningful difference of 1°F between each unit, such as 72 and 73°F. *One property is lacking in the interval scale: There is no true zero.* For example, IQ tests do not measure people who have no intelligence. For temperature, 0°F does not mean no heat at all.

> The **interval level of measurement** ranks data, and precise differences between units of measure do exist; however, there is no meaningful zero.

The final level of measurement is called the *ratio level*. Examples of ratio scales are those used to measure height, weight, area, and number of phone calls received. Ratio scales have differences between units (1 inch, 1 pound, etc.) and a true zero. In addition, the ratio scale contains a true ratio between values. For example, if one person can lift 200 pounds and another can lift 100 pounds, then the ratio between them is 2 to 1. Put another way, the first person can lift twice as much as the second person.

> The **ratio level of measurement** possesses all the characteristics of interval measurement, and there exists a true zero. In addition, true ratios exist when the same variable is measured on two different members of the population.

OBJECTIVE

Identify the measurement level for each variable.

Unusual Stat

Sixty-three percent of us say we would rather hear the bad news first.

Historical Note

When data were first analyzed statistically by Karl Pearson and Francis Galton, almost all were continuous data. In 1899, Pearson began to analyze discrete data. Pearson found that some data, such as eye color, could not be measured, so he termed such data *nominal data.* Ordinal data were introduced by a German numerologist Frederich Mohs in 1822 when he introduced a hardness scale for minerals. For example, the hardest stone is the diamond, which he assigned a hardness value of 1500. Quartz was assigned a hardness value of 100. This does not mean that a diamond is 15 times harder than quartz. It only means that a diamond is harder than quartz. In 1947, a psychologist named Stanley Smith Stevens made a further division of continuous data into two categories, namely, interval and ratio.

TABLE 1–2	Examples of Measurement Scales		
Nominal-level data	**Ordinal-level data**	**Interval-level data**	**Ratio-level data**
Zip code Gender (male, female) Eye color (blue, brown, green, hazel) Political affiliation Religious affiliation Major field (mathematics, computers, etc.) Nationality	Grade (A, B, C, D, F) Judging (first place, second place, etc.) Rating scale (poor, good, excellent) Ranking of tennis players	SAT score IQ Temperature	Height Weight Time Salary Age

FIGURE 1–2

Measurement Scales

1. Nominal Level

Blue   White

Red   Black

Automobile color

2. Ordinal Level

Small   Medium   Large

Pizza size

3. Interval Level

Temperature

4. Ratio Level

6 ft 2"

Height

There is not complete agreement among statisticians about the classification of data into one of the four categories. For example, some researchers classify IQ data as ratio data rather than interval. Also, data can be altered so that they fit into a different category. For instance, if the incomes of all professors of a college are classified into the three categories of low, average, and high, then a ratio variable becomes an ordinal variable. Table 1–2 gives some examples of each type of data. See Figure 1–2.

EXAMPLE 1–4   **Measurement Levels**

What level of measurement would be used to measure each variable?

    a. The ages of patients in a local hospital

    b. The ratings of movies released this month

    c. Colors of athletic shirts sold by Oak Park Health Club

    d. Temperatures of hot tubs in local health clubs

SOLUTION
a. Ratio
b. Ordinal
c. Nominal
d. Interval

Applying the Concepts 1–2

Fatal Transportation Injuries

Read the following information about the number of fatal accidents for the transportation industry in 2010, and answer each question.

Industry	Number of fatalities
Highway accidents	968
Railway accidents	44
Water vehicle accidents	52
Aircraft accidents	151

Source: Bureau of Labor Statistics.

1. Name the variables under study.

2. Categorize each variable as quantitative or qualitative.

3. Categorize each quantitative variable as discrete or continuous.

4. Identify the level of measurement for each variable.

5. The railroad has the fewest fatalities for 2010. Does that mean railroads have fewer accidents than the other industries?

6. What factors other than safety influence a person's choice of transportation?

7. From the information given, comment on the relationship between the variables.

See page 39 for the answers.

Exercises 1–2

1. Explain the difference between qualitative variables and quantitative variables.

2. Explain the difference between discrete and continuous variables.

3. Why are continuous variables rounded when they are used in statistical studies?

4. Name and define the four types of measurement levels used in statistics.

For Exercises 5–10, determine whether the data are qualitative or quantitative.

5. Color of football uniforms

6. Pizza sizes (small, medium, and large)

7. Cholesterol counts for individuals

8. Lightbulb wattage

9. Genders of movie stars

10. Ratings of teachers

For Exercises 11–16, determine whether the data are discrete or continuous.

11. Number of text messages sent in a month

12. Systolic blood pressure readings

13. Heights of basketball players on a local high school team

14. Number of phone calls received during one day at a poison control center

15. Number of students in the mathematics classes during the fall semester at your school for a particular school year

16. Temperatures at a seashore resort

For Exercises 17–22, give the boundaries of each value.

17. 7 feet

18. 6.3 millimeters

19. 143 miles

20. 3.25 pounds

21. 25.8 yards

22. 19 quarts

For Exercises 23–30, classify each as nominal-level, ordinal-level, interval-level, or ratio-level measurement.

23. Telephone numbers

24. Leap years: . . . 2008, 2012, 2016, . . .

25. Amounts of money spent on a medical checkup

26. Scores on a statistical final exam

27. Ratings of fiction books—excellent, good, fair, poor

28. Blood types—O, A, B, AB

29. Online spending

30. Number of flowers in a bouquet

1–3   Data Collection and Sampling Techniques

OBJECTIVE

Identify the four basic sampling techniques.

In research, statisticians use data in many different ways. As stated previously, data can be used to describe situations or events. For example, a manufacturer might want to know something about the consumers who will be purchasing his product so he can plan an effective marketing strategy. In another situation, the management of a company might survey its employees to assess their needs in order to negotiate a new contract with the employees' union. Data can be used to determine whether the educational goals of a school district are being met. Finally, trends in various areas, such as the stock market, can be analyzed, enabling prospective buyers to make more intelligent decisions concerning what stocks to purchase. These examples illustrate a few situations where collecting data will help people make better decisions on courses of action.

Data can be collected in a variety of ways. One of the most common methods is through the use of surveys. Surveys can be done by using a variety of methods. Three of the most common methods are the telephone survey, the mailed questionnaire, and the personal interview.

Telephone surveys have an advantage over personal interview surveys in that they are less costly. Also, people may be more candid in their opinions since there is no face-to-face contact. A major drawback to the telephone survey is that some people in the population will not have phones or will not answer when the calls are made; hence, not all people have a chance of being surveyed. Also, many people now have unlisted numbers and cell phones, so they cannot be surveyed. Finally, even the tone of voice of the interviewer might influence the response of the person who is being interviewed.

Mailed questionnaire surveys can be used to cover a wider geographic area than telephone surveys or personal interviews since mailed questionnaire surveys are less expensive to conduct. Also, respondents can remain anonymous if they desire. Disadvantages of mailed questionnaire surveys include a low number of responses and inappropriate answers to questions. Another drawback is that some people may have difficulty reading or understanding the questions.

Historical Note

A pioneer in census taking was Pierre-Simon de Laplace. In 1780, he developed the Laplace method of estimating the population of a country. The principle behind his method was to take a census of a few selected communities and to determine the ratio of the population to the number of births in these communities. (Good birth records were kept.) This ratio would be used to multiply the number of births in the entire country to estimate the number of citizens in the country.

Personal interview surveys have the advantage of obtaining in-depth responses to questions from the person being interviewed. One disadvantage is that interviewers must be trained in asking questions and recording responses, which makes the personal interview survey more costly than the other two survey methods. Another disadvantage is that the interviewer may be biased in his or her selection of respondents.

Data can also be collected in other ways, such as *surveying records* or *direct observation* of situations.

As stated in Section 1–1, researchers use samples to collect data and information about a particular variable from a large population. Using samples saves time and money and in some cases enables the researcher to get more detailed information about a particular subject. Remember, samples cannot be selected in haphazard ways because the information obtained might be biased. For example, interviewing people on a street corner during the day would not include responses from people working in offices at that time or from people attending school; hence, not all subjects in a particular population would have a chance of being selected.

To obtain samples that are unbiased—i.e., that give each subject in the population an equally likely chance of being selected—statisticians use four basic methods of sampling: random, systematic, stratified, and cluster sampling.

Historical Note

The first census in the United States was conducted in 1790. Its purpose was to ensure proper Congressional representation.

Random Sampling

> A **random sample** is a sample in which all members of the population have an equal chance of being selected.

Random samples are selected by using chance methods or random numbers. One such method is to number each subject in the population. Then place numbered cards in a bowl, mix them thoroughly, and select as many cards as needed. The subjects whose numbers are selected constitute the sample. Since it is difficult to mix the cards thoroughly, there is a chance of obtaining a biased sample. For this reason, statisticians use another method of obtaining numbers. They generate random numbers with a computer or calculator. Before the invention of computers, random numbers were obtained from tables.

Some two-digit random numbers are shown in Table 1–3. To select a random sample of, say, 15 subjects out of 85 subjects, it is necessary to number each subject from 01 to 85. Then select a starting number by closing your eyes and placing your finger on a number in the table. (Although this may sound somewhat unusual, it enables us to find a starting number at random.) In this case suppose your finger landed on the number 12 in the second column. (It is the sixth number down from the top.) Then proceed downward until you have selected 15 different numbers between 01 and 85. When you reach the bottom of the column, go to the top of the next column. If you select a number greater than 85 or the number 00 or a duplicate number, just omit it. In our example, we will use the subjects numbered 12, 27, 75, 62, 57, 13, 31, 06, 16, 49, 46, 71, 53, 41, and 02. A more detailed procedure for selecting a random sample using a table of random numbers is given in Chapter 14, using Table D in Appendix A.

Systematic Sampling

> A **systematic sample** is a sample obtained by selecting every k^{th} member of the population where k is a counting number.

Researchers obtain systematic samples by numbering each subject of the population and then selecting every k^{th} subject. For example, suppose there were 2000 subjects in the

TABLE 1–3   Random Numbers

79	41	71	93	60	35	04	67	96	04	79	10	86
26	52	53	13	43	50	92	09	87	21	83	75	17
18	13	41	30	56	20	37	74	49	56	45	46	83
19	82	02	69	34	27	77	34	24	93	16	77	00
14	57	44	30	93	76	32	13	55	29	49	30	77
29	12	18	50	06	33	15	79	50	28	50	45	45
01	27	92	67	93	31	97	55	29	21	64	27	29
55	75	65	68	65	73	07	95	66	43	43	92	16
84	95	95	96	62	30	91	64	74	83	47	89	71
62	62	21	37	82	62	19	44	08	64	34	50	11
66	57	28	69	13	99	74	31	58	19	47	66	89
48	13	69	97	29	01	75	58	05	40	40	18	29
94	31	73	19	75	76	33	18	05	53	04	51	41
00	06	53	98	01	55	08	38	49	42	10	44	38
46	16	44	27	80	15	28	01	64	27	89	03	27
77	49	85	95	62	93	25	39	63	74	54	82	85
81	96	43	27	39	53	85	61	12	90	67	96	02
40	46	15	73	23	75	96	68	13	99	49	64	11

population and a sample of 50 subjects was needed. Since $2000 \div 50 = 40$, then $k = 40$, and every 40th subject would be selected; however, the first subject (numbered between 1 and 40) would be selected at random. Suppose subject 12 were the first subject selected; then the sample would consist of the subjects whose numbers were 12, 52, 92, etc., until 50 subjects were obtained. When using systematic sampling, you must be careful about how the subjects in the population are numbered. If subjects were arranged in a manner such as wife, husband, wife, husband, and every 40th subject were selected, the sample would consist of all husbands. Numbering is not always necessary. For example, a researcher may select every 10th item from an assembly line to test for defects.

Stratified Sampling

A **stratified sample** is a sample obtained by dividing the population into subgroups or strata according to some characteristic relevant to the study. (There can be several subgroups.) Then subjects are selected from each subgroup.

Samples within the strata should be randomly selected. For example, suppose the president of a two-year college wants to learn how students feel about a certain issue. Furthermore, the president wishes to see if the opinions of first-year students differ from those of second-year students. The president will randomly select students from each subgroup to use in the sample.

Cluster Sampling

> A **cluster sample** is obtained by dividing the population into sections or clusters and then selecting one or more clusters and using all members in the cluster(s) as the members of the sample.

Here the population is divided into groups or clusters by some means such as geographic area or schools in a large school district. Then the researcher randomly selects some of these clusters and uses all members of the selected clusters as the subjects of the samples. Suppose a researcher wishes to survey apartment dwellers in a large city. If there are 10 apartment buildings in the city, the researcher can select at random 2 buildings from the 10 and interview all the residents of these buildings. Cluster sampling is used when the population is large or when it involves subjects residing in a large geographic area. For example, if one wanted to do a study involving the patients in the hospitals in New York City, it would be very costly and time-consuming to try to obtain a random sample of patients since they would be spread over a large area. Instead, a few hospitals could be selected at random, and the patients in these hospitals would be interviewed in a cluster. See Figure 1–3.

The four basic sampling methods are summarized in Table 1–4.

Other Sampling Methods

In addition to the four basic sampling methods, researchers use other methods to obtain samples. One such method is called a **convenience sample.** Here a researcher uses subjects who are convenient. For example, the researcher may interview subjects entering a local mall to determine the nature of their visit or perhaps what stores they will be patronizing. This sample is probably not representative of the general customers for several reasons. For one thing, it was probably taken at a specific time of day, so not all customers entering the mall have an equal chance of being selected since they were not there when the survey was being conducted. But convenience samples can be representative of the population. If the researcher investigates the characteristics of the population and determines that the sample is representative, then it can be used.

Another type of sample that is used in statistics is a *volunteer sample* or *self-selected sample.* Here respondents decide for themselves if they wish to be included in the sample. For example, a radio station in Pittsburgh asks a question about a situation and then asks people to call one number if they agree with the action taken or call another number if they disagree with the action. The results are then announced at the end of the day. Note that most often, only people with strong opinions will call. The station does explain that this is not a "scientific poll."

Since samples are not perfect representatives of the populations from which they are selected, there is always some error in the results. This error is called a *sampling error.*

> **Sampling error** is the difference between the results obtained from a sample and the results obtained from the population from which the sample was selected.

FIGURE 1–3   Sampling Methods

1. Random

Population

Table D	Random Numbers			
10480	15011	01536	02011	81647
22368	46573	25595	85393	30995
24130	48360	22527	97265	76393
42167	93093	06243	61680	07856
37570	39975	81837	16656	06121
77921	06907	11008	42751	27750
99562	72905	56420	69994	98872
96301	91977	05463	07972	18876
89579	14342	63661	10281	17453
85475	36857	43342	53988	
28918	69578	88321		
63553	40961			

Sample

2. Systematic

Population

Sample

3. Stratified

Men

Women

Population

Sample

4. Cluster

Area codes
Population

Sample

TABLE 1–4	**Summary of Sampling Methods**
Random	Subjects are selected by random numbers.
Systematic	Subjects are selected by using every kth number after the first subject is randomly selected from 1 through k.
Stratified	Subjects are selected by dividing up the population into subgroups (strata), and subjects are randomly selected within subgroups.
Cluster	Subjects are selected by using an intact subgroup that is representative of the population.

For example, suppose you select a sample of full-time students at your college and find 56% are female. Then you go to the admissions office and get the genders of all full-time students that semester and find that 54% are female. The difference of 2% is said to be due to sampling error.

In most cases, this difference is unknown, but it can be estimated. This process is shown in Chapter 7.

There is another error that occurs in statistics called *nonsampling error.*

> A **nonsampling error** occurs when the data are obtained erroneously or the sample is biased, i.e., nonrepresentative.

For example, data could be collected by using a defective scale. Each weight might be off by, say, 2 pounds. Also, recording errors can be made. Perhaps the researcher wrote an incorrect data value.

Caution and vigilance should be used when collecting data.

Other sampling techniques, such as *sequential sampling, double sampling,* and *multistage sampling,* are explained in Chapter 14, along with a more detailed explanation of the four basic sampling techniques.

EXAMPLE 1–5 Sampling Methods

State which sampling method was used.

a. Out of 10 hospitals in a municipality, a researcher selects one and collects records for a 24-hour period on the types of emergencies that were treated there.

b. A researcher divides a group of students according to gender, major field, and low, average, and high grade point average. Then she randomly selects six students from each group to answer questions in a survey.

c. The subscribers to a magazine are numbered. Then a sample of these people is selected using random numbers.

d. Every 10th bottle of Super-Duper Cola is selected, and the amount of liquid in the bottle is measured. The purpose is to see if the machines that fill the bottles are working properly.

SOLUTION

a. Cluster

b. Stratified

c. Random

d. Systematic

≡ Applying the Concepts 1–3

American Culture and Drug Abuse

Assume you are a member of the Family Research Council and have become increasingly concerned about the drug use by professional sports players. You set up a plan and conduct a survey on how people believe the American culture (television, movies, magazines, and popular music) influences illegal drug use. Your survey consists of 2250 adults and adolescents from around the country. A consumer group petitions you for more information about your survey. Answer the following questions about your survey.

1. What type of survey did you use (phone, mail, or interview)?

2. What are the advantages and disadvantages of the surveying methods you did not use?

3. What type of scores did you use? Why?

4. Did you use a random method for deciding who would be in your sample?

5. Which of the methods (stratified, systematic, cluster, volunteer, or convenience) did you use?

6. Why was that method more appropriate for this type of data collection?

7. If a convenience sample were obtained consisting of only adolescents, how would the results of the study be affected?

See pages 39–40 for the answers.

≡ Exercises 1–3

1. Name five ways that data can be collected.

2. What is meant by sampling error and nonsampling error?

3. Why are random numbers used in sampling, and how are random numbers generated?

4. Name and define the four basic sampling methods.

For Exercises 5–10, define a population that may have been used and explain how the sample might have been selected.

5. In 2011, 25% of people did not engage in regular physical activity. (Source: SQL Server Reporting Services)

6. The number one automobile that vehicle thieves prefer is the Honda Accord. (Source: LoJack Vehicle Theft Recovery Report, 2010)

7. There are 78 million pet owners in the United States who have dogs. (Source: American Pet Products Association National Pet Owners Survey)

8. Adults aged 19–50 need 1000 milligrams of calcium per day. (Source: Institute of Medicine Report)

9. Taking statins raises the risk of developing diabetes. (Source: *Journal of American Medical Association* and other sources)

10. The average January 2012 temperature in Boston was 34.2°F. This was 5.2° higher than the normal January average temperature. (Source: AccuWeather.com)

For Exercises 11–16, indentify the sampling method that was used.

11. To check the accuracy of a machine that is used for filling ice cream containers, every 20th bottle is selected and weighed.

12. To determine how long people exercise, a researcher interviews 5 people selected from a yoga class, 5 people selected from a weight-lifting class, 5 people selected from an aerobics class, and 5 people from swimming classes.

13. In a large school district, a researcher numbers all the full-time teachers and then randomly selects 30 teachers to be interviewed.

14. In a medical research study, a researcher selects a hospital and interviews all the patients that day.

15. Customers in the Sunrise Coffee Shop are asked how much they spend on coffee per week.

16. Ten counties in Pennsylvania are randomly selected to determine the average county real estate tax that the residents pay.

1–4   Experimental Design

OBJECTIVE ⑥

Explain the difference
between an observational
and an experimental study.

Observational and Experimental Studies

There are several different ways to classify statistical studies. This section explains two types of studies: *observational studies* and *experimental studies.*

> In an **observational study,** the researcher merely observes what is happening or what has happened in the past and tries to draw conclusions based on these observations.

For example, data from the Motorcycle Industry Council (*USA TODAY*) stated that "Motorcycle owners are getting older and richer." Data were collected on the ages and incomes of motorcycle owners for the years 1980 and 1998 and then compared. The findings showed considerable differences in the ages and incomes of motorcycle owners for the two years. In this study, the researcher merely observed what had happened to the motorcycle owners over a period of time. There was no type of research intervention.

There are three main types of observational studies. When all the data are collected at one time, the study is called a *cross-sectional study.* When the data are collected using records obtained from the past, the study is called a *retrospective study.* Finally, if the data are collected over a period of time, say, past and present, the study is called a *longitudinal study.*

Observational studies have advantages and disadvantages. One advantage of an observational study is that it usually occurs in a natural setting. For example, researchers can observe people's driving patterns on streets and highways in large cities. Another advantage of an observational study is that it can be done in situations where it would be unethical or downright dangerous to conduct an experiment. Using observational studies, researchers can study suicides, rapes, murders, etc. In addition, observational studies can be done using variables that cannot be manipulated by the researcher, such as drug users versus nondrug users and right-handedness versus left-handedness.

Observational studies have disadvantages, too. As mentioned previously, since the variables are not controlled by the researcher, a definite cause-and-effect situation cannot be shown since other factors may have had an effect on the results. Observational studies can be expensive and time-consuming. For example, if one wanted to study the habitat of lions in Africa, one would need a lot of time and money, and there would be a certain amount of danger involved. Finally, since the researcher may not be using his or her own measurements, the results could be subject to the inaccuracies of those who collected the data. For example, if the researchers were doing a study of events that occurred in the 1800s, they would have to rely on information and records obtained by others from a previous era. There is no way to ensure the accuracy of these records.

The other type of study is called an *experimental study.*

> In an **experimental study,** the researcher manipulates one of the variables and tries to determine how the manipulation influences other variables.

For example, a study conducted at Virginia Polytechnic Institute and presented in *Psychology Today* divided female undergraduate students into two groups and had the students perform as many sit-ups as possible in 90 sec. The first group was told only to "Do your best," while the second group was told to try to increase the actual number of sit-ups done each day by 10%. After four days, the subjects in the group who were given the vague instructions to "Do your best" averaged 43 sit-ups, while the group that was given the more specific instructions to increase the number of sit-ups by 10% averaged 56 sit-ups by the last day's session. The conclusion then was that athletes who were given specific goals performed better than those who were not given specific goals.

This study is an example of a statistical experiment since the researchers intervened in the study by manipulating one of the variables, namely, the type of instructions given to each group.

In a true experimental study, the subjects should be assigned to groups randomly. Also, the treatments should be assigned to the groups at random. In the sit-up study, the article did not mention whether the subjects were randomly assigned to the groups.

Sometimes when random assignment is not possible, researchers use intact groups. These types of studies are done quite often in education where already intact groups are available in the form of existing classrooms. When these groups are used, the study is said to be a **quasi-experimental study.** The treatments, though, should be assigned at random. Most articles do not state whether random assignment of subjects was used.

Statistical studies usually include one or more *independent variables* and one *dependent variable.*

> The **independent variable** in an experimental study is the one that is being manipulated by the researcher. The independent variable is also called the **explanatory variable.** The resultant variable is called the **dependent variable** or the **outcome variable.**

The outcome variable is the variable that is studied to see if it has changed significantly because of the manipulation of the independent variable. For example, in the sit-up study, the researchers gave the groups two different types of instructions, general and specific. Hence, the independent variable is the type of instruction. The dependent variable, then, is the resultant variable, that is, the number of sit-ups each group was able to perform after four days of exercise. If the differences in the dependent or outcome variable are large and other factors are equal, these differences can be attributed to the manipulation of the independent variable. In this case, specific instructions were shown to increase athletic performance.

In the sit-up study, there were two groups. The group that received the special instruction is called the **treatment group** while the other is called the **control group.** The treatment group receives a specific treatment (in this case, instructions for improvement) while the control group does not.

Both types of statistical studies have advantages and disadvantages. Experimental studies have the advantage that the researcher can decide how to select subjects and how to assign them to specific groups. The researcher can also control or manipulate the independent variable. For example, in studies that require the subjects to consume a certain amount of medicine each day, the researcher can determine the precise dosages and, if necessary, vary the dosage for the groups.

There are several disadvantages to experimental studies. First, they may occur in unnatural settings, such as laboratories and special classrooms. This can lead to several problems. One such problem is that the results might not apply to the natural setting. The age-old question then is, "This mouthwash may kill 10,000 germs in a test tube, but how many germs will it kill in my mouth?"

Another disadvantage with an experimental study is the **Hawthorne effect.** This effect was discovered in 1924 in a study of workers at the Hawthorne plant of the Western Electric Company. In this study, researchers found that the subjects who knew they were participating in an experiment actually changed their behavior in ways that affected the results of the study.

Another problem when conducting statistical studies is called *confounding of variables* or *lurking variables.*

> A **confounding variable** is one that influences the dependent or outcome variable but was not separated from the independent variable.

Researchers try to control most variables in a study, but this is not possible in some studies. For example, subjects who are put on an exercise program might also improve their diet unbeknownst to the researcher and perhaps improve their health in other ways not due to exercise alone. Then diet becomes a confounding variable.

When you read the results of statistical studies, decide if the study was observational or experimental. Then see if the conclusion follows logically, based on the nature of these studies.

Another factor that can influence statistical experiments is called the *placebo effect*. Here the subjects used in the study respond favorably or show improvement due to the fact that they had been selected for the study. They could also be reacting to clues given unintentionally by the researchers. For example, in a study on knee pain done at the Houston VA Medical Center, researchers divided 180 patients into three groups. Two groups had surgery to remove damaged cartilage while those in the third group had simulated surgery. After two years, an equal number of patients in each group reported that they felt better after the surgery. Those patients who had simulated surgery were said to be responding to what is called the placebo effect.

To minimize the placebo effect, researchers use what is called *blinding*. In blinding, the subjects do not know whether they are receiving an actual treatment or a placebo. Many times researchers use a sugar pill that looks like a real medical pill. Often *double blinding* is used. Here both the subjects and the researchers are not told which groups are given the placebos.

Researchers use *blocking* to minimize variability when they suspect that there might be a difference between two or more blocks. For example, in the sit-up study mentioned earlier, if we think that men and women would respond differently to "Do your best" versus "Increase by 10% every day," we would divide the subjects into two blocks (men, women) and then randomize which subjects in each block get the treatment.

When subjects are assigned to groups randomly, and the treatments are assigned randomly, the experiment is said to be a *completely randomized design.*"

Some experiments use what is called a *matched-pair design*. Here one subject is assigned to a treatment group, and another subject is assigned to a control group. But, before the assignment, subjects are paired according to certain characteristics. In earlier years, studies used identical twins, assigning one twin to one group and the other twin to another group. Subjects can be paired on any characteristics such as ages, heights, and weights.

Another way to validate studies is to use *replication*. Here the same experiment is done in another part of the country or in another laboratory. The same study could also be done using adults who are not going to college instead of using college students. Then the results of the second study are compared to the ones in the original study to see if they are the same.

No matter what type of study is conducted, two studies on the same subject sometimes have conflicting conclusions. Why might this occur? An article entitled "Bottom Line: Is It Good for You?" (*USA TODAY Weekend*) states that in the 1960s studies suggested that margarine was better for the heart than butter since margarine contains less saturated fat and users had lower cholesterol levels. In a 1980 study, researchers found that butter was better than margarine since margarine contained trans-fatty acids, which are worse for the heart than butter's saturated fat. Then in a 1998 study, researchers found that margarine was better for a person's health. Now, what is to be believed? Should one use butter or margarine?

The answer here is that you must take a closer look at these studies. Actually, it is not the choice between butter and margarine that counts, but the type of margarine used. In the 1980s, studies showed that solid margarine contains trans-fatty acids, and scientists believe that they are worse for the heart than butter's saturated fat. In the 1998 study, liquid margarine was used. It is very low in trans-fatty acids, and hence it is more healthful than butter because trans-fatty acids have been shown to raise cholesterol. Hence, the conclusion is that it is better to use liquid margarine than solid margarine or butter.

Before decisions based on research studies are made, it is important to get all the facts and examine them in light of the particular situation.

The purpose of a statistical study is to gain and process information obtained from the study in order to answer specific questions about the subject being investigated.

Statistical researchers use a specific procedure to do statistical studies to obtain valid results.

The general guidelines for this procedure are as follows:

1. Formulate the purpose of the study.
2. Identify the variables for the study.
3. Define the population.
4. Decide what sampling method you will use to collect the data.
5. Collect the data.
6. Summarize the data and perform any statistical calculations needed.
7. Interpret the results.

There is also a formal way to write up the study procedure and the results obtained. This information is available on the online resources under "Writing the Research Report."

EXAMPLE 1–6   Experimental Design

Researchers randomly assigned 10 people to each of three different groups. Group 1 was instructed to write an essay about the hassles in their lives. Group 2 was instructed to write an essay about circumstances that made them feel thankful. Group 3 was asked to write an essay about events that they felt neutral about. After the exercise, they were given a questionnaire on their outlook on life. The researchers found that those who wrote about circumstances that made them feel thankful had a more optimistic outlook on life. The conclusion is that focusing on the positive makes you more optimistic about life in general. Based on this study, answer the following questions.

a. Was this an observational or experimental study?

b. What is the independent variable?

c. What is the dependent variable?

d. What may be a confounding variable in this study?

e. What can you say about the sample size?

f. Do you agree with the conclusion? Explain your answer.

SOLUTION

a. This is an experimental study since the variables (types of essays written) were manipulated.

b. The independent variable was the type of essay the participants wrote.

c. The dependent variable was the score on the life outlook questionnaire.

d. Other factors, such as age, upbringing, and income, can affect the results; however, the random assignment of subjects is helpful in eliminating these factors. See the answer for the next question.

e. In this study, the sample uses 30 participants total.

f. Answers will vary.

OBJECTIVE ❼

Explain how statistics can be used and misused.

Uses and Misuses of Statistics

As explained previously, statistical techniques can be used to describe data, compare two or more data sets, determine if a relationship exists between variables, test hypotheses, and make estimates about population characteristics. However, there is another aspect of statistics, and that is the misuse of statistical techniques to sell products that don't work properly, to attempt to prove something true that is really not true, or to get our attention by using statistics to evoke fear, shock, and outrage.

Two sayings that have been around for a long time illustrate this point:

"There are three types of lies—lies, damn lies, and statistics."

"Figures don't lie, but liars figure."

Just because we read or hear the results of a research study or an opinion poll in the media, this does not mean that these results are reliable or that they can be applied to any and all situations. For example, reporters sometimes leave out critical details such as the size of the sample used or how the research subjects were selected. Without this information, you cannot properly evaluate the research and properly interpret the conclusions of the study or survey.

It is the purpose of this section to show some ways that statistics can be misused. You should not infer that all research studies and surveys are suspect, but that there are many factors to consider when making decisions based on the results of research studies and surveys. Here are some ways that statistics can be misrepresented.

Suspect Samples   The first thing to consider is the sample that was used in the research study. Sometimes researchers use very small samples to obtain information. Several years ago, advertisements contained such statements as "Three out of four doctors surveyed recommend brand such and such." If only 4 doctors were surveyed, the results could have been obtained by chance alone; however, if 100 doctors were surveyed, the results might be quite different.

Not only is it important to have a sample size that is large enough, but also it is necessary to see how the subjects in the sample were selected. As stated previously, studies using volunteers sometimes have a built-in bias. Volunteers generally do not represent the population at large. Sometimes they are recruited from a particular socioeconomic background, and sometimes unemployed people volunteer for research studies to get a stipend. Studies that require the subjects to spend several days or weeks in an environment other than their home or workplace automatically exclude people who are employed and cannot take time away from work. Sometimes only college students or retirees are used in studies. In the past, many studies have used only men, but have attempted to generalize the results to both men and women. Opinion polls that require a person to phone or mail in a response most often are not representative of the population in general, since only those with strong feelings for or against the issue usually call or respond by mail.

Another type of sample that may not be representative is the convenience sample. Educational studies sometimes use students in intact classrooms since it is convenient. Quite often, the students in these classrooms do not represent the student population of the entire school district.

When results are interpreted from studies using small samples, convenience samples, or volunteer samples, care should be used in generalizing the results to the entire population.

Ambiguous Averages   In Chapter 3, you will learn that there are four commonly used measures that are loosely called *averages*. They are the *mean, median, mode,* and *midrange.* For the same data set, these averages can differ markedly. People who know this can, without lying, select the one measure of average that lends the most evidence to support their position.

Changing the Subject   Another type of statistical distortion can occur when different values are used to represent the same data. For example, one political candidate who is running for reelection might say, "During my administration, expenditures increased a mere 3%." His opponent, who is trying to unseat him, might say, "During my opponent's administration, expenditures have increased a whopping $6,000,000." Here both figures are correct; however, expressing a 3% increase as $6,000,000 makes it sound like a very large increase. Here again, ask yourself, Which measure better represents the data?

Detached Statistics   A claim that uses a detached statistic is one in which no comparison is made. For example, you may hear a claim such as "Our brand of crackers has one-third fewer calories." Here, no comparison is made. One-third fewer calories than what? Another example is a claim that uses a detached statistic such as "Brand A aspirin works four times faster." Four times faster than what? When you see statements such as this, always ask yourself, Compared to what?

Implied Connections   Many claims attempt to imply connections between variables that may not actually exist. For example, consider the following statement: "Eating fish may help to reduce your cholesterol." Notice the words *may help*. There is no guarantee that eating fish will definitely help you reduce your cholesterol.

"Studies suggest that using our exercise machine will reduce your weight." Here the word *suggest* is used; and again, there is no guarantee that you will lose weight by using the exercise machine advertised.

Another claim might say, "Taking calcium will lower blood pressure in some people." Note the word *some* is used. You may not be included in the group of "some" people. Be careful when you draw conclusions from claims that use words such as *may, in some people,* and *might help.*

Misleading Graphs   Statistical graphs give a visual representation of data that enables viewers to analyze and interpret data more easily than by simply looking at numbers. In Chapter 2, you will see how some graphs are used to represent data. However, if graphs are drawn inappropriately, they can misrepresent the data and lead the reader to draw false conclusions. The misuse of graphs is also explained in Chapter 2.

Faulty Survey Questions   When analyzing the results of a survey using questionnaires, you should be sure that the questions are properly written since the way questions are phrased can often influence the way people answer them. For example, the responses to a question such as "Do you feel that the North Huntingdon School District should build a new football stadium?" might be answered differently than a question such as "Do you favor increasing school taxes so that the North Huntingdon School District can build a new football stadium?" Each question asks something a little different, and the responses could be radically different. When you read and interpret the results obtained from questionnaire surveys, watch out for some of these common mistakes made in the writing of the survey questions.

In Chapter 14, you will find some common ways that survey questions could be misinterpreted by those responding, and could therefore result in incorrect conclusions.

In summary then, statistics, when used properly, can be beneficial in obtaining much information, but when used improperly, can lead to much misinformation. It is like your automobile. If you use your automobile to get to school or work or to go on a vacation, that's good. But if you use it to run over your neighbor's dog because it barks all night long and tears up your flower garden, that's not so good!

Applying the Concepts 1–4

Just a Pinch Between Your Cheek and Gum

As the evidence on the adverse effects of cigarette smoke grew, people tried many different ways to quit smoking. Some people tried chewing tobacco or, as it was called, smokeless tobacco. A small amount of tobacco was placed between the cheek and gum. Certain chemicals from the tobacco were absorbed into the bloodstream and gave the sensation of smoking cigarettes. This prompted studies on the adverse effects of smokeless tobacco. One study in particular used 40 university students as subjects. Twenty were given smokeless tobacco to chew, and twenty given a substance that looked and tasted like smokeless tobacco, but did not contain any of the harmful substances. The students were randomly assigned to one of the groups. The students' blood pressure and heart rate were measured before they started chewing and 20 minutes after they had begun chewing. A significant increase in heart rate occurred in the group that chewed the smokeless tobacco. Answer the following questions.

1. What type of study was this (observational, quasi-experimental, or experimental)?
2. What are the independent and dependent variables?
3. Which was the treatment group?
4. Could the students' blood pressures be affected by knowing that they are part of a study?
5. List some possible confounding variables.
6. Do you think this is a good way to study the effect of smokeless tobacco?

See page 40 for the answers.

≡ Exercises 1–4

1. Explain the difference between an observational and an experimental study.

2. Name and define the three types of observational studies.

3. List some advantages and disadvantages of an observational study.

4. List some advantages and disadvantages of an experimental study.

5. What is the difference between an experimental study and a quasi-experimental study?

6. What is the difference between independent variables and dependent variables?

7. Why are a treatment group and a control group used in a statistical study?

8. Explain the Hawthorne effect.

9. What is a confounding variable?

10. Define the placebo effect in a statistical study.

11. What is meant by blinding and double-blinding?

12. Why do researchers use randomization in statistical studies?

13. What is the difference between a completely randomized design and a matched-pair design?

14. Why is replication used in statistical studies?

For Exercises 15–18, determine whether an observational study or an experimental study was used.

15. Subjects are randomly assigned to three groups. Group 1 receives a placebo daily, group 2 receives a high dose of vitamin B daily, and group 3 receives a multivitamin daily. After 3 months, each participant is asked how many incidents of depression that she or he had, and the occurrences were compared.

16. In a large city, a researcher decides to check the police department records for 2 months to determine what types of vehicles were stolen.

17. In a public park, visitors were asked how many minutes a day they walked their dogs.

18. Subjects were randomly divided into two groups. One group was permitted 4 hours of sleep each night for one week. The other group was allowed to sleep at least 8 hours each night for one week. The blood pressures of both groups were taken at the end of the week and compared.

In Exercises 19–22, identify the independent variable and the dependent variable.

19. According to the *British Journal of Sports Medicine*, a regular 30-minute workout could slash your risk of catching a cold by 43%.

20. The *Journal of Behavioral Medicine* reported that sharing a hug and holding hands can limit the physical effects of stress such as soaring heart rate and elevated blood pressure.

21. A research study stated that meditation helps people make more-rational decisions.

22. A researcher found that the number of times people visited fast-food restaurants increased with increasing income. (Source: healthland.time.com)

For Exercises 23–26, suggest some confounding variables that the researcher might want to consider when doing a study.

23. *Psychology Today* magazine reports that the more intelligent a person is (based on IQ), the more willing the person is to make a cooperative choice rather than a selfish one.

24. *The New England Journal of Medicine* reported that when poor women move to better neighborhoods, they lower the risk of developing obesity and diabetes.

25. A researcher from the University of California found that gratitude can produce positive emotions that can lead to a longer, healthier life.

26. York University in Toronto, Canada, stated that people who had suffered from fibromyalgia were able to reduce their pain by participating in twice-weekly yoga sessions.

For Exercises 27–31, give a reason why the statement made might be misleading.

27. Our product will give you the perfect body.

28. Here is the whole truth about back pain.

29. Our pain medicine will give you 24 hours of pain relief.

30. By reading this book, you will increase your IQ by 20 points.

31. Eating 21 grams of fiber may help you to lose weight.

32. List the steps you should perform when conducting a statistical study.

33. Beneficial Bacteria According to a pilot study of 20 people conducted at the University of Minnesota, daily doses of a compound called arabinogalactan over a period of 6 months resulted in a significant increase in the beneficial lactobacillus species of bacteria. Why can't it be concluded that the compound is beneficial for the majority of people?

34. Comment on the following statement, taken from a magazine advertisement: "In a recent clinical study, Brand ABC (actual brand will not be named) was proved to be 1950% better than creatine!"

35. In an ad for women, the following statement was made: "For every 100 women, 91 have taken the road less traveled." Comment on this statement.

36. In many ads for weight loss products, under the product claims and in small print, the following statement is made: "These results are not typical." What does this say about the product being advertised?

37. In an ad for moisturizing lotion, the following claim is made: ". . . it's the number 1 dermatologist-recommended brand." What is misleading about this claim?

38. An ad for an exercise product stated: "Using this product will burn 74% more calories." What is misleading about this statement?

39. "Vitamin E is a proven antioxidant and may help in fighting cancer and heart disease." Is there anything ambiguous about this claim? Explain.

40. "Just 1 capsule of Brand X can provide 24 hours of acid control." (Actual brand will not be named.) What needs to be more clearly defined in this statement?

41. ". . . Male children born to women who smoke during pregnancy run a risk of violent and criminal behavior that lasts well into adulthood." Can we infer that smoking during pregnancy is responsible for criminal behavior in people?

42. Caffeine and Health In the 1980s, a study linked coffee to a higher risk of heart disease and pancreatic cancer. In the early 1990s, studies showed that drinking coffee posed minimal health threats. However, in 1994, a study showed that pregnant women who drank 3 or more cups of tea daily may be at risk for spontaneous abortion. In 1998, a study claimed that women who drank more than a half-cup of caffeinated tea every day may actually increase their fertility. In 1998, a study showed that over a lifetime, a few extra cups of coffee a day can raise blood pressure, heart rate, and stress (Source: "Bottom Line: Is It Good for You? Or Bad?" by Monika Guttman, *USA TODAY Weekend*). Suggest some reasons why these studies appear to be conflicting.

Extending the Concepts

43. Find an article that describes a statistical study, and identify the study as observational or experimental.

44. For the article that you used in Exercise 43, identify the independent variable(s) and dependent variable for the study.

45. For the article that you selected in Exercise 43, suggest some confounding variables that may have an effect on the results of the study.

46. Select a newspaper or magazine article that involves a statistical study, and write a paper answering these questions.

    a. Is this study descriptive or inferential? Explain your answer.

    b. What are the variables used in the study? In your opinion, what level of measurement was used to obtain the data from the variables?

    c. Does the article define the population? If so, how is it defined? If not, how could it be defined?

    d. Does the article state the sample size and how the sample was obtained? If so, determine the size of the sample and explain how it was selected. If not, suggest a way it could have been obtained.

    e. Explain *in your own words* what procedure (survey, comparison of groups, etc.) might have been used to determine the study's conclusions.

    f. Do you agree or disagree with the conclusions? State your reasons.

1–5   Computers and Calculators

OBJECTIVE

Explain the importance of computers and calculators in statistics.

In the past, statistical calculations were done with pencil and paper. However, with the advent of calculators, numerical computations became much easier. Computers do all the numerical calculation. All one does is to enter the data into the computer and use the appropriate command; the computer will print the answer or display it on the screen. Now the TI-84 Plus graphing calculator accomplishes the same thing.

There are many statistical packages available. This book uses Microsoft Excel and MINITAB. Instructions for using the TI-84 Plus graphing calculator, Excel, and MINITAB have been placed at the end of each relevant section, in subsections entitled Technology Step by Step.

You should realize that the computer and calculator merely give numerical answers and save the time and effort of doing calculations by hand. You are still responsible for understanding and interpreting each statistical concept. In addition, you should realize that the results come from the data and do not appear magically on the computer. Doing calculations by using the procedure tables will help you reinforce this idea.

The author has left it up to instructors to choose how much technology they will incorporate into the course.

≡ Technology   Step by Step

TI-84 Plus

Step by Step

The TI-84 Plus graphing calculator can be used for a variety of statistical graphs and tests.

General Information

To turn calculator on:
Press **ON** key.
To turn calculator off:
Press **2nd [OFF]**.

To reset defaults only:

    1. Press **2nd**, then **[MEM]**.

    2. Select **7**, then **2**, then **2**.

Optional. To reset settings on calculator and clear memory (*note:* this will clear all settings and programs in the calculator's memory):
Press **2nd**, then **[MEM]**. Then press **7**, then **1**, then **2**.
(Also, the contrast may need to be adjusted after this.)
To adjust contrast (if necessary):
Press **2nd**. Then press and hold ▲ to darken or ▼ to lighten contrast.

To clear screen:

Press **CLEAR.**

(*Note:* This will return you to the screen you were using.)

To display a menu:

Press appropriate menu key. Example: **STAT.**

To return to home screen:

Press **2nd,** then **[QUIT].**

To move around on the screens:

Use the arrow keys.

To select items on the menu:

Press the corresponding number or move the cursor to the item, using the arrow keys. Then press **ENTER.**

(*Note:* In some cases, you do not have to press **ENTER,** and in other cases you may need to press **ENTER** twice.)

Entering Data

To enter single-variable data (clear the old list if necessary, see "Editing Data"):

1. Press **STAT** to display the Edit menu.

2. Press **ENTER** to select 1:Edit.

3. Enter the data in L₁ and press **ENTER** after each value.

4. After all data values are entered, press **STAT** to get back to the Edit menu or **2nd [QUIT]** to end.

Example TI1–1

Enter the following data values in L₁: **213, 208, 203, 215, 222.**

To enter multiple-variable data:

The TI-84 Plus will take up to six lists designated L₁, L₂, L₃, L₄, L₅, and L₆.

Output

1. To enter more than one set of data values, complete the preceding steps. Then move the cursor to L₂ by pressing the ▶ key.

2. Repeat the steps in the preceding part.

Editing Data

To correct a data value before pressing **ENTER,** use ◀ and retype the value and press **ENTER.**

To correct a data value in a list after pressing **ENTER,** move the cursor to the incorrect value in list and type in the correct value. Then press **ENTER.**

To delete a data value in a list:

Move the cursor to a value and press **DEL.**

To insert a data value in a list:

1. Move cursor to position where data value is to be inserted; then press **2nd [INS].**

2. Type data value; then press **ENTER.**

To clear a list:

1. Press **STAT,** then **4.**

2. Enter list to be cleared. Example: To clear L₁, press **2nd [L₁].** Then press **ENTER.**

   (*Note:* To clear several lists, follow Step 1, but enter each list to be cleared, separating them with commas. To clear all lists at once, follow Step 1; then press **ENTER.**)

Sorting Data

To sort the data in a list:

1. Enter the data in L₁.

2. Press **STAT 2** to get SortA to sort the list in ascending order.

3. Then press **2nd [L₁] ENTER.**

The calculator will display Done.

Output

4. Press **STAT ENTER** to display the sorted list.

(*Note:* The SortD or **3** sorts the list in descending order.)

Example TI1–2

Sort in ascending order the data values entered in
Example TI1–1.

EXCEL

Step by Step

Excel's Analysis
ToolPak Add-In

General Information

Microsoft Excel 2010 has two different ways to solve statistical problems. First, there are
built-in functions, such as STDEV and CHITEST, available from the standard toolbar by

clicking Formulas, and then selecting the Insert Function icon [fx Insert Function]. Another feature of Excel that
is useful for calculating multiple statistical measures and performing statistical tests for a set of
data is the Data Analysis command found in the Analysis ToolPak Add-in.

To load the Analysis ToolPak:

Click the File tab in the upper left-hand corner of an Excel workbook, then select Options in
the left-hand panel.

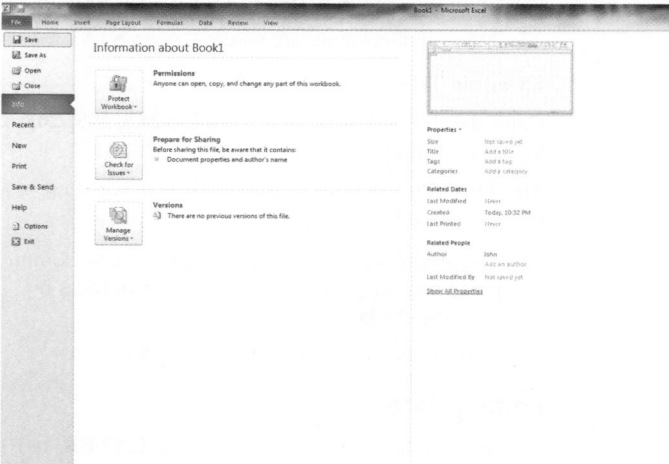

1. Click Add-Ins, and then click the Go button at the bottom of the Excel Options page to the
right of the Manage tool.

2. Check the Analysis ToolPak Add-in and click OK.

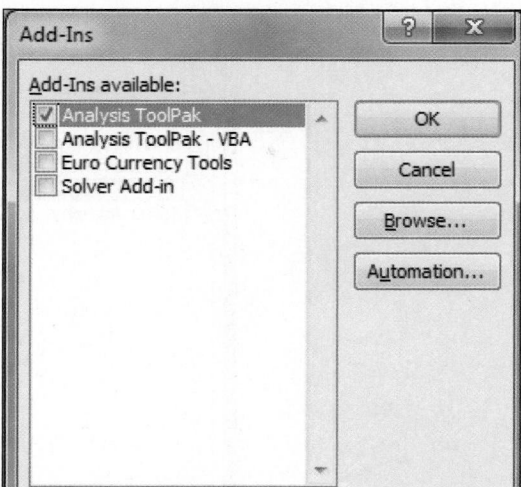

3. Click the Data Tab. The Analysis ToolPak will appear in the Analysis group.

MegaStat

Later in this text you will encounter a few Excel Technology Step by Step operations that will require the use of the MegaStat Add-in for Excel. MegaStat can be purchased from www.mhhe.com/megastat.

1. Save the Zip file containing the MegaStat Excel Add-in file (MegaStat.xls) and the associated help file on your computer's hard drive.

2. Open the Excel software.

3. Click the File tab and select Options (as before with the installation of the Analysis ToolPak).

4. Click the Add-Ins button. MegaStat will not appear as an Application until first installation.

5. Click Go button next to the Manage (Add-Ins) Tool at the bottom of the Excel Options window.

6. Once the Add-Ins Checkbox appears, click Browse to locate the MegaStat.xla file on your computer's hard drive.

7. Select the MegaStat.xla file from the hard drive; click the Checkbox next to it and click OK.

8. The MegaStat Add-in will appear when you select the Add-Ins tab in the Toolbar.

Entering Data

1. Select a cell at the top of a column on an Excel worksheet where you want to enter data. When working with data values for a single variable, you will usually want to enter the values into a single column.

2. Type each data value and press **[Enter]** or **[Tab]** on your keyboard.

You can also add more worksheets to an Excel workbook by clicking the Insert Worksheet icon located at the bottom of an open workbook.

Example XL1–1: Opening an existing Excel workbook/worksheet

1. Open the Microsoft Office Excel 2010 program.

2. Click the File tab, then click Open.

3. Click the name of the library that contains the file, such as My documents, and then click Open.

4. Click the name of the Excel file that you want to open and then click Open.

Note: Excel files have the extension .xls

MINITAB
Step by Step

General Information

MINITAB statistical software provides a wide range of statistical analysis and graphing capabilities.

Take Note

In this text you will see captured MINITAB images from Windows computers running MINITAB Release 16. If you are using an earlier or later release of MINITAB, the screens you see on your computer may bear slight visual differences from the screens pictured in this text.

Start the Program

1. Click the Windows Start Menu, then All Programs.
2. Click the MINITAB folder and then click ▥ Minitab 16, the program icon. The program screen will look similar to the one shown here. You will see the Session Window, the Worksheet Window, and perhaps the Project Manager Window.
3. Click the Project Manager icon on the toolbar to bring the project manager to the front.

To use the program, data must be entered from the keyboard or from a file.

Entering Data from the Keyboard

In MINITAB, all the data for one variable are stored in a column. Step by step instructions for entering these data follow.

Data
213   208   203   215   222

1. Click in row 1 of Worksheet 1***. This makes the worksheet the active window and puts the cursor in the first cell. The small data entry arrow in the upper left-hand corner of the worksheet should be pointing down. If it is not, click it to change the direction in which the cursor will move when you press the [Enter] key.

2. Type in each number, pressing [Enter] after each entry, including the last number typed.

3. *Optional:* Click in the space above row 1 to type in **Weight,** the column label.

Save a Worksheet File

4. Click on the **File Menu.** *Note:* This is *not* the same as clicking the disk icon 💾 .

5. Click **Save Current Worksheet As . . .**

6. In the dialog box you will need to verify three items:

   a) Save in: Click on or type in the disk drive and directory where you will store your data. This may be a thumb drive such as E:\ or a hard-drive folder such as C:\MinitabData.

   b) File Name: Type in the name of the file, such as **MyData.**

   c) Save as Type: If using the Student Edition, we would need to use the portable file format. The default here is MINITAB. An extension of mtw is added to the name.

   Click [Save]. The name of the worksheet will change from Worksheet 1*** to MyData. MTP***. The triple asterisks indicate the active worksheet.

Open the Databank File

The raw data are shown in Appendix B. There is a row for each person's data and a column for each variable. MINITAB data files comprised of data sets used in this book, including the Databank, are available at www.mhhe.com/bluman. Here is how to get the data from a file into a worksheet.

1. Click **File>Open Worksheet.** A sequence of menu instructions will be shown this way.

   Note: This is *not* the same as clicking the file icon 📂 . If the dialog box says **Open Project** instead of **Open Worksheet,** click [Cancel] and use the correct menu item. The **Open Worksheet** dialog box will be displayed.

2. You must check three items in this dialog box.

   a) The **Look In:** dialog box should show the directory where the file is located.

   b) Make sure the **Files of Type:** shows the correct type, MINITAB [*.mtp].

   c) Double-click the file name in the list box Databank.mtp. A dialog box may inform you that a copy of this file is about to be added to the project. Click on the checkbox if you do not want to see this warning again.

3. Click the [OK] button. The data will be copied into a second worksheet. Part of the worksheet is shown here.

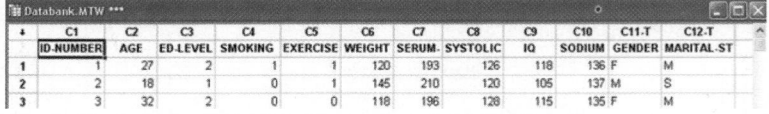

↓	C1	C2	C3	C4	C5	C6	C7	C8	C9	C10	C11-T	C12-T
	ID-NUMBER	AGE	ED-LEVEL	SMOKING	EXERCISE	WEIGHT	SERUM-	SYSTOLIC	IQ	SODIUM	GENDER	MARITAL-ST
1	1	27	2	1	1	120	193	126	118	136	F	M
2	2	18	1	0	1	145	210	120	105	137	M	S
3	3	32	2	0	0	118	196	128	115	135	F	M

   a) You may maximize the window and scroll if desired.

   b) C12-T Marital Status has a T appended to the label to indicate alphanumeric data. MyData.MTW is not erased or overwritten. Multiple worksheets can be available; however, only the active worksheet is available for analysis.

4. To switch between the worksheets, select **Window>MyData.MTW.**

5. Select **File>Exit** to quit. To save the project, click [Yes].

6. Type in the name of the file, **Chapter01.** The Data Window, the Session Window, and settings are all in one file called a project. Projects have an extension of mpj instead of mtw.

   Clicking the disk icon 💾 on the menu bar is the same as selecting **File>Save Project.**

   Clicking the file icon 📂 is the same as selecting **File>Open Project.**

7. Click [Save]. The mpj extension will be added to the name. The computer will return to the Windows desktop. The two worksheets, the Session Window results, and settings are saved in this project file. When a project file is opened, the program will start up right where you left off.

Summary

- The two major areas of statistics are descriptive and inferential. Descriptive statistics includes the collection, organization, summarization, and presentation of data. Inferential statistics includes making inferences from samples to populations, estimations and hypothesis testing, determining relationships, and making predictions. Inferential statistics is based on *probability theory*. (1–1)*

- Data can be classified as qualitative or quantitative. Quantitative data can be either discrete or continuous, depending on the values they can assume. Data can also be measured by various scales. The four basic levels of measurement are nominal, ordinal, interval, and ratio. (1–2)

- Since in most cases the populations under study are large, statisticians use subgroups called samples to get the necessary data for their studies. There are four basic methods used to obtain samples: random, systematic, stratified, and cluster. (1–3)

- There are two basic types of statistical studies: observational studies and experimental studies. When conducting observational studies, researchers observe what is happening or what has happened and then draw conclusions based on these observations. They do not attempt to manipulate the variables in any way. (1–4)

- When conducting an experimental study, researchers manipulate one or more of the independent or explanatory variables and see how this manipulation influences the dependent or outcome variable. (1–4)

- Finally, the applications of statistics are many and varied. People encounter them in everyday life, such as in reading newspapers or magazines, listening to an MP3 player, or watching television. Since statistics is used in almost every field of endeavor, the educated individual should be knowledgeable about the vocabulary, concepts, and procedures of statistics. Also, everyone should be aware that statistics can be misused. (1–4)

- Today, computers and calculators are used extensively in statistics to facilitate the computations. (1–5)

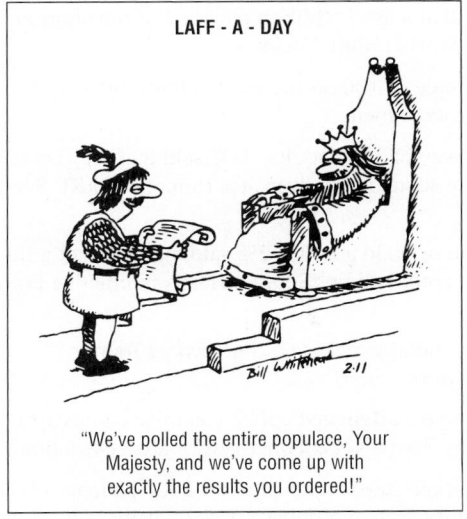

LAFF - A - DAY

"We've polled the entire populace, Your Majesty, and we've come up with exactly the results you ordered!"

© Dave Whitehead. King Features Syndicate.

*The numbers in parentheses indicate the chapter section where the material is explained.

Important Terms

blinding 20	continuous variables 6	descriptive statistics 3	inferential statistics 4
blocks 20	control group 19	discrete variables 6	interval level of measurement 8
boundary 7	convenience sample 14	double blinding 20	
census 3	cross-sectional study 18	experimental study 18	longitudinal study 18
cluster sample 14	data 3	explanatory variable 19	matched-pair design 20
completely randomized design 20	data set 3	Hawthorne effect 19	measurement scales 8
	data value or datum 3	hypothesis testing 4	nominal level of measurement 8
confounding variable 19	dependent variable 19	independent variable 19	

nonsampling error   16

observational study   18

ordinal level of
measurement   8

outcome variable   19

placebo effect   20

population   3

probability   4

qualitative variables   6

quantitative variables   6

quasi-experimental
study   19

random sample   12

random variable   3

ratio level of
measurement   8

replication   20

retrospective study   18

sample   3

sampling error   14

statistics   2

stratified sample   13

systematic sample   12

treatment group   19

variable   3

volunteer sample   14

≡ Review Exercises

Section 1–1

For Exercises 1–8, state whether descriptive or inferential statistics has been used.

1. By 2040 at least 3.5 billion people will run short of water (World Future Society).

2. In a sample of 100 on-the-job fatalities, 90% of the victims were men.

3. In a survey of 1000 adults, 34% said that they posted notes on social media websites (Source: AARP Survey).

4. In a poll of 3036 adults, 32% said that they got a flu shot at a retail clinic (Source: Harris Interactive Poll).

5. Allergy therapy makes bees go away (Source: *Prevention*).

6. Drinking decaffeinated coffee can raise cholesterol levels by 7% (Source: American Heart Association).

7. The average stay in a hospital for 2000 patients who had circulatory system problems was 4.7 days.

8. Experts say that mortgage rates may soon hit bottom (Source: *USA TODAY*).

Section 1–2

For Exercises 9–18, classify each as nominal-level, ordinal-level, interval-level, or ratio-level measurement.

9. Pages in the 25 best-selling mystery novels.

10. Rankings of golfers in a tournament.

11. Temperatures inside 10 pizza ovens.

12. Weights of selected cell phones.

13. Salaries of the coaches in the NFL.

14. Times required to complete a chess game.

15. Ratings of textbooks (poor, fair, good, excellent).

16. Number of amps delivered by battery chargers.

17. Ages of children in a day care center.

18. Categories of magazines in a physician's office (sports, women's, health, men's, news).

For Exercises 19–26, classify each variable as qualitative or quantitative.

19. Marital status of nurses in a hospital.

20. Time it takes to run a marathon.

21. Weights of lobsters in a tank in a restaurant.

22. Colors of automobiles in a shopping center parking lot.

23. Ounces of ice cream in a large milkshake.

24. Capacity of the NFL football stadiums.

25. Ages of people living in a personal care home.

26. Different vitamins taken.

For Exercises 27–34, classify each variable as discrete or continuous.

27. Number of pizzas sold by Pizza Express each day.

28. Relative humidity levels in operating rooms at local hospitals.

29. Number of bananas in a bunch at several local supermarkets.

30. Lifetimes (in hours) of 15 iPod batteries.

31. Weights of the backpacks of first-graders on a school bus.

32. Number of students each day who make appointments with a math tutor at a local college.

33. Blood pressures of runners in a marathon.

34. Ages of children in a preschool.

For Exercises 35–38, give the boundaries of each value.

35. 36 inches.

36. 105.4 miles.

37. 72.6 tons.

38. 5.27 centimeters.

Section 1–3

For Exercises 39–44, classify each sample as random, systematic, stratified, cluster, or other.

39. In a large school district, all teachers from two buildings are interviewed to determine whether they believe the students have less homework to do now than in previous years.

40. Every seventh customer entering a shopping mall is asked to select her or his favorite store.

41. Nursing supervisors are selected using random numbers to determine annual salaries.

42. Every 100th hamburger manufactured is checked to determine its fat content.

43. Mail carriers of a large city are divided into four groups according to gender (male or female) and according to whether they walk or ride on their routes. Then 10 are selected from each group and interviewed to determine whether they have been bitten by a dog in the last year.

44. People are asked to phone in their response to a survey question.

Section 1–4

For Exercises 45–48, identify each study as being either observational or experimental.

45. Subjects were randomly assigned to two groups, and one group was given an herb and the other group a placebo. After 6 months, the numbers of respiratory tract infections each group had were compared.

46. A researcher stood at a busy intersection to see if the color of the automobile that a person drives is related to running red lights.

47. A researcher finds that people who are more hostile have higher total cholesterol levels than those who are less hostile.

48. Subjects are randomly assigned to four groups. Each group is placed on one of four special diets—a low-fat diet, a high-fish diet, a combination of low-fat diet and high-fish diet, and a regular diet. After 6 months, the blood pressures of the groups are compared to see if diet has any effect on blood pressure.

For Exercises 49–52, identify the independent and dependent variables for each study.

49. Various types of coffees are selected from local coffee shops, and the number of milligrams of caffeine per ounce is determined.

50. People who walk at least 3 miles a day are randomly selected, and their blood triglyceride levels are measured in order to determine if the number of miles that they walk has any influence on these levels.

51. In an article in the *British Journal of Nutrition,* two types of mice were randomly selected. One group received a thyme supplement for a specific time, while another group was used as a control group and received no supplements. The brains of the mice were then analyzed, and it was found that the brains of the group of mice that received the thyme supplements had antioxidant levels similar to those of younger mice. It was concluded that the thyme supplement increased the antioxidants in the brains of the mice.

52. It was found that laughing can reduce your aches and pains as much as taking a pain pill.

For Exercises 53–58, explain why the claims of these studies might be suspect.

53. Based on a recent telephone survey, 72% of those contacted shop online.

54. In Greenville County there are 8324 deer.

55. Nursing school graduates from Fairview University earn on average $33,456.

56. Only 5% of men surveyed said that they liked "chick flicks."

57. A recent study shows that high school dropouts spend less time on the Internet than those who graduated; therefore, the Internet raises your IQ.

58. Most shark attacks occur in ocean water that is 3 feet deep; therefore, it is safer to swim in deep water.

≡ STATISTICS TODAY

Is Higher Education "Going Digital"? —Revisited

Researchers at the Pew Research Center used a telephone survey of 2142 graduates and an online survey of 1055 college and university presidents of two-year and four-year public and private colleges to ascertain their findings.

They found out that approximately 89% of public colleges and universities offer online classes while 60% of four-year private colleges offer them. About 23% of the graduates said that they have taken an online course. The college presidents predict that in 10 years, most of their students will have taken an online course.

As to the value of the online courses, 51% of the college presidents say that on-line courses are of equal value to classroom courses, but only 29% of the graduates say that they are of equal value.

Fifty-five percent of the college presidents said that plagiarism has increased over the last 10 years, and 89% said that the use of computers and the Internet have contributed to the increases.

Fifty-seven percent of recent college graduates said that they have used a laptop, smartphone, or computer tablets in the classroom. Most colleges have no rules for their use, but leave it up to the individual instructor to determine the limitations of their use.

≡ Chapter Quiz

Determine whether each statement is true or false. If the statement is false, explain why.

1. Probability is used as a basis for inferential statistics.

2. When the sample does not represent the population, it is called a biased sample.

3. The difference between a sampling measure and a population measure is called a nonsampling error.

4. When the population of college professors is divided into groups according to their rank (instructor, assistant professor, etc.) and then several are selected from each group to make up a sample, the sample is called a cluster sample.

5. The variable temperature is an example of a quantitative variable.

6. The height of basketball players is considered a continuous variable.

7. The boundary of a value such as 6 inches would be 5.9–6.1 inches.

Select the best answer.

8. The number of ads on a one-hour television show is what type of data?
   a. Nominal
   b. Qualitative
   c. Discrete
   d. Continuous

9. What are the boundaries of 25.6 ounces?
   a. 25–26 ounces
   b. 25.55–25.65 ounces
   c. 25.5–25.7 ounces
   d. 20–39 ounces

10. A researcher divided subjects into two groups according to gender and then selected members from each group for her sample. What sampling method was the researcher using?
   a. Cluster
   b. Random
   c. Systematic
   d. Stratified

11. Data that can be classified according to color are measured on what scale?
   a. Nominal
   b. Ratio
   c. Ordinal
   d. Interval

12. A study that involves no researcher intervention is called
   a. An experimental study.
   b. A noninvolvement study.
   c. An observational study.
   d. A quasi-experimental study.

13. A variable that interferes with other variables in the study is called
   a. A confounding variable.
   b. An explanatory variable.
   c. An outcome variable.
   d. An interfering variable.

Use the best answer to complete these statements.

14. Two major branches of statistics are _____ and _____.

15. Two uses of probability are _____ and _____.

16. The group of all subjects under study is called a(n) _____.

17. A group of subjects selected from the group of all subjects under study is called a(n) _____.

18. Three reasons why samples are used in statistics:
   a. _____ *b.* _____ *c.* _____.

19. The four basic sampling methods are
   a. _____ *b.* _____ *c.* _____ *d.* _____.

20. A study that uses intact groups when it is not possible to randomly assign participants to the groups is called a(n) _____ study.

21. In a research study, participants should be assigned to groups using _____ methods, if possible.

22. For each statement, decide whether descriptive or inferential statistics is used.

   a. The average life expectancy in New Zealand is 78.49 years (Source: *World Factbook*).
   b. A diet high in fruits and vegetables will lower blood pressure (Source: Institute of Medicine).
   c. The total amount of estimated losses for Hurricane Katrina was $125 billion (Source: *The World Almanac and Book of Facts*).
   d. Researchers stated that the shape of a person's ears is relative to the person's aggression (Source: *American Journal of Human Biology*).

   e. In 2050, it is estimated that there will be 18 million Americans who are age 85 and over (Source: U.S. Census Bureau).

23. Classify each as nominal-level, ordinal-level, interval-level, or ratio-level of measurement.

   a. Rating of movies as G, PG, and R
   b. Number of candy bars sold on a fund drive
   c. Classification of automobiles as subcompact, compact, standard, and luxury
   d. Temperatures of hair dryers
   e. Weights of suitcases on a commercial airliner

24. Classify each variable as discrete or continuous.

   a. Ages of people working in a large factory
   b. Number of cups of coffee served at a restaurant
   c. The amount of drug injections into a guinea pig
   d. The time it takes a student to drive to school
   e. The number of gallons of milk sold each day at a grocery store

25. Give the boundaries of each.

   a. 32 minutes
   b. 0.48 millimeter
   c. 6.2 inches
   d. 19 pounds
   e. 12.1 quarts

Critical Thinking Challenges

1. World's Busiest Airports A study of the world's busiest airports was conducted by *Airports Council International*. Describe three variables that one could use to determine which airports are the busiest. What *units* would one use to measure these variables? Are these variables categorical, discrete, or continuous?

2. Smoking and Criminal Behavior The results of a study published in *Archives of General Psychiatry* stated that male children born to women who smoke during pregnancy run a risk of violent and criminal behavior that lasts into adulthood. The results of this study were challenged by some people in the media. Give several reasons why the results of this study would be challenged.

3. Piano Lessons Improve Math Ability The results of a study published in *Neurological Research* stated that second-graders who took piano lessons and played a computer math game more readily grasped math problems in fractions and proportions than a similar group who took an English class and played the same math

game. What type of inferential study was this? Give several reasons why the piano lessons could improve a student's math ability.

4. ACL Tears in Collegiate Soccer Players A study of 2958 collegiate soccer players showed that in 46 anterior cruciate ligament (ACL) tears, 36 were in women. Calculate the percentages of tears for each gender.

   a. Can it be concluded that female athletes tear their knees more often than male athletes?
   b. Comment on how this study's conclusion might have been reached.

5. Anger and Snap Judgments Read the article entitled "Anger Can Cause Snap Judgments" and answer the following questions.

   a. Is the study experimental or observational?
   b. What is the independent variable?
   c. What is the dependent variable?
   d. Do you think the sample sizes are large enough to merit the conclusion?

e. Based on the results of the study, what changes would you recommend to persons to help them reduce their anger?

6. Hostile Children Fight Unemployment Read the article entitled "Hostile Children Fight Unemployment" and answer the following questions.

a. Is the study experimental or observational?

b. What is the independent variable?

c. What is the dependent variable?

d. Suggest some confounding variables that may have influenced the results of the study.

e. Identify the three groups of subjects used in the study.

ANGER CAN CAUSE SNAP JUDGMENTS

Anger can make a normally unbiased person act with prejudice, according to a forthcoming study in the journal *Psychological Science*.

Assistant psychology professors David DeSteno at Northeastern University in Boston and Nilanjana Dasgupta at the University of Massachusetts, Amherst, randomly divided 81 study participants into two groups and assigned them a writing task designed to induce angry, sad or neutral feelings. In a subsequent test to uncover nonconscious associations, angry subjects were quicker to connect negatively charged words—like war, death and vomit—with members of the opposite group—even though the groupings were completely arbitrary.

"These automatic responses guide our behavior when we're not paying attention," says DeSteno, and they can lead to discriminatory acts when there is pressure to make a quick decision. "If you're aware that your emotions might be coloring these gut reactions," he says, "you should take time to consider that possibility and adjust your actions accordingly."

—*Eric Strand*

Source: Reprinted with permission from *Psychology Today,* Copyright © (2004) Sussex Publishers, Inc.

UNEMPLOYMENT

Hostile Children Fight Unemployment

Aggressive children may be destined for later long-term unemployment. In a study that began in 1968, researchers at the University of Jyvaskyla in Finland examined about 300 participants at ages 8, 14, 27, and 36. They looked for aggressive behaviors like hurting other children, kicking objects when angry, or attacking others without reason.

Their results, published recently in the *International Journal of Behavioral Development*, suggest that children with low self-control of emotion —especially aggression—were significantly more prone to long-term unemployment. Children with behavioral inhibitions—such as passive and anxious behaviors—were also indirectly linked to unemployment as they lacked the preliminary initiative needed for school success. And while unemployment rates were high in Finland during the last data collection, jobless participants who were aggressive as children were less likely to have a job two years later than their nonaggressive counterparts.

Ongoing unemployment can have serious psychological consequences, including depression, anxiety and stress. But lead researcher Lea Pulkkinen, Ph.D., a Jyvaskyla psychology professor, does have encouraging news for parents: Aggressive children with good social skills and child-centered parents were significantly less likely to be unemployed for more than two years as adults.

—*Tanya Zimbardo*

Source: Reprinted with permission from *Psychology Today,* Copyright © (2001) Sussex Publishers, Inc.

Data Projects

1. **Business and Finance** Investigate the types of data that are collected regarding stock and bonds, for example, price, earnings ratios, and bond ratings. Find as many types of data as possible. For each, identify the level of measurement as nominal, ordinal, interval, or ratio. For any quantitative data, also note if they are discrete or continuous.

2. **Sports and Leisure** Select a professional sport. Investigate the types of data that are collected about that sport, for example, in baseball, the level of play (A, AA, AAA, Major League), batting average, and home-run hits. For each, identify the level of measurement as nominal, ordinal, interval, or ratio. For any quantitative data, also note if they are discrete or continuous.

3. **Technology** Music organization programs on computers and music players maintain information about a song, such as the writer, song length, genre, and your personal rating. Investigate the types of data collected about a song. For each, identify the level of measurement as nominal, ordinal, interval, or ratio. For any quantitative data, also note if they are discrete or continuous.

4. **Health and Wellness** Think about the types of data that can be collected about your health and wellness, things such as blood type, cholesterol level, smoking status, and body mass index. Find as many data items as you can. For each, identify the level of measurement as nominal, ordinal, interval, or ratio. For any quantitative data, also note if they are discrete or continuous.

5. **Politics and Economics** Every 10 years since 1790, the federal government has conducted a census of U.S. residents. Investigate the types of data that were collected in the 2010 census. For each, identify the level of measurement as nominal, ordinal, interval, or ratio. For any quantitative data, also note if they are discrete or continuous. Use the library or a genealogy website to find a census form from 1860. What types of data were collected? How do the types of data differ?

6. **Your Class** Your school probably has a database that contains information about each student, such as age, county of residence, credits earned, and ethnicity. Investigate the types of student data that your college collects and reports. For each, identify the level of measurement as nominal, ordinal, interval, or ratio. For any quantitative data, also note if they are discrete or continuous.

Answers to Applying the Concepts

Section 1–1   Attendance and Grades

1. The variables are grades and attendance.

2. The data consist of specific grades and attendance numbers.

3. These are descriptive statistics; however, if an inference were made to all students, then that would be inferential statistics.

4. The population under study is students at Manatee Community College (MCC).

5. While not specified, we probably have data from a sample of MCC students.

6. Based on the data, it appears that, in general, the better your attendance, the higher your grade.

Section 1–2   Fatal Transportation Injuries

1. The variables are transportation industry and fatal injuries.

2. Transportation industry is a qualitative variable, and the number of fatal injuries is a quantitative variable.

3. The number of fatalities is discrete.

4. The type of industry is nominal, and the number of fatalities is ratio.

5. Even though the number of fatalities for the railroad industry is lowest, you should consider the fact that fewer people use the railroads to travel than the other industries.

6. A person's transportation choice might also be affected by convenience, cost, service, availability, etc.

7. Answers will vary. The railroad industry had the fewest fatalities followed by water vehicle accidents while the aircraft accidents were about three times as many as the water vehicle accidents. Of course, the most fatalities occurred in highway accidents.

Section 1–3   American Culture and Drug Abuse

Answers will vary, so this is one possible answer.

1. I used a telephone survey. The advantage to my survey method is that this was a relatively inexpensive survey method (although more expensive than using the mail) that could get a fairly sizable response. The disadvantage to my survey method is that I have not included anyone without a telephone. (*Note:* My survey used a random dialing method to include unlisted numbers and cell phone exchanges.)

2. A mail survey also would have been fairly inexpensive, but my response rate may have been much lower than what I got with my telephone survey. Interviewing

would have allowed me to use follow-up questions and to clarify any questions of the respondents at the time of the interview. However, interviewing is very labor- and cost-intensive.

3. I used ordinal data on a scale of 1 to 5. The scores were 1 = strongly disagree, 2 = disagree, 3 = neutral, 4 = agree, 5 = strongly agree.

4. The random method that I used was a random dialing method.

5. To include people from each state, I used a stratified random sample, collecting data randomly from each of the area codes and telephone exchanges available.

6. This method allowed me to make sure that I had representation from each area of the United States.

7. Convenience samples may not be representative of the population, and a convenience sample of adolescents would probably differ greatly from the general population with regard to the influence of American culture on illegal drug use.

Section 1–4   Just a Pinch Between Your Cheek and Gum

1. This was an experiment, since the researchers imposed a treatment on each of the two groups involved in the study.

2. The independent variable is whether the participant chewed tobacco or not. The dependent variables are the students' blood pressures and heart rates.

3. The treatment group is the tobacco group—the other group was used as a control.

4. A student's blood pressure might not be affected by knowing that he or she was part of a study. However, if the student's blood pressure were affected by this knowledge, all the students (in both groups) would be affected similarly. This might be an example of the placebo effect.

5. Answers will vary. One possible answer is that confounding variables might include the way that the students chewed the tobacco, whether or not the students smoked (although this would hopefully have been evened out with the randomization), and that all the participants were university students.

6. Answers will vary. One possible answer is that the study design was fine, but that it cannot be generalized beyond the population of university students (or people around that age).

Frequency Distributions and Graphs

OUTLINE

Introduction

2–1 Organizing Data

2–2 Histograms, Frequency Polygons, and Ogives

2–3 Other Types of Graphs

Summary

OBJECTIVES

After completing this chapter, you should be able to

1 Organize data using a frequency distribution.

2 Represent data in frequency distributions graphically, using histograms, frequency polygons, and ogives.

3 Represent data using bar graphs, Pareto charts, time series graphs, pie graphs, and dotplots.

4 Draw and interpret a stem and leaf plot.

≡ STATISTICS TODAY

How Your Identity Can Be Stolen

Identity fraud is a big business today—more than 8.1 million people were victims. The total amount of the fraud in 2010 was $37 billion. The average amount of the fraud for a victim is $4607, and the average time to correct the problem is 40 hours. The ways in which a person's identity can be stolen are presented in the following table:

Lost or stolen wallet, checkbook, or credit card	38%
Friends, acquaintances	15
Corrupt business employees	15
Computer viruses and hackers	9
Stolen mail or fraudulent change of address	8
Online purchases or transactions	4
Other methods	11

Source: Javelin Strategy & Research; Council of Better Business Bureau, Inc.

Looking at the numbers presented in a table does not have the same impact as presenting numbers in a well-drawn chart or graph. The article did not include any graphs. This chapter will show you how to construct appropriate graphs to represent data and help you to get your point across to your audience.

See Statistics Today—Revisited at the end of the chapter for some suggestions on how to represent the data graphically.

Introduction

When conducting a statistical study, the researcher must gather data for the particular variable under study. For example, if a researcher wishes to study the number of people who were bitten by poisonous snakes in a specific geographic area over the past several years, he or she has to gather the data from various doctors, hospitals, or health departments.

To describe situations, draw conclusions, or make inferences about events, the researcher must organize the data in some meaningful way. The most convenient method of organizing data is to construct a *frequency distribution*.

After organizing the data, the researcher must present them so they can be understood by those who will benefit from reading the study. The most useful method of presenting the data is by constructing *statistical charts* and *graphs*. There are many different types of charts and graphs, and each one has a specific purpose.

This chapter explains how to organize data by constructing frequency distributions and how to present the data by constructing charts and graphs. The charts and graphs illustrated here are histograms, frequency polygons, ogives, pie graphs, Pareto charts, and time series graphs. A graph that combines the characteristics of a frequency distribution and a histogram, called a stem and leaf plot, is also explained.

2–1   Organizing Data

OBJECTIVE

Organize data using a frequency distribution.

Suppose a researcher wished to do a study on the ages of the 50 wealthiest people in the world. The researcher first would have to get the data on the ages of the people. In this case, these ages are listed in *Forbes Magazine*. When the data are in original form, they are called **raw data** and are listed next.

45	46	64	57	85
92	51	71	54	48
27	66	76	55	69
54	44	54	75	46
61	68	78	61	83
88	45	89	67	56
81	58	55	62	38
55	56	64	81	38
49	68	91	56	68
46	47	83	71	62

Since little information can be obtained from looking at raw data, the researcher organizes the data into what is called a *frequency distribution*.

A **frequency distribution** is the organization of raw data in table form, using classes and frequencies.

Each raw data value is placed into a quantitative or qualitative category called a **class.** The **frequency** of a class then is the number of data values contained in a specific class. A frequency distribution is shown for the preceding data set.

Class limits	Tally	Frequency
27–35	/	1
36–44	///	3
45–53	7H/ ////	9
54–62	7H/ 7H/ 7H/	15
63–71	7H/ 7H/	10
72–80	///	3
81–89	7H/ //	7
90–98	//	2
		‾‾
		50

Now some general observations can be made from looking at the frequency distribution. For example, it can be stated that the majority of the wealthy people in the study are over 45 years old.

The classes in this distribution are 27–35, 36–44, etc. These values are called *class limits.* The data values 27, 28, 29, 30, 31, 32, 33, 34, 35 can be tallied in the first class; 36, 37, 38, 39, 40, 41, 42, 43, 44 in the second class; and so on.

Two types of frequency distributions that are most often used are the *categorical frequency distribution* and the *grouped frequency distribution.* The procedures for constructing these distributions are shown now.

Categorical Frequency Distributions

The **categorical frequency distribution** is used for data that can be placed in specific categories, such as nominal- or ordinal-level data. For example, data such as political affiliation, religious affiliation, or major field of study would use categorical frequency distributions.

EXAMPLE 2–1 Distribution of Blood Types

Twenty-five army inductees were given a blood test to determine their blood type. The data set is

A	B	B	AB	O
O	O	B	AB	B
B	B	O	A	O
A	O	O	O	AB
AB	A	O	B	A

Construct a frequency distribution for the data.

SOLUTION

Since the data are categorical, discrete classes can be used. There are four blood types: A, B, O, and AB. These types will be used as the classes for the distribution.

The procedure for constructing a frequency distribution for categorical data is given next.

Step 1 Make a table as shown.

A Class	B Tally	C Frequency	D Percent
A			
B			
O			
AB			

Step 2   Tally the data and place the results in column B.

Step 3   Count the tallies and place the results in column C.

Step 4   Find the percentage of values in each class by using the formula

$$\% = \frac{f}{n} \cdot 100$$

where f = frequency of the class and n = total number of values. For example, in the class of type A blood, the percentage is

$$\% = \frac{5}{25} \cdot 100 = 20\%$$

Percentages are not normally part of a frequency distribution, but they can be added since they are used in certain types of graphs such as pie graphs. Also, the decimal equivalent of a percent is called a *relative frequency.*

Step 5   Find the totals for columns C (frequency) and D (percent). The completed table is shown. It is a good idea to add the percent column to make sure it sums to 100%. This column won't always sum to 100% because of rounding.

A Class	B Tally	C Frequency	D Percent
A	卌	5	20
B	卌 //	7	28
0	卌 ////	9	36
AB	////	4	16
		Total 25	100%

For the sample, more people have type O blood than any other type.

Grouped Frequency Distributions

When the range of the data is large, the data must be grouped into classes that are more than one unit in width, in what is called a **grouped frequency distribution.** For example, a distribution of the blood glucose levels in milligrams per deciliter (mg/dL) for 50 randomly selected college students is shown.

Class limits	Class boundaries	Tally	Frequency
58–64	57.5–64.5	/	1
65–71	64.5–71.5	卌 /	6
72–78	71.5–78.5	卌 卌	10
79–85	78.5–85.5	卌 卌 ////	14
86–92	85.5–92.5	卌 卌 //	12
93–99	92.5–99.5	卌	5
100–106	99.5–106.5	//	2
			Total 50

The procedure for constructing the preceding frequency distribution is given in Example 2–2; however, several things should be noted. In this distribution, the values 58 and 64 of the first class are called *class limits.* The **lower class limit** is 58; it represents the smallest data value that can be included in the class. The **upper class limit** is 64; it represents the largest data value that can be included in the class. The numbers in the second column are called **class boundaries.** These numbers are used to separate the classes so that there are no gaps in the frequency distribution. The gaps are due to the limits; for example, there is a gap between 64 and 65.

Students sometimes have difficulty finding class boundaries when given the class limits. The basic rule of thumb is that *the class limits should have the same decimal place value as the data, but the class boundaries should have one additional place value and end in a 5.* For example, if the values in the data set are whole numbers, such as 59, 68, and 82, the limits for a class might be 58–64, and the boundaries are 57.5–64.5. Find the boundaries by subtracting 0.5 from 58 (the lower class limit) and adding 0.5 to 64 (the upper class limit).

$$\text{Lower limit} - 0.5 = 58 - 0.5 = 57.5 = \text{lower boundary}$$
$$\text{Upper limit} + 0.5 = 64 + 0.5 = 64.5 = \text{upper boundary}$$

If the data are in tenths, such as 6.2, 7.8, and 12.6, the limits for a class hypothetically might be 7.8–8.8, and the boundaries for that class would be 7.75–8.85. Find these values by subtracting 0.05 from 7.8 and adding 0.05 to 8.8.

Class boundaries are not always included in frequency distributions; however, they give a more formal approach to the procedure of organizing data, including the fact that sometimes the data have been rounded. You should be familiar with boundaries since you may encounter them in a statistical study.

Finally, the **class width** for a class in a frequency distribution is found by subtracting the lower (or upper) class limit of one class from the lower (or upper) class limit of the next class. For example, the class width in the preceding distribution on the distribution of blood glucose levels is 7, found from $65 - 58 = 7$.

The class width can also be found by subtracting the lower boundary from the upper boundary for any given class. In this case, $64.5 - 57.5 = 7$.

Note: Do not subtract the limits of a single class. It will result in an incorrect answer.

The researcher must decide how many classes to use and the width of each class. To construct a frequency distribution, follow these rules:

1. *There should be between 5 and 20 classes.* Although there is no hard-and-fast rule for the number of classes contained in a frequency distribution, it is of utmost importance to have enough classes to present a clear description of the collected data.

2. *It is preferable but not absolutely necessary that the class width be an odd number.* This ensures that the midpoint of each class has the same place value as the data. The **class midpoint** X_m is obtained by adding the lower and upper boundaries and dividing by 2, or adding the lower and upper limits and dividing by 2:

$$X_m = \frac{\text{lower boundary} + \text{upper boundary}}{2}$$

or

$$X_m = \frac{\text{lower limit} + \text{upper limit}}{2}$$

For example, the midpoint of the first class in the example with glucose levels is

$$\frac{58 + 64}{2} = 61 \quad \text{or} \quad \frac{57.5 + 64.5}{2} = 61$$

The midpoint is the numeric location of the center of the class. Midpoints are necessary for graphing (see Section 2–2). If the class width is an even number, the midpoint is in tenths. For example, if the class width is 6 and the boundaries are 5.5 and 11.5, the midpoint is

$$\frac{5.5 + 11.5}{2} = \frac{17}{2} = 8.5$$

Rule 2 is only a suggestion, and it is not rigorously followed, especially when a computer is used to group data.

3. *The classes must be mutually exclusive.* Mutually exclusive classes have nonoverlapping class limits so that data cannot be placed into two classes. Many times, frequency distributions such as this

Age
10–20
20–30
30–40
40–50

are found in the literature or in surveys. If a person is 40 years old, into which class should she or he be placed? A better way to construct a frequency distribution is to use classes such as

Age
10–20
21–31
32–42
43–53

Recall that boundaries are mutually exclusive. For example, when a class boundary is 5.5 to 10.5, the data values that are included in that class are values from 6 to 10. A data value of 5 goes into the previous class, and a data value of 11 goes into the next-higher class.

4. *The classes must be continuous.* Even if there are no values in a class, the class must be included in the frequency distribution. There should be no gaps in a frequency distribution. The only exception occurs when the class with a zero frequency is the first or last class. A class with a zero frequency at either end can be omitted without affecting the distribution.

5. *The classes must be exhaustive.* There should be enough classes to accommodate all the data.

6. *The classes must be equal in width.* This avoids a distorted view of the data.

    One exception occurs when a distribution has a class that is **open-ended.** That is, the first class has no specific lower limit, or the last class has no specific upper limit. A frequency distribution with an open-ended class is called an **open-ended distribution.** Here are two examples of distributions with open-ended classes.

Age	Frequency
10–20	3
21–31	6
32–42	4
43–53	10
54 and above	8

Minutes	Frequency
Below 110	16
110–114	24
115–119	38
120–124	14
125–129	5

The frequency distribution for age is open-ended for the last class, which means that anybody who is 54 years or older will be tallied in the last class. The distribution for minutes is open-ended for the first class, meaning that any minute values below 110 will be tallied in that class.

The steps for constructing a grouped frequency distribution are summarized in the following Procedure Table.

Procedure Table

Constructing a Grouped Frequency Distribution

Step 1   Determine the classes.

   Find the highest and lowest values.

   Find the range.

   Select the number of classes desired.

   Find the width by dividing the range by the number of classes and rounding up.

   Select a starting point (usually the lowest value or any convenient number less than the lowest value); add the width to get the lower limits.

   Find the upper class limits.

   Find the boundaries.

Step 2   Tally the data.

Step 3   Find the numerical frequencies from the tallies, and find the cumulative frequencies.

Example 2–2 shows the procedure for constructing a grouped frequency distribution, i.e., when the classes contain more than one data value.

EXAMPLE 2–2   Record High Temperatures

These data represent the record high temperatures in degrees Fahrenheit (°F) for each of the 50 states. Construct a grouped frequency distribution for the data, using 7 classes.

112	100	127	120	134	118	105	110	109	112
110	118	117	116	118	122	114	114	105	109
107	112	114	115	118	117	118	122	106	110
116	108	110	121	113	120	119	111	104	111
120	113	120	117	105	110	118	112	114	114

Source: The World Almanac and Book of Facts.

SOLUTION

The procedure for constructing a grouped frequency distribution for numerical data follows.

Step 1   Determine the classes.

   Find the highest value and lowest value: $H = 134$ and $L = 100$.

   Find the range: R = highest value − lowest value = $H - L$, so

$$R = 134 - 100 = 34$$

   Select the number of classes desired (usually between 5 and 20). In this case, 7 is arbitrarily chosen.

   Find the class width by dividing the range by the number of classes.

$$\text{Width} = \frac{R}{\text{number of classes}} = \frac{34}{7} = 4.9$$

Unusual Stats

America's most popular beverages are soft drinks. It is estimated that, on average, each person drinks about 52 gallons of soft drinks per year, compared to 22 gallons of beer.

Round the answer up to the nearest whole number if there is a remainder: $4.9 \approx 5$. (Rounding *up* is different from rounding *off*. A number is rounded up if there is any decimal remainder when dividing. For example, $85 \div 6 = 14.167$ and is rounded up to 15. Also, $53 \div 4 = 13.25$ and is rounded up to 14. Also, after dividing, if there is no remainder, you will need to add an extra class to accommodate all the data.)

Select a starting point for the lowest class limit. This can be the smallest data value or any convenient number less than the smallest data value. In this case, 100 is used. Add the width to the lowest score taken as the starting point to get the lower limit of the next class. Keep adding until there are 7 classes, as shown, 100, 105, 110, etc.

Subtract one unit from the lower limit of the second class to get the upper limit of the first class. Then add the width to each upper limit to get all the upper limits.

$$105 - 1 = 104$$

The first class is 100–104, the second class is 105–109, etc.

Find the class boundaries by subtracting 0.5 from each lower class limit and adding 0.5 to each upper class limit:

$$99.5–104.5, \ 104.5–109.5, \text{ etc.}$$

Step 2   Tally the data.

Step 3   Find the numerical frequencies from the tallies.

The completed frequency distribution is

Class limits	Class boundaries	Tally	Frequency
100–104	99.5–104.5	//	2
105–109	104.5–109.5	7/// ///	8
110–114	109.5–114.5	7/// 7/// 7/// ///	18
115–119	114.5–119.5	7/// 7/// ///	13
120–124	119.5–124.5	7/// //	7
125–129	124.5–129.5	/	1
130–134	129.5–134.5	/	1
			Total 50

The frequency distribution shows that the class 109.5–114.5 contains the largest number of temperatures (18) followed by the class 114.5–119.5 with 13 temperatures. Hence, most of the temperatures (31) fall between 110 and 119°F.

Sometimes it is necessary to use a *cumulative frequency distribution*. A **cumulative frequency distribution** is a distribution that shows the number of data values less than or equal to a specific value (usually an upper boundary). The values are found by adding the frequencies of the classes less than or equal to the upper class boundary of a specific class. This gives an ascending cumulative frequency. In this example, the cumulative frequency for the first class is $0 + 2 = 2$; for the second class it is $0 + 2 + 8 = 10$; for the third class it is $0 + 2 + 8 + 18 = 28$. Naturally, a shorter way to do this would be to just add the cumulative frequency of the class below to the frequency of the given class. For example, the cumulative frequency for the number of data values less than 114.5 can be found by adding $10 + 18 = 28$. The cumulative frequency distribution for the data in this example is as follows:

	Cumulative frequency
Less than 99.5	0
Less than 104.5	2
Less than 109.5	10
Less than 114.5	28
Less than 119.5	41
Less than 124.5	48
Less than 129.5	49
Less than 134.5	50

Cumulative frequencies are used to show how many data values are accumulated up to and including a specific class. In Example 2–2, of the total record high temperatures 28 are less than or equal to 114°F. Forty-eight of the total record high temperatures are less than or equal to 124°F.

After the raw data have been organized into a frequency distribution, it will be analyzed by looking for peaks and extreme values. The peaks show which class or classes have the most data values compared to the other classes. Extreme values, called *outliers,* show large or small data values that are relative to other data values.

When the range of the data values is relatively small, a frequency distribution can be constructed using single data values for each class. This type of distribution is called an **ungrouped frequency distribution** and is shown next.

EXAMPLE 2–3   MPGs for SUVs

The data shown here represent the number of miles per gallon (mpg) that 30 selected four-wheel-drive sport utility vehicles obtained in city driving. Construct a frequency distribution, and analyze the distribution.

12	17	12	14	16	18
16	18	12	16	17	15
15	16	12	15	16	16
12	14	15	12	15	15
19	13	16	18	16	14

Source: Model Year Fuel Economy Guide. United States Environmental Protection Agency.

SOLUTION

Step 1   Determine the classes. Since the range of the data set is small ($19 - 12 = 7$), classes consisting of a single data value can be used. They are 12, 13, 14, 15, 16, 17, 18, 19.

Note: If the data are continuous, class boundaries can be used. Subtract 0.5 from each class value to get the lower class boundary, and add 0.5 to each class value to get the upper class boundary.

Step 2   Tally the data.

Step 3   Find the numerical frequencies from the tallies, and find the cumulative frequencies.

The completed ungrouped frequency distribution is

Class limits	Class boundaries	Tally	Frequency
12	11.5–12.5	𝍷𝍷𝍷𝍷𝍷 /	6
13	12.5–13.5	/	1
14	13.5–14.5	///	3
15	14.5–15.5	𝍷𝍷𝍷𝍷𝍷 /	6
16	15.5–16.5	𝍷𝍷𝍷𝍷𝍷 ///	8
17	16.5–17.5	//	2
18	17.5–18.5	///	3
19	18.5–19.5	/	1

In this case, almost one-half (14) of the vehicles get 15 or 16 miles per gallon. The cumulative frequencies are

	Cumulative frequency
Less than 11.5	0
Less than 12.5	6
Less than 13.5	7
Less than 14.5	10
Less than 15.5	16
Less than 16.5	24
Less than 17.5	26
Less than 18.5	29
Less than 19.5	30

When you are constructing a frequency distribution, the guidelines presented in this section should be followed. However, you can construct several different but correct frequency distributions for the same data by using a different class width, a different number of classes, or a different starting point.

Furthermore, the method shown here for constructing a frequency distribution is not unique, and there are other ways of constructing one. Slight variations exist, especially in computer packages. But regardless of what methods are used, classes should be mutually exclusive, continuous, exhaustive, and of equal width.

In summary, the different types of frequency distributions were shown in this section. The first type, shown in Example 2–1, is used when the data are categorical (nominal), such as blood type or political affiliation. This type is called a categorical frequency distribution. The second type of distribution is used when the range is large and classes several units in width are needed. This type is called a grouped frequency distribution and is shown in Example 2–2. Another type of distribution is used for numerical data and when the range of data is small, as shown in Example 2–3. Since each class is only one unit, this distribution is called an ungrouped frequency distribution.

All the different types of distributions are used in statistics and are helpful when one is organizing and presenting data.

The reasons for constructing a frequency distribution are as follows:

1. To organize the data in a meaningful, intelligible way.

2. To enable the reader to determine the nature or shape of the distribution.

3. To facilitate computational procedures for measures of average and spread (shown in Sections 3–1 and 3–2).

Interesting Fact

Male dogs bite children more often than female dogs do; however, female cats bite children more often than male cats do.

4. To enable the researcher to draw charts and graphs for the presentation of data (shown in Section 2–2).

5. To enable the reader to make comparisons among different data sets.

The factors used to analyze a frequency distribution are essentially the same as those used to analyze histograms and frequency polygons, which are shown in Section 2–2.

≡ Applying the Concepts 2–1

Ages of Presidents at Inauguration

The data represent the ages of our Presidents at the time they were first inaugurated.

57	61	57	57	58	57	61	54	68
51	49	64	50	48	65	52	56	46
54	49	51	47	55	55	54	42	51
56	55	51	54	51	60	62	43	55
56	61	52	69	64	46	54	47	

1. Were the data obtained from a population or a sample? Explain your answer.
2. What was the age of the oldest President?
3. What was the age of the youngest President?
4. Construct a frequency distribution for the data. (Use your own judgment as to the number of classes and class size.)
5. Are there any peaks in the distribution?
6. Identify any possible outliers.
7. Write a brief summary of the nature of the data as shown in the frequency distribution.

See page 108 for the answers.

≡ Exercises 2–1

1. List five reasons for organizing data into a frequency distribution.

2. Name the three types of frequency distributions, and explain when each should be used.

3. How many classes should frequency distributions have? Why should the class width be an odd number?

4. What are open-ended frequency distributions? Why are they necessary?

For Exercises 5–8, find the class boundaries, midpoints, and widths for each class.

5. 43–47

6. 125–131

7. 8.24–11.36

8. 16.3–18.5

For Exercises 9–12, show frequency distributions that are incorrectly constructed. State the reasons why they are wrong.

9.

Class	Frequency
27–32	1
33–38	0
39–44	6
45–49	4
50–55	2

10.

Class	Frequency
5–9	1
9–13	2
13–17	5
17–20	6
20–24	3

11.

Class	Frequency
123–127	3
128–132	7
138–142	2
143–147	19

12.

Class	Frequency
9–13	1
14–19	6
20–25	2
26–28	5
29–32	9

13. Favorite Sport Fifty people were asked to identify their favorite sport. The responses were F = professional football, C = college football, B = baseball, and A = auto racing. Construct a categorical frequency distribution for the data. Which class has the most data values, and which class has the fewest data values? (Based on information from a Harris Interactive survey.)

F	C	F	A	B
C	F	F	B	C
A	B	C	C	F
F	A	F	C	A
C	C	F	F	C
F	F	B	C	F
B	A	F	B	F
F	C	B	A	C
B	F	C	F	A
B	B	F	C	F

14. Trust in Internet Information A survey was taken on how much trust people place in the information they read on the Internet. Construct a categorical frequency distribution for the data. A = trust in all that they read, M = trust in most of what they read, H = trust in about one-half of what they read, S = trust in a small portion of what they read. (Based on information from the *UCLA Internet Report.*)

M	M	M	A	H	M	S	M	H	M
S	M	M	M	A	A	M	M	A	M
M	M	H	M	M	M	H	M	H	M
A	M	M	M	H	M	M	M	M	M

15. Eating at Fast Food Restaurants A survey was taken of 50 individuals. They were asked how many days per week they ate at a fast-food restaurant. Construct a frequency distribution using 8 classes (0–7). Based on the distribution, how often did most people eat at a fast-food restaurant?

1	3	4	0	4
5	2	2	3	1
2	2	2	2	2
2	2	2	2	3
2	2	5	2	4
2	4	5	2	1
4	1	3	2	2
2	0	7	2	3
2	2	2	5	2
3	3	4	1	3

16. Ages of Dogs The ages of 20 dogs in a pet shelter are shown. Construct a frequency distribution using 7 classes.

5	8	7	6	3
9	4	4	5	8
7	4	7	5	7
3	5	8	4	9

17. Energy Used by Plasma TVs Forty plasma TVs were tested, and the number of watts per hour that they used while running for 4 hours per day were recorded. Construct a frequency distribution for the data. Use 6 classes.

480	503	514	472	465
473	475	500	502	506
492	477	483	475	481
512	473	488	485	503
508	484	486	499	512
485	468	507	501	470
497	479	492	468	492
466	472	483	511	481

18. Stories in the World's Tallest Buildings The number of stories in each of a sample of the world's 30 tallest buildings follows. Construct a grouped frequency distribution and a cumulative frequency distribution with 7 classes.

88	88	110	88	80	69	102	78	70	55
79	85	80	100	60	90	77	55	75	55
54	60	75	64	105	56	71	70	65	72

Source: *New York Times Almanac.*

19. Ages of Declaration of Independence Signers The ages of the signers of the Declaration of Independence are shown. (Age is approximate since only the birth year appeared in the source, and one has been omitted since his birth year is unknown.) Construct a grouped frequency distribution and a cumulative frequency distribution for the data, using 7 classes.

41	54	47	40	39	35	50	37	49	42	70	32
44	52	39	50	40	30	34	69	39	45	33	42
44	63	60	27	42	34	50	42	52	38	36	45
35	43	48	46	31	27	55	63	46	33	60	62
35	46	45	34	53	50	50					

Source: *The Universal Almanac.*

20. Salaries of Governors Here are the salaries (in dollars) of the governors of 25 randomly selected states. Construct a grouped frequency distribution with 6 classes.

112,895	117,312	140,533	110,000	115,331
95,000	177,500	120,303	139,590	150,000
173,987	130,000	133,821	144,269	142,542
150,000	145,885	105,000	93,600	166,891
130,273	70,000	113,834	117,817	137,092

Source: *World Almanac.*

21. Charity Donations A random sample of 30 large companies in the United States shows the amount, in millions of dollars, that each company donated to charity for a specific year. Construct a frequency distribution for the data, using 9 classes.

26	25	19	31	14
48	35	43	25	46
17	21	57	58	34
41	12	27	15	53
16	63	82	23	52
56	75	19	26	88

22. Unclaimed Expired Prizes The number of unclaimed expired prizes (in millions of dollars) for lottery tickets bought in a sample of states is shown. Construct a frequency distribution for the data, using 5 classes.

28.5	51.7	19	5
2	1.2	14	14.6
0.8	11.6	3.5	30.1
1.7	1.3	13	14

23. NFL Payrolls The data show the NFL team payrolls (in millions of dollars) for a specific year. Construct a frequency distribution for the payroll, using 7 classes.

99	105	106	102
102	93	109	106
77	91	103	118
97	100	107	103
94	109	100	98
84	92	98	110
94	104	98	123
102	99	100	107

Source: *NFL.*

24. Consumption of Natural Gas Construct a frequency distribution for the energy consumption of natural gas (in billions of Btu) by the 50 states and the District of Columbia. Use 9 classes.

474	475	205	639	197	344	3	409	247	66
377	87	747	1166	223	248	958	406	251	3462
2391	514	371	58	224	530	317	267	769	9
188	289	76	678	331	52	214	165	255	319
34	1300	284	834	114	1082	73	62	95	393
146									

Source: *Time Almanac.*

25. Average Wind Speeds A sample of 40 large cities was selected, and the average of the wind speeds was computed for each city over one year. Construct a frequency distribution, using 7 classes.

12.2	9.1	11.2	9.0
10.5	8.2	8.9	12.2
9.5	10.2	7.1	11.0
6.2	7.9	8.7	8.4
8.9	8.8	7.1	10.1
8.7	10.5	10.2	10.7
7.9	8.3	8.7	8.7
10.4	7.7	12.3	10.7
7.7	7.8	11.8	10.5
9.6	9.6	8.6	10.3

Source: *World Almanac and Book of Facts.*

26. Percentage of People Who Completed 4 or More Years of College Listed by state are the percentages of the population who have completed 4 or more years of a college education. Construct a frequency distribution with 7 classes.

21.4	26.0	25.3	19.3	29.5	35.0	34.7	26.1	25.8	23.4
27.1	29.2	24.5	29.5	22.1	24.3	28.8	20.0	20.4	26.7
35.2	37.9	24.7	31.0	18.9	24.5	27.0	27.5	21.8	32.5
33.9	24.8	31.7	25.6	25.7	24.1	22.8	28.3	25.8	29.8
23.5	25.0	21.8	25.2	28.7	33.6	33.6	30.3	17.3	25.4

Source: *NY Times Almanac.*

Extending the Concepts

27. JFK Assassination A researcher conducted a survey asking people if they believed more than one person was involved in the assassination of John F. Kennedy. The results were as follows: 73% said yes, 19% said no, and 9% had no opinion. Is there anything suspicious about the results?

28. The Value of Pi The ratio of the circumference of a circle to its diameter is known as π (pi). The value of π is an irrational number, which means that the decimal part goes on forever and there is no fixed sequence of numbers that repeats. People have found the decimal part of π to over a million places. We can statistically study the number. Shown here is the value of π to 40 decimal places. Construct an ungrouped frequency distribution for the digits. Based on the distribution, do you think each digit appears equally in the number?

3.1415926535897932384626433832795028841971

Step by Step

EXCEL

Step by Step

Categorical Frequency Table (Qualitative or Discrete Data)

1. In an open workbook, select cell A1 and type in all the blood types from Example 2–1 down column A.
2. Type in the variable name **Blood Type** in cell B1.
3. Select cell B2 and type in the four different blood types down the column.
4. Type in the name **Count** in cell C1.
5. Select cell C2. From the toolbar, select the Formulas tab on the toolbar.
6. Select the Insert Function icon , then select the Statistical category in the Insert Function dialog box.
7. Select the Countif function from the function name list.
8. In the dialog box, type **A1:A25** in the **Range** box. Type in the blood type "A" in quotes in the **Criteria** box. The count or frequency of the number of data corresponding to the blood type should appear below the input. Repeat for the remaining blood types.
9. After all the data have been counted, select cell C6 in the worksheet.
10. From the toolbar select Formulas, then AutoSum and type in C2:C5 to insert the total frequency into cell C6.

After entering data or a heading into a worksheet, you can change the width of a column to fit the input. To automatically change the width of a column to fit the data:

1. Select the column or columns that you want to change.
2. On the Home tab, in the Cells group, select Format.
3. Under Cell Size, click Autofit Column Width.

Making a Grouped Frequency Distribution (Quantitative Data)

1. Press **[Ctrl]-N** for a new workbook.
2. Enter the raw data from Example 2–2 in column A, one number per cell.
3. Enter the upper class boundaries in column B.
4. From the toolbar select the Data tab, then click Data Analysis.
5. In the Analysis Tools, select Histogram and click [OK].
6. In the Histogram dialog box, type **A1:A50** in the Input Range box and type **B1:B7** in the Bin Range box.
7. Select New Worksheet Ply, and check the Cumulative Percentage option. Click [OK].
8. You can change the label for the column containing the upper class boundaries and expand the width of the columns automatically after relabeling:

   Select the Home tab from the toolbar.

Highlight the columns that you want to change.

Select Format, then AutoFit Column Width.

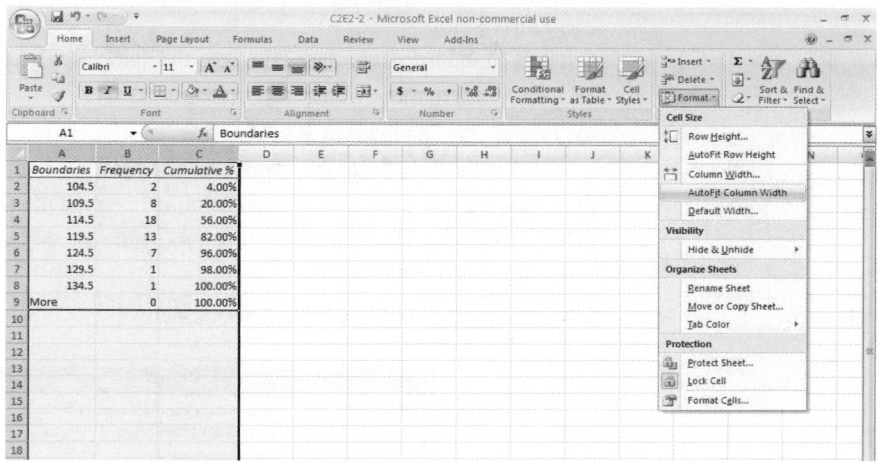

Note: By leaving the Chart Output unchecked, a new worksheet will display the table only.

MINITAB
Step by Step

Make a Categorical Frequency Table (Qualitative or Discrete Data)

1. Type in all the blood types from Example 2–1 down C1 of the worksheet.

   A B B AB O O O B AB B B B O A O A O O O AB AB A O B A

2. Click above row 1 and name the column **BloodType.**
3. Select **Stat>Tables>Tally Individual Values.**

   The cursor should be blinking in the Variables dialog box. If not, click inside the dialog box.
4. Double-click C1 in the Variables list.
5. Check the boxes for the statistics: Counts, Percents, and Cumulative percents.
6. Click [OK]. The results will be displayed in the Session Window as shown.

Tally for Discrete Variables: BloodType

BloodType	Count	Percent	CumPct
A	5	20.00	20.00
AB	4	16.00	36.00
B	7	28.00	64.00
O	9	36.00	100.00
N=	25		

Make a Grouped Frequency Distribution (Quantitative Variable)

1. Select **File>New>Minitab Worksheet.** A new worksheet will be added to the project.
2. Type the data used in Example 2–2 into C1. Name the column **TEMPERATURES.**
3. Use the instructions in the textbook to determine the class limits of 100 to 134 in increments of 5.

   In the next step you will create a new column of data, converting the numeric variable to text categories that can be tallied.

4. Select **Data>Code>Numeric to Text.**

   a) The cursor should be blinking in Code data from columns. If not, click inside the box, then double-click C1 Temperatures in the list. Only quantitative variables will be shown in this list.

   b) Click in the Into columns: then type the name of the new column, **TempCodes.**

   c) Press [Tab] to move to the next dialog box.

   d) Type in the first interval **100:104.**

   Use a colon to indicate the interval from 100 to 104 with no spaces before or after the colon.

   e) Press [Tab] to move to the New: column, and type the text category **100–104.**

   f) Continue to tab to each dialog box, typing the interval and then the category until the last category has been entered.

The dialog box should look like the one shown.

5. Click [OK]. In the worksheet, a new column of data will be created in the first empty column, C2. This new variable will contain the category for each value in C1. The column C2-T contains alphanumeric data.

6. Click **Stat>Tables>Tally Individual Values,** then double-click TempCodes in the Variables list.

   a) Check the boxes for the desired statistics, such as Counts, Percents, and Cumulative percents.

   b) Click [OK].

The table will be displayed in the Session Window. Eighteen states have high temperatures between 110 and 114°F. Eighty-two percent of the states have record high temperatures less than or equal to 119°F.

Tally for Discrete Variables: TempCodes

TempCodes	Count	Percent	CumPct
100–104	2	4.00	4.00
105–109	8	16.00	20.00
110–114	18	36.00	56.00
115–119	13	26.00	82.00
120–124	7	14.00	96.00
125–129	1	2.00	98.00
130–134	1	2.00	100.00
N=	50		

7. Click **File>Save Project As** . . . , and type the name of the project file, **Ch2-1.** This will save the two worksheets and the Session Window.

2–2   Histograms, Frequency Polygons, and Ogives

OBJECTIVE ❷

Represent data in frequency distributions graphically, using histograms, frequency polygons, and ogives.

After you have organized the data into a frequency distribution, you can present them in graphical form. The purpose of graphs in statistics is to convey the data to the viewers in pictorial form. It is easier for most people to comprehend the meaning of data presented graphically than data presented numerically in tables or frequency distributions. This is especially true if the users have little or no statistical knowledge.

Statistical graphs can be used to describe the data set or to analyze it. Graphs are also useful in getting the audience's attention in a publication or a speaking presentation. They can be used to discuss an issue, reinforce a critical point, or summarize a data set. They can also be used to discover a trend or pattern in a situation over a period of time.

The three most commonly used graphs in research are

1. The histogram.

2. The frequency polygon.

3. The cumulative frequency graph, or ogive (pronounced o-jive).

The steps for constructing the histogram, frequency polygon, and the ogive are summarized in the procedure table.

Procedure Table

Constructing a Histogram, Frequency Polygon, and Ogive

Step 1   Draw and label the x and y axes.

Step 2   On the x axis, label the class boundaries of the frequency distribution for the histogram and ogive. Label the midpoints for the frequency polygon.

Step 3   Plot the frequencies for each class, and draw the vertical bars for the histogram and the lines for the frequency polygon and ogive.

(*Note:* Remember that the lines for the frequency polygon begin and end on the x axis while the lines for the ogive begin on the x axis.)

The Histogram

| **Historical Note**

Karl Pearson introduced the histogram in 1891. He used it to show time concepts of various reigns of Prime Ministers.

The **histogram** is a graph that displays the data by using contiguous vertical bars (unless the frequency of a class is 0) of various heights to represent the frequencies of the classes.

EXAMPLE 2–4   Record High Temperatures

Construct a histogram to represent the data shown for the record high temperatures for each of the 50 states (see Example 2–2).

Class boundaries	Frequency
99.5–104.5	2
104.5–109.5	8
109.5–114.5	18
114.5–119.5	13
119.5–124.5	7
124.5–129.5	1
129.5–134.5	1

Step 1   Draw and label the x and y axes. The x axis is always the horizontal axis, and the y axis is always the vertical axis.

Step 2   Represent the frequency on the y axis and the class boundaries on the x axis.

Step 3   Using the frequencies as the heights, draw vertical bars for each class. See Figure 2–1.

FIGURE 2–1   Histogram for Example 2–4

As the histogram shows, the class with the greatest number of data values (18) is 109.5–114.5, followed by 13 for 114.5–119.5. The graph also has one peak with the data clustering around it.

Historical Note

Graphs originated when ancient astronomers drew the position of the stars in the heavens. Roman surveyors also used coordinates to locate landmarks on their maps.

The development of statistical graphs can be traced to William Playfair (1759–1823), an engineer and drafter who used graphs to present economic data pictorially.

The Frequency Polygon

Another way to represent the same data set is by using a frequency polygon.

The **frequency polygon** is a graph that displays the data by using lines that connect points plotted for the frequencies at the midpoints of the classes. The frequencies are represented by the heights of the points.

Example 2–5 shows the procedure for constructing a frequency polygon. Be sure to begin and end on the x axis.

EXAMPLE 2–5   Record High Temperatures

Using the frequency distribution given in Example 2–4, construct a frequency polygon.

Step 1   Find the midpoints of each class. Recall that midpoints are found by adding the upper and lower boundaries and dividing by 2:

$$\frac{99.5 + 104.5}{2} = 102 \qquad \frac{104.5 + 109.5}{2} = 107$$

and so on. The midpoints are

Class boundaries	Midpoints	Frequency
99.5–104.5	102	2
104.5–109.5	107	8
109.5–114.5	112	18
114.5–119.5	117	13
119.5–124.5	122	7
124.5–129.5	127	1
129.5–134.5	132	1

Step 2 Draw the x and y axes. Label the x axis with the midpoint of each class, and then use a suitable scale on the y axis for the frequencies.

Step 3 Using the midpoints for the x values and the frequencies as the y values, plot the points.

Step 4 Connect adjacent points with line segments. Draw a line back to the x axis at the beginning and end of the graph, at the same distance that the previous and next midpoints would be located, as shown in Figure 2–2.

FIGURE 2–2

Frequency Polygon for Example 2–5

The frequency polygon and the histogram are two different ways to represent the same data set. The choice of which one to use is left to the discretion of the researcher.

The Ogive

The third type of graph that can be used represents the cumulative frequencies for the classes. This type of graph is called the *cumulative frequency graph,* or *ogive.* The **cumulative frequency** is the sum of the frequencies accumulated up to the upper boundary of a class in the distribution.

> The **ogive** is a graph that represents the cumulative frequencies for the classes in a frequency distribution.

Example 2–6 shows the procedure for constructing an ogive. Be sure to start on the x axis.

EXAMPLE 2–6   Record High Temperatures

Construct an ogive for the frequency distribution described in Example 2–4.

SOLUTION

Step 1   Find the cumulative frequency for each class.

	Cumulative frequency
Less than 99.5	0
Less than 104.5	2
Less than 109.5	10
Less than 114.5	28
Less than 119.5	41
Less than 124.5	48
Less than 129.5	49
Less than 134.5	50

Step 2   Draw the *x* and *y* axes. Label the *x* axis with the class boundaries. Use an appropriate scale for the *y* axis to represent the cumulative frequencies. (Depending on the numbers in the cumulative frequency columns, scales such as 0, 1, 2, 3, . . . , or 5, 10, 15, 20, . . . , or 1000, 2000, 3000, . . . can be used. Do *not* label the *y* axis with the numbers in the cumulative frequency column.) In this example, a scale of 0, 5, 10, 15, . . . will be used.

Step 3   Plot the cumulative frequency at each upper class boundary, as shown in Figure 2–3. Upper boundaries are used since the cumulative frequencies represent the number of data values accumulated up to the upper boundary of each class.

Step 4   Starting with the first upper class boundary, 104.5, connect adjacent points with line segments, as shown in Figure 2–4. Then extend the graph to the first lower class boundary, 99.5, on the *x* axis.

FIGURE 2–3

Plotting the Cumulative
Frequency for
Example 2–6

FIGURE 2–4

Ogive for Example 2–6

FIGURE 2–5

Finding a Specific Cumulative Frequency

Record High Temperatures

Cumulative frequency graphs are used to visually represent how many values are below a certain upper class boundary. For example, to find out how many record high temperatures are less than 114.5°F, locate 114.5°F on the *x* axis, draw a vertical line up until it intersects the graph, and then draw a horizontal line at that point to the *y* axis. The *y* axis value is 28, as shown in Figure 2–5.

Relative Frequency Graphs

The histogram, the frequency polygon, and the ogive shown previously were constructed by using frequencies in terms of the raw data. These distributions can be converted to distributions using *proportions* instead of raw data as frequencies. These types of graphs are called **relative frequency graphs.**

Graphs of relative frequencies instead of frequencies are used when the proportion of data values that fall into a given class is more important than the actual number of data values that fall into that class. For example, if you wanted to compare the age distribution of adults in Philadelphia, Pennsylvania, with the age distribution of adults of Erie, Pennsylvania, you would use relative frequency distributions. The reason is that since the population of Philadelphia is 1,526,006 and the population of Erie is 101,786, the bars using the actual data values for Philadelphia would be much taller than those for the same classes for Erie.

To convert a frequency into a proportion or relative frequency, divide the frequency for each class by the total of the frequencies. The sum of the relative frequencies will always be 1. These graphs are similar to the ones that use raw data as frequencies, but the values on the *y* axis are in terms of proportions. Example 2–7 shows the three types of relative frequency graphs.

EXAMPLE 2–7   Miles Run per Week

Construct a histogram, frequency polygon, and ogive using relative frequencies for the distribution (shown here) of the miles that 20 randomly selected runners ran during a given week.

Class boundaries	Frequency
5.5–10.5	1
10.5–15.5	2
15.5–20.5	3
20.5–25.5	5
25.5–30.5	4
30.5–35.5	3
35.5–40.5	2
	Total 20

SOLUTION

Step 1   Convert each frequency to a proportion or relative frequency by dividing the frequency for each class by the total number of observations.

For class 5.5–10.5, the relative frequency is $\frac{1}{20} = 0.05$; for class 10.5–15.5, the relative frequency is $\frac{2}{20} = 0.10$; for class 15.5–20.5, the relative frequency is $\frac{3}{20} = 0.15$; and so on.

Place these values in the column labeled Relative frequency.

Class boundaries	Midpoints	Relative frequency
5.5–10.5	8	0.05
10.5–15.5	13	0.10
15.5–20.5	18	0.15
20.5–25.5	23	0.25
25.5–30.5	28	0.20
30.5–35.5	33	0.15
35.5–40.5	38	0.10
		Total 1.00

Step 2   Find the cumulative relative frequencies. To do this, add the frequency in each class to the total frequency of the preceding class. In this case, $0 + 0.05 = 0.05$, $0.05 + 0.10 = 0.15$, $0.15 + 0.15 = 0.30$, $0.30 + 0.25 = 0.55$, etc. Place these values in the column labeled Cumulative relative frequency.

An alternative method would be to find the cumulative frequencies and then convert each one to a relative frequency.

	Cumulative frequency	Cumulative relative frequency
Less than 5.5	0	0.00
Less than 10.5	1	0.05
Less than 15.5	3	0.15
Less than 20.5	6	0.30
Less than 25.5	11	0.55
Less than 30.5	15	0.75
Less than 35.5	18	0.90
Less than 40.5	20	1.00

Step 3   Draw each graph as shown in Figure 2–6. For the histogram and ogive, use the class boundaries along the x axis. For the frequency polygon, use the midpoints on the x axis. The scale on the y axis uses proportions.

FIGURE 2–6

Graphs for Example 2–7

(a) Histogram

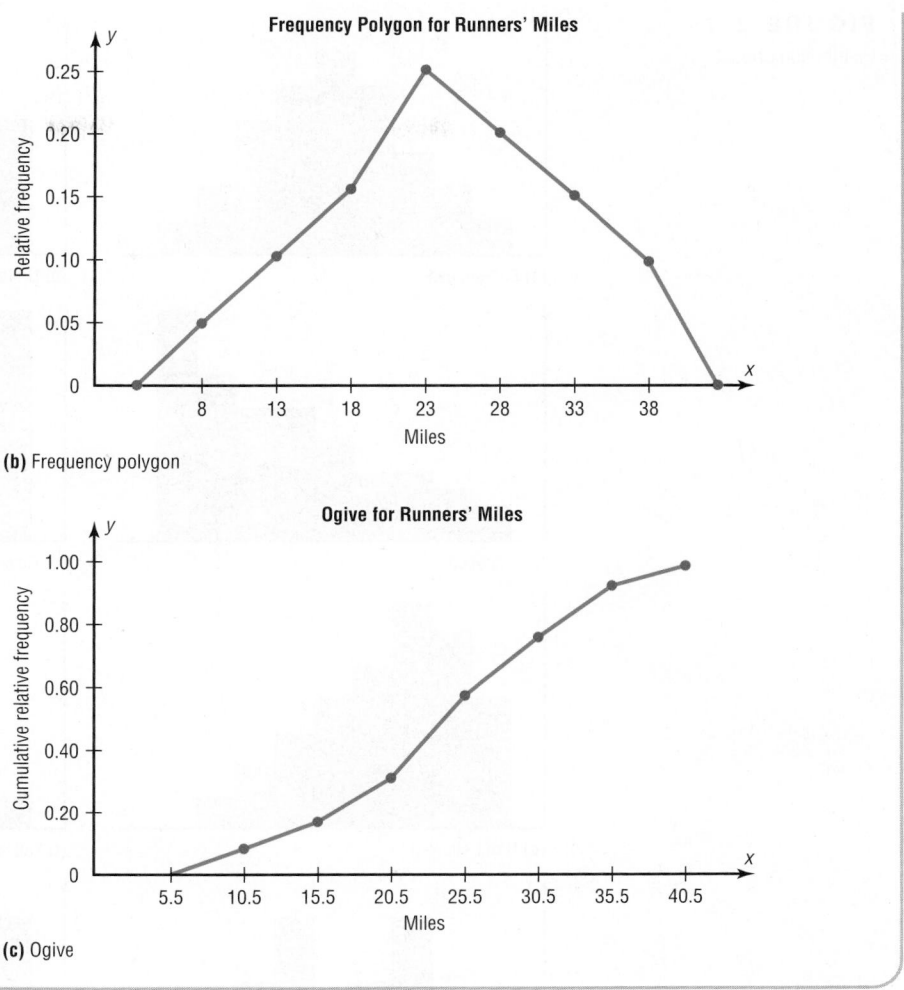

(b) Frequency polygon

(c) Ogive

Distribution Shapes

When one is describing data, it is important to be able to recognize the shapes of the distribution values. In later chapters, you will see that the shape of a distribution also determines the appropriate statistical methods used to analyze the data.

A distribution can have many shapes, and one method of analyzing a distribution is to draw a histogram or frequency polygon for the distribution. Several of the most common shapes are shown in Figure 2–7: *the bell-shaped or mound-shaped, the uniform-shaped, the J-shaped, the reverse J-shaped, the positively or right-skewed shape, the negatively or left-skewed shape, the bimodal-shaped, and the U-shaped.*

Distributions are most often not perfectly shaped, so it is not necessary to have an exact shape but rather to identify an overall pattern.

A *bell-shaped distribution* shown in Figure 2–7(a) has a single peak and tapers off at either end. It is approximately symmetric; i.e., it is roughly the same on both sides of a line running through the center.

A *uniform distribution* is basically flat or rectangular. See Figure 2–7(b).

A *J-shaped distribution* is shown in Figure 2–7(c), and it has a few data values on the left side and increases as one moves to the right. A *reverse J-shaped distribution* is the opposite of the J-shaped distribution. See Figure 2–7(d).

When the peak of a distribution is to the left and the data values taper off to the right, a distribution is said to be *positively or right-skewed*. See Figure 2–7(e). When

FIGURE 2–7
Distribution Shapes

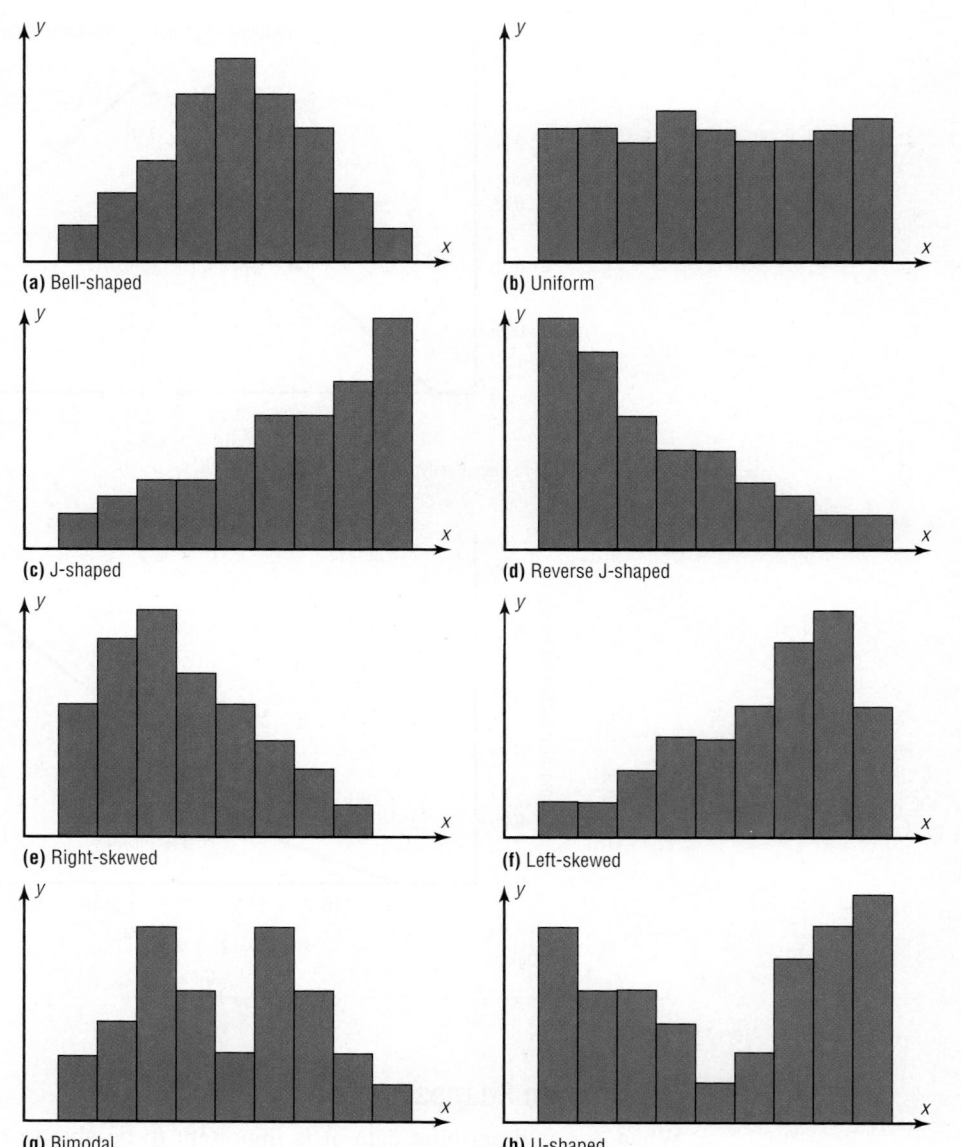

(a) Bell-shaped

(b) Uniform

(c) J-shaped

(d) Reverse J-shaped

(e) Right-skewed

(f) Left-skewed

(g) Bimodal

(h) U-shaped

the data values are clustered to the right and taper off to the left, a distribution is said to be *negatively or left-skewed*. See Figure 2–7(f). Skewness will be explained in detail in Chapter 3. Distributions with one peak, such as those shown in Figure 2–7(a), (e), and (f), are said to be *unimodal*. (The highest peak of a distribution indicates where the mode of the data values is. The mode is the data value that occurs more often than any other data value. Modes are explained in Chapter 3.) When a distribution has two peaks of the same height, it is said to be *bimodal*. See Figure 2–7(g). Finally, the graph shown in Figure 2–7(h) is a *U-shaped* distribution.

Distributions can have other shapes in addition to the ones shown here; however, these are some of the more common ones that you will encounter in analyzing data.

When you are analyzing histograms and frequency polygons, look at the shape of the curve. For example, does it have one peak or two peaks? Is it relatively flat, or is it U-shaped? Are the data values spread out on the graph, or are they clustered around the center? Are there data values in the extreme ends? These may be *outliers*. (See Section 3–3 for an explanation of outliers.) Are there any gaps in the histogram, or does the frequency polygon touch the *x* axis somewhere other than at the ends? Finally, are the data clustered at one end or the other, indicating a *skewed distribution*?

For example, the histogram for the record high temperatures in Figure 2–1 shows a single peaked distribution, with the class 109.5–114.5 containing the largest number of temperatures. The distribution has no gaps, and there are fewer temperatures in the highest class than in the lowest class.

Applying the Concepts 2–2

Selling Real Estate

Assume you are a realtor in Bradenton, Florida. You have recently obtained a listing of the selling prices of the homes that have sold in that area in the last 6 months. You wish to organize those data so you will be able to provide potential buyers with useful information. Use the following data to create a histogram, frequency polygon, and cumulative frequency polygon.

142,000	127,000	99,600	162,000	89,000	93,000	99,500
73,800	135,000	119,500	67,900	156,300	104,500	108,650
123,000	91,000	205,000	110,000	156,300	104,000	133,900
179,000	112,000	147,000	321,550	87,900	88,400	180,000
159,400	205,300	144,400	163,000	96,000	81,000	131,000
114,000	119,600	93,000	123,000	187,000	96,000	80,000
231,000	189,500	177,600	83,400	77,000	132,300	166,000

1. What questions could be answered more easily by looking at the histogram rather than the listing of home prices?

2. What different questions could be answered more easily by looking at the frequency polygon rather than the listing of home prices?

3. What different questions could be answered more easily by looking at the cumulative frequency polygon rather than the listing of home prices?

4. Are there any extremely large or extremely small data values compared to the other data values?

5. Which graph displays these extremes the best?

6. Is the distribution skewed?

See page 108 for the answers.

Exercises 2–2

1. **Do Students Need Summer Development?** For 108 randomly selected college applicants, the following frequency distribution for entrance exam scores was obtained. Construct a histogram, frequency polygon, and ogive for the data. (The data for this exercise will be used for Exercise 13 in this section.)

Class limits	Frequency
90–98	6
99–107	22
108–116	43
117–125	28
126–134	9
	Total 108

Applicants who score above 107 need not enroll in a summer developmental program. In this group, how many students do not have to enroll in the developmental program?

2. **Bear Kills** The number of bears killed in 2010 for 52 counties in Pennsylvania is shown in the frequency distribution. Construct a histogram, frequency polygon, and ogive for the data. Comment on the skewness of the distribution. How many counties had 75 or fewer bears killed? (The data for this exercise will be used for Exercise 14 of this section.)

Class limits	Frequency
1–25	18
26–50	12
51–75	7
76–100	6
101–125	2
126–150	3
151–175	0
176–200	2
201–225	0
226–250	2
	Total 52

Source: Pennsylvania State Game Commission.

3. **Counties, Divisions, or Parishes for 50 States** The number of counties, divisions, or parishes for each of the 50 states is given below. Use the data to construct a grouped frequency distribution with 6 classes, a histogram, a frequency polygon, and an ogive. Analyze the distribution.

67	27	15	75	58	64	8	67	159	5
102	44	92	99	105	120	64	16	23	14
83	87	82	114	56	93	16	10	21	33
62	100	53	88	77	36	67	5	46	66
95	254	29	14	95	39	55	72	23	3

Source: *World Almanac and Book of Facts.*

4. **Number of College Faculty** The number of faculty listed for a variety of private colleges that offer only bachelor's degrees is listed below. Use these data to construct a frequency distribution with 7 classes, a histogram, a frequency polygon, and an ogive. Discuss the shape of this distribution. What proportion of schools have 180 or more faculty?

165	221	218	206	138	135	224	204
70	210	207	154	155	82	120	116
176	162	225	214	93	389	77	135
221	161	128	310				

Source: *World Almanac and Book of Facts.*

5. **Railroad Crossing Accidents** The data show the number of railroad crossing accidents for the 50 states of the United States for a specific year. Construct a histogram, frequency polygon, and ogive for the data. Comment on the skewness of the distribution. (The data in this exercise will be used for Exercise 15 in this section.)

Class limits	Frequency
1–43	24
44–86	17
87–129	3
130–172	4
173–215	1
216–258	0
259–301	0
302–344	1
	Total 50

Source: Federal Railroad Administration.

6. **NFL Salaries** The salaries (in millions of dollars) for 31 NFL teams for a specific season are given in this frequency distribution.

Construct a histogram, a frequency polygon, and an ogive for the data; and comment on the shape of the distribution. (The data for this exercise will be used for Exercise 16 of this section.)

Class limits	Frequency
39.9–42.8	2
42.9–45.8	2
45.9–48.8	5
48.9–51.8	5
51.9–54.8	12
54.9–57.8	5
	Total 31

Source: NFL.com

7. **Super Bowl Scores** The frequency distribution shows the total number of points scored in the Super Bowl games from 1967 to 2012. Construct a histogram, frequency polygon, and ogive for the distribution. If you were to predict the total number of points for the next Super Bowl game, what range of values would you choose? In how many games were the total points greater than 56?

Class limits	Frequency
21–29	5
30–38	10
39–47	13
48–56	10
57–65	4
66–74	3
75–83	1
	Total 46

8. **Costs of Utilities** The frequency distribution represents the cost (in cents) for the utilities of states that supply much of their own power. Construct a histogram, frequency polygon, and ogive for the data. Is the distribution skewed?

Class limits	Frequency
6–8	12
9–11	16
12–14	3
15–17	1
18–20	0
21–23	0
24–26	1
	Total 33

9. **Air Pollution** One of the air pollutants that is measured in selected cities is sulfur dioxide. This pollutant occurs when fossil fuels are burned. This pollutant is measured in micrograms per cubic meter ($\mu g/m^3$). The results obtained from a sample of 24 cities are shown in the frequency distributions. One sample was taken recently,

and the other sample of the same cities was taken 5 years ago. Construct a histogram and compare the two distributions.

Class limits	Frequency (now)	Frequency (5 years ago)
10–14	6	5
15–19	4	4
20–24	3	2
25–29	2	3
30–34	5	6
35–39	1	2
40–44	2	1
45–49	1	1
	Total 24	Total 24

10. **Making the Grade** The frequency distributions shown indicate the percentages of public school students in fourth-grade reading and mathematics who performed at or above the required proficiency levels for the 50 states in the United States. Draw histograms for each, and decide if there is any difference in the performance of the students in the subjects.

Class	Reading frequency	Math frequency
17.5–22.5	7	5
22.5–27.5	6	9
27.5–32.5	14	11
32.5–37.5	19	16
37.5–42.5	3	8
42.5–47.5	1	1
	Total 50	Total 50

Source: *National Center for Educational Statistics.*

11. **Blood Glucose Levels** The frequency distribution shows the blood glucose levels (in milligrams per deciliter) for 50 patients at a medical facility. Construct a histogram, frequency polygon, and ogive for the data. Comment on the shape of the distribution. What range of glucose levels did most patients fall into?

Class limits	Frequency
60–64	2
65–69	1
70–74	5
75–79	12
80–84	18
85–89	6
90–94	5
95–99	1
	Total 50

12. **Waiting Times** The frequency distribution shows the waiting times (in minutes) for 50 patients at a walk-in medical facility. Construct a histogram,

frequency polygon, and ogive for the data. Is the distribution skewed? How many patients waited longer than 30 minutes?

Class limits	Frequency
11–15	7
16–20	9
21–25	15
26–30	9
31–35	5
36–40	3
41–45	2
	Total 50

13. Construct a histogram, frequency polygon, and ogive, using relative frequencies for the data in Exercise 1 of this section.

14. Construct a histogram, frequency polygon, and ogive, using relative frequencies for the data in Exercise 2 of this section.

15. Construct a histogram, frequency polygon, and ogive, using relative frequencies for the data in Exercise 5 of this section.

16. Construct a histogram, frequency polygon, and ogive, using relative frequencies for the data in Exercise 6 of this section.

17. **Cereal Calories** The number of calories per serving for selected ready-to-eat cereals is listed here. Construct a frequency distribution, using 7 classes. Draw a histogram, a frequency polygon, and an ogive for the data, using relative frequencies. Describe the shape of the histogram.

130	190	140	80	100	120	220	220	110	100
210	130	100	90	210	120	200	120	180	120
190	210	120	200	130	180	260	270	100	160
190	240	80	120	90	190	200	210	190	180
115	210	110	225	190	130				

Source: *The Doctor's Pocket Calorie, Fat, and Carbohydrate Counter.*

18. **Protein Grams in Fast Food** The amount of protein (in grams) for a variety of fast-food sandwiches is reported here. Construct a frequency distribution, using 6 classes. Draw a histogram, a frequency polygon, and an ogive for the data, using relative frequencies. Describe the shape of the histogram.

23	30	20	27	44	26	35	20	29	29
25	15	18	27	19	22	12	26	34	15
27	35	26	43	35	14	24	12	23	31
40	35	38	57	22	42	24	21	27	33

Source: *The Doctor's Pocket Calorie, Fat, and Carbohydrate Counter.*

≡ Extending the Concepts

19. Using the histogram shown here, do the following.

a. Construct a frequency distribution; include class limits, class frequencies, midpoints, and cumulative frequencies.

b. Construct a frequency polygon.

c. Construct an ogive.

20. Using the results from Exercise 19, answer these questions.

a. How many values are in the class 27.5–30.5?

b. How many values fall between 24.5 and 36.5?

c. How many values are below 33.5?

d. How many values are above 30.5?

21. Math SAT Scores Shown is an ogive depicting the cumulative frequency of the average mathematics SAT scores by state. Use it to construct a histogram and a frequency polygon.

≡ Technology   Step by Step

TI-84 Plus
Step by Step

Constructing a Histogram

To display the graphs on the screen, enter the appropriate values in the calculator, using the WINDOW menu. The default values are $X_{min} = -10$, $X_{max} = 10$, $Y_{min} = -10$, and $Y_{max} = 10$.

The X_{scl} changes the distance between the tick marks on the x axis and can be used to change the class width for the histogram.

To change the values in the WINDOW:

1. Press **WINDOW.**

2. Move the cursor to the value that needs to be changed. Then type in the desired value and press **ENTER.**

3. Continue until all values are appropriate.

4. Press **[2nd] [QUIT]** to leave the WINDOW menu.

To plot the histogram from raw data:

1. Enter the data in L$_1$.

2. Make sure WINDOW values are appropriate for the histogram.

3. Press **[2nd] [STAT PLOT] ENTER.**

4. Press **ENTER** to turn the plot 1 on, if necessary.

5. Move cursor to the Histogram symbol and press **ENTER,** if necessary. The histogram is the third option.

6. Make sure Xlist is L$_1$.

7. Make sure Freq is 1.

8. Press **GRAPH** to display the histogram.

9. To obtain the frequency (number of data values in each class), press the **TRACE** key, followed by ◄ or ► keys.

Input

Input

Output

Example TI2–1

Plot a histogram for the following data from Example 2–2.

112	100	127	120	134	118	105	110	109	112
110	118	117	116	118	122	114	114	105	109
107	112	114	115	118	117	118	122	106	110
116	108	110	121	113	120	119	111	104	111
120	113	120	117	105	110	118	112	114	114

Press **TRACE** and use the arrow keys to determine the number of values in each group.

To graph a histogram from grouped data:

1. Enter the midpoints into L_1.
2. Enter the frequencies into L_2.
3. Make sure WINDOW values are appropriate for the histogram.
4. Press **[2nd] [STAT PLOT] ENTER.**
5. Press **ENTER** to turn the plot on, if necessary.
6. Move cursor to the histogram symbol, and press **ENTER,** if necessary.
7. Make sure Xlist is L_1.
8. Make sure Freq is L_2.
9. Press **GRAPH** to display the histogram.

Example TI2–2

Plot a histogram for the data from Examples 2–4 and 2–5.

Class boundaries	Midpoints	Frequency
99.5–104.5	102	2
104.5–109.5	107	8
109.5–114.5	112	18
114.5–119.5	117	13
119.5–124.5	122	7
124.5–129.5	127	1
129.5–134.5	132	1

Input   Input   Output

Output

To graph a frequency polygon from grouped data, follow the same steps as for the histogram except change the graph type from histogram (third graph) to a line graph (second graph).

To graph an ogive from grouped data, modify the procedure for the histogram as follows:

1. Enter the upper class boundaries into L_1.
2. Enter the cumulative frequencies into L_2.
3. Change the graph type from histogram (third graph) to line (second graph).
4. Change the Y_{max} from the WINDOW menu to the sample size.

EXCEL
Step by Step

Constructing a Histogram

1. Press **[Ctrl]-N** for a new workbook.
2. Enter the data from Example 2–2 in column A, one number per cell.
3. Enter the upper boundaries into column B.
4. From the toolbar, select the Data tab, then select Data Analysis.
5. In Data Analysis, select Histogram and click [OK].
6. In the Histogram dialog box, type **A1:A50** in the Input Range box and type **B1:B7** in the Bin Range box.

7. Select New Worksheet Ply and Chart Output. Click [OK].

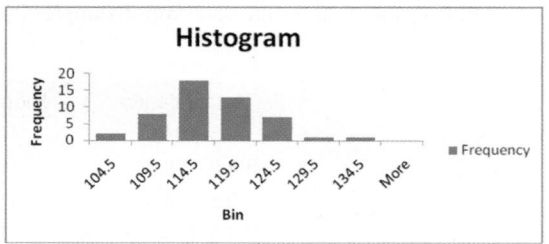

Editing the Histogram

To move the vertical bars of the histogram closer together:

1. Right-click one of the bars of the histogram, and select Format Data Series.

2. Move the Gap Width slider all the way to the left to change the gap width of the bars in the histogram to 0.

To change the label for the horizontal axis:

1. Left-click the mouse over any part of the histogram.

2. Select the Chart Tools tab from the toolbar.

3. Select the Layout tab, Axis Titles and Primary Horizontal Axis Title.

Once the Axis Titles text box is selected, you can type in the name of the variable represented on the horizontal axis.

Constructing a Frequency Polygon

1. Press **[CTRL]-N** for a new notebook.

2. Enter the midpoints of the data from Example 2–2 into column A and the frequencies into column B, including labels.

Note: Classes with frequency 0 have been added at the beginning and the end to "anchor" the frequency polygon to the horizontal axis.

	A	B
1	Midpoints	Frequencies
2	97	0
3	102	2
4	107	8
5	112	18
6	117	13
7	122	7
8	127	1
9	132	1
10	137	0
11		

3. Press and hold the left mouse button, and drag over the Frequencies (including the label) from column B.

4. Select the Insert tab from the toolbar and the Line Chart option.

5. Select the 2-D line chart type.

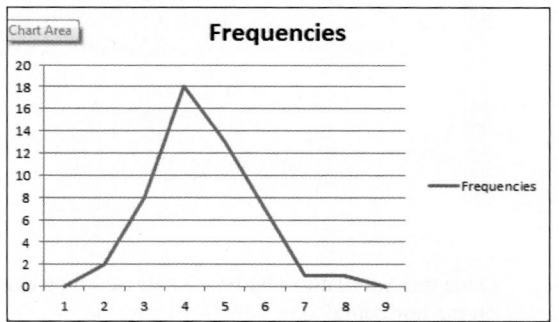

We will need to edit the graph so that the midpoints are on the horizontal axis.

1. Right click the mouse on any region of the chart.
2. Choose Select Data.
3. Select Edit below the Horizontal (Category) Axis Labels panel on the right.
4. Press and hold the left mouse button, and drag over the midpoints (not including the label) for the Axis label range, then click [OK].
5. Click [OK] on the Select Data Source box.

Inserting Labels on the Axes

1. Click the mouse on any region of the graph.
2. Select Chart Tools and then Layout on the toolbar.
3. Select Axis Titles to open the horizontal and vertical axis text boxes. Then manually type in labels for the axes.

Changing the Title

1. Select Chart Tools, Layout from the toolbar.
2. Select Chart Title.
3. Choose one of the options from the Chart Title menu and edit.

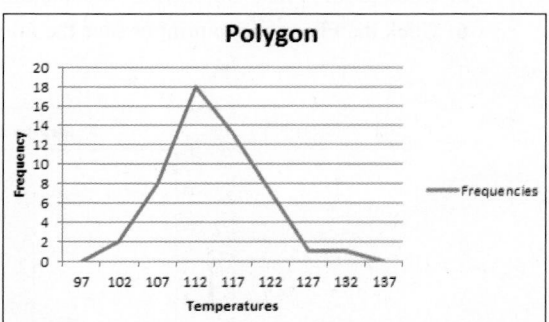

Constructing an Ogive

To create an ogive, use the upper class boundaries (horizontal axis) and cumulative frequencies (vertical axis) from the frequency distribution.

1. Type the upper class boundaries (including a class with frequency 0 before the lowest class to anchor the graph to the horizontal axis) and corresponding cumulative frequencies into adjacent columns of an Excel worksheet.
2. Press and hold the left mouse button, and drag over the Cumulative Frequencies from column B.
3. Select Line Chart, then the 2-D Line option.

As with the frequency polygon, you can insert labels on the axes and a chart title for the ogive.

MINITAB
Step by Step

Construct a Histogram

1. Enter the data from Example 2–2, the high temperatures for the 50 states, into C1.
2. Select **Graph>Histogram**.
3. Select [Simple], then click [OK].
4. Click C1 TEMPERATURES in the Graph variables dialog box.
5. Click [OK]. A new graph window containing the histogram will open.
6. Click the **File** menu to print or save the graph.

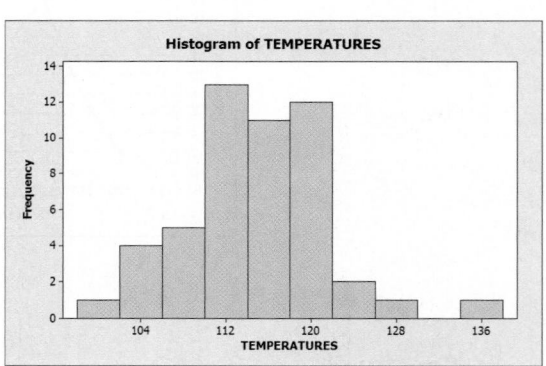

7. Click **File>Exit**.
8. Save the project as **Ch2-3.mpj.**

2–3   Other Types of Graphs

In addition to the histogram, the frequency polygon, and the ogive, several other types of graphs are often used in statistics. They are the bar graph, Pareto chart, time series graph, pie graph, and the dotplot. Figure 2–8 shows an example of each type of graph.

FIGURE 2–8   Other Types of Graphs Used in Statistics

(a) Bar graph

(b) Pareto chart

(c) Time series graph

(d) Pie graph

(e) Dotplot

OBJECTIVE **3**

Represent data using bar graphs, Pareto charts, time series graphs, pie graphs, and dotplots.

Bar Graphs

When the data are qualitative or categorical, bar graphs can be used to represent the data. A bar graph can be drawn using either horizontal or vertical bars.

A **bar graph** represents the data by using vertical or horizontal bars whose heights or lengths represent the frequencies of the data.

EXAMPLE 2–8   **College Spending for First-Year Students**

The table shows the average money spent by first-year college students. Draw a horizontal and vertical bar graph for the data.

Electronics	$728
Dorm decor	344
Clothing	141
Shoes	72

Source: The National Retail Federation.

SOLUTION

1. Draw and label the *x* and *y* axes. For the horizontal bar graph place the frequency scale on the *x* axis, and for the vertical bar graph place the frequency scale on the *y* axis.
2. Draw the bars corresponding to the frequencies. See Figure 2–9.

FIGURE 2–9   Bar Graphs for Example 2–8

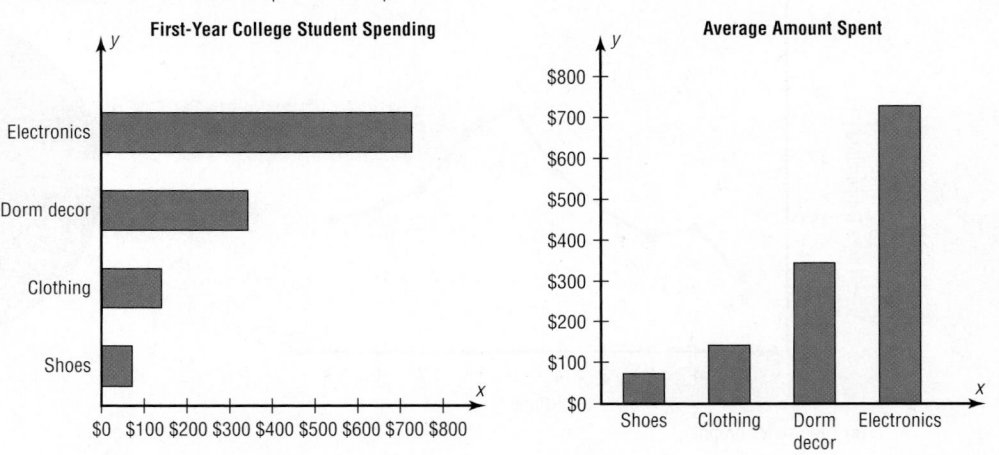

The graphs show that first-year college students spend the most on electronic equipment.

Bar graphs can also be used to compare data for two or more groups. These types of bar graphs are called *compound bar graphs*. Consider the following data for the number (in millions) of never married adults in the United States.

Year	Males	Females
1960	15.3	12.3
1980	24.2	20.2
2000	32.3	27.8
2010	40.2	34.0

Source: U.S. Census Bureau.

Figure 2–10 shows a bar graph that compares the number of never married males with the number of never married females for the years shown. The comparison is made by placing the bars next to each other for the specific years. The heights of the bars can be compared. This graph shows that there have consistently been more never married males

FIGURE 2–10

Example of a Compound Bar Graph

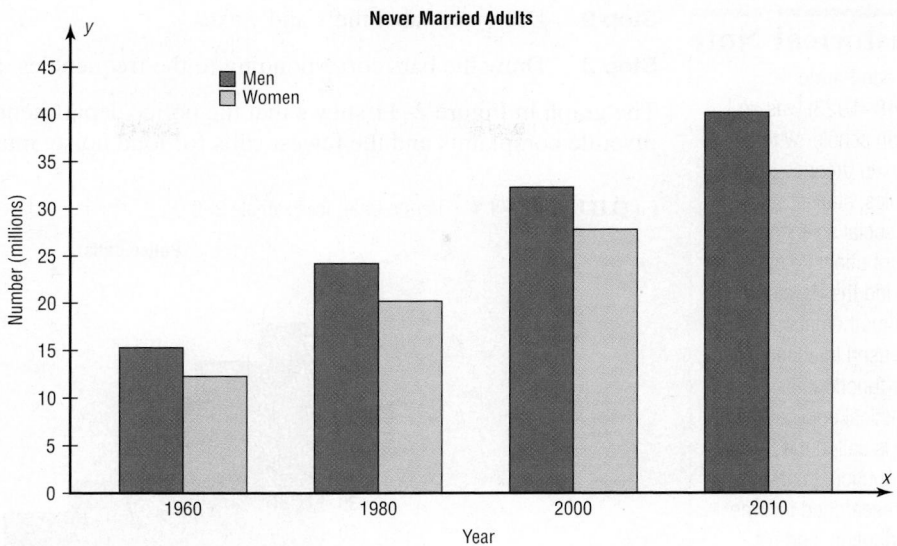

than never married females and that the difference in the two groups has increased slightly over the last 50 years.

Pareto Charts

When the variable displayed on the horizontal axis is qualitative or categorical, a *Pareto chart* can also be used to represent the data.

> A **Pareto chart** is used to represent a frequency distribution for a categorical variable, and the frequencies are displayed by the heights of vertical bars, which are arranged in order from highest to lowest.

EXAMPLE 2–9   Police Calls

The data shown here consist of the number of police calls for specific categories that a local municipality received in 2011. (The data were obtained by the author.) Draw and analyze a Pareto chart for the data.

Category	Number
Juvenile complaint	92
Loud noise/music/party	27
Drug offenses	79
Driving under the influence	38
Disabled vehicle	65

SOLUTION

Step 1   Arrange the data from the largest to smallest according to frequency.

Category	Number
Juvenile complaint	92
Drug offenses	79
Disabled vehicle	65
Driving under the influence	38
Loud noise/music/party	27

Step 2   Draw and label the x and y axes.

Step 3   Draw the bars corresponding to the frequencies. See Figure 2–11.

The graph in Figure 2–11 shows that the police department received the most calls for juvenile complaints and the fewest calls for loud noise, music, and parties.

FIGURE 2–11   Pareto Chart for Example 2–9

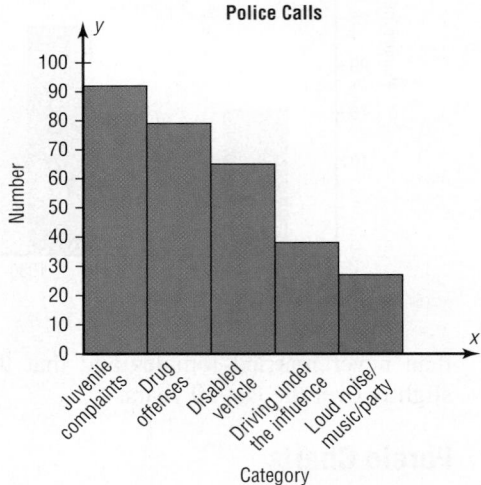

Suggestions for Drawing Pareto Charts

1. Make the bars the same width.
2. Arrange the data from largest to smallest according to frequency.
3. Make the units that are used for the frequency equal in size.

When you analyze a Pareto chart, make comparisons by looking at the heights of the bars.

The Time Series Graph

When data are collected over a period of time, they can be represented by a time series graph.

A **time series graph** represents data that occur over a specific period of time.

Example 2–10 shows the procedure for constructing a time series graph.

EXAMPLE 2–10   Percent of Cigarette Smokers

The data show the percentage of U.S. adults who smoke. Draw and analyze a time series graph for the data.

Year	1970	1980	1990	2000	2010
Percent	37	33	25	23	19

Source: Center for Disease Control and Prevention.

Historical Note

Time series graphs are over 1000 years old. The first ones were used to chart the movements of the planets and the sun.

SOLUTION

Step 1   Draw and label the x and y axes.

Step 2   Label the x axis for years and the y axis for the percent.

Step 3   Plot each point according to the table.

Step 4   Draw line segments connecting adjacent points. Do not try to fit a smooth curve through the data points. See Figure 2–12.

There has been a decrease in the percent of smokers over the 40-year period.

FIGURE 2–12   Figure for Example 2–10

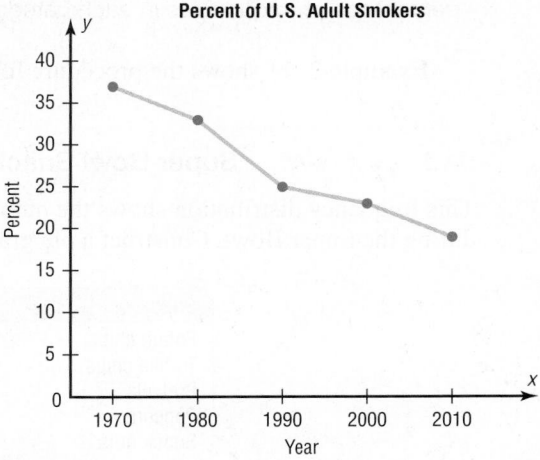

When you analyze a time series graph, look for a trend or pattern that occurs over the time period. For example, is the line ascending (indicating an increase over time) or descending (indicating a decrease over time)? Another thing to look for is the slope, or steepness, of the line. A line that is steep over a specific time period indicates a rapid increase or decrease over that period.

     Two or more data sets can be compared on the same graph called a *compound time series graph* if two or more lines are used, as shown in Figure 2–13. This graph shows the

FIGURE 2–13

Two Time Series Graphs for Comparison

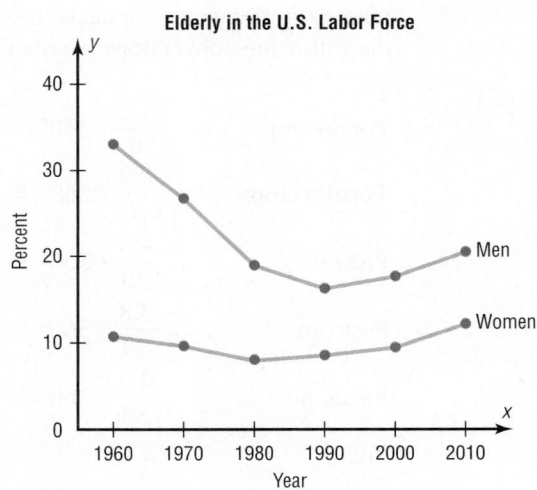

Source: Bureau of Census, U.S. Department of Commerce.

percentage of elderly males and females in the U.S. labor force from 1960 to 2010. It shows that the percentage of elderly men decreased significantly from 1960 to 1990 and then increased slightly after that. For the elderly females, the percentage decreased slightly from 1960 to 1980 and then increased from 1980 to 2010.

The Pie Graph

Pie graphs are used extensively in statistics. The purpose of the pie graph is to show the relationship of the parts to the whole by visually comparing the sizes of the sections. Percentages or proportions can be used. The variable is nominal or categorical.

> A **pie graph** is a circle that is divided into sections or wedges according to the percentage of frequencies in each category of the distribution.

Example 2–11 shows the procedure for constructing a pie graph.

EXAMPLE 2–11   Super Bowl Snack Foods

This frequency distribution shows the number of pounds of each snack food eaten during the Super Bowl. Construct a pie graph for the data.

Snack	Pounds (frequency)
Potato chips	11.2 million
Tortilla chips	8.2 million
Pretzels	4.3 million
Popcorn	3.8 million
Snack nuts	2.5 million
	Total $n = 30.0$ million

Source: USA TODAY Weekend.

SOLUTION

Step 1   Since there are 360° in a circle, the frequency for each class must be converted to a proportional part of the circle. This conversion is done by using the formula

$$\text{Degrees} = \frac{f}{n} \cdot 360°$$

where f = frequency for each class and n = sum of the frequencies. Hence, the following conversions are obtained. The degrees should sum to 360°.[1]

Potato chips	$\dfrac{11.2}{30} \cdot 360°$ =	134°
Tortilla chips	$\dfrac{8.2}{30} \cdot 360°$ =	98°
Pretzels	$\dfrac{4.3}{30} \cdot 360°$ =	52°
Popcorn	$\dfrac{3.8}{30} \cdot 360°$ =	46°
Snack nuts	$\dfrac{2.5}{30} \cdot 360°$ =	30°
Total		360°

[1]*Note:* The degrees column does not always sum to 360° due to rounding.

The graph shows the number of murders (in thousands) that have occurred in the United States since 2001. Based on the graph, do you think the number of murders is increasing, decreasing, or remaining the same?

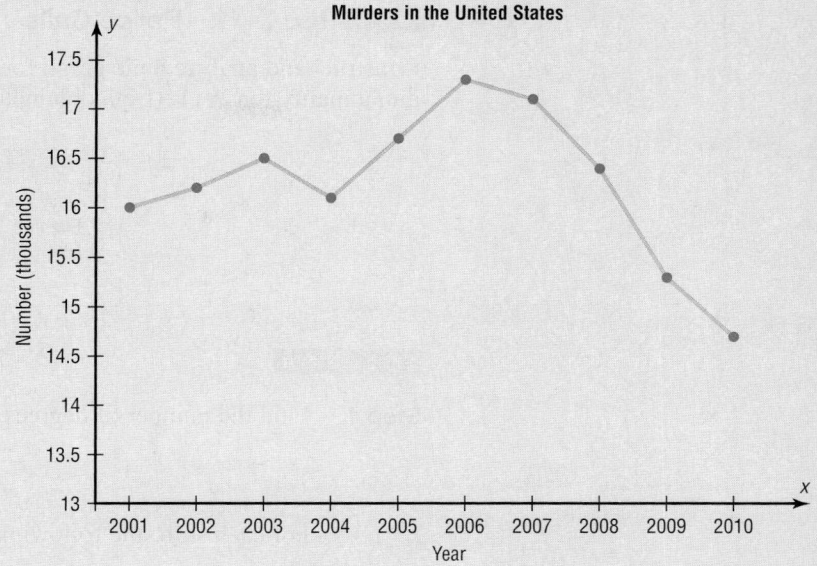

Murders in the United States

Source: Crime in the United States 2010, FBI, Department of Justice.

Step 2　Each frequency must also be converted to a percentage. Recall from Example 2–1 that this conversion is done by using the formula

$$\% = \frac{f}{n} \cdot 100$$

Hence, the following percentages are obtained. The percentages should sum to 100%.[2]

Potato chips	$\frac{11.2}{30} \cdot 100 =$	37.3%
Tortilla chips	$\frac{8.2}{30} \cdot 100 =$	27.3%
Pretzels	$\frac{4.3}{30} \cdot 100 =$	14.3%
Popcorn	$\frac{3.8}{30} \cdot 100 =$	12.7%
Snack nuts	$\frac{2.5}{30} \cdot 100 =$	8.3%
Total		99.9%

FIGURE 2–14　Pie Graph for Example 2–11

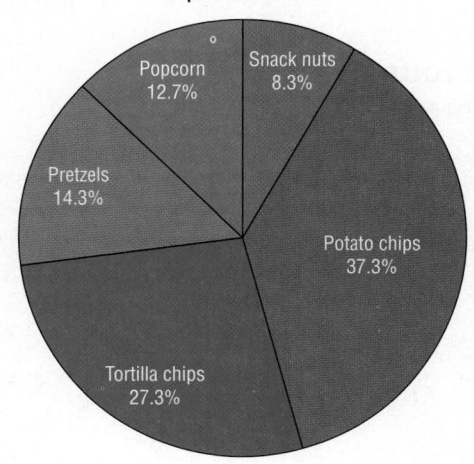

Super Bowl Snacks

Step 3　Next, using a protractor and a compass, draw the graph, using the appropriate degree measures found in Step 1, and label each section with the name and percentages, as shown in Figure 2–14.

[2]*Note:* The percent column does not always sum to 100% due to rounding.

EXAMPLE 2–12   Police Calls

Construct and analyze a pie graph for the calls received each shift by a local municipality for 2011. (Data obtained by author.)

Shift	Frequency
1. Day	2594
2. Evening	2800
3. Night	2436
	7830

SOLUTION

Step 1   Find the number of degrees for each shift, using the formula:

$$\text{Degrees} = \frac{f}{n} \cdot 360°$$

For each shift, the following results are obtained:

Day: $\dfrac{2594}{7830} \cdot 360° = 119°$

Evening: $\dfrac{2800}{7830} \cdot 360° = 129°$

Night: $\dfrac{2436}{7830} \cdot 360° = 112°$

Step 2   Find the percentages:

Day: $\dfrac{2594}{7830} \cdot 100 = 33\%$

Evening: $\dfrac{2800}{7830} \cdot 100 = 36\%$

Night: $\dfrac{2436}{7830} \cdot 100 = 31\%$

Step 3   Using a protractor, graph each section and write its name and corresponding percentage as shown in Figure 2–15.

FIGURE 2–15

Figure for Example 2–12

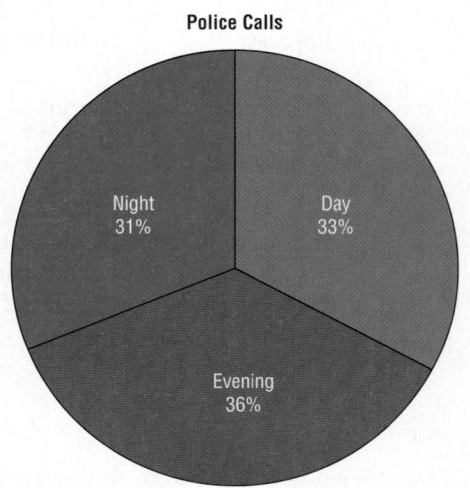

Police Calls

To analyze the nature of the data shown in the pie graph, look at the size of the sections in the pie graph. For example, are any sections relatively large compared to the rest? Figure 2–15 shows that the number of calls for the three shifts are about equal, although slightly more calls were received on the evening shift.

Note: Computer programs can construct pie graphs easily, so the mathematics shown here would only be used if those programs were not available.

Dotplots

A dotplot uses points or dots to represent the data values. If the data values occur more than once, the corresponding points are plotted above one another.

> A **dotplot** is a statistical graph in which each data value is plotted as a point (dot) above the horizontal axis.

Dotplots are used to show how the data values are distributed and to see if there are any extremely high or low data values.

EXAMPLE 2–13   Named Storms

The data show the number of named storms each year for the last 40 years. Construct and analyze a dotplot for the data.

19	15	14	7	6	11	11
9	16	8	8	11	9	8
16	12	13	14	13	12	7
15	15	19	11	4	6	13
10	15	7	12	6	10	
28	12	8	7	12	9	

Source: NOAA.

Step 1   Find the lowest and highest data values, and decide what scale to use on the horizontal axis. The lowest data value is 4 and the highest data value is 28, so a scale from 4 to 28 is needed.

Step 2   Draw a horizontal line, and draw the scale on the line.

Step 3   Plot each data value above the line. If the value occurs more than once, plot the other point above the first point. See Figure 2–16.

FIGURE 2–16   Figure for Example 2–13

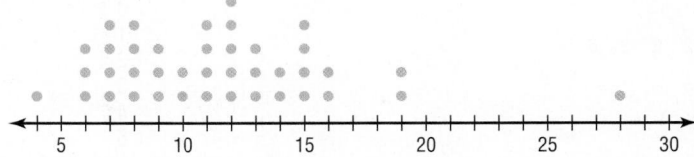

The graph shows that the majority of the named storms occur with frequency between 6 and 16 per year. There are only 3 years when there were 19 or more named storms per year.

Stem and Leaf Plots

The stem and leaf plot is a method of organizing data and is a combination of sorting and graphing. It has the advantage over a grouped frequency distribution of retaining the actual data while showing them in graphical form.

OBJECTIVE **4**

Draw and interpret a stem and leaf plot.

A **stem and leaf plot** is a data plot that uses part of the data value as the stem and part of the data value as the leaf to form groups or classes.

For example, a data value of 34 would have 3 as the stem and 4 as the leaf. A data value of 356 would have 35 as the stem and 6 as the leaf.

Example 2–14 shows the procedure for constructing a stem and leaf plot.

EXAMPLE 2–14   Out Patient Cardiograms

At an outpatient testing center, the number of cardiograms performed each day for 20 days is shown. Construct a stem and leaf plot for the data.

25	31	20	32	13
14	43	02	57	23
36	32	33	32	44
32	52	44	51	45

SOLUTION

Step 1   Arrange the data in order:

02, 13, 14, 20, 23, 25, 31, 32, 32, 32,
32, 33, 36, 43, 44, 44, 45, 51, 52, 57

Note: Arranging the data in order is not essential and can be cumbersome when the data set is large; however, it is helpful in constructing a stem and leaf plot. The leaves in the final stem and leaf plot should be arranged in order.

Step 2   Separate the data according to the first digit, as shown.

02   13, 14   20, 23, 25   31, 32, 32, 32, 32, 33, 36
43, 44, 44, 45   51, 52, 57

FIGURE 2–17

Stem and Leaf Plot for Example 2–14

0	2
1	3 4
2	0 3 5
3	1 2 2 2 2 3 6
4	3 4 4 5
5	1 2 7

Step 3   A display can be made by using the leading digit as the *stem* and the trailing digit as the *leaf*. For example, for the value 32, the leading digit, 3, is the stem and the trailing digit, 2, is the leaf. For the value 14, the 1 is the stem and the 4 is the leaf. Now a plot can be constructed as shown in Figure 2–17.

Leading digit (stem)	Trailing digit (leaf)
0	2
1	3 4
2	0 3 5
3	1 2 2 2 2 3 6
4	3 4 4 5
5	1 2 7

Figure 2–17 shows that the distribution peaks in the center and that there are no gaps in the data. For 7 of the 20 days, the number of patients receiving cardiograms was between 31 and 36. The plot also shows that the testing center treated from a minimum of 2 patients to a maximum of 57 patients in any one day.

If there are no data values in a class, you should write the stem number and leave the leaf row blank. Do not put a zero in the leaf row.

EXAMPLE 2–15 Number of Car Thefts in a Large City

An insurance company researcher conducted a survey on the number of car thefts in a large city for a period of 30 days last summer. The raw data are shown. Construct a stem and leaf plot by using classes 50–54, 55–59, 60–64, 65–69, 70–74, and 75–79.

52	62	51	50	69
58	77	66	53	57
75	56	55	67	73
79	59	68	65	72
57	51	63	69	75
65	53	78	66	55

SOLUTION

Step 1 Arrange the data in order.

50, 51, 51, 52, 53, 53, 55, 55, 56, 57, 57, 58, 59, 62, 63, 65, 65, 66, 66, 67, 68, 69, 69, 72, 73, 75, 75, 77, 78, 79

Step 2 Separate the data according to the classes.

50, 51, 51, 52, 53, 53   55, 55, 56, 57, 57, 58, 59
62, 63   65, 65, 66, 66, 67, 68, 69, 69   72, 73
75, 75, 77, 78, 79

Step 3 Plot the data as shown here.

Leading digit (stem)	Trailing digit (leaf)
5	0 1 1 2 3 3
5	5 5 6 7 7 8 9
6	2 3
6	5 5 6 6 7 8 9 9
7	2 3
7	5 5 7 8 9

The graph for this plot is shown in Figure 2–18.

FIGURE 2–18
Stem and Leaf Plot for Example 2–15

5	0 1 1 2 3 3
5	5 5 6 7 7 8 9
6	2 3
6	5 5 6 6 7 8 9 9
7	2 3
7	5 5 7 8 9

When you analyze a stem and leaf plot, look for peaks and gaps in the distribution. See if the distribution is symmetric or skewed. Check the variability of the data by looking at the spread.

Related distributions can be compared by using a back-to-back stem and leaf plot. The back-to-back stem and leaf plot uses the same digits for the stems of both distributions, but the digits that are used for the leaves are arranged in order out from the stems on both sides. Example 2–16 shows a back-to-back stem and leaf plot.

EXAMPLE 2–16   Number of Stories in Tall Buildings

The number of stories in two selected samples of tall buildings in Atlanta and Philadelphia is shown. Construct a back-to-back stem and leaf plot, and compare the distributions.

Atlanta					Philadelphia				
55	70	44	36	40	61	40	38	32	30
63	40	44	34	38	58	40	40	25	30
60	47	52	32	32	54	40	36	30	30
50	53	32	28	31	53	39	36	34	33
52	32	34	32	50	50	38	36	39	32
26	29								

Source: The World Almanac and Book of Facts.

SOLUTION

Step 1   Arrange the data for both data sets in order.

Step 2   Construct a stem and leaf plot, using the same digits as stems. Place the digits for the leaves for Atlanta on the left side of the stem and the digits for the leaves for Philadelphia on the right side, as shown. See Figure 2–19.

FIGURE 2–19   Back-to-Back Stem and Leaf Plot for Example 2–16

Atlanta		Philadelphia
9 8 6	2	5
8 6 4 4 2 2 2 2 2 1	3	0 0 0 0 2 2 3 4 6 6 6 8 8 9 9
7 4 4 0 0	4	0 0 0 0
5 3 2 2 0 0	5	0 3 4 8
3 0	6	1
0	7	

Step 3   Compare the distributions. The buildings in Atlanta have a large variation in the number of stories per building. Although both distributions are peaked in the 30- to 39-story class, Philadelphia has more buildings in this class. Atlanta has more buildings that have 40 or more stories than Philadelphia does.

Stem and leaf plots are part of the techniques called *exploratory data analysis*. More information on this topic is presented in Chapter 3.

Misleading Graphs

Graphs give a visual representation that enables readers to analyze and interpret data more easily than they could simply by looking at numbers. However, inappropriately drawn graphs can misrepresent the data and lead the reader to false conclusions. For example, a car manufacturer's ad stated that 98% of the vehicles it had sold in the past 10 years were still on the road. The ad then showed a graph similar to the one in Figure 2–20. The graph shows the percentage of the manufacturer's automobiles still on the road and the percentage of its competitors' automobiles still on the road. Is there a large difference? Not necessarily.

Notice the scale on the vertical axis in Figure 2–20. It has been cut off (or truncated) and starts at 95%. When the graph is redrawn using a scale that goes from 0 to 100%, as in Figure 2–21, there is hardly a noticeable difference in the percentages. Thus, changing the units at the starting point on the y axis can convey a very different visual representation of the data.

FIGURE 2–20
Graph of Automaker's Claim Using a Scale from 95 to 100%

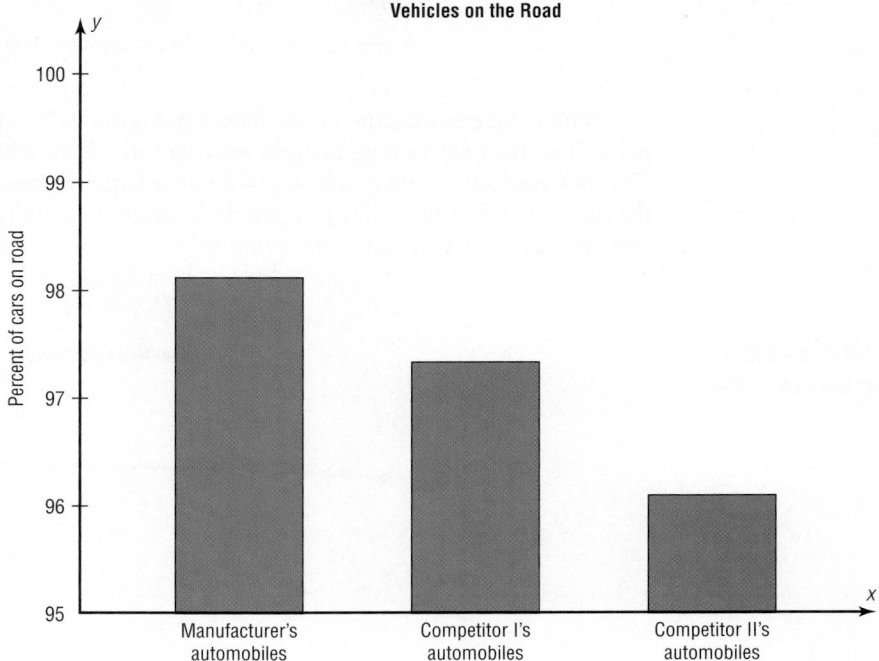

FIGURE 2–21
Graph in Figure 2–20 Redrawn Using a Scale from 0 to 100%

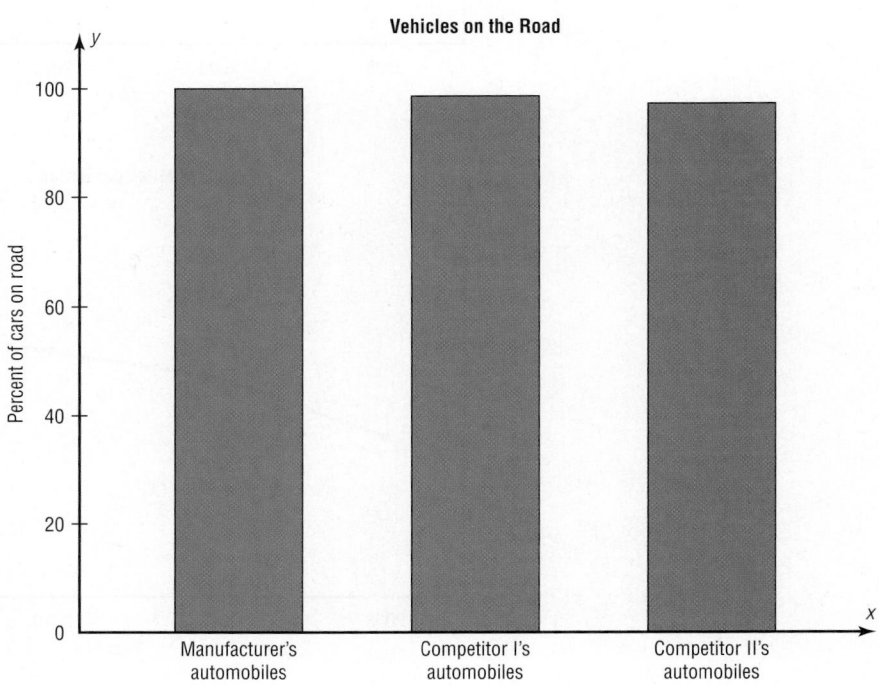

It is not wrong to truncate an axis of the graph; many times it is necessary to do so. However, the reader should be aware of this fact and interpret the graph accordingly. Do not be misled if an inappropriate impression is given.

Let us consider another example. The projected required fuel economy in miles per gallon for General Motors vehicles is shown. In this case, an increase from 21.9 to 23.2 miles per gallon is projected.

Year	2008	2009	2010	2011
MPG	21.9	22.6	22.9	23.2

Source: National Highway Traffic Safety Administration.

When you examine the graph shown in Figure 2–22(a), using a scale of 0 to 25 miles per gallon, the graph shows a slight increase. However, when the scale is changed to 21 to 24 miles per gallon, the graph shows a much larger increase even though the data remain the same. See Figure 2–22(b). Again, by changing the units or starting point on the *y* axis, one can change the visual representation.

FIGURE 2–22

Projected Miles per Gallon

(a)

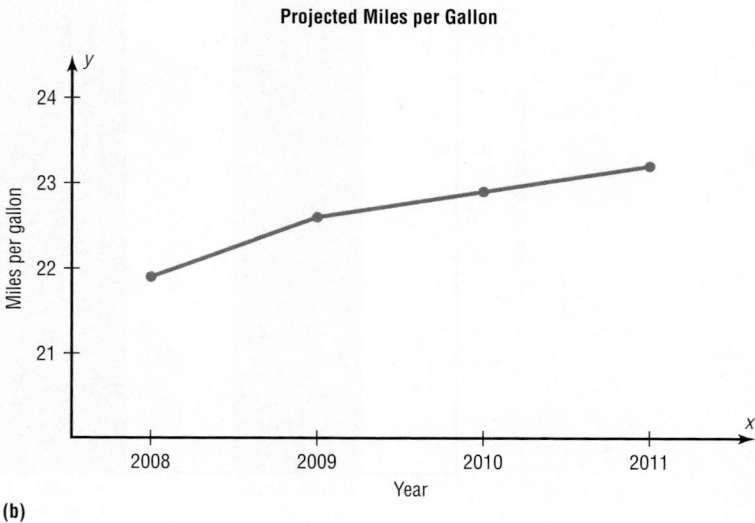

(b)

FIGURE 2–23

Comparison of Costs for a 30-Second Super Bowl Commercial

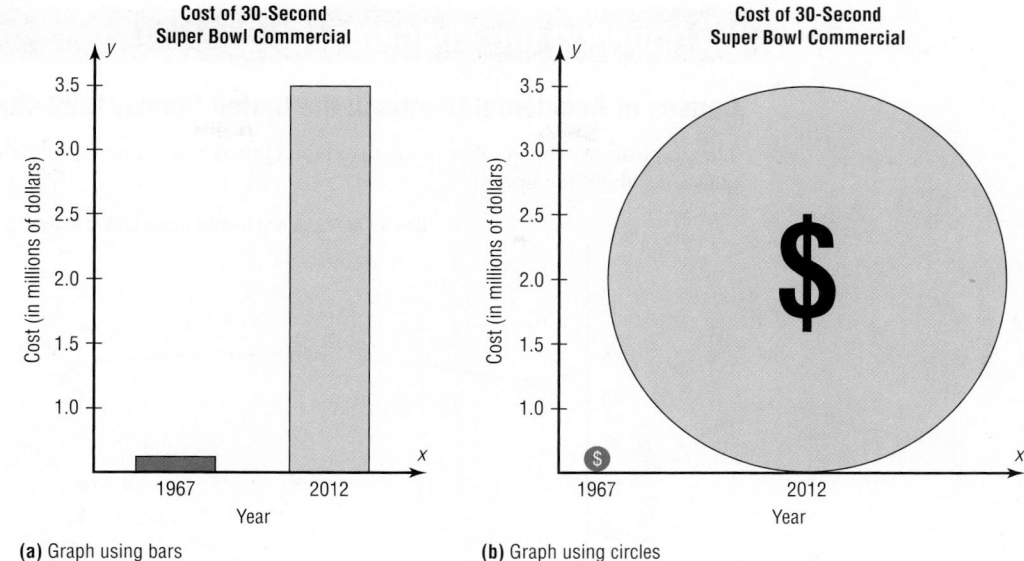

(a) Graph using bars   **(b)** Graph using circles

Another misleading graphing technique sometimes used involves exaggerating a one-dimensional increase by showing it in two dimensions. For example, the average cost of a 30-second Super Bowl commercial has increased from $42,000 in 1967 to $3.5 million in 2012 (Source: *USA TODAY*).

The increase shown by the graph in Figure 2–23(a) represents the change by a comparison of the heights of the two bars in one dimension. The same data are shown two-dimensionally with circles in Figure 2–23(b). Notice that the difference seems much larger because the eye is comparing the areas of the circles rather than the lengths of the diameters.

Note that it is not wrong to use the graphing techniques of truncating the scales or representing data by two-dimensional pictures. But when these techniques are used, the reader should be cautious of the conclusion drawn on the basis of the graphs.

Another way to misrepresent data on a graph is by omitting labels or units on the axes of the graph. The graph shown in Figure 2–24 compares the cost of living, economic growth, population growth, etc., of four main geographic areas in the United States. However, since there are no numbers on the *y* axis, very little information can be gained from this graph, except a crude ranking of each factor. There is no way to decide the actual magnitude of the differences.

Finally, all graphs should contain a source for the information presented. The inclusion of a source for the data will enable you to check the reliability of the organization presenting the data.

FIGURE 2–24

A Graph with No Units on the *y* Axis

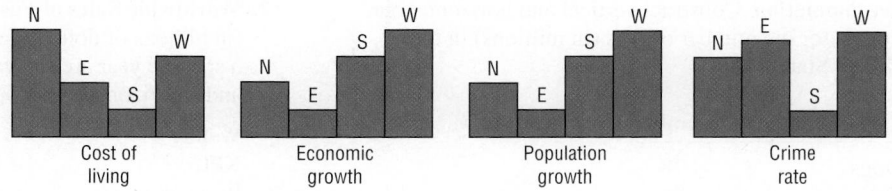

Applying the Concepts 2–3

Causes of Accidental Deaths in the United States, 1999–2009

The graph shows the number of deaths in the United States due to accidents. Answer the following questions about the graph.

Causes of Accidental Deaths in the United States

Source: National Safety Council.

1. Name the variables used in the graph.
2. Are the variables qualitative or quantitative?
3. What type of graph is used here?
4. Which variable shows a decrease in the number of deaths over the years?
5. Which variable or variables show an increase in the number of deaths over the years?
6. The number of deaths in which variable remains about the same over the years?
7. List the approximate number of deaths for each category for the year 2001.
8. In 1999, which variable accounted for the most deaths? In 2009, which variable accounted for the most deaths?
9. In what year were the numbers of deaths from poisoning and falls about the same?

See page 108 for the answers.

Exercises 2–3

1. **Pet Population** Construct vertical and horizontal bar graphs for the number of pets (in millions) in the United States.

Type	Number
Dogs	78
Cats	86
Fish	160
Other	53

Source: AAPA National Pet Owners.

2. **Worldwide Sales of Fast Foods** The worldwide sales (in billions of dollars) for several fast-food franchises for a specific year are shown. Construct a vertical bar graph and a horizontal bar graph for the data.

Wendy's	$ 8.7
KFC	14.2
Pizza Hut	9.3
Burger King	12.7
Subway	10.0

Source: *Franchise Times.*

3. Calories Burned While Exercising Construct a Pareto chart for the following data on exercise.

	Calories burned per minute
Walking, 2 mph	2.8
Bicycling, 5.5 mph	3.2
Golfing	5.0
Tennis playing	7.1
Skiing, 3 mph	9.0
Running, 7 mph	14.5

Source: *Physiology of Exercise.*

4. Roller Coaster Mania The World Roller Coaster Census Report lists the following numbers of roller coasters on each continent. Represent the data graphically, using a Pareto chart.

Africa	17
Asia	315
Australia	22
Europe	413
North America	643
South America	45

Source: www.rcdb.com

5. Online Ad Spending The amount spent (in billions of dollars) for ads online is shown. (The numbers for 2011 through 2015 are projected numbers.) Draw a time series graph and comment on the trend.

Year	2010	2011	2012	2013	2014	2015
Amount	$68.4	$80.2	$94.2	$106.1	$119.8	$132.1

Source: eMarketer.

6. Violent Crimes The number of all violent crimes (murder, nonnegligent homicide, manslaughter, forcible rape, robbery, and aggravated assault) in the United States for each of these years is listed below. Represent the data with a time series graph.

2000	1,425,486	2004	1,360,088	2008	1,394,461
2001	1,439,480	2005	1,390,745	2009	1,325,896
2002	1,423,677	2006	1,435,123	2010	1,246,248
2003	1,383,676	2007	1,422,970		

Source: *World Almanac and Book of Facts.*

7. Super Bowl Viewer's Expenditures The average amount a television viewer spent on merchandise, apparel, and snacks when watching a Super Bowl game is shown. Draw a time series graph for the data and interpret the results.

Year	2005	2007	2009	2011	2012
Amount	$38.35	$56.04	$57.27	$59.33	$63.87

Source: Retail Advertising and Marketing Association.

8. Valentine's Day Spending The data show the average amount of money spent by consumers on Valentine's Day. Draw a time series graph for the data and comment on the trend.

Year	2007	2008	2009	2010	2011	2012
Amount	$120	$123	$103	$103	$110	$126

Source: National Retail Federation.

9. Grading of Schools Parents were asked to grade their child's school for overall performance. The numbers are shown. Draw a pie graph for the data and analyze the graph.

Grade	A	B	C	D	F
Number	337	424	144	48	10

Source: Harris Interactive Survey.

10. Reasons We Travel The following data are based on a survey from American Travel Survey on why people travel. Construct a pie graph for the data and analyze the results.

Purpose	Number
Personal business	146
Visit friends or relatives	330
Work-related	225
Leisure	299

Source: *USA TODAY.*

11. Energy Consumption The data show the percentages of the types of energy consumed in the United States. Draw a pie graph for the data. What percentage of energy used is obtained from fossil fuels (coal, gas, and petroleum)?

Energy	Percent
Natural gas	25
Coal	21
Petroleum	37
Nuclear	9
Renewable	8

Source: U.S. Energy Information Administration.

12. Colors of Automobiles The popular car colors are shown. Construct a pie graph for the data.

White	19%
Silver	18
Black	16
Red	13
Blue	12
Gray	12
Other	10

Source: Dupont Automotive Color Popularity Report.

13. Ages of Football Players The data show the ages of the players of the New England Patriots in 2012. Construct a dotplot for the data, and comment on the distribution.

28	24	26	23	27	25
26	27	28	25	23	33
24	21	23	29	22	
25	23	27	26	30	
34	24	25	24	32	
25	35	25	29	34	
23	22	34	24	22	
26	30	24	33	30	
29	28	30	25	34	
25	24	26	30	28	

Source: *USA Today.*

14. Teacher Strikes In Pennsylvania the numbers of teacher strikes for the last 14 years are shown. Construct a dotplot for the data. Comment on the graph.

9	13	15	7	7	14	9
10	14	18	7	8	8	3

Source: *School Leader News.*

15. Patients at a Medical Care Facility The number of patients seen at a walk-in medical care facility for each of 40 days is shown. Construct a dotplot for the data, and comment on the distribution.

87	72	88	86	90	74	78	88
86	77	75	73	85	84	77	77
76	78	85	80	90	88	91	80
88	80	84	80	84	89	84	75
77	74	89	74	79	75	75	77

16. Commuting Times Fifty off-campus students were asked how long it takes them to get to school. The times (in minutes) are shown. Construct a dotplot and analyze the data.

23	22	29	19	12
18	17	30	11	27
11	18	26	25	20
25	15	24	21	31
29	14	22	25	29
24	12	30	27	21
27	25	21	14	28
17	17	24	20	26
13	20	27	26	17
18	25	21	33	29

17. 50 Home Run Club There are 42 Major League baseball players (as of 2011) that have hit 50 or more home runs in one season. Construct a stem and leaf plot and analyze the data.

50	51	52	54	59	51
54	50	58	51	54	54
56	58	56	70	54	52
58	54	64	52	73	57
50	60	56	50	66	54
52	51	58	63	57	52
51	50	61	52	65	50

Source: *The World Almanac and Book of Facts.*

18. Calories in Salad Dressings A listing of calories per 1 ounce of selected salad dressings (not fat-free) is given below. Construct a stem and leaf plot for the data.

100	130	130	130	110	110	120	130	140	100
140	170	160	130	160	120	150	100	145	145
145	115	120	100	120	160	140	120	180	100
160	120	140	150	190	150	180	160		

19. Length of Major Rivers The data show the lengths (in hundreds of miles) of major rivers in South America and Europe. Construct a back-to-back stem and leaf plot, and compare the distributions.

South America				Europe				
39	21	10	10	5	12	7	6	8
11	10	2	10	5	5	4	6	
10	14	10	12	18	5	13	9	
17	15	10		14	6	6	11	
15	25	16		8	6	3	4	

Source: *The World Almanac and Book of Facts.*

20. Math and Reading Achievement Scores The math and reading achievement scores from the National Assessment of Educational Progress for selected states are listed below. Construct a back-to-back stem and leaf plot with the data, and compare the distributions.

Math					Reading				
52	66	69	62	61	65	76	76	66	67
63	57	59	59	55	71	70	70	66	61
55	59	74	72	73	61	69	78	76	77
68	76	73			77	77	80		

Source: *World Almanac.*

21. State which type of graph (Pareto chart, time series graph, or pie graph) would most appropriately represent the data.

  a. Situations that distract automobile drivers

  b. Number of persons in an automobile used for getting to and from work each day

  c. Amount of money spent for textbooks and supplies for one semester

  d. Number of people killed by tornados in the United States each year for the last 10 years

  e. The number of pets (dogs, cats, birds, fish, etc.) in the United States this year

  f. The average amount of money that a person spent for his or her significant other for Christmas for the last 6 years

22. State which graph (Pareto chart, time series graph, or pie graph) would most appropriately represent the given situation.

  a. The number of students enrolled at a local college for each year during the last 5 years

  b. The budget for the student activities department at a certain college for a specific year

  c. The means of transportation the students use to get to school

  d. The percentage of votes each of the four candidates received in the last election

  e. The record temperatures of a city for the last 30 years

  f. The frequency of each type of crime committed in a city during the year

23. U.S. Health Dollar The U.S. health dollar is spent as indicated below. Construct two different types of graphs to represent the data.

Government administration	9.7%
Nursing home care	5.5
Prescription drugs	10.1
Physician and clinical services	20.3
Hospital care	30.5
Other (OTC drugs, dental, etc.)	23.9

Source: *Time Almanac.*

24. Patents The U.S. Department of Commerce reports the following number of U.S. patents received by foreign countries and the United States in the year 2010. Illustrate the data with a bar graph and a pie graph. Which do you think better illustrates this data set?

Japan	44,814	United Kingdom	4,302
Germany	12,363	China	2,657
South Korea	11,671	Israel	1,819
Taiwan	8,238	Italy	1,796
Canada	4,852	United States	107,792

Source: *World Almanac.*

No doubt you'll each draw your own conclusions from this chart...

Apple Pumpkin Blueberry

Source: Cartoon by Bradford Veley, Marquette, Michigan. Used with permission.

25. Cost of Milk The graph shows the increase in the price of a quart of milk. Why might the increase appear to be larger than it really is?

Cost of Milk

$3.50 — $3.50
$3.00 —
$2.50 —
$2.00 —
$1.50 —
$1.08
$1.00 —
$0.50 —
MILK

Fall 1988   Fall 2011

26. U.S. Population by Age The following information was found in a recent almanac. Use a pie graph to illustrate the information. Is there anything wrong with the data?

U.S. Population by Age in 2011

Under 20 years	27.0%
20 years and over	73.0
65 years and over	13.1

Source: *Time Almanac.*

27. Concealed Weapons Licenses The numbers of concealed weapons licenses issued for two neighboring counties are listed below for the years 2005–2011. Compare the data with the time series graph(s), and comment on the accompanying headline of the story, "Gun sales increase as crime rate decreases."

Year	County 1	County 2
2005	2207	312
2006	2239	428
2007	4476	693
2008	4200	1509
2009	3770	769
2010	3128	423
2011	3906	508

Source: *PA State Police Firearms Report.*

28. Trip Reimbursements The average amount requested for business trip reimbursement is itemized below. Illustrate the data with an appropriate graph. Do you have any questions regarding the data?

Flight	$440
Hotel stay	323
Entertainment	139
Phone usage	95
Transportation	65
Meal	38
Parking	34

Source: *USA TODAY.*

☰ Technology | Step by Step

TI-84 Plus
Step by Step

To graph a time series, follow the procedure for a frequency polygon from Section 2–2, using the following data for the number of outdoor drive-in theaters

Year	1988	1990	1992	1994	1996	1998	2000
Number	1497	910	870	859	826	750	637

Input	Input	Output

EXCEL
Step by Step

Constructing a Pareto Chart

To make a Pareto chart:

1. Enter the snack food categories from Example 2–11 into column A of a new worksheet.
2. Enter the corresponding frequencies in column B. The data should be entered in descending order according to frequency.
3. Highlight the data from columns A and B, and select the Insert tab from the toolbar.
4. Select the Column Chart type.
5. To change the title of the chart, click on the current title of the chart.
6. When the text box containing the title is highlighted, click the mouse in the text box and change the title.

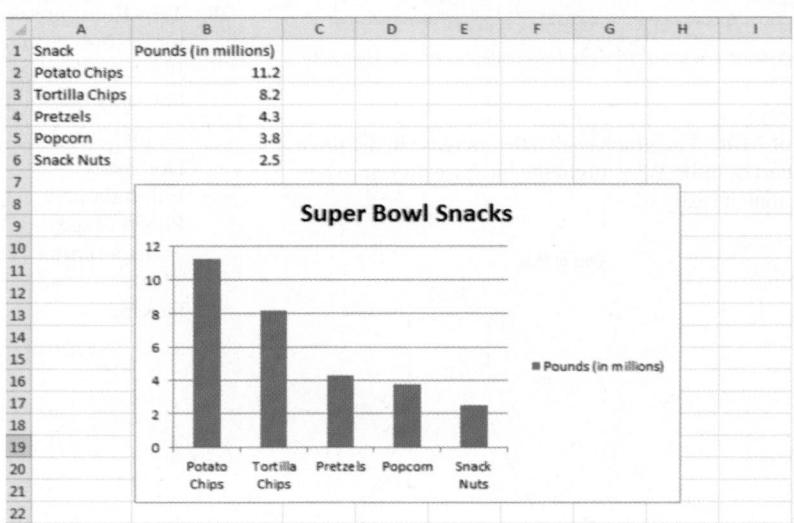

Constructing a Time Series Chart

Example

Year	1999	2000	2001	2002	2003
Vehicles*	156.2	160.1	162.3	172.8	179.4

*Vehicles (in millions) that used the Pennsylvania Turnpike.
Source: Tribune Review.

To make a time series chart:

1. Enter the years 1999 through 2003 from the example in column A of a new worksheet.
2. Enter the corresponding frequencies in column B.
3. Highlight the data from column B and select the Insert tab from the toolbar.
4. Select the Line chart type.

5. Right-click the mouse on any region of the graph.
6. Select the Select Data option.
7. Select Edit from the Horizontal Axis Labels and highlight the years from column A, then click [OK].
8. Click [OK] on the Select Data Source box.
9. Create a title for your chart, such as Number of Vehicles Using the Pennsylvania Turnpike Between 1999 and 2003. Right-click the mouse on any region of the chart. Select the Chart Tools tab from the toolbar, then Layout.
10. Select Chart Title and highlight the current title to change the title.
11. Select Axis Titles to change the horizontal and vertical axis labels.

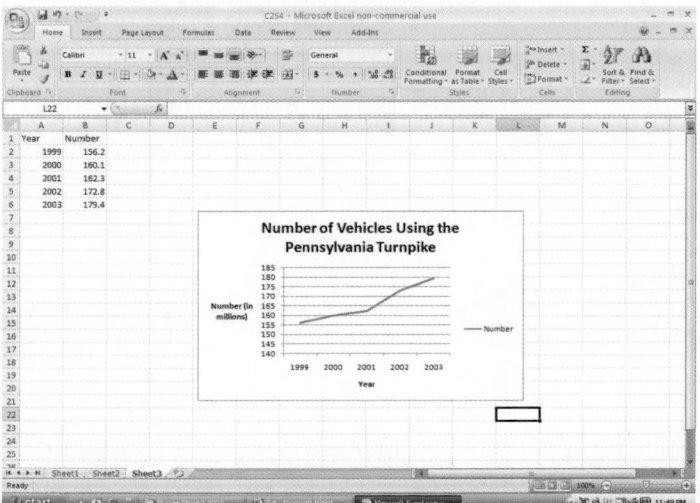

Constructing a Pie Chart

To make a pie chart:

1. Enter the shifts from Example 2–12 into column A of a new worksheet.
2. Enter the frequencies corresponding to each shift in column B.
3. Highlight the data in columns A and B and select Insert from the toolbar; then select the Pie chart type.

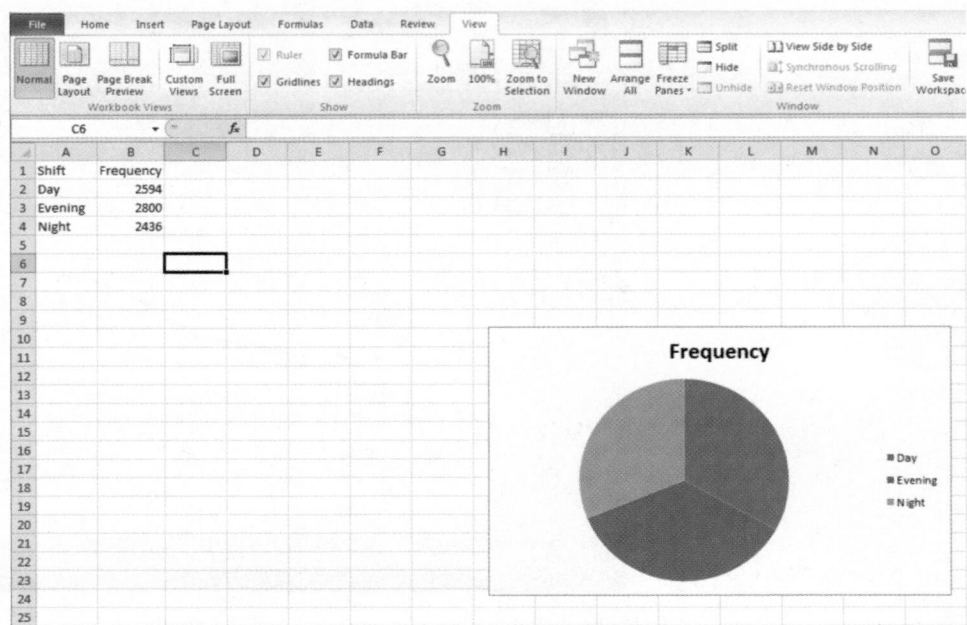

4. Click on any region of the chart. Then select Design from the Chart Tools tab on the toolbar.
5. Select Formulas from the chart Layouts tab on the toolbar.
6. To change the title of the chart, click on the current title of the chart.
7. When the text box containing the title is highlighted, click the mouse in the text box and change the title.

MINITAB
Step by Step

Construct a Bar Chart

The procedure for constructing a bar chart is similar to that for the pie chart.

1. Select **Graph>Bar Chart.**

   a) Click on the drop-down list in Bars Represent: and then select values from a table.

   b) Click on the Simple chart, then click [OK]. The dialog box will be similar to the Pie Chart Dialog Box.

2. Select the frequency column C2 f for Graph variables: and C1 Snack for the Categorical variable.

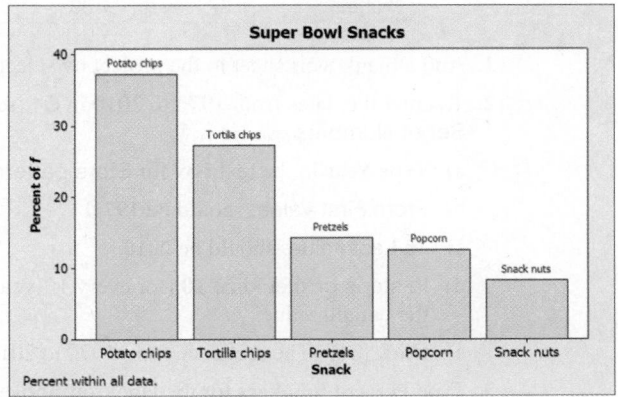

3. Click on [Labels], then type the title in the Titles/Footnote tab: **Super Bowl Snacks.**
4. Click the tab for Data Labels, then click the option to Use labels from column: and select C1 Snacks.
5. Click [OK] twice.

After the graph is made, right-click over any bar to change the appearance such as the color of the bars. To change the gap between them, right-click on the horizontal axis and then choose Edit X scale. In the Space Between Scale Categories select Gap between clusters then change the 1.5 to 0.2. Click [OK]. To change the *y* Scale to percents, right-click on the vertical axis and then choose Graph options and Show Y as a Percent.

Construct a Pareto Chart

Pareto charts are a quality control tool. They are similar to a bar chart with no gaps between the bars, and the bars are arranged by frequency.

1. Select **Stat>Quality Tools>Pareto.**
2. Click the option to Chart defects table.
3. Click in the box for the Labels in: and select C1 Snack.
4. Click on the frequencies column C2 f.

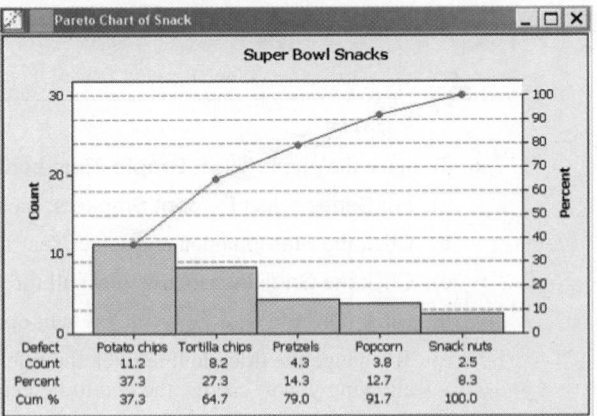

5. Click on [Options].

   a) Type Snack for the X axis label and Count for the Y axis label.

   b) Type in the title, **Super Bowl Snacks.**

6. Click [OK] twice. The chart is completed.

Construct a Time Series Plot

The data used are the percentage of U.S. adults who smoke (Example 2–10).

Year	1970	1980	1990	2000	2010
Number	37	33	25	23	19

1. Add a blank worksheet to the project by selecting **File>New>New-Minitab Worksheet.**

2. To enter the dates from 1970 to 2010 in C1, select **Calc>Make Patterned Data>Simple Set of Numbers.**

   a) Type **Year** in the text box for Store patterned data in.

   b) From First value: should be **1970.**

   c) To Last value: should be **2010.**

   d) In steps of should be **10** (for every 10-year increment). The last two boxes should be 1, the default value.

   e) Click [OK]. The sequence from 1970 to 2010 will be entered in C1 whose label will be Year.

3. Type **Percent Smokers** for the label row above row 1 in C2.

4. Type **37** for the first number, then press [Enter].

5. Continue entering each value in a row of C2.

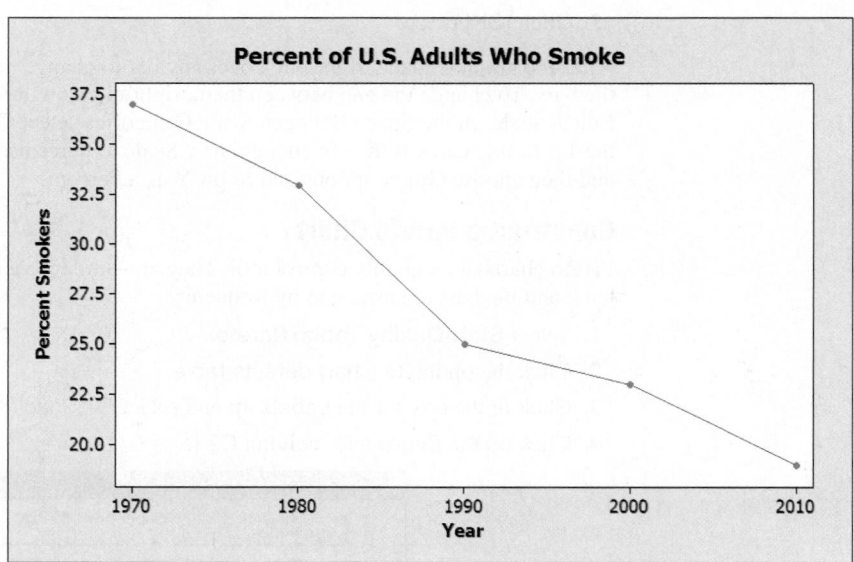

6. To make the graph, select **Graph>Time series plot,** then Simple, and press [OK].

   a) For Series select Percent Smokers; then click [Time/scale].

   b) Click the Stamp option and select Year for the Stamp column.

   c) Click the Gridlines tab and select all three boxes, Y major, Y minor, and X major.

   d) Click [OK] twice. A new window will open that contains the graph.

   e) To change the title, double-click the title in the graph window. A dialog box will open, allowing you to change the text to Percent of U.S. Adults Who Smoke.

Construct a Pie Chart

1. Enter the summary data for snack foods and frequencies from Example 2–11 into C1 and C2.

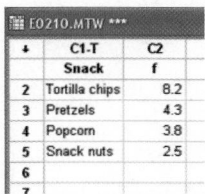

2. Name them **Snack** and **f.**
3. Select **Graph>Pie Chart.**

   a) Click the option for **Chart summarized data.**

   b) Press [Tab] to move to **Categorical variable,** then double-click C1 to select it.

   c) Press [Tab] to move to **Summary variables,** and select the column with the frequencies f.

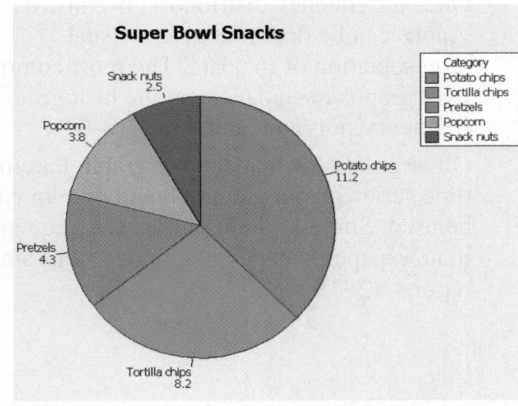

4. Click the [Labels] tab, then **Titles/Footnotes.**

   a) Type in the title: **Super Bowl Snacks.**

   b) Click the Slice Labels tab, then the options for **Category name** and **Frequency.**

   c) Click the option to **Draw a line from label to slice.**

   d) Click [OK] twice to create the chart.

Construct a Stem and Leaf Plot

1. Type in the data for Example 2–15. Label the column **CarThefts.**
2. Select **STAT>EDA>Stem-and-Leaf.** This is the same as **Graph>Stem-and-Leaf.**
3. Double-click on C1 CarThefts in the column list.
4. Click in the **Increment** text box, and enter the class width of **5.**

5. Click [OK]. This character graph will be displayed in the session window.

Stem-and-Leaf Display: CarThefts

Stem-and-leaf of CarThefts   N = 30
Leaf Unit = 1.0

6	5	011233
13	5	5567789
15	6	23
15	6	55667899
7	7	23
5	7	55789

Summary

- When data are collected, the values are called raw data. Since very little knowledge can be obtained from raw data, they must be organized in some meaningful way. A frequency distribution using classes is the common method that is used. (2–1)

- Once a frequency distribution is constructed, graphs can be drawn to give a visual representation of the data. The most commonly used graphs in statistics are the histogram, frequency polygon, and ogive. (2–2)

- Other graphs such as the bar graph, Pareto chart, time series graph, pie graph and dotplot can also be used. Some of these graphs are frequently seen in newspapers, magazines, and various statistical reports. (2–3)

- A stem and leaf plot uses part of the data values as stems and part of the data values as leaves. This graph has the advantage of a frequency distribution and a histogram. (2–3)

- Finally, graphs can be misleading if they are drawn improperly. For example, increases and decreases over time in time series graphs can be exaggerated by truncating the scale on the y axis. One-dimensional increases or decreases can be exaggerated by using two-dimensional figures. Finally, when labels or units are purposely omitted, there is no actual way to decide the magnitude of the differences between the categories. (2–3)

Important Terms

bar graph 75

categorical frequency
distribution 43

class 42

class boundaries 45

class midpoint 45

class width 45

compound bar graphs 76

cumulative frequency 59

cumulative frequency
distribution 48

dotplot 83

frequency 42

frequency distribution 42

frequency polygon 58

grouped frequency
distribution 44

histogram 57

lower class limit 44

ogive 59

open-ended distribution 46

Pareto chart 77

pie graph 80

raw data 42

relative frequency
graph 61

stem and leaf plot 84

time series graph 78

ungrouped frequency
distribution 49

upper class limit 44

Important Formulas

Formula for the percentage of values in each class:

$$\% = \frac{f}{n} \cdot 100$$

where

f = frequency of class
n = total number of values

Formula for the range:

$$R = \text{highest value} - \text{lowest value}$$

Formula for the class width:

$$\text{Class width} = \text{upper boundary} - \text{lower boundary}$$

Formula for the class midpoint:

$$X_m = \frac{\text{lower boundary} + \text{upper boundary}}{2}$$

or

$$X_m = \frac{\text{lower limit} + \text{upper limit}}{2}$$

Formula for the degrees for each section of a pie graph:

$$\text{Degrees} = \frac{f}{n} \cdot 360°$$

Review Exercises

Section 2–1

1. **How People Get Their News** The Brunswick Research Organization surveyed 50 randomly selected individuals and asked them the primary way they received the daily news. Their choices were via newspaper (N), television (T), radio (R), or Internet (I). Construct a categorical frequency distribution for the data and interpret the results.

N	N	T	T	T	I	R	R	I	T
I	N	R	R	I	N	N	I	T	N
I	R	T	T	T	T	N	R	R	I
R	R	I	N	T	R	T	I	I	T
T	I	N	T	T	I	R	N	R	T

2. **Men's World Hockey Champions** The United States won the Men's World Hockey Championship in 1933 and 1960. Below are listed the world champions for the last 30 years. Use this information to construct a frequency distribution of the champions. What is the difficulty with these data?

1982	USSR	1992	Sweden
1983	USSR	1993	Russia
1984	Not held	1994	Canada
1985	Czechoslovakia	1995	Finland
1986	USSR	1996	Czech Republic
1987	Sweden	1997	Canada
1988	Not held	1998	Sweden
1989	USSR	1999	Czech Republic
1990	Sweden	2000	Czech Republic
1991	Sweden	2001	Czech Republic
2002	Slovakia	2007	Canada
2003	Canada	2008	Russia
2004	Canada	2009	Russia
2005	Czech Republic	2010	Czech Republic
2006	Sweden	2011	Finland

Source: *Time Almanac.*

3. **BUN Count** The blood urea nitrogen (BUN) count of 20 randomly selected patients is given here in milligrams per deciliter (mg/dl). Construct an ungrouped frequency distribution for the data.

17	18	13	14
12	17	11	20
13	18	19	17
14	16	17	12
16	15	19	22

4. **Wind Speed** The data show the average wind speed for 30 days in a large city. Construct an ungrouped frequency distribution for the data.

8	15	9	8	9	10
8	10	14	9	8	8
12	9	8	8	14	9
9	13	13	10	12	9
13	8	11	11	9	8
9	13	9	8	8	10

5. **College Completions** The percentage (rounded to the nearest whole percent) of persons from each state

completing 4 years or more of college is listed below. Organize the data into a grouped frequency distribution with 5 classes. The data for this exercise will be used for Exercises 7, 9, and 11.

Percentage of persons completing 4 years of college

23	25	24	34	22	24	27	37	33	24
26	23	38	24	24	17	28	23	30	25
30	22	33	24	28	36	24	19	25	31
34	31	27	24	29	28	21	25	26	15
26	22	27	21	25	28	24	21	25	26

Source: *New York Times Almanac.*

6. **Ages of the Vice Presidents at the Time of Their Death** The ages of the Vice Presidents of the United States at the time of their death are listed below. Use the data to construct a frequency distribution. Use 6 classes. The data for this exercise will be used for Exercises 8, 10, and 12.

90	83	80	73	70	51	68	79	70	71
72	74	67	54	81	66	62	63	68	57
66	96	78	55	60	66	57	71	60	85
76	98	77	88	78	81	64	66	77	93	70

Source: *World Almanac and Book of Facts.*

Section 2–2

7. Find the relative frequency for the frequency distribution for the data in Exercise 5.

8. Find the relative frequency for the frequency distribution for the data in Exercise 6.

9. Construct a histogram, frequency polygon, and ogive for the data in Exercise 5.

10. Construct a histogram, frequency polygon, and ogive for the data in Exercise 6.

11. Construct a histogram, frequency polygon, and ogive, using relative frequencies for the data in Exercise 5.

12. Construct a histogram, frequency polygon, and ogive, using relative frequencies for the data in Exercise 6.

Section 2–3

13. **Activities While Driving** A survey of 1200 drivers showed the percentage of respondents who did the following while driving. Construct a vertical bar graph and a horizontal bar graph for the data.

Drink beverage	80%
Talk on cell phone	73
Eat a meal	41
Experience road rage	23
Smoke	21

Source: Nationwide Mutual Insurance Company.

14. **Calories of Nuts** The data show the number of calories per ounce in selected types of nuts. Construct vertical and horizontal bar graphs for the data.

Types	Calories
Peanuts	160
Almonds	170
Macadamia	200
Pecans	190
Cashews	160

15. **Classroom Technology** The number of teachers who use the types of technology in the classroom is shown. Construct a Pareto chart for the data. (*Note:* The respondents could select more than one category.)

Type	Number
Websites	280
Online games	215
Online videos	165
Online images	220

Source: Vera Quest Research.

16. **Pet Care** The data (in billions of dollars) show the estimated amount of money spent on pet care in the United States. Construct a Pareto chart for the data.

Type of care	Amount spent
Veterinarian care	$14
Supplies and medicine	11
Grooming and boarding	4
Animal purchases	2

Source: American Pet Products Association.

17. **Space Launches** The data show the number of U.S. space launches for the 10-year periods from 1960 to 2009. Construct a time series graph for the data and analyze the graph.

Year	60–69	70–79	80–89	90–99	100–109
Launches	614	247	199	300	206

Source: NASA.

18. **High School Dropout Rate** The data show the high school dropout rate for students for the years 2003 to 2009. Construct a time series graph and analyze the graph.

Year	2003	2004	2005	2006	2007	2008	2009
Percent	9.9	10.3	9.4	9.3	8.7	8.0	8.1

Source: U.S. Department of Commerce.

19. Spending of College Freshmen The average amounts spent by college freshmen for school items are shown. Construct a pie graph for the data.

Electronics/computers	$728
Dorm items	344
Clothing	141
Shoes	72

Source: National Retail Federation.

20. Career Changes A survey asked if people would like to spend the rest of their careers with their present employers. The results are shown. Construct a pie graph for the data and analyze the results.

Answer	Number of people
Yes	660
No	260
Undecided	80

21. Peyton Manning's Colts Career Peyton Manning played for the Indianapolis Colts for 14 years. (He did not play in 2011.) The data show the number of touchdowns he scored for the years 1998–2010. Construct a dotplot for the data and comment on the graph.

26	33	27	49	31	27	33
26	26	29	28	31	33	

Source: NFL.com

22. Songs on CDs The data show the number of songs on each of 40 CDs from the author's collection. Construct a dotplot for the data and comment on the graph.

10	14	18	11
11	15	16	10
10	17	10	15
22	9	14	12
18	12	12	15
21	22	20	15
10	19	20	21
17	9	13	15
11	12	12	9
14	20	12	10

23. Museum Visitors The number of visitors to the Railroad Museum during 24 randomly selected hours is shown here. Construct a stem and leaf plot for the data.

67	62	38	73	34	43	72	35
53	55	58	63	47	42	51	62
32	29	47	62	29	38	36	41

24. Public Libraries The numbers of public libraries in operation for selected states are listed below. Organize the data with a stem and leaf plot.

102	176	210	142	189	176	108	113	205
209	184	144	108	192	176			

Source: World Almanac.

25. Pain Relief The graph below shows the time it takes Quick Pain Relief to relieve a person's pain. The graph below that shows the time a competitor's product takes to relieve pain. Why might these graphs be misleading?

26. Casino Payoffs The graph shows the payoffs obtained from the White Oak Casino compared to the nearest competitor's casino. Why is this graph misleading?

≡ STATISTICS TODAY

How Your Identity Can Be Stolen —Revisited

Data presented in numerical form do not convey an easy-to-interpret conclusion; however, when data are presented in graphical form, readers can see the visual impact of the numbers. In the case of identity fraud, the reader can see that most of the identity frauds are due to lost or stolen wallets, checkbooks, or credit cards, and very few identity frauds are caused by online purchases or transactions.

Identity Fraud

Online purchases or transactions 4%

Stolen mail or fraudulent change of address 8%

Other methods 11%

Computer viruses and hackers 9%

Corrupt business employees 15%

Friends, acquaintances 15%

Lost or stolen wallet, checkbook, or credit card 38%

The Federal Trade Commission suggests some ways to protect your identity:

1. Shred all financial documents no longer needed.
2. Protect your Social Security number.
3. Don't give out personal information on the phone, through the mail, or over the Internet.
4. Never click on links sent in unsolicited emails.
5. Don't use an obvious password for your computer documents.
6. Keep your personal information in a secure place at home.

≡ Data Analysis

A Data Bank is found in Appendix B, or on the World Wide Web by following links from www.mhhe.com/math/stat/bluman

1. From the Data Bank located in Appendix B, choose one of the following variables: age, weight, cholesterol level, systolic pressure, IQ, or sodium level. Select at least 30 values. For these values, construct a grouped frequency distribution. Draw a histogram, frequency polygon, and ogive for the distribution. Describe briefly the shape of the distribution.

2. From the Data Bank, choose one of the following variables: educational level, smoking status, or exercise. Select at least 20 values. Construct an ungrouped

frequency distribution for the data. For the distribution, draw a Pareto chart and describe briefly the nature of the chart.

3. From the Data Bank, select at least 30 subjects and construct a categorical distribution for their marital status. Draw a pie graph and describe briefly the findings.

4. Using the data from Data Set IV in Appendix B, construct a frequency distribution and draw a histogram. Describe briefly the shape of the distribution of the tallest buildings in New York City.

5. Using the data from Data Set XI in Appendix B, construct a frequency distribution and draw a frequency polygon. Describe briefly the shape of the distribution for the number of pages in statistics books.

6. Using the data from Data Set IX in Appendix B, divide the United States into four regions, as follows:

Northeast	CT ME MA NH NJ NY PA RI VT
Midwest	IL IN IA KS MI MN MD MS NE ND OH SD WI
South	AL AR DE DC FL GA KY LA MD NC OK SC TN TX VA WV
West	AK AZ CA CO HI ID MT NV NM OR UT WA WY

Find the total population for each region, and draw a Pareto chart and a pie graph for the data. Analyze the results. Explain which chart might be a better representation for the data.

7. Using the data from Data Set I in Appendix B, make a stem and leaf plot for the record low temperatures in the United States. Describe the nature of the plot.

Chapter Quiz

Determine whether each statement is true or false. If the statement is false, explain why.

1. In the construction of a frequency distribution, it is a good idea to have overlapping class limits, such as 10–20, 20–30, 30–40.

2. Histograms can be drawn by using vertical or horizontal bars.

3. It is not important to keep the width of each class the same in a frequency distribution.

4. Frequency distributions can aid the researcher in drawing charts and graphs.

5. The type of graph used to represent data is determined by the type of data collected and by the researcher's purpose.

6. In construction of a frequency polygon, the class limits are used for the x axis.

7. Data collected over a period of time can be graphed by using a pie graph.

Select the best answer.

8. What is another name for the ogive?
 a. Histogram
 b. Frequency polygon
 c. Cumulative frequency graph
 d. Pareto chart

9. What are the boundaries for 8.6–8.8?
 a. 8–9
 b. 8.5–8.9
 c. 8.55–8.85
 d. 8.65–8.75

10. What graph should be used to show the relationship between the parts and the whole?
 a. Histogram
 b. Pie graph
 c. Pareto chart
 d. Ogive

11. Except for rounding errors, relative frequencies should add up to what sum?
 a. 0
 b. 1
 c. 50
 d. 100

Complete these statements with the best answers.

12. The three types of frequency distributions are _____, _____, and _____.

13. In a frequency distribution, the number of classes should be between _____ and _____.

14. Data such as blood types (A, B, AB, O) can be organized into a(n) _____ frequency distribution.

15. Data collected over a period of time can be graphed using a(n) _____ graph.

16. A statistical device used in exploratory data analysis that is a combination of a frequency distribution and a histogram is called a(n) _____.

17. On a Pareto chart, the frequencies should be represented on the _____ axis.

18. Housing Arrangements A questionnaire on housing arrangements showed this information obtained from 25 respondents. Construct a frequency distribution for the data (H = house, A = apartment, M = mobile home, C = condominium). These data will be used in Exercise 19.

H	C	H	M	H	A	C	A	M
C	M	C	A	M	A	C	C	M
C	C	H	A	H	H	M		

19. Construct a pie graph for the data in Exercise 18.

20. Items Purchased at a Convenience Store When 30 randomly selected customers left a convenience store, each was asked the number of items he or she purchased. Construct an ungrouped frequency distribution for the data. These data will be used in Exercise 21.

2	9	4	3	6
6	2	8	6	5
7	5	3	8	6
6	2	3	2	4
6	9	9	8	9
4	2	1	7	4

21. Construct a histogram, a frequency polygon, and an ogive for the data in Exercise 20.

22. Coal Consumption The following data represent the energy consumption of coal (in billions of Btu) by each of the 50 states and the District of Columbia. Use the data to construct a frequency distribution and a relative frequency distribution with 7 classes.

631	723	267	60	372	15	19	92	306	38
413	8	736	156	478	264	1015	329	679	1498
52	1365	142	423	365	350	445	776	1267	0
26	356	173	373	335	34	937	250	33	84
0	253	84	1224	743	582	2	33	0	426
474									

Source: *Time Almanac.*

23. Construct a histogram, frequency polygon, and ogive for the data in Exercise 22. Analyze the histogram.

24. Recycled Trash Construct a Pareto chart and a horizontal bar graph for the number of tons (in millions) of trash recycled per year by Americans based on an Environmental Protection Agency study.

Type	Amount
Paper	320.0
Iron/steel	292.0
Aluminum	276.0
Yard waste	242.4
Glass	196.0
Plastics	41.6

Source: *USA TODAY.*

25. Identity Thefts The results of a survey of 84 people whose identities were stolen using various methods are shown. Draw a pie chart for the information.

Lost or stolen wallet, checkbook, or credit card	38
Retail purchases or telephone transactions	15
Stolen mail	9
Computer viruses or hackers	8
Phishing	4
Other	10
	84

Source: Javelin Strategy and Research.

26. Needless Deaths of Children *The New England Journal of Medicine* predicted the number of needless deaths due to childhood obesity. Draw a time series graph for the data.

Year	2020	2025	2030	2035
Deaths	130	550	1500	3700

27. Museum Visitors The number of visitors to the Historic Museum for 25 randomly selected hours is shown. Construct a stem and leaf plot for the data.

15	53	48	19	38
86	63	98	79	38
62	89	67	39	26
28	35	54	88	76
31	47	53	41	68

28. Parking Meter Revenue In a small city the number of quarters collected from the parking meters is shown. Construct a dotplot for the data.

13	12	11	7	16
10	16	15	7	11
3	5	14	3	6
8	3	10	9	3
5	7	8	9	9
9	2	6	4	11
7	4	2	8	10
7	17	4	11	8
2	5	5	14	6
3	9	3	12	3

29. Water Usage The graph shows the average number of gallons of water a person uses for various activities. Can you see anything misleading about the way the graph is drawn?

Critical Thinking Challenges

1. The Great Lakes Shown are various statistics about the Great Lakes. Using appropriate graphs (your choice) and summary statements, write a report analyzing the data.

	Superior	Michigan	Huron	Erie	Ontario
Length (miles)	350	307	206	241	193
Breadth (miles)	160	118	183	57	53
Depth (feet)	1,330	923	750	210	802
Volume (cubic miles)	2,900	1,180	850	116	393
Area (square miles)	31,700	22,300	23,000	9,910	7,550
Shoreline (U.S., miles)	863	1,400	580	431	300

Source: The World Almanac and Book of Facts.

2. Teacher Strikes In Pennsylvania there were more teacher strikes in 2004 than there were in all other states combined. Because of the disruptions, state legislators want to pass a bill outlawing teacher strikes and submitting contract disputes to binding arbitration. The graph shows the number of teacher strikes in Pennsylvania for the school years 1997 to 2011. Use the graph to answer these questions.

a. In what year did the largest number of strikes occur? How many were there?

b. In what year did the smallest number of teacher strikes occur? How many were there?

c. In what year was the average duration of the strikes the longest? How long was it?

d. In what year was the average duration of the strikes the shortest? How long was it?

e. In what year was the number of teacher strikes the same as the average duration of the strikes?

f. Find the difference in the number of strikes for the school years 1997–1998 and 2010–2011.

g. Do you think teacher strikes should be outlawed? Justify your conclusions.

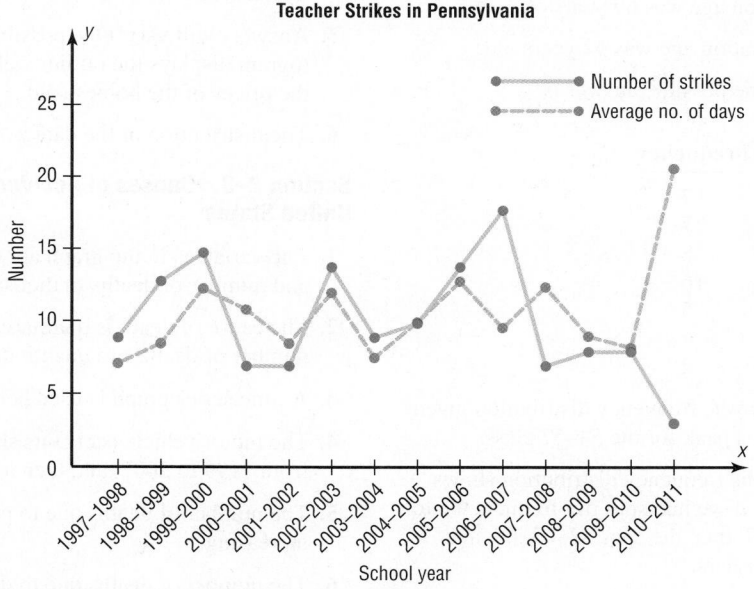

Teacher Strikes in Pennsylvania

Source: Pennsylvania School Boards Association.

Data Projects

Where appropriate, use the TI-84 Plus, Excel, MINITAB, or a computer program of your choice to complete the following exercises.

1. Business and Finance Consider the 30 stocks listed as the Dow Jones Industrials. For each, find its earnings per share. Randomly select 30 stocks traded on the NASDAQ. For each, find its earnings per share. Create a frequency table with 5 categories for each data set. Sketch a histogram for each. How do the two data sets compare?

2. **Sports and Leisure** Use systematic sampling to create a sample of 25 National League and 25 American League baseball players from the most recently completed season. Find the number of home runs for each player. Create a frequency table with 5 categories for each data set. Sketch a histogram for each. How do the two leagues compare?

3. **Technology** Randomly select 50 songs from your music player or music organization program. Find the length (in seconds) for each song. Use these data to create a frequency table with 6 categories. Sketch a frequency polygon for the frequency table. Is the shape of the distribution of times uniform, skewed, or bell-shaped? Also note the genre of each song. Create a Pareto chart showing the frequencies of the various categories. Finally, note the year each song was released. Create a pie chart organized by decade to show the percentage of songs from various time periods.

4. **Health and Wellness** Use information from the Red Cross to create a pie chart depicting the percentages of Americans with various blood types. Also find information about blood donations and the percentage of each type donated. How do the charts compare? Why is the collection of type O blood so important?

5. **Politics and Economics** Consider the U.S. Electoral College System. For each of the 50 states, determine the number of delegates received. Create a frequency table with 8 classes. Is this distribution uniform, skewed, or bell-shaped?

6. **Your Class** Have each person in class take his or her pulse and determine the heart rate (beats in 1 minute). Use the data to create a frequency table with 6 classes. Then have everyone in the class do 25 jumping jacks and immediately take the pulse again after the activity. Create a frequency table for those data as well. Compare the two results. Are they similarly distributed? How does the range of scores compare?

Answers to Applying the Concepts

Section 2–1   Ages of Presidents at Inauguration

1. The data were obtained from the population of all Presidents at the time this text was written.

2. The oldest inauguration age was 69 years old.

3. The youngest inauguration age was 42 years old.

4. Answers will vary. One possible answer is

Age at inauguration	Frequency
42–45	2
46–49	7
50–53	8
54–57	16
58–61	5
62–65	4
66–69	2

5. Answers will vary. For the frequency distribution given in question 4, there is a peak for the 54–57 class.

6. Answers will vary. This frequency distribution shows no outliers. However, if we had split our frequency into 14 classes instead of 7, then the ages 42, 43, 68, and 69 might appear as outliers.

7. Answers will vary. The data appear to be unimodal and fairly symmetric, centering on 55 years of age.

Section 2–2   Selling Real Estate

1. A histogram of the data gives price ranges and the counts of homes in each price range. We can also talk about how the data are distributed by looking at a histogram.

2. A frequency polygon shows increases or decreases in the number of home prices around values.

3. A cumulative frequency polygon shows the number of homes sold at or below a given price.

4. The house that sold for $321,550 is an extreme value in this data set.

5. Answers will vary. One possible answer is that the histogram displays the outlier well since there is a gap in the prices of the homes sold.

6. The distribution of the data is skewed to the right.

Section 2–3   Causes of Accidental Deaths in the United States

1. The variables in the graph are the year, cause of death, and number of deaths in thousands.

2. The cause of death is qualitative, while the year and number of deaths are quantitative.

3. A time series graph is used here.

4. The motor vehicle accidents showed a slight increase from 1999 to 2007, and then a decrease.

5. The number of deaths due to poisoning and falls is increasing.

6. The number of deaths due to drowning remains about the same over the years.

7. For 2001, about 44,000 people died in motor vehicle accidents, about 15,000 people died from falls, about 14,000 people died from poisoning, and about 3000 people died from drowning.

8. In 1999, motor vehicle accidents claimed the most lives, while in 2009, poisoning claimed the most lives.

9. Around 2002, the number of deaths from falls and poisoning were about the same.

Data Description

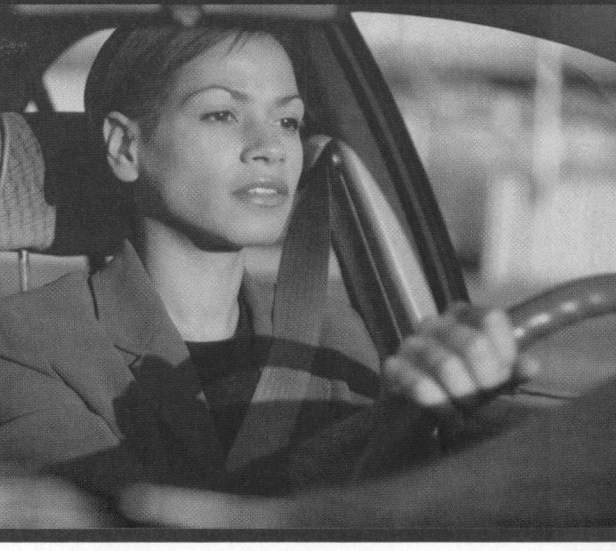

⚞ STATISTICS TODAY

How Long Are You Delayed by Road Congestion?

No matter where you live, at one time or another, you have been stuck in traffic. To see whether there are more traffic delays in some cities than in others, statisticians make comparisons using descriptive statistics. A statistical study by the Texas Transportation Institute found that a driver is delayed by road congestion an average of 36 hours per year. To see how selected cities compare to this average, see Statistics Today—Revisited at the end of the chapter.

This chapter will show you how to obtain and interpret descriptive statistics such as measures of average, measures of variation, and measures of position.

OUTLINE

Introduction

3–1 Measures of Central Tendency

3–2 Measures of Variation

3–3 Measures of Position

3–4 Exploratory Data Analysis

Summary

OBJECTIVES

After completing this chapter, you should be able to

1 Summarize data, using measures of central tendency, such as the mean, median, mode, and midrange.

2 Describe data, using measures of variation, such as the range, variance, and standard deviation.

3 Identify the position of a data value in a data set, using various measures of position, such as percentiles, deciles, and quartiles.

4 Use the techniques of exploratory data analysis, including boxplots and five-number summaries, to discover various aspects of data.

Introduction

Chapter 2 showed how you can gain useful information from raw data by organizing them into a frequency distribution and then presenting the data by using various graphs. This chapter shows the statistical methods that can be used to summarize data. The most familiar of these methods is the finding of averages.

For example, you may read that the average speed of a car crossing midtown Manhattan during the day is 5.3 miles per hour or that the average number of minutes an American father of a 4-year-old spends alone with his child each day is 42.[1]

In the book *American Averages* by Mike Feinsilber and William B. Meed, the authors state:

> *"Average" when you stop to think of it is a funny concept. Although it describes all of us it describes none of us. . . . While none of us wants to be the average American, we all want to know about him or her.*

The authors go on to give examples of averages:

> *The average American man is five feet, nine inches tall; the average woman is five feet, 3.6 inches.*
> *The average American is sick in bed seven days a year missing five days of work.*
> *On the average day, 24 million people receive animal bites.*
> *By his or her 70th birthday, the average American will have eaten 14 steers, 1050 chickens, 3.5 lambs, and 25.2 hogs.[2]*

In these examples, the word *average* is ambiguous, since several different methods can be used to obtain an average. Loosely stated, the average means the center of the distribution or the most typical case. Measures of average are also called *measures of central tendency* and include the *mean, median, mode,* and *midrange.*

Knowing the average of a data set is not enough to describe the data set entirely. Even though a shoe store owner knows that the average size of a man's shoe is size 10, she would not be in business very long if she ordered only size 10 shoes.

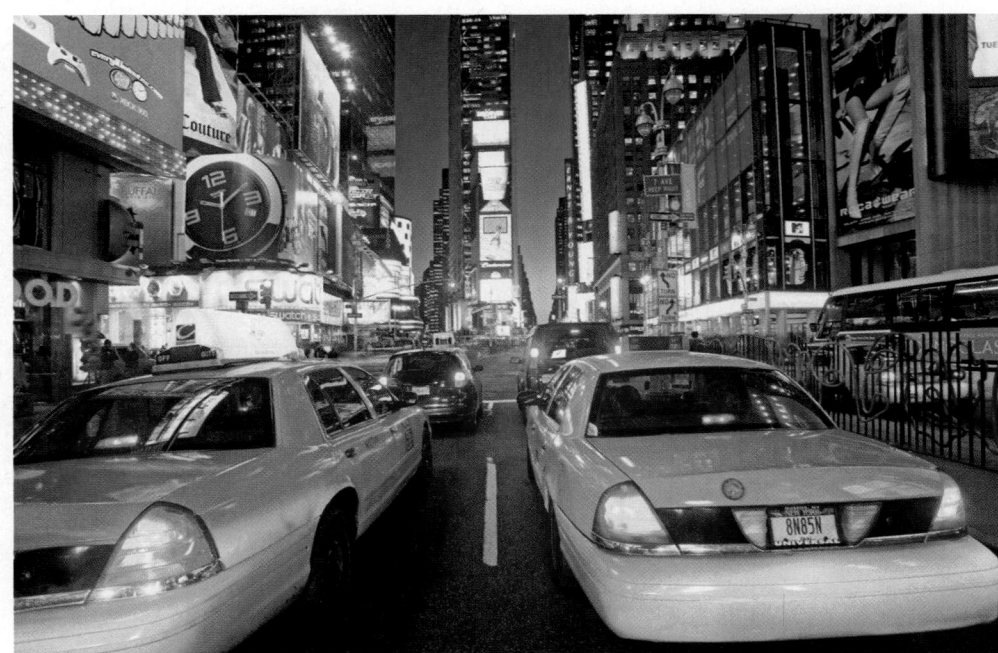

[1]"Harper's Index," *Harper's* magazine.

[2]Mike Feinsilber and William B. Meed, *American Averages* (New York: Bantam Doubleday Dell).

As this example shows, in addition to knowing the average, you must know how the data values are dispersed. That is, do the data values cluster around the average, or are they spread more evenly throughout the distribution? The measures that determine the spread of the data values are called *measures of variation,* or *measures of dispersion.* These measures include the *range, variance,* and *standard deviation.*

Finally, another set of measures is necessary to describe data. These measures are called *measures of position.* They tell where a specific data value falls within the data set or its relative position in comparison with other data values. The most common position measures are *percentiles, deciles,* and *quartiles.* These measures are used extensively in psychology and education. Sometimes they are referred to as *norms.*

The measures of central tendency, variation, and position explained in this chapter are part of what is called *traditional statistics.*

Section 3–4 shows the techniques of what is called *exploratory data analysis.* These techniques include the *boxplot* and the *five-number summary.* They can be used to explore data to see what they show (as opposed to the traditional techniques, which are used to confirm conjectures about the data).

3–1   Measures of Central Tendency

OBJECTIVE

Summarize data, using measures of central tendency, such as the mean, median, mode, and midrange.

Chapter 1 stated that statisticians use samples taken from populations; however, when populations are small, it is not necessary to use samples since the entire population can be used to gain information. For example, suppose an insurance manager wanted to know the average weekly sales of all the company's representatives. If the company employed a large number of salespeople, say, nationwide, he would have to use a sample and make an inference to the entire sales force. But if the company had only a few salespeople, say, only 87 agents, he would be able to use all representatives' sales for a randomly chosen week and thus use the entire population.

Measures found by using all the data values in the population are called *parameters.* Measures obtained by using the data values from samples are called *statistics;* hence, the average of the sales from a sample of representatives is a *statistic,* and the average of sales obtained from the entire population is a *parameter.*

> A **statistic** is a characteristic or measure obtained by using the data values from a sample.
>
> A **parameter** is a characteristic or measure obtained by using all the data values from a specific population.

Historical Note

In 1796, Adolphe Quetelet investigated the characteristics (heights, weights, etc.) of French conscripts to determine the "average man." Florence Nightingale was so influenced by Quetelet's work that she began collecting and analyzing medical records in the military hospitals during the Crimean War. Based on her work, hospitals began keeping accurate records on their patients.

These concepts as well as the symbols used to represent them will be explained in detail in this chapter.

General Rounding Rule In statistics the basic rounding rule is that when computations are done in the calculation, rounding should not be done until the final answer is calculated. When rounding is done in the intermediate steps, it tends to increase the difference between that answer and the exact one. But in the textbook and solutions manual, it is not practical to show long decimals in the intermediate calculations; hence, the values in the examples are carried out to enough places (usually three or four) to obtain the same answer that a calculator would give after rounding on the last step.

There are specific rounding rules for many statistics, and they will be given in the appropriate sections.

The Mean

The *mean,* also known as the *arithmetic average,* is found by adding the values of the data and dividing by the total number of values. For example, the mean of 3, 2, 6, 5, and 4 is found by adding $3 + 2 + 6 + 5 + 4 = 20$ and dividing by 5; hence, the mean of the data is $20 \div 5 = 4$. The values of the data are represented by X's. In this data set, $X_1 = 3$, $X_2 = 2$,

$X_3 = 6$, $X_4 = 5$, and $X_5 = 4$. To show a sum of the total X values, the symbol Σ (the capital Greek letter sigma) is used, and ΣX means to find the sum of the X values in the data set. The summation notation is explained on the online resource section under "Algebra Review."

> The **mean** is the sum of the values, divided by the total number of values.
>
> The **sample mean**, denoted by $\overline{X}$ (pronounced "X bar"), is calculated by using sample data. The sample mean is a statistic.
>
> $$\overline{X} = \frac{X_1 + X_2 + X_3 + \cdots + X_n}{n} = \frac{\Sigma X}{n}$$
>
> where n represents the total number of values in the sample.
>
> The **population mean**, denoted by μ (pronounced "mew"), is calculated by using all the values in the population. The population mean is a parameter.
>
> $$\mu = \frac{X_1 + X_2 + X_3 + \cdots + X_N}{N} = \frac{\Sigma X}{N}$$
>
> where N represents the total number of values in the population.

In statistics, Greek letters are used to denote parameters, and Roman letters are used to denote statistics. Assume that the data are obtained from samples unless otherwise specified.

Rounding Rule for the Mean The mean should be rounded to one more decimal place than occurs in the raw data. For example, if the raw data are given in whole numbers, the mean should be rounded to the nearest tenth. If the data are given in tenths, the mean should be rounded to the nearest hundredth, and so on.

EXAMPLE 3–1   Police Incidents

The number of calls that a local police department responded to for a sample of 9 months is shown. Find the mean. (Data were obtained by the author.)

$$475, 447, 440, 761, 993, 1052, 783, 671, 621$$

SOLUTION

$$\overline{X} = \frac{\Sigma x}{n} = \frac{475 + 447 + 440 + 761 + 993 + 1052 + 783 + 671 + 621}{9}$$

$$= \frac{6243}{9} \approx 693.7$$

Hence, the mean number of incidents per month to which the police responded is 693.7.

EXAMPLE 3–2   Hospital Infections

The data show the number of patients in a sample of six hospitals who acquired an infection while hospitalized. Find the mean.

$$110 \qquad 76 \qquad 29 \qquad 38 \qquad 105 \qquad 31$$

Source: Pennsylvania Health Care Cost Containment Council.

SOLUTION

$$\overline{X} = \frac{\Sigma X}{n} = \frac{110 + 76 + 29 + 38 + 105 + 31}{6} = \frac{389}{6} = 64.8$$

The mean of the number of hospital infections for the six hospitals is 64.8.

The mean, in most cases, is not an actual data value.

The procedure for finding the mean for grouped data assumes that the mean of all the raw data values in each class is equal to the midpoint of the class. In reality, this is not true, since the average of the raw data values in each class usually will not be exactly equal to the midpoint. However, using this procedure will give an acceptable approximation of the mean, since some values fall above the midpoint and other values fall below the midpoint for each class, and the midpoint represents an estimate of all values in the class.

The steps for finding the mean for grouped data are shown in the next Procedure Table.

Procedure Table

Finding the Mean for Grouped Data

Step 1   Make a table as shown.

A Class	B Frequency f	C Midpoint X_m	D $f \cdot X_m$

Step 2   Find the midpoints of each class and place them in column C.

Step 3   Multiply the frequency by the midpoint for each class, and place the product in column D.

Step 4   Find the sum of column D.

Step 5   Divide the sum obtained in column D by the sum of the frequencies obtained in column B.

The formula for the mean is

$$\overline{X} = \frac{\Sigma f \cdot X_m}{n}$$

[*Note:* The symbols $\Sigma f \cdot X_m$ mean to find the sum of the product of the frequency (f) and the midpoint (X_m) for each class.]

EXAMPLE 3–3   Miles Run per Week

Using the following frequency distribution (taken from Example 2–7), find the mean. The data represent the number of miles run during one week for a sample of 20 runners.

Class boundaries	Frequency
5.5–10.5	1
10.5–15.5	2
15.5–20.5	3
20.5–25.5	5
25.5–30.5	4
30.5–35.5	3
35.5–40.5	2
	Total 20

SOLUTION

The procedure for finding the mean for grouped data is given here.

Step 1   Make a table as shown.

A Class	B Frequency f	C Midpoint X_m	D $f \cdot X_m$
5.5–10.5	1		
10.5–15.5	2		
15.5–20.5	3		
20.5–25.5	5		
25.5–30.5	4		
30.5–35.5	3		
35.5–40.5	2		
	$n = 20$		

The histogram shows the ages of the top 50 wealthiest individuals according to *Forbes Magazine* for a recent year. The mean age is 66 years. The median age is 68 years. Explain why these two statistics are not enough to adequately describe the data.

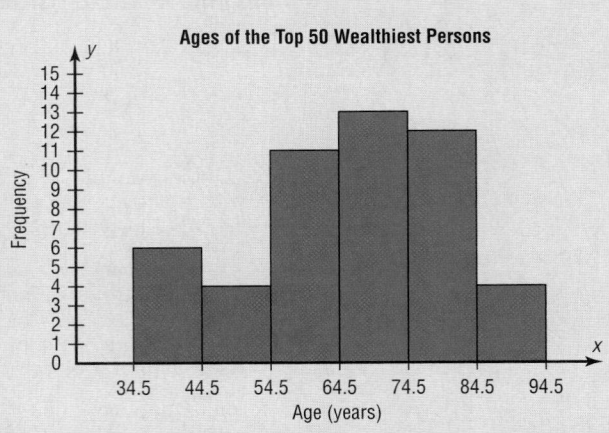

Ages of the Top 50 Wealthiest Persons

Step 2   Find the midpoints of each class and enter them in column C.

$$X_m = \frac{5.5 + 10.5}{2} = 8 \qquad \frac{10.5 + 15.5}{2} = 13 \quad \text{etc.}$$

Step 3   For each class, multiply the frequency by the midpoint, as shown, and place the product in column D.

$$1 \cdot 8 = 8 \qquad 2 \cdot 13 = 26 \quad \text{etc.}$$

The completed table is shown here.

A Class	B Frequency f	C Midpoint X_m	D $f \cdot X_m$
5.5–10.5	1	8	8
10.5–15.5	2	13	26
15.5–20.5	3	18	54
20.5–25.5	5	23	115
25.5–30.5	4	28	112
30.5–35.5	3	33	99
35.5–40.5	2	38	76
$n = 20$			$\Sigma f \cdot X_m = 490$

Step 4   Find the sum of column D.

Step 5   Divide the sum by n to get the mean.

$$\overline{X} = \frac{\Sigma f \cdot X_m}{n} = \frac{490}{20} = 24.5 \text{ miles}$$

Historical Note

The concept of median was used by Gauss at the beginning of the 19th century and introduced as a statistical concept by Francis Galton around 1874. The mode was first used by Karl Pearson in 1894.

The Median

An article recently reported that the median income for college professors was $43,250. This measure of central tendency means that one-half of all the professors surveyed earned more than $43,250, and one-half earned less than $43,250.

The *median* is the halfway point in a data set. Before you can find this point, the data must be arranged in ascending or increasing order. When the data set is ordered, it is called a **data array.** The median either will be a specific value in the data set or will fall between two values, as shown in the next examples.

> The **median** is the midpoint of the data array. The symbol for the median is MD.

The Procedure Table for finding the median is shown next.

Procedure Table

Finding the Median

Step 1   Arrange the data values in ascending order.

Step 2   Determine the number of values in the data set.

Step 3   *a.* If n is odd, select the middle data value as the median.

　　　　　b. If n is even, find the mean of the two middle values. That is, add them and divide the sum by 2.

EXAMPLE 3–4   Police Officers Killed

The number of police officers killed in the line of duty over the last 11 years is shown. Find the median.

177   153   122   141   189   155   162   165   149   157   240

Source: National Law Enforcement Officers Memorial Fund.

SOLUTION

Step 1   Arrange the data in ascending order.

122, 141, 149, 153, 155, 157, 162, 165, 177, 189, 240

Step 2   There are an odd number of data values, namely, 11.

Step 3   Select the middle data value.

122, 141, 149, 153, 155, 157, 162, 165, 177, 189, 240

↑

Median

The median number of police officers killed for the 11-year period is 157.

EXAMPLE 3–5   Tornadoes in the United States

The number of tornadoes that have occurred in the United States over an 8-year period follows. Find the median.

684, 764, 656, 702, 856, 1133, 1132, 1303

Source: *The Universal Almanac.*

SOLUTION

Step 1   Arrange the data values in ascending order.

656,   684,   702,   764,   856,   1132,   1133,   1303

Step 2   There are an even number of data values, namely, 8.

Step 3   The middle two data values are 764 and 856.

656, 684, 702, 764, 856, 1132, 1133, 1303

↑

Median

Since the middle point falls halfway between 764 and 856, find the median MD by adding the two values and dividing by 2.

$$MD = \frac{764 + 856}{2} = \frac{1620}{2} = 810$$

The median number of tornadoes is 810.

The Mode

The third measure of average is called the *mode.* The mode is the value that occurs most often in the data set. It is sometimes said to be the most typical case.

> The value that occurs most often in a data set is called the **mode**.

A data set that has only one value that occurs with the greatest frequency is said to be **unimodal.**

If a data set has two values that occur with the same greatest frequency, both values are considered to be the mode and the data set is said to be **bimodal.** If a data set has more than two values that occur with the same greatest frequency, each value is used as the mode, and the data set is said to be **multimodal.** When no data value occurs more than once, the data set is said to have *no mode. Note: Do not say that the mode is zero.* That would be incorrect, because in some data, such as temperature, zero can be an actual value. A data set can have more than one mode or no mode at all. These situations will be shown in some of the examples that follow.

EXAMPLE 3–6   NFL Signing Bonuses

Find the mode of the signing bonuses of eight NFL players for a specific year. The bonuses in millions of dollars are

18.0, 14.0, 34.5, 10, 11.3, 10, 12.4, 10

Source: *USA TODAY.*

SOLUTION

It is helpful to arrange the data in order, although it is not necessary.

10, 10, 10, 11.3, 12.4, 14.0, 18.0, 34.5

Since $10 million occurred 3 times—a frequency larger than any other number—the mode is $10 million.

EXAMPLE 3–7   Licensed Nuclear Reactors

The data show the number of licensed nuclear reactors in the United States for a recent 15-year period. Find the mode.

Source: *The World Almanac and Book of Facts.*

104	104	104	104	104
107	109	109	109	110
109	111	112	111	109

SOLUTION

Since the values 104 and 109 both occur 5 times, the modes are 104 and 109. The data set is said to be bimodal.

EXAMPLE 3–8   Accidental Firearm Deaths

The number of accidental deaths due to firearms for a six-year period is shown. Find the mode.

$$649, 789, 642, 613, 610, 600$$

Source: National Safety Council.

SOLUTION

Since each value occurs only once, there is no mode.

The mode for grouped data is the modal class. The **modal class** is the class with the largest frequency.

EXAMPLE 3–9   Miles Run per Week

Find the modal class for the frequency distribution of miles that 20 runners ran in one week, used in Example 2–7.

Class	Frequency	
5.5–10.5	1	
10.5–15.5	2	
15.5–20.5	3	
20.5–25.5	5	← Modal class
25.5–30.5	4	
30.5–35.5	3	
35.5–40.5	2	

SOLUTION

The modal class is 20.5–25.5, since it has the largest frequency. Sometimes the midpoint of the class is used rather than the boundaries; hence, the mode could also be given as 23 miles per week.

The mode is the only measure of central tendency that can be used in finding the most typical case when the data are nominal or categorical.

EXAMPLE 3–10   Area Boat Registrations

The data show the number of boats registered for six counties in southwestern Pennsylvania. Find the mode.

Westmoreland	11,008
Butler	9,002
Washington	6,843
Beaver	6,367
Fayette	4,208
Armstrong	3,782

Source: Pennsylvania Fish and Boat Commission.

SOLUTION

Since the category with the highest frequency is Westmoreland, the most typical case is Westmoreland. Hence, the mode is Westmoreland.

An extremely high or extremely low data value in a data set can have a striking effect on the mean of the data set. These extreme values are called *outliers*. This is one reason why, when analyzing a frequency distribution, you should be aware of any of these values. For the data set shown in Example 3–11, the mean, median, and mode can be quite different because of extreme values. A method for identifying outliers is given in Section 3–3.

EXAMPLE 3–11   Salaries of Personnel

A small company consists of the owner, the manager, the salesperson, and two technicians, all of whose annual salaries are listed here. (Assume that this is the entire population.)

Staff	Salary
Owner	$100,000
Manager	40,000
Salesperson	24,000
Technician	18,000
Technician	18,000

Find the mean, median, and mode.

SOLUTION

$$\mu = \frac{\Sigma X}{N} = \frac{\$100,000 + 40,000 + 24,000 + 18,000 + 18,000}{5} = \frac{\$200,000}{5} = \$40,000$$

Hence, the mean is $40,000, the median is $24,000, and the mode is $18,000.

In Example 3–11, the mean is much higher than the median or the mode. This is so because the extremely high salary of the owner tends to raise the value of the mean. In this and similar situations, the median should be used as the measure of central tendency.

The Midrange

The *midrange* is a rough estimate of the middle. It is found by adding the lowest and highest values in the data set and dividing by 2. It is a very rough estimate of the average and can be affected by one extremely high or low value.

> The **midrange** is defined as the sum of the lowest and highest values in the data set, divided by 2. The symbol MR is used for the midrange.
>
> $$MR = \frac{\text{lowest value} + \text{highest value}}{2}$$

EXAMPLE 3–12   **Bank Failures**

The number of bank failures for a recent five-year period is shown. Find the midrange.

$$3, 30, 148, 157, 71$$

Source: Federal Deposit Insurance Corporation.

SOLUTION

The lowest data value is 3, and the highest data value is 157.

$$MR = \frac{3 + 157}{2} = \frac{160}{2} = 80$$

The midrange for the number of bank failures is 80.

EXAMPLE 3–13   **NFL Signing Bonuses**

Find the midrange of data for the NFL signing bonuses in Example 3–6. The bonuses in millions of dollars are

$$18.0, 14.0, 34.5, 10, 11.3, 10, 12.4, 10$$

SOLUTION

The lowest bonus is $10 million, and the largest bonus is $34.5 million.

$$MR = \frac{10 + 34.5}{2} = \frac{44.5}{2} = \$22.25 \text{ million}$$

Notice that this amount is larger than seven of the eight amounts and is not typical of the average of the bonuses. The reason is that there is one very high bonus, namely, $34.5 million.

    In statistics, several measures can be used for an average. The most common measures are the mean, median, mode, and midrange. Each has its own specific purpose and use. Exercises 36 through 38 show examples of other averages, such as the harmonic mean, the geometric mean, and the quadratic mean. Their applications are limited to specific areas, as shown in the exercises.

The Weighted Mean

Sometimes, you must find the mean of a data set in which not all values are equally represented. Consider the case of finding the average cost of a gallon of gasoline for three taxis. Suppose the drivers buy gasoline at three different service stations at a cost of $3.22, $3.53, and $3.63 per gallon. You might try to find the average by using the formula

$$\bar{X} = \frac{\Sigma X}{n}$$

$$= \frac{3.22 + 3.53 + 3.63}{3} = \frac{10.38}{3} = \$3.46$$

But not all drivers purchased the same number of gallons. Hence, to find the true average cost per gallon, you must take into consideration the number of gallons each driver purchased.

    The type of mean that considers an additional factor is called the *weighted mean,* and it is used when the values are not all equally represented.

Find the **weighted mean** of a variable X by multiplying each value by its corresponding weight and dividing the sum of the products by the sum of the weights.

$$\overline{X} = \frac{w_1X_1 + w_2X_2 + \cdots + w_nX_n}{w_1 + w_2 + \cdots + w_n} = \frac{\Sigma wX}{\Sigma w}$$

where $w_1, w_2, \ldots, w_n$ are the weights and $X_1, X_2, \ldots, X_n$ are the values.

Example 3–14 shows how the weighted mean is used to compute a grade point average. Since courses vary in their credit value, the number of credits must be used as weights.

EXAMPLE 3–14 Grade Point Average

A student received an A in English Composition I (3 credits), a C in Introduction to Psychology (3 credits), a B in Biology I (4 credits), and a D in Physical Education (2 credits). Assuming A = 4 grade points, B = 3 grade points, C = 2 grade points, D = 1 grade point, and F = 0 grade points, find the student's grade point average.

SOLUTION

Course	Credits (w)	Grade (X)
English Composition I	3	A (4 points)
Introduction to Psychology	3	C (2 points)
Biology I	4	B (3 points)
Physical Education	2	D (1 point)

$$\overline{X} = \frac{\Sigma wX}{\Sigma w} = \frac{3 \cdot 4 + 3 \cdot 2 + 4 \cdot 3 + 2 \cdot 1}{3 + 3 + 4 + 2} = \frac{32}{12} \approx 2.7$$

The grade point average is 2.7.

Unusual Stat

Of people in the United States, 45% live within 15 minutes of their best friend.

TABLE 3–1	Summary of Measures of Central Tendency	
Measure	**Definition**	**Symbol(s)**
Mean	Sum of values, divided by total number of values	$\mu, \overline{X}$
Median	Middle point in data set that has been ordered	MD
Mode	Most frequent data value	None
Midrange	Lowest value plus highest value, divided by 2	MR

Table 3–1 summarizes the measures of central tendency.

Researchers and statisticians must know which measure of central tendency is being used and when to use each measure of central tendency. The properties and uses of the four measures of central tendency are summarized next.

Properties and Uses of Central Tendency

The Mean

1. The mean is found by using all the values of the data.
2. The mean varies less than the median or mode when samples are taken from the same population and all three measures are computed for these samples.
3. The mean is used in computing other statistics, such as the variance.
4. The mean for the data set is unique and not necessarily one of the data values.

5. The mean cannot be computed for the data in a frequency distribution that has an open-ended class.

6. The mean is affected by extremely high or low values, called outliers, and may not be the appropriate average to use in these situations.

The Median

1. The median is used to find the center or middle value of a data set.

2. The median is used when it is necessary to find out whether the data values fall into the upper half or lower half of the distribution.

3. The median is used for an open-ended distribution.

4. The median is affected less than the mean by extremely high or extremely low values.

The Mode

1. The mode is used when the most typical case is desired.

2. The mode is the easiest average to compute.

3. The mode can be used when the data are nominal or categorical, such as religious preference, gender, or political affiliation.

4. The mode is not always unique. A data set can have more than one mode, or the mode may not exist for a data set.

The Midrange

1. The midrange is easy to compute.

2. The midrange gives the midpoint.

3. The midrange is affected by extremely high or low values in a data set.

Distribution Shapes

Frequency distributions can assume many shapes. The three most important shapes are positively skewed, symmetric, and negatively skewed. Figure 3–1 shows histograms of each.

In a **positively skewed** or **right-skewed distribution,** the majority of the data values fall to the left of the mean and cluster at the lower end of the distribution; the "tail" is to the right. Also, the mean is to the right of the median, and the mode is to the left of the median.

FIGURE 3–1

Types of Distributions

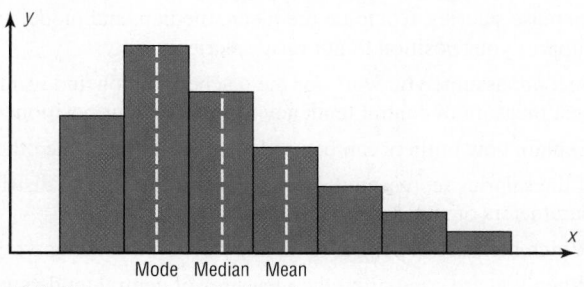

(a) Positively skewed or right-skewed

(b) Symmetric

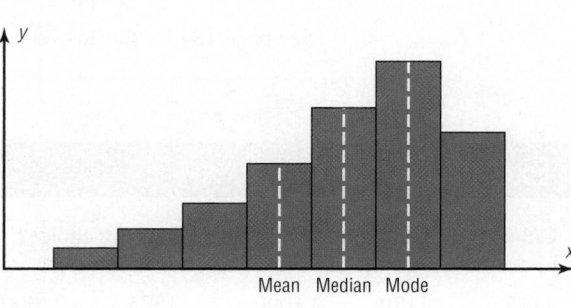

(c) Negatively skewed or left-skewed

For example, if an instructor gave an examination and most of the students did poorly, their scores would tend to cluster on the left side of the distribution. A few high scores would constitute the tail of the distribution, which would be on the right side. Another example of a positively skewed distribution is the incomes of the population of the United States. Most of the incomes cluster about the low end of the distribution; those with high incomes are in the minority and are in the tail at the right of the distribution.

In a **symmetric distribution,** the data values are evenly distributed on both sides of the mean. In addition, when the distribution is unimodal, the mean, median, and mode are the same and are at the center of the distribution. Examples of symmetric distributions are IQ scores and heights of adult males.

When the majority of the data values fall to the right of the mean and cluster at the upper end of the distribution, with the tail to the left, the distribution is said to be **negatively skewed** or **left-skewed.** Also, the mean is to the left of the median, and the mode is to the right of the median. As an example, a negatively skewed distribution results if the majority of students score very high on an instructor's examination. These scores will tend to cluster to the right of the distribution.

When a distribution is extremely skewed, the value of the mean will be pulled toward the tail, but the majority of the data values will be greater than the mean or less than the mean (depending on which way the data are skewed); hence, the median rather than the mean is a more appropriate measure of central tendency. An extremely skewed distribution can also affect other statistics.

A measure of skewness for a distribution is discussed in Exercise 48 in Section 3–2.

Applying the Concepts 3–1

Teacher Salaries

The following data from several years ago represent salaries (in dollars) from a school district in Greenwood, South Carolina.

| 10,000 | 11,000 | 11,000 | 12,500 | 14,300 | 17,500 |
| 18,000 | 16,600 | 19,200 | 21,560 | 16,400 | 107,000 |

1. First, assume you work for the school board in Greenwood and do not wish to raise taxes to increase salaries. Compute the mean, median, and mode, and decide which one would best support your position to not raise salaries.

2. Second, assume you work for the teachers' union and want a raise for the teachers. Use the best measure of central tendency to support your position.

3. Explain how outliers can be used to support one or the other position.

4. If the salaries represented every teacher in the school district, would the averages be parameters or statistics?

5. Which measure of central tendency can be misleading when a data set contains outliers?

6. When you are comparing the measures of central tendency, does the distribution display any skewness? Explain.

See page 184 for the answers.

Exercises 3–1

1. **Calories in Salads** Are salads a healthy menu choice? Listed below are the number of calories in selected entrée salads at several popular restaurants. Find the mean, median, mode and midrange for the data.

1165	1180	1090	1595	900	1100	985	1120	940	730
1270	1005	1180	700	1260	605	920	855	935	835
590	860	840	755	1450					

2. **Airport Parking** The number of short-term parking spaces at 15 airports is shown. Find the mean, median, mode, and midrange for the data.

750	3400	1962	700	203
900	8662	260	1479	5905
9239	690	9822	1131	2516

Source: *USA Today.*

3. **Natural Gas Drilling Sites** The number of natural gas drilling sites in Pennsylvania counties with drilling operations is listed below. Find the mean, median, mode and midrange for the data and discuss the differences in these measures of central tendency. Which best describes the center of the data?

9	112	1	1	6	1008	109	6	14	58
20	136	85	3	58	185	6	415	2	43
26	2	2	2	473	53	76	19	41	462
693	1	2	560	4	191	98			

Source: *Pennsylvania Dept. of Environmental Protection.*

4. **Observers in the Frogwatch Program** The number of observers in the Frogwatch USA program (a wildlife conservation program dedicated to helping conserve frogs and toads) for the top 10 states with the most observers is 484, 483, 422, 396, 378, 352, 338, 331, 318, and 302. The top 10 states with the most active watchers list these numbers of visits: 634, 464, 406, 267, 219, 194, 191, 150, 130, and 114. Find the mean, median, mode, and midrange for the data. Compare the measures of central tendency for these two groups of data.

Source: www.nwf.org/frogwatch

5. **Violent Crimes** Shown are the ten U.S. cities (with population over 100,000) with the fewest number of violent crimes reported in 2010. Find the mean, median, mode, and midrange of the data.

Temecula, CA	74	Irvine, CA	120
Murriefa, CA	99	Cary, NC	120
Surprise, AZ	106	Amherst, NY	121
Round Rock, TX	116	Simi Valley, CA	129
Frisco, TX	119	Norman, OK	132

Source: *Time Almanac 2012.*

6. **Earnings of Nonliving Celebrities** *Forbes* magazine prints an annual Top-Earning Nonliving Celebrities list (based on royalties and estate earnings). Find the mean, median, mode, and midrange for the data. Comment on the skewness. Figures represent millions of dollars.

Kurt Cobain	50	Ray Charles	10
Elvis Presley	42	Marilyn Monroe	8
Charles M. Schulz	35	Johnny Cash	8
John Lennon	24	J.R.R. Tolkien	7
Albert Einstein	20	George Harrison	7
Andy Warhol	19	Bob Marley	7
Theodore Geisel	10		
(Dr. Seuss)			

Source: articles.moneycentral.msn.com

7. **Moons of Jupiter** The planet Jupiter has at least 62 moons. In 1610 Galileo first observed the four brightest moons with a telescope. They are listed below with their diameters. Find the mean, median, mode, and midrange, and discuss which of these measures have any meaningful application with respect to these data. (Just for reference, the diameter of Earth is 3959 miles.)

Io	3643 km	2264 miles
Europa	3122	1940
Ganymede	5262	3270
Callisto	4821	2996

Source: *Time Almanac 2012.*

8. **Top-Paid CEOs** The data shown are the total compensation (in millions of dollars) for the 50 top-paid CEOs for a recent year. Compare the averages, and state which one you think is the best measure.

17.5	18.0	36.8	31.7	31.7
17.3	24.3	47.7	38.5	17.0
23.7	16.5	25.1	17.4	18.0
37.6	19.7	21.4	28.6	21.6
19.3	20.0	16.9	25.2	19.8
25.0	17.2	20.4	20.1	29.1
19.1	25.2	23.2	25.9	24.0
41.7	24.0	16.8	26.8	31.4
16.9	17.2	24.1	35.2	19.1
22.9	18.2	25.4	35.4	25.5

Source: *USA TODAY.*

9. **College Enrollments** The enrollments at a random selection of independent religiously controlled undergraduate schools are indicated below. Find the mean, median, mode, and midrange. Compare the mean and median and what that says about the data.

1469	1860	1422	1023	2532	1409	1648
1080	2082	1371	1197	1484	1106	1241

Source: *World Almanac 2012.*

10. **Foreign Workers** The number of foreign workers' certificates for the New England states and the northwestern states is shown. Find the mean, median, and mode for both areas and compare the results.

New England states	Northwest states
6768	1870
3196	622
1112	620
819	23
1019	172
1795	112

Source: Department of Labor.

11. **Distances of Stars** Of the 25 brightest stars, the distances from earth (in light-years) for those with distances less than 100 light-years are found below. Find the mean, median, mode, and midrange for the data.

8.6	36.7	42.2	16.8	33.7	77.5	87.9
4.4	25.3	11.4	65.1	25.1	51.5	

Source: *New York Times Almanac 2010.*

12. **Contest Spelling Words** The last words given and spelled correctly at the National Spelling Bee for the past 21 years are spelled out below. Count the number of letters in each word, and find the mean, median, mode, and midrange for the data.

fibranne	euonym	autochthonous
antipyretic	chiaroscurist	appoggiatura
lyceum	logorrhea	Ursprache
kamikaze	demarche	serrefine
antediluvian	succedaneum	guerdon
xanthosis	propispicience	stromuhr
vivisepulture	pococurante	cymatrichous

Source: *World Almanac 2012.*

13. **Executive Bonuses** A random sample of bonuses (in millions of dollars) paid by large companies to their executives is shown. Find the mean and modal class for the data.

Class boundaries	Frequency
0.5–3.5	11
3.5–6.5	12
6.5–9.5	4
9.5–12.5	2
12.5–15.5	1

14. **Hourly Compensation for Production Workers** The hourly compensation costs (in U.S. dollars) for production workers in selected countries are represented below. Find the mean and modal class for the data.

Class	Frequency
2.48–7.48	7
7.49–12.49	3
12.50–17.50	1
17.51–22.51	7
22.52–27.52	5
27.53–32.53	5

Compare the mean of these grouped data to the U.S. mean of $21.97.

Source: *New York Times Almanac.*

15. **Automobile Fuel Efficiency** Thirty automobiles were tested for fuel efficiency (in miles per gallon). This frequency distribution was obtained. Find the mean and modal class for the data.

Class boundaries	Frequency
7.5–12.5	3
12.5–17.5	5
17.5–22.5	15
22.5–27.5	5
27.5–32.5	2

16. **Percentage of Foreign-Born People** The percentage of foreign-born population for each of the 50 states is represented here. Find the mean and modal class for the data. Do you think the mean is the best average for this set of data? Explain.

Percentage	Frequency
0.8–4.4	26
4.5–8.1	11
8.2–11.8	4
11.9–15.5	5
15.6–19.2	2
19.3–22.9	1
23.0–26.6	1

Source: *World Almanac.*

17. **Percentage of College-Educated Population over 25** Below are the percentages of the population over 25 years of age who have completed 4 years of college or more for the 50 states and the District of Columbia. Find the mean and modal class.

Percentage	Frequency
15.2–19.6	3
19.7–24.1	15
24.2–28.6	19
28.7–33.1	6
33.2–37.6	7
37.7–42.1	0
42.2–46.6	1

Source: *New York Times Almanac.*

18. **Net Worth of Corporations** These data represent the net worth (in millions of dollars) of 45 national corporations. Find the mean and modal class for the data.

Class limits	Frequency
10–20	2
21–31	8
32–42	15
43–53	7
54–64	10
65–75	3

19. **Specialty Coffee Shops** A random sample of 30 states shows the number of specialty coffee shops for a specific company. Find the mean and modal class for the data.

Class boundaries	Frequency
0.5–19.5	12
19.5–38.5	7
38.5–57.5	5
57.5–76.5	3
76.5–95.5	3

20. **Commissions Earned** This frequency distribution represents the commission earned (in dollars) by 100 salespeople employed at several branches of a large chain store. Find the mean and modal class for the data.

Class limits	Frequency
150–158	5
159–167	16
168–176	20
177–185	21
186–194	20
195–203	15
204–212	3

21. Copier Service Calls This frequency distribution represents the data obtained from a sample of 75 copying machine service technicians. The values represent the days between service calls for various copying machines. Find the mean and modal class for the data.

Class boundaries	Frequency
15.5–18.5	14
18.5–21.5	12
21.5–24.5	18
24.5–27.5	10
27.5–30.5	15
30.5–33.5	6

22. Enrollments for Selected Independent Religiously Controlled 4-Year Colleges Listed below are the enrollments for selected independent religiously controlled 4-year colleges that offer bachelor's degrees only. Construct a grouped frequency distribution with six classes and find the mean and modal class.

1013 1867 1268 1666 2309 1231 3005 2895 2166 1136
1532 1461 1750 1069 1723 1827 1155 1714 2391 2155
1412 1688 2471 1759 3008 2511 2577 1082 1067 1062
1319 1037 2400

Source: *World Almanac.*

23. Find the weighted mean price of three models of automobiles sold. The number and price of each model sold are shown in this list.

Model	Number	Price
A	8	$10,000
B	10	12,000
C	12	8,000

24. Fat Grams Using the weighted mean, find the average number of grams of fat per ounce of meat or fish that a person would consume over a 5-day period if he ate these:

Meat or fish	Fat (g/oz)
3 oz fried shrimp	3.33
3 oz veal cutlet (broiled)	3.00
2 oz roast beef (lean)	2.50
2.5 oz fried chicken drumstick	4.40
4 oz tuna (canned in oil)	1.75

Source: *The World Almanac and Book of Facts.*

25. Diet Cola Preference A recent survey of a new diet cola reported the following percentages of people who liked the taste. Find the weighted mean of the percentages.

Area	% Favored	Number surveyed
1	40	1000
2	30	3000
3	50	800

26. Costs of Helicopters The costs of three models of helicopters are shown here. Find the weighted mean of the costs of the models.

Model	Number sold	Cost
Sunscraper	9	$427,000
Skycoaster	6	365,000
High-flyer	12	725,000

27. Final Grade An instructor grades exams, 20%; term paper, 30%; final exam, 50%. A student had grades of 83, 72, and 90, respectively, for exams, term paper, and final exam. Find the student's final average. Use the weighted mean.

28. Final Grade Another instructor gives four 1-hour exams and one final exam, which counts as two 1-hour exams. Find a student's grade if she received 62, 83, 97, and 90 on the 1-hour exams and 82 on the final exam.

29. For these situations, state which measure of central tendency—mean, median, or mode—should be used.

a. The most typical case is desired.

b. The distribution is open-ended.

c. There is an extreme value in the data set.

d. The data are categorical.

e. Further statistical computations will be needed.

f. The values are to be divided into two approximately equal groups, one group containing the larger values and one containing the smaller values.

30. Describe which measure of central tendency—mean, median, or mode—was probably used in each situation.

a. One-half of the factory workers make more than $5.37 per hour, and one-half make less than $5.37 per hour.

b. The average number of children per family in the Plaza Heights Complex is 1.8.

c. Most people prefer red convertibles over any other color.

d. The average person cuts the lawn once a week.

e. The most common fear today is fear of speaking in public.

f. The average age of college professors is 42.3 years.

31. What types of symbols are used to represent sample statistics? Give an example. What types of symbols are used to represent population parameters? Give an example.

32. A local fast-food company claims that the average salary of its employees is $13.23 per hour. An employee states that most employees make minimum wage. If both are being truthful, how could both be correct?

≡ Extending the Concepts

33. If the mean of five values is 64, find the sum of the values.

34. If the mean of five values is 8.2 and four of the values are 6, 10, 7, and 12, find the fifth value.

35. Find the mean of 10, 20, 30, 40, and 50.

    a. Add 10 to each value and find the mean.

    b. Subtract 10 from each value and find the mean.

    c. Multiply each value by 10 and find the mean.

    d. Divide each value by 10 and find the mean.

    e. Make a general statement about each situation.

36. Harmonic Mean The *harmonic mean* (HM) is defined as the number of values divided by the sum of the reciprocals of each value. The formula is

$$HM = \frac{n}{\Sigma(1/X)}$$

For example, the harmonic mean of 1, 4, 5, and 2 is

$$HM = \frac{4}{1/1 + 1/4 + 1/5 + 1/2} \approx 2.051$$

This mean is useful for finding the average speed. Suppose a person drove 100 miles at 40 miles per hour and returned driving 50 miles per hour. The average miles per hour is *not* 45 miles per hour, which is found by adding 40 and 50 and dividing by 2. The average is found as shown.

    Since

$$\text{Time} = \text{distance} \div \text{rate}$$

then

$$\text{Time 1} = \frac{100}{40} = 2.5 \text{ hours to make the trip}$$

$$\text{Time 2} = \frac{100}{50} = 2 \text{ hours to return}$$

Hence, the total time is 4.5 hours, and the total miles driven are 200. Now, the average speed is

$$\text{Rate} = \frac{\text{distance}}{\text{time}} = \frac{200}{4.5} \approx 44.444 \text{ miles per hour}$$

This value can also be found by using the harmonic mean formula

$$HM = \frac{2}{1/40 + 1/50} \approx 44.444$$

Using the harmonic mean, find each of these.

    a. A salesperson drives 300 miles round trip at 30 miles per hour going to Chicago and 45 miles per hour returning home. Find the average miles per hour.

    b. A bus driver drives the 50 miles to West Chester at 40 miles per hour and returns driving 25 miles per hour. Find the average miles per hour.

    c. A carpenter buys $500 worth of nails at $50 per pound and $500 worth of nails at $10 per pound. Find the average cost of 1 pound of nails.

37. Geometric Mean The *geometric mean* (GM) is defined as the *n*th root of the product of *n* values. The formula is

$$GM = \sqrt[n]{(X_1)(X_2)(X_3) \cdots (X_n)}$$

The geometric mean of 4 and 16 is

$$GM = \sqrt{(4)(16)} = \sqrt{64} = 8$$

The geometric mean of 1, 3, and 9 is

$$GM = \sqrt[3]{(1)(3)(9)} = \sqrt[3]{27} = 3$$

The geometric mean is useful in finding the average of percentages, ratios, indexes, or growth rates. For example, if a person receives a 20% raise after 1 year of service and a 10% raise after the second year of service, the average percentage raise per year is not 15 but 14.89%, as shown.

$$GM = \sqrt{(1.2)(1.1)} \approx 1.1489$$

or

$$GM = \sqrt{(120)(110)} \approx 114.89\%$$

His salary is 120% at the end of the first year and 110% at the end of the second year. This is equivalent to an average of 14.89%, since 114.89% − 100% = 14.89%.

    This answer can also be shown by assuming that the person makes $10,000 to start and receives two raises of 20% and 10%.

$$\text{Raise 1} = 10,000 \cdot 20\% = \$2000$$
$$\text{Raise 2} = 12,000 \cdot 10\% = \$1200$$

His total salary raise is $3200. This total is equivalent to

$$\$10,000 \cdot 14.89\% = \$1489.00$$
$$\underline{\$11,489 \cdot 14.89\% = \quad 1710.71}$$
$$\$3199.71 \approx \$3200$$

Find the geometric mean of each of these.

    a. The growth rates of the Living Life Insurance Corporation for the past 3 years were 35, 24, and 18%.

    b. A person received these percentage raises in salary over a 4-year period: 8, 6, 4, and 5%.

    c. A stock increased each year for 5 years at these percentages: 10, 8, 12, 9, and 3%.

d. The price increases, in percentages, for the cost of food in a specific geographic region for the past 3 years were 1, 3, and 5.5%.

38. Quadratic Mean A useful mean in the physical sciences (such as voltage) is the *quadratic mean* (QM), which is found by taking the square root of the average of the squares of each value. The formula is

$$QM = \sqrt{\frac{\Sigma X^2}{n}}$$

The quadratic mean of 3, 5, 6, and 10 is

$$QM = \sqrt{\frac{3^2 + 5^2 + 6^2 + 10^2}{4}}$$
$$= \sqrt{42.5} \approx 6.519$$

Find the quadratic mean of 8, 6, 3, 5, and 4.

39. Median for Grouped Data An approximate median can be found for data that have been grouped into a frequency distribution. First it is necessary to find the median class. This is the class that contains the median value. That is the $n/2$ data value. Then it is assumed that the data values are evenly distributed throughout the median class. The formula is

$$MD = \frac{n/2 - cf}{f}(w) + L_m$$

where n = sum of frequencies
  cf = cumulative frequency of class immediately preceding the median class
  w = width of median class
  f = frequency of median class
  L_m = lower boundary of median class

Using this formula, find the median for data in the frequency distribution of Exercise 16.

Technology   Step by Step

EXCEL

Step by Step

Finding Measures of Central Tendency

Example XL3–1

Find the mean, mode, and median of the data from Example 3–7. The data represent the population of licensed nuclear reactors in the United States for a recent 15-year period.

104	104	104	104	104
107	109	109	109	110
109	111	112	111	109

1. On an Excel worksheet enter the numbers in cells A2–A16. Enter a label for the variable in cell A1.

On the same worksheet as the data:

2. Compute the mean of the data: key in **=AVERAGE(A2:A16)** in a blank cell.

3. Compute the mode of the data: key in **=MODE(A2:A16)** in a blank cell.

4. Compute the median of the data: key in **=MEDIAN(A2:A16)** in a blank cell.

These and other statistical functions can also be accessed without typing them into the worksheet directly.

1. Select the Formulas tab from the toolbar and select the Insert Function Icon f_x.

2. Select the Statistical category for statistical functions.

3. Scroll to find the appropriate function and click [OK].

	A	B	C
1	Number of Reactors		
2	104	107.7333	mean
3	104	104	mode
4	104	109	median
5	104		
6	104		
7	107		
8	109		
9	109		
10	109		
11	110		
12	109		
13	111		
14	112		
15	111		
16	109		

(Excel reports only the first mode in a bimodal or multimodal distribution.)

3–2   Measures of Variation

In statistics, to describe the data set accurately, statisticians must know more than the measures of central tendency. Consider Example 3–15.

OBJECTIVE ②

Describe data, using measures of variation, such as the range, variance, and standard deviation.

EXAMPLE 3–15   Comparison of Outdoor Paint

A testing lab wishes to test two experimental brands of outdoor paint to see how long each will last before fading. The testing lab makes 6 gallons of each paint to test. Since different chemical agents are added to each group and only six cans are involved, these two groups constitute two small populations. The results (in months) are shown. Find the mean of each group.

Brand A	Brand B
10	35
60	45
50	30
30	35
40	40
20	25

SOLUTION

The mean for brand A is

$$\mu = \frac{\Sigma X}{N} = \frac{210}{6} = 35 \text{ months}$$

The mean for brand B is

$$\mu = \frac{\Sigma X}{N} = \frac{210}{6} = 35 \text{ months}$$

Since the means are equal in Example 3–15, you might conclude that both brands of paint last equally well. However, when the data sets are examined graphically, a somewhat different conclusion might be drawn. See Figure 3–2.

As Figure 3–2 shows, even though the means are the same for both brands, the spread, or variation, is quite different. Figure 3–2 shows that brand B performs more

FIGURE 3–2
Examining Data Sets
Graphically

Variation of paint (in months)

(a) Brand A

Variation of paint (in months)

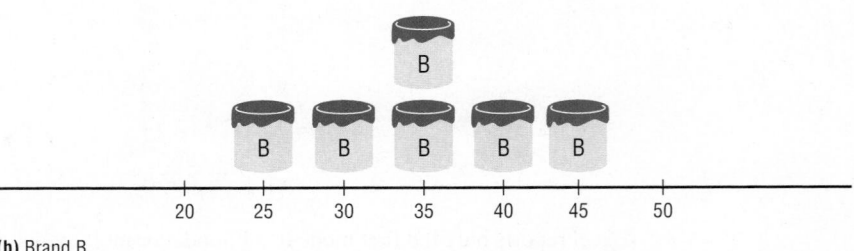

(b) Brand B

consistently; it is less variable. For the spread or variability of a data set, three measures are commonly used: *range, variance,* and *standard deviation.* Each measure will be discussed in this section.

Range

The range is the simplest of the three measures and is defined now.

> The **range** is the highest value minus the lowest value. The symbol R is used for the range.
>
> $$R = \text{highest value} - \text{lowest value}$$

EXAMPLE 3–16   Comparison of Outdoor Paint

Find the ranges for the paints in Example 3–15.

SOLUTION

For brand A, the range is

$$R = 60 - 10 = 50 \text{ months}$$

For brand B, the range is

$$R = 45 - 25 = 20 \text{ months}$$

Make sure the range is given as a single number.

The range for brand A shows that 50 months separate the largest data value from the smallest data value. For brand B, 20 months separate the largest data value from the smallest data value, which is less than one-half of brand A's range.

One extremely high or one extremely low data value can affect the range markedly, as shown in Example 3–17.

EXAMPLE 3–17   Employee Salaries

The salaries for the staff of the XYZ Manufacturing Co. are shown here. Find the range.

Staff	Salary
Owner	$100,000
Manager	40,000
Sales representative	30,000
Workers	25,000
	15,000
	18,000

SOLUTION

The range is $R = \$100,000 - \$15,000 = \$85,000$.

Since the owner's salary is included in the data for Example 3–17, the range is a large number. To have a more meaningful statistic to measure the variability, statisticians use measures called the *variance* and *standard deviation.*

Population Variance and Standard Deviation

Before these measures can be defined, it is necessary to know what *data variation* means. It is based on the difference or distance each data value is from the mean. This difference or distance is called a *deviation*. In the outdoor paint example, the mean for brand A paint is $\mu = 35$ months, and for a specific can, say, the can that lasted for 50 months, the deviation is $X - \mu$ or $50 - 35 = 15$. Hence, the deviation for that data value is 15 months. If you find the sum of the deviations for all data values about the mean (without rounding), this sum will always be zero. That is, $\Sigma(X - \mu) = 0$. (You can see this if you sum all the deviations for the paint example.)

To eliminate this problem, we sum the squares, that is, $\Sigma(X - \mu)^2$ and find the mean of these squares by dividing by N (the total number of data values), symbolically $\Sigma(X - \mu)^2/N$. This measure is called the *population variance* and is symbolized by σ^2, where σ is the symbol for Greek lowercase letter sigma.

Since this measure (σ^2) is in square units and the data are in regular units, statisticians take the square root of the variance and call it the *standard deviation*.

Formally defined,

The **population variance** is the average of the squares of the distance each value is from the mean. The symbol for the population variance is σ^2 (σ is the Greek lower-case letter sigma).

The formula for the population variance is

$$\sigma^2 = \frac{\Sigma(X - \mu)^2}{N}$$

where X = individual value
μ = population mean
N = population size

The **population standard deviation** is the square root of the variance. The symbol for the population standard deviation is σ.

The corresponding formula for the population standard deviation is

$$\sigma = \sqrt{\sigma^2} = \sqrt{\frac{\Sigma(X - \mu)^2}{N}}$$

To find the variance and standard deviation for a data set, the following Procedure Table can be used.

Procedure Table

Finding the Population Variance and Population Standard Deviation

Step 1   Find the mean for the data.

$$\mu = \frac{\Sigma X}{N}$$

Step 2   Find the deviation for each data value.

$$X - \mu$$

Step 3   Square each of the deviations.

$$(X - \mu)^2$$

Step 4   Find the sum of the squares.

$$\Sigma(X - \mu)^2$$

Step 5   Divide by N to get the variance.

$$\sigma^2 = \frac{\Sigma(X - \mu)^2}{N}$$

Step 6   Take the square root of the variance to get the standard deviation.

$$\sigma = \sqrt{\frac{\Sigma(X - \mu)^2}{N}}$$

Interesting Fact

The average American drives about 10,000 miles a year.

Rounding Rule for the Standard Deviation The rounding rule for the standard deviation is the same as that for the mean. The final answer should be rounded to one more decimal place than that of the original data.

EXAMPLE 3–18   Comparison of Outdoor Paint

Find the variance and standard deviation for the data set for brand A paint in Example 3–15. The number of months brand A lasted before fading was

10, 60, 50, 30, 40, 20

SOLUTION

Step 1   Find the mean for the data.

$$\mu = \frac{\Sigma X}{N} = \frac{10 + 60 + 50 + 30 + 40 + 20}{6} = \frac{210}{6} = 35$$

Step 2   Subtract the mean from each data value $(X - \mu)$.

$$10 - 35 = -25 \qquad 50 - 35 = +15 \qquad 40 - 35 = +5$$
$$60 - 35 = +25 \qquad 30 - 35 = -5 \qquad 20 - 35 = -15$$

Step 3   Square each result $(\overline{X} - \mu)^2$.

$$(-25)^2 = 625 \qquad (+15)^2 = 225 \qquad (+5)^2 = 25$$
$$(+25)^2 = 625 \qquad (-5)^2 = 25 \qquad (-15)^2 = 225$$

Step 4   Find the sum of the squares $\Sigma(\overline{X} - \mu)^2$.

$$625 + 625 + 225 + 25 + 25 + 225 = 1750$$

Step 5   Divide the sum by N to get the variance $\dfrac{[\Sigma(\overline{X} - \mu)^2]}{N}$.

$$\text{Variance} = 1750 \div 6 \approx 291.7$$

Step 6   Take the square root of the variance to get the standard deviation. Hence, the standard deviation equals $\sqrt{291.7}$, or 17.1. It is helpful to make a table.

A Values X	B $X - \mu$	C $(X - \mu)^2$
10	−25	625
60	+25	625
50	+15	225
30	−5	25
40	+5	25
20	−15	225
		1750

Column A contains the raw data X. Column B contains the differences $X - \mu$ obtained in step 2. Column C contains the squares of the differences obtained in step 3.

The preceding computational procedure reveals several things. First, the square root of the variance gives the standard deviation; and vice versa, squaring the standard deviation gives the variance. Second, the variance is actually the average of the square of the distance that each value is from the mean. Therefore, if the values are near the mean, the variance will be small. In contrast, if the values are far from the mean, the variance will be large.

You might wonder why the squared distances are used instead of the actual distances. As previously stated, the reason is that the sum of the distances will always be zero. To verify this result for a specific case, add the values in column B of the table in Example 3–18. When each value is squared, the negative signs are eliminated.

Finally, why is it necessary to take the square root? Again, the reason is that since the distances were squared, the units of the resultant numbers are the squares of the units of the original raw data. Finding the square root of the variance puts the standard deviation in the same units as the raw data.

When you are finding the square root, always use its positive value, since the variance and standard deviation of a data set can never be negative.

EXAMPLE 3–19   Comparison of Outdoor Paint

Find the variance and standard deviation for brand B paint data in Example 3–15. The months brand B lasted before fading were

$$35, 45, 30, 35, 40, 25$$

SOLUTION

Step 1   Find the mean.

$$\mu = \frac{\Sigma X}{N} = \frac{35 + 45 + 30 + 35 + 40 + 25}{6} = \frac{210}{6} = 35$$

Step 2   Subtract the mean from each value, and place the result in column B of the table.

$$35 - 35 = 0 \qquad 45 - 35 = 10 \qquad 30 - 35 = -5$$
$$35 - 35 = 0 \qquad 40 - 35 = 5 \qquad 25 - 35 = -10$$

Step 3   Square each result and place the squares in column C of the table.

A X	B $X - \mu$	C $(X - \mu)^2$
35	0	0
45	10	100
30	−5	25
35	0	0
40	5	25
25	−10	100

Step 4   Find the sum of the squares in column C.

$$\Sigma(X - \mu)^2 = 0 + 100 + 25 + 0 + 25 + 100 = 250$$

Step 5   Divide the sum by N to get the variance.

$$\sigma^2 = \frac{\Sigma(X - \mu)^2}{N} = \frac{250}{6} = 41.7$$

Step 6   Take the square root to get the standard deviation.

$$\sigma = \sqrt{\frac{\Sigma(X - \mu)^2}{N}} = \sqrt{41.7} \approx 6.5$$

Hence, the standard deviation is 6.5.

Since the standard deviation of brand A is 17.1 (see Example 3–18) and the standard deviation of brand B is 6.5, the data are more variable for brand A. *In summary, when the means are equal, the larger the variance or standard deviation is, the more variable the data are.*

Sample Variance and Standard Deviation

When computing the variance for a sample, one might expect the following expression to be used:

$$\frac{\Sigma(X - \overline{X})^2}{n}$$

where $\overline{X}$ is the sample mean and n is the sample size. *This formula is not usually used, however, since in most cases the purpose of calculating the statistic is to estimate the corresponding parameter.* For example, the sample mean $\overline{X}$ is used to estimate the population mean μ. The expression

$$\frac{\Sigma(X - \overline{X})^2}{n}$$

does not give the best estimate of the population variance because when the population is large and the sample is small (usually less than 30), the variance computed by this formula usually underestimates the population variance. Therefore, instead of dividing by n, find the variance of the sample by dividing by $n - 1$, giving a slightly larger value and an *unbiased* estimate of the population variance.

Formula for the Sample Variance

The formula for the sample variance (denoted by s^2) is

$$s^2 = \frac{\Sigma(X - \overline{X})^2}{n - 1}$$

where X = individual value
$\overline{X}$ = sample mean
n = sample size

To find the standard deviation of a sample, you must take the square root of the sample variance, which was found by using the preceding formula.

Formula for the Sample Standard Deviation

The formula for the sample standard deviation, denoted by s, is

$$s = \sqrt{s^2} = \sqrt{\frac{\Sigma(X - \overline{X})^2}{n - 1}}$$

where X = individual value
$\overline{X}$ = sample mean
n = sample size

The procedure for finding the sample variance and the sample standard deviation is the same as the procedure for finding the population variance and the population standard deviation *except* the sum of the squares is divided by $n - 1$ (sample size minus 1) instead of N (population size). Refer to the previous Procedure Table if necessary. The next example shows these steps.

EXAMPLE 3–20   Teacher Strikes

The number of public school teacher strikes in Pennsylvania for a random sample of school years is shown. Find the sample variance and the sample standard deviation.

$$9 \quad 10 \quad 14 \quad 7 \quad 8 \quad 3$$

Source: Pennsylvania School Board Association.

SOLUTION

Step 1   Find the mean of the data values.

$$\overline{X} = \frac{\Sigma X}{n} = \frac{9 + 10 + 14 + 7 + 8 + 3}{6} = \frac{51}{6} = 8.5$$

Step 2   Find the deviation for each data value $(X - \overline{X})$.

$$
\begin{array}{lll}
9 - 8.5 = 0.5 & 10 - 8.5 = 1.5 & 14 - 8.5 = 5.5 \\
7 - 8.5 = -1.5 & 8 - 8.5 = -0.5 & 3 - 8.5 = -5.5
\end{array}
$$

Step 3   Square each of the deviations $(X - \overline{X})^2$.

$$
\begin{array}{lll}
(0.5)^2 = 0.25 & (1.5)^2 = 2.25 & (5.5)^2 = 30.25 \\
(-1.5)^2 = 2.25 & (-0.5)^2 = 0.25 & (-5.5)^2 = 30.25
\end{array}
$$

Step 4   Find the sum of the squares.

$$\Sigma(X - \overline{X})^2 = 0.25 + 2.25 + 30.25 + 2.25 + 0.25 + 30.25 = 65.5$$

Step 5   Divide by $n - 1$ to get the variance.

$$s^2 = \frac{\Sigma(X - \overline{X})^2}{n - 1} = \frac{65.5}{6 - 1} = \frac{65.5}{5} = 13.1$$

Step 6   Take the square root of the variance to get the standard deviation.

$$s = \sqrt{\frac{\Sigma(X - \overline{X})^2}{n - 1}} = \sqrt{13.1} \approx 3.6 \text{ (rounded)}$$

Here the sample variance is 13.1, and the sample standard deviation is 3.6.

Shortcut formulas for computing the variance and standard deviation are presented next and will be used in the remainder of the chapter and in the exercises. These formulas are mathematically equivalent to the preceding formulas and do not involve using the mean. They save time when repeated subtracting and squaring occur in the original formulas. They are also more accurate when the mean has been rounded.

Shortcut or Computational Formulas for s^2 and s

The shortcut formulas for computing the variance and standard deviation for data obtained from samples are as follows.

Variance	Standard deviation
$s^2 = \dfrac{n(\Sigma X^2) - (\Sigma X)^2}{n(n - 1)}$	$s = \sqrt{\dfrac{n(\Sigma X^2) - (\Sigma X)^2}{n(n - 1)}}$

Note that ΣX^2 is not the same as $(\Sigma X)^2$. The notation ΣX^2 means to square the values first, then sum; $(\Sigma X)^2$ means to sum the values first, then square the sum.
Example 3–21 explains how to use the shortcut formulas.

EXAMPLE 3–21   Teacher Strikes

The number of public school teacher strikes in Pennsylvania for a random sample of school years is shown. Find the sample variance and sample standard deviation.

$$9, 10, 14, 7, 8, 3$$

SOLUTION

Step 1   Find the sum of the values:

$$\Sigma X = 9 + 10 + 14 + 7 + 8 + 3 = 51$$

Step 2   Square each value and find the sum:

$$\Sigma X^2 = 9^2 + 10^2 + 14^2 + 7^2 + 8^2 + 3^2 = 499$$

Step 3   Substitute in the formula and solve:

$$s^2 = \frac{n(\Sigma X^2) - (\Sigma X)^2}{n(n-1)}$$

$$= \frac{6(499) - 51^2}{6(6-1)}$$

$$= \frac{2994 - 2601}{6(5)}$$

$$= \frac{393}{30}$$

$$= 13.1$$

The variance is 13.1.

$$s = \sqrt{13.1} \approx 3.6 \text{ (rounded)}$$

Hence, the sample variance is 13.1, and the sample standard deviation is 3.6. Notice that these are the same results as the results in Example 3–20.

Variance and Standard Deviation for Grouped Data

The procedure for finding the variance and standard deviation for grouped data is similar to that for finding the mean for grouped data, and it uses the midpoints of each class.

This procedure uses the shortcut formula, and X_m is the symbol for the class midpoint.

Shortcut or Computational Formula for s^2 and s for Grouped Data

Sample variance:

$$s^2 = \frac{n(\Sigma f \cdot X_m^2) - (\Sigma f \cdot X_m)^2}{n(n-1)}$$

Sample standard deviation

$$s = \sqrt{\frac{n(\Sigma f \cdot X_m^2) - (\Sigma f \cdot X_m)^2}{n(n-1)}}$$

where X_m is the midpoint of each class and f is the frequency of each class.

The steps for finding the sample variance and sample standard deviation for grouped data are summarized in this Procedure Table.

Procedure Table

Finding the Sample Variance and Standard Deviation for Grouped Data

Step 1 Make a table as shown, and find the midpoint of each class.

A Class	B Frequency	C Midpoint	D $f \cdot X_m$	E $f \cdot X_m^2$

Step 2 Multiply the frequency by the midpoint for each class, and place the products in column D.

Step 3 Multiply the frequency by the square of the midpoint, and place the products in column E.

Step 4 Find the sums of columns B, D, and E. (The sum of column B is n. The sum of column D is $\Sigma f \cdot X_m$. The sum of column E is $\Sigma f \cdot X_m^2$.)

Step 5 Substitute in the formula and solve to get the variance.

$$s^2 = \frac{n(\Sigma f \cdot X_m^2) - (\Sigma f \cdot X_m)^2}{n(n-1)}$$

Step 6 Take the square root to get the standard deviation.

EXAMPLE 3–22   **Miles Run per Week**

Find the sample variance and the sample standard deviation for the frequency distribution of the data in Example 2–7. The data represent the number of miles that 20 runners ran during one week.

Class	Frequency	Midpoint
5.5–10.5	1	8
10.5–15.5	2	13
15.5–20.5	3	18
20.5–25.5	5	23
25.5–30.5	4	28
30.5–35.5	3	33
35.5–40.5	2	38

SOLUTION

Step 1 Make a table as shown, and find the midpoint of each class.

Unusual Stat

At birth men outnumber women by 2%. By age 25, the number of men living is about equal to the number of women living. By age 65, there are 14% more women living than men.

A Class	B Frequency f	C Midpoint X_m	D $f \cdot X_m$	E $f \cdot X_m^2$
5.5–10.5	1	8		
10.5–15.5	2	13		
15.5–20.5	3	18		
20.5–25.5	5	23		
25.5–30.5	4	28		
30.5–35.5	3	33		
35.5–40.5	2	38		

Step 2   Multiply the frequency by the midpoint for each class, and place the products in column D.

$$1 \cdot 8 = 8 \qquad 2 \cdot 13 = 26 \qquad \ldots \qquad 2 \cdot 38 = 76$$

Step 3   Multiply the frequency by the square of the midpoint, and place the products in column E.

$$1 \cdot 8^2 = 64 \qquad 2 \cdot 13^2 = 338 \qquad \ldots \qquad 2 \cdot 38^2 = 2888$$

Step 4   Find the sums of columns B, D, and E. The sum of column B is n, the sum of column D is $\Sigma f \cdot X_m$, and the sum of column E is $\Sigma f \cdot X_m^2$. The completed table is shown.

A Class	B Frequency	C Midpoint	D $f \cdot X_m$	E $f \cdot X_m^2$
5.5–10.5	1	8	8	64
10.5–15.5	2	13	26	338
15.5–20.5	3	18	54	972
20.5–25.5	5	23	115	2,645
25.5–30.5	4	28	112	3,136
30.5–35.5	3	33	99	3,267
35.5–40.5	2	38	76	2,888
	$n = 20$		$\Sigma f \cdot X_m = 490$	$\Sigma f \cdot X_m^2 = 13{,}310$

Step 5   Substitute in the formula and solve for s^2 to get the variance.

$$s^2 = \frac{n(\Sigma f \cdot X_m^2) - (\Sigma f \cdot X_m)^2}{n(n-1)}$$

$$= \frac{20(13{,}310) - 490^2}{20(20-1)}$$

$$= \frac{266{,}200 - 240{,}100}{20(19)}$$

$$= \frac{26{,}100}{380}$$

$$\approx 68.7$$

Step 6   Take the square root to get the standard deviation.

$$s \approx \sqrt{68.7} \approx 8.3$$

Be sure to use the number found in the sum of column B (i.e., the sum of the frequencies) for n. Do not use the number of classes.

The three measures of variation are summarized in Table 3–2.

TABLE 3–2   Summary of Measures of Variation

Measure	Definition	Symbol(s)
Range	Distance between highest value and lowest value	R
Variance	Average of the squares of the distance that each value is from the mean	σ^2, s^2
Standard deviation	Square root of the variance	σ, s

Uses of the Variance and Standard Deviation

1. As previously stated, variances and standard deviations can be used to determine the spread of the data. If the variance or standard deviation is large, the data are more dispersed. This information is useful in comparing two (or more) data sets to determine which is more (most) variable.

2. The measures of variance and standard deviation are used to determine the consistency of a variable. For example, in the manufacture of fittings, such as nuts and bolts, the variation in the diameters must be small, or else the parts will not fit together.

3. The variance and standard deviation are used to determine the number of data values that fall within a specified interval in a distribution. For example, Chebyshev's theorem (explained later) shows that, for any distribution, at least 75% of the data values will fall within 2 standard deviations of the mean.

4. Finally, the variance and standard deviation are used quite often in inferential statistics. These uses will be shown in later chapters of this textbook.

Coefficient of Variation

Historical Note

Karl Pearson devised the coefficient of variation to compare the deviations of two different groups such as the heights of men and women.

Whenever two samples have the same units of measure, the variance and standard deviation for each can be compared directly. For example, suppose an automobile dealer wanted to compare the standard deviation of miles driven for the cars she received as trade-ins on new cars. She found that for a specific year, the standard deviation for Buicks was 422 miles and the standard deviation for Cadillacs was 350 miles. She could say that the variation in mileage was greater in the Buicks. But what if a manager wanted to compare the standard deviations of two different variables, such as the number of sales per salesperson over a 3-month period and the commissions made by these salespeople?

A statistic that allows you to compare standard deviations when the units are different, as in this example, is called the *coefficient of variation.*

The **coefficient of variation,** denoted by CVar, is the standard deviation divided by the mean. The result is expressed as a percentage.

For samples,	**For populations,**
$\text{CVar} = \dfrac{s}{\overline{X}} \cdot 100$	$\text{CVar} = \dfrac{\sigma}{\mu} \cdot 100$

EXAMPLE 3–23   Sales of Automobiles

The mean of the number of sales of cars over a 3-month period is 87, and the standard deviation is 5. The mean of the commissions is $5225, and the standard deviation is $773. Compare the variations of the two.

SOLUTION

The coefficients of variation are

$$\text{CVar} = \frac{s}{\overline{X}} = \frac{5}{87} \cdot 100 = 5.7\% \quad \text{sales}$$

$$\text{CVar} = \frac{773}{5225} \cdot 100 = 14.8\% \quad \text{commissions}$$

Since the coefficient of variation is larger for commissions, the commissions are more variable than the sales.

EXAMPLE 3–24   Pages in Women's Fitness Magazines

The mean for the number of pages of a sample of women's fitness magazines is 132, with a variance of 23; the mean for the number of advertisements of a sample of women's fitness magazines is 182, with a variance of 62. Compare the variations.

SOLUTION

The coefficients of variation are

$$\text{CVar} = \frac{\sqrt{23}}{132} \cdot 100 = 3.6\% \quad \text{pages}$$

$$\text{CVar} = \frac{\sqrt{62}}{182} \cdot 100 = 4.3\% \quad \text{advertisements}$$

The number of advertisements is more variable than the number of pages since the coefficient of variation is larger for advertisements.

Range Rule of Thumb

The range can be used to approximate the standard deviation. The approximation is called the **range rule of thumb.**

The Range Rule of Thumb

A rough estimate of the standard deviation is

$$s \approx \frac{\text{range}}{4}$$

In other words, if the range is divided by 4, an approximate value for the standard deviation is obtained. For example, the standard deviation for the data set 5, 8, 8, 9, 10, 12, and 13 is 2.7, and the range is $13 - 5 = 8$. The range rule of thumb is $s \approx 2$. The range rule of thumb in this case underestimates the standard deviation somewhat; however, it is in the ballpark.

A note of caution should be mentioned here. The range rule of thumb is only an *approximation* and should be used when the distribution of data values is unimodal and roughly symmetric.

The range rule of thumb can be used to estimate the largest and smallest data values of a data set. The smallest data value will be approximately 2 standard deviations below the mean, and the largest data value will be approximately 2 standard deviations above the mean of the data set. The mean for the previous data set is 9.3; hence,

$$\text{Smallest data value} = \overline{X} - 2s = 9.3 - 2(2.7) = 3.9$$

$$\text{Largest data value} = \overline{X} + 2s = 9.3 + 2(2.7) = 14.7$$

Notice that the smallest data value was 5, and the largest data value was 13. Again, these are rough approximations. For many data sets, almost all data values will fall within 2 standard deviations of the mean. Better approximations can be obtained by using Chebyshev's theorem and the empirical rule. These are explained next.

Chebyshev's Theorem

As stated previously, the variance and standard deviation of a variable can be used to determine the spread, or dispersion, of a variable. That is, the larger the variance or standard deviation, the more the data values are dispersed. For example, if two variables measured in the same units have the same mean, say, 70, and the first variable has a standard deviation of 1.5 while the second variable has a standard deviation of 10, then the data for the second variable will be more spread out than the data for the first variable. *Chebyshev's theorem*, developed by the Russian mathematician Chebyshev (1821–1894), specifies the proportions of the spread in terms of the standard deviation.

> **Chebyshev's theorem** The proportion of values from a data set that will fall within k standard deviations of the mean will be at least $1 - 1/k^2$, where k is a number greater than 1 (k is not necessarily an integer).

This theorem states that at least three-fourths, or 75%, of the data values will fall within 2 standard deviations of the mean of the data set. This result is found by substituting $k = 2$ in the expression

$$1 - \frac{1}{k^2} \quad \text{or} \quad 1 - \frac{1}{2^2} = 1 - \frac{1}{4} = \frac{3}{4} = 75\%$$

For the example in which variable 1 has a mean of 70 and a standard deviation of 1.5, at least three-fourths, or 75%, of the data values fall between 67 and 73. These values are found by adding 2 standard deviations to the mean and subtracting 2 standard deviations from the mean, as shown:

$$70 + 2(1.5) = 70 + 3 = 73$$

and

$$70 - 2(1.5) = 70 - 3 = 67$$

For variable 2, at least three-fourths, or 75%, of the data values fall between 50 and 90. Again, these values are found by adding and subtracting, respectively, 2 standard deviations to and from the mean.

$$70 + 2(10) = 70 + 20 = 90$$

and

$$70 - 2(10) = 70 - 20 = 50$$

Furthermore, the theorem states that at least eight-ninths, or 88.89%, of the data values will fall within 3 standard deviations of the mean. This result is found by letting $k = 3$ and substituting in the expression.

$$1 - \frac{1}{k^2} \quad \text{or} \quad 1 - \frac{1}{3^2} = 1 - \frac{1}{9} = \frac{8}{9} = 88.89\%$$

For variable 1, at least eight-ninths, or 88.89%, of the data values fall between 65.5 and 74.5, since

$$70 + 3(1.5) = 70 + 4.5 = 74.5$$

and

$$70 - 3(1.5) = 70 - 4.5 = 65.5$$

For variable 2, at least eight-ninths, or 88.89%, of the data values fall between 40 and 100. In summary, then, Chebyshev's theorem states

- At least three-fourths, or 75%, of all data values fall within 2 standard deviations of the mean.
- At least eight-ninths, or 89%, of all data values fall within 3 standard deviations of the mean.

FIGURE 3–3
Chebyshev's Theorem

This theorem can be applied to any distribution regardless of its shape (see Figure 3–3). Examples 3–25 and 3–26 illustrate the application of Chebyshev's theorem.

EXAMPLE 3–25   Prices of Homes

The mean price of houses in a certain neighborhood is $50,000, and the standard deviation is $10,000. Find the price range for which at least 75% of the houses will sell.

SOLUTION

Chebyshev's theorem states that three-fourths, or 75%, of the data values will fall within 2 standard deviations of the mean. Thus,

$$\$50,000 + 2(\$10,000) = \$50,000 + \$20,000 = \$70,000$$

and

$$\$50,000 - 2(\$10,000) = \$50,000 - \$20,000 = \$30,000$$

Hence, at least 75% of all homes sold in the area will have a price range from $30,000 to $70,000.

Chebyshev's theorem can be used to find the minimum percentage of data values that will fall between any two given values. The procedure is shown in Example 3–26.

EXAMPLE 3–26   Travel Allowances

A survey of local companies found that the mean amount of travel allowance for couriers was $0.25 per mile. The standard deviation was $0.02. Using Chebyshev's theorem, find the minimum percentage of the data values that will fall between $0.20 and $0.30.

SOLUTION

Step 1   Subtract the mean from the larger value.

$$\$0.30 - \$0.25 = \$0.05$$

Step 2   Divide the difference by the standard deviation to get k.

$$k = \frac{0.05}{0.02} = 2.5$$

Step 3   Use Chebyshev's theorem to find the percentage.

$$1 - \frac{1}{k^2} = 1 - \frac{1}{2.5^2} = 1 - \frac{1}{6.25} = 1 - 0.16 = 0.84 \qquad \text{or} \qquad 84\%$$

Hence, at least 84% of the data values will fall between $0.20 and $0.30.

FIGURE 3–4
The Empirical Rule

The Empirical (Normal) Rule

Chebyshev's theorem applies to any distribution regardless of its shape. However, when a distribution is *bell-shaped* (or what is called *normal*), the following statements, which make up the **empirical rule,** are true.

- Approximately 68% of the data values will fall within 1 standard deviation of the mean.

- Approximately 95% of the data values will fall within 2 standard deviations of the mean.

- Approximately 99.7% of the data values will fall within 3 standard deviations of the mean.

For example, suppose that the scores on a national achievement exam have a mean of 480 and a standard deviation of 90. If these scores are normally distributed, then approximately 68% will fall between 390 and 570 (480 + 90 = 570 and 480 − 90 = 390). Approximately 95% of the scores will fall between 300 and 660 (480 + 2 · 90 = 660 and 480 − 2 · 90 = 300). Approximately 99.7% will fall between 210 and 750 (480 + 3 · 90 = 750 and 480 − 3 · 90 = 210). See Figure 3–4. (The empirical rule is explained in greater detail in Chapter 6.)

Because the empirical rule requires that the distribution be approximately bell-shaped, the results are more accurate than those of Chebyshev's theorem, which applies to all distributions.

≣ Applying the Concepts 3–2

Blood Pressure

The table lists means and standard deviations. The mean is the number before the plus/minus, and the standard deviation is the number after the plus/minus. The results are from a study attempting to find the average blood pressure of older adults. Use the results to answer the questions.

	Normotensive		Hypertensive	
	Men ($n = 1200$)	**Women** ($n = 1400$)	**Men** ($n = 1100$)	**Women** ($n = 1300$)
Age	55 ± 10	55 ± 10	60 ± 10	64 ± 10
Blood pressure (mm Hg)				
Systolic	123 ± 9	121 ± 11	153 ± 17	156 ± 20
Diastolic	78 ± 7	76 ± 7	91 ± 10	88 ± 10

1. Apply Chebyshev's theorem to the systolic blood pressure of normotensive men. At least how many of the men in the study fall within 1 standard deviation of the mean?

2. At least how many of those men in the study fall within 2 standard deviations of the mean?

Assume that blood pressure is normally distributed among older adults. Answer the following questions, using the empirical rule instead of Chebyshev's theorem.

3. What are the ranges for the diastolic blood pressure (normotensive and hypertensive) of older women?

4. Do the normotensive, male, systolic blood pressure ranges overlap with the hypertensive, male, systolic blood pressure ranges?

See page 184 for the answers.

≡ Exercises 3–2

1. What is the relationship between the variance and the standard deviation?

2. Why might the range *not* be the best estimate of variability?

3. What are the symbols used to represent the population variance and standard deviation?

4. What are the symbols used to represent the sample variance and standard deviation?

5. Why is the unbiased estimator of variance used?

6. The three data sets have the same mean and range, but is the variation the same? Prove your answer by computing the standard deviation. Assume the data were obtained from samples.

   a. 5, 7, 9, 11, 13, 15, 17
   b. 5, 6, 7, 11, 15, 16, 17
   c. 5, 5, 5, 11, 17, 17, 17

7. **Unemployment Benefits** The average weekly unemployment benefits (in dollars) for a random selection of states are listed below. Calculate the range, variance, and standard deviation for the data.

239	214	327	416	321	289	209	356
190	272	252	272	310	276	251	

   Source: *World Almanac 2012.*

8. **Cigarette Taxes** The increases (in cents) in cigarette taxes for 17 states in a 6-month period are

   60, 20, 40, 40, 45, 12, 34, 51, 30, 70, 42, 31, 69, 32, 8, 18, 50

   Find the range, variance, and standard deviation for the data. Use the range rule of thumb to estimate the standard deviation. Compare the estimate to the actual standard deviation.

   Source: Federation of Tax Administrators.

9. **Bowling Scores** The scores from the last 10 years' U.S. Bowling Congress Championships are shown below for men and for women. Find the range, variance, and standard deviation for each data set. Which set of data is more variable?

Men	823 837 858 791 812 814 832 862 833 826
Women	752 764 754 774 771 745 736 816 792 793

   Source: *Time Almanac 2012.*

10. **Size of U.S. States** The total surface area (in square miles) for each of six selected eastern states is listed here.

28,995	PA	37,534	FL
31,361	NY	27,087	VA
20,966	ME	37,741	GA

    The total surface area for each of six selected western states is listed (in square miles).

72,964	AZ	70,763	NV
101,510	CA	62,161	OR
66,625	CO	54,339	UT

    Find the standard deviation for each data set. Which set is more variable?

    Source: *New York Times Almanac.*

11. **Multiple Births** The numbers of various multiple births in the United States for the past 10 years are listed. Find the range, variance, and standard deviation of the data sets. Which set of data is the most variable?

Triplets			Quadruplets			Quintuplets		
5877	7110	5937	345	468	369	46	85	91
6898	6118	6885	434	355	501	69	67	85
6208	6742	6750	418	506	439	68	77	86
	6742			512			67	

    Source: *World Almanac 2012.*

12. **Starting Teachers' Salaries** Starting teachers' salaries (in equivalent U.S. dollars) for upper secondary education in selected countries are listed. Find the range, variance, and standard deviation for the data. Which set

of data is more variable? (The U.S. average starting salary at this time was $29,641.)

Europe		Asia	
Sweden	$48,704	Korea	$26,852
Germany	41,441	Japan	23,493
Spain	32,679	India	18,247
Finland	32,136	Malaysia	13,647
Denmark	30,384	Philippines	9,857
Netherlands	29,326	Thailand	5,862
Scotland	27,789		

Source: *World Almanac.*

13. **Ages of U.S. Astronaut Candidates** The average age of U.S. astronaut candidates in the past has been 34, but candidates have ranged in age from 26 to 46. Use the range rule of thumb to estimate the standard deviation of the applicants' ages.

Source: www.nasa.gov

14. **Times Spent in Rush-Hour Traffic** A sample of 12 drivers shows the time that they spent (in minutes) stopped in rush-hour traffic on a specific snowy day last winter. Find the range, variance, and standard deviation for the data.

52	56	53
61	49	51
53	58	53
60	71	58

15. **Prison Executions** The numbers of prisoners executed by the state since 1977 for the top 12 states are listed below. Find the range, variance, and standard deviation of the data.

TX	355	LA	27	AR	27
VA	94	MO	66	AZ	22
AL	34	NC	39	FL	60
OK	79	GA	39	SC	35

Source: *New York Times Almanac 2010.*

16. **Passenger Vehicle Deaths** The number of people killed in each state from passenger vehicle crashes for a specific year is shown. Find the range, variance, and standard deviation for the data.

778	309	1110	324	705
1067	826	76	205	152
218	492	65	186	712
193	262	452	875	82
730	1185	2707	1279	390
305	123	948	343	602
69	451	951	104	985
155	450	2080	565	875
414	981	2786	82	793
214	130	396	620	797

Source: National Highway Traffic Safety Administration.

17. **Annual Precipitation Days** The number of annual precipitation days for one-half of the 50 largest U.S. cities is listed below. Find the range, variance, and standard deviation of the data.

135	128	136	78	116	77	111	79	44	97
116	123	88	102	26	82	156	133	107	35
112	98	45	122	125					

18. Use the data from Exercises 7, 15, and 17 (unemployment, prisoners, precipitation days) and compare the standard deviation with that obtained by the range rule of thumb (R/4.) Comment on the results.

19. **Cost per Load of Laundry Detergents** The costs per load (in cents) of 35 laundry detergents tested by a consumer organization are shown here. Find the variance and standard deviation for the data.

Class limits	Frequency
13–19	2
20–26	7
27–33	12
34–40	5
41–47	6
48–54	1
55–61	0
62–68	2

20. **Automotive Fuel Efficiency** Thirty automobiles were tested for fuel efficiency (in miles per gallon). This frequency distribution was obtained. Find the variance and standard deviation for the data.

Class boundaries	Frequency
7.5–12.5	3
12.5–17.5	5
17.5–22.5	15
22.5–27.5	5
27.5–32.5	2

21. **Murders in Cities** The data show the number of murders in 25 selected cities. Find the variance and standard deviation for the data.

Class limits	Frequency
34–96	13
97–159	2
160–222	0
223–285	5
286–348	1
349–411	1
412–474	0
475–537	1
538–600	2

22. **Reaction Times** In a study of reaction times to a specific stimulus, a psychologist recorded these data (in seconds). Find the variance and standard deviation for the data.

Class limits	Frequency
2.1–2.7	12
2.8–3.4	13
3.5–4.1	7
4.2–4.8	5
4.9–5.5	2
5.6–6.2	1

23. **FM Radio Stations** A random sample of 30 states shows the number of low-power FM radio stations for each state. Find the variance and standard deviation for the data.

Class limits	Frequency
1–9	5
10–18	7
19–27	10
28–36	3
37–45	3
46–54	2

Source: Federal Communications Commission.

24. **Murder Rates** The data represent the murder rate per 100,000 individuals in a sample of selected cities in the United States. Find the variance and standard deviation for the data.

Class limits	Frequency
5–11	8
12–18	5
19–25	7
26–32	1
33–39	1
40–46	3

Source: FBI and U.S. Census Bureau.

25. **Battery Lives** Eighty randomly selected batteries were tested to determine their lifetimes (in hours). The following frequency distribution was obtained. Find the variance and standard deviation for the data.

Class boundaries	Frequency
62.5–73.5	5
73.5–84.5	14
84.5–95.5	18
95.5–106.5	25
106.5–117.5	12
117.5–128.5	6

Can it be concluded that the lifetimes of these brands of batteries are consistent?

26. **Baseball Team Batting Averages** Team batting averages for major league baseball in 2005 are represented below. Find the variance and standard deviation for each league. Compare the results.

NL		AL	
0.252–0.256	4	0.256–0.261	2
0.257–0.261	6	0.262–0.267	5
0.262–0.266	1	0.268–0.273	4
0.267–0.271	4	0.274–0.279	2
0.272–0.276	1	0.280–0.285	1

Source: World Almanac.

27. **Missing Work** The average number of days that construction workers miss per year is 11. The standard deviation is 2.3. The average number of days that factory workers miss per year is 8 with a standard deviation of 1.8. Which class is more variable in terms of days missed?

28. **Suspension Bridges** The lengths (in feet) of the main span of the longest suspension bridges in the United States and the rest of the world are shown below. Which set of data is more variable?

United States 4205, 4200, 3800, 3500, 3478, 2800, 2800, 2310
World   6570, 5538, 5328, 4888, 4626, 4544, 4518, 3970

Source: World Almanac.

29. **Hospital Emergency Waiting Times** The mean of the waiting times in an emergency room is 80.2 minutes with a standard deviation of 10.5 minutes for people who are admitted for additional treatment. The mean waiting time for patients who are discharged after receiving treatment is 120.6 minutes with a standard deviation of 18.3 minutes. Which times are more variable?

30. **Ages of Accountants** The average age of the accountants at Three Rivers Corp. is 26 years, with a standard deviation of 6 years; the average salary of the accountants is $31,000, with a standard deviation of $4000. Compare the variations of age and income.

31. Using Chebyshev's theorem, solve these problems for a distribution with a mean of 80 and a standard deviation of 10.
    a. At least what percentage of values will fall between 60 and 100?
    b. At least what percentage of values will fall between 65 and 95?

32. The mean of a distribution is 20 and the standard deviation is 2. Use Chebyshev's theorem.
    a. At least what percentage of the values will fall between 10 and 30?
    b. At least what percentage of the values will fall between 12 and 28?

33. In a distribution of 160 values with a mean of 72, at least 120 fall within the interval 67–77. Approximately what percentage of values should fall in the interval 62–82? Use Chebyshev's theorem.

34. **Calories** The average number of calories in a regular-size bagel is 240. If the standard deviation is 38 calories, find the range in which at least 75% of the data will lie. Use Chebyshev's theorem.

35. **Time Spent Online** Americans spend an average of 3 hours per day online. If the standard deviation is 32 minutes, find the range in which at least 88.89% of the data will lie. Use Chebyshev's theorem.

Source: www.cs.cmu.edu

36. Solid Waste Production The average college student produces 640 pounds of solid waste each year. If the standard deviation is approximately 85 pounds, within what weight limits will at least 88.89% of all students' garbage lie?

Source: Environmental Sustainability Committee, www.esc.mtu.edu

37. Sale Price of Homes The average sale price of new one-family houses in the United States for 2003 was $246,300. Find the range of values in which at least 75% of the sale prices will lie if the standard deviation is $48,500.

Source: New York Times Almanac.

38. Trials to Learn a Maze The average of the number of trials it took a sample of mice to learn to traverse a maze was 12. The standard deviation was 3. Using Chebyshev's theorem, find the minimum percentage of data values that will fall in the range of 4–20 trials.

39. Farm Sizes The average farm in the United States in 2004 contained 443 acres. The standard deviation is 42 acres. Use Chebyshev's theorem to find the minimum percentage of data values that will fall in the range of 338–548 acres.

Source: World Almanac.

40. Citrus Fruit Consumption The average U.S. yearly per capita consumption of citrus fruit is 26.8 pounds. Suppose that the distribution of fruit amounts consumed is bell-shaped with a standard deviation equal to 4.2 pounds. What percentage of Americans would you expect to consume more than 31 pounds of citrus fruit per year?

Source: USDA/Economic Research Service.

41. SAT Scores The national average for mathematics SATs in 2011 was 514. Suppose that the distribution of scores was approximately bell-shaped and that the standard deviation was approximately 40. Within what boundaries would you expect 68% of the scores to fall? What percentage of scores would be above 594?

42. Work Hours for College Faculty The average full-time faculty member in a postsecondary degree-granting institution works an average of 53 hours per week.

a. If we assume the standard deviation is 2.8 hours, what percentage of faculty members work more than 58.6 hours a week?

b. If we assume a bell-shaped distribution, what percentage of faculty members work more than 58.6 hours a week?

Source: National Center for Education Statistics.

⬟ Extending the Concepts

43. Serum Cholesterol Levels For this data set, find the mean and standard deviation of the variable. The data represent the serum cholesterol levels of 30 individuals. Count the number of data values that fall within 2 standard deviations of the mean. Compare this with the number obtained from Chebyshev's theorem. Comment on the answer.

211	240	255	219	204
200	212	193	187	205
256	203	210	221	249
231	212	236	204	187
201	247	206	187	200
237	227	221	192	196

44. Ages of Consumers For this data set, find the mean and standard deviation of the variable. The data represent the ages of 30 customers who ordered a product advertised on television. Count the number of data values that fall within 2 standard deviations of the mean. Compare this with the number obtained from Chebyshev's theorem. Comment on the answer.

42	44	62	35	20
30	56	20	23	41
55	22	31	27	66
21	18	24	42	25
32	50	31	26	36
39	40	18	36	22

45. Using Chebyshev's theorem, complete the table to find the minimum percentage of data values that fall within k standard deviations of the mean.

k	1.5	2	2.5	3	3.5
Percent					

46. Use this data set: 10, 20, 30, 40, 50

a. Find the standard deviation.

b. Add 5 to each value, and then find the standard deviation.

c. Subtract 5 from each value and find the standard deviation.

d. Multiply each value by 5 and find the standard deviation.

e. Divide each value by 5 and find the standard deviation.

f. Generalize the results of parts b through e.

g. Compare these results with those in Exercise 35 of Exercises 3–1.

47. Mean Deviation The mean deviation is found by using this formula:

$$\text{Mean deviation} = \frac{\Sigma |X - \overline{X}|}{n}$$

where X = value

$\overline{X}$ = mean

n = number of values

$|\ |$ = absolute value

Find the mean deviation for these data.

5, 9, 10, 11, 11, 12, 15, 18, 20, 22

48. Pearson Coefficient of Skewness A measure to determine the skewness of a distribution is called the *Pearson coefficient (PC) of skewness.* The formula is

$$PC = \frac{3(\overline{X} - MD)}{s}$$

The values of the coefficient usually range from -3 to $+3$. When the distribution is symmetric, the coefficient

is zero; when the distribution is positively skewed, it is positive; and when the distribution is negatively skewed, it is negative.

Using the formula, find the coefficient of skewness for each distribution, and describe the shape of the distribution.

a. Mean = 10, median = 8, standard deviation = 3.

b. Mean = 42, median = 45, standard deviation = 4.

c. Mean = 18.6, median = 18.6, standard deviation = 1.5.

d. Mean = 98, median = 97.6, standard deviation = 4.

49. All values of a data set must be within $s\sqrt{n-1}$ of the mean. If a person collected 25 data values that had a mean of 50 and a standard deviation of 3 and you saw that one data value was 67, what would you conclude?

▰ Technology   Step by Step

EXCEL
Step by Step

Finding Measures of Variation
Example XL3–2

Find the sample variance, sample standard deviation, and range of the data from Example 3–20.

9	10	14	7	8	3

1. On an Excel worksheet enter the data in cells A2–A7. Enter a label for the variable in cell A1.

2. In a blank cell enter **=VAR(A2:A7)** for the sample variance.

3. In a blank cell enter **=STDEV(A2:A7)** for the sample standard deviation.

4. For the range, compute the difference between the maximum and the minimum values by entering **=Max(A2:A7)-Min(A2:A7)**.

Note: The command for computing the population variance is VAR.P and for the population standard deviation is STDEV.P

These and other statistical functions can also be accessed without typing them into the worksheet directly.

1. Select the Formulas tab from the Toolbar and select the Insert Function Icon, f_x.

2. Select the Statistical category for statistical functions.

3. Scroll to find the appropriate function and click [OK].

▰	A	B	C	D
1	Strikes			
2	9		Variance	13.1
3	10		Standard Deviation	3.619392214
4	14		Range	11
5	7			
6	8			
7	3			

3–3   Measures of Position

OBJECTIVE ❸

Identify the position of a
data value in a data set,
using various measures
of position, such as
percentiles, deciles, and
quartiles.

In addition to measures of central tendency and measures of variation, there are measures of position or location. These measures include standard scores, percentiles, deciles, and quartiles. They are used to locate the relative position of a data value in the data set. For example, if a value is located at the 80th percentile, it means that 80% of the values fall below it in the distribution and 20% of the values fall above it. The *median* is the value that corresponds to the 50th percentile, since one-half of the values fall below it and one-half of the values fall above it. This section discusses these measures of position.

Standard Scores

There is an old saying, "You can't compare apples and oranges." But with the use of statistics, it can be done to some extent. Suppose that a student scored 90 on a music test and 45 on an English exam. Direct comparison of raw scores is impossible, since the exams might not be equivalent in terms of number of questions, value of each question, and so on. However, a comparison of a relative standard similar to both can be made. This comparison uses the mean and standard deviation and is called a *standard score* or *z* score. (We also use *z* scores in later chapters.)

A standard score or *z* score tells how many standard deviations a data value is above or below the mean for a specific distribution of values. If a standard score is zero, then the data value is the same as the mean.

A **z score** or **standard score** for a value is obtained by subtracting the mean from the value and dividing the result by the standard deviation. The symbol for a standard score is *z*. The formula is

$$z = \frac{\text{value} - \text{mean}}{\text{standard deviation}}$$

For samples, the formula is

$$z = \frac{X - \overline{X}}{s}$$

For populations, the formula is

$$z = \frac{X - \mu}{\sigma}$$

The *z* score represents the number of standard deviations that a data value falls above or below the mean.

For the purpose of this section, it will be assumed that when we find *z* scores, the data were obtained from samples.

EXAMPLE 3–27   Test Scores

Interesting Fact

The average number
of faces that a person
learns to recognize and
remember during his or
her lifetime is 10,000.

A student scored 65 on a calculus test that had a mean of 50 and a standard deviation of 10; she scored 30 on a history test with a mean of 25 and a standard deviation of 5. Compare her relative positions on the two tests.

SOLUTION

First, find the *z* scores. For calculus the *z* score is

$$z = \frac{X - \overline{X}}{s} = \frac{65 - 50}{10} = 1.5$$

For history the z score is

$$z = \frac{30 - 25}{5} = 1.0$$

Since the z score for calculus is larger, her relative position in the calculus class is higher than her relative position in the history class.

Note that if the z score is positive, the score is above the mean. If the z score is 0, the score is the same as the mean. And if the z score is negative, the score is below the mean.

EXAMPLE 3–28   Test Scores

Find the z score for each test, and state which is higher.

Test A	$X = 38$	$\bar{X} = 40$	$s = 5$
Test B	$X = 94$	$\bar{X} = 100$	$s = 10$

SOLUTION

For test A,

$$z = \frac{X - \bar{X}}{s} = \frac{38 - 40}{5} = -0.4$$

For test B,

$$z = \frac{94 - 100}{10} = -0.6$$

The score for test A is relatively higher than the score for test B.

When all data for a variable are transformed into z scores, the resulting distribution will have a mean of 0 *and a standard deviation of* 1. *A z score, then, is actually the number of standard deviations each value is from the mean for a specific distribution.* In Example 3–27, the calculus score of 65 was actually 1.5 standard deviations above the mean of 50. This will be explained in greater detail in Chapter 6.

Percentiles

Percentiles are position measures used in educational and health-related fields to indicate the position of an individual in a group.

Percentiles divide the data set into 100 equal groups.

Percentiles are symbolized by

$$P_1, P_2, P_3, \ldots, P_{99}$$

and divide the distribution into 100 groups.

TABLE 3–3   Percentile Ranks and Scaled Scores on the Test of English as a Foreign Language*

Scaled score	Section 1: Listening comprehension	Section 2: Structure and written expression	Section 3: Vocabulary and reading comprehension	Total scaled score	Percentile rank
68	99	98			
66	98	96	98	660	99
64	96	94	96	640	97
62	92	90	93	620	94
60	87	84	88	600	89
→58	81	76	81	580	82
56	73	68	72	560	73
54	64	58	61	540	62
52	54	48	50	520	50
50	42	38	40	500	39
48	32	29	30	480	29
46	22	21	23	460	20
44	14	15	16	440	13
42	9	10	11	420	9
40	5	7	8	400	5
38	3	4	5	380	3
36	2	3	3	360	1
34	1	2	2	340	1
32		1	1	320	
30		1	1	300	
Mean	51.5	52.2	51.4	517	Mean
S.D.	7.1	7.9	7.5	68	S.D.

*Based on the total group of 1,178,193 examinees.

Source: Reprinted by permission of Educational Testing Service, the copyright owner. However, the test question and any other testing information are provided in their entirety by McGraw-Hill Companies, Inc. No endorsement of this publication by Educational Testing Service should be inferred.

In many situations, the graphs and tables showing the percentiles for various measures such as test scores, heights, or weights have already been completed. Table 3–3 shows the percentile ranks for scaled scores on the Test of English as a Foreign Language. If a student had a scaled score of 58 for section 1 (listening and comprehension), that student would have a percentile rank of 81. Hence, that student did better than 81% of the students who took section 1 of the exam.

Figure 3–5 shows percentiles in graphical form of weights of girls from ages 2 to 18. To find the percentile rank of an 11-year-old who weighs 82 pounds, start at the 82-pound weight on the left axis and move horizontally to the right. Find 11 on the horizontal axis and move up vertically. The two lines meet at the 50th percentile curved line; hence, an 11-year-old girl who weighs 82 pounds is in the 50th percentile for her age group. If the lines do not meet exactly on one of the curved percentile lines, then the percentile rank must be approximated.

Percentiles are also used to compare an individual's test score with the national norm. For example, tests such as the National Educational Development Test (NEDT) are taken by students in ninth or tenth grade. A student's scores are compared with those of other

FIGURE 3–5

Weights of Girls by Age and Percentile Rankings

Source: Distributed by Mead Johnson Nutritional Division. Reprinted with permission.

students locally and nationally by using percentile ranks. A similar test for elementary school students is called the California Achievement Test.

Percentiles are not the same as percentages. That is, if a student gets 72 correct answers out of a possible 100, she obtains a percentage score of 72. There is no indication of her position with respect to the rest of the class. She could have scored the highest, the lowest, or somewhere in between. On the other hand, if a raw score of 72 corresponds to the 64th percentile, then she did better than 64% of the students in her class.

Percentile graphs can be constructed as shown in Example 3–29 and Figure 3–6. Percentile graphs use the same values as the cumulative relative frequency graphs described in Section 2–2, except that the proportions have been converted to percents.

EXAMPLE 3–29   Systolic Blood Pressure

The frequency distribution for the systolic blood pressure readings (in millimeters of mercury, mm Hg) of 200 randomly selected college students is shown here. Construct a percentile graph.

A Class boundaries	B Frequency	C Cumulative frequency	D Cumulative percent
89.5–104.5	24		
104.5–119.5	62		
119.5–134.5	72		
134.5–149.5	26		
149.5–164.5	12		
164.5–179.5	4		
	200		

SOLUTION

Step 1 Find the cumulative frequencies and place them in column C.

Step 2 Find the cumulative percentages and place them in column D. To do this step, use the formula

$$\text{Cumulative }\% = \frac{\text{cumulative frequency}}{n} \cdot 100$$

For the first class,

$$\text{Cumulative }\% = \frac{24}{200} \cdot 100 = 12\%$$

The completed table is shown here.

A Class boundaries	B Frequency	C Cumulative frequency	D Cumulative percent
89.5–104.5	24	24	12
104.5–119.5	62	86	43
119.5–134.5	72	158	79
134.5–149.5	26	184	92
149.5–164.5	12	196	98
164.5–179.5	4	200	100
	200		

Step 3 Graph the data, using class boundaries for the x axis and the percentages for the y axis, as shown in Figure 3–6.

Once a percentile graph has been constructed, one can find the approximate corresponding percentile ranks for given blood pressure values and find approximate blood pressure values for given percentile ranks.

For example, to find the percentile rank of a blood pressure reading of 130, find 130 on the x axis of Figure 3–6 and draw a vertical line to the graph. Then move horizontally to the value on the y axis. Note that a blood pressure of 130 corresponds to approximately the 70th percentile.

If the value that corresponds to the 40th percentile is desired, start on the y axis at 40 and draw a horizontal line to the graph. Then draw a vertical line to the x axis and read the value. In Figure 3–6, the 40th percentile corresponds to a value of approximately 118. Thus, if a person has a blood pressure of 118, he or she is at the 40th percentile.

Finding values and the corresponding percentile ranks by using a graph yields only approximate answers. Several mathematical methods exist for computing percentiles for data. These methods can be used to find the approximate percentile rank of a data value

FIGURE 3–6

Percentile Graph for
Example 3–29

or to find a data value corresponding to a given percentile. When the data set is large (100 or more), these methods yield better results. Examples 3–30 and 3–31 show these methods.

Percentile Formula

The percentile corresponding to a given value X is computed by using the following formula:

$$\text{Percentile} = \frac{(\text{number of values below } X) + 0.5}{\text{total number of values}} \cdot 100$$

EXAMPLE 3–30   Test Scores

A teacher gives a 20-point test to 10 students. The scores are shown here. Find the percentile rank of a score of 12.

$$18, 15, 12, 6, 8, 2, 3, 5, 20, 10$$

SOLUTION

Arrange the data in order from lowest to highest.

$$2, 3, 5, 6, 8, 10, 12, 15, 18, 20$$

Then substitute into the formula.

$$\text{Percentile} = \frac{(\text{number of values below } X) + 0.5}{\text{total number of values}} \cdot 100$$

Since there are six values below a score of 12, the solution is

$$\text{Percentile} = \frac{6 + 0.5}{10} \cdot 100 = 65\text{th percentile}$$

Thus, a student whose score was 12 did better than 65% of the class.

Note: One assumes that a score of 12 in Example 3–30, for instance, means theoretically any value between 11.5 and 12.5.

EXAMPLE 3–31   Test Scores

Using the data in Example 3–30, find the percentile rank for a score of 6.

SOLUTION

There are three values below 6. Thus,

$$\text{Percentile} = \frac{3 + 0.5}{10} \cdot 100 = 35\text{th percentile}$$

A student who scored 6 did better than 35% of the class.

The steps for finding a value corresponding to a given percentile are summarized in this Procedure Table.

Procedure Table

Finding a Data Value Corresponding to a Given Percentile

Step 1   Arrange the data in order from lowest to highest.

Step 2   Substitute into the formula

$$c = \frac{n \cdot p}{100}$$

where n = total number of values
p = percentile

Step 3A   If c is not a whole number, round up to the next whole number. Starting at the lowest value, count over to the number that corresponds to the rounded-up value.

Step 3B   If c is a whole number, use the value halfway between the cth and $(c + 1)$st values when counting up from the lowest value.

Examples 3–32 and 3–33 show a procedure for finding a value corresponding to a given percentile.

EXAMPLE 3–32   Test Scores

Using the scores in Example 3–30, find the value corresponding to the 25th percentile.

SOLUTION

Step 1   Arrange the data in order from lowest to highest.

$$2, 3, 5, 6, 8, 10, 12, 15, 18, 20$$

Step 2   Compute

$$c = \frac{n \cdot p}{100}$$

where n = total number of values
p = percentile

Thus,

$$c = \frac{10 \cdot 25}{100} = 2.5$$

Step 3   Since c is not a whole number, round it up to the next whole number; in this case, $c = 3$. Start at the lowest value and count over to the third value, which is 5. Hence, the value 5 corresponds to the 25th percentile.

EXAMPLE 3–33

Using the data set in Example 3–30, find the value that corresponds to the 60th percentile.

SOLUTION

Step 1   Arrange the data in order from lowest to highest.

$$2, 3, 5, 6, 8, 10, 12, 15, 18, 20$$

Step 2   Substitute in the formula.

$$c = \frac{n \cdot p}{100} = \frac{10 \cdot 60}{100} = 6$$

Step 3   Since c is a whole number, use the value halfway between the c and $c + 1$ values when counting up from the lowest value—in this case, the 6th and 7th values.

$$2, 3, 5, 6, 8, 10, 12, 15, 18, 20$$

6th value   7th value

The value halfway between 10 and 12 is 11. Find it by adding the two values and dividing by 2.

$$\frac{10 + 12}{2} = 11$$

Hence, 11 corresponds to the 60th percentile. Anyone scoring 11 would have done better than 60% of the class.

Quartiles and Deciles

Quartiles divide the distribution into four equal groups, denoted by Q_1, Q_2, Q_3.
    Note that Q_1 is the same as the 25th percentile; Q_2 is the same as the 50th percentile, or the median; Q_3 corresponds to the 75th percentile, as shown:

    Quartiles can be computed by using the formula given for computing percentiles on page 153. For Q_1 use $p = 25$. For Q_2 use $p = 50$. For Q_3 use $p = 75$. However, an easier method for finding quartiles is found in this Procedure Table.

Procedure Table
Finding Data Values Corresponding to Q_1, Q_2, and Q_3
Step 1   Arrange the data in order from lowest to highest.
Step 2   Find the median of the data values. This is the value for Q_2.
Step 3   Find the median of the data values that fall below Q_2. This is the value for Q_1.
Step 4   Find the median of the data values that fall above Q_2. This is the value for Q_3.

Example 3–34 shows how to find the values of Q_1, Q_2, and Q_3.

EXAMPLE 3–34

Find Q_1, Q_2, and Q_3 for the data set 15, 13, 6, 5, 12, 50, 22, 18.

SOLUTION

Step 1   Arrange the data in order from lowest to highest.

$$5, 6, 12, 13, 15, 18, 22, 50$$

Step 2   Find the median (Q_2).

$$5, 6, 12, 13, 15, 18, 22, 50$$
$$\uparrow$$
$$\text{MD}$$

$$\text{MD} = \frac{13 + 15}{2} = 14$$

Step 3   Find the median of the data values less than 14.

$$5, 6, 12, 13$$
$$\uparrow$$
$$Q_1$$

$$Q_1 = \frac{6 + 12}{2} = 9$$

So Q_1 is 9.

Step 4   Find the median of the data values greater than 14.

$$15, 18, 22, 50$$
$$\uparrow$$
$$Q_3$$

$$Q_3 = \frac{18 + 22}{2} = 20$$

Here Q_3 is 20. Hence, $Q_1 = 9$, $Q_2 = 14$, and $Q_3 = 20$.

In addition to dividing the data set into four groups, quartiles can be used as a rough measure of variability. This measure of variability which uses quartiles is called the *interquartile range* and is the range of the middle 50% of the data values.

> The **interquartile range (IQR)** is the difference between the third and first quartiles.
> $$\text{IQR} = Q_3 - Q_1$$

EXAMPLE 3–35

Find the interquartile range for the data set in Example 3–34.

SOLUTION

First it is necessary to find the values of Q_1 and Q_3. These values were found in Example 3–34: $Q_1 = 9$ and $Q_3 = 20$. Next subtract the value of Q_1 from Q_3 to get the interquartile range.

$$\text{IQR} = Q_3 - Q_1 = 20 - 9 = 11$$

The interquartile range is equal to 11.

Like the standard deviation, the more variable the data set is, the larger the value of the interquartile range will be.

Deciles divide the distribution into 10 groups, as shown. They are denoted by D_1, D_2, etc.

Unusual Stat

Of the alcoholic beverages consumed in the United States, 85% is beer.

Note that D_1 corresponds to P_{10}; D_2 corresponds to P_{20}; etc. Deciles can be found by using the formulas given for percentiles. Taken altogether then, these are the relationships among percentiles, deciles, and quartiles.

Deciles are denoted by $D_1, D_2, D_3, \ldots, D_9$, and they correspond to $P_{10}, P_{20}, P_{30}, \ldots, P_{90}$.

Quartiles are denoted by Q_1, Q_2, Q_3 and they correspond to P_{25}, P_{50}, P_{75}.

The median is the same as P_{50} or Q_2 or D_5.

The position measures are summarized in Table 3–4.

TABLE 3–4	Summary of Position Measures	
Measure	**Definition**	**Symbol(s)**
Standard score or z score	Number of standard deviations that a data value is above or below the mean	z
Percentile	Position in hundredths that a data value holds in the distribution	P_n
Decile	Position in tenths that a data value holds in the distribution	D_n
Quartile	Position in fourths that a data value holds in the distribution	Q_n

Outliers

A data set should be checked for extremely high or extremely low values. These values are called *outliers.*

> An **outlier** is an extremely high or an extremely low data value when compared with the rest of the data values.

An outlier can strongly affect the mean and standard deviation of a variable. For example, suppose a researcher mistakenly recorded an extremely high data value. This value would then make the mean and standard deviation of the variable much larger than they really were.

Since these measures (mean and standard deviation) are affected by outliers, they are called *nonresistant statistics.* The median and interquartile range are less affected by outliers, so they are called *resistant* statistics. Sometimes when a distribution is skewed or contains outliers, the median and interquartile range can be used to more accurately describe the data than the mean and standard deviation. Outliers can have an effect on other statistics as well.

There are several ways to check a data set for outliers. One method is shown in this Procedure Table.

Procedure Table

Procedure for Identifying Outliers

Step 1   Arrange the data in order from lowest to highest and find Q_1 and Q_3.

Step 2   Find the interquartile range: IQR $= Q_3 - Q_1$.

Step 3   Multiply the IQR by 1.5.

Step 4   Subtract the value obtained in step 3 from Q_1 and add the value obtained in step 3 to Q_3.

Step 5   Check the data set for any data value that is smaller than $Q_1 - 1.5(\text{IQR})$ or larger than $Q_3 + 1.5(\text{IQR})$.

This procedure is shown in Example 3–36.

EXAMPLE 3–36   Outliers

Check the following data set for outliers.

$$5, 6, 12, 13, 15, 18, 22, 50$$

SOLUTION

The data value 50 is extremely suspect. These are the steps in checking for an outlier.

Step 1   Find Q_1 and Q_3. This was done in Example 3–34; Q_1 is 9 and Q_3 is 20.

Step 2   Find the interquartile range (IQR), which is $Q_3 - Q_1$.

$$\text{IQR} = Q_3 - Q_1 = 20 - 9 = 11$$

Step 3   Multiply this value by 1.5.

$$1.5(11) = 16.5$$

Step 4   Subtract the value obtained in step 3 from Q_1, and add the value obtained in step 3 to Q_3.

$$9 - 16.5 = -7.5 \qquad \text{and} \qquad 20 + 16.5 = 36.5$$

Step 5   Check the data set for any data values that fall outside the interval from -7.5 to 36.5. The value 50 is outside this interval; hence, it can be considered an outlier.

There are several reasons why outliers may occur. First, the data value may have resulted from a measurement or observational error. Perhaps the researcher measured the variable incorrectly. Second, the data value may have resulted from a recording error. That is, it may have been written or typed incorrectly. Third, the data value may have been obtained from a subject that is not in the defined population. For example, suppose test scores were obtained from a seventh-grade class, but a student in that class was actually in the sixth grade and had special permission to attend the class. This student might have scored extremely low on that particular exam on that day. Fourth, the data value might be a legitimate value that occurred by chance (although the probability is extremely small).

There are no hard-and-fast rules on what to do with outliers, nor is there complete agreement among statisticians on ways to identify them. Obviously, if they occurred as a result of an error, an attempt should be made to correct the error or else the data value should be omitted entirely. When they occur naturally by chance, the statistician must make a decision about whether to include them in the data set.

When a distribution is normal or bell-shaped, data values that are beyond 3 standard deviations of the mean can be considered suspected outliers.

⬛ Applying the Concepts 3–3

Determining Dosages

In an attempt to determine necessary dosages of a new drug (HDL) used to control sepsis, assume you administer varying amounts of HDL to 40 mice. You create four groups and label them *low dosage, moderate dosage, large dosage,* and *very large dosage.* The dosages also vary within each group. After the mice are injected with the HDL and the sepsis bacteria, the time until the onset of sepsis is recorded. Your job as a statistician is to effectively communicate the results of the study.

1. Which measures of position could be used to help describe the data results?
2. If 40% of the mice in the top quartile survived after the injection, how many mice would that be?
3. What information can be given from using percentiles?
4. What information can be given from using quartiles?
5. What information can be given from using standard scores?

See page 184 for the answers.

⬛ Exercises 3–3

1. What is a z score?

2. Define *percentile rank.*

3. What is the difference between a percentage and a percentile?

4. Define *quartile.*

5. What is the relationship between quartiles and percentiles?

6. What is a decile?

7. How are deciles related to percentiles?

8. To which percentile, quartile, and decile does the median correspond?

9. Vacation Days If the average number of vacation days for a selection of various countries has a mean of 29.4 days and a standard deviation of 8.6 days, find the z scores for the average number of vacation days in each of these countries.

Canada	26 days
Italy	42 days
United States	13 days

Source: www.infoplease.com

10. Age of Senators The average age of Senators in the 108th Congress was 59.5 years. If the standard deviation was 11.5 years, find the z scores corresponding to the

oldest and youngest Senators: Robert C. Byrd (D, WV), 86, and John Sununu (R, NH), 40.

Source: *CRS Report for Congress.*

11. Driver's License Exam Scores The average score on a state CDL license exam is 76 with a standard deviation of 5. Find the corresponding z score for each raw score.

a.	79	*d.*	65
b.	70	*e.*	77
c.	88		

12. Teacher's Salary The average teacher's salary in a particular state is $54,166. If the standard deviation is $10,200, find the salaries corresponding to the following z scores.

a.	2	*d.*	2.5
b.	−1	*e.*	−1.6
c.	0		

13. Which has a better relative position: a score of 75 on a statistics test with a mean of 60 and a standard deviation of 10 or a score of 36 on an accounting test with a mean of 30 and a variance of 16?

14. College and University Debt A student graduated from a 4-year college with an outstanding loan of $9650 where the average debt is $8455 with a standard deviation of $1865. Another student graduated from a university with an outstanding loan of $12,360 where the average of the outstanding loans was $10,326 with a standard deviation of $2143. Which student had a higher debt in relationship to his or her peers?

15. Annual Miles Driven The average miles driven annually per licensed driver in the United States is approximately 14,090 miles. If we assume a fairly mound-shaped distribution with a standard deviation of approximately 3500 miles, find the following:

    a.   *z* score for 16,000 miles

    b.   *z* score for 10,000 miles

    c.   Number of miles corresponding to *z* scores of 1.6, −0.5, and 0.

Source: *World Almanac 2012.*

16. Which score indicates the highest relative position?

    a.   A score of 3.2 on a test with $\overline{X} = 4.6$ and $s = 1.5$

    b.   A score of 630 on a test with $\overline{X} = 800$ and $s = 200$

    c.   A score of 43 on a test with $\overline{X} = 50$ and $s = 5$

17. Basketball Scores

    a.   Shown are all the scores from the second round of the NCAA Men's Basketball Championships 2012. Rank all of the individual scores, and use this set of data to find the percentile corresponding to each of the following scores: 78, 66, and 59.

72–65	70–64	77–54	78–59	73–49	79–70
65–59	66–63	81–66	77–64	68–60	68–64
62–59	79–66	75–70	67–63	58–57	77–58
79–65	74–59	65–60	58–44	72–69	65–50
58–41	88–68	69–62	75–68	61–54	89–67
71–45	86–84				

Using the same set of data, find the score corresponding to each percentile value.

    b.   90th percentile

    c.   80th percentile

    d.   65th percentile

18. College Room and Board Costs Room and board costs for selected schools are summarized in this distribution. Find the approximate cost of room and board corresponding to each of the following percentiles.

Costs (in dollars)	Frequency
3000.5–4000.5	5
4000.5–5000.5	6
5000.5–6000.5	18
6000.5–7000.5	24
7000.5–8000.5	19
8000.5–9000.5	8
9000.5–10,000.5	5

    a.   30th percentile

    b.   50th percentile

    c.   75th percentile

    d.   90th percentile

Source: *World Almanac.*

Using the same data, find the approximate percentile rank of each of the following costs.

    e.   5500   *g.*   6500

    f.   7200   *h.*   8300

19. Achievement Test Scores The data shown represent the scores on a national achievement test for a group of 10th-grade students. Find the approximate percentile ranks of these scores by constructing a percentile graph.

    a.   220   *d.*   280

    b.   245   *e.*   300

    c.   276

Score	Frequency
196.5–217.5	5
217.5–238.5	17
238.5–259.5	22
259.5–280.5	48
280.5–301.5	22
301.5–322.5	6

For the same data, find the approximate scores that correspond to these percentiles.

    f.   15th   *i.*   65th

    g.   29th   *j.*   80th

    h.   43rd

20. Airplane Speeds The airborne speeds in miles per hour of 21 planes are shown. Find the approximate values that correspond to the given percentiles by constructing a percentile graph.

Class	Frequency
366–386	4
387–407	2
408–428	3
429–449	2
450–470	1
471–491	2
492–512	3
513–533	4
	21

Source: *The World Almanac and Book of Facts.*

    a.   9th   *d.*   60th

    b.   20th   *e.*   75th

    c.   45th

Using the same data, find the approximate percentile ranks of the following speeds in miles per hour (mph).

    f.   380 mph   *i.*   505 mph

    g.   425 mph   *j.*   525 mph

    h.   455 mph

21. Average Weekly Earnings The average weekly earnings in dollars for various industries are listed below. Find the percentile rank of each value.

804   736   659   489   777   623   597   524   228

For the same data, what value corresponds to the 40th percentile?

Source: *New York Times Almanac.*

22. **Test Scores** Find the percentile rank for each test score in the data set.

    12, 28, 35, 42, 47, 49, 50

    What value corresponds to the 60th percentile?

23. **Hurricane Damage** Find the percentile rank for each value in the data set. The data represent the values in billions of dollars of the damage of 10 hurricanes.

    1.1, 1.7, 1.9, 2.1, 2.2, 2.5, 3.3, 6.2, 6.8, 20.3

    What value corresponds to the 40th percentile?

    Source: Insurance Services Office.

24. **Test Scores** Find the percentile rank for each test score in the data set.

    5, 12, 15, 16, 20, 21

    What test score corresponds to the 33rd percentile?

25. **Gasoline Taxes** A random selection of state gasoline taxes per gallon is given below. Find the first and third quartile values for the data.

    16   18   35.3   25   23.5   27.1   32.5   16   22
    17.5   19   29.5   7.5   12

    Source: *World Almanac 2012.*

26. **Sheep Population** The data show the number of sheep in the top 12 major sheep-producing states. Find the first and third quartiles for the data.

Arizona	160,000	New Mexico	120,000
California	610,000	Oregon	225,000
Colorado	375,000	Texas	830,000
Idaho	220,000	Utah	290,000
Montana	255,000	Washington	60,000
Nevada	75,000	Wyoming	375,000

Source: U.S. Department of Agriculture.

27. **Earthquakes** Eleven major earthquakes had Richter magnitudes as shown. Find the first and third quartiles for the data.

    7.0, 6.2, 7.7, 8.0, 6.4, 6.2, 7.2, 5.4, 6.4, 6.5, 7.2

28. **Police Calls in Schools** The number of incidents in which police were needed for a sample of 9 schools in Allegheny County is 7, 37, 3, 8, 48, 11, 6, 0, 10. Find the first and third quartiles for the data.

29. Check each data set for outliers.
    a. 16, 18, 22, 19, 3, 21, 17, 20
    b. 24, 32, 54, 31, 16, 18, 19, 14, 17, 20
    c. 321, 343, 350, 327, 200

30. Check each data set for outliers.
    a. 88, 72, 97, 84, 86, 85, 100
    b. 145, 119, 122, 118, 125, 116
    c. 14, 16, 27, 18, 13, 19, 36, 15, 20

Extending the Concepts

31. Another measure of the average is called the *midquartile;* it is the numerical value halfway between Q_1 and Q_3, and the formula is

    $$\text{Midquartile} = \frac{Q_1 + Q_3}{2}$$

    Using this formula and other formulas, find Q_1, Q_2, Q_3, the midquartile, and the interquartile range for each data set.
    a. 5, 12, 16, 25, 32, 38
    b. 53, 62, 78, 94, 96, 99, 103

32. An employment evaluation exam has a variance of 250. Two particular exams with raw scores of 142 and 165 have z scores of -0.5 and 0.955, respectively. Find the mean of the distribution.

33. A particular standardized test has scores that have a mound-shaped distribution with mean equal to 125 and standard deviation equal to 18. Tom had a raw score of 158, Dick scored at the 98th percentile, and Harry had a z score of 2.00. Arrange these three students in order of their scores from lowest to highest. Explain your reasoning.

Technology Step by Step

TI-84 Plus
Step by Step

Calculating Descriptive Statistics

To calculate various descriptive statistics:

1. Enter data into L1.
2. Press **STAT** to get the menu.
3. Press → to move cursor to CALC; then press 1 for 1-Var Stats.
4. Press **2nd [L1]**, then **ENTER**.

The calculator will display

$\bar{x}$ sample mean

$\sum x$ sum of the data values

$\sum x^2$ sum of the squares of the data values

S_x sample standard deviation

σ_x population standard deviation

n number of data values

minX   smallest data value

Q_1 lower quartile

Med   median

Q_3 upper quartile

maxX   largest data value

Example TI3–1

Find the various descriptive statistics for the teacher strikes data from Example 3–20: 9, 10, 14, 7, 8, 3

Input	Input	Output

Following the steps just shown, we obtain these results, as shown on the screen:

The mean is 8.5.

The sum of x is 51.

The sum of x^2 is 499.

The sample standard deviation S_x is 3.619392214.

The population standard deviation σ_x is 3.304037934.

The sample size n is 6.

The smallest data value is 3.

Q_1 is 7.

The median is 8.5.

Q_3 is 10.

The largest data value is 14.

To calculate the mean and standard deviation from grouped data:

1. Enter the midpoints into **L1**.
2. Enter the frequencies into **L2**.
3. Press **STAT** to get the menu.
4. Use the arrow keys to move the cursor to CALC; then press 1 for 1-Var Stats.
5. Press **2nd [L1]**, **2nd [L2]**, then ENTER.

Example TI3–2

Calculate the mean and standard deviation for the data given in Examples 3–3 and 3–22.

Class	Frequency	Midpoint
5.5–10.5	1	8
10.5–15.5	2	13
15.5–20.5	3	18
20.5–25.5	5	23
25.5–30.5	4	28
30.5–35.5	3	33
35.5–40.5	2	38

Input	Input	Output

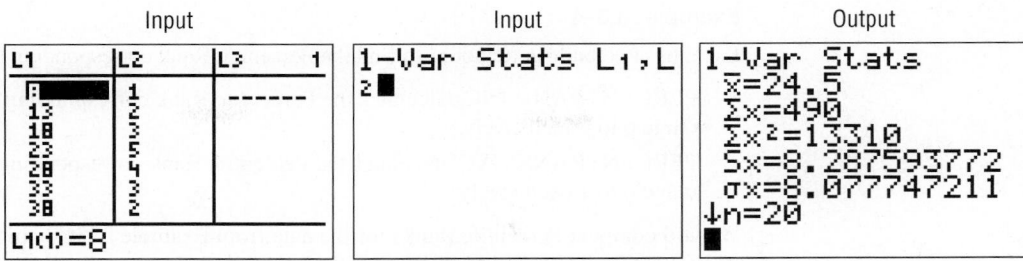

The sample mean is 24.5, and the sample standard deviation is 8.287593772.

To graph a percentile graph, follow the procedure for an ogive (Section 2–2), but use the cumulative percent in L2, 100 for Ymax, and the data from Example 3–29.

Input	Input	Output

EXCEL
Step by Step

Measures of Position
Example XL3–3

Find the z scores for each value of the data from Example 3–36.

$$5 \quad 6 \quad 12 \quad 13 \quad 15 \quad 18 \quad 22 \quad 50$$

1. On an Excel worksheet enter the data in cells A2–A9. Enter a label for the variable in cell A1.
2. Label cell B1 as z score.
3. Select cell B2.
4. Select the Formulas tab from the toolbar and Insert Function f_x .
5. Select the Statistical category for statistical functions and scroll in the function list to STANDARDIZE and click [OK].

In the STANDARDIZE dialog box:

6. Type A2 for the X value.
7. Type average(A2:A9) for the mean.
8. Type stdev(A2:A9) for the Standard_dev. Then click [OK].
9. Repeat the procedure above for each data value in column A.

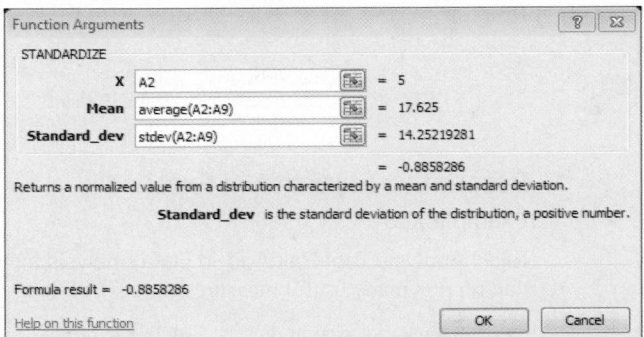

Example XL3–4

Excel has two built-in functions to find the Percentile Rank corresponding to a value in a set of data.

PERCENTRANK.INC calculates the Percentile Rank corresponding to a data value in the range 0 to 1 inclusively.

PERCENTRANK.EXC calculates the Percentile Rank corresponding to a data value in the range 0 to 1 exclusively.

We will compute Percentile Ranks for the data from Example 3–36, using both PERCENTRANK.INC and PERCENTRANK.EXC to demonstrate the difference between the two functions.

$$5 \quad 6 \quad 12 \quad 13 \quad 15 \quad 18 \quad 22 \quad 50$$

1. On an Excel worksheet enter the data in cells A2–A9. Enter the label **Data** in cell A1.
2. Label cell B1 as **Percent Rank INC** and cell C1 as **Percent Rank EXC.**
3. Select cell B2.
4. Select the Formulas tab from the toolbar and Insert Function .
5. Select the Statistical category for statistical functions and scroll in the function list to PERCENTRANK.INC (PERCENTRANK.EXC) and click [OK].

In the PERCENTRANK.INC (PERCENTRANK.EXC) dialog boxes:

6. Type A2:A9 for the Array.
7. Type A2 for X, then click [OK]. You can leave the Significance box blank unless you want to change the number of significant digits of the output (the default is 3 significant digits).
8. Repeat the procedure above for each data value in the set.

The function results for both PERCENTRANK.INC and PERCENTRANK.EXC are shown below.

Note: Both functions return the Percentile Ranks as a number between 0 and 1. You may convert these to numbers between 0 and 100 by multiplying each function value by 100.

Descriptive Statistics in Excel

Example XL3–5

Excel Analysis Tool-Pak Add-in Data Analysis includes an item called Descriptive Statistics that reports many useful measures for a set of data.

1. Enter the data set shown in cells A1 to A9 of a new worksheet.

$$12 \quad 17 \quad 15 \quad 16 \quad 16 \quad 14 \quad 18 \quad 13 \quad 10$$

See the Excel Step by Step in Chapter 1 for the instructions on loading the Analysis Tool-Pak Add-in.

2. Select the Data tab on the toolbar and select Data Analysis.
3. In the Analysis Tools dialog box, scroll to Descriptive Statistics, then click [OK].
4. Type A1:A9 in the Input Range box and check the Grouped by Columns option.
5. Select the Output Range option and type in cell C1.
6. Check the Summary statistics option and click [OK].

Below is the summary output for this data set.

Column1	
Mean	14.55555556
Standard Error	0.85165054
Median	15
Mode	16
Standard Deviation	2.554951619
Sample Variance	6.527777778
Kurtosis	-0.3943866
Skewness	-0.51631073
Range	8
Minimum	10
Maximum	18
Sum	131
Count	9

MINITAB
Step by Step

Calculate Descriptive Statistics from Data
Example MT3–1

1. Enter the data from Example 3–20 on teacher strikes into C1 of MINITAB. Name the column **Strikes.**
2. Select **Stat>Basic Statistics>Display Descriptive Statistics.**
3. The cursor will be blinking in the Variables text box. Double-click C1 Strikes.
4. Click [Statistics] to view the statistics that can be calculated with this command.
   a) Check the boxes for Mean, Standard deviation, Variance, Coefficient of variation, Median, Minimum, Maximum, and N nonmissing.

   b) Remove the checks from other options.

5. Click [OK] twice. The results will be displayed in the session window as shown.

Descriptive Statistics: Strikes

Variable	N	Mean	StDev	Variance	CoefVar	Minimum	Median	Maximum
Strikes	6	8.50	3.62	13.10	42.58	3.00	8.50	14.00

Session window results are in text format. A high-resolution graphical window displays the descriptive statistics, a histogram, and a boxplot.

6. Select **Stat>Basic Statistics>Graphical Summary.**

7. Double-click C1 Strikes.

8. Click [OK].

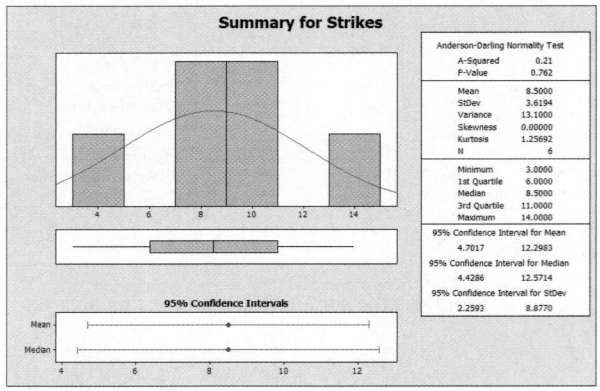

The graphical summary will be displayed in a separate window as shown.

Calculate Descriptive Statistics from a Frequency Distribution

Multiple menu selections must be used to calculate the statistics from a table. We will use data given in Example 3–22 on miles run per week.

Enter Midpoints and Frequencies

1. Select **File>New>New Worksheet** to open an empty worksheet.

2. To enter the midpoints into C1, select **Calc>Make Patterned Data>Simple Set of Numbers.**

   a) Type **X** to name the column.

   b) Type in **8** for the First value, **38** for the Last value, and **5** for Steps.

   c) Click [OK].

3. Enter the frequencies in C2. Name the column **f.**

Calculate Columns for f·X and f·X²

4. Select **Calc>Calculator.**

   a) Type in **fX** for the variable and **f*X** in the Expression dialog box. Click [OK].

   b) Select **Edit>Edit Last Dialog** and type in **fX2** for the variable and **f*X**2** for the expression.

   c) Click [OK]. There are now four columns in the worksheet.

Calculate the Column Sums

5. Select **Calc>Column Statistics.**

   This command stores results in constants, not columns.

   Click [OK] after each step.

   a) Click the option for Sum; then select C2 f for the Input column, and type **n** for Store result in.

   b) Select **Edit>Edit Last Dialog;** then select C3 fX for the column and type **sumX** for storage.

c) Edit the last dialog box again. This time select C4 fX2 for the column, then type **sumX2** for storage.

To verify the results, navigate to the Project Manager window, then the constants folder of the worksheet. The sums are 20, 490, and 13,310.

Calculate the Mean, Variance, and Standard Deviation

6. Select **Calc>Calculator.**

   a) Type **Mean** for the variable, then click in the box for the Expression and type **sumX/n.** Click [OK]. If you double-click the constants instead of typing them, single quotes will surround the names. The quotes are not required unless the column name has spaces.

   b) Click the **EditLast Dialog** icon and type **Variance** for the variable.

   c) In the expression box type in

   (sumX2-sumX**2/n)/(n-1)

   d) Edit the last dialog box and type **S** for the variable. In the expression box, drag the mouse over the previous expression to highlight it.

   e) Click the button in the keypad for parentheses. Type **SQRT** at the beginning of the line, upper- or lowercase will work. The expression should be SQRT((sumX2-sumX**2/n)/(n-1)).

   f) Click [OK].

Display Results

   g) Select **Data>Display Data,** then highlight all columns and constants in the list.

   h) Click [Select] then [OK].

The session window will display all our work! Create the histogram with instructions from Chapter 2.

Data Display

n	20.0000
sumX	490.000
sumX2	13310.0

Row	X	f	fX	fX2	Mean	Variance	S
1	8	1	8	64	24.5	68.6842	8.28759
2	13	2	26	338			
3	18	3	54	972			
4	23	5	115	2645			
5	28	4	112	3136			
6	33	3	99	3267			
7	38	2	76	2888			

3–4   Exploratory Data Analysis

OBJECTIVE

Use the techniques of exploratory data analysis, including boxplots and five-number summaries, to discover various aspects of data.

In traditional statistics, data are organized by using a frequency distribution. From this distribution various graphs such as the histogram, frequency polygon, and ogive can be constructed to determine the shape or nature of the distribution. In addition, various statistics such as the mean and standard deviation can be computed to summarize the data.

The purpose of traditional analysis is to confirm various conjectures about the nature of the data. For example, from a carefully designed study, a researcher might want to know if the proportion of Americans who are exercising today has increased from 10 years ago. This study would contain various assumptions about the population, various definitions such as the definition of exercise, and so on.

In **exploratory data analysis (EDA),** data can be organized using a *stem and leaf plot.* (See Chapter 2.) The measure of central tendency used in EDA is the *median.* The measure of variation used in EDA is the *interquartile range Q_3–Q_1.* In EDA the data are represented graphically using a *boxplot* (sometimes called a box and whisker plot). The purpose of exploratory data analysis is to examine data to find out what information can be discovered about the data, such as the center and the spread. Exploratory data analysis was developed by John Tukey and presented in his book *Exploratory Data Analysis* (Addison-Wesley, 1977).

The Five-Number Summary and Boxplots

A **boxplot** can be used to graphically represent the data set. These plots involve five specific values:

1. The lowest value of the data set (i.e., minimum)
2. Q_1
3. The median
4. Q_3
5. The highest value of the data set (i.e., maximum)

These values are called a **five-number summary** of the data set.

A **boxplot** is a graph of a data set obtained by drawing a horizontal line from the minimum data value to Q_1, drawing a horizontal line from Q_3 to the maximum data value, and drawing a box whose vertical sides pass through Q_1 and Q_3 with a vertical line inside the box passing through the median or Q_2.

Procedure Table

Constructing a Boxplot

Step 1   Find the five-number summary for the data.

Step 2   Draw a horizontal axis and place the scale on the axis. The scale should start on or below the minimum data value and end on or above the maximum data value.

Step 3   Locate the lowest data value, Q_1, the median, Q_3, and the highest data value; then draw a box whose vertical sides go through Q_1 and Q_3. Draw a vertical line through the median. Finally, draw a line from the minimum data value to the left side of the box, and draw a line from the maximum data value to the right side of the box.

EXAMPLE 3–37   Number of Meteorites Found

The number of meteorites found in 10 states of the United States is 89, 47, 164, 296, 30, 215, 138, 78, 48, 39. Construct a boxplot for the data.

Source: Natural History Museum.

SOLUTION

Step 1   Find the five-number summary for the data.

Arrange the data in order:

30, 39, 47, 48, 78, 89, 138, 164, 215, 296

Find the median.

30, 39, 47, 48, 78, 89, 138, 164, 215, 296
↑
Median

$$\text{Median} = \frac{78 + 89}{2} = 83.5$$

Find Q_1.

30, 39, 47, 48, 78
↑
Q_1

Find Q_3.

89, 138, 164, 215, 296
↑
Q_3

The minimum data value is 30, and the maximum data value is 296.

Step 2   Draw a horizontal axis and the scale.

Step 3   Draw the box above the scale using Q_1 and Q_3. Draw a vertical line through the median, and draw lines from the lowest data value to the box and from the highest data value to the box. See Figure 3–7.

FIGURE 3–7   Boxplot for Example 3–37

Information Obtained from a Boxplot

1. *a.* If the median is near the center of the box, the distribution is approximately symmetric.
   b. If the median falls to the left of the center of the box, the distribution is positively skewed.
   c. If the median falls to the right of the center, the distribution is negatively skewed.
2. *a.* If the lines are about the same length, the distribution is approximately symmetric.
   b. If the right line is larger than the left line, the distribution is positively skewed.
   c. If the left line is larger than the right line, the distribution is negatively skewed.

The boxplot in Figure 3–7 indicates that the distribution is slightly positively skewed. If the boxplots for two or more data sets are graphed on the same axis, the distributions can be compared. To compare the averages, use the location of the medians. To compare the variability, use the interquartile range, i.e., the length of the boxes. Example 3–38 shows this procedure.

EXAMPLE 3–38   Sodium Content of Cheese

A dietitian is interested in comparing the sodium content of real cheese with the sodium content of a cheese substitute. The data for two random samples are shown. Compare the distributions, using boxplots.

Real cheese				Cheese substitute			
310	420	45	40	270	180	250	290
220	240	180	90	130	260	340	310

Source: *The Complete Book of Food Counts.*

SOLUTION

Step 1   Find the five-number summary for each data set. For real cheese

$$40 \quad 45 \quad 90 \quad 180 \quad 220 \quad 240 \quad 310 \quad 420$$
$$\uparrow \qquad\qquad \uparrow \qquad\qquad \uparrow$$
$$Q_1 \qquad\quad MD \qquad\quad Q_3$$

$$Q_1 = \frac{45 + 90}{2} = 67.5 \qquad MD = \frac{180 + 220}{2} = 200$$

$$Q_3 = \frac{240 + 310}{2} = 275$$

For cheese substitute

$$130 \quad 180 \quad 250 \quad 260 \quad 270 \quad 290 \quad 310 \quad 340$$
$$\uparrow \qquad\qquad \uparrow \qquad\qquad \uparrow$$
$$Q_1 \qquad\quad MD \qquad\quad Q_3$$

$$Q_1 = \frac{180 + 250}{2} = 215 \qquad MD = \frac{260 + 270}{2} = 265$$

$$Q_3 = \frac{290 + 310}{2} = 300$$

FIGURE 3–8   Boxplots for Example 3–38

Real cheese

Cheese substitute

Step 2   Draw the horizontal axis and the scale.

Step 3   Draw the boxplots. See Figure 3–8. Compare the plots. It is quite apparent that the distribution for the cheese substitute data has a higher median than the median for the distribution for the real cheese data. The variation or spread for the distribution of the real cheese data is larger than the variation for the distribution of the cheese substitute data.

A *modified boxplot* can be drawn and used to check for outliers. See Exercise 19 in Extending the Concepts in this section.

In exploratory data analysis, *hinges* are used instead of quartiles to construct boxplots. When the data set consists of an even number of values, hinges are the same as quartiles. Hinges for a data set with an odd number of values differ somewhat from quartiles. However, since most calculators and computer programs use quartiles, they will be used in this textbook.

Table 3–5 shows the correspondence between the traditional and the exploratory data analysis approach.

TABLE 3–5   Traditional versus EDA Techniques

Traditional	Exploratory data analysis
Frequency distribution	Stem and leaf plot
Histogram	Boxplot
Mean	Median
Standard deviation	Interquartile range

Applying the Concepts 3–4

The Noisy Workplace

Assume you work for OSHA (Occupational Safety and Health Administration) and have complaints about noise levels from some of the workers at a state power plant. You charge the power plant with taking decibel readings at six different areas of the plant at different times of the day and week. The results of the data collection are listed. Use boxplots to initially explore the data and make recommendations about which plant areas workers must be provided with protective ear wear. The safe hearing level is approximately 120 decibels.

Area 1	Area 2	Area 3	Area 4	Area 5	Area 6
30	64	100	25	59	67
12	99	59	15	63	80
35	87	78	30	81	99
65	59	97	20	110	49
24	23	84	61	65	67
59	16	64	56	112	56
68	94	53	34	132	80
57	78	59	22	145	125
100	57	89	24	163	100
61	32	88	21	120	93
32	52	94	32	84	56
45	78	66	52	99	45
92	59	57	14	105	80
56	55	62	10	68	34
44	55	64	33	75	21

See page 184 for the answers.

⬢ Exercises 3–4

For Exercises 1–6, identify the five-number summary and find the interquartile range.

1. 8, 12, 32, 6, 27, 19, 54

2. 19, 16, 48, 22, 7

3. 362, 589, 437, 316, 192, 188

4. 147, 243, 156, 632, 543, 303

5. 14.6, 19.8, 16.3, 15.5, 18.2

6. 9.7, 4.6, 2.2, 3.7, 6.2, 9.4, 3.8

For Exercises 7–10, use each boxplot to identify the maximum value, minimum value, median, first quartile, third quartile, and interquartile range.

7.

8.

9.

10.

11. Earned Run Average Construct a boxplot for the following data and comment on the shape of the distribution representing the number of games pitched by major league baseball's earned run average (ERA) leaders for the past few years.

30   34   29   30   34   29   31   33   34   27   30   27   34   32

Source: *World Almanac.*

12. Innings Pitched Construct a boxplot for the following data which represent the number of innings pitched by the ERA leaders for the past few years. Comment on the shape of the distribution.

192 228 186 199 238 217 213 234 264 187
214 115 238 246

Source: *World Almanac.*

13. Teacher Strikes The number of teacher strikes over a 13-year period in Pennsylvania is shown. Construct a boxplot for the data. Is the distribution symmetric?

20	18	7	13
7	14	5	9
9	9	10	17
15			

Source: Pennsylvania School Boards Association.

14. Visitors Who Travel to Foreign Countries Construct a boxplot for the number (in millions) of visitors who traveled to a foreign country each year for a random selection of years. Comment on the skewness of the distribution.

4.3	0.5	0.6	0.8	0.5
0.4	3.8	1.3	0.4	0.3

15. Protein Contest of Energy Bars The numbers of grams of protein in a random selection of granola and protein bars are listed below. Construct a boxplot for the data.

14	15	11	4	26	10	24
15	12	15	27	8	10	10

Compare your results to a boxplot for the amount of protein found in single servings of various high-protein drinks, as shown below.

18	42	40	40	15	10	15
15	20	21	42	20	34	

16. Size of Dams These data represent the volumes in cubic yards of the largest dams in the United States and in South America. Construct a boxplot of the data for each region and compare the distributions.

United States	South America
125,628	311,539
92,000	274,026
78,008	105,944
77,700	102,014
66,500	56,242
62,850	46,563
52,435	
50,000	

Source: *New York Times Almanac.*

17. Graduation Rates The graduation rates of several large state schools are shown below. Identify the five-number summary and the interquartile range, and draw a boxplot.

59.0 64.0 48.0 40.4 69.0 40.0 70.0 60.0
77.0 60.0 77.0 78.0 59.0 85.0

18. Number of Tornadoes A four-month record for the number of tornadoes in 2003–2005 is given here.

	2005	2004	2003
April	132	125	157
May	123	509	543
June	316	268	292
July	138	124	167

a. Which month had the highest mean number of tornadoes for this 3-year period?

b. Which year has the highest mean number of tornadoes for this 4-month period?

c. Construct three boxplots and compare the distributions.

Source: NWS, Storm Prediction Center.

Extending the Concepts

19. Unhealthy Smog Days A *modified boxplot* can be drawn by placing a box around Q_1 and Q_3 and then extending the whiskers to the highest and/or lowest values within 1.5 times the interquartile range (that is, $Q_3 - Q_1$). *Mild outliers* are values greater than $Q_3 + 1.5(\text{IQR})$ or less than $Q_1 - 1.5(\text{IQR})$. Extreme outliers are values greater than $Q_3 + 3(\text{IQR})$ or less than $Q_1 - 3(\text{IQR})$.

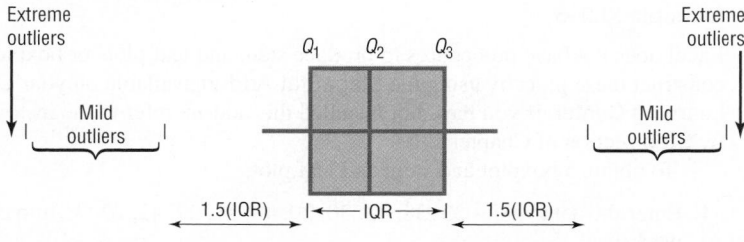

For the data shown here, draw a modified boxplot and identify any mild or extreme outliers. The data represent the number of unhealthy smog days for a specific year for the highest 10 locations.

97	39	43	66	91
43	54	42	53	39

Source: U.S. Public Interest Research Group and Clean Air Network.

≡ Technology | Step by Step

TI-84 Plus
Step by Step

Constructing a Boxplot

To draw a boxplot:

1. Enter data into L_1.
2. Change values in WINDOW menu, if necessary. (*Note:* Make X_{min} somewhat smaller than the smallest data value and X_{max} somewhat larger than the largest data value.) Change Y_{min} to 0 and Y_{max} to 1.
3. Press **[2nd] [STAT PLOT]**, then **1** for Plot **1**.
4. Press **ENTER** to turn on Plot 1.
5. Move cursor to Boxplot symbol (fifth graph) on the Type: line, then press ENTER.
6. Make sure Xlist is L_1.
7. Make sure Freq is 1.
8. Press **GRAPH** to display the boxplot.
9. Press **TRACE** followed by ← or → to obtain the values from the five-number summary on the boxplot.

To display two boxplots on the same screen, follow the above steps and use the 2: Plot 2 and L_2 symbols.

Example TI3–3

Construct a boxplot for the data values:

$$33, 38, 43, 30, 29, 40, 51, 27, 42, 23, 31$$

Input	Input	Output

Using the **TRACE** key along with the ← and → keys, we obtain the five-number summary. The minimum value is 23; Q_1 is 29; the median is 33; Q_3 is 42; the maximum value is 51.

EXCEL
Step by Step

Constructing a Stem and Leaf Plot and a Boxplot
Example XL3–6

Excel does not have procedures to produce stem and leaf plots or boxplots. However, you may construct these plots by using the **MegaStat Add-in** available on your CD or from the Online Learning Center. If you have not installed this add-in, refer to the instructions in the Excel Step by Step section of Chapter 1.

   To obtain a boxplot and stem and leaf plot:

1. Enter the data values 33, 38, 43, 30, 29, 40, 51, 27, 42, 23, 31 into column A of a new Excel worksheet.
2. Select the Add-Ins tab, then MegaStat from the toolbar.
3. Select Descriptive Statistics from the MegaStat menu.
4. Enter the cell range A1:A11 in the Input range.

5. Check both Boxplot and Stem and Leaf Plot. *Note:* You may leave the other output options unchecked for this example. Click [OK].

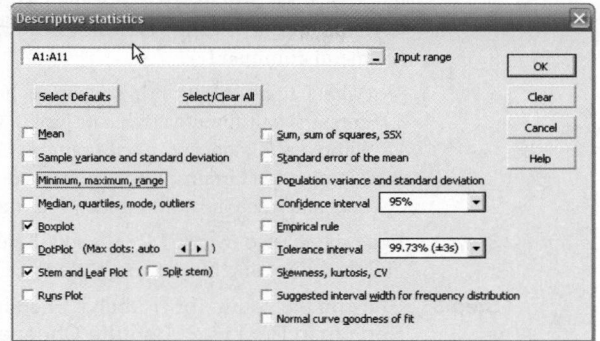

The stem and leaf plot and the boxplot are shown below.

MINITAB
Step by Step

Construct a Boxplot

1. Type in the data 89, 47,164, 296, 30, 215, 138, 78, 48, 39. Label the column **Meteorites**.
2. Select **Stat>EDA>Boxplot**.

Note: Choose simple Y if all data is in one column.

3. Double-click **Meteorites** to select it for the graph variable.
4. Click on [Labels].
   a) In the Title 1: of the Title/Footnotes folder, type **Number of Meteorites**.
   b) Press the [Tab] key and type **Your Name** in the text box for Subtitle 1:.
5. Click [OK] twice. The graph will be displayed in a graph window.

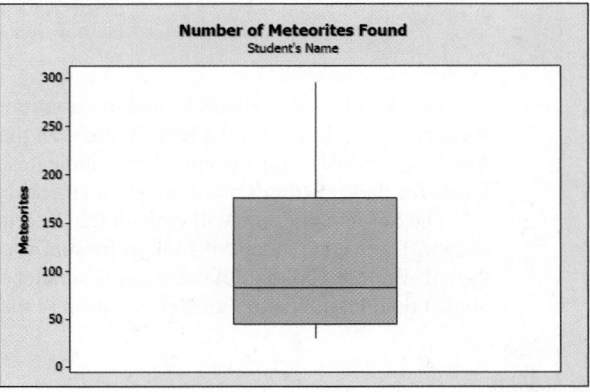

Compare Two Distributions Using Boxplots

A sample of real cheese and another sample of a cheese substitute are tested for their sodium levels in milligrams. The data are used in Section 3–4, Example 3–38 of the text.

Step 1 Type the data into C1 and C2 of a Minitab work-sheet as shown.

a. Select **Stat>EDA>Boxplot** then **Multiple Y's** and **Simple**. **Graph>Boxplot** is an alternative menu command.

Note: Choose Multiple Y's when each column contains a different variable or group. Choose Simple if all data are in one column. Choose Simple with Groups if one column contains all the data and a second column identifies the group.

Step 2 Drag the mouse over C1 Real and C2 Substitute, and then click the button for [**Select**].

Step 3 Click on the button for [**Labels**]. Then in the Title dialog box type **Comparison of Sodium in Real vs Substitute Cheese** and next click [**OK**].

Step 4 Click the button for [**Scale**].

a. Click the tab for **Gridlines** as shown.

b. Check the box for **Y major ticks**.

Step 5 Click [**OK**] twice. Hover the mouse over the box to see the details. The quartiles may not be the same as those calculated in the text. The method varies by technology. The values will be similar.

	C1	C2
	Real	Substitute
2	420	180
3	45	250
4	40	290
5	220	130
6	240	260
7	180	340
8	90	310
9		

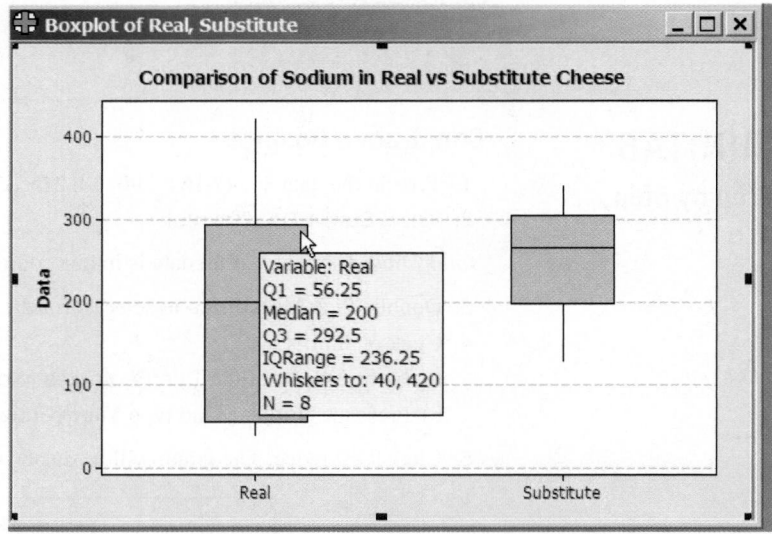

The boxplots show there is greater variation in the sodium levels for the real cheese. The median level is lower for the real cheese than the median for the sodium in the cheese substitute. The longer whisker for the real cheese indicates the distribution is skewed right. The sodium levels for the substitutes are more symmetrical and not as spread out.

The Session window will contain the descriptive statistics for sodium for each cheese type as shown. The mean amount of sodium for real cheese is 193.1 milligrams compared to 253.8 for the substitute. Even though the mean is smaller for the real group, the standard deviation is almost double, indicating greater variation in the sodium levels for the real cheese.

Descriptive Statistics: Sodium

Variable	Group	N	N*	Mean	SE Mean	StDev	Minimum	Q1	Median	Q3	Maximum
Sodium	RealCheese	8	0	193.1	47.1	133.2	40.0	56.3	200.0	292.5	420.0
	Substitute	8	0	253.8	24.3	68.6	130.0	197.5	265.0	305.0	340.0

Summary

- This chapter explains the basic ways to summarize data. These include measures of central tendency. They are the mean, median, mode, and midrange. The weighted mean can also be used. (3–1)

- To summarize the variation of data, statisticians use measures of variation or dispersion. The three most common measures of variation are the range, variance, and standard deviation. The coefficient of variation can be used to compare the variation of two data sets. The data values are distributed according to Chebyshev's theorem or the empirical rule. (3–2)

- There are several measures of the position of data values in the set. There are standard scores or z scores, percentiles, quartiles, and deciles. Sometimes a data set contains an extremely high or extremely low data value, called an outlier. (3–3)

- Other methods can be used to describe a data set. These methods are the five-number summary and boxplots. These methods are called exploratory data analysis. (3–4)

The techniques explained in Chapter 2 and this chapter are the basic techniques used in descriptive statistics.

Important Terms

bimodal 116

boxplot 168

Chebyshev's theorem 140

coefficient of variation 138

data array 115

decile 157

empirical rule 142

exploratory data analysis (EDA) 168

five-number summary 168

interquartile range (IQR) 156

mean 112

median 115

midrange 118

modal class 117

mode 116

multimodal 116

negatively skewed or left-skewed distribution 122

nonresistant statistic 157

outlier 157

parameter 111

percentile 149

positively skewed or right-skewed distribution 121

quartile 155

range 129

range rule of thumb 139

resistant statistic 157

standard deviation 134

statistic 111

symmetric distribution 122

unimodal 116

variance 134

weighted mean 120

z score or standard score 148

Important Formulas

Formula for the mean for individual data:

Sample	Population

$$\overline{X} = \frac{\Sigma X}{n} \qquad \mu = \frac{\Sigma X}{N}$$

Formula for the mean for grouped data:

$$\overline{X} = \frac{\Sigma f \cdot X_m}{n}$$

Formula for the weighted mean:

$$\overline{X} = \frac{\Sigma wX}{\Sigma w}$$

Formula for the midrange:

$$MR = \frac{\text{lowest value + highest value}}{2}$$

Formula for the range:

$$R = \text{highest value} - \text{lowest value}$$

Formula for the variance for population data:

$$\sigma^2 = \frac{\Sigma(X - \mu)^2}{N}$$

Formula for the variance for sample data (shortcut formula for the unbiased estimator):

$$s^2 = \frac{n(\Sigma X^2) - (\Sigma X)^2}{n(n-1)}$$

Formula for the variance for grouped data:

$$s^2 = \frac{n(\Sigma f \cdot X_m^2) - (\Sigma f \cdot X_m)^2}{n(n-1)}$$

Formula for the standard deviation for population data:

$$\sigma = \sqrt{\frac{\Sigma(X - \mu)^2}{N}}$$

Formula for the standard deviation for sample data (shortcut formula):

$$s = \sqrt{\frac{n(\Sigma X^2) - (\Sigma X)^2}{n(n-1)}}$$

Formula for the standard deviation for grouped data:

$$s = \sqrt{\frac{n(\Sigma f \cdot X_m^2) - (\Sigma f \cdot X_m)^2}{n(n-1)}}$$

Formula for the coefficient of variation:

$$\text{CVar} = \frac{s}{\overline{X}} \cdot 100 \quad \text{or} \quad \text{CVar} = \frac{\sigma}{\mu} \cdot 100$$

Range rule of thumb:

$$s \approx \frac{\text{range}}{4}$$

Expression for Chebyshev's theorem: The proportion of values from a data set that will fall within k standard deviations of the mean will be at least

$$1 - \frac{1}{k^2}$$

where k is a number greater than 1.

Formula for the z score (standard score):

Sample		Population

$$z = \frac{X - \overline{X}}{s} \quad \text{or} \quad z = \frac{X - \mu}{\sigma}$$

Formula for the cumulative percentage:

$$\text{Cumulative \%} = \frac{\text{cumulative frequency}}{n} \cdot 100$$

Formula for the percentile rank of a value X:

$$\text{Percentile} = \frac{\text{number of values below } X + 0.5}{\text{total number of values}} \cdot 100$$

Formula for finding a value corresponding to a given percentile:

$$c = \frac{n \cdot p}{100}$$

Formula for interquartile range:

$$\text{IQR} = Q_3 - Q_1$$

≣ Review Exercises

Section 3–1

1. **Net Worth of Wealthy People** The net worth (in billions of dollars) of a sample of the richest people in the United States is shown. Find the mean, median, mode, and midrange for the data.

59	52	28	26	19
19	18	17	17	17

    Source: *Forbes* magazine.

2. **Shark Attacks** The number of shark attacks and deaths over a recent 5-year period is shown. Find the mean, median, mode, and midrange for the data.

Attacks	71	64	61	65	57
Deaths	1	4	4	7	4

3. **Battery Lives** Twelve batteries were tested to see how many hours they would last. The frequency distribution is shown here.

Hours	Frequency
1–3	1
4–6	4
7–9	5
10–12	1
13–15	1

    Find the mean and modal class.

4. **SAT Scores** The mean SAT math scores for selected states are represented. Find the mean class and modal class.

Score	Frequency
478–504	4
505–531	6
532–558	2
559–585	2
586–612	2

    Source: *World Almanac.*

5. **Households of Four Television Networks** A survey showed the number of viewers and number of households of four television networks. Find the average number of viewers, using the weighted mean.

Households	1.4	0.8	0.3	1.6
Viewers (in millions)	1.6	0.8	0.4	1.8

    Source: Nielsen Media Research.

6. **Investment Earnings** An investor calculated these percentages of each of three stock investments with payoffs as shown. Find the average payoff. Use the weighted mean.

Stock	Percent	Payoff
A	30	$10,000
B	50	3,000
C	20	1,000

Section 3–2

7. Tornado Occurrences The data show the number of tornados recorded for each month of a specific year. Find the range, variance, and standard deviation for the data.

33   10   62   132   123   316   123   133   18   150
26   138

Source: Storm Prediction Center.

8. Tallest Buildings The number of stories in the 13 tallest buildings in Houston are shown. Find the range, variance, and standard deviation for the data.

75   71   64   56   53   55   47   55   52   50   50
50   47

Source: *World Almanac.*

9. Rise in Tides Shown here is a frequency distribution for the rise in tides at 30 selected locations in the United States. Find the variance and standard deviation for the data.

Rise in tides (inches)	Frequency
12.5–27.5	6
27.5–42.5	3
42.5–57.5	5
57.5–72.5	8
72.5–87.5	6
87.5–102.5	2

10. Fuel Capacity The fuel capacity in gallons for randomly selected cars is shown here. Find the variance and standard deviation for the data.

Class	Frequency
10–12	6
13–15	4
16–18	14
19–21	15
22–24	8
25–27	2
28–30	1
	50

11. If the range of a data set is 24, find the approximate value of the standard deviation, using the range rule of thumb.

12. If the range of a data set is 56, find the approximate value of the standard deviation, using the range rule of thumb.

13. Textbooks in Professors' Offices If the average number of textbooks in professors' offices is 16, the standard deviation is 5, and the average age of the professors is 43, with a standard deviation of 8, which data set is more variable?

14. Magazines in Bookstores A survey of bookstores showed that the average number of magazines carried is 56, with a standard deviation of 12. The same survey showed that the average length of time each store had been in business was 6 years, with a standard deviation

of 2.5 years. Which is more variable, the number of magazines or the number of years?

15. Cost of Car Rentals A survey of car rental agencies shows that the average cost of a car rental is $0.32 per mile. The standard deviation is $0.03. Using Chebyshev's theorem, find the range in which at least 75% of the data values will fall.

16. Average Earnings of Workers The average earnings of year-round full-time workers 25–34 years old with a bachelor's degree or higher were $58,500 in 2003. If the standard deviation is $11,200, what can you say about the percentage of these workers who earn.

   a. Between $47,300 and $69,700?
   b. More than $80,900?
   c. How likely is it that someone earns more than $100,000?

Source: *New York Times Almanac.*

17. Labor Charges The average labor charge for automobile mechanics is $54 per hour. The standard deviation is $4. Find the minimum percentage of data values that will fall within the range of $48 to $60. Use Chebyshev's theorem.

18. Costs to Train Employees For a certain type of job, it costs a company an average of $231 to train an employee to perform the task. The standard deviation is $5. Find the minimum percentage of data values that will fall in the range of $219 to $243. Use Chebyshev's theorem.

19. Commuter Times The mean of the times it takes a commuter to get to work in Baltimore is 29.7 minutes. If the standard deviation is 6 minutes, within what limits would you expect approximately 68% of the times to fall? Assume the distribution is approximately bell-shaped.

20. Exam Completion Time The mean time it takes a group of students to complete a statistics final exam is 44 minutes, and the standard deviation is 9 minutes. Within what limits would you expect approximately 95% of the students to complete the exam? Assume the variable is approximately normally distributed.

21. High Temperatures The reported high temperatures of 23 cities of the United States in October are shown. Find the z values for

   a. A temperature of 80°
   b. A temperature of 56°

62   72   66   79   83   61   62   85   72   64   74   71
42   38   91   66   77   90   74   63   64   68   42

Section 3–3

22. Exam Grades Which of these exam grades has a better relative position?
   a. A grade of 82 on a test with $\overline{X} = 85$ and $s = 6$
   b. A grade of 56 on a test with $\overline{X} = 60$ and $s = 5$

23. **NFL Salaries** The salaries (in millions of dollars) for 29 NFL teams for the 1999–2000 season are given in this frequency distribution.

Class limits	Frequency
39.9–42.8	2
42.9–45.8	2
45.9–48.8	5
48.9–51.8	5
51.9–54.8	12
54.9–57.8	3

Source: www.NFL.com

a. Construct a percentile graph.
b. Find the values that correspond to the 35th, 65th, and 85th percentiles.
c. Find the percentile of values 44, 48, and 54.

24. **Printer Repairs** The frequency distribution shows the number of days it took to fix each of 80 computer's printers.

Class limits	Frequency
1–3	7
4–6	9
7–9	32
10–12	20
13–15	12
	80

a. Construct a percentile graph.
b. Find the 20th, 50th, and 70th percentiles.
c. Find the percentile values of 5, 10, and 14.

25. Check each data set for outliers.

a. 506, 511, 517, 514, 400, 521
b. 3, 7, 9, 6, 8, 10, 14, 16, 20, 12

26. Check each data set for outliers.

a. 14, 18, 27, 26, 19, 13, 5, 25
b. 112, 157, 192, 116, 153, 129, 131

Section 3–4

27. **Top Movie Sites** The number of sites at which the top nine movies (based on the daily gross earnings) opened in a particular week is indicated below.

3017	3687	2525
2516	2820	2579
3211	3044	2330

Construct a boxplot for the data.

28. **Hours Worked** The data shown here represent the number of hours that 12 part-time employees at a toy store worked during the weeks before and after Christmas. Construct two boxplots and compare the distributions.

Before	38	16	18	24	12	30	35	32	31	30	24	35
After	26	15	12	18	24	32	14	18	16	18	22	12

≣ STATISTICS TODAY

How Long Are You Delayed by Road Congestion? —Revisited

The average number of hours per year that a driver is delayed by road congestion is listed here.

Los Angeles	56
Atlanta	53
Seattle	53
Houston	50
Dallas	46
Washington	46
Austin	45
Denver	45
St. Louis	44
Orlando	42
U.S. average	36

Source: Texas Transportation Institute.

By making comparisons using averages, you can see that drivers in these 10 cities are delayed by road congestion more than the national average.

Data Analysis

A Data Bank is found in Appendix B, or on the World Wide Web by following links from www.mhhe.com/math/stat/bluman/

1. From the Data Bank, choose one of the following variables: age, weight, cholesterol level, systolic pressure, IQ, or sodium level. Select at least 30 values, and find the mean, median, mode, and midrange. State which measurement of central tendency best describes the average and why.

2. Find the range, variance, and standard deviation for the data selected in Exercise 1.

3. From the Data Bank, choose 10 values from any variable, construct a boxplot, and interpret the results.

4. Randomly select 10 values from the number of suspensions in the local school districts in southwestern Pennsylvania in Data Set V in Appendix B. Find the mean, median, mode, range, variance, and standard deviation of the number of suspensions by using the Pearson coefficient of skewness.

5. Using the data from Data Set VII in Appendix B, find the mean, median, mode, range, variance, and standard deviation of the acreage owned by the municipalities. Comment on the skewness of the data, using the Pearson coefficient of skewness.

Chapter Quiz

Determine whether each statement is true or false. If the statement is false, explain why.

1. When the mean is computed for individual data, all values in the data set are used.

2. The mean cannot be found for grouped data when there is an open class.

3. A single, extremely large value can affect the median more than the mean.

4. One-half of all the data values will fall above the mode, and one-half will fall below the mode.

5. In a data set, the mode will always be unique.

6. The range and midrange are both measures of variation.

7. One disadvantage of the median is that it is not unique.

8. The mode and midrange are both measures of variation.

9. If a person's score on an exam corresponds to the 75th percentile, then that person obtained 75 correct answers out of 100 questions.

Select the best answer.

10. What is the value of the mode when all values in the data set are different?

    a. 0
    b. 1
    c. There is no mode.
    d. It cannot be determined unless the data values are given.

11. When data are categorized as, for example, places of residence (rural, suburban, urban), the most appropriate measure of central tendency is the

    a. Mean
    b. Median
    c. Mode
    d. Midrange

12. P_{50} corresponds to

    a. Q_2
    b. D_5
    c. IQR
    d. Midrange

13. Which is not part of the five-number summary?

    a. Q_1 and Q_3
    b. The mean
    c. The median
    d. The smallest and the largest data values

14. A statistic that tells the number of standard deviations a data value is above or below the mean is called

    a. A quartile
    b. A percentile
    c. A coefficient of variation
    d. A z score

15. When a distribution is bell-shaped, approximately what percentage of data values will fall within 1 standard deviation of the mean?

    a. 50%
    b. 68%
    c. 95%
    d. 99.7%

Complete these statements with the best answer.

16. A measure obtained from sample data is called a(n) _____.

17. Generally, Greek letters are used to represent _____, and Roman letters are used to represent _____.

18. The positive square root of the variance is called the _____.

19. The symbol for the population standard deviation is _____.

20. When the sum of the lowest data value and the highest data value is divided by 2, the measure is called the _____.

21. If the mode is to the left of the median and the mean is to the right of the median, then the distribution is _____ skewed.

22. An extremely high or extremely low data value is called a(n) _____.

23. Miles per Gallon The number of highway miles per gallon of the 10 worst vehicles is shown.

12   15   13   14   15   16   17   16   17   18

Source: *Pittsburgh Post Gazette.*

Find each of these.

a. Mean   *e.* Range
b. Median   *f.* Variance
c. Mode   *g.* Standard deviation
d. Midrange

24. Errors on a Typing Test The distribution of the number of errors that 10 students made on a typing test is shown.

Errors	Frequency
0–2	1
3–5	3
6–8	4
9–11	1
12–14	1

Find each of these.

a. Mean   *c.* Variance
b. Modal class   *d.* Standard deviation

25. Employee Years of Service In an advertisement, a retail store stated that its employees averaged 9 years of service. The distribution is shown here.

Number of employees	Years of service
8	2
2	6
3	10

Using the weighted mean, calculate the correct average.

26. Newspapers for Sale The average number of newspapers for sale in an airport newsstand is 56 with a standard deviation of 6. The average number of newspapers for sale in a convenience store is 44 with a standard deviation of 5. Which data set is more variable?

27. Delivery Charges The average delivery charge for a refrigerator is $32. The standard deviation is $4. Find the minimum percentage of data values that will fall in the range of $20 to $44. Use Chebyshev's theorem.

28. SAT Scores The average national SAT score is 1019. If we assume a bell-shaped distribution and a standard deviation equal to 110, what percentage of scores will you expect to fall above 1129? Above 799?

Source: *New York Times Almanac.*

29. If the range of a data set is 18, estimate the standard deviation of the data.

30. Test Scores A student scored 76 on a general science test where the class mean and standard deviation were 82 and 8, respectively; he also scored 53 on a psychology test where the class mean and standard deviation were 58 and 3, respectively. In which class was his relative position higher?

31. Exam Scores On a philosophy comprehensive exam, this distribution was obtained from 25 students.

Score	Frequency
40.5–45.5	3
45.5–50.5	8
50.5–55.5	10
55.5–60.5	3
60.5–65.5	1

a. Construct a percentile graph.
b. Find the values that correspond to the 22nd, 78th, and 99th percentiles.
c. Find the percentiles of the values 52, 43, and 64.

32. Gas Prices for Rental Cars The first column of these data represents the prebuy gas price of a rental car, and the second column represents the price charged if the car is returned without refilling the gas tank for a selected car rental company. Draw two boxplots for the data and compare the distributions. (*Note:* The data were collected several years ago.)

Prebuy cost	No prebuy cost
$1.55	$3.80
1.54	3.99
1.62	3.99
1.65	3.85
1.72	3.99
1.63	3.95
1.65	3.94
1.72	4.19
1.45	3.84
1.52	3.94

Source: *USA TODAY.*

Critical Thinking Challenges

1. Average Cost of Weddings Averages give us information to help us see where we stand and enable us to make comparisons. Here is a study on the average cost of a wedding. What type of average—mean, median, mode, or midrange—might have been used for each category?

Wedding Costs

The average cost of a wedding varies each year. For example, in 2009 the average cost was $19,580, in 2010 it was $24,070, and in 2011 it was $20,548.

The average cost of the reception location was $2435. The average cost of catering was $3645. The average cost for a wedding dress was $823 and for a man's suit $284. The cost for wedding flowers was $1500. The average cost for a bride's ring was $784 and for a groom's ring $572.

Overall, most costs went down from the 2010 numbers in tipping and wedding cakes.

2. **Average Cost of Smoking** This article states that the average yearly cost of smoking a pack of cigarettes a day is $1190. Find the average cost of a pack of cigarettes in your area, and compute the cost per day for 1 year. Compare your answer with the one in the article.

Burning Through the Cash

Everyone knows the health-related reasons to quit smoking, so here's an economic argument: A pack a day adds up to $1190 a year on average; it's more in states that have higher taxes on tobacco. To calculate what you or a loved one spends, visit ashline.org/ASH/quit/contemplation/index.html and try out their smoker's calculator. You'll be stunned.

Source: Reprinted with permission from the April 2002 Reader's Digest. Copyright © by The Reader's Digest Assn., Inc.

3. **Ages of U.S. Residents** The table shows the median ages of residents for the 10 oldest states and the 10 youngest states of the United States including Washington, D.C. Explain why the median is used instead of the mean.

10 Oldest			10 Youngest		
Rank	State	Median age	Rank	State	Median age
1	West Virginia	38.9	51	Utah	27.1
2	Florida	38.7	50	Texas	32.3
3	Maine	38.6	49	Alaska	32.4
4	Pennsylvania	38.0	48	Idaho	33.2
5	Vermont	37.7	47	California	33.3
6	Montana	37.5	46	Georgia	33.4
7	Connecticut	37.4	45	Mississippi	33.8
8	New Hampshire	37.1	44	Louisiana	34.0
9	New Jersey	36.7	43	Arizona	34.2
10	Rhode Island	36.7	42	Colorado	34.3

Source: U.S. Census Bureau.

Data Projects

Where appropriate, use MINITAB, the TI-84 Plus, Excel, or a computer program of your choice to complete the following exercises.

1. **Business and Finance** Use the data collected in data project 1 of Chapter 2 regarding earnings per share. Determine the mean, mode, median, and midrange for the two data sets. Is one measure of center more appropriate than the other for these data? Do the measures of center appear similar? What does this say about the symmetry of the distribution?

2. **Sports and Leisure** Use the data collected in data project 2 of Chapter 2 regarding home runs. Determine the mean, mode, median, and midrange for the two data sets. Is one measure of center more appropriate than the other for these data? Do the measures of center appear similar? What does this say about the symmetry of the distribution?

3. **Technology** Use the data collected in data project 3 of Chapter 2. Determine the mean for the frequency table created in that project. Find the actual mean length of all

50 songs. How does the grouped mean compare to the actual mean?

4. **Health and Wellness** Use the data collected in data project 6 of Chapter 2 regarding heart rates. Determine the mean and standard deviation for each set of data. Do the means seem very different from one another? Do the standard deviations appear very different from one another?

5. **Politics and Economics** Use the data collected in data project 5 of Chapter 2 regarding delegates. Use the formulas for population mean and standard deviation to

compute the parameters for all 50 states. What is the z score associated with California? Delaware? Ohio? Which states are more than 2 standard deviations from the mean?

6. **Your Class** Use your class as a sample. Determine the mean, median, and standard deviation for the age of students in your class. What z score would a 40-year-old have? Would it be unusual to have an age of 40? Determine the skew of the data, using the Pearson coefficient of skewness. (See Exercise 48 in Exercise 3–2.)

Answers to Applying the Concepts

Section 3–1   Teacher Salaries

1. The sample mean is \$22,921.67, the sample median is \$16,500, and the sample mode is \$11,000. If you work for the school board and do not want to raise salaries, you could say that the average teacher salary is \$22,921.67.

2. If you work for the teachers' union and want a raise for the teachers, either the sample median of \$16,500 or the sample mode of \$11,000 would be a good measure of center to report.

3. The outlier is \$107,000. With the outlier removed, the sample mean is \$15,278.18, the sample median is \$16,400, and the sample mode is still \$11,000. The mean is greatly affected by the outlier and allows the school board to report an average teacher salary that is not representative of a "typical" teacher salary.

4. If the salaries represented every teacher in the school district, the averages would be parameters, since we have data from the entire population.

5. The mean can be misleading in the presence of outliers, since it is greatly affected by these extreme values.

6. Since the mean is greater than both the median and the mode, the distribution is skewed to the right (positively skewed).

Section 3–2   Blood Pressure

1. Chebyshev's theorem does not work for scores within 1 standard deviation of the mean.

2. At least 75% (900) of the normotensive men will fall in the interval 105–141 mm Hg.

3. About 95% (1330) of the normotensive women have diastolic blood pressures between 62 and 90 mm Hg. About 95% (1235) of the hypertensive women have diastolic blood pressures between 68 and 108 mm Hg.

4. About 95% (1140) of the normotensive men have systolic blood pressures between 105 and 141 mm Hg. About 95% (1045) of the hypertensive men have systolic blood pressures between 119 and 187 mm Hg. These two ranges do overlap.

Section 3–3   Determining Dosages

1. The quartiles could be used to describe the data results.

2. Since there are 10 mice in the upper quartile, this would mean that 4 of them survived.

3. The percentiles would give us the position of a single mouse with respect to all other mice.

4. The quartiles divide the data into four groups of equal size.

5. Standard scores would give us the position of a single mouse with respect to the mean time until the onset of sepsis.

Section 3–4   The Noisy Workplace

Boxplot of Noise Level Versus Area

From this boxplot, we see that about 25% of the readings in area 5 are above the safe hearing level of 120 decibels. Those workers in area 5 should definitely have protective ear wear. One of the readings in area 6 is above the safe hearing level. It might be a good idea to provide protective ear wear to those workers in area 6 as well. Areas 1–4 appear to be "safe" with respect to hearing level, with area 4 being the safest.

Probability and Counting Rules

STATISTICS TODAY

Would You Bet Your Life?

Humans not only bet money when they gamble, but also bet their lives by engaging in unhealthy activities such as smoking, drinking, using drugs, and exceeding the speed limit when driving. Many people don't care about the risks involved in these activities since they do not understand the concepts of probability. On the other hand, people may fear activities that involve little risk to health or life because these activities have been sensationalized by the press and media.

In his book *Probabilities in Everyday Life* (Ivy Books, p. 191), John D. McGervey states

> When people have been asked to estimate the frequency of death from various causes, the most overestimated categories are those involving pregnancy, tornadoes, floods, fire, and homicide. The most underestimated categories include deaths from diseases such as diabetes, strokes, tuberculosis, asthma, and stomach cancer (although cancer in general is overestimated).

The question then is, Would you feel safer if you flew across the United States on a commercial airline or if you drove? How much greater is the risk of one way to travel over the other? See Statistics Today—Revisited at the end of the chapter for the answer.

In this chapter, you will learn about probability—its meaning, how it is computed, and how to evaluate it in terms of the likelihood of an event actually happening.

OUTLINE

Introduction
4–1 Sample Spaces and Probability
4–2 The Addition Rules for Probability
4–3 The Multiplication Rules and Conditional Probability
4–4 Counting Rules
4–5 Probability and Counting Rules
Summary

OBJECTIVES

After completing this chapter, you should be able to

1 Determine sample spaces and find the probability of an event, using classical probability or empirical probability.

2 Find the probability of compound events, using the addition rules.

3 Find the probability of compound events, using the multiplication rules.

4 Find the conditional probability of an event.

5 Find the total number of outcomes in a sequence of events, using the fundamental counting rule.

6 Find the number of ways that *r* objects can be selected from *n* objects, using the permutation rule.

7 Find the number of ways that *r* objects can be selected from *n* objects without regard to order, using the combination rule.

8 Find the probability of an event, using the counting rules.

Introduction

A cynical person once said, "The only two sure things are death and taxes." This philosophy no doubt arose because so much in people's lives is affected by chance. From the time you awake until you go to bed, you make decisions regarding the possible events that are governed at least in part by chance. For example, should you carry an umbrella to work today? Will your car battery last until spring? Should you accept that new job?

Probability as a general concept can be defined as the chance of an event occurring. Many people are familiar with probability from observing or playing games of chance, such as card games, slot machines, or lotteries. In addition to being used in games of chance, probability theory is used in the fields of insurance, investments, and weather forecasting and in various other areas. Finally, as stated in Chapter 1, probability is the basis of inferential statistics. For example, predictions are based on probability, and hypotheses are tested by using probability.

The basic concepts of probability are explained in this chapter. These concepts include *probability experiments, sample spaces,* the *addition* and *multiplication rules,* and the *probabilities of complementary events.* Also in this chapter, you will learn the rule for counting, the differences between permutations and combinations, and how to figure out how many different combinations for specific situations exist. Finally, Section 4–5 explains how the counting rules and the probability rules can be used together to solve a wide variety of problems.

4–1   Sample Spaces and Probability

The theory of probability grew out of the study of various games of chance using coins, dice, and cards. Since these devices lend themselves well to the application of concepts of probability, they will be used in this chapter as examples. This section begins by explaining some basic concepts of probability. Then the types of probability and probability rules are discussed.

Basic Concepts

Processes such as flipping a coin, rolling a die, or drawing a card from a deck are called *probability experiments.*

OBJECTIVE

Determine sample spaces and find the probability of an event, using classical probability or empirical probability.

> A **probability experiment** is a chance process that leads to well-defined results called outcomes.
>
> An **outcome** is the result of a single trial of a probability experiment.

A trial means flipping a coin once, rolling one die once, or the like. When a coin is tossed, there are two possible outcomes: head or tail. (*Note:* We exclude the possibility of a coin landing on its edge.) In the roll of a single die, there are six possible outcomes: 1, 2, 3, 4, 5, or 6. In any experiment, the set of all possible outcomes is called the *sample space.*

> A **sample space** is the set of all possible outcomes of a probability experiment.

Some sample spaces for various probability experiments are shown here.

Experiment	Sample space
Toss one coin	Head, tail
Roll a die	1, 2, 3, 4, 5, 6
Answer a true/false question	True, false
Toss two coins	Head-head, tail-tail, head-tail, tail-head

It is important to realize that when two coins are tossed, there are *four* possible outcomes, as shown in the fourth experiment above. Both coins could fall heads up. Both coins could fall tails up. Coin 1 could fall heads up and coin 2 tails up. Or coin 1 could fall tails up and coin 2 heads up. Heads and tails will be abbreviated as H and T throughout this chapter.

EXAMPLE 4–1 Rolling Dice

Find the sample space for rolling two dice.

SOLUTION

Since each die can land in six different ways, and two dice are rolled, the sample space can be presented by a rectangular array, as shown in Figure 4–1. The sample space is the list of pairs of numbers in the chart.

FIGURE 4–1

Sample Space for Rolling Two Dice (Example 4–1)

Die 1	Die 2					
	1	2	3	4	5	6
1	(1, 1)	(1, 2)	(1, 3)	(1, 4)	(1, 5)	(1, 6)
2	(2, 1)	(2, 2)	(2, 3)	(2, 4)	(2, 5)	(2, 6)
3	(3, 1)	(3, 2)	(3, 3)	(3, 4)	(3, 5)	(3, 6)
4	(4, 1)	(4, 2)	(4, 3)	(4, 4)	(4, 5)	(4, 6)
5	(5, 1)	(5, 2)	(5, 3)	(5, 4)	(5, 5)	(5, 6)
6	(6, 1)	(6, 2)	(6, 3)	(6, 4)	(6, 5)	(6, 6)

EXAMPLE 4–2 Drawing Cards

Find the sample space for drawing one card from an ordinary deck of cards.

SOLUTION

Since there are 4 suits (hearts, clubs, diamonds, and spades) and 13 cards for each suit (ace through king), there are 52 outcomes in the sample space. See Figure 4–2.

FIGURE 4–2 Sample Space for Drawing a Card (Example 4–2)

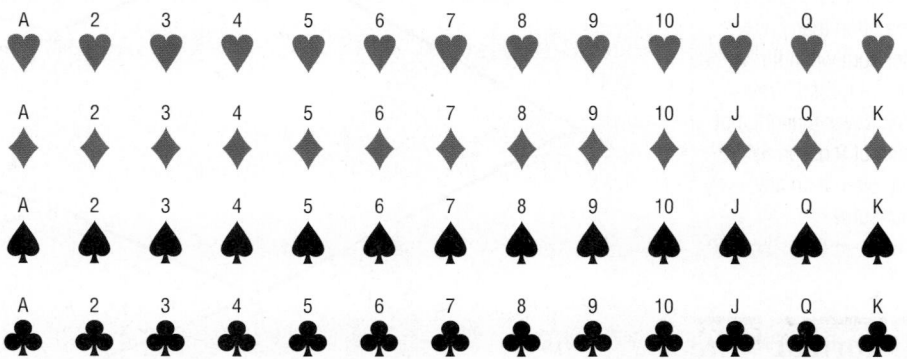

EXAMPLE 4–3 Gender of Children

Find the sample space for the gender of the children if a family has three children. Use B for boy and G for girl.

SOLUTION

There are two genders, boy and girl, and each child could be either gender. Hence, there are eight possibilities, as shown here.

BBB   BBG   BGB   GBB   GGG   GGB   GBG   BGG

In Examples 4–1 through 4–3, the sample spaces were found by observation and reasoning; however, another way to find all possible outcomes of a probability experiment is to use a *tree diagram.*

> A **tree diagram** is a device consisting of line segments emanating from a starting point and also from the outcome point. It is used to determine all possible outcomes of a probability experiment.

EXAMPLE 4–4   Gender of Children

Use a tree diagram to find the sample space for the gender of three children in a family, as in Example 4–3.

SOLUTION

Since there are two possibilities (boy or girl) for the first child, draw two branches from a starting point and label one B and the other G. Then if the first child is a boy, there are two possibilities for the second child (boy or girl), so draw two branches from B and label one B and the other G. Do the same if the first child is a girl. Follow the same procedure for the third child. The completed tree diagram is shown in Figure 4–3. To find the outcomes for the sample space, trace through all the possible branches, beginning at the starting point for each one.

FIGURE 4–3   Tree Diagram for Example 4–4

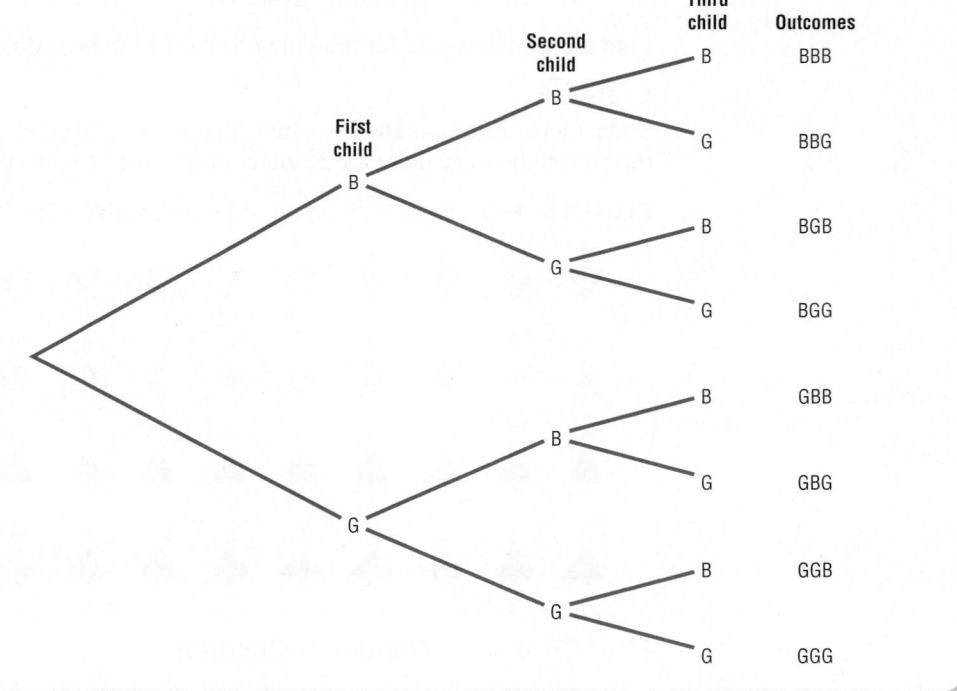

An outcome was defined previously as the result of a single trial of a probability experiment. In many problems, one must find the probability of two or more outcomes. For this reason, it is necessary to distinguish between an outcome and an event.

> An **event** consists of a set of outcomes of a probability experiment.

Historical Note

During the mid-1600s, a professional gambler named Chevalier de Méré made a considerable amount of money on a gambling game. He would bet unsuspecting patrons that in four rolls of a die, he could get at least one 6. He was so successful at the game that some people refused to play. He decided that a new game was necessary to continue his winnings. By reasoning, he figured he could roll at least one double 6 in 24 rolls of two dice, but his reasoning was incorrect and he lost systematically. Unable to figure out why, he contacted a mathematician named Blaise Pascal (1623–1662) to find out why.

Pascal became interested and began studying probability theory. He corresponded with a French government official, Pierre de Fermat (1601–1665), whose hobby was mathematics. Together the two formulated the beginnings of probability theory.

An event can be one outcome or more than one outcome. For example, if a die is rolled and a 6 shows, this result is called an *outcome,* since it is a result of a single trial. An event with one outcome is called a **simple event.** The event of getting an odd number when a die is rolled is called a **compound event,** since it consists of three outcomes or three simple events. In general, a compound event consists of two or more outcomes or simple events.

There are three basic interpretations of probability:

1. Classical probability

2. Empirical or relative frequency probability

3. Subjective probability

Classical Probability

Classical probability uses sample spaces to determine the numerical probability that an event will happen. You do not actually have to perform the experiment to determine that probability. Classical probability is so named because it was the first type of probability studied formally by mathematicians in the 17th and 18th centuries.

Classical probability assumes that all outcomes in the sample space are equally likely to occur. For example, when a single die is rolled, each outcome has the same probability of occurring. Since there are six outcomes, each outcome has a probability of $\frac{1}{6}$. When a card is selected from an ordinary deck of 52 cards, you assume that the deck has been shuffled, and each card has the same probability of being selected. In this case, it is $\frac{1}{52}$.

Equally likely events are events that have the same probability of occurring.

Formula for Classical Probability

The probability of any event E is

$$\frac{\text{Number of outcomes in } E}{\text{Total number of outcomes in the sample space}}$$

This probability is denoted by

$$P(E) = \frac{n(E)}{n(S)}$$

where $n(E)$ is the number of outcomes in E and $n(S)$ is the number of outcomes in the sample space S.

Probabilities can be expressed as fractions, decimals, or—where appropriate—percentages. If you ask, "What is the probability of getting a head when a coin is tossed?" typical responses can be any of the following three.

"One-half."

"Point five."

"Fifty percent."[1]

These answers are all equivalent. In most cases, the answers to examples and exercises given in this chapter are expressed as fractions or decimals, but percentages are used where appropriate.

[1]Strictly speaking, a percent is not a probability. However, in everyday language, probabilities are often expressed as percents (i.e., there is a 60% chance of rain tomorrow). For this reason, some probabilities will be expressed as percents throughout this book.

Rounding Rule for Probabilities   Probabilities should be expressed as reduced fractions or rounded to three decimal places. When the probability of an event is an extremely small decimal, it is permissible to round the decimal to the first nonzero digit after the point. For example, 0.0000587 would be 0.00006. When obtaining probabilities from one of the tables in Appendix A, use the number of decimal places given in the table. If decimals are converted to percentages to express probabilities, move the decimal point two places to the right and add a percent sign.

EXAMPLE 4–5   Drawing Cards

Find the probability of getting a red face card (jack, queen, or king) when randomly drawing a card from an ordinary deck.

SOLUTION

There are 52 cards in an ordinary deck of cards, and there are 6 red face cards (jack, queen, and king of hearts and jack, queen, and king of diamonds). Hence, the probability of getting a red face card is

$$\frac{6}{52} = \frac{3}{26} \approx 0.115$$

EXAMPLE 4–6   Gender of Children

If a family has three children, find the probability that exactly two of the three children are girls.

SOLUTION

The sample space for the gender of the children for a family with three children has eight outcomes, that is, BBB, BBG, BGB, GBB, GGG, GGB, GBG, and BGG. (See Examples 4–3 and 4–4.) Since there are three ways to have two girls, namely, GGB, GBG, and BGG, P(two girls) $= \frac{3}{8}$.

Historical Note

Ancient Greeks and Romans made crude dice from animal bones, various stones, minerals, and ivory. When the dice were tested mathematically, some were found to be quite accurate.

In probability theory, it is important to understand the meaning of the words *and* and *or*. For example, if you were asked to find the probability of getting a queen *and* a heart when you were drawing a single card from a deck, you would be looking for the queen of hearts. Here the word *and* means "at the same time." The word *or* has two meanings. For example, if you were asked to find the probability of selecting a queen *or* a heart when one card is selected from a deck, you would be looking for one of the 4 queens or one of the 13 hearts. In this case, the queen of hearts would be included in both cases and counted twice. So there would be $4 + 13 - 1 = 16$ possibilities.

On the other hand, if you were asked to find the probability of getting a queen *or* a king, you would be looking for one of the 4 queens or one of the 4 kings. In this case, there would be $4 + 4 = 8$ possibilities. In the first case, both events can occur at the same time; we say that this is an example of the *inclusive or*. In the second case, both events cannot occur at the same time, and we say that this is an example of the *exclusive or*.

EXAMPLE 4–7   Drawing Cards

A card is drawn from an ordinary deck. Find the probability of getting

   a. A king

   b. The 4 of spades

   c. A face card (jack, queen, or king)

   d. A red card

   e. A club

SOLUTION

a. Refer to the sample space in Figure 4–2. There are 4 kings in the event E and a total of 52 cards; hence,

$$P(\text{king}) = \frac{4}{52} = \frac{1}{13} \approx 0.077$$

b. Since there is only one 4 of spades, the probability is

$$P(4\spadesuit) = \frac{1}{52} \approx 0.019$$

c. There are 3 face cards for each suit, and there are 4 suits (hearts, clubs, diamonds, and spades). So there are 12 face cards; hence,

$$P(\text{face card}) = \frac{12}{52} = \frac{3}{13} \approx 0.231$$

d. There are 26 red cards: 13 diamonds and 13 hearts. Hence,

$$P(\text{red card}) = \frac{26}{52} = \frac{1}{2} = 0.5$$

e. There are 13 clubs, so the probability of selecting a club is

$$P(\clubsuit) = \frac{13}{52} = \frac{1}{4} = 0.25$$

There are four basic probability rules. These rules are helpful in solving probability problems, in understanding the nature of probability, and in deciding if your answers to the problems are correct.

Probability Rules

1. The probability of any event E is a number (either a fraction or decimal) between and including 0 and 1. This is denoted by $0 \le P(E) \le 1$.
2. The sum of the probabilities of all the outcomes in a sample space is 1.
3. If an event E cannot occur (i.e., the event contains no members in the sample space), its probability is 0.
4. If an event E is certain, then the probability of E is 1.

Rule 1 states that probability values range from 0 to 1. When the probability of an event is close to 0, its occurrence is highly unlikely. When the probability of an event is near 0.5, there is about a 50-50 chance that the event will occur; and when the probability of an event is close to 1, the event is highly likely to occur. See Figure 4–4.

FIGURE 4–4
Range of Probability

Rule 2 can be illustrated by the example of rolling a single die. Each outcome in the sample space has a probability of $\frac{1}{6}$, and the sum of the probabilities of all the outcomes is 1, as shown.

Outcome	1	2	3	4	5	6
Probability	$\frac{1}{6}$	$\frac{1}{6}$	$\frac{1}{6}$	$\frac{1}{6}$	$\frac{1}{6}$	$\frac{1}{6}$
Sum	$\frac{1}{6}$ +	$\frac{1}{6}$ +	$\frac{1}{6}$ +	$\frac{1}{6}$ +	$\frac{1}{6}$ +	$\frac{1}{6} = \frac{6}{6} = 1$

Rule 3 is illustrated in Example 4–8.

EXAMPLE 4–8   Rolling a Die

When a single die is rolled, find the probability of getting a 9.

SOLUTION

Since the sample space is 1, 2, 3, 4, 5, and 6, it is impossible to get a 9. Hence, the probability is $P(9) = \frac{0}{6} = 0$.

Rule 4 states that if $P(E) = 1$, then the event E is certain to occur. This rule is illustrated in Example 4–9.

EXAMPLE 4–9   Rolling a Die

When a single die is rolled, what is the probability of getting a number less than 7?

SOLUTION

Since all outcomes—1, 2, 3, 4, 5, and 6—are less than 7, the probability is

$$P(\text{number less than 7}) = \frac{6}{6} = 1$$

The event of getting a number less than 7 is certain.

Complementary Events

Another important concept in probability theory is that of *complementary events*. When a die is rolled, for instance, the sample space consists of the outcomes 1, 2, 3, 4, 5, and 6. The event E of getting odd numbers consists of the outcomes 1, 3, and 5. The event of not getting an odd number is called the *complement* of event E, and it consists of the outcomes 2, 4, and 6.

> The **complement of an event** E is the set of outcomes in the sample space that are not included in the outcomes of event E. The complement of E is denoted by $\bar{E}$ (read "E bar").

Example 4–10 further illustrates the concept of complementary events.

EXAMPLE 4–10   Finding Complements

Find the complement of each event:

    a. Selecting a month that has 31 days

    b. Selecting a day of the week that begins with the letter T

    c. Rolling two dice and getting a sum that is an odd number

    d. Selecting a letter of the alphabet that is used as a vowel or consonant

SOLUTION

    a. Select a month that has fewer than 31 days, i.e., February, April, June, September, and November.

    b. Select a day of the week that does not begin with a T, i.e., Sunday, Monday, Wednesday, Friday, and Saturday.

    c. Rolling two dice and getting a sum that is an even number, i.e., a sum of 2, 4, 6, 8, 10, or 12.

    d. Since y is the only letter that is used as a vowel or a consonant, the complement is selecting a letter other than y.

The outcomes of an event and the outcomes of the complement make up the entire sample space. For example, if two coins are tossed, the sample space is HH, HT, TH, and TT. The complement of "getting all heads" is not "getting all tails," since the event "all heads" is HH, and the complement of HH is HT, TH, and TT. Hence, the complement of the event "all heads" is the event "getting at least one tail."

Since the event and its complement make up the entire sample space, it follows that the sum of the probability of the event and the probability of its complement will equal 1. That is, $P(E) + P(\overline{E}) = 1$. For example, let E = all heads, or HH, and let $\overline{E}$ = at least one tail, or HT, TH, TT. Then $P(E) = \frac{1}{4}$ and $P(\overline{E}) = \frac{3}{4}$; hence, $P(E) + P(\overline{E}) = \frac{1}{4} + \frac{3}{4} = 1$.

The rule for complementary events can be stated algebraically in three ways.

Rule for Complementary Events

$$P(\overline{E}) = 1 - P(E) \qquad \text{or} \qquad P(E) = 1 - P(\overline{E}) \qquad \text{or} \qquad P(E) + P(\overline{E}) = 1$$

Stated in words, the rule is: *If the probability of an event or the probability of its complement is known, then the other can be found by subtracting the probability from* 1. This rule is important in probability theory because at times the best solution to a problem is to find the probability of the complement of an event and then subtract from 1 to get the probability of the event itself.

Probabilities can be represented pictorially by **Venn diagrams.** Figure 4–5(a) shows the probability of a simple event E. The area inside the circle represents the probability of event E, that is, $P(E)$. The area inside the rectangle represents the probability of all the events in the sample space $P(S)$.

The Venn diagram that represents the probability of the complement of an event $P(\overline{E})$ is shown in Figure 4–5(b). In this case, $P(\overline{E}) = 1 - P(E)$, which is the area inside the rectangle but outside the circle representing $P(E)$. Recall that $P(S) = 1$ and $P(E) = 1 - P(\overline{E})$. The reasoning is that $P(E)$ is represented by the area of the circle and $P(\overline{E})$ is the probability of the events that are outside the circle.

FIGURE 4–5
Venn Diagram for the Probability and Complement

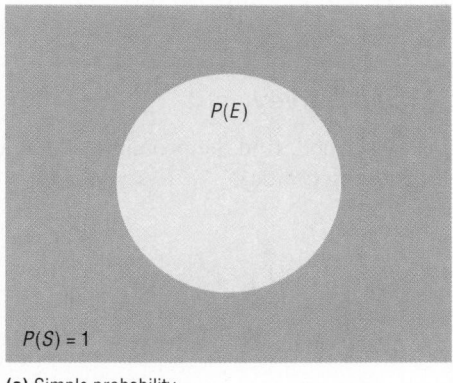

(a) Simple probability

(b) $P(\overline{E}) = 1 - P(E)$

EXAMPLE 4–11   Favorite Ice Cream Flavors

In a study, it was found that 23% of the people surveyed said that vanilla was their favorite flavor of ice cream. If a person is selected at random, find the probability that the person's favorite flavor of ice cream is not vanilla.

Source: Rasmussen Report.

SOLUTION

$$P(\text{not vanilla}) = 1 - P(\text{vanilla})$$
$$= 1 - 0.23 = 0.77 = 77\%$$

Empirical Probability

The difference between classical and **empirical probability** is that classical probability assumes that certain outcomes are equally likely (such as the outcomes when a die is rolled), while empirical probability relies on actual experience to determine the likelihood of outcomes. In empirical probability, one might actually roll a given die 6000 times, observe the various frequencies, and use these frequencies to determine the probability of an outcome.

Suppose, for example, that a researcher for the American Automobile Association (AAA) asked 50 people who plan to travel over the Thanksgiving holiday how they will get to their destination. The results can be categorized in a frequency distribution as shown.

Method	Frequency
Drive	41
Fly	6
Train or bus	3
	50

Now probabilities can be computed for various categories. For example, the probability of selecting a person who is driving is $\frac{41}{50}$, since 41 out of the 50 people said that they were driving.

Formula for Empirical Probability

Given a frequency distribution, the probability of an event being in a given class is

$$P(E) = \frac{\text{frequency for the class}}{\text{total frequencies in the distribution}} = \frac{f}{n}$$

This probability is called *empirical probability* and is based on observation.

EXAMPLE 4–12   Travel Survey

In the travel survey just described, find the probability that a person will travel by airplane over the Thanksgiving holiday.

SOLUTION

$$P(E) = \frac{f}{n} = \frac{6}{50} = \frac{3}{25}$$

Note: These figures are based on an AAA survey.

EXAMPLE 4–13   Distribution of Blood Types

In a sample of 50 people, 21 had type O blood, 22 had type A blood, 5 had type B blood, and 2 had type AB blood. Set up a frequency distribution and find the following probabilities.

    a. A person has type O blood.

    b. A person has type A or type B blood.

    c. A person has neither type A nor type O blood.

    d. A person does not have type AB blood.

Source: The American Red Cross.

SOLUTION

Type	Frequency
A	22
B	5
AB	2
0	21
	Total 50

a. $P(O) = \dfrac{f}{n} = \dfrac{21}{50}$

b. $P(A \text{ or } B) = \dfrac{22}{50} + \dfrac{5}{50} = \dfrac{27}{50}$

(Add the frequencies of the two classes.)

c. $P(\text{neither A nor O}) = \dfrac{5}{50} + \dfrac{2}{50} = \dfrac{7}{50}$

(Neither A nor O means that a person has either type B or type AB blood.)

d. $P(\text{not AB}) = 1 - P(\text{AB}) = 1 - \dfrac{2}{50} = \dfrac{48}{50} = \dfrac{24}{25}$

(Find the probability of not AB by subtracting the probability of type AB from 1.)

EXAMPLE 4–14   Hospital Stays for Knee Replacements

Hospital records indicated that knee replacement patients stayed in the hospital for the number of days shown in the distribution.

Number of days stayed	Frequency
3	15
4	32
5	56
6	19
7	5
	127

Find these probabilities.

a. A patient stayed exactly 5 days.   c. A patient stayed at most 4 days.

b. A patient stayed fewer than 6 days.   d. A patient stayed at least 5 days.

SOLUTION

a. $P(5) = \dfrac{56}{127}$

b. $P(\text{fewer than 6 days}) = \dfrac{15}{127} + \dfrac{32}{127} + \dfrac{56}{127} = \dfrac{103}{127}$

(Fewer than 6 days means 3, 4, or 5 days.)

c. $P(\text{at most 4 days}) = \dfrac{15}{127} + \dfrac{32}{127} = \dfrac{47}{127}$

(At most 4 days means 3 or 4 days.)

d. $P(\text{at least 5 days}) = \dfrac{56}{127} + \dfrac{19}{127} + \dfrac{5}{127} = \dfrac{80}{127}$

(At least 5 days means 5, 6, or 7 days.)

Empirical probabilities can also be found by using a relative frequency distribution, as shown in Section 2–2. For example, the relative frequency distribution of the travel survey shown previously is

Method	Frequency	Relative frequency
Drive	41	0.82
Fly	6	0.12
Train or bus	3	0.06
	50	1.00

These frequencies are the same as the relative frequencies explained in Chapter 2.

Law of Large Numbers

When a coin is tossed one time, it is common knowledge that the probability of getting a head is $\frac{1}{2}$. But what happens when the coin is tossed 50 times? Will it come up heads 25 times? Not all the time. You should expect about 25 heads if the coin is fair. But due to chance variation, 25 heads will not occur most of the time.

If the empirical probability of getting a head is computed by using a small number of trials, it is usually not exactly $\frac{1}{2}$. However, as the number of trials increases, the empirical probability of getting a head will approach the theoretical probability of $\frac{1}{2}$, if in fact the coin is fair (i.e., balanced). This phenomenon is an example of the **law of large numbers.**

You should be careful to not think that the number of heads and number of tails tend to "even out." As the number of trials increases, the proportion of heads to the total number of trials will approach $\frac{1}{2}$. This law holds for any type of gambling game—tossing dice, playing roulette, and so on.

It should be pointed out that the probabilities that the proportions steadily approach may or may not agree with those theorized in the classical model. If not, it can have important implications, such as "the die is not fair." Pit bosses in Las Vegas watch for empirical trends that do not agree with classical theories, and they will sometimes take a set of dice out of play if observed frequencies are too far out of line with classical expected frequencies.

Subjective Probability

The third type of probability is called *subjective probability.* **Subjective probability** uses a probability value based on an educated guess or estimate, employing opinions and inexact information.

In subjective probability, a person or group makes an educated guess at the chance that an event will occur. This guess is based on the person's experience and evaluation of a solution. For example, a sportswriter may say that there is a 70% probability that the Pirates will win the pennant next year. A physician might say that, on the basis of her diagnosis, there is a 30% chance the patient will need an operation. A seismologist might say there is an 80% probability that an earthquake will occur in a certain area. These are only a few examples of how subjective probability is used in everyday life.

All three types of probability (classical, empirical, and subjective) are used to solve a variety of problems in business, engineering, and other fields.

Probability and Risk Taking

An area in which people fail to understand probability is risk taking. Actually, people fear situations or events that have a relatively small probability of happening rather than those events that have a greater likelihood of occurring. For example, many people think that the crime rate is increasing every year. However, in his book entitled *How Risk Affects Your Everyday Life,* author James Walsh states: "Despite widespread concern about the number of crimes committed in the United States, FBI and Justice Department statistics show that the national crime rate has remained fairly level for 20 years. It even dropped slightly in the early 1990s."

He further states, "Today most media coverage of risk to health and well-being focuses on shock and outrage." Shock and outrage make good stories and can scare us about the wrong dangers. For example, the author states that if a person is 20% overweight, the loss of life expectancy is 900 days (about 3 years), but loss of life expectancy from exposure to radiation emitted by nuclear power plants is 0.02 day. As you can see, being overweight is much more of a threat than being exposed to radioactive emission.

Many people gamble daily with their lives, for example, by using tobacco, drinking and driving, and riding motorcycles. When people are asked to estimate the probabilities or frequencies of death from various causes, they tend to overestimate causes such as accidents, fires, and floods and to underestimate the probabilities of death from diseases (other than cancer), strokes, etc. For example, most people think that their chances of dying of a heart attack are 1 in 20, when in fact they are almost 1 in 3; the chances of dying by pesticide poisoning are 1 in 200,000 (*True Odds* by James Walsh). The reason people think this way is that the news media sensationalize deaths resulting from catastrophic events and rarely mention deaths from disease.

When you are dealing with life-threatening catastrophes such as hurricanes, floods, automobile accidents, or texting while driving, it is important to get the facts. That is, get the actual numbers from accredited statistical agencies or reliable statistical studies, and then compute the probabilities and make decisions based on your knowledge of probability and statistics.

In summary, then, when you make a decision or plan a course of action based on probability, make sure that you understand the true probability of the event occurring. Also, find out how the information was obtained (i.e., from a reliable source). Weigh the cost of the action and decide if it is worth it. Finally, look for other alternatives or courses of action with less risk involved.

Applying the Concepts 4–1

Tossing a Coin

Assume you are at a carnival and decide to play one of the games. You spot a table where a person is flipping a coin, and since you have an understanding of basic probability, you believe that the odds of winning are in your favor. When you get to the table, you find out that all you have to do is to guess which side of the coin will be facing up after it is tossed. You are assured that the coin is fair, meaning that each of the two sides has an equally likely chance of occurring. You think back about what you learned in your statistics class about probability before you decide what to bet on. Answer the following questions about the coin-tossing game.

1. What is the sample space?
2. What are the possible outcomes?
3. What does the classical approach to probability say about computing probabilities for this type of problem?

You decide to bet on heads, believing that it has a 50% chance of coming up. A friend of yours, who had been playing the game for awhile before you got there, tells you that heads has come up the last 9 times in a row. You remember the law of large numbers.

4. What is the law of large numbers, and does it change your thoughts about what will occur on the next toss?
5. What does the empirical approach to probability say about this problem, and could you use it to solve this problem?
6. Can subjective probabilities be used to help solve this problem? Explain.
7. Assume you could win $1 million if you could guess what the results of the next toss will be. What would you bet on? Why?

See pages 253–254 for the answers.

Exercises 4–1

1. What is a probability experiment?

2. Define *sample space*.

3. What is the difference between an outcome and an event?

4. What are equally likely events?

5. What is the range of the values of the probability of an event?

6. When an event is certain to occur, what is its probability?

7. If an event cannot happen, what value is assigned to its probability?

8. What is the sum of the probabilities of all the outcomes in a sample space?

9. If the probability that it will rain tomorrow is 0.20, what is the probability that it won't rain tomorrow? Would you recommend taking an umbrella?

10. A probability experiment is conducted. Which of these cannot be considered a probability outcome?

a. $\frac{2}{3}$ d. 1.65   g. 1

b. 0.63   e. -0.44 h. 125%

c. $-\frac{3}{5}$ f. 0   i. 24%

11. Classify each statement as an example of classical probability, empirical probability, or subjective probability.

a. The probability that a person will watch the 6 o'clock evening news is 0.15.

b. The probability of winning at a Chuck-a-Luck game is $\frac{5}{36}$.

c. The probability that a bus will be in an accident on a specific run is about 6%.

d. The probability of getting a royal flush when five cards are selected at random is $\frac{1}{649,740}$.

12. Classify each statement as an example of classical probability, empirical probability, or subjective probability.

a. The probability that a student will get a C or better in a statistics course is about 70%.

b. The probability that a new fast-food restaurant will be a success in Chicago is 35%.

c. The probability that interest rates will rise in the next 6 months is 0.50.

d. The probability that the unemployment rate will fall next month is 0.03.

13. **Rolling a Die** If a die is rolled one time, find these probabilities.

a. Getting a 2

b. Getting a number greater than 6

c. Getting an odd number

d. Getting an odd or even number

14. **Rolling a Die** If a die is rolled one time, find these probabilities:

a. Getting a number less than 7

b. Getting a number greater than or equal to 3

c. Getting a number greater than 2 and an even number

d. Getting a number less than 1

15. **Rolling Two Dice** If two dice are rolled one time, find the probability of getting these results.

a. A sum of 9

b. A sum of 7 or 11

c. Doubles

16. **Rolling Two Dice** If two dice are rolled one time, find the probability of getting these results:

a. A sum less than 9

b. A sum greater than or equal to 10

c. A 3 on one die or on both dice.

17. **Drawing a Card** If one card is drawn from a deck, find the probability of getting these results.

a. A queen

b. A club

c. A queen of clubs

d. A 3 or an 8

e. A 6 or a spade

18. **Drawing a Card** If a card is drawn from a deck, find the probability of getting these results:

a. A 6 and a spade

b. A black king

c. A red card and a 7

d. A diamond or a heart

e. A black card

19. **Shopping Mall Promotion** A shopping mall has set up a promotion as follows. With any mall purchase of $50 or more, the customer gets to spin the wheel shown here. If a number 1 comes up, the customer wins $10. If the number 2 comes up, the customer wins $5; and if the number 3 or 4 comes up, the customer wins a discount coupon. Find the following probabilities.

a. The customer wins $10.

b. The customer wins money.

c. The customer wins a coupon.

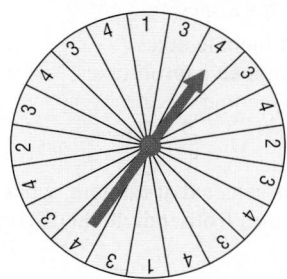

20. Selecting a State Choose one of the 50 states at random.

   a. What is the probability that it begins with the letter M?

   b. What is the probability that it doesn't begin with a vowel?

21. Human Blood Types Human blood is grouped into four types. The percentages of Americans with each type are listed below.

     O 43%   A 40%   B 12%   AB 5%

Choose one American at random. Find the probability that this person

   a. Has type O blood

   b. Has type A or B

   c. Does not have type O or A

Source: www.infoplease.com

22. Murder Victims Of all the murder victims in 2010 whose relation to the offender was known, 24.8% were killed by a family member and 53% by an acquaintance. The rest were killed by a stranger. What is the probability that a randomly selected murder victim was killed by a stranger?

Source: *World Almanac 2012.*

23. Prime Numbers A prime number is a number that is evenly divisible only by 1 and itself. The prime numbers less than 100 are listed below.

  2   3   5   7   11   13   17   19   23   29   31
  37   41   43   47   53   59   61   67   71   73   79
  83   89   97

Choose one of these numbers at random. Find the probability that

   a. The number is even

   b. The sum of the number's digits is even

   c. The number is greater than 50

24. Rural Speed Limits Rural speed limits for all 50 states are indicated below.

60 mph	65 mph	70 mph	75 mph
1 (HI)	18	18	13

Choose one state at random. Find the probability that its speed limit is

   a. 60 or 70 miles per hour

   b. Greater than 65 miles per hour

   c. 70 miles per hour or less

Source: *World Almanac.*

25. Gender of Children A couple has three children. Find each probability.

   a. All boys

   b. All girls or all boys

   c. Exactly two boys or two girls

   d. At least one child of each gender

26. Sources of Energy Uses in the United States A breakdown of the sources of energy used in the United States is shown below. Choose one energy source at random. Find the probability that it is

   a. Not oil

   b. Natural gas or oil

   c. Nuclear

Oil 39%	Natural gas 24%	Coal 23%
Nuclear 8%	Hydropower 3%	Other 3%

Source: www.infoplease.com

27. Craps Game In a game of craps, a player loses on the roll if a 2, 3, or 12 is tossed on the first roll. Find the probability of losing on the first roll.

28. Computers in Elementary Schools Elementary and secondary schools were classified by the number of computers they had.

Computers	1–10	11–20	21–50	51–100	100+
Schools	3170	4590	16,741	23,753	34,803

Choose one school at random. Find the probability that it has

   a. 50 or fewer computers

   b. More than 100 computers

   c. No more than 20 computers

Source: *World Almanac.*

29. College Debt The following information shows the amount of debt students who graduated from college incur for a specific year.

$1 to $5000	$5001 to $20,000	$20,001 to $50,000	$50,000+
27%	40%	19%	14%

If a person who graduates has some debt, find the probability that

   a. It is less than $5001

   b. It is more than $20,000

   c. It is between $1 and $20,000

   d. It is more than $50,000

Source: *USA TODAY.*

30. Population of Hawaii The population of Hawaii is 22.7% white, 1.5% African-American, 37.7% Asian, 0.2% Native American/Alaskan, 9.46% Native Hawaiian/Pacific Islander, 8.9% Hispanic, 19.4% two or more races, and 0.14% some other. Choose one Hawaiian resident at random. What is the probability that he/she is a Native Hawaiian or Pacific Islander? Asian? White?

31. Arrests for Property Crimes The total arrests for property crimes in the United States in a recent year were itemized as follows.

Larceny/theft	1,334,933
Burglary	299,351
Motor vehicle theft	81,797
Arson	12,204

Choose one arrest at random; what is the probability that it was for burglary? What is the probability that it was not for larceny/theft?

Source: *Time Almanac.*

32. Living Arrangements for Children Here are the living arrangements of children under 18 years old living in the United States in a recent year. Numbers are in thousands.

Both parents	51,823
Mother only	17,283
Father only	2,572
Neither parent	3,041

Choose one child at random; what is the probability that the child lives with both parents? With the mother present?

Source: *Time Almanac.*

33. Health Insurance In 2010 in the United States, there were 49,904,000 people not covered by health insurance. The numbers of those not covered in selected states are shown below (numbers in thousands.)

CA   7209   FL   3854   TX   6181   NY   2886

Choose a person not covered by health insurance; what is the probability that the person is from California or Texas? What is the probability that the person is not from one of these four listed states?

Source: *World Almanac.*

34. Federal Government Revenue The source of federal government revenue for a specific year is

50% from individual income taxes
32% from social insurance payroll taxes
10% from corporate income taxes
3% from excise taxes
5% other

If a revenue source is selected at random, what is the probability that it comes from individual or corporate income taxes?

Source: *New York Times Almanac.*

35. Selecting a Bill A box contains a $1 bill, a $5 bill, a $10 bill, and a $20 bill. A bill is selected at random, and it is not replaced; then a second bill is selected at random. Draw a tree diagram and determine the sample space.

36. Tossing Coins Draw a tree diagram and determine the sample space for tossing four coins.

37. Selecting Numbered Balls Four balls numbered 1 through 4 are placed in a box. A ball is selected at random, and its number is noted; then it is replaced. A second ball is selected at random, and its number is noted. Draw a tree diagram and determine the sample space.

38. Family Dinner Combinations A family special at a neighborhood restaurant offers dinner for four for $39.99. There are 3 appetizers available, 4 entrees, and 3 desserts from which to choose. The special includes one of each. Represent the possible dinner combinations with a tree diagram.

39. Required First-Year College Courses First-year students at a particular college must take one English class, one class in mathematics, a first-year seminar, and an elective. There are 2 English classes to choose from, 3 mathematics classes, 5 electives, and everyone takes the same first-year seminar. Represent the possible schedules, using a tree diagram.

40. Tossing a Coin and Rolling a Die A coin is tossed; if it falls heads up, it is tossed again. If it falls tails up, a die is rolled. Draw a tree diagram and determine the outcomes.

≡ Extending the Concepts

41. Distribution of CEO Ages The distribution of ages of CEOs is as follows:

Age	Frequency
21–30	1
31–40	8
41–50	27
51–60	29
61–70	24
71–up	11

Source: Information based on
USA TODAY Snapshot.

If a CEO is selected at random, find the probability that his or her age is
a. Between 31 and 40
b. Under 31
c. Over 30 and under 51
d. Under 31 or over 60

42. Tossing a Coin A person flipped a coin 100 times and obtained 73 heads. Can the person conclude that the coin was unbalanced?

43. Medical Treatment A medical doctor stated that with a certain treatment, a patient has a 50% chance of recovering without surgery. That is, "Either he will get well or he won't get well." Comment on this statement.

44. **Wheel Spinner** The wheel spinner shown here is spun twice. Find the sample space, and then determine the probability of the following events.

a. An odd number on the first spin and an even number on the second spin (*Note:* 0 is considered even.)

b. A sum greater than 4

c. Even numbers on both spins

d. A sum that is odd

e. The same number on both spins

45. **Tossing Coins** Toss three coins 128 times and record the number of heads (0, 1, 2, or 3); then record your results with the theoretical probabilities. Compute the empirical probabilities of each.

46. **Tossing Coins** Toss two coins 100 times and record the number of heads (0, 1, 2). Compute the probabilities of each outcome, and compare these probabilities with the theoretical results.

47. **Odds** Odds are used in gambling games to make them fair. For example, if you rolled a die and won every time

you rolled a 6, then you would win on average once every 6 times. So that the game is fair, the odds of 5 to 1 are given. This means that if you bet $1 and won, you could win $5. On average, you would win $5 once in 6 rolls and lose $1 on the other 5 rolls—hence the term *fair game.*

In most gambling games, the odds given are not fair. For example, if the odds of winning are really 20 to 1, the house might offer 15 to 1 in order to make a profit.

Odds can be expressed as a fraction or as a ratio, such as $\frac{5}{1}$, 5:1, or 5 to 1. Odds are computed in favor of the event or against the event. The formulas for odds are

$$\text{Odds in favor} = \frac{P(E)}{1 - P(E)}$$

$$\text{Odds against} = \frac{P(\overline{E})}{1 - P(\overline{E})}$$

In the die example,

$$\text{Odds in favor of a 6} = \frac{\frac{1}{6}}{\frac{5}{6}} = \frac{1}{5} \text{ or } 1{:}5$$

$$\text{Odds against a 6} = \frac{\frac{5}{6}}{\frac{1}{6}} = \frac{5}{1} \text{ or } 5{:}1$$

Find the odds in favor of and against each event.

a. Rolling a die and getting a 2

b. Rolling a die and getting an even number

c. Drawing a card from a deck and getting a spade

d. Drawing a card and getting a red card

e. Drawing a card and getting a queen

f. Tossing two coins and getting two tails

g. Tossing two coins and getting exactly one tail

4–2   The Addition Rules for Probability

OBJECTIVE ❷

Find the probability of compound events, using the addition rules.

Many problems involve finding the probability of two or more events. For example, at a large political gathering, you might wish to know, for a person selected at random, the probability that the person is a female or is a Republican. In this case, there are three possibilities to consider:

1. The person is a female.

2. The person is a Republican.

3. The person is both a female and a Republican.

Consider another example. At the same gathering there are Republicans, Democrats, and Independents. If a person is selected at random, what is the probability that the person is a Democrat or an Independent? In this case, there are only two possibilities:

1. The person is a Democrat.

2. The person is an Independent.

The difference between the two examples is that in the first case, the person selected can be a female and a Republican at the same time. In the second case, the person selected cannot be both a Democrat and an Independent at the same time. In the second case, the

Historical Note

The first book on probability, *The Book of Chance and Games,* was written by Jerome Cardan (1501–1576). Cardan was an astrologer, philosopher, physician, mathematician, and gambler. This book contained techniques on how to cheat and how to catch others at cheating.

two events are said to be *mutually exclusive;* in the first case, they are not mutually exclusive.

> Two events are **mutually exclusive events** or **disjoint events** if they cannot occur at the same time (i.e., they have no outcomes in common).

In another situation, the events of getting a 4 and getting a 6 when a single card is drawn from a deck are mutually exclusive events, since a single card cannot be both a 4 and a 6. On the other hand, the events of getting a 4 and getting a heart on a single draw are not mutually exclusive, since you can select the 4 of hearts when drawing a single card from an ordinary deck.

EXAMPLE 4–15   Determining Mutually Exclusive Events

Determine whether the two events are mutually exclusive. Explain your answer.

a. Randomly selecting a female student
Randomly selecting a student who is a junior

b. Randomly selecting a person with type A blood
Randomly selecting a person with type O blood

c. Rolling a die and getting an odd number
Rolling a die and getting a number less than 3

d. Randomly selecting a person who is under 21 years of age
Randomly selecting a person who is over 30 years of age

SOLUTION

a. These events are not mutually exclusive since a student can be both female and a junior.

b. These events are mutually exclusive since a person cannot have type A blood and type O blood at the same time.

c. These events are not mutually exclusive since the number 1 is both an odd number and a number less than 3.

d. These events are mutually exclusive since a person cannot be both under 21 and over 30 years of age at the same time.

EXAMPLE 4–16   Drawing a Card

Determine which events are mutually exclusive and which events are not when a single card is drawn from a deck.

a. Getting a king; getting a diamond

b. Getting a 4; getting a king

c. Getting a face card; getting a club

d. Getting a face card; getting a 10

SOLUTION

a. These events are not mutually exclusive since the king of diamonds represents both events.

b. These events are mutually exclusive since you cannot draw one card that is both a 4 and a king.

c. These events are not mutually exclusive since a jack, queen, or king can be clubs.

d. These events are mutually exclusive since a 10 and a face card cannot be drawn at the same time when one card is drawn.

FIGURE 4–6

Venn Diagram for Addition Rule 1 When the Events Are Mutually Exclusive

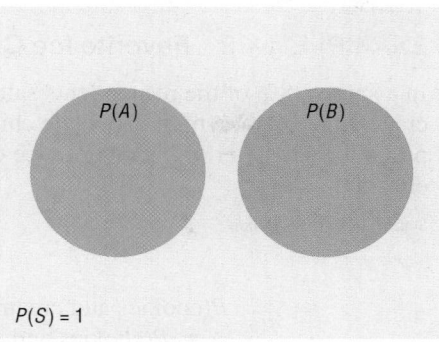

$P(S) = 1$

Mutually exclusive events
$P(A \text{ or } B) = P(A) + P(B)$

The probability of two or more events can be determined by the *addition rules.* The first addition rule is used when the events are mutually exclusive.

Addition Rule 1

When two events A and B are mutually exclusive, the probability that A or B will occur is

$$P(A \text{ or } B) = P(A) + P(B)$$

Figure 4–6 shows a Venn diagram that represents two mutually exclusive events A and B. In this case, $P(A \text{ or } B) = P(A) + P(B)$, since these events are mutually exclusive and do not overlap. In other words, the probability of occurrence of event A or event B is the sum of the areas of the two circles.

EXAMPLE 4–17   Coffee Shop Selection

A city has 9 coffee shops: 3 Starbucks, 2 Caribou Coffees, and 4 Crazy Mocho Coffees. If a person selects one shop at random to buy a cup of coffee, find the probability that it is either a Starbucks or Crazy Mocho Coffees.

SOLUTION

Since there are 3 Starbucks and 4 Crazy Mochos, and a total of 9 coffee shops, $P(\text{Starbucks or Crazy Mocho}) = P(\text{Starbucks}) + P(\text{Crazy Mocho}) = \frac{3}{9} + \frac{4}{9} = \frac{7}{9} \approx 0.778$. The events are mutually exclusive.

EXAMPLE 4–18   Research and Development Employees

The corporate research and development centers for three local companies have the following numbers of employees:

U.S. Steel	110
Alcoa	750
Bayer Material Science	250

If a research employee is selected at random, find the probability that the employee is employed by U.S. Steel or Alcoa.

Source: *Pittsburgh Tribune Review.*

SOLUTION

$$P(\text{U.S. Steel or Alcoa}) = P(\text{U.S. Steel}) + P(\text{Alcoa})$$

$$= \frac{110}{1110} + \frac{750}{1110} = \frac{860}{1110} = \frac{86}{111}$$

EXAMPLE 4–19   Favorite Ice Cream

In a survey, 8% of the respondents said that their favorite ice cream flavor is cookies and cream, and 6% like mint chocolate chip. If a person is selected at random, find the probability that her or his favorite ice cream flavor is either cookies and cream or mint chocolate chip.

Source: Rasmussen Report.

SOLUTION

$$P(\text{cookies and cream or mint chocolate chip})$$
$$= P(\text{cookies and cream}) + P(\text{mint chocolate chip})$$
$$= 0.08 + 0.06 = 0.14 = 14\%$$

These events are mutually exclusive.

The probability rules can be extended to three or more events. For three mutually exclusive events *A*, *B*, and *C*,

$$P(A \text{ or } B \text{ or } C) = P(A) + P(B) + P(C)$$

When events are not mutually exclusive, addition rule 2 can be used to find the probability of the events.

Addition Rule 2

If *A* and *B* are *not* mutually exclusive, then
$$P(A \text{ or } B) = P(A) + P(B) - P(A \text{ and } B)$$

Note: This rule can also be used when the events are mutually exclusive, since $P(A \text{ and } B)$ will always equal 0. However, it is important to make a distinction between the two situations.

Figure 4–7 represents the probability of two events that are *not* mutually exclusive. In this case, $P(A \text{ or } B) = P(A) + P(B) - P(A \text{ and } B)$. The area in the intersection or overlapping part of both circles corresponds to $P(A \text{ and } B)$; and when the area of circle *A* is added to the area of circle *B*, the overlapping part is counted twice. It must therefore be subtracted once to get the correct area or probability.

FIGURE 4–7

Venn Diagram for Addition Rule 2 When Events Are Not Mutually Exclusive

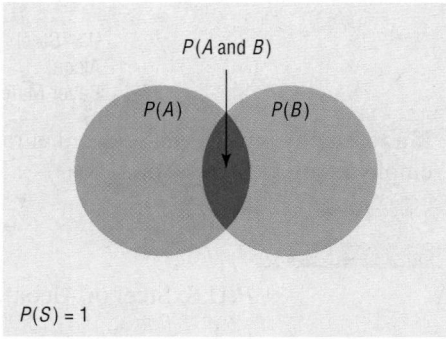

Nonmutually exclusive events
$P(A \text{ or } B) = P(A) + P(B) - P(A \text{ and } B)$

EXAMPLE 4–20   Drawing a Card

A single card is drawn at random from an ordinary deck of cards. Find the probability that it is either an ace or a black card.

SOLUTION

Since there are 4 aces and 26 black cards (13 spades and 13 clubs), 2 of the aces are black cards, namely, the ace of spades and the ace of clubs. Hence, the probabilities of the two outcomes must be subtracted since they have been counted twice.

$$P(\text{ace or black card}) = P(\text{ace}) + P(\text{black card}) - P(\text{black aces})$$

$$= \frac{4}{52} + \frac{26}{52} - \frac{2}{52} = \frac{28}{52} = \frac{7}{13} \approx 0.538$$

EXAMPLE 4–21   Selecting a Medical Staff Person

In a hospital unit there are 8 nurses and 5 physicians; 7 nurses and 3 physicians are females. If a staff person is selected, find the probability that the subject is a nurse or a male.

SOLUTION

The sample space is shown here.

Staff	Females	Males	Total
Nurses	7	1	8
Physicians	3	2	5
Total	10	3	13

The probability is

$$P(\text{nurse or male}) = P(\text{nurse}) + P(\text{male}) - P(\text{male nurse})$$

$$= \frac{8}{13} + \frac{3}{13} - \frac{1}{13} = \frac{10}{13} \approx 0.769$$

EXAMPLE 4–22   Driving While Intoxicated

On New Year's Eve, the probability of a person driving while intoxicated is 0.32, the probability of a person having a driving accident is 0.09, and the probability of a person having a driving accident while intoxicated is 0.06. What is the probability of a person driving while intoxicated or having a driving accident?

SOLUTION

$$P(\text{intoxicated or accident}) = P(\text{intoxicated}) + P(\text{accident})$$
$$- P(\text{intoxicated and accident})$$
$$= 0.32 + 0.09 - 0.06 = 0.35$$

For three events that are *not* mutually exclusive,

$$P(A \text{ or } B \text{ or } C) = P(A) + P(B) + P(C) - P(A \text{ and } B) - P(A \text{ and } C)$$
$$- P(B \text{ and } C) + P(A \text{ and } B \text{ and } C)$$

See Exercises 23 and 24 in this section.

In summary, then, when the two events are mutually exclusive, use addition rule 1. When the events are not mutually exclusive, use addition rule 2.

Interesting Fact

Card Shuffling

How many times does a deck of cards need to be shuffled so that the cards are in random order? Actually, this question is not easy to answer since there are many variables. First, several different methods are used to shuffle a deck of cards. Some of the methods are the riffle method, the overhand method, the Corgi method, and the Faro method.

Another factor that needs to be considered is what is meant by the cards being in a random order. There are several statistical tests that can be used to determine if a deck of cards is randomized after several shuffles, but these tests give somewhat different results.

Two mathematicians, Persi Diaconis and Dave Bayer, concluded that a deck of cards starts to become random after 5 good shuffles and is completely random after 7 shuffles. However, a later study done by Trefthen concluded that only 6 shuffles are necessary. The difference was based on what is considered a randomized deck of cards.

Applying the Concepts 4–2

Which Pain Reliever Is Best?

Assume that following an injury you received from playing your favorite sport, you obtain and read information on new pain medications. In that information you read of a study that was conducted to test the side effects of two new pain medications. Use the following table to answer the questions and decide which, if any, of the two new pain medications you will use.

	Number of side effects in 12-week clinical trial		
Side effect	Placebo $n = 192$	Drug A $n = 186$	Drug B $n = 188$
Upper respiratory congestion	10	32	19
Sinus headache	11	25	32
Stomach ache	2	46	12
Neurological headache	34	55	72
Cough	22	18	31
Lower respiratory congestion	2	5	1

1. How many subjects were in the study?

2. How long was the study?

3. What were the variables under study?

4. What type of variables are they, and what level of measurement are they on?

5. Are the numbers in the table exact figures?

6. What is the probability that a randomly selected person was receiving a placebo?

7. What is the probability that a person was receiving a placebo or drug A? Are these mutually exclusive events? What is the complement to this event?

8. What is the probability that a randomly selected person was receiving a placebo or experienced a neurological headache?

9. What is the probability that a randomly selected person was not receiving a placebo or experienced a sinus headache?

See page 254 for the answers.

Exercises 4–2

1. Define mutually exclusive events, and give an example of two events that are mutually exclusive and two events that are not mutually exclusive.

2. Explain briefly why addition rule 2 can be used when two events are mutually exclusive.

3. Determine whether these events are mutually exclusive.

   a. Roll a die: Get an even number and get a number less than 3.

   b. Roll a die: Get a prime number (2, 3, 5) and get an odd number.

   c. Roll a die: Get a number greater than 3 and get a number less than 3.

   d. Select a student in your class: The student has blond hair and the student has blue eyes.

4. Determine whether these events are mutually exclusive.

   a. Roll two dice: Get a sum of 7 or get doubles.

   b. Select a student in your college: The student is a sophomore and the student is a business major.

   c. Select any course: It is a calculus course and it is an English course.

   d. Select a registered voter: The voter is a Republican and the voter is a Democrat.

5. **College Degrees Awarded** The table below represents the college degrees awarded in a recent academic year by gender.

	Bachelor's	Master's	Doctorate
Men	573,079	211,381	24,341
Women	775,424	301,264	21,683

Choose a degree at random. Find the probability that it is

a. A bachelor's degree

b. A doctorate or a degree awarded to a woman

c. A doctorate awarded to a woman

d. Not a master's degree

Source: www.nces.ed.gov

6. **Riding to School** The probability that John will drive to school is 0.37, the probability that he will ride with friends is 0.23, and the probability that his parents will take him is 0.4. He is not allowed to have passengers in the car when he is driving. What is the probability that John will have company on the way to school?

7. **Medical Specialities** The following doctors were observed on staff at a local hospital.

	MD	Doctor of Osteopathy
Pathology	6	1
Pediatrics	7	2
Orthopedics	20	2

Choose one doctor at random; what is the probability that

a. She is a pathologist?

b. He is an orthopedist or an MD?

8. **U.S. Population** The data show the U.S. population by age.

Under 20 years	27.0%
20 years and over	73.0
65 years and over	13.1

Choose one person from the United States at random. Find the probability that the person is

a. From 20 years to 64 years

b. Under 20 or 65 and over

c. Not 65 and over

9. **Selecting an Instructor** At a convention there are 7 mathematics instructors, 5 computer science instructors, 3 statistics instructors, and 4 science instructors. If an instructor is selected, find the probability of getting a science instructor or a math instructor.

10. **Selecting a Movie** A media rental store rented the following number of movie titles in each of these categories: 170 horror, 230 drama, 120 mystery, 310 romance, and 150 comedy. If a person selects a movie to rent, find the probability that it is a romance or a comedy. Is this event likely or unlikely to occur? Explain your answer.

11. **Selecting a Student** In a statistics class there are 18 juniors and 10 seniors; 6 of the seniors are females, and 12 of the juniors are males. If a student is selected at random, find the probability of selecting the following.

a. A junior or a female

b. A senior or a female

c. A junior or a senior

12. **Selecting a Book** At a used-book sale, 100 books are adult books and 160 are children's books. Of the adult books, 70 are nonfiction while 60 of the children's books are nonfiction. If a book is selected at random, find the probability that it is

a. Fiction

b. Not a children's nonfiction book

c. An adult book or a children's nonfiction book

13. **Young Adult Residences** According to the Bureau of the Census, the following statistics describe the number (in thousands) of young adults living at home or in a dormitory in the year 2004.

	Ages 18–24	Ages 25–34
Male	7922	2534
Female	5779	995

Source: *World Almanac.*

Choose one student at random. Find the probability that the student is

a. A female student aged 25–34 years

b. Male or aged 18–24 years

c. Under 25 years of age and not male

14. **Endangered Species** The chart below shows the numbers of endangered and threatened species both here in the United States and abroad.

	Endangered		Threatened	
	United States	Foreign	United States	Foreign
Mammals	68	251	10	20
Birds	77	175	13	6
Reptiles	14	64	22	16
Amphibians	11	8	10	1

Source: www.infoplease.com

Choose one species at random. Find the probability that it is

a. Threatened and in the United States

b. An endangered foreign bird

c. A mammal or a threatened foreign species

15. **Multiple Births** The number of multiple births in the United States for a recent year indicated that there were 128,665 sets of twins, 7110 sets of triplets, 468 sets of quadruplets, and 85 sets of quintuplets. Choose one set of siblings at random.

a. Find the probability that it represented more than two babies.

b. Find the probability that it represented quads or quints.

c. Now choose one baby from these multiple births. What is the probability that the baby was a triplet?

16. Licensed Drivers in the United States In a recent year there were the following numbers (in thousands) of licensed drivers in the United States.

	Male	Female
Age 19 and under	4746	4517
Age 20	1625	1553
Age 21	1679	1627

Source: *World Almanac.*

Choose one driver at random. Find the probability that the driver is

a. Male and 19 years or under

b. Age 20 or female

c. At least 20 years old

17. Student Survey In a recent survey, the following data were obtained in response to the question, "If the number of summer classes were increased, would you be more likely to enroll in one or more of them?"

Class	Yes	No	No opinion
Freshmen	15	8	5
Sophomores	24	4	2

If a student is selected at random, find the probability that the student

a. Has no opinion

b. Is a freshman or is against the issue

c. Is a sophomore and favors the issue

18. Mail Delivery A local postal carrier distributes first-class letters, advertisements, and magazines. For a certain day, she distributed the following numbers of each type of item.

Delivered to	First-class letters	Ads	Magazines
Home	325	406	203
Business	732	1021	97

If an item of mail is selected at random, find these probabilities.

a. The item went to a home.

b. The item was an ad, or it went to a business.

c. The item was a first-class letter, or it went to a home.

19. Medical Tests on Emergency Patients The frequency distribution shown here illustrates the number of medical tests conducted on 30 randomly selected emergency patients.

Number of tests performed	Number of patients
0	12
1	8
2	2
3	3
4 or more	5

If a patient is selected at random, find these probabilities.

a. The patient has had exactly 2 tests done.

b. The patient has had at least 2 tests done.

c. The patient has had at most 3 tests done.

d. The patient has had 3 or fewer tests done.

e. The patient has had 1 or 2 tests done.

20. College Fundraiser A social organization of 32 members sold college sweatshirts as a fundraiser. The results of their sale are shown below.

No. of sweatshirts	No. of students
0	2
1–5	13
6–10	8
11–15	4
16–20	4
20+	1

Choose one student at random. Find the probability that the student sold

a. More than 10 sweatshirts

b. At least one sweatshirt

c. 1–5 or more than 15 sweatshirts

21. Door-to-Door Sales A sales representative who visits customers at home finds she sells 0, 1, 2, 3, or 4 items according to the following frequency distribution.

Items sold	Frequency
0	8
1	10
2	3
3	2
4	1

Find the probability that she sells the following.

a. Exactly 1 item

b. More than 2 items

c. At least 1 item

d. At most 3 items

22. Medical Patients A recent study of 300 patients found that of 100 alcoholic patients, 87 had elevated cholesterol levels, and of 200 nonalcoholic patients, 43 had elevated cholesterol levels. If a patient is selected at random, find the probability that the patient is the following.

a. An alcoholic with elevated cholesterol level

b. A nonalcoholic

c. A nonalcoholic with nonelevated cholesterol level

23. Selecting a Card If one card is drawn from an ordinary deck of cards, find the probability of getting the following.

a. A king or a queen or a jack

b. A club or a heart or a spade

c. A king or a queen or a diamond

d. An ace or a diamond or a heart

e. A 9 or a 10 or a spade or a club

24. Rolling Die Two dice are rolled. Find the probability of getting

a. A sum of 8, 9, or 10

b. Doubles or a sum of 7

c. A sum greater than 9 or less than 4

d. Based on the answers to *a*, *b*, and *c*, which is least likely to occur?

25. Corn Products U.S. growers harvested 11 billion bushels of corn in 2005. About 1.9 billion bushels were exported, and 1.6 billion bushels were used for ethanol. Choose one bushel of corn at random. What is the probability that it was used either for export or for ethanol?

Source: www.census.gov

26. Rolling Dice Three dice are rolled. Find the probability of getting

a. Triples   b. A sum of 5

Extending the Concepts

27. Purchasing a Pizza The probability that a customer selects a pizza with mushrooms or pepperoni is 0.55, and the probability that the customer selects only mushrooms is 0.32. If the probability that he or she selects only pepperoni is 0.17, find the probability of the customer selecting both items.

28. Building a New Home In building new homes, a contractor finds that the probability of a home buyer selecting a two-car garage is 0.70 and of selecting a one-car garage is 0.20. Find the probability that the buyer will select no garage. The builder does not build houses with three-car or more garages.

29. In Exercise 28, find the probability that the buyer will not want a two-car garage.

30. Suppose that $P(A) = 0.42$, $P(B) = 0.38$, and $P(A \text{ or } B) = 0.70$. Are A and B mutually exclusive? Explain.

31. The probability of event A occurring is $m/(2m + n)$, and the probability of event B occurring is $n/(2m + n)$. Find the probability of A or B occurring if the events are mutually exclusive.

32. Events A and B are mutually exclusive with $P(A)$ equal to 0.392 and $P(A \text{ or } B)$ equal to 0.653. Find

a. $P(B)$

b. $P(\text{not } A)$

c. $P(A \text{ and } B)$

"I know you haven't had an accident in thirteen years. We're raising your rates because you're about due one."

© Bob Schochet. King Features Syndicate.

Technology   Step by Step

TI-84 Plus
Step by Step

To construct a relative frequency table:

1. Enter the data values in L_1 and the frequencies in L_2.

2. Move the cursor to the top of the L_3 column so that L_3 is highlighted.

3. Type L_2 divided by the sample size, then press **ENTER**.

Example TI4–1

Construct a relative frequency table for the knee replacement data from Example 4–14:

L1	L2	◆3	3
3	15	------	
4	32		
5	56		
6	19		
7	5		
------	------	------	

L3 =L2/127■

L1	L2	L3	3
3	15	.11811	
4	32	.25197	
5	56	.44094	
6	19	.14961	
7	5	.03937	
------	------	------	

L3(1)=.1181102362...

EXCEL
Step by Step

Constructing a Relative Frequency Distribution

Use the data from Example 4–14.

1. In a new worksheet, type the label **DAYS** in cell A1. Beginning in cell A2, type in the data for the variable representing the number of days knee replacement patients stayed in the hospital.

2. In cell B1, type the label for the frequency, **COUNT.** Beginning in cell B2, type in the frequencies.

3. In cell B7, compute the total frequency by selecting the sum icon Σ from the toolbar and press **Enter.**

4. In cell C1, type a label for the relative frequencies, **RF.** In cell C2, type **=(B2)/(B7)** and **Enter.** In cell C3, type **=(B3)/(B7)** and **Enter.** Repeat this for each of the remaining frequencies.

5. To find the total relative frequency, select the sum icon Σ from the toolbar and **Enter.** This sum should be 1.

Constructing a Contingency Table

Example XL4–1

For this example, you will need to have the MegaStat Add-In installed on Excel (refer to Chapter 1, Excel Step by Step instructions for instructions on installing MegaStat).

1. Open the Databank.xls file from the CD-ROM that came with your text. To do this:

   Double-click My Computer on the Desktop.

   Double-click the Bluman CD-ROM icon in the CD drive holding the disk.

   Double-click the datasets folder. Then double-click the all_data-sets folder.

   Double-click the bluman_es_data-sets_excel-windows folder. In this folder double-click the Databank.xls file. The Excel program will open automatically once you open this file.

2. Highlight the column labeled SMOKING STATUS to copy these data onto a new Excel worksheet.

3. Click the Microsoft Office Button, select New Blank Workbook, then Create.

4. With cell A1 selected, click the Paste icon on the toolbar to paste the data into the new workbook.

5. Return to the Databank.xls file. Highlight the column labeled Gender. Copy and paste these data into column B of the worksheet containing the SMOKING STATUS data.

6. Type in the categories for SMOKING STATUS, **0, 1,** and **2** into cells C2–C4. In cell D2, type M for male and in cell D3, type F for female.

7. On the toolbar, select **Add-Ins.** Then select **MegaStat.** *Note:* You may need to open MegaStat from the file MegaStat.xls saved on your computer's hard drive.

8. Select **Chi-Square/Crosstab>Crosstabulation.**

9. In the Row variable Data range box, type A1:A101. In the Row variable Specification range box, type C2:C4. In the Column variable Data range box, type B1:B101. In the Column variable Specification range box, type D2:D3. Remove any checks from the Output Options. Then click [OK].

Crosstabulation

| | | GENDER | | |
		M	F	Total
SMOKING STATUS	0	21	25	46
	1	19	18	37
	2	9	8	17
	Total	49	51	100

MINITAB
Step by Step

Calculate Relative Frequency Probabilities

The random variable X represents the number of days patients stayed in the hospital from Example 4–14.

1. In C1 of a worksheet, type in the values of X. Name the column **X.**

2. In C2 enter the frequencies. Name the column **f.**

3. To calculate the relative frequencies and store them in a new column named Px:

   a) Select **Calc>Calculator.**

   b) Type **Px** in the box for Store result in variable:.

   c) Click in the Expression box, then double-click C2 f.

d) Type or click the division operator.

e) Scroll down the function list to Sum, then click [Select].

f) Double-click C2 f to select it.

g) Click [OK].

The dialog box and completed worksheet are shown.

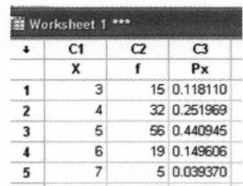

If the original data, rather than the table, are in a worksheet, use **Stat>Tables>Tally** to make the tables with percents (Section 2–1).

MINITAB can also make a two-way classification table.

Construct a Contingency Table

1. Select **File>Open Worksheet** to open the Databank.mtw file.

2. Select **Stat>Tables>Crosstabulation . . .**

   a) Double-click **C4 SMOKING STATUS** to select it **For rows:**.

   b) Select **C11 GENDER** for the **For Columns:** Field.

   c) Click on option for **Counts** and then [OK].

The session window and completed dialog box are shown.

Tabulated statistics: SMOKING STATUS, GENDER

Rows: SMOKING STATUS   Columns: GENDER

	F	M	All
0	25	22	47
1	18	19	37
2	7	9	16
All	50	50	100

Cell Contents: Count

In this sample of 100 there are 25 females who do not smoke compared to 22 men. Sixteen individuals smoke 1 pack or more per day.

4–3   The Multiplication Rules and Conditional Probability

Section 4–2 showed that the addition rules are used to compute probabilities for mutually exclusive and non-mutually exclusive events. This section introduces the multiplication rules.

The Multiplication Rules

OBJECTIVE ③

Find the probability of compound events, using the multiplication rules.

The *multiplication rules* can be used to find the probability of two or more events that occur in sequence. For example, if you toss a coin and then roll a die, you can find the probability of getting a head on the coin *and* a 4 on the die. These two events are said to be *independent* since the outcome of the first event (tossing a coin) does not affect the probability outcome of the second event (rolling a die).

> Two events A and B are **independent events** if the fact that A occurs does not affect the probability of B occurring.

Here are other examples of independent events:

Rolling a die and getting a 6, and then rolling a second die and getting a 3.

Drawing a card from a deck and getting a queen, replacing it, and drawing a second card and getting a queen.

To find the probability of two independent events that occur in sequence, you must find the probability of each event occurring separately and then multiply the answers. For example, if a coin is tossed twice, the probability of getting two heads is $\frac{1}{2} \cdot \frac{1}{2} = \frac{1}{4}$. This result can be verified by looking at the sample space HH, HT, TH, TT. Then $P(\text{HH}) = \frac{1}{4}$.

Multiplication Rule 1

When two events are independent, the probability of both occurring is

$$P(A \text{ and } B) = P(A) \cdot P(B)$$

EXAMPLE 4–23   Tossing a Coin

A coin is flipped and a die is rolled. Find the probability of getting a head on the coin and a 4 on the die.

SOLUTION

The sample space for the coin is H, T; and for the die it is 1, 2, 3, 4, 5, 6.

$$P(\text{head and 4}) = P(\text{head}) \cdot P(4) = \frac{1}{2} \cdot \frac{1}{6} = \frac{1}{12} \approx 0.083$$

The problem in Example 4–23 can also be solved by using the sample space

H1   H2   H3   H4   H5   H6   T1   T2   T3   T4   T5   T6

The solution is $\frac{1}{12}$, since there is only one way to get the head-4 outcome.

EXAMPLE 4–24   Drawing a Card

A card is drawn from a deck and replaced; then a second card is drawn. Find the probability of getting a queen and then an ace.

SOLUTION

The probability of getting a queen is $\frac{4}{52}$, and since the card is replaced, the probability of getting an ace is $\frac{4}{52}$. Hence, the probability of getting a queen and an ace is

$$P(\text{queen and ace}) = P(\text{queen}) \cdot P(\text{ace}) = \frac{4}{52} \cdot \frac{4}{52} = \frac{16}{2704} = \frac{1}{169} \approx 0.006$$

EXAMPLE 4–25   Selecting a Colored Ball

An urn contains 3 red balls, 2 blue balls, and 5 white balls. A ball is selected and its color noted. Then it is replaced. A second ball is selected and its color noted. Find the probability of each of these.

    a. Selecting 2 blue balls

    b. Selecting 1 blue ball and then 1 white ball

    c. Selecting 1 red ball and then 1 blue ball

SOLUTION

    a. $P(\text{blue and blue}) = P(\text{blue}) \cdot P(\text{blue}) = \frac{2}{10} \cdot \frac{2}{10} = \frac{4}{100} = \frac{1}{25} = 0.04$

    b. $P(\text{blue and white}) = P(\text{blue}) \cdot P(\text{white}) = \frac{2}{10} \cdot \frac{5}{10} = \frac{10}{100} = \frac{1}{10} = 0.1$

    c. $P(\text{red and blue}) = P(\text{red}) \cdot P(\text{blue}) = \frac{3}{10} \cdot \frac{2}{10} = \frac{6}{100} = \frac{3}{50} = 0.06$

       Multiplication rule 1 can be extended to three or more independent events by using the formula

$$P(A \text{ and } B \text{ and } C \text{ and } \ldots \text{ and } K) = P(A) \cdot P(B) \cdot P(C) \cdots P(K)$$

       When a small sample is selected from a large population and the subjects are not replaced, the probability of the event occurring changes so slightly that for the most part, it is considered to remain the same. Examples 4–26 and 4–27 illustrate this concept.

EXAMPLE 4–26   Survey on Stress

A Harris poll found that 46% of Americans say they suffer great stress at least once a week. If three people are selected at random, find the probability that all three will say that they suffer great stress at least once a week.

Source: *100% American.*

SOLUTION

Let *S* denote stress. Then

$$P(S \text{ and } S \text{ and } S) = P(S) \cdot P(S) \cdot P(S)$$
$$= (0.46)(0.46)(0.46) \approx 0.097$$

There is a 9.7% chance that all three people will say they suffer great stress at least once a week.

EXAMPLE 4–27   Male Color Blindness

Approximately 9% of men have a type of color blindness that prevents them from distinguishing between red and green. If 3 men are selected at random, find the probability that all of them will have this type of red-green color blindness.

Source: *USA TODAY.*

SOLUTION

Let C denote red-green color blindness. Then

$$P(C \text{ and } C \text{ and } C) = P(C) \cdot P(C) \cdot P(C)$$
$$= (0.09)(0.09)(0.09)$$
$$= 0.000729$$

Hence, the rounded probability is 0.0007.

There is a 0.07% chance that all three men selected will have this type of red-green color blindness.

In Examples 4–23 through 4–27, the events were independent of one another, since the occurrence of the first event in no way affected the outcome of the second event. On the other hand, when the occurrence of the first event changes the probability of the occurrence of the second event, the two events are said to be *dependent*. For example, suppose a card is drawn from a deck and *not* replaced, and then a second card is drawn. What is the probability of selecting an ace on the first card and a king on the second card?

Before an answer to the question can be given, you must realize that the events are dependent. The probability of selecting an ace on the first draw is $\frac{4}{52}$. If that card is *not* replaced, the probability of selecting a king on the second card is $\frac{4}{51}$, since there are 4 kings and 51 cards remaining. The outcome of the first draw has affected the outcome of the second draw.

Dependent events are formally defined now.

> When the outcome or occurrence of the first event affects the outcome or occurrence of the second event in such a way that the probability is changed, the events are said to be **dependent events**.

Here are some examples of dependent events:

Drawing a card from a deck, not replacing it, and then drawing a second card

Selecting a ball from an urn, not replacing it, and then selecting a second ball

Being a lifeguard and getting a suntan

Having high grades and getting a scholarship

Parking in a no-parking zone and getting a parking ticket

To find probabilities when events are dependent, use the multiplication rule with a modification in notation. For the problem just discussed, the probability of getting an ace on the first draw is $\frac{4}{52}$, and the probability of getting a king on the second draw is $\frac{4}{51}$. By the multiplication rule, the probability of both events occurring is

$$\frac{4}{52} \cdot \frac{4}{51} = \frac{16}{2652} = \frac{4}{663} \approx 0.006$$

The event of getting a king on the second draw *given* that an ace was drawn the first time is called a *conditional probability*.

The **conditional probability** of an event B in relationship to an event A is the probability that event B occurs after event A has already occurred. The notation for conditional probability is $P(B|A)$. This notation does not mean that B is divided by A; rather, it means the probability that event B occurs given that event A has already occurred. In the card example, $P(B|A)$ is the probability that the second card is a king given that the first card is an ace, and it is equal to $\frac{4}{51}$ since the first card was *not* replaced.

Multiplication Rule 2

When two events are dependent, the probability of both occurring is

$$P(A \text{ and } B) = P(A) \cdot P(B|A)$$

EXAMPLE 4–28   Overqualified Workers

In a recent survey, 33% of the respondents said that they feel that they are overqualified (O) for their present job. Of these, 24% said that they were looking for a new job (J). If a person is selected at random, find the probability that the person feels that he or she is overqualified and is also looking for a new job.

SOLUTION

$$P(O \text{ and } J) = P(O) \cdot P(J|O) = (0.33)(0.24) \approx 0.079$$

There is about a 7.9% probability that the person feels that he or she is overqualified and is also looking for a new job.

EXAMPLE 4–29   Homeowner's and Automobile Insurance

World Wide Insurance Company found that 53% of the residents of a city had home-owner's insurance (H) with the company. Of these clients, 27% also had automobile insurance (A) with the company. If a resident is selected at random, find the probability that the resident has both homeowner's and automobile insurance with World Wide Insurance Company.

SOLUTION

$$P(H \text{ and } A) = P(H) \cdot P(A|H) = (0.53)(0.27) = 0.1431 \approx 0.143$$

There is about a 14.3% probability that a resident has both homeowner's and automobile insurance with World Wide Insurance Company.

This multiplication rule can be extended to three or more events, as shown in Example 4–30.

EXAMPLE 4–30   Drawing Cards

Three cards are drawn from an ordinary deck and not replaced. Find the probability of these events.

    a. Getting 3 jacks

    b. Getting an ace, a king, and a queen in order

    c. Getting a club, a spade, and a heart in order

    d. Getting 3 clubs

SOLUTION

a. $P(3 \text{ jacks}) = \dfrac{4}{52} \cdot \dfrac{3}{51} \cdot \dfrac{2}{50} = \dfrac{24}{132,600} = \dfrac{1}{5525} \approx 0.0002$

b. $P(\text{ace and king and queen}) = \dfrac{4}{52} \cdot \dfrac{4}{51} \cdot \dfrac{4}{50} = \dfrac{64}{132,600} = \dfrac{8}{16,575} \approx 0.0005$

c. $P(\text{club and spade and heart}) = \dfrac{13}{52} \cdot \dfrac{13}{51} \cdot \dfrac{13}{50} = \dfrac{2197}{132,600} = \dfrac{169}{10,200} \approx 0.017$

d. $P(3 \text{ clubs}) = \dfrac{13}{52} \cdot \dfrac{12}{51} \cdot \dfrac{11}{50} = \dfrac{1716}{132,600} = \dfrac{11}{850} \approx 0.013$

Tree diagrams can be used as an aid to finding the solution to probability problems when the events are sequential. Example 4–31 illustrates the use of tree diagrams.

EXAMPLE 4–31   Selecting Colored Balls

Box 1 contains 2 red balls and 1 blue ball. Box 2 contains 3 blue balls and 1 red ball. A coin is tossed. If it falls heads up, box 1 is selected and a ball is drawn. If it falls tails up, box 2 is selected and a ball is drawn. Find the probability of selecting a red ball.

SOLUTION

The first two branches designate the selection of either box 1 or box 2. Then from box 1, either a red ball or a blue ball can be selected. Likewise, a red ball or blue ball can be selected from box 2. Hence, a tree diagram of the example is shown in Figure 4–8.

Next determine the probabilities for each branch. Since a coin is being tossed for the box selection, each branch has a probability of $\frac{1}{2}$, that is, heads for box 1 or tails for box 2. The probabilities for the second branches are found by using the basic probability rule. For example, if box 1 is selected and there are 2 red balls and 1 blue ball, the probability of selecting a red ball is $\frac{2}{3}$ and the probability of selecting a blue ball is $\frac{1}{3}$. If box 2 is selected and it contains 3 blue balls and 1 red ball, then the probability of selecting a red ball is $\frac{1}{4}$ and the probability of selecting a blue ball is $\frac{3}{4}$.

Next multiply the probability for each outcome, using the rule $P(A \text{ and } B) = P(A) \cdot P(B|A)$. For example, the probability of selecting box 1 and selecting a red ball is $\frac{1}{2} \cdot \frac{2}{3} = \frac{2}{6}$. The probability of selecting box 1 and a blue ball is $\frac{1}{2} \cdot \frac{1}{3} = \frac{1}{6}$. The probability of selecting box 2 and selecting a red ball is $\frac{1}{2} \cdot \frac{1}{4} = \frac{1}{8}$. The probability of selecting box 2 and a blue ball is $\frac{1}{2} \cdot \frac{3}{4} = \frac{3}{8}$. (Note that the sum of these probabilities is 1.)

Finally, a red ball can be selected from either box 1 or box 2 so $P(\text{red}) = \frac{2}{6} + \frac{1}{8} = \frac{8}{24} + \frac{3}{24} = \frac{11}{24}$.

FIGURE 4–8   Tree Diagram for Example 4–31

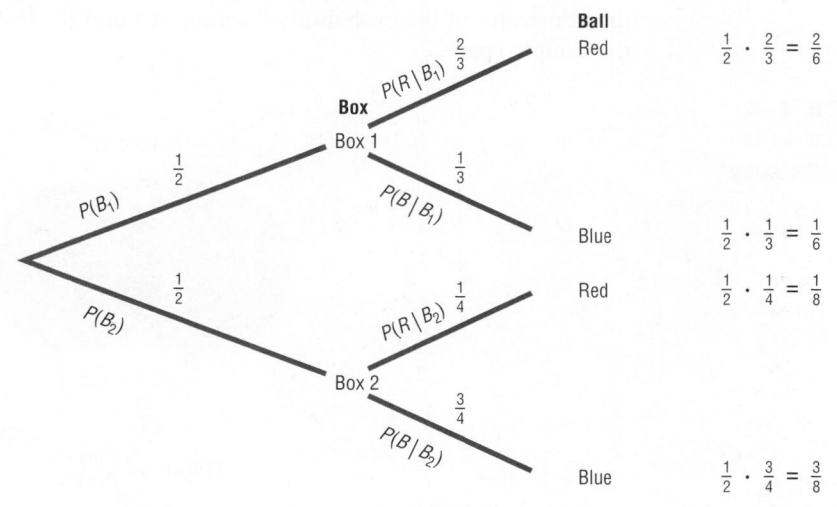

Tree diagrams can be used when the events are independent or dependent, and they can also be used for sequences of three or more events.

OBJECTIVE ❹

Find the conditional probability of an event.

Conditional Probability

The conditional probability of an event B in relationship to an event A was defined as the probability that event B occurs after event A has already occurred.

The conditional probability of an event can be found by dividing both sides of the equation for multiplication rule 2 by $P(A)$, as shown:

$$P(A \text{ and } B) = P(A) \cdot P(B|A)$$

$$\frac{P(A \text{ and } B)}{P(A)} = \frac{\cancel{P(A)} \cdot P(B|A)}{\cancel{P(A)}}$$

$$\frac{P(A \text{ and } B)}{P(A)} = P(B|A)$$

Formula for Conditional Probability

The probability that the second event B occurs given that the first event A has occurred can be found by dividing the probability that both events occurred by the probability that the first event has occurred. The formula is

$$P(B|A) = \frac{P(A \text{ and } B)}{P(A)}$$

The Venn diagram for conditional probability is shown in Figure 4–9. In this case,

$$P(B|A) = \frac{P(A \text{ and } B)}{P(A)}$$

which is represented by the area in the intersection or overlapping part of the circles A and B, divided by the area of circle A. The reasoning here is that if you assume A has occurred, then A becomes the sample space for the next calculation and is the denominator of the probability fraction $P(A \text{ and } B)/P(A)$. The numerator $P(A \text{ and } B)$ represents the probability of the part of B that is contained in A. Hence, $P(A \text{ and } B)$ becomes the numerator of the probability fraction $P(A \text{ and } B)/P(A)$. Imposing a condition reduces the sample space.

FIGURE 4–9
Venn Diagram for
Conditional Probability

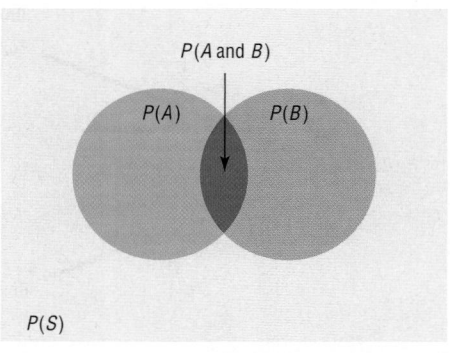

$$P(B|A) = \frac{P(A \text{ and } B)}{P(A)}$$

Examples 4–32, 4–33, and 4–34 illustrate the use of this rule.

EXAMPLE 4–32   Selecting Colored Chips

A box contains black chips and white chips. A person selects two chips without replacement. If the probability of selecting a black chip *and* a white chip is $\frac{15}{56}$ and the probability of selecting a black chip on the first draw is $\frac{3}{8}$, find the probability of selecting the white chip on the second draw, *given* that the first chip selected was a black chip.

SOLUTION

Let

$$B = \text{selecting a black chip} \qquad W = \text{selecting a white chip}$$

Then

$$P(W|B) = \frac{P(B \text{ and } W)}{P(B)} = \frac{15/56}{3/8}$$

$$= \frac{15}{56} \div \frac{3}{8} = \frac{15}{56} \cdot \frac{8}{3} = \frac{\overset{5}{\cancel{15}}}{\underset{7}{\cancel{56}}} \cdot \frac{\overset{1}{\cancel{8}}}{\underset{1}{\cancel{3}}} = \frac{5}{7} \approx 0.714$$

Hence, the probability of selecting a white chip on the second draw given that the first chip selected was black is $\frac{5}{7} \approx 0.714$.

EXAMPLE 4–33   Parking Tickets

The probability that Sam parks in a no-parking zone *and* gets a parking ticket is 0.06, and the probability that Sam cannot find a legal parking space and has to park in the no-parking zone is 0.20. On Tuesday, Sam arrives at school and has to park in a no-parking zone. Find the probability that he will get a parking ticket.

SOLUTION

Let

$$N = \text{parking in a no-parking zone} \qquad T = \text{getting a ticket}$$

Then

$$P(T|N) = \frac{P(N \text{ and } T)}{P(N)} = \frac{0.06}{0.20} = 0.30$$

Hence, Sam has a 0.30 probability or 30% chance of getting a parking ticket, given that he parked in a no-parking zone.

The conditional probability of events occurring can also be computed when the data are given in table form, as shown in Example 4–34.

EXAMPLE 4–34   Survey on Women in the Military

A recent survey asked 100 people if they thought women in the armed forces should be permitted to participate in combat. The results of the survey are shown.

Gender	Yes	No	Total
Male	32	18	50
Female	8	42	50
Total	40	60	100

Find these probabilities.

a. The respondent answered yes, given that the respondent was a female.

b. The respondent was a male, given that the respondent answered no.

SOLUTION

Let

M = respondent was a male Y = respondent answered yes

F = respondent was a female N = respondent answered no

a. The problem is to find $P(Y|F)$. The rule states

$$P(Y|F) = \frac{P(F \text{ and } Y)}{P(F)}$$

The probability $P(F \text{ and } Y)$ is the number of females who responded yes, divided by the total number of respondents:

$$P(F \text{ and } Y) = \frac{8}{100}$$

The probability $P(F)$ is the probability of selecting a female:

$$P(F) = \frac{50}{100}$$

Then

$$P(Y|F) = \frac{P(F \text{ and } Y)}{P(F)} = \frac{8/100}{50/100}$$

$$= \frac{8}{100} \div \frac{50}{100} = \frac{\overset{4}{\cancel{8}}}{\underset{1}{\cancel{100}}} \cdot \frac{\overset{1}{\cancel{100}}}{\underset{25}{\cancel{50}}} = \frac{4}{25} = 0.16$$

b. The problem is to find $P(M|N)$.

$$P(M|N) = \frac{P(N \text{ and } M)}{P(N)} = \frac{18/100}{60/100}$$

$$= \frac{18}{100} \div \frac{60}{100} = \frac{\overset{3}{\cancel{18}}}{\underset{1}{\cancel{100}}} \cdot \frac{\overset{1}{\cancel{100}}}{\underset{10}{\cancel{60}}} = \frac{3}{10} = 0.3$$

Probabilities for "At Least"

The multiplication rules can be used with the complementary event rule (Section 4–1) to simplify solving probability problems involving "at least." Examples 4–35, 4–36, and 4–37 illustrate how this is done.

EXAMPLE 4–35   Drawing Cards

A person selects 3 cards from an ordinary deck and replaces each card after it is drawn. Find the probability that the person will get at least one heart.

SOLUTION

It is much easier to find the probability that the person will not select a heart in three draws and subtract this value from 1. To do the problem directly, you would have to find the probability of selecting 1 heart, 2 hearts, and 3 hearts and then add the results.

Let

$$E = \text{at least 1 heart is drawn} \qquad \text{and} \qquad \overline{E} = \text{no hearts are drawn}$$

$$P(\overline{E}) = \frac{39}{52} \cdot \frac{39}{52} \cdot \frac{39}{52} = \frac{3}{4} \cdot \frac{3}{4} \cdot \frac{3}{4} = \frac{27}{64}$$

$$P(E) = 1 - P(\overline{E})$$

$$= 1 - \frac{27}{64} = \frac{37}{64} \approx 0.578 = 57.8\%$$

Hence, a person will select at least one heart about 57.8% of the time.

EXAMPLE 4–36   Tossing Coins

A coin is tossed 5 times. Find the probability of getting at least 1 tail.

SOLUTION

It is easier to find the probability of the complement of the event, which is "all heads," and then subtract the probability from 1 to get the probability of at least 1 tail.

$$P(E) = 1 - P(\overline{E})$$

$$P(\text{at least 1 tail}) = 1 - P(\text{all heads})$$

$$P(\text{all heads}) = \left(\frac{1}{2}\right)^5 = \frac{1}{32}$$

Hence,

$$P(\text{at least 1 tail}) = 1 - \frac{1}{32} = \frac{31}{32} \approx 0.969$$

There is a 96.9% chance of getting at least one tail.

EXAMPLE 4–37   Ties

The Neckware Association of America reported that 3% of ties sold in the United States are bow ties. If 4 customers who purchased a tie are randomly selected, find the probability that at least 1 purchased a bow tie.

SOLUTION

Let E = at least 1 bow tie is purchased and $\overline{E}$ = no bow ties are purchased. Then

$$P(E) = 0.03 \qquad \text{and} \qquad P(\overline{E}) = 1 - 0.03 = 0.97$$

$$P(\text{no bow ties are purchased}) = (0.97)(0.97)(0.97)(0.97) \approx 0.885; \text{ hence,}$$
$$P(\text{at least one bow tie is purchased}) = 1 - 0.885 = 0.115.$$

There is an 11.5% chance of a person purchasing at least one bow tie.

Applying the Concepts 4–3

Guilty or Innocent?

In July 1964, an elderly woman was mugged in Costa Mesa, California. In the vicinity of the crime a tall, bearded man sat waiting in a yellow car. Shortly after the crime was committed, a young, tall woman, wearing her blond hair in a ponytail, was seen running from the scene of the crime and getting into the car, which sped off. The police broadcast a description of the suspected muggers. Soon afterward, a couple fitting the description was arrested and convicted of the crime. Although the evidence in the case was largely circumstantial, the two people arrested were nonetheless convicted of the crime. The prosecutor based his entire case on basic probability theory, showing the unlikeness of another couple being in that area while having all the same characteristics that the elderly woman described. The following probabilities were used.

Characteristic	Assumed probability
Drives yellow car	1 out of 12
Man over 6 feet tall	1 out of 10
Man wearing tennis shoes	1 out of 4
Man with beard	1 out of 11
Woman with blond hair	1 out of 3
Woman with hair in a ponytail	1 out of 13
Woman over 6 feet tall	1 out of 100

1. Compute the probability of another couple being in that area with the same characteristics.

2. Would you use the addition or multiplication rule? Why?

3. Are the characteristics independent or dependent?

4. How are the computations affected by the assumption of independence or dependence?

5. Should any court case be based solely on probabilities?

6. Would you convict the couple who was arrested even if there were no eyewitnesses?

7. Comment on why in today's justice system no person can be convicted solely on the results of probabilities.

8. In actuality, aren't most court cases based on uncalculated probabilities?

See page 254 for the answers.

Exercises 4–3

1. State which events are independent and which are dependent.

    a. Tossing a coin and drawing a card from a deck

    b. Drawing a ball from an urn, not replacing it, and then drawing a second ball

    c. Getting a raise in salary and purchasing a new car

    d. Driving on ice and having an accident

2. State which events are independent and which are dependent.

    a. Having a large shoe size and having a high IQ

    b. A father being left-handed and a daughter being left-handed

    c. Smoking excessively and having lung cancer

    d. Eating an excessive amount of ice cream and smoking an excessive amount of cigarettes

3. **Video and Computer Games** Sixty-nine percent of U.S. heads of household play video or computer games. Choose 4 heads of household at random. Find the probability that

    a. None play video or computer games.

    b. All four do.

    Source: www.theesa.com

4. **Seat Belt Use** The Gallup Poll reported that 52% of Americans used a seat belt the last time they got into a car. If 4 people are selected at random, find the probability that they all used a seat belt the last time they got into a car.

    Source: *100% American.*

5. **Automobile Sales** An automobile salesperson finds the probability of making a sale is 0.21. If she talks to 4 customers, find the probability that she will make 4 sales. Is the event likely or unlikely to occur? Explain your answer.

6. **Prison Populations** If 25% of U.S. federal prison inmates are not U.S. citizens, find the probability that 2 randomly selected federal prison inmates will not be U.S. citizens.

    Source: *Harper's Index.*

7. **Government Employees** In 2010 about 69.6% of full-time law enforcement workers were sworn officers, and of those, 88.2% were male. Females, however, make up 60.8% of civilian employees. Choose one law enforcement worker at random and find the following.

    a. The probability that she is a female sworn officer

    b. The probability that he is a male civilian employee

    c. The probability that he or she is male or a civilian employee

    Source: *World Almanac.*

8. **Working Women and Computer Use** It is reported that 72% of working women use computers at work. Choose 5 working women at random. Find

    a. The probability that at least 1 doesn't use a computer at work

    b. The probability that all 5 use a computer in their jobs

    Source: www.infoplease.com

9. **Text Messages via Cell Phones** Thirty-five percent of adults who own cell phones use their phones to send and receive text messages. Choose 4 cell phone owners at random. What is the probability that none use their phones for texting?

10. **Selecting Marbles** A bag contains 9 red marbles, 8 white marbles, and 6 blue marbles. Randomly choose two marbles, one at a time, and without replacement. Find the following.

    a. The probability that the first marble is red and the second is white

    b. The probability that both are the same color

    c. The probability that the second marble is blue

11. **Cable Television** In 2006, 86% of U.S. households had cable TV. Choose 3 households at random. Find the probability that

    a. None of the 3 households had cable TV

    b. All 3 households had cable TV

    c. At least 1 of the 3 households had cable TV

    Source: www.infoplease.com

12. **Flashlight Batteries** A flashlight has 6 batteries, 2 of which are defective. If 2 are selected at random without replacement, find the probability that both are defective.

13. **Drawing a Card** Four cards are drawn from a deck *without* replacement. Find these probabilities.

    a. All are kings.

    b. All are diamonds.

    c. All are red cards.

14. **Scientific Study** In a scientific study there are 8 guinea pigs, 5 of which are pregnant. If 3 are selected at random without replacement, find the probability that all are pregnant.

15. **Cards** If 2 cards are selected from a standard deck of 52 cards without replacement, find these probabilities.

    a. Both are spades.

    b. Both are the same suit.

    c. Both are kings.

16. **Winning a Door Prize** At a gathering consisting of 10 men and 20 women, two door prizes are awarded. Find the probability that both prizes are won by men. The winning ticket is not replaced. Would you consider this event likely or unlikely to occur?

17. In a box of 24 iPods, 3 are defective. If 3 are sold, find the probability that all are defective. Would you consider this event likely or unlikely to occur?

18. **Sales** A manufacturer makes two models of an item: model I, which accounts for 80% of unit sales, and model II, which accounts for 20% of unit sales. Because of defects, the manufacturer has to replace (or exchange) 10% of its model I and 18% of its model II. If a model is selected at random, find the probability that it will be defective.

19. **Student Financial Aid** In a recent year 8,073,000 male students and 10,980,000 female students were enrolled as undergraduates. Receiving aid were 60.6% of the male students and 65.2% of the female students. Of those receiving aid, 44.8% of the males got federal aid and 50.4% of the females got federal aid. Choose 1 student at random. (*Hint:* Make a tree diagram.) Find the probability that the student is

    a. A male student without aid

    b. A male student, given that the student has aid

    c. A female student or a student who receives federal aid

    Source: www.nces.gov

20. **Selecting Colored Balls** Urn 1 contains 5 red balls and 3 black balls. Urn 2 contains 3 red balls and 1 black ball. Urn 3 contains 4 red balls and 2 black balls. If an urn is selected at random and a ball is drawn, find the probability it will be red.

21. **Automobile Insurance** An insurance company classifies drivers as low-risk, medium-risk, and high-risk. Of those insured, 60% are low-risk, 30% are medium-risk, and 10% are high-risk. After a study, the company finds that during a 1-year period, 1% of the low-risk drivers had an accident, 5% of the medium-risk drivers had an accident, and 9% of the high-risk drivers had an accident. If a driver is selected at random, find the probability that the driver will have had an accident during the year.

22. **Defective Items** A production process produces an item. On average, 15% of all items produced are defective. Each item is inspected before being shipped, and the inspector misclassifies an item 10% of the time. What proportion of the items will be "classified as good"? What is the probability that an item is defective given that it was classified as good?

23. **Prison Populations** For a recent year, 0.99 of the incarcerated population is adults and 0.07 of the incarcerated are female. If an incarcerated person is selected at random, find the probability that the person is a female given that the person is an adult.

    Source: Bureau of Justice.

24. Rolling Dice Roll two standard dice and add the numbers. What is the probability of getting a number larger than 9 for the first time on the third roll?

25. Heart Disease Twenty-five percent of all deaths (all ages) are caused by diseases of the heart. Ischemic heart disease accounts for 16.4% of all deaths and heart failure for 2.3%. Choose one death at random. What is the probability that it is from ischemic heart disease given that it was from heart disease? Choose two deaths at random; what is the probability that at least one is from heart disease?

Source: *Time Almanac.*

26. Country Club Activities At the Avonlea Country Club, 73% of the members play bridge and swim, and 82% play bridge. If a member is selected at random, find the probability that the member swims, given that the member plays bridge.

27. College Courses At a large university, the probability that a student takes calculus and is on the dean's list is 0.042. The probability that a student is on the dean's list is 0.21. Find the probability that the student is taking calculus, given that he or she is on the dean's list.

28. Congressional Terms Below is given the summary from the 112th Congress of Senators whose terms end in 2013, 2015, or 2017.

	2013	2015	2017
Democrat	21	20	1
Republican	8	15	13

Choose one of these Senators at random and find

a. *P*(Democrat and term expires in 2015)

b. *P*(Republican or term expires in 2013)

c. *P*(Republican given term expires in 2017)

Are the events "Republican" and "term expires in 2015" independent? Explain.

Source: *Time Almanac 2012.*

29. Pizza and Salads In a pizza restaurant, 95% of the customers order pizza. If 65% of the customers order pizza and a salad, find the probability that a customer who orders pizza will also order a salad.

30. Gift Baskets The Gift Basket Store had the following premade gift baskets containing the following combinations in stock.

	Cookies	Mugs	Candy
Coffee	20	13	10
Tea	12	10	12

Choose 1 basket at random. Find the probability that it contains

a. Coffee or candy

b. Tea given that it contains mugs

c. Tea and cookies

Source: www.infoplease.com

31. Blood Types and Rh Factors In addition to being grouped into four types, human blood is grouped by its Rhesus (Rh) factor. Consider the figures below which show the distributions of these groups for Americans.

	O	A	B	AB
Rh+	37%	34%	10%	4%
Rh−	6	6	2	1

Choose one American at random. Find the probability that the person

a. Is a universal donor, i.e., has O-negative blood

b. Has type O blood given that the person is Rh+

c. Has A+ or AB− blood

d. Has Rh− given that the person has type B

Source: www.infoplease.com

32. Doctor Specialties Below are listed the numbers of doctors in various specialties by gender.

	Pathology	Pediatrics	Psychiatry
Male	12,575	33,020	27,803
Female	5,604	33,351	12,292

Choose one doctor at random.

a. Find *P* (male|pediatrician).

b. Find *P* (pathologist|female).

c. Are the characteristics "female" and "pathologist" independent? Explain.

Source: *World Almanac.*

33. Lightning Strikes It has been said that the probability of being struck by lightning is about 1 in 750,000, but under what circumstances? Below are listed the numbers of deaths from lightning since 1996.

	Golf/ball field	Boating/ in water	Outside/camping	Construction	Under a tree	Phone	Other
1996–2000	16	23	117	9	40	0	30
2001–2005	17	16	112	3	35	0	23
2006–2010	15	17	91	0	42	1	16

Choose one fatality at random and find each probability.

a. Given that the death was after 2000, what is the probability that it occurred under a tree?

b. Find the probability that the death was from camping or being outside and was before 2001.

c. Find the probability that the death was from camping or being outside given that it was before 2001.

Source: Noaa.gov/hazstats

34. Foreign Adoptions The following foreign adoptions (in the United States) occurred during these particular years.

	2006	2010
China	6493	3401
Ethiopia	732	2513
Russia	3706	1082

Choose one adoption at random from this chart.

a. What is the probability that it was from Ethiopia given that it was from 2010?

b. What is the probability that it was from Russia and in 2006?

c. What is the probability that it did not occur in 2006 and was not from Ethiopia?

d. Choose two adoptions at random; what is the probability that they were both from China?

Source: *World Almanac.*

35. Leisure Time Exercise Only 27% of U.S. adults get enough leisure time exercise to achieve cardiovascular fitness. Choose 3 adults at random. Find the probability that

a. All 3 get enough daily exercise

b. At least 1 of the 3 gets enough exercise

Source: www.infoplease.com

36. Customer Purchases In a department store there are 120 customers, 90 of whom will buy at least 1 item. If 5 customers are selected at random, one by one, find the probability that all will buy at least 1 item.

37. Marital Status of Women According to the *Statistical Abstract of the United States,* 70.3% of females ages 20 to 24 have never been married. Choose 5 young women in this age category at random. Find the probability that

a. None has ever been married

b. At least 1 has been married

Source: *New York Times Almanac.*

38. Fatal Accidents The American Automobile Association (AAA) reports that of the fatal car and truck accidents, 54% are caused by car driver error. If 3 accidents are chosen at random, find the probability that

a. All are caused by car driver error

b. None is caused by car driver error

c. At least 1 is caused by car driver error

Source: AAA quoted on CNN.

39. On-Time Airplane Arrivals The greater Cincinnati airport led major U.S. airports in on-time arrivals in the last quarter of 2005 with an 84.3% on-time rate. Choose 5 arrivals at random and find the probability that at least 1 was not on time.

Source: www.census.gov

40. On-Time Flights A flight from Pittsburgh to Charlotte has a 90% on-time record. From Charlotte to Jacksonville, North Carolina, the flight is on time 80% of the time. The return flight from Jacksonville to Charlotte is on time 50% of the time and from Charlotte to Pittsburgh, 90% of the time. Consider a round trip from Pittsburgh to Jacksonville on these flights. Assume the flights are independent.

a. What is the probability that all 4 flights are on time?

b. What is the probability that at least 1 flight is not on time?

c. What is the probability that at least 1 flight is on time?

d. Which events are complementary?

41. Reading to Children Fifty-eight percent of American children (ages 3 to 5) are read to every day by someone at home. Suppose 5 children are randomly selected. What is the probability that at least 1 is read to every day by someone at home?

Source: Federal Interagency Forum on Child and Family Statistics.

42. Doctoral Assistantships Of Ph.D. students, 60% have paid assistantships. If 3 students are selected at random, find the probabilities that

a. All have assistantships

b. None has an assistantship

c. At least 1 has an assistantship

Source: U.S. Department of Education, *Chronicle of Higher Education.*

43. Selecting Cards If 4 cards are drawn from a deck of 52 and not replaced, find the probability of getting at least 1 club.

44. Autism In recent years it was thought that approximately 1 in 110 children exhibited some form of autism. The most recent CDC study concluded that the proportion may be as high as 1 in 88. If indeed these new figures are correct, choose 3 children at random and find these probabilities.

a. What is the probability that none have autism?

b. What is the probability that at least 1 has autism?

c. Choose 10 children at random, What is the probability that at least 1 has autism?

Source: Cdc.gov

45. Family and Children's Computer Games It was reported that 19.8% of computer games sold in 2005 were classified as "family and children's." Choose 5 purchased computer games at random. Find the probability that

a. None of the 5 was family and children's

b. At least 1 of the 5 was family and children's

Source: www.theesa.com

46. Medication Effectiveness A medication is 75% effective against a bacterial infection. Find the probability that if 12 people take the medication, at least 1 person's infection will not improve.

47. **Tossing a Coin** A coin is tossed 5 times; find the probability of getting at least 1 tail. Would you consider this event likely to happen? Explain your answer.

48. **Selecting a Letter of the Alphabet** If 3 letters of the alphabet are selected at random, find the probability of getting at least 1 letter x. Letters can be used more than once. Would you consider this event likely to happen? Explain your answer.

49. **Rolling a Die** A die is rolled 6 times. Find the probability of getting at least one 4. Would you consider this event likely or unlikely? Explain your answer.

50. **High School Grades of First-Year College Students** Forty-seven percent of first-year college students enrolled in 2005 had an average grade of A in high school compared to 20% of first-year college students in 1970. Choose 6 first-year college students at random enrolled in 2005. Find the probability that

    a. All had an A average in high school
    b. None had an A average in high school
    c. At least 1 had an A average in high school

    Source: www.census.gov

51. **Rolling a Die** If a die is rolled 3 times, find the probability of getting at least 1 even number.

52. **Selecting a Flower** In a large vase, there are 8 roses, 5 daisies, 12 lilies, and 9 orchids. If 4 flowers are selected at random, and not replaced, find the probability that at least 1 of the flowers is a rose. Would you consider this event likely to occur? Explain your answer.

Extending the Concepts

53. Let A and B be two mutually exclusive events. Are A and B independent events? Explain your answer.

54. **Types of Vehicles** The Bargain Auto Mall has the following cars in stock.

	SUV	Compact	Mid-sized
Foreign	20	50	20
Domestic	65	100	45

    Are the events "compact" and "domestic" independent? Explain.

55. **College Enrollment** An admissions director knows that the probability a student will enroll after a campus visit is 0.55, or $P(E) = 0.55$. While students are on campus visits, interviews with professors are arranged. The admissions director computes these conditional probabilities for students enrolling after visiting three professors, DW, LP, and MH.

    $P(E|DW) = 0.95$ $P(E|LP) = 0.55$ $P(E|MH) = 0.15$

    Is there something wrong with the numbers? Explain.

56. **Commercials** Event A is the event that a person remembers a certain product commercial. Event B is the event that a person buys the product. If $P(B) = 0.35$, comment on each of these conditional probabilities if you were vice president for sales.

    a. $P(B|A) = 0.20$
    b. $P(B|A) = 0.35$
    c. $P(B|A) = 0.55$

57. Given a sample space with events A and B such that $P(A) = 0.342$, $P(B) = 0.279$, and $P(A \text{ or } B) = 0.601$. Are A and B mutually exclusive? Are A and B independent? Find $P(A|B)$, $P(\text{not } B)$, and $P(A \text{ and } B)$.

58. **Child's Board Game** In a child's board game of the tortoise and the hare, the hare moves by roll of a standard die and the tortoise by a six-sided die with the numbers 1, 1, 1, 2, 2, and 3. Roll each die once. What is the probability that the tortoise moves ahead of the hare?

59. **Bags Containing Marbles** Two bags contain marbles. Bag 1 contains 1 black marble and 9 white marbles. Bag 2 contains 1 black marble and x white marbles. If you choose a bag at random, then choose a marble at random, the probability of getting a black marble is $\frac{2}{15}$. How many white marbles are in bag 2?

4–4   Counting Rules

Many times a person must know the number of all possible outcomes for a sequence of events. To determine this number, three rules can be used: the *fundamental counting rule,* the *permutation rule,* and the *combination rule.* These rules are explained here, and they will be used in Section 4–5 to find probabilities of events.

The first rule is called the **fundamental counting rule.**

The Fundamental Counting Rule

Fundamental Counting Rule

In a sequence of n events in which the first one has k_1 possibilities and the second event has k_2 and the third has k_3, and so forth, the total number of possibilities of the sequence will be

$$k_1 \cdot k_2 \cdot k_3 \cdots k_n$$

Note: In this case *and* means to multiply.

Examples 4–38 through 4–41 illustrate the fundamental counting rule.

EXAMPLE 4–38   Tossing a Coin and Rolling a Die

A coin is tossed and a die is rolled. Find the number of outcomes for the sequence of events.

Interesting Fact

Possible games of chess: 25×10^{115}.

SOLUTION

Since the coin can land either heads up or tails up and since the die can land with any one of six numbers showing face up, there are $2 \cdot 6 = 12$ possibilities. A tree diagram can also be drawn for the sequence of events. See Figure 4–10.

FIGURE 4–10
Complete Tree Diagram for Example 4–38

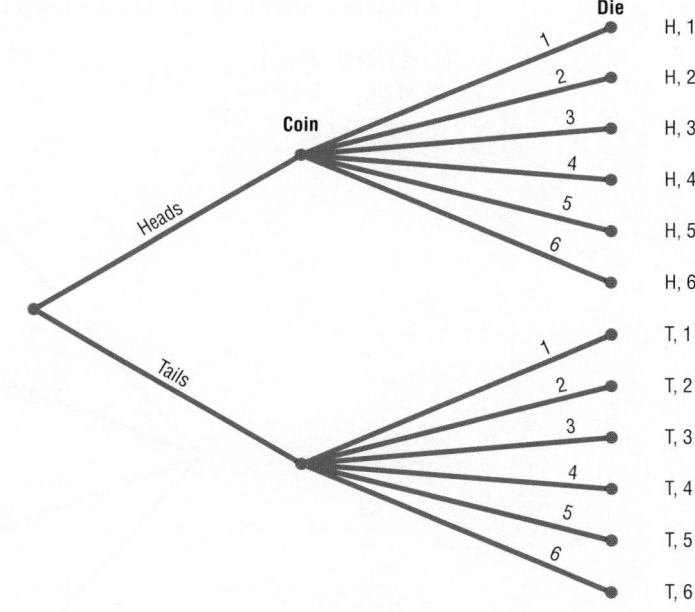

EXAMPLE 4–39   Types of Paint

A paint manufacturer wishes to manufacture several different paints. The categories include

Color	Red, blue, white, black, green, brown, yellow
Type	Latex, oil
Texture	Flat, semigloss, high gloss
Use	Outdoor, indoor

How many different kinds of paint can be made if you can select one color, one type, one texture, and one use?

SOLUTION

You can choose one color and one type and one texture and one use. Since there are 7 color choices, 2 type choices, 3 texture choices, and 2 use choices, the total number of possible different paints is as follows:

Color		Type		Texture		Use	
7	·	2	·	3	·	2	= 84

EXAMPLE 4–40   Distribution of Blood Types

There are four blood types, A, B, AB, and O. Blood can also be Rh+ and Rh−. Finally, a blood donor can be classified as either male or female. How many different ways can a donor have his or her blood labeled?

SOLUTION

Since there are 4 possibilities for blood type, 2 possibilities for Rh factor, and 2 possibilities for the gender of the donor, there are $4 \cdot 2 \cdot 2$, or 16, different classification categories, as shown.

Blood type		Rh		Gender	
4	·	2	·	2	= 16

A tree diagram for the events is shown in Figure 4–11.

FIGURE 4–11

Complete Tree Diagram
for Example 4–40

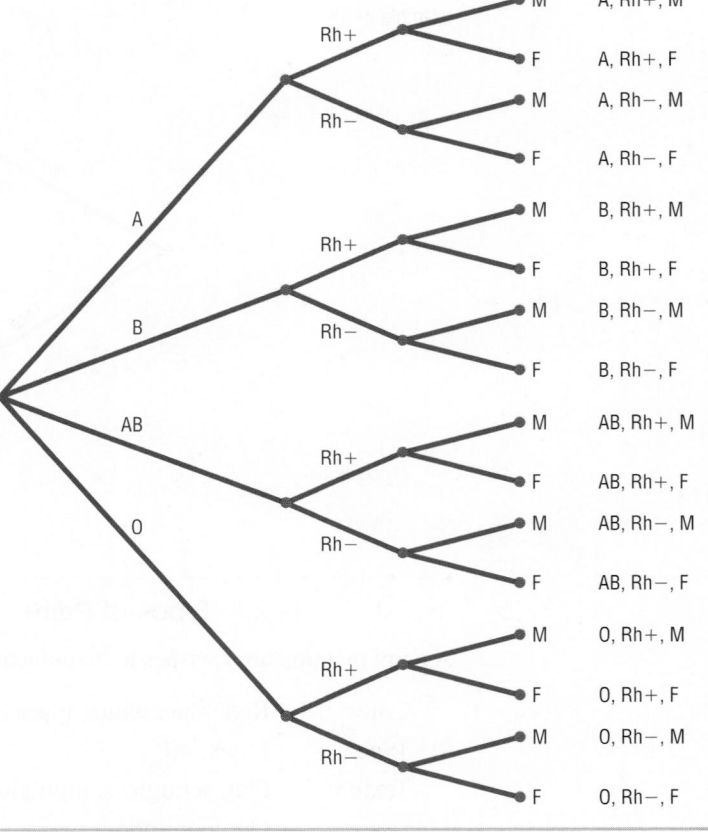

When determining the number of different possibilities of a sequence of events, you must know whether repetitions are permissible.

EXAMPLE 4-41   Railroad Memorial License Plates

The first year the state of Pennsylvania issued railroad memorial license plates, the plates had a picture of a steam engine followed by four digits. Assuming that repetitions are allowed, how many railroad memorial plates could be issued?

SOLUTION

Since there are four spaces to fill for each space, the total number of plates that can be issued is $10 \cdot 10 \cdot 10 \cdot 10 = 10,000$. *Note:* Actually there was such a demand for the plates, Pennsylvania had to use letters also.

Now if repetitions are not permitted, the first digit in the plate in Example 4-41 could be selected in 10 ways, the second digit in 9 ways, etc. So the total number of plates that could be issued is $10 \cdot 9 \cdot 8 \cdot 7 = 5040$.

The same situation occurs when one is drawing balls from an urn or cards from a deck. If the ball or card is replaced before the next one is selected, then repetitions are permitted, since the same one can be selected again. But if the selected ball or card is not replaced, then repetitions are not permitted, since the same ball or card cannot be selected the second time.

These examples illustrate the fundamental counting rule. In summary: *If repetitions are permitted, then the numbers stay the same going from left to right. If repetitions are not permitted, then the numbers decrease by* 1 *for each place left to right.*

Two other rules that can be used to determine the total number of possibilities of a sequence of events are the permutation rule and the combination rule.

Factorial Notation

Historical Note

In 1808 Christian Kramp first used factorial notation.

These rules use *factorial notation.* The factorial notation uses the exclamation point.

$$5! = 5 \cdot 4 \cdot 3 \cdot 2 \cdot 1$$
$$9! = 9 \cdot 8 \cdot 7 \cdot 6 \cdot 5 \cdot 4 \cdot 3 \cdot 2 \cdot 1$$

To use the formulas in the permutation and combination rules, a special definition of 0! is needed: $0! = 1$.

Factorial Formulas

For any counting number n

$$n! = n(n - 1)(n - 2) \cdots 1$$
$$0! = 1$$

Permutations

A **permutation** is an arrangement of n objects in a specific order.

Examples 4-42 and 4-43 illustrate permutations.

EXAMPLE 4-42   Business Location

Suppose a business owner has a choice of 5 locations in which to establish her business. She decides to rank each location according to certain criteria, such as price of the store and parking facilities. How many different ways can she rank the 5 locations?

SOLUTION

There are

$$5! = 5 \cdot 4 \cdot 3 \cdot 2 \cdot 1 = 120$$

different possible rankings. The reason is that she has 5 choices for the first location, 4 choices for the second location, 3 choices for the third location, etc.

In Example 4–42 all objects were used up. But what happens when not all objects are used up? The answer to this question is given in Example 4–43.

EXAMPLE 4–43   Business Location

Suppose the business owner in Example 4–42 wishes to rank only the top 3 of the 5 locations. How many different ways can she rank them?

SOLUTION

Using the fundamental counting rule, she can select any one of the 5 for first choice, then any one of the remaining 4 locations for her second choice, and finally, any one of the remaining locations for her third choice, as shown.

First choice	Second choice	Third choice	
5	4	3	= 60

The solutions in Examples 4–42 and 4–43 are permutations.

OBJECTIVE 6

Find the number of ways that *r* objects can be selected from *n* objects, using the permutation rule.

Permutation Rule 1

The arrangement of *n* objects in a specific order using *r* objects at a time is called a *permutation of n objects taking r objects at a time.* It is written as $_nP_r$, and the formula is

$$_nP_r = \frac{n!}{(n - r)!}$$

The notation $_nP_r$ is used for permutations.

$$_6P_4 \text{ means } \quad \frac{6!}{(6 - 4)!} \quad or \quad \frac{6!}{2!} = \frac{6 \cdot 5 \cdot 4 \cdot 3 \cdot 2 \cdot \cancel{1}}{2 \cdot \cancel{1}} = 360$$

Although Examples 4–42 and 4–43 were solved by the multiplication rule, they can now be solved by the permutation rule.

In Example 4–42, five locations were taken and then arranged in order; hence,

$$_5P_5 = \frac{5!}{(5 - 5)!} = \frac{5!}{0!} = \frac{5 \cdot 4 \cdot 3 \cdot 2 \cdot 1}{1} = 120$$

(Recall that 0! = 1.)

In Example 4–43, three locations were selected from 5 locations, so $n = 5$ and $r = 3$; hence,

$$_5P_3 = \frac{5!}{(5 - 3)!} = \frac{5!}{2!} = \frac{5 \cdot 4 \cdot 3 \cdot 2 \cdot \cancel{1}}{2 \cdot \cancel{1}} = 60$$

Examples 4–44 and 4–45 illustrate the permutation rule.

EXAMPLE 4–44   Radio Show Guests

A radio talk show host can select 3 of 6 special guests for her program. The order of appearance of the guests is important. How many different ways can this be done?

SOLUTION

Since the order of appearance on the show is important, there are $_6P_3$ ways to select the guests.

$$_6P_3 = \frac{6!}{(6-3)!} = \frac{6!}{3!} = \frac{6 \cdot 5 \cdot 4 \cdot 3!}{3!} = 120$$

Hence, there can be 120 different ways to select 3 guests and present them on the program in a specific order.

EXAMPLE 4–45   School Musical Plays

A school musical director can select 2 musical plays to present next year. One will be presented in the fall, and one will be presented in the spring. If she has 9 to pick from, how many different possibilities are there?

SOLUTION

Order is important since one play can be presented in the fall and the other play in the spring.

$$_9P_2 = \frac{9!}{(9-2)!} = \frac{9!}{7!} = \frac{9 \cdot 8 \cdot 7!}{7!} = 72$$

There are 72 different possibilities.

In the previous examples, all items involving permutations were different, but when some of the items are identical, a second permutation rule can be used.

Permutation Rule 2

The number of permutations of n objects when r_1 objects are identical, r_2 objects are identical, . . . , r_p objects are identical, etc., is

$$\frac{n!}{r_1!\, r_2! \cdots r_p!}$$

where $r_1 + r_2 + \cdots + r_p = n$.

EXAMPLE 4–46   Letter Permutations

How many permutations of the letters can be made from the word *STATISTICS*?

SOLUTION

In the word *STATISTICS*, there are 3 S's, 3 T's, 2 I's, 1 A, and 1 C.

$$\frac{10!}{3!3!2!1!1!} = \frac{10 \cdot 9 \cdot 8 \cdot 7 \cdot 6 \cdot 5 \cdot 4 \cdot 3 \cdot 2 \cdot 1}{3 \cdot 2 \cdot 1 \cdot 3 \cdot 2 \cdot 1 \cdot 2 \cdot 1 \cdot 1 \cdot 1} = 50,400$$

There are 50,400 permutations that can be made from the word *STATISTICS*.

Combinations

Suppose a dress designer wishes to select two colors of material to design a new dress, and she has on hand four colors. How many different possibilities can there be in this situation?

This type of problem differs from previous ones in that the order of selection is not important. That is, if the designer selects yellow and red, this selection is the same as the selection red and yellow. This type of selection is called a *combination*. The difference between a permutation and a combination is that in a combination, the order or arrangement of the objects is not important; by contrast, order *is* important in a permutation. Example 4–46 illustrates this difference.

> A selection of distinct objects without regard to order is called a **combination.**

The difference between a combination and a permutation can be shown using the letters A, B, C, and D. The permutations for the letters A, B, C, and D are

AB	BA	CA	DA
AC	BC	CB	DB
AD	BD	CD	DC

In permutations, AB is different from BA. But in combinations, AB is the same as BA since the order of the objects does not matter in combinations. Therefore, if duplicates are removed from a list of permutations, what is left is a list of combinations, as shown.

AB	B̶A̶	C̶A̶	D̶A̶
AC	BC	C̶B̶	D̶B̶
AD	BD	CD	D̶C̶

Hence, the combinations of A, B, C, and D are AB, AC, AD, BC, BD, and CD. (Alternatively, BA could be listed and AB crossed out, etc.) The combinations have been listed alphabetically for convenience, but this is not a requirement.

Combinations are used when the order or arrangement is not important, as in the selecting process. Suppose a committee of 5 students is to be selected from 25 students. The 5 selected students represent a combination, since it does not matter who is selected first, second, etc.

Combination Rule

The number of combinations of *r* objects selected from *n* objects is denoted by $_nC_r$ and is given by the formula

$$_nC_r = \frac{n!}{(n-r)!r!}$$

EXAMPLE 4–47   Combinations

How many combinations of 4 objects are there, taken 2 at a time?

SOLUTION

Since this is a combination problem, the answer is

$$_4C_2 = \frac{4!}{(4-2)!2!} = \frac{4!}{2!2!} = \frac{\overset{2}{\cancel{4}} \cdot 3 \cdot \cancel{2!}}{2 \cdot 1 \cdot \cancel{2!}} = 6$$

This is the same result shown on the previous page.

Notice that the expression for $_nC_r$ is

$$\frac{n!}{(n-r)!r!}$$

which is the formula for permutations with *r*! in the denominator. In other words,

$$_nC_r = \frac{_nP_r}{r!}$$

This *r*! divides out the duplicates from the number of permutations. For each two letters, there are two permutations but only one combination. Hence, dividing the number of permutations by *r*! eliminates the duplicates. This result can be verified for other values of *n* and *r*. *Note:* $_nC_n = 1$.

EXAMPLE 4–48   Flier Types

An advertising executive must select 3 different photographs for an advertising flier. If she has 10 different photographs that can be used, how many ways can she select 3 of them?

SOLUTION

$$_{10}C_3 = \frac{10!}{(10-3)!3!} = \frac{10!}{7!3!} = \frac{10 \cdot 9 \cdot 8}{3 \cdot 2 \cdot 1} = 120$$

Hence, there are 120 different ways to select 3 photographs from 10 photographs.

EXAMPLE 4–49   Committee Selection

In a club there are 7 women and 5 men. A committee of 3 women and 2 men is to be chosen. How many different possibilities are there?

SOLUTION

Here, you must select 3 women from 7 women, which can be done in $_7C_3$, or 35, ways. Next, 2 men must be selected from 5 men, which can be done in $_5C_2$, or 10, ways. Finally, by the fundamental counting rule, the total number of different ways is $35 \cdot 10 = 350$, since you are choosing both men and women. Using the formula gives

$$_7C_3 \cdot {}_5C_2 = \frac{7!}{(7-3)!3!} \cdot \frac{5!}{(5-2)!2!} = 350$$

Table 4–1 summarizes the counting rules.

TABLE 4–1	**Summary of Counting Rules**	
Rule	**Definition**	**Formula**
Fundamental counting rule	The number of ways a sequence of n events can occur if the first event can occur in k_1 ways, the second event can occur in k_2 ways, etc.	$k_1 \cdot k_2 \cdot k_3 \cdots k_n$
Permutation rule 1	The number of permutations of n objects taking r objects at a time (order is important)	$_nP_r = \dfrac{n!}{(n-r)!}$
Permutation rule 2	The number of permutations of n objects when r_1 objects are identical, r_2 objects are identical, . . . , r_p objects are identical	$\dfrac{n!}{r_1! \, r_2! \cdots r_p!}$
Combination rule	The number of combinations of r objects taken from n objects (order is not important)	$_nC_r = \dfrac{n!}{(n-r)!r!}$

Applying the Concepts 4–4

Garage Door Openers

Garage door openers originally had a series of four on/off switches so that homeowners could personalize the frequencies that opened their garage doors. If all garage door openers were set at the same frequency, anyone with a garage door opener could open anyone else's garage door.

1. Use a tree diagram to show how many different positions 4 consecutive on/off switches could be in.

After garage door openers became more popular, another set of 4 on/off switches was added to the systems.

2. Find a pattern of how many different positions are possible with the addition of each on/off switch.

3. How many different positions are possible with 8 consecutive on/off switches?

4. Is it reasonable to assume, if you owned a garage door opener with 8 switches, that someone could use his or her garage door opener to open your garage door by trying all the different possible positions?

In 1989 it was reported that the ignition keys for 1988 Dodge Caravans were made from a single blank that had five cuts on it. Each cut was made at one out of five possible levels. In 1988, assume there were 420,000 Dodge Caravans sold in the United States.

5. How many different possible keys can be made from the same key blank?

6. How many different 1988 Dodge Caravans could any one key start?

Look at the ignition key for your car and count the number of cuts on it. Assume that the cuts are made at one of any of five possible levels. Most car companies use one key blank for all their makes and models of cars.

7. Conjecture how many cars your car company sold over recent years, and then figure out how many other cars your car key could start. What would you do to decrease the odds of someone being able to open another vehicle with his or her key?

See pages 254–255 for the answers.

Exercises 4–4

1. **Zip Codes** How many 5-digit zip codes are possible if digits can be repeated? If there cannot be repetitions?

2. **Letter Permutations** List all the permutations of the letters in the word *MATH*.

3. **Video Games** How many different ways can 6 different video game cartridges be arranged on a shelf?

4. **Visiting Nurses** How many different ways can a visiting nurse visit 9 patients if she wants to visit them all in one day?

5. **Quinto Lottery** A lottery game called Quinto is played by choosing five numbers each, from 0 through 9. How many numbers are possible? Although repeats are allowed, how many numbers are possible if repeats are not allowed?

6. **Show Programs** Three bands and two comics are performing for a student talent show. How many different programs (in terms of order) can be arranged? How many if the comics must perform between bands?

7. **Dogs at a Show** Eight dogs are selected for the final round of a dog show to compete for best of show. How many different ways can they line up to enter the ring? The judge then randomly chooses the dogs to parade around the ring in a circle. In how many ways can this be done?

8. **Radio Station Call Letters** The call letters of a radio station must have 4 letters. The first letter must be a K or a W. How many different station call letters can be made if repetitions are not allowed? If repetitions are allowed?

9. **Knitting Pattern** A knitted hat pattern comes in 4 styles with 4 stitch options and 3 sizes, and there are 7 yarns appropriate for the hat. Disregarding size, how many different hats can be made?

10. **Secret Code Word** How many 4-letter code words can be made using the letters in the word *pencil* if repetitions are permitted? If repetitions are not permitted?

11. **Passwords** Given the characters A, B, C, H, I, T, U, V, 1, 2, 3, and 4, how many seven-character passwords can be made? (No repeats are allowed.) How many if you have to use all four numbers as the first four characters in the password?

12. **Automobile Trips** There are 2 major roads from city X to city Y and 4 major roads from city Y to city Z. How many different trips can be made from city X to city Z, passing through city Y?

13. Evaluate each expression.

   a. 8!   e. $_7P_5$ i. $_5P_5$

   b. 10!   f. $_{12}P_4$ j. $_6P_2$

   c. 0!   g. $_5P_3$

   d. 1!   h. $_6P_0$

14. Evaluate each expression.

   a. 6!   e. $_9P_6$

   b. 11!   f. $_{11}P_4$

   c. 2!   g. $_8P_0$

   d. 9!   h. $_{10}P_2$

15. **Sports Car Stripes** How many different 4-color code stripes can be made on a sports car if each code consists of the colors green, red, blue, and white? All colors are used only once.

16. **Manufacturing Tests** An inspector must select 3 tests to perform in a certain order on a manufactured part. He has a choice of 7 tests. How many ways can he perform 3 different tests?

17. **Threatened Species of Reptiles** There are 22 threatened species of reptiles in the United States. In

how many ways can you choose 4 to write about? (Order is not important.)

Source: www.infoplease.com

18. **Inspecting Restaurants** How many different ways can a city health department inspector visit 5 restaurants in a city with 10 restaurants?

19. How many different 4-letter permutations can be formed from the letters in the word *decagon*?

20. **Cell Phone Models** A particular cell phone company offers 4 models of phones, each in 6 different colors and each available with any one of 5 calling plans. How many combinations are possible?

21. **ID Cards** How many different ID cards can be made if there are 6 digits on a card and no digit can be used more than once?

22. **Free-Sample Requests** An online coupon service has 13 offers for free samples. How many different requests are possible if a customer must request exactly 3 free samples? How many are possible if the customer may request up to 3 free samples?

23. **Ticket Selection** How many different ways can 4 tickets be selected from 50 tickets if each ticket wins a different prize?

24. **Movie Selections** The Foreign Language Club is showing a four-movie marathon of subtitled movies. How many ways can they choose 4 from the 11 available?

25. **Task Assignments** How many ways can an adviser choose 4 students from a class of 12 if they are all assigned the same task? How many ways can the students be chosen if they are each given a different task?

26. **Agency Cases** An investigative agency has 7 cases and 5 agents. How many different ways can the cases be assigned if only 1 case is assigned to each agent?

27. **Signal Flags** How many different flag signals, each consisting of 7 flags hung vertically, can be made when there are 3 indistinguishable red flags, 2 blue flags, and 2 white flags?

28. **Word Permutations** How many permutations can be made using all the letters in the word *MASSACHUSETTS*?

29. **Code Words** How many different 9-letter code words can be made using the symbols %, %, %, %, &, &, &, +, +?

30. **Toothpaste Display** How many different ways can 5 identical tubes of tartar control toothpaste, 3 identical tubes of bright white toothpaste, and 4 identical tubes of mint toothpaste be arranged in a grocery store counter display?

31. **Book Arrangements** How many different ways can 6 identical hardback books, 3 identical paperback books, and 3 identical boxed books be arranged on a shelf in a bookstore?

32. **Letter Permutations** How many different permutations of the letters in the word *CINCINNATI* are there?

33. Evaluate each expression.

   a. $_5C_2$ d. $_6C_2$
   b. $_8C_3$ e. $_6C_4$
   c. $_7C_4$

34. Evaluate each expression.

   a. $_3C_0$ d. $_{12}C_2$
   b. $_3C_3$ e. $_4C_3$
   c. $_9C_7$

35. **Selecting Coins** How many ways can a person select 3 coins from a box consisting of a penny, a nickel, a dime, a quarter, a half-dollar, and a one-dollar coin?

36. **Selecting Players** How many ways can 4 baseball players and 3 basketball players be selected from 12 baseball players and 9 basketball players?

37. **Selecting a Committee** How many ways can a committee of 4 people be selected from a group of 10 people?

38. **Selecting Christmas Presents** If a person can select 3 presents from 10 presents under a Christmas tree, how many different combinations are there?

39. **Buffet Desserts** In how many ways can you choose 3 kinds of ice cream and 2 toppings from a dessert buffet with 10 kinds of ice cream and 6 kinds of toppings?

40. **Bridge Foursomes** How many different tables of 4 can you make from 16 potential bridge players? How many different tables if 4 of the players insist on playing together?

41. **Music Recital** Six students are performing one song each in a jazz vocal recital. Two students have repertoires of five numbers, and the others have four songs each prepared. How many different programs are possible without regard to order? Assume that the repertory selections are all unique.

42. **Freight Train Cars** In a train yard there are 4 tank cars, 12 boxcars, and 7 flatcars. How many ways can a train be made up consisting of 2 tank cars, 5 boxcars, and 3 flatcars? (In this case, order is not important.)

43. **Selecting a Committee** There are 7 women and 5 men in a department. How many ways can a committee of 4 people be selected? How many ways can this committee be selected if there must be 2 men and 2 women on the committee? How many ways can this committee be selected if there must be at least 2 women on the committee?

44. **Selecting Cereal Boxes** Wake Up cereal comes in 2 types, crispy and crunchy. If a researcher has 10 boxes of each, how many ways can she select 3 boxes of each for a quality control test?

45. Hawaiian Words The Hawaiian alphabet consists of 7 consonants and 5 vowels. How many three-letter "words" are possible if there are never two consonants together and if a word must always end in a vowel?

46. Selecting a Jury How many ways can a jury of 6 women and 6 men be selected from 10 women and 12 men?

47. How many ways can you pick 4 students from 10 students (6 men, 4 women) if you must have an equal number of each gender or all of the same gender?

48. Investigative Team The state narcotics bureau must form a 5-member investigative team. If it has 25 agents from which to choose, how many different possible teams can be formed?

49. Dominoes A domino is a flat rectangular block whose face is divided into two square parts, each part showing from zero to six pips (or dots). Playing a game consists of playing dominoes with a matching number of pips. Explain why there are 28 dominoes in a complete set.

50. Charity Event Participants There are 16 seniors and 15 juniors in a particular social organization. In how many ways can 4 seniors and 2 juniors be chosen to participate in a charity event?

51. Selecting Commercials How many ways can a person select 7 television commercials from 11 television commercials?

52. DVD Selection How many ways can a person select 8 DVDs from a display of 13 DVDs?

53. Candy Bar Selection How many ways can a person select 6 candy bars from a list of 10 and 6 salty snacks from a list of 12 to put in a vending machine?

54. Selecting a Location An advertising manager decides to have an ad campaign in which 8 special calculators will be hidden at various locations in a shopping mall. If he has 17 locations from which to pick, how many different possible combinations can he choose?

Permutations and Combinations

55. Selecting Posters A buyer decides to stock 8 different posters. How many ways can she select these 8 if there are 20 from which to choose?

56. Test Marketing Products Anderson Research Company decides to test-market a product in 6 areas. How many different ways can 3 areas be selected in a certain order for the first test?

57. Selecting Rats How many different ways can a researcher select 5 rats from 20 rats and assign each to a different test?

58. Selecting Musicals How many different ways can a theatrical group select 2 musicals and 3 dramas from 11 musicals and 8 dramas to be presented during the year?

59. Textbook Selection How many different ways can an instructor select 2 textbooks from a possible 17?

60. DVD Selection How many ways can a person select 8 DVDs from 10 DVDs?

61. Public Service Announcements How many different ways can 5 public service announcements be run during 1 hour?

62. Signal Flags How many different signals can be made by using at least 3 different flags if there are 5 different flags from which to select?

63. Dinner Selections How many ways can a dinner patron select 3 appetizers and 2 vegetables if there are 6 appetizers and 5 vegetables on the menu?

64. Air Pollution The Environmental Protection Agency must investigate 9 mills for complaints of air pollution. How many different ways can a representative select 5 of these to investigate this week?

65. Selecting Officers In a board of directors composed of 8 people, how many ways can one chief executive officer, one director, and one treasurer be selected?

66. The presidents, vice presidents, and secretary-treasurers from each of four classes are eligible for an all-school council. How many ways can four officers be chosen from these representatives? How many ways can they be chosen if the president must be selected from the sitting presidents, the vice president from the sitting vice presidents, the secretary from the sitting secretary-treasurers, and the treasurer from everybody who's left?

Extending the Concepts

67. Selecting Coins How many different ways can you select one or more coins if you have 2 nickels, 1 dime, and 1 half-dollar?

68. People Seated in a Circle In how many ways can 3 people be seated in a circle? 4? n? (*Hint:* Think of them standing in a line before they sit down and/or draw diagrams.)

69. Seating in a Movie Theater How many different ways can 5 people—A, B, C, D, and E—sit in a row at a movie theater if (*a*) A and B must sit together; (*b*) C must sit to the right of, but not necessarily next to, B; (*c*) D and E will not sit next to each other?

70. Poker Hands Using combinations, calculate the number of each type of poker hand in a deck of cards. (A poker hand consists of 5 cards dealt in any order.)

a. Royal flush

b. Straight flush (not including a royal flush)

c. Four of a kind

d. Full house

71. How many different combinations can be made from $(x + 2)$ things taken x at a time?

72. A game of concentration (memory) is played with a standard 52-card deck. How many potential two-card matches are there (e.g., one jack "matches" any other jack)?

⬛ Technology | Step by Step

TI-84 Plus
Step by Step

Factorials, Permutations, and Combinations

Factorials $n!$

1. Type the value of n.

2. Press **MATH** and move the cursor to PRB, then press **4** for !.

3. Press **ENTER.**

Permutations $_nP_r$

1. Type the value of n.

2. Press **MATH** and move the cursor to PRB, then press **2** for $_nP_r$.

3. Type the value of r.

4. Press **ENTER.**

Combinations $_nC_r$

1. Type the value of n.

2. Press **MATH** and move the cursor to PRB, then press **3** for $_nC_r$.

3. Type the value of r.

4. Press **ENTER.**

Example TI 4–2

Calculate 5! (Example 4–42 from the text).

Calculate $_6P_3$ (Example 4–44 from the text).

Calculate $_{10}C_3$ (Example 4–48 from the text).

Input   Input   Output

EXCEL
Step by Step

Permutations, Combinations, and Factorials

To find a value of a permutation, for example, $_5P_3$:

1. In an open cell in an Excel worksheet, select the Formulas tab on the toolbar. Then click the Insert function icon $\overset{fx}{\underset{\text{Insert Function}}{}}$.

2. Select the Statistical function category, then the PERMUT function, and click [OK].

3. Type **5** in the Number box.
4. Type **3** in the Number_chosen box and click [OK].

The selected cell will display the answer: 60.

    To find a value of a combination, for example, $_5C_3$:

1. In an open cell, select the Formulas tab on the toolbar. Click the Insert function icon.
2. Select the All function category, then the COMBIN function, and click [OK].

3. Type **5** in the Number box.

4. Type **3** in the Number_chosen box and click [OK].

The selected cell will display the answer: 10.
To find a factorial of a number, for example, 7!:

1. In an open cell, select the Formulas tab on the toolbar. Click the Insert function icon.

2. Select the Math & Trig function category, then the FACT function, and click [OK].

3. Type **7** in the Number box and click [OK].

The selected cell will display the answer: 5040.

MINITAB
Step by Step

Factorials, Permutations, and Combinations

Examples used:

4–42 Location Ranks 5!
4–44 Radio Show Guests $_6P_3$
4–48 Flyer Type $_{10}C_3$

The results are stored in a constant; MINITAB has 1000 of them available in each worksheet. They are numbered from K1 to K1000. By default, MINITAB assigns the values of missing constants, e, and pi to the last three stored constants: K998 = *; K999 = 2.71828; and K1000 = 3.14159. To reduce clutter, MINITAB does not list these in the Constants subfolder.

1. To calculate 5!, select **Calc>Calculator.**

   a) Type K1 in the Store result in variable, then press the Tab key on your keyboard or click in the Expression dialog box.

   b) Scroll down the function list to Factorial, then click [Select].

   c) Type a 5 to replace the number of items that is highlighted.

   d) Click [OK]. The value of 5! = 120 will be stored in a constant that is not visible.

   e) To see the constant, click the icon for Project Manager, then the Constants item in the worksheet folder. Right-click on the Untitled name, then choose Rename and type 5Factorial. Storing the constant makes it available to be used in future calculations.

f) To view the constants in the Session window, select **Data>Data display**, then choose K1 5factorial and [OK].

2. To calculate $_6P_3$, select **Calc>Calculator**.

a) Type K2 in the Store result in variable, then press the Tab key on your keyboard or click in the Expression dialog box.

b) Scroll down the function list to Permutations, then click [Select].

c) Type a 6 to replace the number of items, then 3 to replace number to choose.

d) Click [OK]. Name the constant and display it, using the instructions in steps 1e and 1f.

3. To calculate $_{10}C_3$, select **Calc>Calculator**.

a) Type K3 in the Store result in variable, then press the Tab key on your keyboard or click in the Expression dialog box.

b) Scroll down the function list to Combinations, then click [Select].

c) Type a 10 to replace the number of items, then 3 to replace number to choose.

d) Click [OK]. Name the constant and display it, using the instructions in steps 1e and 1f.

The Project Manager is shown. Coincidence! The values are all 120. These values can be very large and exceed the storage capability for constants. Values larger in absolute value than 1.001000E+18 in K1 are converted to missing. In scientific notation that is 1.001000×10^{18}.

4–5   Probability and Counting Rules

The counting rules can be combined with the probability rules in this chapter to solve many types of probability problems. By using the fundamental counting rule, the permutation rules, and the combination rule, you can compute the probability of outcomes of many experiments, such as getting a full house when 5 cards are dealt or selecting a committee of 3 women and 2 men from a club consisting of 10 women and 10 men.

EXAMPLE 4–50   Four Aces

Find the probability of getting 4 aces when 5 cards are drawn from an ordinary deck of cards.

SOLUTION

There are $_{52}C_5$ ways to draw 5 cards from a deck. There is only 1 way to get 4 aces (that is, $_4C_4$), but there are 48 possibilities to get the fifth card. Therefore, there are 48 ways to get 4 aces and 1 other card. Hence,

$$P(4 \text{ aces}) = \frac{_4C_4 \cdot 48}{_{52}C_5} = \frac{1 \cdot 48}{2,598,960} = \frac{48}{2,598,960} = \frac{1}{54,145}$$

EXAMPLE 4–51   Defective Transistors

A box contains 24 transistors, 4 of which are defective. If 4 are sold at random, find the following probabilities.

    a. Exactly 2 are defective.   *c.* All are defective.
    b. None is defective.   *d.* At least 1 is defective.

SOLUTION

There are $_{24}C_4$ ways to sell 4 transistors, so the denominator in each case will be 10,626.

    a. Two defective transistors can be selected as $_4C_2$ and two nondefective ones as $_{20}C_2$. Hence,

$$P(\text{exactly 2 defectives}) = \frac{_4C_2 \cdot {}_{20}C_2}{_{24}C_4} = \frac{1140}{10,626} = \frac{190}{1771}$$

b. The number of ways to choose no defectives is $_{20}C_4$. Hence,

$$P(\text{no defectives}) = \frac{_{20}C_4}{_{24}C_4} = \frac{4845}{10{,}626} = \frac{1615}{3542}$$

c. The number of ways to choose 4 defectives from 4 is $_4C_4$, or 1. Hence,

$$P(\text{all defective}) = \frac{1}{_{24}C_4} = \frac{1}{10{,}626}$$

d. To find the probability of at least 1 defective transistor, find the probability that there are no defective transistors, and then subtract that probability from 1.

$$P(\text{at least 1 defective}) = 1 - P(\text{no defectives})$$

$$= 1 - \frac{_{20}C_4}{_{24}C_4} = 1 - \frac{1615}{3542} = \frac{1927}{3542}$$

EXAMPLE 4–52 Magazines

A store has 6 *TV Graphic* magazines and 8 *Newstime* magazines on the counter. If two customers purchased a magazine, find the probability that one of each magazine was purchased.

SOLUTION

$$P(1 \ \textit{TV Graphic} \text{ and } 1 \ \textit{Newstime}) = \frac{_6C_1 \cdot {}_8C_1}{_{14}C_2} = \frac{6 \cdot 8}{91} = \frac{48}{91}$$

EXAMPLE 4–53 State Lottery Number

In the Pennsylvania State Lottery, a person selects a three-digit number and repetitions are permitted. If a winning number is selected, find the probability that it will have all three digits the same.

SOLUTION

Since there are 10 different digits, there are $10 \cdot 10 \cdot 10 = 1000$ ways to select a winning number. When all of the digits are the same, that is, 000, 111, 222, . . . , 999, there are 10 possibilities, so the probability of selecting a winning number which has 3 identical digits is $\frac{10}{1000} = \frac{1}{100}$.

EXAMPLE 4–54 Tennis Tournament

There are 8 married couples in a tennis club. If 1 man and 1 woman are selected at random to plan the summer tournament, find the probability that they are married to each other.

SOLUTION

Since there are 8 ways to select the man and 8 ways to select the woman, there are $8 \cdot 8$, or 64, ways to select 1 man and 1 woman. Since there are 8 married couples, the solution is $\frac{8}{64} = \frac{1}{8}$.

    As indicated at the beginning of this section, the counting rules and the probability rules can be used to solve a large variety of probability problems found in business, gambling, economics, biology, and other fields.

Gambling is big business. There are state lotteries, casinos, sports betting, and church bingos. It seems that today everybody is either watching or playing Texas Hold 'Em Poker.

Using permutations, combinations, and the probability rules, mathematicians can find the probabilities of various gambling games. Here are the probabilities of the various 5-card poker hands.

Hand	Number of ways	Probability
Straight flush	40	0.000015
Four of a kind	624	0.000240
Full house	3,744	0.001441
Flush	5,108	0.001965
Straight	10,200	0.003925
Three of a kind	54,912	0.021129
Two pairs	123,552	0.047539
One pair	1,098,240	0.422569
Less than one pair	1,302,540	0.501177
Total	2,598,960	1.000000

The chance of winning at gambling games can be compared by using what is called the house advantage, house edge, or house percentage. For example, the house advantage for roulette is about 5.26%, which means in the long run, the house wins 5.26 cents on every $1 bet; or you will lose, on average, 5.26 cents on every $1 you bet. The lower the house advantage, the more favorable the game is to you.

For the game of craps, the house advantage is anywhere between 1.4 and 15%, depending on what you bet on. For the game called Keno, the house advantage is 29.5%. The house advantage for Chuck-a-Luck is 7.87%, and for Baccarat, it is either 1.36 or 1.17%, depending on your bet.

Slot machines have a house advantage anywhere from about 4 to 10% depending on the geographic location, such as Atlantic City, Las Vegas, and Mississippi, and the amount put in the machine, such as 5 cents, 25 cents, and $1.

Actually, gamblers found winning strategies for the game blackjack or 21, such as card counting. However, the casinos retaliated by using multiple decks and by banning card counters.

≡ Applying the Concepts 4–5

Counting Rules and Probability

One of the biggest problems for students when doing probability problems is to decide which formula or formulas to use. Another problem is to decide whether two events are independent or dependent. Use the following problem to help develop a better understanding of these concepts.

Assume you are given a five-question multiple-choice quiz. Each question has 5 possible answers: A, B, C, D, and E.

1. How many events are there?
2. Are the events independent or dependent?
3. If you guess at each question, what is the probability that you get all of them correct?
4. What is the probability that a person guesses answer A for each question?

Assume that you are given a five-question matching test in which you are to match the correct answers in the right column with the questions in the left column. You can use each answer only once.

5. How many events are there?

6. Are the events independent or dependent?

7. What is the probability of getting them all correct if you are guessing?

8. What is the difference between the two problems?

See page 255 for the answers.

Exercises 4–5

1. **Selecting Cards** Find the probability of getting 2 face cards (king, queen, or jack) when 2 cards are drawn from a deck without replacement.

2. **Selecting Cards** Cards numbered 1–10 are shuffled and dealt face down. What is the probability that they are in order?

3. **Management Seminar** In a company there are 7 executives: 4 women and 3 men. Three are selected to attend a management seminar. Find these probabilities.

   a. All 3 selected will be women.

   b. All 3 selected will be men.

   c. 2 men and 1 woman will be selected.

   d. 1 man and 2 women will be selected.

4. **Senate Partisanship** The composition of the Senate of the 111th Congress is

   41 Republicans   2 Independent   57 Democrats

   A new committee is being formed to study ways to benefit the arts in education. If 3 Senators are selected at random to head the committee, what is the probability that they will all be Republicans? What is the probability that they will all be Democrats? What is the probability that there will be 1 from each party, including the Independent?

   Source: *New York Times Almanac.*

5. **Job Applications** Six men and seven women apply for two identical jobs. If the jobs are filled at random, find the following:

   a. The probability that both are filled by men.

   b. The probability that both are filled by women.

   c. The probability that one man and one woman are hired.

   d. The probability that the one man and one woman who are twins are hired.

6. **Defective Resistors** A package contains 12 resistors, 3 of which are defective. If 4 are selected, find the probability of getting

   a. 0 defective resistors

   b. 1 defective resistor

   c. 3 defective resistors

7. **Winning Tickets** If 50 tickets are sold and 2 prizes are to be awarded, find the probability that one person will win 2 prizes if that person buys 2 tickets.

8. **Getting a Full House** Find the probability of getting a full house (3 cards of one denomination and 2 of another) when 5 cards are dealt from an ordinary deck.

9. **World-Class Orchestras** *Encyclopaedia Britannica*'s list of 20 World Class Orchestras includes the following from the United States: Boston Symphony Orchestra, Chicago Symphony Orchestra, Cleveland Orchestra, Los Angeles Philharmonic, New York Philharmonic, Philadelphia Orchestra, and the San Francisco Symphony. Choose 5 at random from the list of 20 for a benefit CD. What is the probability that the collection will include at least one group from the United States? At least 2 from the United States? That all 5 will be from the United States?

   Source: *Time Almanac 2012.*

10. **Selecting Cards** The red face cards and the black cards numbered 2–9 are put into a bag. Four cards are drawn at random without replacement. Find the following probabilities.

    a. All 4 cards are red.

    b. 2 cards are red and 2 cards are black.

    c. At least 1 of the cards is red.

    d. All 4 cards are black.

11. **Socks in a Drawer** A drawer contains 11 identical red socks and 8 identical black socks. Suppose that you choose 2 socks at random in the dark.

    a. What is the probability that you get a pair of red socks?

    b. What is the probability that you get a pair of black socks?

    c. What is the probability that you get 2 unmatched socks?

    d. Where did the other red sock go?

12. **Selecting Books** Find the probability of selecting 3 science books and 4 math books from 8 science books and 9 math books. The books are selected at random.

13. **Rolling Three Dice** When 3 dice are rolled, find the probability of getting a sum of 7.

14. **Football Team Selection** A football team consists of 20 freshmen and 20 sophomores, 15 juniors, and 10 seniors. Four players are selected at random to serve as captains. Find the probability that

    a. All 4 are seniors

    b. There is 1 each: freshman, sophomore, junior, and senior

    c. There are 2 sophomores and 2 freshmen

    d. At least 1 of the students is a senior

15. **Arrangement of Washers** Find the probability that if 5 different-sized washers are arranged in a row, they will be arranged in order of size.

16. Using the information in Exercise 70 in Section 4–4, find the probability of each poker hand.

    a. Royal flush

    b. Straight flush

    c. Four of a kind

17. **Plant Selection** All holly plants are dioecious—a male plant must be planted within 30 to 40 feet of the female plants in order to yield berries. A home improvement store has 12 unmarked holly plants for sale, 8 of which are female. If a homeowner buys 3 plants at random, what is the probability that berries will be produced?

Summary

In this chapter, the basic concepts of probability are explained.

- There are three basic types of probability: classical probability, empirical probability, and subjective probability. Classical probability uses sample spaces. Empirical probability uses frequency distributions, and subjective probability uses an educated guess to determine the probability of an event. The probability of any event is a number from 0 to 1. If an event cannot occur, the probability is 0. If an event is certain, the probability is 1. The sum of the probability of all the events in the sample space is 1. To find the probability of the complement of an event, subtract the probability of the event from 1. (4–1)

- Two events are mutually exclusive if they cannot occur at the same time; otherwise, the events are not mutually exclusive. To find the probability of two mutually exclusive events occurring, add the probability of each event. To find the probability of two events when they are not mutually exclusive, add the possibilities of the individual events and then subtract the probability that both events occur at the same time. These types of probability problems can be solved by using the addition rules. (4–2)

- Two events are independent if the occurrence of the first event does not change the probability of the second event occurring. Otherwise, the events are dependent. To find the probability of two independent events occurring, multiply the probabilities of each event. To find the probability that two dependent events occur, multiply the probability that the first event occurs by the probability that the second event occurs, given that the first event has already occurred. The complement of an event is found by selecting the outcomes in the sample space that are not involved in the outcomes of the event. These types of problems can be solved by using the multiplication rules and the complementary event rules. (4–3)

- Finally, when a large number of events can occur, the fundamental counting rule, the permutation rules, and the combination rule can be used to determine the number of ways that these events can occur. (4–4)

- The counting rules and the probability rules can be used to solve more-complex probability problems. (4–5)

Important Terms

classical probability 189	empirical probability 194	mutually exclusive events 202	simple event 189
combination 232	equally likely events 189		subjective probability 196
complement of an event 192	event 188	outcome 186	tree diagram 188
compound event 189	fundamental counting rule 226	permutation 229	Venn diagrams 193
conditional probability 215		probability 186	
dependent events 215	independent events 213	probability experiment 186	
disjoint events 202	law of large numbers 196	sample space 186	

Important Formulas

Formula for classical probability:

$$P(E) = \frac{\text{number of outcomes in } E}{\text{total number of outcomes in sample space}} = \frac{n(E)}{n(S)}$$

Formula for empirical probability:

$$P(E) = \frac{\text{frequency for class}}{\text{total frequencies in distribution}} = \frac{f}{n}$$

Addition rule 1, for two mutually exclusive events:

$$P(A \text{ or } B) = P(A) + P(B)$$

Addition rule 2, for events that are not mutually exclusive:

$$P(A \text{ or } B) = P(A) + P(B) - P(A \text{ and } B)$$

Multiplication rule 1, for independent events:

$$P(A \text{ and } B) = P(A) \cdot P(B)$$

Multiplication rule 2, for dependent events:

$$P(A \text{ and } B) = P(A) \cdot P(B|A)$$

Formula for conditional probability:

$$P(B|A) = \frac{P(A \text{ and } B)}{P(A)}$$

Formula for complementary events:

$$P(\overline{E}) = 1 - P(E) \quad \text{or} \quad P(E) = 1 - P(\overline{E})$$
$$\text{or} \quad P(E) + P(\overline{E}) = 1$$

Fundamental counting rule: In a sequence of n events in which the first one has k_1 possibilities, the second event has k_2 possibilities, the third has k_3 possibilities, etc., the total number of possibilities of the sequence will be

$$k_1 \cdot k_2 \cdot k_3 \cdots k_n$$

Permutation rule 1: The number of permutations of n objects taking r objects at a time when order is important is

$$_nP_r = \frac{n!}{(n-r)!}$$

Permutation rule 2: The number of permutations of n objects when r_1 objects are identical, r_2 objects are identical, . . . , r_p objects are identical is

$$\frac{n!}{r_1! \, r_2! \cdots r_p!}$$

Combination rule: The number of combinations of r objects selected from n objects when order is not important is

$$_nC_r = \frac{n!}{(n-r)!r}$$

Review Exercises

Section 4–1

1. When a standard die is rolled, find the probability of getting

   a. A 5

   b. A number larger than 2

   c. An odd number

2. **Selecting a Card** When a card is selected from a deck, find the probability of getting

   a. A club

   b. A face card or a heart

   c. A 6 and a spade

   d. A king

   e. A red card

3. **Software Selection** The top-10 selling computer software titles last year consisted of 3 for doing taxes, 5 antivirus or security programs, and 2 "other." Choose one title at random.

   a. What is the probability that it is not used for doing taxes?

   b. What is the probability that it is used for taxes or is one of the "other" programs?

   Source: www.infoplease.com

4. **Motor Vehicle Producers** The top five motor vehicle producers in the world are listed below with the number of vehicles produced in 2010 (in thousands of vehicles).

China	16,144
Japan	9,197
United States	7,632
Germany	5,700
South Korea	4,184

   Choose one vehicle at random;

   a. What is the probability that it was produced in the United States?

   b. What is the probability that it was not produced in Asia?

   c. What is the probability that it was produced in Germany or Japan?

   Source: *World Almanac 2012.*

5. **Fitness Center Members** At a particular fitness center, 64.1% of the members take at least one class, 18.6% work with a personal trainer, and 9.2% do both. If a member of the center is selected at random, what is the probability that she does neither?

6. **Rolling Two Dice** When two dice are rolled, find the probability of getting

   a. A sum of 5 or 6
   b. A sum greater than 9
   c. A sum less than 4 or greater than 9
   d. A sum that is divisible by 4
   e. A sum of 14
   f. A sum less than 13

Section 4–2

7. **Budget Rental Cars** Cheap Rentals has nothing but budget cars for rental. The probability that a car has air conditioning is 0.5, and the probability that a car has a CD player is 0.37. The probability that a car has both air conditioning and a CD player is 0.06. What is the probability that a randomly selected car has neither air conditioning nor a CD player?

8. **Breakfast Drink** In a recent survey, 18 people preferred milk, 29 people preferred coffee, and 13 people preferred juice as their primary drink for breakfast. If a person is selected at random, find the probability that the person preferred juice as her or his primary drink.

9. **Car and Boat Ownership** The probability that a person owns a car is 0.80, that a person owns a boat is 0.30, and that a person owns both a car and a boat is 0.12. Find the probability that a person owns either a boat or a car.

10. **Car Purchases** There is a 0.39 probability that John will purchase a new car, a 0.73 probability that Mary will purchase a new car, and a 0.36 probability that both will purchase a new car. Find the probability that neither will purchase a new car.

11. **Online Course Selection** Roughly 1 in 6 students enrolled in higher education took at least one online course last fall. Choose 5 enrolled students at random. Find the probability that

    a. All 5 took online courses
    b. None of the 5 took a course online
    c. At least 1 took an online course

    Source: www.encarta.msn.com

12. **Purchasing Sweaters** During a sale at a men's store, 16 white sweaters, 3 red sweaters, 9 blue sweaters, and 7 yellow sweaters were purchased. If a customer is selected at random, find the probability that he bought

    a. A blue sweater
    b. A yellow or a white sweater
    c. A red, a blue, or a yellow sweater
    d. A sweater that was not white

Section 4–3

13. **Drawing Cards** Three cards are drawn from an ordinary deck *without* replacement. Find the probability of getting

    a. All black cards
    b. All spades
    c. All queens

14. **Coin Toss and Card Drawn** A coin is tossed and a card is drawn from a deck. Find the probability of getting

    a. A head and a 6
    b. A tail and a red card
    c. A head and a club

15. **Movie Releases** The top five countries for movie releases for a specific year are the United States with 471 releases, United Kingdom with 386, Japan with 79, Germany with 316, and France with 132. Choose 1 new release at random. Find the probability that it is

    a. European
    b. From the United States
    c. German or French
    d. German given that it is European

    Source: www.showbizdata.com

16. **Factory Output** A manufacturing company has three factories: X, Y, and Z. The daily output of each is shown here.

Product	Factory X	Factory Y	Factory Z
TVs	18	32	15
Stereos	6	20	13

If 1 item is selected at random, find these probabilities.

    a. It was manufactured at factory X or is a stereo.
    b. It was manufactured at factory Y or factory Z.
    c. It is a TV or was manufactured at factory Z.

17. **Effectiveness of Vaccine** A vaccine has a 90% probability of being effective in preventing a certain disease. The probability of getting the disease if a person is not vaccinated is 50%. In a certain geographic region, 25% of the people get vaccinated. If a person is selected at random, find the probability that he or she will contract the disease.

18. **T-shirt Factories** Two T-shirt printing factories produce T-shirts for a local sports team. Factory A produces 60% of the shirts and factory B produces 40%. Five percent of the shirts from factory A are defective, and 6% of the shirts from factory B are defective. Choose 1 shirt at random. Given that the shirt is defective, what is the probability that it came from factory A?

19. **Car Purchase** The probability that Sue will live on campus and buy a new car is 0.37. If the probability that she will live on campus is 0.73, find the probability that she will buy a new car, given that she lives on campus.

20. **Applying Shipping Labels** Four unmarked packages have lost their shipping labels, and you must reapply them. What is the probability that you apply the labels and get all 4 of them correct? Exactly 3 correct? Exactly 2? At least 1 correct?

21. **Health Club Membership** Of the members of the Blue River Health Club, 43% have a lifetime membership and

exercise regularly (three or more times a week). If 75% of the club members exercise regularly, find the probability that a randomly selected member is a life member, given that he or she exercises regularly.

22. Bad Weather The probability that it snows and the bus arrives late is 0.023. José hears the weather forecast, and there is a 40% chance of snow tomorrow. Find the probability that the bus will be late, given that it snows.

23. Education Level and Smoking At a large factory, the employees were surveyed and classified according to their level of education and whether they smoked. The data are shown in the table.

| | Educational level | | |
Smoking habit	Not high school graduate	High school graduate	College graduate
Smoke	6	14	19
Do not smoke	18	7	25

If an employee is selected at random, find these probabilities.

a. The employee smokes, given that he or she graduated from college.

b. Given that the employee did not graduate from high school, he or she is a smoker.

24. War Veterans Approximately 11% of the civilian population are veterans. Choose 5 civilians at random. What is the probability that none are veterans? What is the probability that at least 1 is a veteran?

Source: www.factfinder.census.gov

25. DVD Players Eighty-one percent of U.S. households have DVD players. Choose 6 households at random. What is the probability that at least 1 does not have a DVD player?

Source: www.infoplease.com

26. Chronic Sinusitis The U.S. Department of Health and Human Services reports that 15% of Americans have chronic sinusitis. If 5 people are selected at random, find the probability that at least 1 has chronic sinusitis.

Source: *100% American.*

Section 4–4

27. Automobile License Plate An automobile license plate consists of 3 letters followed by 4 digits. How many different plates can be made if repetitions are allowed? If repetitions are not allowed? If repetitions are allowed in the letters but not in the digits?

28. Types of Copy Paper White copy paper is offered in 5 different strengths and 11 different degrees of brightness, recycled or not, and acid-free or not. How many different types of paper are available for order?

29. Baseball Players How many ways can 3 outfielders and 4 infielders be chosen from 5 outfielders and 7 infielders?

30. Carry-on Items The following items are allowed as airline carry-on items: (1) safety razors, (2) eyedrops and saline, (3) nail clippers and tweezers, (4) blunt-tipped scissors, (5) mobile phones, (6) umbrellas, (7) common lighters, (8) beverages purchased after security screening, and (9) musical instruments. Suppose that your airline allows only 6 of these items. In how many ways can you pick 3 not to take?

31. Names for Boys The top 10 names for boys in America in the 1880s were John, William, Charles, George, James, Frank, Joseph, Harry, Henry, and Edward. The top 10 names for boys in the 1980s were Michael, Christopher, Matthew, Joshua, David, Daniel, James, John, Robert, and Brian. In how many ways can you choose 5 names from these lists?

32. Committee Representation There are 6 Republican, 5 Democrat, and 4 Independent candidates. How many different ways can a committee of 3 Republicans, 2 Democrats, and 1 Independent be selected?

33. Song Selections A promotional MP3 player is available with the capacity to store 100 songs, which can be reordered at the push of a button. How many different arrangements of these songs are possible? (*Note:* Factorials get very big, very fast! How large a factorial will your calculator calculate?)

34. Employee Health Care Plans A new employee has a choice of 5 health care plans, 3 retirement plans, and 2 different expense accounts. If a person selects 1 of each option, how many different options does she or he have?

35. Course Enrollment There are 12 students who wish to enroll in a particular course. There are only 4 seats left in the classroom. How many different ways can 4 students be selected to attend the class?

36. Candy Selection A candy store allows customers to select 3 different candies to be packaged and mailed. If there are 13 varieties available, how many possible selections can be made?

37. House Numbers A home improvement store has the following house numbers: 335666 left after a sale. How many different six-digit house numbers can be made from those numbers?

38. Word Permutations From which word can you make more permutations, *MATHEMATICS* or *PROBABILITY*? How many more?

39. Book Selection If a student can select 5 novels from a reading list of 20 for a course in literature, how many different possible ways can this selection be done?

40. Course Selection If a student can select one of 3 language courses, one of 5 mathematics courses, and one of 4 history courses, how many different schedules can be made?

Section 4–5

41. **License Plates** License plates are to be issued with 3 letters followed by 4 single digits. How many such license plates are possible? If the plates are issued at random, what is the probability that the license plate says USA followed by a number that is divisible by 5?

42. A certain state's license plate has 3 letters followed by 4 numbers. Repeats are not allowed for the letters, but they are for the numbers. How many such license plates are possible? If they are issued at random, what is the probability that the 3 letters are 3 consecutive letters in alphabetical order?

43. **Territorial Selection** Several territories and colonies today are still under the jurisdiction of another country. France holds the most with 16 territories, the United Kingdom has 15, the United States has 14, and several other countries have territories as well. Choose 3

territories at random from those held by France, the United Kingdom, and the United States. What is the probability that all 3 belong to the same country?

Source: www.infoplease.com

44. **Yahtzee** Yahtzee is a game played with 5 dice. Players attempt to score points by rolling various combinations. When all 5 dice show the same number, it is called a *Yahtzee* and scores 50 points for the first one and 100 points for each subsequent Yahtzee in the same game. What is the probability that a person throws a Yahtzee on the very first roll? What is the probability that a person throws two Yahtzees on two successive turns?

45. **Personnel Classification** For a survey, a subject can be classified as follows:

Gender: male or female
Marital status: single, married, widowed, divorced
Occupation: administration, faculty, staff

Draw a tree diagram for the different ways a person can be classified.

☰ STATISTICS TODAY

Would You Bet Your Life?— Revisited

In his book *Probabilities in Everyday Life,* John D. McGervey states that the chance of being killed on any given commercial airline flight is almost 1 in 1 million and that the chance of being killed during a transcontinental auto trip is about 1 in 8000. The corresponding probabilities are $1/1,000,000 = 0.000001$ as compared to $1/8000 = 0.000125$. Since the second number is 125 times greater than the first number, you have a much higher risk driving than flying across the United States.

☰ Chapter Quiz

Determine whether each statement is true or false. If the statement is false, explain why.

1. Subjective probability has little use in the real world.

2. Classical probability uses a frequency distribution to compute probabilities.

3. In classical probability, all outcomes in the sample space are equally likely.

4. When two events are not mutually exclusive, $P(A \text{ or } B) = P(A) + P(B)$.

5. If two events are dependent, they must have the same probability of occurring.

6. An event and its complement can occur at the same time.

7. The arrangement ABC is the same as BAC for combinations.

8. When objects are arranged in a specific order, the arrangement is called a combination.

Select the best answer.

9. The probability that an event happens is 0.42. What is the probability that the event won't happen?
   a. −0.42   c. 0
   b. 0.58   d. 1

10. When a meteorologist says that there is a 30% chance of showers, what type of probability is the person using?
    a. Classical   c. Relative
    b. Empirical   d. Subjective

11. The sample space for tossing 3 coins consists of how many outcomes?

    a. 2   *c.* 6

    b. 4   *d.* 8

12. The complement of guessing 5 correct answers on a 5-question true/false exam is

    a. Guessing 5 incorrect answers

    b. Guessing at least 1 incorrect answer

    c. Guessing at least 1 correct answer

    d. Guessing no incorrect answers

13. When two dice are rolled, the sample space consists of how many events?

    a. 6   *c.* 36

    b. 12   *d.* 54

14. What is $_nP_0$?

    a. 0   *c.* n

    b. 1   *d.* It cannot be determined.

15. What is the number of permutations of 6 different objects taken all together?

    a. 0   *c.* 36

    b. 1   *d.* 720

16. What is 0!?

    a. 0   *c.* Undefined

    b. 1   *d.* 10

17. What is $_nC_n$?

    a. 0   *c.* n

    b. 1   *d.* It cannot be determined.

Complete the following statements with the best answer.

18. The set of all possible outcomes of a probability experiment is called the _____.

19. The probability of an event can be any number between and including _____ and _____.

20. If an event cannot occur, its probability is _____.

21. The sum of the probabilities of the events in the sample space is _____.

22. When two events cannot occur at the same time, they are said to be _____.

23. When a card is drawn, find the probability of getting

    a. A jack   *b.* A 4

    c. A card less than 6 (an ace is considered above 6)

24. **Selecting a Card** When a card is drawn from a deck, find the probability of getting

    a. A diamond   *b.* A 5 or a heart

    c. A 5 and a heart   *d.* A king

    e. A red card

25. **Selecting a Sweater** At a men's clothing store, 12 men purchased blue golf sweaters, 8 purchased green sweaters, 4 purchased gray sweaters, and 7 bought black sweaters. If a customer is selected at random, find the probability that he purchased

    a. A blue sweater

    b. A green or gray sweater

    c. A green or black or blue sweater

    d. A sweater that was not black

26. **Rolling Dice** When 2 dice are rolled, find the probability of getting

    a. A sum of 6 or 7

    b. A sum greater than 8

    c. A sum less than 3 or greater than 8

    d. A sum that is divisible by 3

    e. A sum of 16

    f. A sum less than 11

27. **Appliance Ownership** The probability that a person owns a microwave oven is 0.75, that a person owns a compact disk player is 0.25, and that a person owns both a microwave and a CD player is 0.16. Find the probability that a person owns either a microwave or a CD player, but not both.

28. **Starting Salaries** Of the physics graduates of a university, 30% received a starting salary of $30,000 or more. If 5 of the graduates are selected at random, find the probability that all had a starting salary of $30,000 or more.

29. **Selecting Cards** Five cards are drawn from an ordinary deck *without* replacement. Find the probability of getting

    a. All red cards

    b. All diamonds

    c. All aces

30. **Scholarships** The probability that Samantha will be accepted by the college of her choice and obtain a scholarship is 0.35. If the probability that she is accepted by the college is 0.65, find the probability that she will obtain a scholarship given that she is accepted by the college.

31. **New-Car Warranty** The probability that a customer will buy a new car and an extended warranty is 0.16. If the probability that a customer will purchase a new car is 0.30, find the probability that the customer will also purchase the extended warranty.

32. **Bowling and Club Membership** Of the members of the Spring Lake Bowling Lanes, 57% have a lifetime membership and bowl regularly (three or more times a week). If 70% of the club members bowl regularly, find the probability that a randomly selected member is a lifetime member, given that he or she bowls regularly.

33. **Work and Weather** The probability that Mike has to work overtime and it rains is 0.028. Mike hears the weather forecast, and there is a 50% chance of rain. Find the probability that he will have to work overtime, given that it rains.

34. **Education of Factory Employees** At a large factory, the employees were surveyed and classified according to their level of education and whether they attend a sports event at least once a month. The data are shown in the table.

	Educational level		
Sports event	**High school graduate**	**Two-year college degree**	**Four-year college degree**
Attend	16	20	24
Do not attend	12	19	25

If an employee is selected at random, find the probability that

a. The employee attends sports events regularly, given that he or she graduated from college (2- or 4-year degree)

b. Given that the employee is a high school graduate, he or she does not attend sports events regularly

35. **Heart Attacks** In a certain high-risk group, the chances of a person having suffered a heart attack are 55%. If 6 people are chosen, find the probability that at least 1 will have had a heart attack.

36. **Rolling a Die** A single die is rolled 4 times. Find the probability of getting at least one 5.

37. **Eye Color** If 85% of all people have brown eyes and 6 people are selected at random, find the probability that at least 1 of them has brown eyes.

38. **Singer Selection** How many ways can 5 sopranos and 4 altos be selected from 7 sopranos and 9 altos?

39. **Speaker Selection** How many different ways can 8 speakers be seated on a stage?

40. **Stocking Machines** A soda machine servicer must restock and collect money from 15 machines, each one at a different location. How many ways can she select 4 machines to service in 1 day?

41. **ID Cards** One company's ID cards consist of 5 letters followed by 2 digits. How many cards can be made if repetitions are allowed? If repetitions are not allowed?

42. How many different arrangements of the letters in the word *number* can be made?

43. **Physics Test** A physics test consists of 25 true/false questions. How many different possible answer keys can be made?

44. **Cellular Telephones** How many different ways can 5 cellular telephones be selected from 8 cellular phones?

45. **Fruit Selection** On a lunch counter, there are 3 oranges, 5 apples, and 2 bananas. If 3 pieces of fruit are selected, find the probability that 1 orange, 1 apple, and 1 banana are selected.

46. **Cruise Ship Activities** A cruise director schedules 4 different movies, 2 bridge games, and 3 tennis games for a two-day period. If a couple selects 3 activities, find the probability that they attend 2 movies and 1 tennis game.

47. **Committee Selection** At a sorority meeting, there are 6 seniors, 4 juniors, and 2 sophomores. If a committee of 3 is to be formed, find the probability that 1 of each will be selected.

48. **Banquet Meal Choices** For a banquet, a committee can select beef, pork, chicken, or veal; baked potatoes or mashed potatoes; and peas or green beans for a vegetable. Draw a tree diagram for all possible choices of a meat, a potato, and a vegetable.

49. **Toy Display** A toy store manager wants to display 7 identical stuffed dogs, 4 identical stuffed cats, and 3 identical stuffed teddy bears on a shelf. How many different arrangements can be made?

50. **Commercial Order** A local television station must show commercial X twice, commercial Y twice, and commercial Z three times during a 2-hour show. How many different ways can this be done?

⬛ Critical Thinking Challenges

1. **Con Man Game** Consider this problem: A con man has 3 coins. One coin has been specially made and has a head on each side. A second coin has been specially made, and on each side it has a tail. Finally, a third coin has a head and a tail on it. All coins are of the same denomination. The con man places the 3 coins in his pocket, selects one, and shows you one side. It is heads. He is willing to bet you even money that it is the two-headed coin. His reasoning is that it can't be the two-tailed coin since a head is showing; therefore, there is a 50-50 chance of it being the two-headed coin. Would you take the bet?

2. **de Méré Dice Game** Chevalier de Méré won money when he bet unsuspecting patrons that in 4 rolls of 1 die, he could get at least one 6; but he lost money when he bet that in 24 rolls of 2 dice, he could get at least a double 6. Using the probability rules, find the probability of each event and explain why he won the majority of the time on the first game but lost the majority of the time when playing the second game. (*Hint:* Find the probabilities of losing each game and subtract from 1.)

3. **Classical Birthday Problem** How many people do you think need to be in a room so that 2 people will have the same birthday (month and day)? You might think it is 366. This would, of course, guarantee it (excluding leap year), but how many people would need to be in a room so that there would be a 90% probability that 2 people would be born on the same day? What about a 50% probability?

Actually, the number is much smaller than you may think. For example, if you have 50 people in a room, the probability that 2 people will have the same birthday is 97%. If you have 23 people in a room, there is a 50% probability that 2 people were born on the same day!

The problem can be solved by using the probability rules. It must be assumed that all birthdays are equally likely, but this assumption will have little effect on the answers. The way to find the answer is by using the complementary event rule as P(2 people having the same birthday) $= 1 - P$(all have different birthdays).

For example, suppose there were 3 people in the room. The probability that each had a different birthday would be

$$\frac{365}{365} \cdot \frac{364}{365} \cdot \frac{363}{365} = \frac{{}_{365}P_3}{365^3} = 0.992$$

Hence, the probability that at least 2 of the 3 people will have the same birthday will be

$$1 - 0.992 = 0.008$$

Hence, for k people, the formula is

P(at least 2 people have the same birthday)

$$= 1 - \frac{{}_{365}P_k}{365^k}$$

Using your calculator, complete the table and verify that for at least a 50% chance of 2 people having the same birthday, 23 or more people will be needed.

Number of people	Probability that at least 2 have the same birthday
1	0.000
2	0.003
5	0.027
10	
15	
20	
21	
22	
23	

4. We know that if the probability of an event happening is 100%, then the event is a certainty. Can it be concluded that if there is a 50% chance of contracting a communicable disease through contact with an infected person, there would be a 100% chance of contracting the disease if 2 contacts were made with the infected person? Explain your answer.

≡ Data Projects

1. **Business and Finance** Select a pizza restaurant and a sandwich shop. For the pizza restaurant look at the menu to determine how many sizes, crust types, and toppings are available. How many different pizza types are possible? For the sandwich shop determine how many breads, meats, veggies, cheeses, sauces, and condiments are available. How many different sandwich choices are possible?

2. **Sports and Leisure** When poker games are shown on television, there are often percentages displayed that show how likely it is that a certain hand will win. Investigate how these percentages are determined. Show an example with two competing hands in a Texas Hold 'Em game. Include the percentages that each hand will win after the deal, the flop, the turn, and the river.

3. **Technology** A music player or music organization program can keep track of how many different artists are in a library. First note how many different artists are in your music library. Then find the probability that if

25 songs are selected at random, none will have the same artist.

4. **Health and Wellness** Assume that the gender distribution of babies is such that one-half the time females are born and one-half the time males are born. In a family of 3 children, what is the probability that all are girls? In a family of 4? Is it unusual that in a family with 4 children all would be girls? In a family of 5?

5. **Politics and Economics** Consider the U.S. Senate. Find out about the composition of any three of the Senate's standing committees. How many different committees of Senators are possible, knowing the party composition of the Senate and the number of committee members from each party for each committee?

6. **Your Class** Research the famous Monty Hall probability problem. Conduct a simulation of the Monty Hall problem online using a simulation program or in class using live "contestants." After 50 simulations compare your results to those stated in the research you did. Did your simulation support the conclusions?

≡ Answers to Applying the Concepts

Section 4–1   Tossing a Coin

1. The sample space is the listing of all possible outcomes of the coin toss.

2. The possible outcomes are heads or tails.

3. Classical probability says that a fair coin has a 50% chance of coming up heads and a 50% chance of coming up tails.

4. The law of large numbers says that as you increase the number of trials, the overall results will approach the

theoretical probability. However, since the coin has no "memory," it still has a 50% chance of coming up heads and a 50% chance of coming up tails on the next toss. Knowing what has already happened should not change your opinion on what will happen on the next toss.

5. The empirical approach to probability is based on running an experiment and looking at the results. You cannot do that at this time.

6. Subjective probabilities could be used if you believe the coin is biased.

7. Answers will vary; however, they should address that a fair coin has a 50% chance of coming up heads and a 50% chance of coming up tails on the next flip.

Section 4–2   Which Pain Reliever Is Best?

1. There were $192 + 186 + 188 = 566$ subjects in the study.

2. The study lasted for 12 weeks.

3. The variables are the type of pain reliever and the side effects.

4. Both variables are qualitative and nominal.

5. The numbers in the table are exact figures.

6. The probability that a randomly selected person was receiving a placebo is $192/566 = 0.339$ (about 34%).

7. The probability that a randomly selected person was receiving a placebo or drug A is $(192 + 186)/566 = 378/566 = 0.668$ (about 67%). These are mutually exclusive events. The complement is that a randomly selected person was receiving drug B.

8. The probability that a randomly selected person was receiving a placebo or experienced a neurological headache is $(192 + 55 + 72)/566 = 319/566 = 0.564$ (about 56%).

9. The probability that a randomly selected person was not receiving a placebo or experienced a sinus headache is $(186 + 188)/566 + 11/566 = 385/566 = 0.680$ (about 68%).

Section 4–3   Guilty or Innocent?

1. The probability of another couple with the same characteristics being in that area is $\frac{1}{12} \cdot \frac{1}{10} \cdot \frac{1}{4} \cdot \frac{1}{11} \cdot \frac{1}{3} \cdot \frac{1}{13} \cdot \frac{1}{100} = \frac{1}{20,592,000}$, assuming the characteristics are independent of one another.

2. You would use the multiplication rule, since you are looking for the probability of multiple events happening together.

3. We do not know if the characteristics are dependent or independent, but we assumed independence for the calculation in question 1.

4. The probabilities would change if there were dependence among two or more events.

5. Answers will vary. One possible answer is that probabilities can be used to explain how unlikely it is to have a

set of events occur at the same time (in this case, how unlikely it is to have another couple with the same characteristics in that area).

6. Answers will vary. One possible answer is that if the only eyewitness was the woman who was mugged and the probabilities are accurate, it seems very unlikely that a couple matching these characteristics would be in that area at that time. This might cause you to convict the couple.

7. Answers will vary. One possible answer is that our probabilities are theoretical and serve a purpose when appropriate, but that court cases are based on much more than impersonal chance.

8. Answers will vary. One possible answer is that juries decide whether to convict a defendant if they find evidence "beyond a reasonable doubt" that the person is guilty. In probability terms, this means that if the defendant was actually innocent, then the chance of seeing the events that occurred is so unlikely as to have occurred by chance. Therefore, the jury concludes that the defendant is guilty.

Section 4–4   Garage Door Openers

1. Four on/off switches lead to 16 different settings.

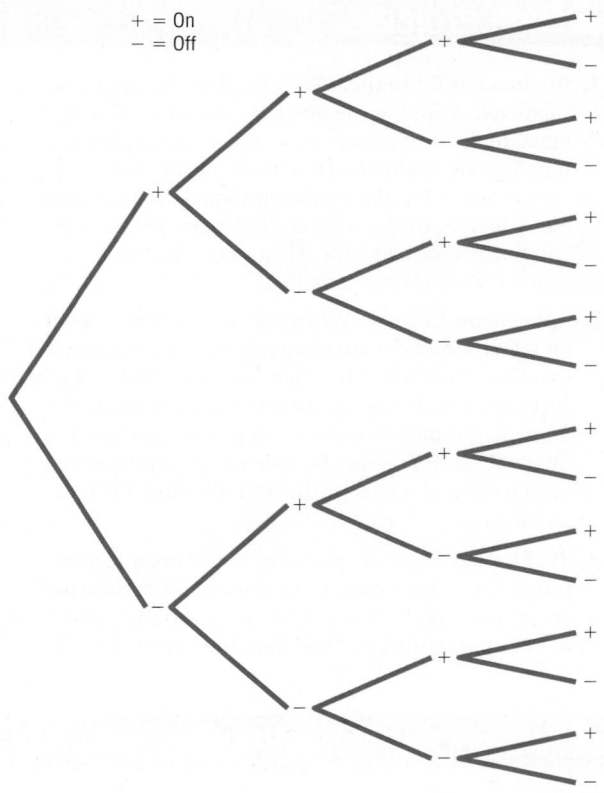

+ = On
− = Off

2. With 5 on/off switches, there are $2^5 = 32$ different settings. With 6 on/off switches, there are $2^6 = 64$ different settings. In general, if there are k on/off switches, there are 2^k different settings.

3. With 8 consecutive on/off switches, there are $2^8 = 256$ different settings.

4. It is less likely for someone to be able to open your garage door if you have 8 on/off settings (probability about 0.4%) than if you have 4 on/off switches (probability about 6.0%). Having 8 on/off switches in the opener seems pretty safe.

5. Each key blank could be made into $5^5 = 3125$ possible keys.

6. If there were 420,000 Dodge Caravans sold in the United States, then any one key could start about $420,000/3125 = 134.4$, or about 134, different Caravans.

7. Answers will vary.

Section 4–5 Counting Rules and Probability

1. There are five different events: each multiple-choice question is an event.

2. These events are independent.

3. If you guess on 1 question, the probability of getting it correct is 0.20. Thus, if you guess on all 5 questions, the probability of getting all of them correct is $(0.20)^5 = 0.00032$.

4. The probability that a person would guess answer A for a question is 0.20, so the probability that a person would guess answer A for each question is $(0.20)^5 = 0.00032$.

5. There are five different events: each matching question is an event.

6. These are dependent events.

7. The probability of getting them all correct if you are guessing is $\frac{1}{5} \cdot \frac{1}{4} \cdot \frac{1}{3} \cdot \frac{1}{2} \cdot \frac{1}{1} = \frac{1}{120} = 0.008$.

8. The difference between the two problems is that we are sampling without replacement in the second problem, so the denominator changes in the event probabilities.

5

Discrete Probability Distributions

 STATISTICS TODAY

≡ STATISTICS TODAY

Is Pooling Worthwhile?

Blood samples are used to screen people for certain diseases. When the disease is rare, health care workers sometimes combine or pool the blood samples of a group of individuals into one batch and then test it. If the test result of the batch is negative, no further testing is needed since none of the individuals in the group has the disease. However, if the test result of the batch is positive, each individual in the group must be tested.

Consider this hypothetical example: Suppose the probability of a person having the disease is 0.05, and a pooled sample of 15 individuals is tested. What is the probability that no further testing will be needed for the individuals in the sample? The answer to this question can be found by using what is called the *binomial distribution*. See Statistics Today—Revisited at the end of the chapter.

This chapter explains probability distributions in general and a specific, often used distribution called the binomial distribution. The Poisson, hypergeometric, geometric, and multinomial distributions are also explained.

OUTLINE

Introduction
5–1   Probability Distributions
5–2   Mean, Variance, Standard Deviation, and Expectation
5–3   The Binomial Distribution
5–4   Other Types of Distributions
Summary

OBJECTIVES

After completing this chapter, you should be able to

1. Construct a probability distribution for a random variable.

2. Find the mean, variance, standard deviation, and expected value for a discrete random variable.

3. Find the exact probability for X successes in n trials of a binomial experiment.

4. Find the mean, variance, and standard deviation for the variable of a binomial distribution.

5. Find probabilities for outcomes of variables, using the Poisson, hypergeometric, geometric, and multinomial distributions.

Introduction

Many decisions in business, insurance, and other real-life situations are made by assigning probabilities to all possible outcomes pertaining to the situation and then evaluating the results. For example, a saleswoman can compute the probability that she will make 0, 1, 2, or 3 or more sales in a single day. An insurance company might be able to assign probabilities to the number of vehicles a family owns. A self-employed speaker might be able to compute the probabilities for giving 0, 1, 2, 3, or 4 or more speeches each week. Once these probabilities are assigned, statistics such as the mean, variance, and standard deviation can be computed for these events. With these statistics, various decisions can be made. The saleswoman will be able to compute the average number of sales she makes per week, and if she is working on commission, she will be able to approximate her weekly income over a period of time, say, monthly. The public speaker will be able to plan ahead and approximate his average income and expenses. The insurance company can use its information to design special computer forms and programs to accommodate its customers' future needs.

This chapter explains the concepts and applications of what is called a *probability distribution*. In addition, special probability distributions, such as the *binomial, multinomial, Poisson, hypergeometric,* and *geometric* distributions, are explained.

5–1   Probability Distributions

OBJECTIVE

Construct a probability distribution for a random variable.

Before probability distribution is defined formally, the definition of a variable is reviewed. In Chapter 1, a *variable* was defined as a characteristic or attribute that can assume different values. Various letters of the alphabet, such as X, Y, or Z, are used to represent variables. Since the variables in this chapter are associated with probability, they are called *random variables*.

For example, if a die is rolled, a letter such as X can be used to represent the outcomes. Then the value that X can assume is 1, 2, 3, 4, 5, or 6, corresponding to the outcomes of rolling a single die. If two coins are tossed, a letter, say Y, can be used to represent the number of heads, in this case 0, 1, or 2. As another example, if the temperature at 8:00 A.M. is 43° and at noon it is 53°, then the values T that the temperature assumes are said to be random, since they are due to various atmospheric conditions at the time the temperature was taken.

> A **random variable** is a variable whose values are determined by chance.

Also recall from Chapter 1 that you can classify variables as discrete or continuous by observing the values the variable can assume. If a variable can assume only a specific number of values, such as the outcomes for the roll of a die or the outcomes for the toss of a coin, then the variable is called a *discrete variable.*

Discrete variables have a finite number of possible values or an infinite number of values that can be counted. The word *counted* means that they can be enumerated using the numbers 1, 2, 3, etc. For example, the number of joggers in Riverview Park each day and the number of phone calls received after a TV commercial airs are examples of discrete variables, since they can be counted.

Variables that can assume all values in the interval between any two given values are called *continuous variables.* For example, if the temperature goes from 62° to 78° in a 24-hour period, it has passed through every possible number from 62 to 78. *Continuous random variables are obtained from data that can be measured rather than counted.* Continuous random variables can assume an infinite number of values and can be decimal and fractional values. On a continuous scale, a person's weight might be exactly

183.426 pounds if a scale could measure weight to the thousandths place; however, on a digital scale that measures only to tenths of a pound, the weight would be 183.4 pounds. Examples of continuous variables are heights, weights, temperatures, and time. In this chapter only discrete random variables are used; Chapter 6 explains continuous random variables.

The procedure shown here for constructing a probability distribution for a discrete random variable uses the probability experiment of tossing three coins. Recall that when three coins are tossed, the sample space is represented as TTT, TTH, THT, HTT, HHT, HTH, THH, HHH; and if X is the random variable for the number of heads, then X assumes the value 0, 1, 2, or 3.

Probabilities for the values of X can be determined as follows:

No heads	One head			Two heads			Three heads
TTT	TTH	THT	HTT	HHT	HTH	THH	HHH
$\frac{1}{8}$	$\frac{1}{8}$	$\frac{1}{8}$	$\frac{1}{8}$	$\frac{1}{8}$	$\frac{1}{8}$	$\frac{1}{8}$	$\frac{1}{8}$
$\frac{1}{8}$	$\frac{3}{8}$			$\frac{3}{8}$			$\frac{1}{8}$

Hence, the probability of getting no heads is $\frac{1}{8}$, one head is $\frac{3}{8}$, two heads is $\frac{3}{8}$, and three heads is $\frac{1}{8}$. From these values, a probability distribution can be constructed by listing the outcomes and assigning the probability of each outcome, as shown here.

Number of heads X	0	1	2	3
Probability $P(X)$	$\frac{1}{8}$	$\frac{3}{8}$	$\frac{3}{8}$	$\frac{1}{8}$

> A **discrete probability distribution** consists of the values a random variable can assume and the corresponding probabilities of the values. The probabilities are determined theoretically or by observation.

Discrete probability distributions can be shown by using a graph or a table. Probability distributions can also be represented by a formula. See Exercises 31–36 at the end of this section for examples.

EXAMPLE 5–1   Rolling a Die

Construct a probability distribution for rolling a single die.

SOLUTION

Since the sample space is 1, 2, 3, 4, 5, 6 and each outcome has a probability of $\frac{1}{6}$, the distribution is as shown.

Outcome X	1	2	3	4	5	6
Probability $P(X)$	$\frac{1}{6}$	$\frac{1}{6}$	$\frac{1}{6}$	$\frac{1}{6}$	$\frac{1}{6}$	$\frac{1}{6}$

When probability distributions are shown graphically, the values of X are placed on the x axis and the probabilities $P(X)$ on the y axis. These graphs are helpful in determining the shape of the distribution (right-skewed, left-skewed, or symmetric).

EXAMPLE 5–2   Tossing Coins

Represent graphically the probability distribution for the sample space for tossing three coins.

Number of heads X	0	1	2	3
Probability $P(X)$	$\frac{1}{8}$	$\frac{3}{8}$	$\frac{3}{8}$	$\frac{1}{8}$

SOLUTION

The values that X assumes are located on the x axis, and the values for $P(X)$ are located on the y axis. The graph is shown in Figure 5–1.

FIGURE 5–1   Probability Distribution for Example 5–2

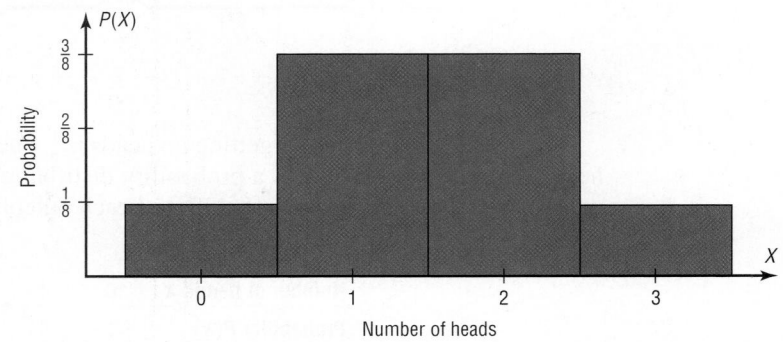

Note that for visual appearances, it is not necessary to start with 0 at the origin.

Examples 5–1 and 5–2 are illustrations of *theoretical* probability distributions. You did not need to actually perform the experiments to compute the probabilities. In contrast, to construct actual probability distributions, you must observe the variable over a period of time. They are empirical, as shown in Example 5–3.

EXAMPLE 5–3   Baseball World Series

The baseball World Series is played by the winner of the National League and that of the American League. The first team to win four games wins the World Series. In other words, the series will consist of four to seven games, depending on the individual victories. The data shown consist of 40 World Series events. The number of games played in each series is represented by the variable X. Find the probability $P(X)$ for each X, construct a probability distribution, and draw a graph for the data.

X	Number of series played
4	8
5	7
6	9
7	16
	Total 40

SOLUTION

The probability $P(X)$ can be computed for each X by dividing the number of series played for each X by the total.

For 4 games, $\frac{8}{40} = 0.200$ For 6 games, $\frac{9}{40} = 0.225$

For 5 games, $\frac{7}{40} = 0.175$ For 7 games, $\frac{16}{40} = 0.400$

The probability distribution is

Number of games X	4	5	6	7
Probability $P(X)$	0.200	0.175	0.225	0.400

The graph is shown in Figure 5–2.

FIGURE 5–2
Probability Distribution for
Example 5–3

Two Requirements for a Probability Distribution

1. The sum of the probabilities of all the events in the sample space must equal 1; that is, $\Sigma P(X) = 1$.
2. The probability of each event in the sample space must be between or equal to 0 and 1. That is, $0 \leq P(X) \leq 1$.

The first requirement states that the sum of the probabilities of all the events must be equal to 1. This sum cannot be less than 1 or greater than 1 since the sample space includes *all* possible outcomes of the probability experiment. The second requirement states that the probability of any individual event must be a value from 0 to 1. The reason (as stated in Chapter 4) is that the range of the probability of any individual value can be 0, 1, or any value between 0 and 1. A probability cannot be a negative number or greater than 1.

EXAMPLE 5–4   Probability Distributions

Determine whether each distribution is a probability distribution.

a.

X	5	8	11	14
$P(X)$	0.2	0.6	0.1	0.3

b.

X	1	2	3	4	5
$P(X)$	$\frac{1}{4}$	$\frac{1}{8}$	$\frac{3}{8}$	$\frac{1}{8}$	$\frac{1}{8}$

c.

X	1	2	3	4
$P(X)$	$\frac{1}{4}$	$\frac{1}{4}$	$\frac{1}{4}$	$\frac{1}{4}$

d.

X	4	8	12
$P(X)$	-0.5	0.6	0.4

≡ SPEAKING OF STATISTICS   Coins, Births, and Other Random (?) Events

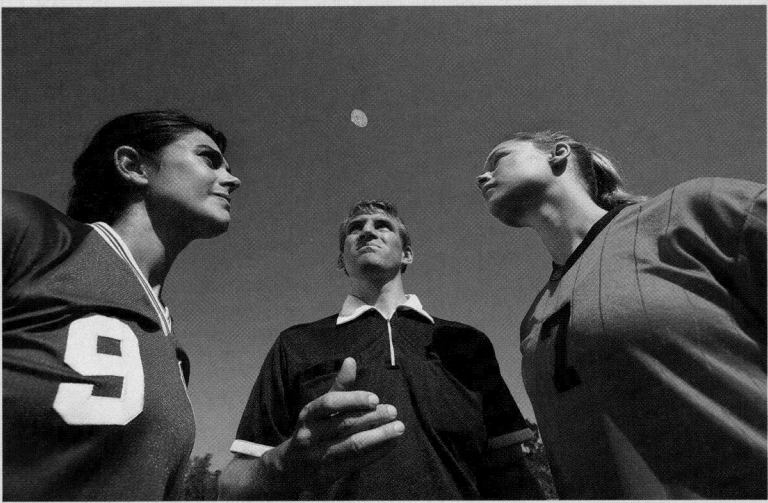

Examples of random events such as tossing coins are used in almost all books on probability. But is flipping a coin really a random event?

Tossing coins dates back to ancient Roman times when the coins usually consisted of the Emperor's head on one side (i.e., heads) and another icon such as a ship on the other side (i.e., tails). Tossing coins was used in both fortune telling and ancient Roman games.

A Chinese form of divination called the *I-Ching* (pronounced E-Ching) is thought to be at least 4000 years old. It consists of 64 hexagrams made up of six horizontal lines. Each line is either broken or unbroken, representing the yin and the yang. These 64 hexagrams are supposed to represent all possible situations in life. To consult the *I-Ching,* a question is asked and then three coins are tossed six times. The way the coins fall, either heads up or heads down, determines whether the line is broken (yin) or unbroken (yang). Once the hexagram is determined, its meaning is consulted and interpreted to get the answer to the question. (*Note:* Another method used to determine the hexagram employs yarrow sticks.)

In the 16th century, a mathematician named Abraham DeMoivre used the outcomes of tossing coins to study what later became known as the normal distribution; however, his work at that time was not widely known.

Mathematicians usually consider the outcomes of a coin toss to be a random event. That is, each probability of getting a head is $\frac{1}{2}$, and the probability of getting a tail is $\frac{1}{2}$. Also, it is not possible to predict with 100% certainty which outcome will occur. But new studies question this theory. During World War II a South African mathematician named John Kerrich tossed a coin 10,000 times while he was interned in a German prison camp. Unfortunately, the results of his experiment were never recorded, so we don't know the number of heads that occurred.

Several studies have shown that when a coin-tossing device is used, the probability that a coin will land on the same side on which it is placed on the coin-tossing device is about 51%. It would take about 10,000 tosses to become aware of this bias. Furthermore, researchers showed that when a coin is spun on its edge, the coin falls tails up about 80% of the time since there is more metal on the heads side of a coin. This makes the coin slightly heavier on the heads side than on the tails side.

Another assumption commonly made in probability theory is that the number of male births is equal to the number of female births and that the probability of a boy being born is $\frac{1}{2}$ and the probability of a girl being born is $\frac{1}{2}$. We know this is not exactly true.

In the later 1700s, a French mathematician named Pierre Simon Laplace attempted to prove that more males than females are born. He used records from 1745 to 1770 in Paris and showed that the percentage of females born was about 49%. Although these percentages vary somewhat from location to location, further surveys show they are generally true worldwide. Even though there are discrepancies, we generally consider the outcomes to be 50-50 since these discrepancies are relatively small.

Based on this article, would you consider the coin toss at the beginning of a football game fair?

a. No. The sum of the probabilities is greater than 1.

b. Yes. The sum of the probabilities of all the events is equal to 1. Each probability is greater than or equal to 0 and less than or equal to 1.

c. Yes. The sum of the probabilities of all the events is equal to 1. Each probability is greater than or equal to 0 and less than or equal to 1.

d. No. One of the probabilities is less than 0.

Many variables in business, education, engineering, and other areas can be analyzed by using probability distributions. Section 5–2 shows methods for finding the mean and standard deviation for a probability distribution.

≡ Applying the Concepts 5–1

Dropping College Courses

Use the following table to answer the questions.

Reason for dropping a college course	Frequency	Percentage
Too difficult	45	
Illness	40	
Change in work schedule	20	
Change of major	14	
Family-related problems	9	
Money	7	
Miscellaneous	6	
No meaningful reason	3	

1. What is the variable under study? Is it a random variable?

2. How many people were in the study?

3. Complete the table.

4. From the information given, what is the probability that a student will drop a class because of illness? Money? Change of major?

5. Would you consider the information in the table to be a probability distribution?

6. Are the categories mutually exclusive?

7. Are the categories independent?

8. Are the categories exhaustive?

9. Are the two requirements for a discrete probability distribution met?

See page 309 for the answers.

≡ Exercises 5–1

1. Define and give three examples of a random variable.

2. Explain the difference between a discrete and a continuous random variable.

3. Give three examples of a discrete random variable.

4. Give three examples of a continuous random variable.

5. List three continuous random variables and three discrete random variables associated with a major league baseball game.

6. What is a probability distribution? Give an example.

For Exercises 7 through 12, determine whether the distribution represents a probability distribution. If it does not, state why.

7.

X	3	6	8	12
$P(X)$	0.3	0.5	0.7	-0.8

8.

X	5	7	9
$P(X)$	0.6	0.8	-0.4

9.

X	-2	0	2	5
$P(X)$	0.3	0.4	0.2	0.1

10.

X	20	30	40	50
P(X)	0.05	0.35	0.4	0.2

11.

X	1	2	3	4
P(X)	0.4	0.3	0.2	1

12.

X	3	7	9	12	14
P(X)	$\frac{4}{13}$	$\frac{1}{13}$	$\frac{3}{13}$	$\frac{1}{13}$	$\frac{2}{13}$

For Exercises 13 through 18, state whether the variable is discrete or continuous.

13. The number of cheeseburgers a fast-food restaurant serves each day

14. The number of people who play the state lottery each day

15. The weight of an automobile

16. The time it takes to have a medical physical exam

17. The number of mathematics majors in your school

18. The blood pressures of all patients admitted to a hospital on a specific day

For Exercises 19 through 26, construct a probability distribution for the data and draw a graph for the distribution.

19. Medical Tests The probabilities that a patient will have 0, 1, 2, or 3 medical tests performed on entering a hospital are $\frac{6}{15}$, $\frac{5}{15}$, $\frac{3}{15}$, and $\frac{1}{15}$, respectively.

20. Investment Return The probabilities of a return on an investment of $5000, $7000, and $9000 are $\frac{1}{2}$, $\frac{3}{8}$, and $\frac{1}{8}$, respectively.

21. Birthday Cake Sales The probabilities that a bakery has a demand for 2, 3, 5, or 7 birthday cakes on any given day are 0.35, 0.41, 0.15, and 0.09, respectively.

22. DVD Rentals The probabilities that a customer will rent 0, 1, 2, 3, or 4 DVDs on a single visit to the rental store are 0.15, 0.25, 0.3, 0.25, and 0.05, respectively.

23. Loaded Die A die is loaded in such a way that the probabilities of getting 1, 2, 3, 4, 5, and 6 are $\frac{1}{2}$, $\frac{1}{6}$, $\frac{1}{12}$, $\frac{1}{12}$, $\frac{1}{12}$, and $\frac{1}{12}$, respectively.

24. Item Selection The probabilities that a customer selects 1, 2, 3, 4, and 5 items at a convenience store are 0.32, 0.12, 0.23, 0.18, and 0.15, respectively.

25. Student Classes The probabilities that a student is registered for 2, 3, 4, or 5 classes are 0.01, 0.34, 0.62, and 0.03, respectively.

26. Garage Space The probabilities that a randomly selected home has garage space for 0, 1, 2, or 3 cars are 0.22, 0.33, 0.37, and 0.08, respectively.

27. Triangular Numbers The first six triangular numbers (1, 3, 6, 10, 15, 21) are printed one each on one side of a card. The cards are placed face down and mixed. Choose two cards at random, and let x be the sum of the two numbers. Construct the probability distribution for this random variable x.

28. Child Play in Day Care In a popular day care center, the probability that a child will play with the computer is 0.45; the probability that he or she will play dress-up is 0.27; play with blocks, 0.18; and paint, 0.1. Construct the probability distribution for this discrete random variable.

29. Goals in Hockey The probability that a hockey team scores a total of 1 goal in a game is 0.124; 2 goals, 0.297; 3 goals, 0.402; 4 goals, 0.094; and 5 goals, 0.083. Construct the probability distribution for this discrete random variable and draw the graph.

30. Mathematics Tutoring Center At a drop-in mathematics tutoring center, each teacher sees 4 to 8 students per hour. The probability that a tutor sees 4 students in an hour is 0.117; 5 students, 0.123; 6 students, 0.295; and 7 students, 0.328. Find the probability that a tutor sees 8 students in an hour, construct the probability distribution, and draw the graph.

Extending the Concepts

A probability distribution can be written in formula notation such as $P(X) = 1/X$, where $X = 2, 3, 6$. The distribution is shown as follows:

X	2	3	6
P(X)	$\frac{1}{2}$	$\frac{1}{3}$	$\frac{1}{6}$

For Exercises 31 through 36, write the distribution for the formula and determine whether it is a probability distribution.

31. $P(X) = X/6$ for $X = 1, 2, 3$

32. $P(X) = X$ for $X = 0.2, 0.3, 0.5$

33. $P(X) = X/6$ for $X = 3, 4, 7$

34. $P(X) = X + 0.1$ for $X = 0.1, 0.02, 0.04$

35. $P(X) = X/7$ for $X = 1, 2, 4$

36. $P(X) = X/(X + 2)$ for $X = 0, 1, 2$

37. Computer Games The probability that a child plays one computer game is one-half as likely as that of playing two computer games. The probability of playing three games is twice as likely as that of playing two games, and the probability of playing four games is the average of the other three. Let X be the number of computer games played. Construct the probability distribution for this random variable and draw the graph.

5–2   Mean, Variance, Standard Deviation, and Expectation

The mean, variance, and standard deviation for a probability distribution are computed differently from the mean, variance, and standard deviation for samples. This section explains how these measures—as well as a new measure called the *expectation*—are calculated for probability distributions.

Mean

In Chapter 3, the mean for a sample or population was computed by adding the values and dividing by the total number of values, as shown in these formulas:

Sample mean: $\overline{X} = \dfrac{\Sigma X}{n}$ Population mean: $\mu = \dfrac{\Sigma X}{N}$

> **Historical Note**
>
> A professor, Augustin Louis Cauchy (1789–1857), wrote a book on probability. While he was teaching at the Military School of Paris, one of his students was Napoleon Bonaparte.

But how would you compute the mean of the number of spots that show on top when a die is rolled? You could try rolling the die, say, 10 times, recording the number of spots, and finding the mean; however, this answer would only approximate the true mean. What about 50 rolls or 100 rolls? Actually, the more times the die is rolled, the better the approximation. You might ask, then, How many times must the die be rolled to get the exact answer? *It must be rolled an infinite number of times.* Since this task is impossible, the previous formulas cannot be used because the denominators would be infinity. Hence, a new method of computing the mean is necessary. This method gives the exact theoretical value of the mean as if it were possible to roll the die an infinite number of times.

Before the formula is stated, an example will be used to explain the concept. Suppose two coins are tossed repeatedly, and the number of heads that occurred is recorded. What will be the mean of the number of heads? The sample space is

HH, HT, TH, TT

and each outcome has a probability of $\frac{1}{4}$. Now, in the long run, you would *expect* two heads (HH) to occur approximately $\frac{1}{4}$ of the time, one head to occur approximately $\frac{1}{2}$ of the time (HT or TH), and no heads (TT) to occur approximately $\frac{1}{4}$ of the time. Hence, on average, you would expect the number of heads to be

$\frac{1}{4} \cdot 2 + \frac{1}{2} \cdot 1 + \frac{1}{4} \cdot 0 = 1$

That is, if it were possible to toss the coins many times or an infinite number of times, the *average* of the number of heads would be 1.

Hence, to find the mean for a probability distribution, you must multiply each possible outcome by its corresponding probability and find the sum of the products.

Formula for the Mean of a Probability Distribution

The mean of a random variable with a discrete probability distribution is

$$\mu = X_1 \cdot P(X_1) + X_2 \cdot P(X_2) + X_3 \cdot P(X_3) + \cdots + X_n \cdot P(X_n)$$
$$= \Sigma X \cdot P(X)$$

where $X_1, X_2, X_3, \ldots, X_n$ are the outcomes and $P(X_1), P(X_2), P(X_3), \ldots, P(X_n)$ are the corresponding probabilities.

Note: $\Sigma X \cdot P(X)$ means to sum the products.

Rounding Rule for the Mean, Variance, and Standard Deviation for a Probability Distribution   The rounding rule for the mean, variance, and standard deviation for variables of a probability distribution is this: The mean, variance, and standard deviation should be rounded to one more decimal place than the outcome X. When fractions are used, they should be reduced to lowest terms.

Examples 5–5 through 5–8 illustrate the use of the formula.

EXAMPLE 5–5   Rolling a Die

Find the mean of the number of spots that appear when a die is tossed.

SOLUTION

In the toss of a die, the mean can be computed thus.

Outcome X	1	2	3	4	5	6
Probability $P(X)$	$\frac{1}{6}$	$\frac{1}{6}$	$\frac{1}{6}$	$\frac{1}{6}$	$\frac{1}{6}$	$\frac{1}{6}$

$$\mu = \Sigma X \cdot P(X) = 1 \cdot \tfrac{1}{6} + 2 \cdot \tfrac{1}{6} + 3 \cdot \tfrac{1}{6} + 4 \cdot \tfrac{1}{6} + 5 \cdot \tfrac{1}{6} + 6 \cdot \tfrac{1}{6}$$
$$= \tfrac{21}{6} = 3\tfrac{1}{2} \text{ or } 3.5$$

That is, when a die is tossed many times, the theoretical mean will be 3.5. Note that even though the die cannot show a 3.5, the theoretical average is 3.5.

The reason why this formula gives the theoretical mean is that in the long run, each outcome would occur approximately $\frac{1}{6}$ of the time. Hence, multiplying the outcome by its corresponding probability and finding the sum would yield the theoretical mean. In other words, outcome 1 would occur approximately $\frac{1}{6}$ of the time, outcome 2 would occur approximately $\frac{1}{6}$ of the time, etc.

EXAMPLE 5–6   Children in a Family

In families with five children, find the mean number of children who will be girls.

SOLUTION

First, it is necessary to find the probability distribution for the number of females. There are 32 outcomes, and there is one way for a family to have no girls. There are five ways to have one girl, that is, FMMMM, MFMMM, MMFMM, MMMFM, MMMMF. Continue with two females and three males, three females and two males, four females and one male, and five females. You can draw a tree diagram to help you.

The probability distribution is

Number of girls X	0	1	2	3	4	5
Probability $P(X)$	$\frac{1}{32}$	$\frac{5}{32}$	$\frac{10}{32}$	$\frac{10}{32}$	$\frac{5}{32}$	$\frac{1}{32}$

The mean is

$$\mu = \Sigma X \cdot P(X) = 0 \cdot \tfrac{1}{32} + 1 \cdot \tfrac{5}{32} + 2 \cdot \tfrac{10}{32} + 3 \cdot \tfrac{10}{32} + 4 \cdot \tfrac{5}{32} + 5 \cdot \tfrac{1}{32} = 2\tfrac{1}{2} = 2.5$$

Hence, the mean number of females is 2.5.

EXAMPLE 5–7   Tossing Coins

If three coins are tossed, find the mean of the number of heads that occur. (See the table preceding Example 5–1.)

SOLUTION

The probability distribution is

Number of heads X	0	1	2	3
Probability $P(X)$	$\frac{1}{8}$	$\frac{3}{8}$	$\frac{3}{8}$	$\frac{1}{8}$

The mean is

$$\mu = \Sigma X \cdot P(X) = 0 \cdot \tfrac{1}{8} + 1 \cdot \tfrac{3}{8} + 2 \cdot \tfrac{3}{8} + 3 \cdot \tfrac{1}{8} = \tfrac{12}{8} = 1\tfrac{1}{2} \text{ or } 1.5$$

The value 1.5 cannot occur as an outcome. Nevertheless, it is the long-run or theoretical average.

EXAMPLE 5–8   Number of Trips of Five Nights or More

The probability distribution shown represents the number of trips of five nights or more that American adults take per year. (That is, 6% do not take any trips lasting five nights or more, 70% take one trip lasting five nights or more per year, etc.) Find the mean.

Number of trips X	0	1	2	3	4
Probability $P(X)$	0.06	0.70	0.20	0.03	0.01

SOLUTION

$$\begin{aligned}
\mu &= \Sigma X \cdot P(X) \\
&= (0)(0.06) + (1)(0.70) + (2)(0.20) + (3)(0.03) + (4)(0.01) \\
&= 0 + 0.70 + 0.40 + 0.09 + 0.04 \\
&= 1.23
\end{aligned}$$

Hence, the mean of the number of trips lasting five nights or more per year taken by American adults is 1.23.

Variance and Standard Deviation

For a probability distribution, the mean of the random variable describes the measure of the so-called long-run or theoretical average, but it does not tell anything about the spread of the distribution. Recall from Chapter 3 that to measure this spread or variability, statisticians use the variance and standard deviation. These formulas were used:

$$\sigma^2 = \frac{\Sigma(X - \mu)^2}{N} \qquad \text{or} \qquad \sigma = \sqrt{\frac{\Sigma(X - \mu)^2}{N}}$$

These formulas cannot be used for a random variable of a probability distribution since N is infinite, so the variance and standard deviation must be computed differently.

To find the variance for the random variable of a probability distribution, subtract the theoretical mean of the random variable from each outcome and square the difference. Then multiply each difference by its corresponding probability and add the products. The formula is

$$\sigma^2 = \Sigma[(X - \mu)^2 \cdot P(X)]$$

Finding the variance by using this formula is somewhat tedious. So for simplified computations, a shortcut formula can be used. This formula is algebraically equivalent to the longer one and is used in the examples that follow.

Formula for the Variance of a Probability Distribution

Find the variance of a probability distribution by multiplying the square of each outcome by its corresponding probability, summing those products, and subtracting the square of the mean. The formula for the variance of a probability distribution is

$$\sigma^2 = \Sigma[X^2 \cdot P(X)] - \mu^2$$

The standard deviation of a probability distribution is

$$\sigma = \sqrt{\sigma^2} \qquad \text{or} \qquad \sigma = \sqrt{\Sigma[X^2 \cdot P(X)] - \mu^2}$$

Remember that the variance and standard deviation cannot be negative.

EXAMPLE 5–9   Rolling a Die

Compute the variance and standard deviation for the probability distribution in Example 5–5.

SOLUTION

Recall that the mean is $\mu = 3.5$, as computed in Example 5–5. Square each outcome and multiply by the corresponding probability, sum those products, and then subtract the square of the mean.

$$\sigma^2 = (1^2 \cdot \tfrac{1}{6} + 2^2 \cdot \tfrac{1}{6} + 3^2 \cdot \tfrac{1}{6} + 4^2 \cdot \tfrac{1}{6} + 5^2 \cdot \tfrac{1}{6} + 6^2 \cdot \tfrac{1}{6}) - (3.5)^2 = 2.917$$

To get the standard deviation, find the square root of the variance.

$$\sigma = \sqrt{2.917} \approx 1.708$$

Hence, the standard deviation for rolling a die is 1.708.

EXAMPLE 5–10   Selecting Numbered Balls

A box contains 5 balls. Two are numbered 3, one is numbered 4, and two are numbered 5. The balls are mixed and one is selected at random. After a ball is selected, its number is recorded. Then it is replaced. If the experiment is repeated many times, find the variance and standard deviation of the numbers on the balls.

SOLUTION

Let X be the number on each ball. The probability distribution is

Number on ball X	3	4	5
Probability $P(X)$	$\tfrac{2}{5}$	$\tfrac{1}{5}$	$\tfrac{2}{5}$

The mean is

$$\mu = \Sigma X \cdot P(X) = 3 \cdot \tfrac{2}{5} + 4 \cdot \tfrac{1}{5} + 5 \cdot \tfrac{2}{5} = 4$$

The variance is

$$\sigma = \Sigma[X^2 \cdot P(X)] - \mu^2$$
$$= 3^2 \cdot \tfrac{2}{5} + 4^2 \cdot \tfrac{1}{5} + 5^2 \cdot \tfrac{2}{5} - 4^2$$
$$= 16\tfrac{4}{5} - 16$$
$$= \tfrac{4}{5} \text{ or } 0.8$$

The standard deviation is

$$\sigma = \sqrt{\frac{4}{5}} = \sqrt{0.8} \approx 0.894$$

The mean, variance, and standard deviation can also be found by using vertical columns, as shown.

X	$P(X)$	$X \cdot P(X)$	$X^2 \cdot P(X)$
3	0.4	1.2	3.6
4	0.2	0.8	3.2
5	0.4	2.0	10
		$\Sigma X \cdot P(X) = 4.0$	16.8

Find the mean by summing the $\Sigma X \cdot P(X)$ column, and find the variance by summing the $X^2 \cdot P(X)$ column and subtracting the square of the mean.

$$\sigma^2 = 16.8 - 4^2 = 16.8 - 16 = 0.8$$

and

$$\sigma = \sqrt{0.8} \approx 0.894$$

EXAMPLE 5–11   On Hold for Talk Radio

A talk radio station has four telephone lines. If the host is unable to talk (i.e., during a commercial) or is talking to a person, the other callers are placed on hold. When all lines are in use, others who are trying to call in get a busy signal. The probability that 0, 1, 2, 3, or 4 people will get through is shown in the probability distribution. Find the variance and standard deviation for the distribution.

X	0	1	2	3	4
$P(X)$	0.18	0.34	0.23	0.21	0.04

Should the station have considered getting more phone lines installed?

SOLUTION

The mean is

$$\mu = \Sigma X \cdot P(X)$$
$$= 0 \cdot (0.18) + 1 \cdot (0.34) + 2 \cdot (0.23) + 3 \cdot (0.21) + 4 \cdot (0.04)$$
$$= 1.59$$

The variance is

$$\sigma^2 = \Sigma[X^2 \cdot P(X)] - \mu^2$$
$$= [0^2 \cdot (0.18) + 1^2 \cdot (0.34) + 2^2 \cdot (0.23) + 3^2 \cdot (0.21) + 4^2 \cdot (0.04)] - 1.59^2$$
$$= (0 + 0.34 + 0.92 + 1.89 + 0.64) - 2.528$$
$$= 3.79 - 2.528 = 1.262$$

The standard deviation is $\sigma = \sqrt{\sigma^2}$, or $\sigma = \sqrt{1.262} \approx 1.123$.

No. The mean number of people calling at any one time is 1.59. Since the standard deviation is 1.123, most callers would be accommodated by having four phone lines because $\mu + 2\sigma$ would be $1.59 + 2(1.123) = 3.836 \approx 4.0$. Very few callers would get a busy signal since at least 75% of the callers would either get through or be put on hold. (See Chebyshev's theorem in Section 3–2.)

Expectation

Another concept related to the mean for a probability distribution is that of expected value or expectation. Expected value is used in various types of games of chance, in insurance, and in other areas, such as decision theory.

> The **expected value** of a discrete random variable of a probability distribution is the theoretical average of the variable. The formula is
>
> $$\mu = E(X) = \Sigma X \cdot P(X)$$
>
> The symbol $E(X)$ is used for the expected value.

The formula for the expected value is the same as the formula for the theoretical mean. The expected value, then, is the theoretical mean of the probability distribution. That is, $E(X) = \mu$.

When expected value problems involve money, it is customary to round the answer to the nearest cent.

EXAMPLE 5–12   Winning Tickets

One thousand tickets are sold at $1 each for a color television valued at $350. What is the expected value of the gain if you purchase one ticket?

SOLUTION

The problem can be set up as follows:

	Win	**Lose**
Gain X	$349	−$1
Probability P(X)	$\dfrac{1}{1000}$	$\dfrac{999}{1000}$

Two things should be noted. First, for a win, the net gain is $349, since you do not get the cost of the ticket ($1) back. Second, for a loss, the gain is represented by a negative number, in this case −$1. The solution, then, is

$$E(X) = \$349 \cdot \frac{1}{1000} + (-\$1) \cdot \frac{999}{1000} = -\$0.65$$

Hence, a person would lose, on average, $0.65 on each ticket purchased.

Expected value problems of this type can also be solved by finding the overall gain (i.e., the value of the prize won or the amount of money won, not considering the cost of the ticket for the prize or the cost to play the game) and subtracting the cost of the tickets or the cost to play the game, as shown:

$$E(X) = \$350 \cdot \frac{1}{1000} - \$1 = -\$0.65$$

Here, the overall gain ($350) must be used.

Note that the expectation is −$0.65. This does not mean that you lose $0.65, since you can only win a television set valued at $350 or lose $1 on the ticket. What this expectation means is that the average of the losses is $0.65 for each of the 1000 ticket holders. Here is another way of looking at this situation: If you purchased one ticket each week over a long time, the average loss would be $0.65 per ticket, since theoretically, on average, you would win the television set once for each 1000 tickets purchased.

EXAMPLE 5–13   Selecting Balls

Six balls numbered 1, 2, 3, 5, 8, and 13 are placed in a box. A ball is selected at random, and its number is recorded and then it is replaced. Find the expected value of the numbers that will occur.

SOLUTION

Since the balls are replaced, the probability for each number is $\frac{1}{6}$, so the probability distribution is

Number (X)	1	2	3	5	8	13
Probability P(X)	$\frac{1}{6}$	$\frac{1}{6}$	$\frac{1}{6}$	$\frac{1}{6}$	$\frac{1}{6}$	$\frac{1}{6}$

The expected value is

$$E(X) = 1 \cdot \tfrac{1}{6} + 2 \cdot \tfrac{1}{6} + 3 \cdot \tfrac{1}{6} + 5 \cdot \tfrac{1}{6} + 8 \cdot \tfrac{1}{6} + 13 \cdot \tfrac{1}{6} = 5\tfrac{1}{3}$$

EXAMPLE 5–14   Bond Investment

A financial adviser suggests that his client select one of two types of bonds in which to invest $5000. Bond X pays a return of 4% and has a default rate of 2%. Bond Y has a $2\frac{1}{2}\%$ return and a default rate of 1%. Find the expected rate of return and decide which bond would be a better investment. When the bond defaults, the investor loses all the investment.

SOLUTION

The return on bond X is \$5000 $\cdot$ 4% = \$200. The expected return then is

$$E(X) = \$200(0.98) - \$5000(0.02) = \$96$$

The return on bond Y is \$5000 $\cdot$ $2\frac{1}{2}\%$ = \$125. The expected return then is

$$E(X) = \$125(0.99) - \$5000(0.01) = \$73.75$$

Hence, bond X would be a better investment since the expected return is higher.

In gambling games, if the expected value of the game is zero, the game is said to be fair. If the expected value of a game is positive, then the game is in favor of the player. That is, the player has a better than even chance of winning. If the expected value of the game is negative, then the game is said to be in favor of the house. That is, in the long run, the players will lose money.

In his book *Probabilities in Everyday Life* (Ivy Books, 1986), author John D. McGervy gives the expectations for various casino games. For keno, the house wins \$0.27 on every \$1.00 bet. For Chuck-a-Luck, the house wins about \$0.52 on every \$1.00 bet. For roulette, the house wins about \$0.90 on every \$1.00 bet. For craps, the house wins about \$0.88 on every \$1.00 bet. The bottom line here is that if you gamble long enough, sooner or later you will end up losing money.

Applying the Concepts 5–2

Radiation Exposure

On March 28, 1979, the nuclear generating facility at Three Mile Island, Pennsylvania, began discharging radiation into the atmosphere. People exposed to even low levels of radiation can experience health problems ranging from very mild to severe, even causing death. A local newspaper reported that 11 babies were born with kidney problems in the three-county area surrounding the Three Mile Island nuclear power plant. The expected value for that problem in infants in that area was 3. Answer the following questions.

1. What does *expected value* mean?
2. Would you expect the exact value of 3 all the time?

3. If a news reporter stated that the number of cases of kidney problems in newborns was nearly four times as many as was usually expected, do you think pregnant mothers living in that area would be overly concerned?

4. Is it unlikely that 11 occurred by chance?

5. Are there any other statistics that could better inform the public?

6. Assume that 3 out of 2500 babies were born with kidney problems in that three-county area the year before the accident. Also assume that 11 out of 2500 babies were born with kidney problems in that three-county area the year after the accident. What is the real percentage increase in that abnormality?

7. Do you think that pregnant mothers living in that area should be overly concerned after looking at the results in terms of rates?

See page 309 for the answers.

Exercises 5–2

1. **Defective DVDs** From past experience, a company found that in cartons of DVDs, 90% contain no defective DVDs, 5% contain one defective DVD, 3% contain two defective DVDs, and 2% contain three defective DVDs. Find the mean, variance, and standard deviation for the number of defective DVDs.

2. **Suit Sales** The number of suits sold per day at a retail store is shown in the table, with the corresponding probabilities. Find the mean, variance, and standard deviation of the distribution.

Number of suits sold X	19	20	21	22	23
Probability $P(X)$	0.2	0.2	0.3	0.2	0.1

If the manager of the retail store wants to be sure that he has enough suits for the next 5 days, how many should the manager purchase?

3. **Number of Credit Cards** A bank vice president feels that each savings account customer has, on average, three credit cards. The following distribution represents the number of credit cards people own. Find the mean, variance, and standard deviation. Is the vice president correct?

Number of cards X	0	1	2	3	4
Probability $P(X)$	0.18	0.44	0.27	0.08	0.03

4. **Trivia Quiz** The probabilities that a player will get 5 to 10 questions right on a trivia quiz are shown below. Find the mean, variance, and standard deviation for the distribution.

X	5	6	7	8	9	10
$P(X)$	0.05	0.2	0.4	0.1	0.15	0.1

5. **Cellular Phone Sales** The probability that a cellular phone company kiosk sells X number of new phone contracts per day is shown below. Find the mean, variance, and standard deviation for this probability distribution.

X	4	5	6	8	10
$P(X)$	0.4	0.3	0.1	0.15	0.05

What is the probability that they will sell 6 or more contracts three days in a row?

6. **Traffic Accidents** The county highway department recorded the following probabilities for the number of accidents per day on a certain freeway for one month. The number of accidents per day and their corresponding probabilities are shown. Find the mean, variance, and standard deviation.

Number of accidents X	0	1	2	3	4
Probability $P(X)$	0.4	0.2	0.2	0.1	0.1

7. **Leading Digits** Suppose that we wanted to check the occurrence of leading digits in real-life data such as stock prices, population numbers, death rates, lengths of rivers to see if they occur randomly. Disregarding zero as a leading digit, we might expect the other nine to occur with equal likelihood. Construct the probability distribution for the leading digits 1–9, assuming equal probability for each, and calculate the mean, variance, and standard deviation for this distribution.

8. **Benford's Law** The leading digits in actual data, such as stock prices, population numbers, death rates, and lengths of rivers, do not occur randomly as one might suppose, but instead follow a distribution according to Benford's law. Below is the probability distribution for the leading digits in real-life lists of data. Calculate the mean for the distribution.

X	1	2	3	4	5	6	7	8	9
$P(X)$	0.301	0.176	0.125	0.097	0.079	0.067	0.058	0.051	0.046

9. **Students Using the Math Lab** The number of students using the Math Lab per day is found in the distribution below. Find the mean, variance, and standard deviation for this probability distribution.

X	6	8	10	12	14
P(X)	0.15	0.3	0.35	0.1	0.1

What is the probability that fewer than 8 or more than 12 use the lab in a given day?

10. **Pizza Deliveries** A pizza shop owner determines the number of pizzas that are delivered each day. Find the mean, variance, and standard deviation for the distribution shown. If the manager stated that 45 pizzas were delivered on one day, do you think that this is a believable claim?

Number of deliveries X	35	36	37	38	39
Probability P(X)	0.1	0.2	0.3	0.3	0.1

11. **Grab Bags** A craft store has 25 assorted grab bags on sale for $3.00 each. Fifteen of the bags contain $3.00 worth of merchandise, six contain $2.00 worth, two contain $5.00 worth of merchandise, and there are one each containing $10.00 and $20.00 worth of merchandise. Suppose that you purchase one bag; what is your expected gain or loss?

12. **Job Bids** A landscape contractor bids on jobs where he can make $3000 profit. The probabilities of getting 1, 2, 3, or 4 jobs per month are shown.

Number of jobs	1	2	3	4
Probability	0.2	0.3	0.4	0.1

Find the contractor's expected profit per month.

13. **Rolling Dice** If a person rolls doubles when she tosses two dice, she wins $5. For the game to be fair, how much should she pay to play the game?

14. **Dice Game** A person pays $2 to play a certain game by rolling a single die once. If a 1 or a 2 comes up, the person wins nothing. If, however, the player rolls a 3, 4, 5,

or 6, he or she wins the difference between the number rolled and $2. Find the expectation for this game. Is the game fair?

15. **Lottery Prizes** A lottery offers one $1000 prize, one $500 prize, and five $100 prizes. One thousand tickets are sold at $3 each. Find the expectation if a person buys one ticket.

16. In Exercise 15, find the expectation if a person buys two tickets. Assume that the player's ticket is replaced after each draw and that the same ticket can win more than one prize.

17. **Winning the Lottery** For a daily lottery, a person selects a three-digit number. If the person plays for $1, she can win $500. Find the expectation. In the same daily lottery, if a person boxes a number, she will win $80. Find the expectation if the number 123 is played for $1 and boxed. (When a number is "boxed," it can win when the digits occur in any order.)

18. **Life Insurance** A 35-year-old woman purchases a $100,000 term life insurance policy for an annual payment of $360. Based on a period life table for the U.S. government, the probability that she will survive the year is 0.999057. Find the expected value of the policy for the insurance company.

19. **Roulette** A roulette wheel has 38 numbers, 1 through 36, 0, and 00. One-half of the numbers from 1 through 36 are red, and the other half are black; 0 and 00 are green. A ball is rolled, and it falls into one of the 38 slots, giving a number and a color. The payoffs (winnings) for a $1 bet are as follows:

Red or black	$1	0	$35
Odd or even	$1	00	$35
1–18	$1	Any single number	$35
9–36	$1	0 or 00	$17

If a person bets $1, find the expected value for each.

    a. Red   *d.* Any single number
    b. Even   *e.* 0 or 00
    c. 00

Extending the Concepts

20. **Rolling Dice** Construct a probability distribution for the sum shown on the faces when two dice are rolled. Find the mean, variance, and standard deviation of the distribution.

21. **Rolling a Die** When one die is rolled, the expected value of the number of dots is 3.5. In Exercise 20, the mean number of dots was found for rolling two dice. What is the mean number of dots if three dice are rolled?

22. The formula for finding the variance for a probability distribution is

$$\sigma^2 = \Sigma[(X - \mu)^2 \cdot P(X)]$$

Verify algebraically that this formula gives the same result as the shortcut formula shown in this section.

23. Complete the following probability distribution if $P(6)$ equals two-thirds of $P(4)$. Then find μ, σ^2, and σ for the distribution.

X	1	2	4	6	9
$P(X)$	0.23	0.18	?	?	0.015

24. **Rolling Two Dice** Roll two dice 100 times and find the mean, variance, and standard deviation of the sum of the dots. Compare the result with the theoretical results obtained in Exercise 20.

25. **Extracurricular Activities** Conduct a survey of the number of extracurricular activities your classmates are enrolled in. Construct a probability distribution and find the mean, variance, and standard deviation.

26. **Promotional Campaign** In a recent promotional campaign, a company offered these prizes and the corresponding probabilities. Find the expected value of winning. The tickets are free.

Number of prizes	Amount	Probability
1	$100,000	$\dfrac{1}{1,000,000}$
2	10,000	$\dfrac{1}{50,000}$
5	1,000	$\dfrac{1}{10,000}$
10	100	$\dfrac{1}{1000}$

If the winner has to mail in the winning ticket to claim the prize, what will be the expectation if the cost of the stamp is considered? Use the current cost of a stamp for a first-class letter.

27. **Probability Distribution** A bag contains five balls numbered 1, 2, 4, 7, and *. Choose two balls at random without replacement and add the numbers. If one ball has the *, double the amount on the other ball. Construct the probability distribution for this random variable X and calculate μ, σ^2, and σ.

≡ Technology | **Step by Step**

TI-84 Plus

Step by Step

Calculating the Mean and Variance of a Discrete Random Variable

To calculate the mean and variance for a discrete random variable by using the formulas:

1. Enter the x values into L_1 and the probabilities into L_2.
2. Move the cursor to the top of the L_3 column so that L_3 is highlighted.
3. Type L_1 multiplied by L_2, then press **ENTER**.
4. Move the cursor to the top of the L_4 column so that L_4 is highlighted.
5. Type L_1 followed by the x^2 key multiplied by L_2, then press **ENTER**.
6. Type **2nd QUIT** to return to the home screen.
7. Type **2nd LIST**, move the cursor to MATH, type 5 for sum, then type L_3, then press **ENTER**. (This is the mean.)
8. Type **2nd ENTER**, move the cursor to L_3, type L_4, then press **ENTER**.

Example TI5–1

Number on ball X	0	2	4	6	8
Probability $P(X)$	$\frac{1}{5}$	$\frac{1}{5}$	$\frac{1}{5}$	$\frac{1}{5}$	$\frac{1}{5}$

Using the data from Example TI5–1 gives the following:

L1	L2	**L3** 3
0	.2	------
2	.2	
4	.2	
6	.2	
8	.2	
------	------	------

L3 =L1*L2

L1	L2	L3 3
0	.2	0
2	.2	.4
4	.2	.8
6	.2	1.2
8	.2	1.6
------	------	------

L3(1)=0

This study shows that a part of the brain reacts to the impact of losing, and it might explain why people tend to increase their bets after losing when gambling. Explain how this type of split decision making may influence fighter pilots, fire-fighters, or police officers, as the article states.

THE GAMBLER'S FALLACY

WHY WE EXPECT TO STRIKE IT RICH AFTER A LOSING STREAK

A GAMBLER USUALLY WAGERS more after taking a loss, in the misguided belief that a run of bad luck increases the probability of a win. We tend to cling to the misconception that past events can skew future odds. "On some level, you're thinking, 'If I just lost, it's going to even out.' The extent to which you're disturbed by a loss seems to go along with risky behavior," says University of Michigan psychologist William Gehring, Ph.D., co-author of a new study linking dicey decision-making to neurological activity originating in the medial frontal cortex, long thought to be an area of the brain used in error detection.

Because people are so driven to up the ante after a loss, Gehring believes that the medial frontal cortex unconsciously influences future decisions based on the impact of the loss, in addition to registering the loss itself.

Gehring drew this conclusion by asking 12 subjects fitted with electrode caps to choose either the number 5 or 25, with the larger number representing the riskier bet.

On any given round, both numbers could amount to a loss, both could amount to a gain or the results could split, one number signifying a loss, the other a gain.

The medial frontal cortex responded to the outcome of a gamble within a quarter of a second, registering sharp electrical impulses only after a loss. Gehring points out that if the medial frontal cortex simply detected errors it would have reacted after participants chose the lesser of two possible gains. In other words, choosing "5" during a round in which both numbers paid off and betting on "25" would have yielded a larger profit.

After the study appeared in *Science*, Gehring received several e-mails from stock traders likening the "gambler's fallacy" to impulsive trading decisions made directly after off-loading a losing security. Researchers speculate that such risky, split-second decision-making could extend to fighter pilots, firemen and policemen—professions in which rapid-fire decisions are crucial and frequent.

—*Dan Schulman*

The mean is 4 and the variance is 8.

To calculate the mean and standard deviation for a discrete random variable without using the formulas, modify the procedure to calculate the mean and standard deviation from grouped data (Chapter 3) by entering the x values into L_1 and the probabilities into L_2.

The mean is 4 and the standard deviation is 2.828427125. To calculate the variance, square the standard deviation.

5–3   The Binomial Distribution

OBJECTIVE ❸

Find the exact probability for *X* successes in *n* trials of a binomial experiment.

Many types of probability problems have only two outcomes or can be reduced to two outcomes. For example, when a coin is tossed, it can land heads or tails. When a baby is born, it will be either male or female. In a basketball game, a team either wins or loses. A true/false item can be answered in only two ways, true or false. Other situations can be reduced to two outcomes. For example, a medical treatment can be classified as effective or ineffective, depending on the results. A person can be classified as having normal or abnormal blood pressure, depending on the measure of the blood pressure gauge. A multiple-choice question, even though there are four or five answer choices, can be classified as correct or incorrect. Situations like these are called *binomial experiments*.

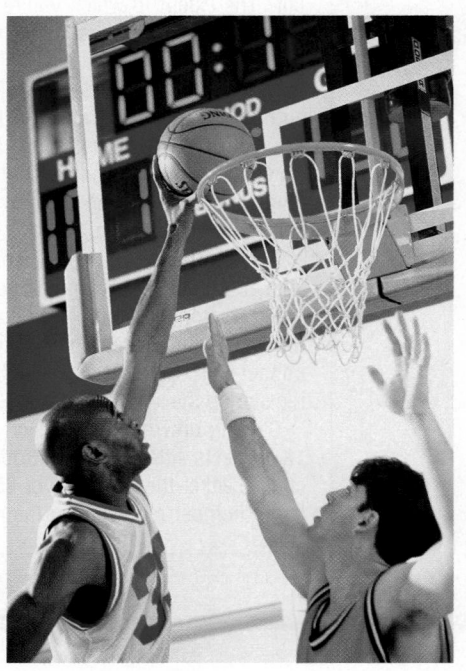

Each repetition of the experiment is called a *trial*.

Historical Note

In 1653, Blaise Pascal created a triangle of numbers called *Pascal's triangle* that can be used in the binomial distribution.

A **binomial experiment** is a probability experiment that satisfies the following four requirements:

1. There must be a fixed number of trials.
2. Each trial can have only two outcomes or outcomes that can be reduced to two outcomes. These outcomes can be considered as either success or failure.
3. The outcomes of each trial must be independent of one another.
4. The probability of a success must remain the same for each trial.

The word *success* does not imply that something good or positive has occurred. For example, in a probability experiment, we might want to select 10 people and let *S* represent the number of people who were in an automobile accident in the last six months. In this case, a success would not be a positive or good thing.

EXAMPLE 5–15

Decide whether each experiment is a binomial experiment. If not, state the reason why.

  a. Selecting 20 university students and recording their class rank
  b. Selecting 20 students from a university and recording their gender

    c. Drawing five cards from a deck without replacement and recording whether they are red or black cards

    d. Selecting five students from a large school and asking them if they are on the dean's list

    e. Recording the number of children in 50 randomly selected families

SOLUTION

    a. No. There are five possible outcomes: freshman, sophomore, junior, senior, and graduate student.

    b. Yes. All four requirements are met.

    c. No. Since the cards are not replaced, the events are not independent.

    d. Yes. All four requirements are met.

    e. No. There can be more than two categories for the answers.

A binomial experiment and its results give rise to a special probability distribution called the *binomial distribution*.

> The outcomes of a binomial experiment and the corresponding probabilities of these outcomes are called a **binomial distribution.**

In binomial experiments, the outcomes are usually classified as successes or failures. For example, the correct answer to a multiple-choice item can be classified as a success, but any of the other choices would be incorrect and hence classified as a failure. The notation that is commonly used for binomial experiments and the binomial distribution is defined now.

Notation for the Binomial Distribution

$P(S)$	The symbol for the probability of success
$P(F)$	The symbol for the probability of failure
p	The numerical probability of a success
q	The numerical probability of a failure

$$P(S) = p \qquad \text{and} \qquad P(F) = 1 - p = q$$

n	The number of trials
X	The number of successes in n trials

Note that $0 \leq X \leq n$ and $X = 0, 1, 2, 3, \ldots, n$.

The probability of a success in a binomial experiment can be computed with this formula.

Binomial Probability Formula

In a binomial experiment, the probability of exactly X successes in n trials is

$$P(X) = \frac{n!}{(n - X)!X!} \cdot p^X \cdot q^{n-X}$$

An explanation of why the formula works is given following Example 5–16.

EXAMPLE 5–16   Tossing Coins

A coin is tossed 3 times. Find the probability of getting exactly two heads.

SOLUTION

This problem can be solved by looking at the sample space. There are three ways to get two heads.

$$\text{HHH, } \underline{\text{HHT, HTH, THH,}} \text{ TTH, THT, HTT, TTT}$$

The answer is $\frac{3}{8}$, or 0.375.

Looking at the problem in Example 5–16 from the standpoint of a binomial experiment, one can show that it meets the four requirements.

1. There are a fixed number of trials (three).

2. There are only two outcomes for each trial, heads or tails.

3. The outcomes are independent of one another (the outcome of one toss in no way affects the outcome of another toss).

4. The probability of a success (heads) is $\frac{1}{2}$ in each case.

In this case, $n = 3$, $X = 2$, $p = \frac{1}{2}$, and $q = \frac{1}{2}$. Hence, substituting in the formula gives

$$P(2 \text{ heads}) = \frac{3!}{(3 - 2)!2!} \cdot \left(\frac{1}{2}\right)^2 \left(\frac{1}{2}\right)^1 = \frac{3}{8} = 0.375$$

which is the same answer obtained by using the sample space.

The same example can be used to explain the formula. First, note that there are three ways to get exactly two heads and one tail from a possible eight ways. They are HHT, HTH, and THH. In this case, then, the number of ways of obtaining two heads from three coin tosses is $_3C_2$, or 3, as shown in Chapter 4. In general, the number of ways to get X successes from n trials without regard to order is

$$_nC_X = \frac{n!}{(n - X)!X!}$$

This is the first part of the binomial formula. (Some calculators can be used for this.)

Next, each success has a probability of $\frac{1}{2}$ and can occur twice. Likewise, each failure has a probability of $\frac{1}{2}$ and can occur once, giving the $(\frac{1}{2})^2(\frac{1}{2})^1$ part of the formula. To generalize, then, each success has a probability of p and can occur X times, and each failure has a probability of q and can occur $n - X$ times. Putting it all together yields the binomial probability formula.

When sampling is done without replacement, such as in surveys, the events are dependent events; however, the events can be considered independent if the size of the sample is no more than 5% of the size of the population. That is, $n \leq 0.05N$. The reason is that when one item is selected from a large number of items and is not replaced before the second item is selected, the change in the probability of the second item being selected is so small that it can be ignored.

EXAMPLE 5–17   Survey on Doctor Visits

A survey found that one out of five Americans says he or she has visited a doctor in any given month. If 10 people are selected at random, find the probability that exactly 3 will have visited a doctor last month.

Source: *Reader's Digest.*

SOLUTION

In this case, $n = 10$, $X = 3$, $p = \frac{1}{5}$, and $q = \frac{4}{5}$. Hence,

$$P(3) = \frac{10!}{(10 - 3)!3!}\left(\frac{1}{5}\right)^3\left(\frac{4}{5}\right)^7 \approx 0.201$$

So, there is a 0.201 probability that in a random sample of 10 people, exactly 3 of them visited a doctor in the last month.

EXAMPLE 5–18   Survey on Employment

A survey from Teenage Research Unlimited (Northbrook, Illinois) found that 30% of teenage consumers receive their spending money from part-time jobs. If 5 teenagers are selected at random, find the probability that at least 3 of them will have part-time jobs.

SOLUTION

To find the probability that at least 3 have part-time jobs, it is necessary to find the individual probabilities for 3, or 4, or 5 and then add them to get the total probability.

$$P(3) = \frac{5!}{(5 - 3)!3!}(0.3)^3(0.7)^2 \approx 0.132$$

$$P(4) = \frac{5!}{(5 - 4)!4!}(0.3)^4(0.7)^1 \approx 0.028$$

$$P(5) = \frac{5!}{(5 - 5)!5!}(0.3)^5(0.7)^0 \approx 0.002$$

Hence,

$$P(\text{at least three teenagers have part-time jobs})$$
$$= 0.132 + 0.028 + 0.002 = 0.162$$

Computing probabilities by using the binomial probability formula can be quite tedious at times, so tables have been developed for selected values of n and p. Table B in Appendix A gives the probabilities for individual events. Example 5–19 shows how to use Table B to compute probabilities for binomial experiments.

EXAMPLE 5–19   Tossing Coins

Solve the problem in Example 5–16 by using Table B.

SOLUTION

Since $n = 3$, $X = 2$, and $p = 0.5$, the value 0.375 is found as shown in Figure 5–3.

FIGURE 5–3   Using Table B for Example 5–19

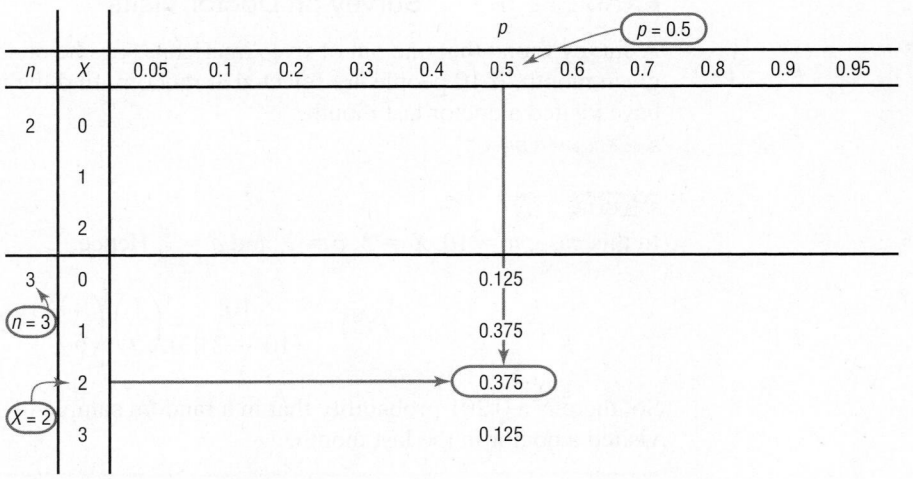

EXAMPLE 5–20   Survey on Fear of Being Home Alone at Night

Public Opinion reported that 5% of Americans are afraid of being alone in a house at night. If a random sample of 20 Americans is selected, find these probabilities by using the binomial table.

    a. There are exactly 5 people in the sample who are afraid of being alone at night.

    b. There are at most 3 people in the sample who are afraid of being alone at night.

    c. There are at least 3 people in the sample who are afraid of being alone at night.

Source: *100% American* by Daniel Evan Weiss.

SOLUTION

    a. $n = 20$, $p = 0.05$, and $X = 5$. From the table, we get 0.002.

    b. $n = 20$ and $p = 0.05$. "At most 3 people" means 0, or 1, or 2, or 3.

      Hence, the solution is

$$P(X \leq 3) = P(0) + P(1) + P(2) + P(3) = 0.358 + 0.377 + 0.189 + 0.060$$

$$= 0.984$$

    c. $n = 20$ and $p = 0.05$. "At least 3 people" means 3, 4, 5, . . . , 20. This problem can best be solved by finding $P(X \leq 2) = P(0) + P(1) + P(2)$ and subtracting from 1.

$$P(0) + P(1) + P(2) = 0.358 + 0.377 + 0.189 = 0.924$$

$$P(X \geq 3) = 1 - 0.924 = 0.076$$

EXAMPLE 5–21   Driving While Intoxicated

A report from the Secretary of Health and Human Services stated that 70% of single-vehicle traffic fatalities that occur at night on weekends involve an intoxicated driver. If a sample of 15 single-vehicle traffic fatalities that occur on a weekend night is selected, find the probability that between 10 and 15, inclusive, accidents involved drivers who were intoxicated.

SOLUTION

$n = 15$, $p = 0.70$, and X is 10, 11, 12, 13, 14, or 15.

For $X = 10$,	$P(10) = 0.206$	For $X = 13$,	$P(13) = 0.092$
For $X = 11$,	$P(11) = 0.219$	For $X = 14$,	$P(14) = 0.031$
For $X = 12$,	$P(12) = 0.170$	For $X = 15$,	$P(15) = 0.005$

$$P(10 \leq X \leq 15) = 0.206 + 0.219 + 0.170 + 0.092 + 0.031 + 0.005 = 0.723$$

Hence, the probability that between 10 and 15 drivers, inclusive, were intoxicated is 0.723.

The mean, variance, and standard deviation for a binomial variable can be found by using the formulas in Section 5–2; however, shorter but mathematically equivalent formulas for the mean, variance, and standard deviation are used.

OBJECTIVE ❹

Find the mean, variance, and standard deviation for the variable of a binomial distribution.

Mean, Variance, and Standard Deviation for the Binomial Distribution

The mean, variance, and standard deviation of a variable that has the *binomial distribution* can be found by using the following formulas.

Mean: $\mu = n \cdot p$ Variance: $\sigma^2 = n \cdot p \cdot q$ Standard deviation: $\sigma = \sqrt{n \cdot p \cdot q}$

EXAMPLE 5–22   **Tossing a Coin**

A coin is tossed 4 times. Find the mean, variance, and standard deviation of the number of heads that will be obtained.

SOLUTION

With the formulas for the binomial distribution and $n = 4$, $p = \frac{1}{2}$, and $q = \frac{1}{2}$, the results are

$$\mu = n \cdot p = 4 \cdot \tfrac{1}{2} = 2$$
$$\sigma^2 = n \cdot p \cdot q = 4 \cdot \tfrac{1}{2} \cdot \tfrac{1}{2} = 1$$
$$\sigma = \sqrt{1} = 1$$

In this case, the mean is two heads. The variance is 1 and the standard deviation is 1.

From Example 5–22, when four coins are tossed many, many times, the average of the number of heads that appear is 2, and the standard deviation of the number of heads is 1. Note that these are theoretical values.

As stated previously, this problem can be solved by using the formulas for expected value. The distribution is shown.

No. of heads X	0	1	2	3	4
Probability $P(X)$	$\frac{1}{16}$	$\frac{4}{16}$	$\frac{6}{16}$	$\frac{4}{16}$	$\frac{1}{16}$

$$\mu = E(X) = \Sigma X \cdot P(X) = 0 \cdot \tfrac{1}{16} + 1 \cdot \tfrac{4}{16} + 2 \cdot \tfrac{6}{16} + 3 \cdot \tfrac{4}{16} + 4 \cdot \tfrac{1}{16} = \tfrac{32}{16} = 2$$
$$\sigma^2 = \Sigma X^2 \cdot P(X) - \mu^2$$
$$= 0^2 \cdot \tfrac{1}{16} + 1^2 \cdot \tfrac{4}{16} + 2^2 \cdot \tfrac{6}{16} + 3^2 \cdot \tfrac{4}{16} + 4^2 \cdot \tfrac{1}{16} - 2^2 = \tfrac{80}{16} - 4 = 1$$
$$\sigma = \sqrt{1} = 1$$

Hence, the simplified binomial formulas give the same results.

EXAMPLE 5–23   Rolling a Die

An 8-sided die (with the numbers 1 through 8 on the faces) is rolled 560 times. Find the mean, variance, and standard deviation of the number of 7s that will be rolled.

SOLUTION

This is a binomial experiment with $n = 560$, $p = \frac{1}{8}$, and $q = \frac{7}{8}$ so that

$$\mu^2 = n \cdot p = 560 \cdot \tfrac{1}{8} = 70$$

$$\sigma^2 = n \cdot p \cdot q = 560 \cdot \tfrac{1}{8} \cdot \tfrac{7}{8} = 61\tfrac{1}{4} = 61.25$$

$$\sigma = \sqrt{61.25} = 7.826$$

In this case, the mean of the number of 7s obtained is 70. The variance is 61.25, and the standard deviation is 7.826.

EXAMPLE 5–24   Likelihood of Twins

The *Statistical Bulletin* published by Metropolitan Life Insurance Co. reported that 2% of all American births result in twins. If a random sample of 8000 births is taken, find the mean, variance, and standard deviation of the number of births that would result in twins.

Source: *100% American* by Daniel Evan Weiss.

SOLUTION

This is a binomial situation, since a birth can result in either twins or not twins (i.e., two outcomes).

$$\mu = n \cdot p = (8000)(0.02) = 160$$

$$\sigma^2 = n \cdot p \cdot q = (8000)(0.02)(0.98) = 156.8$$

$$\sigma = \sqrt{n \cdot p \cdot q} = \sqrt{156.8} = 12.522$$

For the sample, the average number of births that would result in twins is 160; the variance is 156.8, or 157; and the standard deviation is 12.522, or 13 if rounded.

≡ Applying the Concepts 5–3

Unsanitary Restaurants

Health officials routinely check the sanitary condition of restaurants. Assume you visit a popular tourist spot and read in the newspaper that in 3 out of every 7 restaurants checked, unsatisfactory health conditions were found. Assuming you are planning to eat out 10 times while you are there on vacation, answer the following questions.

1. How likely is it that you will eat at three restaurants with unsanitary conditions?

2. How likely is it that you will eat at four or five restaurants with unsanitary conditions?

3. Explain how you would compute the probability of eating in at least one restaurant with unsanitary conditions. Could you use the complement to solve this problem?

4. What is the most likely number to occur in this experiment?

5. How variable will the data be around the most likely number?

6. How do you know that this is a binomial distribution?

7. If it is a binomial distribution, does that mean that the likelihood of a success is always 50% since there are only two possible outcomes?

Check your answers by using the following computer-generated table.

Mean = 4.29   Std. dev. = 1.56492

X	P(X)	Cum. prob.
0	0.00371	0.00371
1	0.02784	0.03155
2	0.09396	0.12552
3	0.18793	0.31344
4	0.24665	0.56009
5	0.22199	0.78208
6	0.13874	0.92082
7	0.05946	0.98028
8	0.01672	0.99700
9	0.00279	0.99979
10	0.00021	1.00000

See page 309 for the answers.

Exercises 5–3

1. Which of the following are binomial experiments or can be reduced to binomial experiments?

   a. Surveying 100 people to determine if they like Sudsy Soap

   b. Tossing a coin 100 times to see how many heads occur

   c. Drawing a card with replacement from a deck and getting a heart

   d. Asking 1000 people which brand of cigarettes they smoke

   e. Testing four different brands of aspirin to see which brands are effective

2. Which of the following are binomial experiments or can be reduced to binomial experiments?

   a. Testing one brand of aspirin by using 10 people to determine whether it is effective

   b. Asking 100 people if they smoke

   c. Checking 1000 applicants to see whether they were admitted to White Oak College

   d. Surveying 300 prisoners to see how many different crimes they were convicted of

   e. Surveying 300 prisoners to see whether this is their first offense

3. Compute the probability of *X* successes, using Table B in Appendix A.

   a. $n = 2, p = 0.30, X = 1$

   b. $n = 4, p = 0.60, X = 3$

   c. $n = 5, p = 0.10, X = 0$

   d. $n = 10, p = 0.40, X = 4$

   e. $n = 12, p = 0.90, X = 2$

4. Compute the probability of *X* successes, using Table B in Appendix A.

   a. $n = 15, p = 0.80, X = 12$

   b. $n = 17, p = 0.05, X = 0$

   c. $n = 20, p = 0.50, X = 10$

   d. $n = 16, p = 0.20, X = 3$

5. Compute the probability of *X* successes, using the binomial formula.

   a. $n = 6, X = 3, p = 0.03$

   b. $n = 4, X = 2, p = 0.18$

   c. $n = 5, X = 3, p = 0.63$

6. Compute the probability of *X* successes, using the binomial formula.

   a. $n = 9, X = 0, p = 0.42$

   b. $n = 10, X = 5, p = 0.37$

For Exercises 7 through 16, assume all variables are binomial. (Note: If values are not found in Table B of Appendix A, use the binomial formula.)

7. **Today's Marriages** A television commercial claims that 1 out of 5 of "today's marriages" began as an online relationship. Assuming that this is true, calculate the following for eight randomly selected "today's marriages."

a.   The probability that at least one began online

b.   The probability that two or three began online

c.   What is the probability that exactly one began online?

 8. **Multiple-Choice Exam** A student takes a 20-question, multiple-choice exam with five choices for each question and guesses on each question. Find the probability of guessing at least 15 out of 20 correctly. Would you consider this event likely or unlikely to occur? Explain your answer.

 9. **Driving to Work Alone** It is reported that 77% of workers aged 16 and over drive to work alone. Choose 8 workers at random. Find the probability that

a.   All drive to work alone

b.   More than one-half drive to work alone

c.   Exactly 3 drive to work alone

Source: www.factfinder.census.gov

10. **High School Dropouts** Approximately 10.3% of American high school students drop out of school before graduation. Choose 10 students entering high school at random. Find the probability that

a.   No more than 2 drop out

b.   At least 6 graduate

c.   All 10 stay in school and graduate

Source: www.infoplease.com

11. **Survey on Concern for Criminals** In a survey, 3 of 4 students said the courts show "too much concern" for criminals. Find the probability that at most 3 out of 7 randomly selected students will agree with this statement.

Source: *Harper's Index.*

12. **Union Workers** In 2010 almost 15 million U.S. workers belonged to trade unions, constituting 11.9% of the total labor force. Choose 15 U.S. workers at random. What is the probability that exactly one-third of them belong to a trade union? At least one-third? What is the probability that at least 9 did not belong?

Source: *Time Almanac 2012.*

13. **College Education and Business World Success** R. H. Bruskin Associates Market Research found that 40% of Americans do not think that having a college education is important to succeed in the business world. If a random sample of 5 Americans is selected, find these probabilities.

a.   Exactly 2 people will agree with that statement.

b.   At most 3 people will agree with that statement.

c.   At least 2 people will agree with that statement.

d.   Fewer than 3 people will agree with that statement.

Source: *100% American* by Daniel Evans Weiss.

14. **Destination Weddings** Twenty-six percent of couples who plan to marry this year are planning destination weddings. In a random sample of 12 couples who plan to marry, find the probability that

a.   Exactly 6 couples will have a destination wedding

b.   At least 6 couples will have a destination wedding

c.   Fewer than 5 couples will have a destination wedding

Source: *Time* magazine.

15. **People Who Have Some College Education** Fifty-three percent of all persons in the U.S. population have at least some college education. Choose 10 persons at random. Find the probability that

a.   Exactly one-half have some college education

b.   At least 5 do not have any college education

c.   Fewer than 5 have some college education

Source: *New York Times Almanac.*

16. **Guidance Missile System** A missile guidance system has 5 fail-safe components. The probability of each failing is 0.05. Find these probabilities.

a.   Exactly 2 will fail.

b.   More than 2 will fail.

c.   All will fail.

d.   Compare the answers for parts *a*, *b*, and *c*, and explain why these results are reasonable.

17. Find the mean, variance, and standard deviation for each of the values of n and p when the conditions for the binomial distribution are met.

a. $n = 100, p = 0.75$

b. $n = 300, p = 0.3$

c. $n = 20, p = 0.5$

d. $n = 10, p = 0.8$

18. Find the mean, variance, and standard deviation for each of the values of n and p when the conditions for the binomial distributions are met.

a. $n = 1000, p = 0.1$

b. $n = 500, p = 0.25$

c. $n = 50, p = \frac{2}{5}$

d. $n = 36, p = \frac{1}{6}$

19. **Social Security Recipients** A study found that 1% of Social Security recipients are too young to vote. If 800 Social Security recipients are randomly selected, find the mean, variance, and standard deviation of the number of recipients who are too young to vote.

Source: *Harper's Index.*

20. **Tossing Coins** Find the mean, variance, and standard deviation for the number of heads when 10 coins are tossed.

21. **American and Foreign-Born Citizens** In 2009 the percentage of the U.S. population who was foreign-born was 12.2. Choose 60 U.S. residents at random. How many would you expect to be American-born? Find the mean, variance, and standard deviation for the number who are foreign-born.

Source: *World Almanac 2012.*

22. Federal Government Employee E-mail Use It has been reported that 83% of federal government employees use e-mail. If a sample of 200 federal government employees is selected, find the mean, variance, and standard deviation of the number who use e-mail.

Source: *USA TODAY.*

23. Watching Fireworks A survey found that 21% of Americans watch fireworks on television on July 4. Find the mean, variance, and standard deviation of the number of individuals who watch fireworks on television on July 4 if a random sample of 1000 Americans is selected.

Source: USA Snapshot, *USA TODAY.*

24. Alternate Sources of Fuel Eighty-five percent of Americans favor spending government money to develop alternative sources of fuel for automobiles. For a random sample of 120 Americans, find the mean, variance, and standard deviation for the number who favor government spending for alternative fuels.

Source: www.pollingreport.com

25. Survey on Bathing Pets A survey found that 25% of pet owners had their pets bathed professionally rather than do it themselves. If 18 pet owners are randomly selected, find the probability that exactly 5 people have their pets bathed professionally.

Source: USA Snapshot, *USA TODAY.*

26. Survey on Answering Machine Ownership In a survey, 63% of Americans said they own an answering machine. If 14 Americans are selected at random, find the probability that exactly 9 own an answering machine.

Source: USA Snapshot, *USA TODAY.*

27. Poverty and the Federal Government One out of every three Americans believes that the U.S. government should take "primary responsibility" for eliminating poverty in the United States. If 10 Americans are selected, find the probability that at most 3 will believe that the U.S. government should take primary responsibility for eliminating poverty.

Source: *Harper's Index.*

28. Internet Purchases Thirty-two percent of adult Internet users have purchased products or services online. For a random sample of 200 adult Internet users, find the mean, variance, and standard deviation for the number who have purchased goods or services online.

Source: www.infoplease.com

29. Survey on Internet Awareness In a 2011 survey, 58% of American adults said they use the Internet. If 20 American adults are selected at random, find the probability that exactly 12 will say they use the Internet.

Source: *Harper's Index.*

30. Job Elimination In a recent year, 13% of businesses have eliminated jobs. If 5 businesses are selected at random, find the probability that at least 3 have eliminated jobs during that year.

Source: *USA TODAY.*

31. Survey of High School Seniors Of graduating high school seniors, 14% said that their generation will be remembered for their social concerns. If 7 graduating seniors are selected at random, find the probability that either 2 or 3 will agree with that statement.

Source: *USA TODAY.*

32. Is this a binomial distribution? Explain.

X	0	1	2	3
$P(X)$	0.064	0.288	0.432	0.216

≡ Extending the Concepts

33. Children in a Family The graph shown here represents the probability distribution for the number of girls in a family of three children. From this graph, construct a probability distribution.

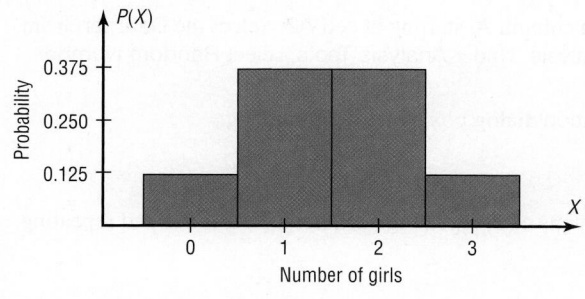

34. Construct a binomial distribution graph for the number of defective computer chips in a lot of 4 if $p = 0.3$.

35. Show that the mean for a binomial random variable X with $n = 3$ is $3p$.

≣Technology | Step by Step

TI-84 Plus
Step by Step

Binomial Random Variables

To find the probability for a binomial variable:
Press **2nd [DISTR]** then **A (ALPHA MATH)** for binompdf.
The form is binompdf(n, p, X).

Example: $n = 20$, $X = 5$, $p = .05$ (Example 5–20a from the text)
binompdf(20,.05,5), then press **ENTER** for the probability.

Example: $n = 20$, $X = 0, 1, 2, 3$, $p = .05$ (Example 5–20b from the text).
binompdf(20,.05,{0,1,2,3}), then press **ENTER.**
The calculator will display the probabilities in a list. Use the arrow keys to view the entire display.

To find the cumulative probability for a binomial random variable:
Press **2nd [DISTR]** then **B (ALPHA APPS)** for binomcdf
The form is binomcdf(n, p, X). This will calculate the cumulative probability for values from 0 to X.

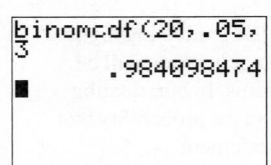

Example: $n = 20$, $X = 0, 1, 2, 3$, $p = .05$ (Example 5–20b from the text)
binomcdf(20,.05,3), then press **ENTER.**

To construct a binomial probability table:

1. Enter the X values (0 through n) into L_1.
2. Move the cursor to the top of the L_2 column so that L_2 is highlighted.
3. Type the command binompdf(n, p, L_1), then press **ENTER.**

Example: $n = 20$, $p = .05$ (Example 5–20 from the text)

EXCEL
Step by Step

Creating a Binomial Distribution and Graph

These instructions will demonstrate how Excel can be used to construct a binomial distribution table for $n = 20$ and $p = 0.35$.

1. Type **X** for the binomial variable label in cell A1 of an Excel worksheet.
2. Type **P(X)** for the corresponding probabilities in cell B1.
3. Enter the integers from 0 to 20 in column A, starting at cell A2. Select the Data tab from the toolbar. Then select Data Analysis. Under Analysis Tools, select Random Number Generation and click [OK].
4. In the Random Number Generation dialog box, enter the following:
   a) Number of Variables: **1**
   b) Distribution: Patterned
   c) Parameters: From **0** to **20** in steps of **1**, repeating each number: **1** times and repeating each sequence **1** times
   d) Output range: **A2:A21**

5. Then click [OK].

Random Number
Generation Dialog Box

6. To determine the probability corresponding to the first value of the binomial random variable, select cell B2 and type: **=BINOMDIST(0,20,.35,FALSE).** This will give the probability of obtaining 0 successes in 20 trials of a binomial experiment for which the probability of success is 0.35.

7. Repeat step **6,** changing the first parameter, for each of the values of the random variable from column A.

Note: If you wish to obtain the cumulative probabilities for each of the values in column A, you can type: **=BINOMDIST(0,20,.35,TRUE)** and repeat for each of the values in column A.

To create the graph:

1. Select the Insert tab from the toolbar and the Column Chart.

2. Select the Clustered Column (the first column chart under the 2-D Column selections).

3. You will need to edit the data for the chart.

   a) Right-click the mouse on any location of the chart. Click the Select Data option. The Select Data Source dialog box will appear.

   b) Click **X** in the Legend Entries box and click Remove.

   c) Click the Edit button under Horizontal Axis Labels to insert a range for the variable X.

   d) When the Axis Labels box appears, highlight cells A2 to A21 on the worksheet, then click [OK].

4. To change the title of the chart:

   a) Left-click once on the current title.

   b) Type a new title for the chart, for example, Binomial Distribution (20, .35, .65).

MINITAB
Step by Step

The Binomial Distribution

Calculate a Binomial Probability

From Example 5–20, it is known that 5% of the population is afraid of being alone at night. If a random sample of 20 Americans is selected, what is the probability that exactly 5 of them are afraid?

$$n = 20 \qquad p = 0.05 \ (5\%) \qquad \text{and} \qquad X = 5 \ (5 \text{ out of } 20)$$

No data need to be entered in the worksheet.

1. Select **Calc>Probability Distributions>Binomial.**

2. Click the option for Probability.

3. Click in the text box for Number of trials:.

4. Type in **20,** then Tab to Probability of success, then type **.05.**

5. Click the option for Input constant, then type in **5.** Leave the text box for Optional storage empty. If the name of a constant such as K1 is entered here, the results are stored but not displayed in the session window.

6. Click [OK]. The results are visible in the session window.

Probability Density Function
Binomial with n = 20 and p = 0.05
x	f(x)
5	0.0022446

Construct a Binomial Distribution

These instructions will use $n = 20$ and $p = 0.05$.

1. Select **Calc>Make Patterned Data>Simple Set of Numbers.**

2. You must enter three items:

   a) Enter **X** in the box for Store patterned data in:. MINITAB will use the first empty column of the active worksheet and name it X.

   b) Press Tab. Enter the value of **0** for the first value. Press Tab.

   c) Enter **20** for the last value. This value should be n. In steps of:, the value should be 1.

3. Click [OK].

4. Select **Calc>Probability Distributions>Binomial.**

5. In the dialog box you must enter five items.

   a) Click the button for Probability.

   b) In the box for Number of trials enter **20.**

   c) Enter **.05** in the Probability of success.

d) Check the button for Input columns, then type the column name, **X,** in the text box.

e) Click in the box for Optional storage, then type **Px.**

6. Click [OK]. The first available column will be named Px, and the calculated probabilities will be stored in it.

7. To view the completed table, click the worksheet icon on the toolbar. This table matches Table B, the binomial distribution found in Appendix A.

Graph a Binomial Distribution

The table must be available in the worksheet.

1. Select **Graph>Scatterplot,** then Simple.

a) Double-click on C2 Px for the Y variable and C1 X for the X variable.

b) Click [Data view], then Project lines, then [OK]. Deselect any other type of display that may be selected in this list.

c) Click on [Labels], then Title/Footnotes.

d) Type an appropriate title, such as **Binomial Distribution n = 20, p = .05.**

e) Press Tab to the Subtitle 1, then type in Your Name then [OK].

f) Optional: Click [Scales] then [Gridlines], then check the box for Y major ticks.

g) Click [OK] twice.

↓	C1	C2
	X	Px
1	0	0.358
2	1	0.377
3	2	0.189
4	3	0.060
5	4	0.013
6	5	0.002
7	6	0.000
8	7	0.000
9	8	0.000
10	9	0.000
11	10	0.000
12	11	0.000
13	12	0.000
14	13	0.000
15	14	0.000
16	15	0.000
17	16	0.000
18	17	0.000
19	18	0.000
20	19	0.000
21	20	0.000

The graph will be displayed in a window. Right-click the control box to save, print, or close the graph.

5–4   Other Types of Distributions

OBJECTIVE 5

Find probabilities for outcomes of variables, using the Poisson, hypergeometric, geometric, and multinomial distributions.

In addition to the binomial distribution, other types of distributions are used in statistics. Four of the most commonly used distributions are the multinomial distribution, the Poisson distribution, the hypergeometric distribution, and the geometric distribution. They are described next.

The Multinomial Distribution

Recall that for an experiment to be binomial, two outcomes are required for each trial. But if each trial in an experiment has more than two outcomes, a distribution called the **multinomial distribution** must be used. For example, a survey might require the responses of "approve," "disapprove," or "no opinion." In another situation, a person may have a choice of one of five activities for Friday night, such as a movie, dinner, baseball game, play, or party. Since these situations have more than two possible outcomes for each trial, the binomial distribution cannot be used to compute probabilities.

The multinomial distribution can be used for such situations.

> A **multinomial experiment** is a probability experiment that satisfies the following four requirements:
>
> 1. There must be a fixed number of trials.
> 2. Each trial has a specific—but not necessarily the same—number of outcomes.
> 3. The trials are independent.
> 4. The probability of a particular outcome remains the same.

> **Formula for the Multinomial Distribution**
>
> If X consists of events $E_1, E_2, E_3, \ldots, E_k$, which have corresponding probabilities $p_1, p_2, p_3, \ldots, p_k$ of occurring, and X_1 is the number of times E_1 will occur, X_2 is the number of times E_2 will occur, X_3 is the number of times E_3 will occur, etc., then the probability that X will occur is
>
> $$P(X) = \frac{n!}{X_1! \cdot X_2! \cdot X_3! \cdots X_k!} \cdot p_1^{X_1} \cdot p_2^{X_2} \cdots p_k^{X_k}$$
>
> where $X_1 + X_2 + X_3 + \cdots + X_k = n$ and $p_1 + p_2 + p_3 + \cdots + p_k = 1$.

EXAMPLE 5–25   Leisure Activities

In a large city, 50% of the people choose a movie, 30% choose dinner and a play, and 20% choose shopping as a leisure activity. If a sample of 5 people is randomly selected, find the probability that 3 are planning to go to a movie, 1 to a play, and 1 to a shopping mall.

SOLUTION

We know that $n = 5$, $X_1 = 3$, $X_2 = 1$, $X_3 = 1$, $p_1 = 0.50$, $p_2 = 0.30$, and $p_3 = 0.20$. Substituting in the formula gives

$$P(X) = \frac{5!}{3! \cdot 1! \cdot 1!} \cdot (0.50)^3 (0.30)^1 (0.20)^1 = 0.15$$

There is a 0.15 probability that if 5 people are randomly selected, 3 will go to a movie, 1 to a play, and 1 to a shopping mall.

Again, note that the multinomial distribution can be used even though replacement is not done, provided that the sample is small in comparison with the population.

EXAMPLE 5–26   Coffee Shop Customers

A small airport coffee shop manager found that the probabilities a customer buys 0, 1, 2, or 3 cups of coffee are 0.3, 0.5, 0.15, and 0.05, respectively. If 8 customers enter the shop, find the probability that 2 will purchase something other than coffee, 4 will purchase 1 cup of coffee, 1 will purchase 2 cups, and 1 will purchase 3 cups.

SOLUTION

Let $n = 8$, $X_1 = 2$, $X_2 = 4$, $X_3 = 1$, and $X_4 = 1$.

$$p_1 = 0.3 \quad p_2 = 0.5 \quad p_3 = 0.15 \quad \text{and} \quad p_4 = 0.05$$

Then

$$P(X) = \frac{8!}{2!4!1!1!} \cdot (0.3)^2(0.5)^4(0.15)^1(0.05)^1 \approx 0.0354$$

There is a 0.0354 probability that the results will occur as described.

EXAMPLE 5–27   Selecting Colored Balls

A box contains 4 white balls, 3 red balls, and 3 blue balls. A ball is selected at random, and its color is written down. It is replaced each time. Find the probability that if 5 balls are selected, 2 are white, 2 are red, and 1 is blue.

SOLUTION

We know that $n = 5$, $X_1 = 2$, $X_2 = 2$, $X_3 = 1$; $p_1 = \frac{4}{10}$, $p_2 = \frac{3}{10}$, and $p_3 = \frac{3}{10}$; hence,

$$P(X) = \frac{5!}{2!2!1!} \cdot \left(\frac{4}{10}\right)^2\left(\frac{3}{10}\right)^2\left(\frac{3}{10}\right)^1 = \frac{81}{625} = 0.1296$$

There is a 0.1296 probability that the results will occur as described.

Historical Notes

Simeon D. Poisson (1781–1840) formulated the distribution that bears his name. It appears only once in his writings and is only one page long. Mathematicians paid little attention to it until 1907, when a statistician named W. S. Gosset found real applications for it.

Thus, the multinomial distribution is similar to the binomial distribution but has the advantage of allowing you to compute probabilities when there are more than two outcomes for each trial in the experiment. That is, the multinomial distribution is a general distribution, and the binomial distribution is a special case of the multinomial distribution.

The Poisson Distribution

A discrete probability distribution that is useful when n is large and p is small and when the independent variables occur over a period of time is called the **Poisson distribution.** In addition to being used for the stated conditions (that is, n is large, p is small, and the variables occur over a period of time), the Poisson distribution can be used when a density of items is distributed over a given area or volume, such as the number of plants growing per acre or the number of defects in a given length of videotape.

A **Poisson experiment** is a probability experiment that satisfies the following requirements:

1. The random variable X is the number of occurrences of an event over some interval (i.e., length, area, volume, period of time, etc.).
2. The occurrences occur randomly.
3. The occurrences are independent of one another.
4. The average number of occurrences over an interval is known.

FIGURE 5–4
Using Table C

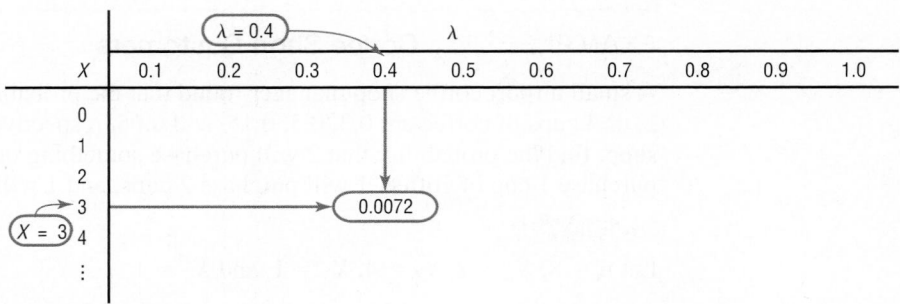

Formula for the Poisson Distribution

The probability of X occurrences in an interval of time, volume, area, etc., for a variable where λ (Greek letter lambda) is the mean number of occurrences per unit (time, volume, area, etc.) is

$$P(X; \lambda) = \frac{e^{-\lambda}\lambda^X}{X!} \qquad \text{where } X = 0, 1, 2, \ldots$$

The letter e is a constant approximately equal to 2.7183.

Round the answers to four decimal places.

EXAMPLE 5–28 Typographical Errors

If there are 200 typographical errors randomly distributed in a 500-page manuscript, find the probability that a given page contains exactly 3 errors.

SOLUTION

First, find the mean number λ of errors. Since there are 200 errors distributed over 500 pages, each page has an average of

$$\lambda = \frac{200}{500} = \frac{2}{5} = 0.4$$

or 0.4 error per page. Since $X = 3$, substituting into the formula yields

$$P(X; \lambda) = \frac{e^{-\lambda}\lambda^X}{X!} = \frac{(2.7183)^{-0.4}(0.4)^3}{3!} \approx 0.0072$$

Thus, there is less than a 1% chance that any given page will contain exactly 3 errors.

Since the mathematics involved in computing Poisson probabilities is somewhat complicated, tables have been compiled for these probabilities. Table C in Appendix A gives P for various values for λ and X.

In Example 5–28, where X is 3 and λ is 0.4, the table gives the value 0.0072 for the probability. See Figure 5–4.

EXAMPLE 5–29 Toll-Free Telephone Calls

A sales firm receives, on average, 3 calls per hour on its toll-free number. For any given hour, find the probability that it will receive the following.

a. At most 3 calls   *b.* At least 3 calls   *c.* 5 or more calls

SOLUTION

a. "At most 3 calls" means 0, 1, 2, or 3 calls. Hence,

$$P(0; 3) + P(1; 3) + P(2; 3) + P(3; 3)$$
$$= 0.0498 + 0.1494 + 0.2240 + 0.2240$$
$$= 0.6472$$

b. "At least 3 calls" means 3 or more calls. It is easier to find the probability of 0, 1, and 2 calls and then subtract this answer from 1 to get the probability of at least 3 calls.

$$P(0; 3) + P(1; 3) + P(2; 3) = 0.0498 + 0.1494 + 0.2240 = 0.4232$$

and

$$1 - 0.4232 = 0.5768$$

c. For the probability of 5 or more calls, it is easier to find the probability of getting 0, 1, 2, 3, or 4 calls and subtract this answer from 1. Hence,

$$P(0; 3) + P(1; 3) + P(2; 3) + P(3; 3) + P(4; 3)$$
$$= 0.0498 + 0.1494 + 0.2240 + 0.2240 + 0.1680$$
$$= 0.8152$$

and

$$1 - 0.8152 = 0.1848$$

Thus, for the events described, the part *a* event is most likely to occur, and the part *c* event is least likely to occur.

The Poisson distribution can also be used to approximate the binomial distribution when the expected value $\lambda = n \cdot p$ is less than 5, as shown in Example 5–30. (The same is true when $n \cdot q < 5$.)

EXAMPLE 5–30   Left-Handed People

If approximately 2% of the people in a room of 200 people are left-handed, find the probability that exactly 5 people there are left-handed.

SOLUTION

Since $\lambda = n \cdot p$, then $\lambda = (200)(0.02) = 4$. Hence,

$$P(X; \lambda) = \frac{(2.7183)^{-4}(4)^5}{5!} \approx 0.1563$$

which is verified by the formula $_{200}C_5(0.02)^5(0.98)^{195} \approx 0.1579$. The difference between the two answers is based on the fact that the Poisson distribution is an approximation and rounding has been used.

The Hypergeometric Distribution

When sampling is done *without* replacement, the binomial distribution does not give exact probabilities, since the trials are not independent. The smaller the size of the population, the less accurate the binomial probabilities will be.

For example, suppose a committee of 4 people is to be selected from 7 women and 5 men. What is the probability that the committee will consist of 3 women and 1 man?

To solve this problem, you must find the number of ways a committee of 3 women and 1 man can be selected from 7 women and 5 men. This answer can be found by using combinations; it is

$$_7C_3 \cdot {}_5C_1 = 35 \cdot 5 = 175$$

Next, find the total number of ways a committee of 4 people can be selected from 12 people. Again, by the use of combinations, the answer is

$$_{12}C_4 = 495$$

Finally, the probability of getting a committee of 3 women and 1 man from 7 women and 5 men is

$$P(X) = \frac{175}{495} = \frac{35}{99}$$

The results of the problem can be generalized by using a special probability distribution called the hypergeometric distribution. The **hypergeometric distribution** is a distribution of a variable that has two outcomes when sampling is done without replacement.

A **hypergeometric experiment** is a probability experiment that satisfies the following requirements:
1. There are a fixed number of trials.
2. There are two outcomes, and they can be classified as success or failure.
3. The sample is selected without replacement.

The probabilities for the hypergeometric distribution can be calculated by using the formula given next.

Formula for the Hypergeometric Distribution

Given a population with only two types of objects (females and males, defective and nondefective, successes and failures, etc.), such that there are a items of one kind and b items of another kind and $a + b$ equals the total population, the probability $P(X)$ of selecting without replacement a sample of size n with X items of type a and $n - X$ items of type b is

$$P(X) = \frac{{}_aC_X \cdot {}_bC_{n-X}}{{}_{a+b}C_n}$$

The basis of the formula is that there are ${}_aC_X$ ways of selecting the first type of items, ${}_bC_{n-X}$ ways of selecting the second type of items, and ${}_{a+b}C_n$ ways of selecting n items from the entire population.

EXAMPLE 5–31   Assistant Manager Applicants

Ten people apply for a job as assistant manager of a restaurant. Five have completed college and five have not. If the manager selects 3 applicants at random, find the probability that all 3 are college graduates.

SOLUTION

Assigning the values to the variables gives

$$a = 5 \text{ college graduates} \qquad n = 3$$
$$b = 5 \text{ nongraduates} \qquad X = 3$$

and $n - X = 0$. Substituting in the formula gives

$$P(X) = \frac{{}_5C_3 \cdot {}_5C_0}{{}_{10}C_3} = \frac{10}{120} = \frac{1}{12} \approx 0.083$$

There is a 0.083 probability that all 3 applicants will be college graduates.

EXAMPLE 5–32   House Insurance

A recent study found that 2 out of every 10 houses in a neighborhood have no insurance. If 5 houses are selected from 10 houses, find the probability that exactly 1 will be uninsured.

SOLUTION

In this example, $a = 2$, $b = 8$, $n = 5$, $X = 1$, and $n - X = 4$.

$$P(X) = \frac{{}_2C_1 \cdot {}_8C_4}{{}_{10}C_5} = \frac{2 \cdot 70}{252} = \frac{140}{252} = \frac{5}{9} \approx 0.556$$

There is a 0.556 probability that out of 5 houses, 1 house will be uninsured.

In many situations where objects are manufactured and shipped to a company, the company selects a few items and tests them to see whether they are satisfactory or defective. If a certain percentage is defective, the company then can refuse the whole shipment. This procedure saves the time and cost of testing every single item. To make the judgment about whether to accept or reject the whole shipment based on a small sample of tests, the company must know the probability of getting a specific number of defective items. To calculate the probability, the company uses the hypergeometric distribution.

EXAMPLE 5–33   Defective Compressor Tanks

A lot of 12 compressor tanks is checked to see whether there are any defective tanks. Three tanks are checked for leaks. If 1 or more of the 3 is defective, the lot is rejected. Find the probability that the lot will be rejected if there are actually 3 defective tanks in the lot.

SOLUTION

Since the lot is rejected if at least 1 tank is found to be defective, it is necessary to find the probability that none are defective and subtract this probability from 1.

Here, $a = 3$, $b = 9$, $n = 3$, and $X = 0$; so

$$P(X) = \frac{{}_3C_0 \cdot {}_9C_3}{{}_{12}C_3} = \frac{1 \cdot 84}{220} \approx 0.38$$

Hence,

$$P(\text{at least 1 defective}) = 1 - P(\text{no defectives}) = 1 - 0.38 = 0.62$$

There is a 0.62, or 62%, probability that the lot will be rejected when 3 of the 12 tanks are defective.

The Geometric Distribution

Another useful distribution is called the *geometric distribution*. This distribution can be used when we have an experiment that has two outcomes and is repeated until a successful outcome is obtained. For example, we could flip a coin until a head is obtained, or we could roll a die until we get a 6. In these cases, our successes would come on the nth trial. The geometric probability distribution tells us when the success is likely to occur.

A **geometric experiment** is a probability experiment if it satisfies the following requirements:
1. Each trial has two outcomes that can be either success or failure.
2. The outcomes are independent of each other.
3. The probability of a success is the same for each trial.
4. The experiment continues until a success is obtained.

Formula for the Geometric Distribution

If p is the probability of a success on each trial of a binomial experiment and n is the number of the trial at which the first success occurs, then the probability of getting the first success on the nth trial is

$$P(n) = p(1 - p)^{n-1}$$

where $n = 1, 2, 3, \ldots .$

EXAMPLE 5–34   Tossing Coins

A coin is tossed. Find the probability of getting the first head on the third toss.

SOLUTION

The objective for tossing a coin and getting a head on the third toss is TTH. The probability for this outcome is

$$\left(\frac{1}{2}\right)\left(\frac{1}{2}\right)\left(\frac{1}{2}\right) = \frac{1}{8}$$

Now by using the formula, you get the same results.

$$\begin{aligned}
P(n) &= p(1 - p)^{n-1} \\
&= \frac{1}{2}\left(1 - \frac{1}{2}\right)^{3-1} \\
&= \frac{1}{2}\left(\frac{1}{2}\right)^{2} \\
&= \frac{1}{8}
\end{aligned}$$

Hence, there is a 1 out of 8 chance or 0.125 probability of getting the first head on the third toss of a coin.

EXAMPLE 5–35   Blood Types

In the United States, approximately 42% of people have type A blood. If 4 people are selected at random, find the probability that the fourth person is the first one selected with type A blood.

SOLUTION

Let $p = 0.42$ and $n = 4$.

$$\begin{aligned}
P(n) &= p(1 - p)^{n-1} \\
P(4) &= (0.42)(1 - 0.42)^{4-1} \\
&= (0.42)(0.58)^{3} \\
&\approx 0.0819 \approx 0.082
\end{aligned}$$

There is a 0.082 probability that the fourth person selected will be the first one to have type A blood.

A summary of the discrete distributions used in this chapter is shown in Table 5–1.

TABLE 5–1 Summary of Discrete Distributions

1. Binomial distribution

$$P(X) = \frac{n!}{(n - X)!X!} \cdot p^X \cdot q^{n-X}$$

$$\mu = n \cdot p \qquad \sigma = \sqrt{n \cdot p \cdot q}$$

It is used when there are only two outcomes for a fixed number of independent trials and the probability for each success remains the same for each trial.

2. Multinomial distribution

$$P(X) = \frac{n!}{X_1! \cdot X_2! \cdot X_3! \cdots X_k!} \cdot p_1^{X_1} \cdot p_2^{X_2} \cdots p_k^{X_k}$$

where

$$X_1 + X_2 + X_3 + \cdots + X_k = n \qquad \text{and} \qquad p_1 + p_2 + p_3 + \cdots + p_k = 1$$

It is used when the distribution has more than two outcomes, the probabilities for each trial remain constant, outcomes are independent, and there are a fixed number of trials.

3. Poisson distribution

$$P(X; \lambda) = \frac{e^{-\lambda}\lambda^X}{X!} \qquad \text{where } X = 0, 1, 2, \ldots$$

It is used when n is large and p is small, and the independent variable occurs over a period of time, or a density of items is distributed over a given area or volume.

4. Hypergeometric distribution

$$P(X) = \frac{{}_aC_X \cdot {}_bC_{n-X}}{{}_{a+b}C_n}$$

It is used when there are two outcomes and sampling is done without replacement.

5. Geometric distribution

$$P(n) = p(1 - p)^{n-1} \qquad \text{where } n = 1, 2, 3, \ldots$$

It is used when there are two outcomes and we are interested in the probability that the first success occurs on the nth trial.

Applying the Concepts 5–4

Rockets and Targets

During the latter days of World War II, the Germans developed flying rocket bombs. These bombs were used to attack London. Allied military intelligence didn't know whether these bombs were fired at random or had a sophisticated aiming device. To determine the answer, they used the Poisson distribution.

To assess the accuracy of these bombs, London was divided into 576 square regions. Each region was $\frac{1}{4}$ square kilometer in area. They then compared the number of actual hits with the theoretical number of hits by using the Poisson distribution. If the values in both distributions were close, then they would conclude that the rockets were fired at random. The actual distribution is as follows:

Hits	0	1	2	3	4	5
Regions	229	211	93	35	7	1

1. Using the Poisson distribution, find the theoretical values for each number of hits. In this case, the number of bombs was 535, and the number of regions was 576. So

$$\lambda = \frac{535}{576} \approx 0.929$$

For 3 hits,

$$P(X) = \frac{e^{-\lambda} \cdot \lambda^X}{X!}$$

$$= \frac{(2.7183)^{-0.929}(0.929)^3}{3!} \approx 0.0528$$

Hence, the number of hits is $(0.0528)(576) = 30.4128$.
Complete the table for the other number of hits.

Hits	0	1	2	3	4	5
Regions				30.4		

2. Write a brief statement comparing the two distributions.

3. Based on your answer to question 2, can you conclude that the rockets were fired at random?

See page 309 for the answer.

Exercises 5–4

1. Use the multinomial formula and find the probabilities for each.

    a. $n = 6, X_1 = 3, X_2 = 2, X_3 = 1, p_1 = 0.5, p_2 = 0.3, p_3 = 0.2$

    b. $n = 5, X_1 = 1, X_2 = 2, X_3 = 2, p_1 = 0.3, p_2 = 0.6, p_3 = 0.1$

    c. $n = 4, X_1 = 1, X_2 = 1, X_3 = 2, p_1 = 0.8, p_2 = 0.1, p_3 = 0.1$

2. Use the multinomial formula and find the probabilities for each.

    a. $n = 3, X_1 = 1, X_2 = 1, X_3 = 1, p_1 = 0.5, p_2 = 0.3, p_3 = 0.2$

    b. $n = 5, X_1 = 1, X_2 = 3, X_3 = 1, p_1 = 0.7, p_2 = 0.2, p_3 = 0.1$

    c. $n = 7, X_1 = 2, X_2 = 3, X_3 = 2, p_1 = 0.4, p_2 = 0.5, p_3 = 0.1$

3. **M&M's Color Distribution** According to the manufacturer, M&M's are produced and distributed in the following proportions: 13% brown, 13% red, 14% yellow, 16% green, 20% orange, and 24% blue. In a random sample of 12 M&M's, what is the probability of having 2 of each color?

4. **Truck Inspection Violations** The probabilities are 0.50, 0.40, and 0.10 that a trailer truck will have no violations, 1 violation, or 2 or more violations when it is given a safety inspection by state police. If 5 trailer trucks are inspected, find the probability that 3 will have no violations, 1 will have 1 violation, and 1 will have 2 or more violations.

5. **Reusable Grocery Bags** In a magazine survey, 60% of respondents said that they use reusable grocery bags; 32%,

plastic; and 8%, paper. In a random sample of 10 grocery shoppers, what is the probability that 6 will use reusable bags and that 2 each will request paper or plastic?

Source: *Everyday with Rachel Ray,* April 2012.

6. **Mendel's Theory** According to Mendel's theory, if tall and colorful plants are crossed with short and colorless plants, the corresponding probabilities are $\frac{9}{16}, \frac{3}{16}, \frac{3}{16}$, and $\frac{1}{16}$ for tall and colorful, tall and colorless, short and colorful, and short and colorless, respectively. If 8 plants are selected, find the probability that 1 will be tall and colorful, 3 will be tall and colorless, 3 will be short and colorful, and 1 will be short and colorless.

7. Find each probability $P(X; \lambda)$, using Table C in Appendix A.

    a. $P(5; 4)$

    b. $P(2; 4)$

    c. $P(6; 3)$

8. Find each probability $P(X; \lambda)$ using Table C in Appendix A.

    a. $P(10; 7)$

    b. $P(9; 8)$

    c. $P(3; 4)$

9. **Study of Robberies** A recent study of robberies for a certain geographic region showed an average of 1 robbery per 20,000 people. In a city of 80,000 people, find the probability of the following.

    a.   0 robberies

    b.   1 robbery

    c.   2 robberies

    d.   3 or more robberies

10. **Misprints on Manuscript Pages** In a 400-page manuscript, there are 200 randomly distributed misprints. If a page is selected, find the probability that it has 1 misprint.

11. **Colors of Flowers** A nursery provides red impatiens for commercial landscaping. If 5% are variegated instead of pure red, find the probability that in an order for 200 plants, exactly 14 are variegated.

12. **Mail Ordering** A mail-order company receives an average of 5 orders per 500 solicitations. If it sends out 100 advertisements, find the probability of receiving at least 2 orders.

13. **Company Mailing** Of a company's mailings 1.5% are returned because of incorrect or incomplete addresses. In a mailing of 200 pieces, find the probability that none will be returned.

14. **Emission Inspection Failures** If 3% of all cars fail the emissions inspection, find the probability that in a sample of 90 cars, 3 will fail. Use the Poisson approximation.

15. **Phone Inquiries** The average number of phone inquiries per day at the poison control center is 4. Find the probability it will receive 5 calls on a given day. Use the Poisson approximation.

16. **Defective Calculators** In a batch of 2000 calculators, there are, on average, 8 defective ones. If a random sample of 150 is selected, find the probability of 5 defective ones.

17. **School Newspaper Staff** A school newspaper staff is comprised of 5 seniors, 4 juniors, 5 sophomores, and 7 freshmen. If 4 staff members are chosen at random for a publicity photo, what is the probability that there will be 1 student from each class?

18. **Missing Pages from Books** A bookstore owner examines 5 books from each lot of 25 to check for missing pages. If he finds at least 2 books with missing pages, the entire lot is returned. If, indeed, there are 5 books with missing pages, find the probability that the lot will be returned.

19. **Hors d'Oeuvres Selection** A plate of hors d'oeuvres contains two types of filled puff pastry—chicken and

shrimp. The entire platter contains 15 pastries— 8 chicken and 7 shrimp. From the outside the pastries appear identical, and they are randomly distributed on the tray. Choose 3 at random; what is the probability that all 3 have the same filling?

20. **Defective Computer Keyboards** A shipment of 24 computer keyboards is rejected if 4 are checked for defects and at least 1 is found to be defective. Find the probability that the shipment will be returned if there are actually 6 defective keyboards.

21. **Defective Electronics** A shipment of 24 electric typewriters is rejected if 3 are checked for defects and at least 1 is found to be defective. Find the probability that the shipment will be returned if there are actually 6 typewriters that are defective.

22. **Job Applications** Ten people apply for a job at Computer Warehouse. Five are college graduates and five are not. If the manager selects 3 applicants at random, find the probability that all 3 are college graduates.

23. **Selling Carpet** A person works in a large home improvement store and approaches customers to tell them about the store's carpet sale. He then asks them if they would like to talk to a sales representative. From past experience, the person has found that the probability of getting a "yes" is about 0.32. Find the probability that the person's first "yes" will occur with the fifth customer.

24. **Winning a Prize** A soda pop manufacturer runs a contest and places a winning bottle cap on every sixth bottle. If a person buys the soda pop, find the probability that the person will (*a*) win on his first purchase, (*b*) win on his third purchase, or (*c*) not win on any of his first five purchases.

25. **Shooting an Arrow** Mark shoots arrows at a target and hits the bull's-eye about 40% of the time. Find the probability that he hits the bull's-eye on the third shot.

26. **Amusement Park Game** At an amusement park basketball game, the player gets 3 throws for $1. If the player makes a basket, the player wins a prize. Mary makes about 80% of her shots. Find the probability that Mary wins a prize on her third shot.

⊟ Extending the Concepts

Another type of problem that can be solved uses what is called the *negative binomial distribution,* which is a generalization of the binomial distribution. In this case, it tells the average number of trials needed to get *k* successes of a binomial experiment. The formula is

$$\mu = \frac{k}{p}$$

where *k* = the number of successes
     p = the probability of a success

Use this formula for Exercises 27–30.

27. **Drawing Cards** A card is randomly drawn from a deck of cards and then replaced. The process continues until 3 clubs are obtained. Find the average number of trials needed to get 3 clubs.

28. **Rolling an 8-Sided Die** An 8-sided die is rolled. The sides are numbered 1 through 8. Find the average number of rolls it takes to get two 5s.

29. **Drawing Cards** Cards are drawn at random from a deck and replaced after each draw. Find the average number of cards that would be drawn to get 4 face cards.

30. Blood Type About 4% of the citizens of the United States have type AB blood. If an agency needed type AB blood and donors came in at random, find the average number of donors that would be needed to get a person with type AB blood.

The mean of a geometric distribution is $\mu = 1/p$, and the standard deviation is $\sigma = \sqrt{q/p^2}$, where p = the probability of the outcome and $q = 1 - p$. Use these formulas for Exercises 31–34.

31. Shower or Bath Preferences It is estimated that 4 out of 5 men prefer showers to baths. Find the mean and standard deviation for the distribution of men who prefer showers to baths.

32. Lessons Outside of School About 2 out of every 3 children take some kind of lessons outside of school.

These lessons include music, art, and sports. Find the mean and standard deviation of the distribution of the number of children who take lessons outside of school.

33. Teachers and Summer Vacations One in five teachers stated that he or she became a teacher because of the long summer vacations. Find the mean and standard deviation for the distribution of teachers who say they became teachers because of the long summer vacation.

34. Work versus Conscience One worker in four in America admits that she or he has to do some things at work that go against her or his consciences. Find the mean and standard deviation for the distribution of workers who admit to having to do some things at work that go against their consciences.

≣ Technology   Step by Step

TI-84 Plus

Step by Step

Poisson Random Variables

To find the probability for a Poisson random variable:
Press **2nd [DISTR]** then **C (ALPHA PRGM)** for poissonpdf

Note the form is different from that used in text, $P(X; \lambda)$.

Example: $\lambda = 0.4$, $X = 3$ (Example 5–28 from the text)
poissonpdf(.4,3)

Example: $\lambda = 3$, $X = 0, 1, 2, 3$ (Example 5–29a from the text)
poissonpdf(3,{0,1,2,3})
The calculator will display the probabilities in a list. Use the arrow keys to view the entire display.

 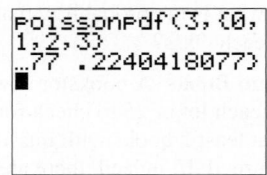

To find the cumulative probability for a Poisson random variable:
Press **2nd [DISTR]** then **D (ALPHA VARS)** for poissoncdf   (Note: On the TI-84 Plus use D.)
The form is poissoncdf(λ,X). This will calculate the cumulative probability for values from 0 to X.

Example: $\lambda = 3$, $X = 0, 1, 2, 3$ (Example 5–29a from the text)
poissoncdf(3,3)

To construct a Poisson probability table:

1. Enter the X values 0 through a large possible value of X into L_1.

2. Move the cursor to the top of the L_2 column so that L_2 is highlighted.

3. Enter the command poissonpdf(λ,L_1) then press **ENTER**.

Example: $\lambda = 3$, $X = 0, 1, 2, 3, \ldots, 10$ (Example 5–29 from the text)

Other Discrete Distributions

Excel can be used to calculate probabilities (and cumulative probabilities). The built-in discrete probability distribution functions available in Excel include the hypergeometric, Poisson, and geometric.

Calculating a Hypergeometric Probability

We will use Excel to calculate the probability from Example 5–31.

1. Select the Insert Function icon *fx* from the Toolbar.
2. Select the Statistical function category from the list of available categories.
3. Select the HYPGEOM.DIST function from the function list. The Function Arguments dialog box will appear.

4. Type 3 for Sample_s, the number of successes in the sample.
5. Type 3 for Number_sample, the size of the sample.
6. Type 5 for Population_s, the number of successes in the population.
7. Type 10 for Number_pop, the size of the population.
8. Type FALSE for Cumulative, since the probability to be calculated is for a single event.
9. Click OK.

Note: If you are calculating a cumulative probability, you should type TRUE for Cumulative.

Calculating a Poisson Probability

We will use Excel to calculate the probability from Example 5–30

1. Select the Insert Function Icon $\frac{fx}{=}$ from the Toolbar.
2. Select the Statistical function category from the list of available categories.
3. Select the POISSON.DIST function from the function list. The Function Arguments dialog box will appear.

4. Type 5 for *X*, the number of occurrences.
5. Type .02*200 or 4 for the Mean.
6. Type FALSE for Cumulative, since the probability to be calculated is for a single event.
7. Click OK.

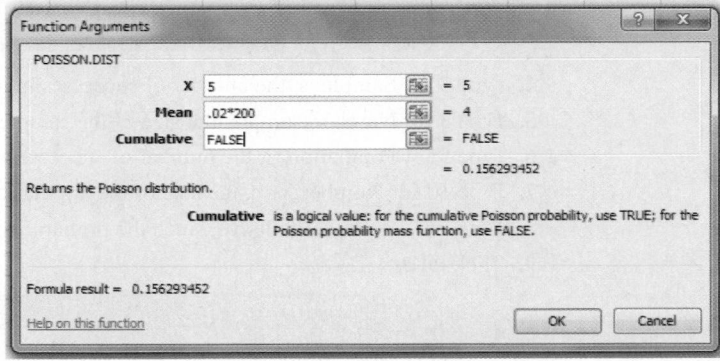

Calculating a Geometric Probability

We will use Excel to calculate the probability from Example 5–35.

Note: Excel does not have a built-in Geometric Probability Distribution function. We must use the built-in Negative Binomial Distribution function—which gives the probability that there will be a certain number of failures until a certain number of successes occur—to calculate probabilities for the Geometric Distribution. The Geometric Distribution is a special case of the Negative Binomial for which the threshold number of successes is 1.

Select the Insert Function Icon $\frac{fx}{=}$ from the Toolbar.

1. Select the Statistical function category from the list of available categories.

2. Select the NEGBINOM.DIST function from the function list. The Function Arguments dialog box will appear.

3. When the NEGBINOM.DIST Function Arguments box appears, type 3 for Number_f, the number of failures (until the first success).

4. Type 1 for Number_s, the threshold number of successes.

5. Type .42 for Probability_s, the probability of a success.

6. Type FALSE for cumulative.

7. Click OK.

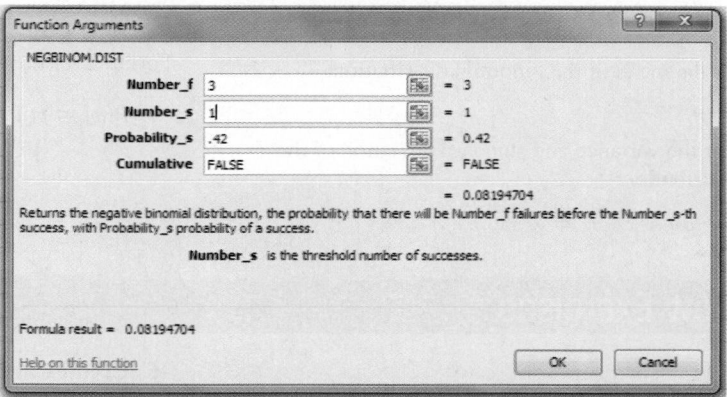

Summary

- A discrete probability distribution consists of the values a random variable can assume and the corresponding probabilities of these values. There are two requirements of a probability distribution: the sum of the probabilities of the events must equal 1, and the probability of any single event must be a number from 0 to 1. Probability distributions can be graphed. (5–1)

- The mean, variance, and standard deviation of a probability distribution can be found. The expected value of a discrete random variable of a probability distribution can also be found. This is basically a measure of the average. (5–2)

- A binomial experiment has four requirements. There must be a fixed number of trials. Each trial can have only two outcomes. The outcomes are independent of each other, and the probability of a success must remain the same for each trial. The probabilities of the outcomes can be found by using the binomial formula or the binomial table. (5–3)

- In addition to the binomial distribution, there are some other commonly used probability distributions. They are the multinomial distribution, the Poisson distribution, the hypergeometric distribution, and the geometric distribution. (5–4)

Important Terms

binomial distribution 277

binomial experiment 276

discrete probability
distribution 259

expected value 269

geometric distribution 295

geometric
experiment 295

hypergeometric
distribution 294

hypergeometric
experiment 294

multinomial
distribution 290

multinomial experiment 290

Poisson distribution 291

Poisson experiment 291

random variable 258

Important Formulas

Formula for the mean of a probability distribution:

$$\mu = \Sigma X \cdot P(X)$$

Formulas for the variance and standard deviation of a probability distribution:

$$\sigma^2 = \Sigma[X^2 \cdot P(X)] - \mu^2$$

$$\sigma = \sqrt{\Sigma[X^2 \cdot P(X)] - \mu^2}$$

Formula for expected value:

$$E(X) = \Sigma X \cdot P(X)$$

Binomial probability formula:

$$P(X) = \frac{n!}{(n-X)!X!} \cdot p^X \cdot q^{n-X} \text{ where } X = 0, 1, 2, 3, \ldots, n$$

Formula for the mean of the binomial distribution:

$$\mu = n \cdot p$$

Formulas for the variance and standard deviation of the binomial distribution:

$$\sigma^2 = n \cdot p \cdot q \qquad \sigma = \sqrt{n \cdot p \cdot q}$$

Formula for the multinomial distribution:

$$P(X) = \frac{n!}{X_1! \cdot X_2! \cdot X_3! \cdots X_k!} \cdot p_1^{X_1} \cdot p_2^{X_2} \cdots p_k^{X_k}$$

(The X's sum to n and the p's sum to 1.)

Formula for the Poisson distribution:

$$P(X; \lambda) = \frac{e^{-\lambda}\lambda^X}{X!} \qquad \text{where } X = 0, 1, 2, \ldots$$

Formula for the hypergeometric distribution:

$$P(X) = \frac{{}_aC_X \cdot {}_bC_{n-X}}{{}_{a+b}C_n}$$

Formula for the geometric distribution:

$$P(n) = p(1-p)^{n-1} \qquad \text{where } n = 1, 2, 3, \ldots$$

Review Exercises

Section 5–1

For Exercises 1 through 3, determine whether the distribution represents a probability distribution. If it does not, state why.

1.

X	1	2	3	4	5
P(X)	$\frac{1}{10}$	$\frac{3}{10}$	$\frac{1}{10}$	$\frac{2}{10}$	$\frac{3}{10}$

2.

X	5	10	15
P(X)	0.3	0.4	0.1

3.

X	8	12	16	20
P(X)	$\frac{5}{6}$	$\frac{1}{12}$	$\frac{1}{12}$	$\frac{1}{12}$

4. Emergency Calls The number of emergency calls that a local police department receives per 24-hour period is distributed as shown here. Construct a graph for the data.

Number of calls X	10	11	12	13	14
Probability P(X)	0.02	0.12	0.40	0.31	0.15

5. Credit Cards A large retail company encourages its employees to get customers to apply for the store credit card. Below is the distribution for the number of credit card applications received per employee for an 8-hour shift.

X	0	1	2	3	4	5
P(X)	0.27	0.28	0.20	0.15	0.08	0.02

a. What is the probability that an employee will get 2 or 3 applications during any given shift?

b. Find the mean, variance, and standard deviation for this probability distribution.

6. Coins in a Box A box contains 5 pennies, 3 dimes, 1 quarter, and 1 half-dollar. A coin is drawn at random. Construct a probability distribution and draw a graph for the data.

7. Tie Purchases At Tyler's Tie Shop, Tyler found the probabilities that a customer will buy 0, 1, 2, 3, or 4 ties, as shown. Construct a graph for the distribution.

Number of ties X	0	1	2	3	4
Probability P(X)	0.30	0.50	0.10	0.08	0.02

Section 5–2

8. **Customers in a Bank** A bank has a drive-through service. The number of customers arriving during a 15-minute period is distributed as shown. Find the mean, variance, and standard deviation for the distribution.

Number of customers X	0	1	2	3	4
Probability P(X)	0.12	0.20	0.31	0.25	0.12

9. **Arrivals at an Airport** At a small rural airport, the number of arrivals per hour during the day has the distribution shown. Find the mean, variance, and standard deviation for the data.

Number X	5	6	7	8	9	10
Probability P(X)	0.14	0.21	0.24	0.18	0.16	0.07

10. **Cans of Paint Purchased** During a recent paint sale at Corner Hardware, the number of cans of paint purchased was distributed as shown. Find the mean, variance, and standard deviation of the distribution.

Number of cans X	1	2	3	4	5
Probability P(X)	0.42	0.27	0.15	0.10	0.06

11. **Inquiries Received** The number of inquiries received per day for a college catalog is distributed as shown. Find the mean, variance, and standard deviation for the data.

Number of inquiries X	22	23	24	25	26	27
Probability P(X)	0.08	0.19	0.36	0.25	0.07	0.05

12. **Outdoor Regatta** A producer plans an outdoor regatta for May 3. The cost of the regatta is $8000. This includes advertising, security, printing tickets, entertainment, etc. The producer plans to make $15,000 profit if all goes well. However, if it rains, the regatta will have to be canceled. According to the weather report, the probability of rain is 0.3. Find the producer's expected profit.

13. **Card Game** A game is set up as follows: All the diamonds are removed from a deck of cards, and these 13 cards are placed in a bag. The cards are mixed up, and then one card is chosen at random (and then replaced). The player wins according to the following rules.

If the ace is drawn, the player loses $20.
If a face card is drawn, the player wins $10.
If any other card (2–10) is drawn, the player wins $2.

How much should be charged to play this game in order for it to be fair?

14. Using Exercise 13, how much should be charged if instead of winning $2 for drawing a 2–10, the player wins the amount shown on the card in dollars?

Section 5–3

15. Let x be a binomial random variable with $n = 12$ and $p = 0.3$. Find the following:
   a. $P(X = 8)$
   b. $P(X < 5)$
   c. $P(X \geq 10)$
   d. $P(4 < X \leq 9)$

16. **Internet Access via Cell Phone** In a retirement community, 14% of cell phone users use their cell phones to access the Internet. In a random sample of 10 cell phone users, what is the probability that exactly 2 have used their phones to access the Internet? More than 2?

17. **Computer Literacy Test** If 80% of job applicants are able to pass a computer literacy test, find the mean, variance, and standard deviation of the number of people who pass the examination in a sample of 150 applicants.

18. **Flu Shots** It has been reported that 63% of adults aged 65 and over got their flu shots last year. In a random sample of 300 adults aged 65 and over, find the mean, variance, and standard deviation for the number who got their flu shots.

Source: U.S. Center for Disease Control and Prevention.

19. **U.S. Police Chiefs and the Death Penalty** The chance that a U.S. police chief believes the death penalty "significantly reduces the number of homicides" is 1 in 4. If a random sample of 8 police chiefs is selected, find the probability that at most 3 believe that the death penalty significantly reduces the number of homicides.

Source: *Harper's Index.*

20. **Household Wood Burning** *American Energy Review* reported that 27% of American households burn wood. If a random sample of 500 American households is selected, find the mean, variance, and standard deviation of the number of households that burn wood.

Source: *100% American* by Daniel Evan Weiss.

21. **Pizza for Breakfast** Three out of four American adults under age 35 have eaten pizza for breakfast. If a random sample of 20 adults under age 35 is selected, find the probability that exactly 16 have eaten pizza for breakfast.

Source: *Harper's Index.*

22. **Unmarried Women** According to survey records, 75.4% of women aged 20–24 have never been married. In a random sample of 250 young women aged 20–24, find the mean, variance, and standard deviation for the number who are or who have been married.

Source: www.infoplease.com

Section 5–4

23. **Accuracy Count of Votes** After a recent national election, voters were asked how confident they were that votes in their state would be counted accurately. The results are shown below.

    46% Very confident   41% Somewhat confident
    9% Not very confident   4% Not at all confident

    If 10 voters are selected at random, find the probability that 5 would be very confident, 3 somewhat confident, 1 not very confident, and 1 not at all confident.

    Source: *New York Times.*

24. **Defective DVDs** Before a DVD leaves the factory, it is given a quality control check. The probabilities that a DVD contains 0, 1, or 2 defects are 0.90, 0.06, and 0.04, respectively. In a sample of 12 recorders, find the probability that 8 have 0 defects, 3 have 1 defect, and 1 has 2 defects.

25. **Christmas Lights** In a Christmas display, the probability that all lights are the same color is 0.50; that 2 colors are used is 0.40; and that 3 or more colors are used is 0.10. If a sample of 10 displays is selected, find the probability that 5 have only 1 color of light, 3 have 2 colors, and 2 have 3 or more colors.

26. **Lost Luggage in Airlines** Transportation officials reported that 8.25 out of every 1000 airline passengers lost luggage during their travels last year. If we randomly select 400 airline passengers, what is the probability that 5 lost some luggage?

    Source: U.S. Department of Transportation.

27. **Computer Assistance** Computer Help Hot Line receives, on average, 6 calls per hour asking for assistance. The distribution is Poisson. For any randomly selected hour, find the probability that the company will receive

    a. At least 6 calls
    b. 4 or more calls
    c. At most 5 calls

28. **Boating Accidents** The number of boating accidents on Lake Emilie follows a Poisson distribution. The probability of an accident is 0.003. If there are 1000 boats on the lake during a summer month, find the probability that there will be 6 accidents.

29. **Drawing Cards** If 5 cards are drawn from a deck, find the probability that 2 will be hearts.

30. **Car Sales** Of the 50 automobiles in a used-car lot, 10 are white. If 5 automobiles are selected to be sold at an auction, find the probability that exactly 2 will be white.

31. **Items Donated to a Food Bank** At a food bank a case of donated items contains 10 cans of soup, 8 cans of vegetables, and 8 cans of fruit. If 3 cans are selected at random to distribute, find the probability of getting 1 can of vegetables and 2 cans of fruit.

32. **Tossing a Die** A die is rolled until a 3 is obtained. Find the probability that the first 3 will be obtained on the fourth roll.

33. **Selecting a Card** A card is selected at random from an ordinary deck and then replaced. Find the probability that the first heart will appear on the fourth draw.

▤ STATISTICS TODAY

Is Pooling Worthwhile?— Revisited

In the case of the pooled sample, the probability that only one test will be needed can be determined by using the binomial distribution. The question being asked is, In a sample of 15 individuals, what is the probability that no individual will have the disease? Hence, $n = 15$, $p = 0.05$, and $X = 0$. From Table B in Appendix A, the probability is 0.463, or 46% of the time, only one test will be needed. For screening purposes, then, pooling samples in this case would save considerable time, money, and effort as opposed to testing every individual in the population.

▤ Chapter Quiz

Determine whether each statement is true or false. If the statement is false, explain why.

1. The expected value of a random variable can be thought of as a long-run average.

2. The number of courses a student is taking this semester is an example of a continuous random variable.

3. When the binomial distribution is used, the outcomes must be dependent.

4. A binomial experiment has a fixed number of trials.

Complete these statements with the best answer.

5. Random variable values are determined by _____.

6. The mean for a binomial variable can be found by using the expression _____.

7. One requirement for a probability distribution is that the sum of all the events in the sample space equal ____.

Select the best answer.

8. What is the sum of the probabilities of all outcomes in a probability distribution?

    a. 0   c. 1
    b. $\frac{1}{2}$ d. It cannot be determined.

9. How many outcomes are there in a binomial experiment?

    a. 0   *c.* 2

    b. 1   *d.* It varies.

10. The number of trials for a binomial experiment

    a. Can be infinite   *c.* Is unlimited

    b. Is unchanged   *d.* Must be fixed

For exercises 11 through 14, determine if the distribution represents a probability distribution. If not, state why.

11.
X	1	2	3	4	5
$P(X)$	$\frac{1}{7}$	$\frac{2}{7}$	$\frac{2}{7}$	$\frac{3}{7}$	$\frac{2}{7}$

12.
X	3	6	9	12	15
$P(X)$	0.3	0.5	0.1	0.08	0.02

13.
X	50	75	100
$P(X)$	0.5	0.2	0.3

14.
X	4	8	12	16
$P(X)$	$\frac{1}{6}$	$\frac{3}{12}$	$\frac{1}{2}$	$\frac{1}{12}$

15. **Calls for a Fire Company** The number of fire calls the Conestoga Valley Fire Company receives per day is distributed as follows:

Number X	5	6	7	8	9
Probability $P(X)$	0.28	0.32	0.09	0.21	0.10

Construct a graph for the data.

16. **Telephones per Household** A study was conducted to determine the number of telephones each household has. The data are shown here.

Number of telephones	0	1	2	3	4
Frequency	2	30	48	13	7

Construct a probability distribution and draw a graph for the data.

17. **CD Purchases** During a recent CD sale at Matt's Music Store, the number of CDs customers purchased was distributed as follows:

Number X	0	1	2	3	4
Probability $P(X)$	0.10	0.23	0.31	0.27	0.09

Find the mean, variance, and standard deviation of the distribution.

18. **Calls for a Crisis Hot Line** The number of calls received per day at a crisis hot line is distributed as follows:

Number X	30	31	32	33	34
Probability $P(X)$	0.05	0.21	0.38	0.25	0.11

Find the mean, variance, and standard deviation of the distribution.

19. **Selecting a Card** There are 6 playing cards placed face down in a box. They are the 4 of diamonds, the 5 of hearts, the 2 of clubs, the 10 of spades, the 3 of diamonds, and the 7 of hearts. A person selects a card. Find the expected value of the draw.

20. **Selecting a Card** A person selects a card from an ordinary deck of cards. If it is a black card, she wins $2. If it is a red card between or including 3 and 7, she wins $10. If it is a red face card, she wins $25; and if it is a black jack, she wins an extra $100. Find the expectation of the game.

21. **Carpooling** If 40% of all commuters ride to work in carpools, find the probability that if 8 workers are selected, 5 will ride in carpools.

22. **Employed Women** If 60% of all women are employed outside the home, find the probability that in a sample of 20 women,

    a. Exactly 15 are employed

    b. At least 10 are employed

    c. At most 5 are not employed outside the home

23. **Driver's Exam** If 80% of the applicants are able to pass a driver's proficiency road test, find the mean, variance, and standard deviation of the number of people who pass the test in a sample of 300 applicants.

24. **Meeting Attendance** A history class has 75 members. If there is a 12% absentee rate per class meeting, find the mean, variance, and standard deviation of the number of students who will be absent from each class.

25. **Income Tax Errors** The probability that a person will make 0, 1, 2, or 3 errors on his or her income tax return is 0.50, 0.30, 0.15, and 0.05, respectively. If 30 claims are selected, find the probability that 15 will contain 0 errors, 8 will contain 1 error, 5 will contain 2 errors, and 2 will contain 3 errors.

26. **Quality Control Check** Before a television set leaves the factory, it is given a quality control check. The probability that a television contains 0, 1, or 2 defects is 0.88, 0.08, and 0.04, respectively. In a sample of 16 televisions, find the probability that 9 will have 0 defects, 4 will have 1 defect, and 3 will have 2 defects.

27. **Bowling Team Uniforms** Among the teams in a bowling league, the probability that the uniforms are all 1 color is 0.45, that 2 colors are used is 0.35, and that 3 or more colors are used is 0.20. If a sample of 12 uniforms is selected, find the probability that 5 contain only 1 color, 4 contain 2 colors, and 3 contain 3 or more colors.

28. **Elm Trees** If 8% of the population of trees are elm trees, find the probability that in a sample of 100 trees, there are exactly 6 elm trees. Assume the distribution is approximately Poisson.

29. **Sports Score Hot Line Calls** Sports Scores Hot Line receives, on the average, 8 calls per hour requesting the latest sports scores. The distribution is Poisson in

nature. For any randomly selected hour, find the probability that the company will receive

a. At least 8 calls

b. 3 or more calls

c. At most 7 calls

30. Color of Raincoats There are 48 raincoats for sale at a local men's clothing store. Twelve are black. If 6 raincoats are selected to be marked down, find the probability that exactly 3 will be black.

31. Youth Group Officers A youth group has 8 boys and 6 girls. If a slate of 4 officers is selected, find the probability that exactly

a. 3 are girls

b. 2 are girls

c. 4 are boys

32. Blood Types About 4% of the citizens of the United States have type AB blood. If an agency needs type AB blood and donors come in at random, find the probability that the sixth person is the first person with type AB blood.

33. Alcohol Abstainers About 35% of Americans abstain from the consumption of alcohol. If Americans are selected at random, find the probability that the 10th person selected will be the first one who doesn't drink alcohol.

≡ Critical Thinking Challenges

1. Lottery Numbers Pennsylvania has a lottery entitled "Big 4." To win, a player must correctly match four digits from a daily lottery in which four digits are selected. Find the probability of winning.

2. Lottery Numbers In the Big 4 lottery, for a bet of $100, the payoff is $5000. What is the expected value of winning? Is it worth it?

3. Lottery Numbers If you played the same four-digit number every day (or any four-digit number for that matter) in the Big 4, how often (in years) would you win, assuming you have average luck?

4. Chuck-a-Luck In the game Chuck-a-Luck, three dice are rolled. A player bets a certain amount (say $1.00) on a number from 1 to 6. If the number appears on 1 die, the person wins $1.00. If it appears on 2 dice, the person wins $2.00, and if it appears on all 3 dice, the person wins $3.00. What are the chances of winning $1.00? $2.00? $3.00?

5. Chuck-a-Luck What is the expected value of the game of Chuck-a-Luck if a player bets $1.00 on one number?

≡ Data Projects

1. Business and Finance Assume that a life insurance company would like to make a profit of $250 on a $100,000 policy sold to a person whose probability of surviving the year is 0.9985. What premium should the company charge the customer? If the company would like to make a $250 profit on a $100,000 policy at a premium of $500, what is the lowest life expectancy it should accept for a customer?

2. Sports and Leisure Baseball, hockey, and basketball all use a seven-game series to determine their championship. Find the probability that with two evenly matched teams a champion will be found in 4 games. Repeat for 5, 6, and 7 games. Look at the historical results for the three sports. How do the actual results compare to the theoretical?

3. Technology Use your most recent itemized phone bill for the data in this problem. Assume that incoming and outgoing calls are equal in the population (why is this a reasonable assumption?). This means assume $p = 0.5$. For the number of calls you made last month, what would be the mean number of outgoing calls in a random selection of calls? Also, compute the standard deviation. Was the number of outgoing calls you made an unusual amount given the above? In a selection of

12 calls, what is the probability that less than 3 were outgoing?

4. Health and Wellness Use Red Cross data to determine the percentage of the population with an Rh factor that is positive (A+, B+, AB+, or O+ blood types). Use that value for p. How many students in your class have a positive Rh factor? Is this an unusual amount?

5. Politics and Economics Find out what percentage of citizens in your state is registered to vote. Assuming that this is a binomial variable, what would be the mean number of registered voters in a random group of citizens with a sample size equal to the number of students in your class? Also determine the standard deviation. How many students in your class are registered to vote? Is this an unusual number, given the above?

6. Your Class Have each student in class toss 4 coins on her or his desk, and note how many heads are showing. Create a frequency table displaying the results. Compare the frequency table to the theoretical probability distribution for the outcome when 4 coins are tossed. Find the mean for the frequency table. How does it compare with the mean for the probability distribution?

≡ Answers to Applying the Concepts

Section 5–1   Dropping College Courses

1. The random variable under study is the reason for dropping a college course.

2. There were a total of 144 people in the study.

3. The complete table is as follows:

Reason for dropping a college course	Frequency	Percentage
Too difficult	45	31.25
Illness	40	27.78
Change in work schedule	20	13.89
Change of major	14	9.72
Family-related problems	9	6.25
Money	7	4.86
Miscellaneous	6	4.17
No meaningful reason	3	2.08

4. The probability that a student will drop a class because of illness is about 28%. The probability that a student will drop a class because of money is about 5%. The probability that a student will drop a class because of a change of major is about 10%.

5. The information is not itself a probability distribution, but it can be used as one.

6. The categories are not necessarily mutually exclusive, but we treated them as such in computing the probabilities.

7. The categories are not independent.

8. The categories are exhaustive.

9. Since all the probabilities are between 0 and 1, inclusive, and the probabilities sum to 1, the requirements for a discrete probability distribution are met.

Section 5–2   Radiation Exposure

1. The expected value is the mean in a discrete probability distribution.

2. We would expect variation from the expected value of 3.

3. Answers will vary. One possible answer is that pregnant mothers in that area might be overly concerned upon hearing that the number of cases of kidney problems in newborns was nearly 4 times what was usually expected. Other mothers (particularly those who had taken a statistics course!) might ask for more information about the claim.

4. Answers will vary. One possible answer is that it does seem unlikely to have 11 newborns with kidney problems when we expect only 3 newborns to have kidney problems.

5. The public might better be informed by percentages or rates (e.g., rate per 1000 newborns).

6. The increase of 8 babies born with kidney problems represents a 0.32% increase (less than $\frac{1}{2}$%).

7. Answers will vary. One possible answer is that the percentage increase does not seem to be something to be overly concerned about.

Section 5–3   Unsanitary Restaurants

1. The probability of eating at 3 restaurants with unsanitary conditions out of the 10 restaurants is 0.18793.

2. The probability of eating at 4 or 5 restaurants with unsanitary conditions out of the 10 restaurants is $0.24665 + 0.22199 = 0.46864 \approx 0.469$.

3. To find this probability, you could add the probabilities for eating at 1, 2, . . . , 10 unsanitary restaurants. An easier way to compute the probability is to subtract the probability of eating at no unsanitary restaurants from 1 (using the complement rule).

4. The highest probability for this distribution is 4, but the expected number of unsanitary restaurants that you would eat at is $10 \cdot \frac{3}{7} = 4.29$.

5. The standard deviation for this distribution is $\sqrt{(10)(\frac{3}{7})(\frac{4}{7})} \approx 1.565$.

6. We have two possible outcomes: "success" is eating in an unsanitary restaurant; "failure" is eating in a sanitary restaurant. The probability that one restaurant is unsanitary is independent of the probability that any other restaurant is unsanitary. The probability that a restaurant is unsanitary remains constant at $\frac{3}{7}$. And we are looking at the number of unsanitary restaurants that we eat at out of 10 "trials."

7. The likelihood of success will vary from situation to situation. Just because we have two possible outcomes, this does not mean that each outcome occurs with probability 0.50.

Section 5–4   Rockets and Targets

1. The theoretical values for the number of hits are as follows:

Hits	0	1	2	3	4	5
Regions	227.5	211.3	98.2	30.4	7.1	1.3

2. The actual values are very close to the theoretical values.

3. Since the actual values are close to the theoretical values, it does appear that the rockets were fired at random.

The Normal Distribution

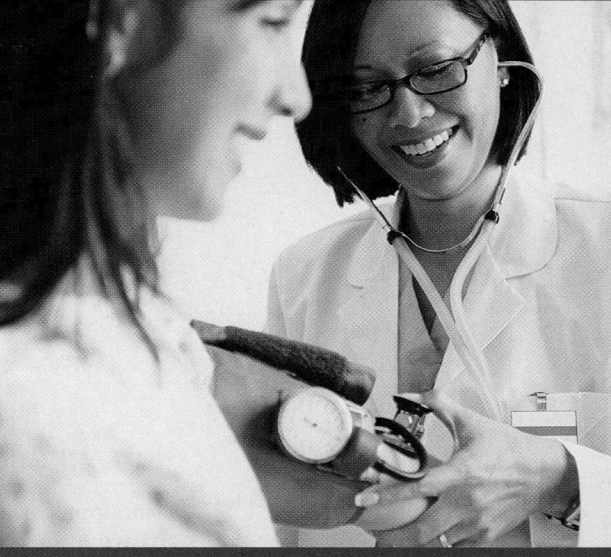

OUTLINE

Introduction
6–1 Normal Distributions
6–2 Applications of the Normal Distribution
6–3 The Central Limit Theorem
6–4 The Normal Approximation to the Binomial Distribution
Summary

OBJECTIVES

After completing this chapter, you should be able to

1 Identify the properties of a normal distribution.

2 Identify distributions as symmetric or skewed.

3 Find the area under the standard normal distribution, given various *z* values.

4 Find probabilities for a normally distributed variable by transforming it into a standard normal variable.

5 Find specific data values for given percentages, using the standard normal distribution.

6 Use the central limit theorem to solve problems involving sample means for large samples.

7 Use the normal approximation to compute probabilities for a binomial variable.

STATISTICS TODAY

What Is Normal?

Medical researchers have determined so-called normal intervals for a person's blood pressure, cholesterol, triglycerides, and the like. For example, the normal range of systolic blood pressure is 110 to 140. The normal interval for a person's triglycerides is from 30 to 200 milligrams per deciliter (mg/dl). By measuring these variables, a physician can determine if a patient's vital statistics are within the normal interval or if some type of treatment is needed to correct a condition and avoid future illnesses. The question then is, How does one determine the so-called normal intervals? See Statistics Today—Revisited at the end of the chapter.

In this chapter, you will learn how researchers determine normal intervals for specific medical tests by using a normal distribution. You will see how the same methods are used to determine the lifetimes of batteries, the strength of ropes, and many other traits.

FIGURE 6–1

Histograms and Normal Model for the Distribution of Heights of Adult Women

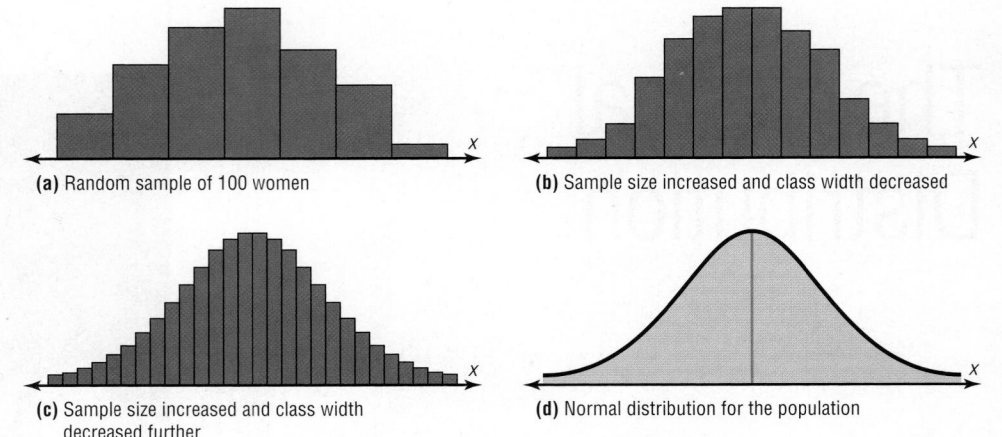

(a) Random sample of 100 women

(b) Sample size increased and class width decreased

(c) Sample size increased and class width decreased further

(d) Normal distribution for the population

Introduction

Historical Note

The name *normal curve* was used by several statisticians, namely, Francis Galton, Charles Sanders, Wilhelm Lexis, and Karl Pearson near the end of the 19th century.

Random variables can be either discrete or continuous. Discrete variables and their distributions were explained in Chapter 5. Recall that a discrete variable cannot assume all values between any two given values of the variables. On the other hand, a continuous variable can assume all values between any two given values of the variables. Examples of continuous variables are the height of adult men, body temperature of rats, and cholesterol level of adults. Many continuous variables, such as the examples just mentioned, have distributions that are bell-shaped, and these are called *approximately normally distributed variables.* For example, if a researcher selects a random sample of 100 adult women, measures their heights, and constructs a histogram, the researcher gets a graph similar to the one shown in Figure 6–1(a). Now, if the researcher increases the sample size and decreases the width of the classes, the histograms will look like the ones shown in Figure 6–1(b) and (c). Finally, if it were possible to measure exactly the heights of all adult females in the United States and plot them, the histogram would approach what is called a *normal distribution curve,* as shown in Figure 6–1(d). This distribution is also known as a *bell curve* or a *Gaussian distribution curve,* named for the German mathematician Carl Friedrich Gauss (1777–1855), who derived its equation.

No variable fits a normal distribution perfectly, since a normal distribution is a theoretical distribution. However, a normal distribution can be used to describe many variables, because the deviations from a normal distribution are very small. This concept will be explained further in Section 6–1.

This chapter will also present the properties of a normal distribution and discuss its applications. Then a very important fact about a normal distribution called the *central limit theorem* will be explained. Finally, the chapter will explain how a normal distribution curve can be used as an approximation to other distributions, such as the binomial distribution. Since a binomial distribution is a discrete distribution, a correction for continuity may be employed when a normal distribution is used for its approximation.

6–1   Normal Distributions

In mathematics, curves can be represented by equations. For example, the equation of the circle shown in Figure 6–2 is $x^2 + y^2 = r^2$, where r is the radius. A circle can be used to represent many physical objects, such as a wheel or a gear. Even though it is not possible to manufacture a wheel that is perfectly round, the equation and the properties of a circle can be used to study many aspects of the wheel, such as area, velocity, and acceleration. In a similar manner, the theoretical curve, called a *normal distribution curve,* can be used to study many variables that are not perfectly normally distributed but are nevertheless approximately normal.

> If a random variable has a probability distribution whose graph is continuous, bell-shaped, and symmetric, it is called a **normal distribution.** The graph is called a *normal distribution curve.*

FIGURE 6–2

Graph of a Circle and an Application

Circle

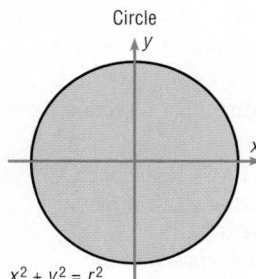

$x^2 + y^2 = r^2$

Wheel

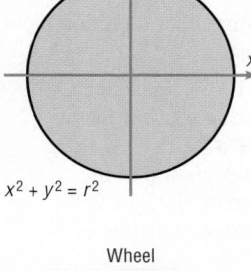

The mathematical equation for a normal distribution is

$$y = \frac{e^{-(X-\mu)^2/(2\sigma^2)}}{\sigma\sqrt{2\pi}}$$

where $e \approx 2.718$ ($\approx$ means "is approximately equal to")

$\pi \approx 3.14$

μ = population mean

σ = population standard deviation

This equation may look formidable, but in applied statistics, tables or technology is used for specific problems instead of the equation.

Another important consideration in applied statistics is that the area under a normal distribution curve is used more often than the values on the y axis. Therefore, when a normal distribution is pictured, the y axis is sometimes omitted.

Circles can be different sizes, depending on their diameters (or radii), and can be used to represent wheels of different sizes. Likewise, normal curves have different shapes and can be used to represent different variables.

The shape and position of a normal distribution curve depend on two parameters, the *mean* and the *standard deviation.* Each normally distributed variable has its own normal distribution curve, which depends on the values of the variable's mean and standard deviation.

Suppose one normally distributed variable has $\mu = 0$ and $\sigma = 1$, and another normally distributed variable has $\mu = 0$ and $\sigma = 2$. As you can see in Figure 6–3(a), when

FIGURE 6–3

Shapes of Normal Distributions

(a) Same means but different standard deviations

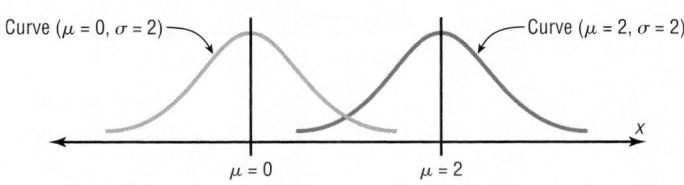

(b) Different means but same standard deviations

OBJECTIVE ①

Identify the properties of a normal distribution.

the value of the standard deviation increases, the shape of the curve spreads out. If one normally distributed variable has $\mu = 0$ and $\sigma = 2$ and another normally distributed variable has $\mu = 2$, and $\sigma = 2$, then the shapes of the curve are the same, but the curve with $\mu = 2$ moves 2 units to the right. See Figure 6–3(b).

The properties of a normal distribution, including those mentioned in the definition, are explained next.

Historical Notes

The discovery of the equation for a normal distribution can be traced to three mathematicians. In 1733, the French mathematician Abraham DeMoivre derived an equation for a normal distribution based on the random variation of the number of heads appearing when a large number of coins were tossed. Not realizing any connection with the naturally occurring variables, he showed this formula to only a few friends. About 100 years later, two mathematicians, Pierre Laplace in France and Carl Gauss in Germany, derived the equation of the normal curve independently and without any knowledge of DeMoivre's work. In 1924, Karl Pearson found that DeMoivre had discovered the formula before Laplace or Gauss.

Summary of the Properties of the Theoretical Normal Distribution

1. A normal distribution curve is bell-shaped.
2. The mean, median, and mode are equal and are located at the center of the distribution.
3. A normal distribution curve is unimodal (i.e., it has only one mode).
4. The curve is symmetric about the mean, which is equivalent to saying that its shape is the same on both sides of a vertical line passing through the center.
5. The curve is continuous; that is, there are no gaps or holes. For each value of X, there is a corresponding value of Y.
6. The curve never touches the x axis. Theoretically, no matter how far in either direction the curve extends, it never meets the x axis—but it gets increasingly close.
7. The total area under a normal distribution curve is equal to 1.00, or 100%. This fact may seem unusual, since the curve never touches the x axis, but one can prove it mathematically by using calculus. (The proof is beyond the scope of this text.)
8. The area under the part of a normal curve that lies within 1 standard deviation of the mean is approximately 0.68, or 68%; within 2 standard deviations, about 0.95, or 95%; and within 3 standard deviations, about 0.997, or 99.7%. See Figure 6–4, which also shows the area in each region.

The values given in item 8 of the summary follow the *empirical rule* for data given in Section 3–2.

You must know these properties in order to solve problems involving distributions that are approximately normal.

Recall from Chapter 2 that the graphs of distributions can have many shapes. When the data values are evenly distributed about the mean, a distribution is said to be a **symmetric distribution.** (A normal distribution is symmetric.) Figure 6–5(a) shows a symmetric distribution. When the majority of the data values fall to the left or right of the mean, the distribution is said to be *skewed.* When the majority of the data values fall to the

FIGURE 6–4

Areas Under a Normal Distribution Curve

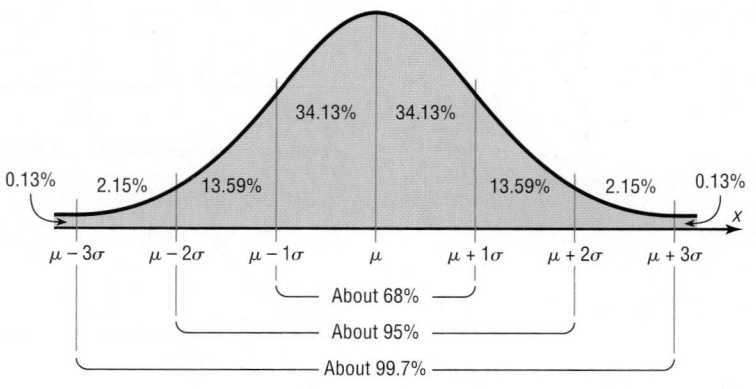

FIGURE 6–5
Normal and Skewed Distributions

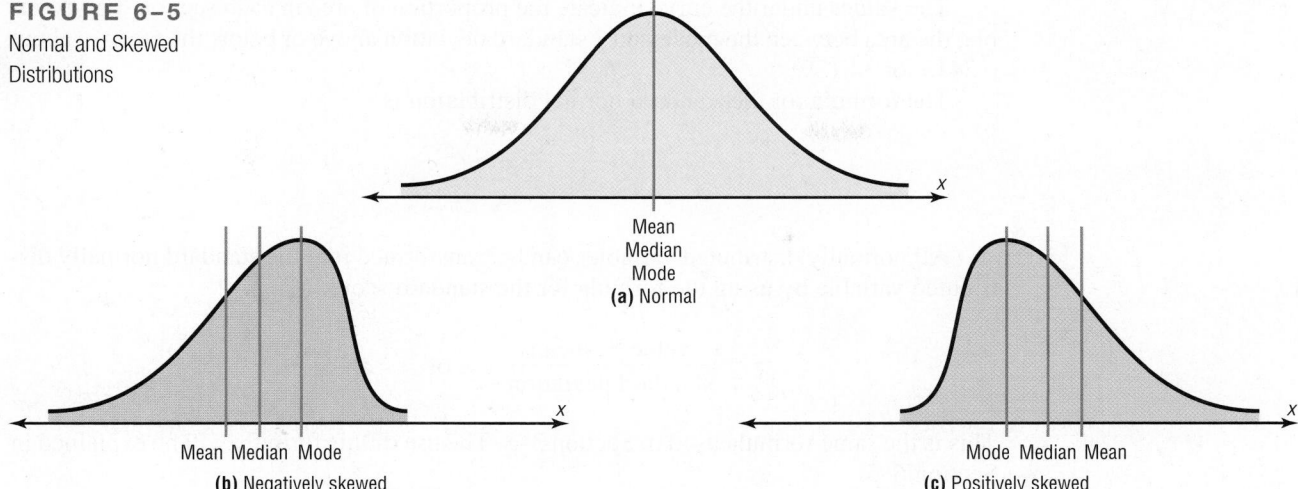

(a) Normal

(b) Negatively skewed

(c) Positively skewed

OBJECTIVE

Identify distributions as symmetric or skewed.

right of the mean, the distribution is said to be a **negatively or left-skewed distribution.** The mean is to the left of the median, and the mean and the median are to the left of the mode. See Figure 6–5(b). When the majority of the data values fall to the left of the mean, a distribution is said to be a **positively or right-skewed distribution.** The mean falls to the right of the median, and both the mean and the median fall to the right of the mode. See Figure 6–5(c).

The "tail" of the curve indicates the direction of skewness (right is positive, left is negative). These distributions can be compared with the ones shown in Figure 3–1. Both types follow the same principles.

The Standard Normal Distribution

Since each normally distributed variable has its own mean and standard deviation, as stated earlier, the shape and location of these curves will vary. In practical applications, then, you would have to have a table of areas under the curve for each variable. To simplify this situation, statisticians use what is called the *standard normal distribution.*

OBJECTIVE

Find the area under the standard normal distribution, given various *z* values.

The **standard normal distribution** is a normal distribution with a mean of 0 and a standard deviation of 1.

The standard normal distribution is shown in Figure 6–6.

FIGURE 6–6
Standard Normal Distribution

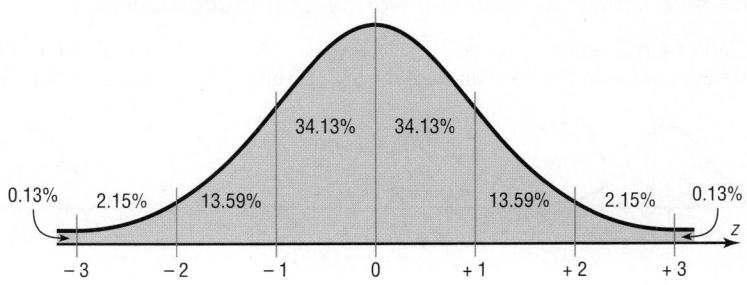

The values under the curve indicate the proportion of area in each section. For example, the area between the mean and 1 standard deviation above or below the mean is about 0.3413, or 34.13%.

The formula for the standard normal distribution is

$$y = \frac{e^{-z^2/2}}{\sqrt{2\pi}}$$

All normally distributed variables can be transformed into the standard normally distributed variable by using the formula for the standard score:

$$z = \frac{\text{value} - \text{mean}}{\text{standard deviation}} \qquad \text{or} \qquad z = \frac{X - \mu}{\sigma}$$

This is the same formula used in Section 3–3. The use of this formula will be explained in Section 6–3.

As stated earlier, the area under a normal distribution curve is used to solve practical application problems, such as finding the percentage of adult women whose height is between 5 feet 4 inches and 5 feet 7 inches, or finding the probability that a new battery will last longer than 4 years. Hence, the major emphasis of this section will be to show the procedure for finding the area under the standard normal distribution curve for any z value. The applications will be shown in Section 6–2. Once the X values are transformed by using the preceding formula, they are called z values. The **z value** or **z score** is actually the number of standard deviations that a particular X value is away from the mean. Table E in Appendix A gives the area (to four decimal places) under the standard normal curve for any z value from -3.49 to 3.49.

Finding Areas Under the Standard Normal Distribution Curve

For the solution of problems using the standard normal distribution, a two-step process is recommended with the use of the Procedure Table shown.

The two steps are as follows:

Step 1   Draw the normal distribution curve and shade the area.

Step 2   Find the appropriate figure in the Procedure Table and follow the directions given.

There are three basic types of problems, and all three are summarized in the Procedure Table. Note that this table is presented as an aid in understanding how to use the standard normal distribution table and in visualizing the problems. After learning the procedures, you should not find it necessary to refer to the Procedure Table for every problem.

Procedure Table

Finding the Area Under the Standard Normal Distribution Curve

1. To the left of any z value:
   Look up the z value in the table and use the area given.

2. To the right of any z value:
   Look up the z value and subtract the area from 1.

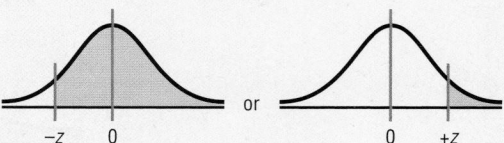

3. Between any two z values:
   Look up both z values and subtract the corresponding areas.

FIGURE 6–7

FIGURE 6–7
Table E Area Value for
$z = 1.39$

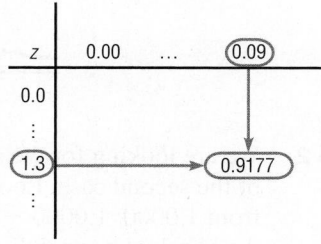

Table E in Appendix A gives the area under the normal distribution curve to the left of any z value given in two decimal places. For example, the area to the left of a z value of 1.39 is found by looking up 1.3 in the left column and 0.09 in the top row. Where the row and column lines meet gives an area of 0.9177. See Figure 6–7.

EXAMPLE 6–1

Find the area under the standard normal distribution curve to the left of $z = 2.09$.

SOLUTION

Step 1   Draw the figure. The desired area is shown in Figure 6–8.

FIGURE 6–8
Area Under the Standard
Normal Distribution Curve for
Example 6–1

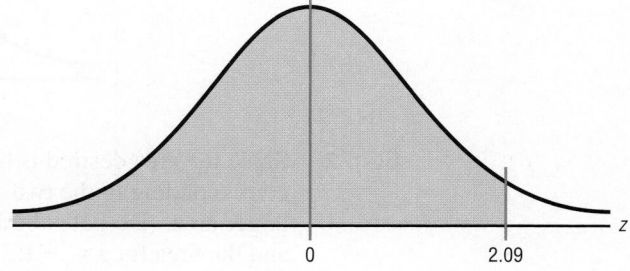

Step 2   We are looking for the area under the standard normal distribution curve to the left of $z = 2.09$. Since this is an example of the first case, look up the area in the table. It is 0.9817. Hence, 98.17% of the area is to the left of $z = 2.09$.

EXAMPLE 6–2

Find the area under the standard normal distribution curve to the right of $z = -1.14$.

SOLUTION

Step 1   Draw the figure. The desired area is shown in Figure 6–9.

FIGURE 6–9
Area Under the Standard
Normal Distribution Curve for
Example 6–2

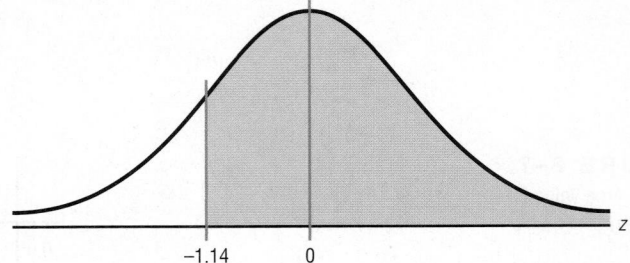

Step 2   We are looking for the area to the right of $z = -1.14$. This is an example of the second case. Look up the area for $z = -1.14$. It is 0.1271. Subtract it from 1.0000: $1.0000 - 0.1271 = 0.8729$. Hence, 87.29% of the area under the standard normal distribution curve is to the right of $z = -1.14$.

Note: In this situation, we subtract the area 0.1271 from 1.0000 because the table gives the area up to -1.14. So, to get the area under the curve to the right of -1.14, subtract the area 0.1271 from 1.0000, the total area under the standard normal distribution curve.

EXAMPLE 6–3

Find the area under the standard normal distribution curve between $z = 1.62$ and $z = -1.35$.

SOLUTION

Step 1   Draw the figure as shown. The desired area is shown in Figure 6–10.

FIGURE 6–10
Area Under the Standard
Normal Distribution Curve
for Example 6–3

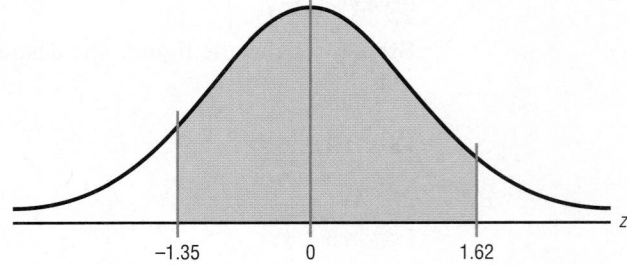

Step 2   Since the area desired is between two given z values, look up the areas corresponding to the two z values and subtract the smaller area from the larger area. (Do not subtract the z values.) The area for $z = 1.62$ is 0.9474, and the area for $z = -1.35$ is 0.0885. The area between the two z values is $0.9474 - 0.0885 = 0.8589$, or 85.89%.

A Normal Distribution Curve as a Probability Distribution Curve

A normal distribution curve can be used as a probability distribution curve for normally distributed variables. Recall that a normal distribution is a *continuous distribution,* as opposed to a discrete probability distribution, as explained in Chapter 5. The fact that it is continuous means that there are no gaps in the curve. In other words, for every z value on the x axis, there is a corresponding height, or frequency, value.

The area under the standard normal distribution curve can also be thought of as a probability or as the proportion of the population with a given characteristic. That is, if it were possible to select a z value at random, the probability of choosing one, say, between 0 and 2.00 would be the same as the area under the curve between 0 and 2.00. In this case, the area is 0.4772. Therefore, the probability of randomly selecting a z value between 0 and 2.00 is 0.4772. The problems involving probability are solved in the same manner as the previous examples involving areas in this section. For example, if the problem is to find the probability of selecting a z value between 2.25 and 2.94, solve it by using the method shown in case 3 of the Procedure Table.

For probabilities, a special notation is used to denote the probability of a standard normal variable z. For example, if the problem is to find the probability of any z value between 0 and 2.32, this probability is written as $P(0 < z < 2.32)$.

Note: In a continuous distribution, the probability of any exact z value is 0 since the area would be represented by a vertical line above the value. But vertical lines in theory have no area. So $P(a \leq z \leq b) = P(a < z < b)$.

EXAMPLE 6–4

Find the probability for each. (Assume this is a standard normal distribution.)

　　a. $P(0 < z < 2.53)$　　　*b.* $P(z < 1.73)$　　　*c.* $P(z > 1.98)$

SOLUTION

 a. $P(0 < z < 2.53)$ is used to find the area under the standard normal distribution curve between $z = 0$ and $z = 2.53$. First, draw the curve and shade the desired area. This is shown in Figure 6–11. Second, find the area in Table E corresponding to $z = 2.53$. It is 0.9943. Third, find the area in Table E corresponding to $z = 0$. It is 0.5000. Finally, subtract the two areas: $0.9943 - 0.5000 = 0.4943$. Hence, the probability is 0.4943, or 49.43%.

FIGURE 6–11
Area Under the Standard
Normal Distribution Curve for
Part *a* of Example 6–4

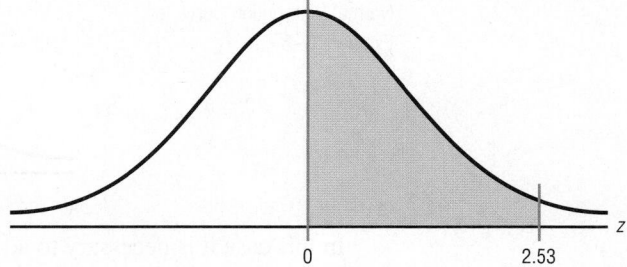

 b. $P(z < 1.73)$ is used to find the area under the standard normal distribution curve to the left of $z = 1.73$. First, draw the curve and shade the desired area. This is shown in Figure 6–12. Second, find the area in Table E corresponding to 1.73. It is 0.9582. Hence, the probability of obtaining a z value less than 1.73 is 0.9582, or 95.82%.

FIGURE 6–12
Area Under the Standard
Normal Distribution Curve
for Part *b* of Example 6–4

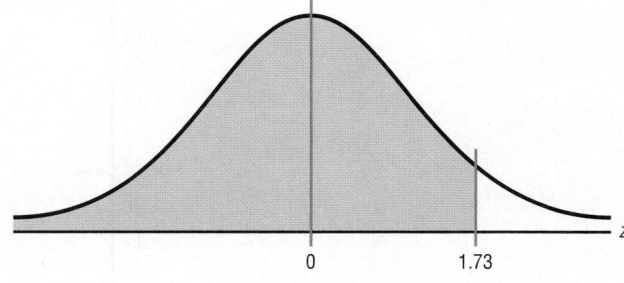

 c. $P(z > 1.98)$ is used to find the area under the standard normal distribution curve to the right of $z = 1.98$. First, draw the curve and shade the desired area.

See Figure 6–13. Second, find the area corresponding to $z = 1.98$ in Table E. It is 0.9761. Finally, subtract this area from 1.0000. It is $1.0000 - 0.9761 = 0.0239$. Hence, the probability of obtaining a z value greater than 1.98 is 0.0239, or 2.39%.

FIGURE 6–13

Area Under the Standard Normal Distribution Curve for Part c of Example 6–4

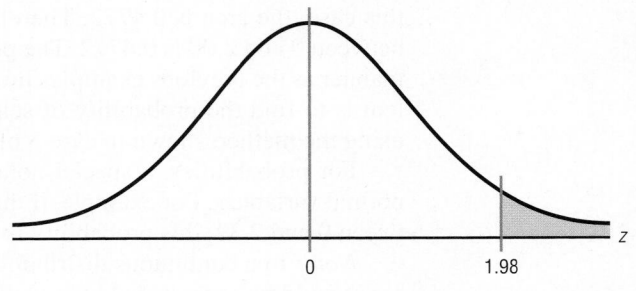

Sometimes, one must find a specific z value for a given area under the standard normal distribution curve. The procedure is to work backward, using Table E.

Since Table E is cumulative, it is necessary to locate the cumulative area up to a given z value. Example 6–5 shows this.

EXAMPLE 6–5

Find the z value such that the area under the standard normal distribution curve between 0 and the z value is 0.2123.

SOLUTION

Draw the figure. The area is shown in Figure 6–14.

FIGURE 6–14

Area Under the Standard Normal Distribution Curve for Example 6–5

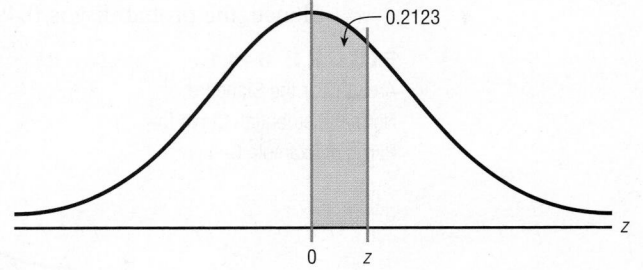

In this case it is necessary to add 0.5000 to the given area of 0.2123 to get the cumulative area of 0.7123. Look up the area in Table E. The value in the left column is 0.5, and the top value is 0.06. Add these two values to get $z = 0.56$. See Figure 6–15.

FIGURE 6–15

Finding the z Value from Table E for Example 6–5

FIGURE 6–16

The Relationship Between
Area and Probability

$$P = \tfrac{3}{12} = \tfrac{1}{4}$$

(a) Clock

$$\text{Area} = 3 \cdot \tfrac{1}{12} = \tfrac{3}{12} = \tfrac{1}{4}$$

(b) Rectangle

If the exact area cannot be found, use the closest value. For example, if you wanted to find the z value for an area 0.9241, the closest area is 0.9236, which gives a z value of 1.43. See Table E in Appendix C.

The rationale for using an area under a continuous curve to determine a probability can be understood by considering the example of a watch that is powered by a battery. When the battery goes dead, what is the probability that the minute hand will stop somewhere between the numbers 2 and 5 on the face of the watch? In this case, the values of the variable constitute a continuous variable since the hour hand can stop anywhere on the dial's face between 0 and 12 (one revolution of the minute hand). Hence, the sample space can be considered to be 12 units long, and the distance between the numbers 2 and 5 is $5 - 2$, or 3 units. Hence, the probability that the minute hand stops on a number between 2 and 5 is $\tfrac{3}{12} = \tfrac{1}{4}$. See Figure 6–16(a).

The problem could also be solved by using a graph of a continuous variable. Let us assume that since the watch can stop anytime at random, the values where the minute hand would land are spread evenly over the range of 0 through 12. The graph would then consist of a *continuous uniform distribution* with a range of 12 units. Now if we required the area under the curve to be 1 (like the area under the standard normal distribution), the height of the rectangle formed by the curve and the x axis would need to be $\tfrac{1}{12}$. The reason is that the area of a rectangle is equal to the base times the height. If the base is 12 units long, then the height has to be $\tfrac{1}{12}$ since $12 \cdot \tfrac{1}{12} = 1$.

The area of the rectangle with a base from 2 through 5 would be $3 \cdot \tfrac{1}{12}$, or $\tfrac{1}{4}$. See Figure 6–16(b). Notice that the area of the small rectangle is the same as the probability found previously. Hence, the area of this rectangle corresponds to the probability of this event. The same reasoning can be applied to the standard normal distribution curve shown in Example 6–5.

Finding the area under the standard normal distribution curve is the first step in solving a wide variety of practical applications in which the variables are normally distributed. Some of these applications will be presented in Section 6–2.

Applying the Concepts 6–1

Assessing Normality

Many times in statistics it is necessary to see if a set of data values is approximately normally distributed. There are special techniques that can be used. One technique is to draw a histogram for the data and see if it is approximately bell-shaped. (*Note:* It does not have to be exactly symmetric to be bell-shaped.)

The numbers of branches of the 50 top libraries are shown.

67	84	80	77	97	59	62	37	33	42
36	54	18	12	19	33	49	24	25	22
24	29	9	21	21	24	31	17	15	21
13	19	19	22	22	30	41	22	18	20
26	33	14	14	16	22	26	10	16	24

Source: The World Almanac and Book of Facts.

1. Construct a frequency distribution for the data.

2. Construct a histogram for the data.

3. Describe the shape of the histogram.

4. Based on your answer to question 3, do you feel that the distribution is approximately normal?

In addition to the histogram, distributions that are approximately normal have about 68% of the values fall within 1 standard deviation of the mean, about 95% of the data values fall within 2 standard deviations of the mean, and almost 100% of the data values fall within 3 standard deviations of the mean. (See Figure 6–5.)

5. Find the mean and standard deviation for the data.

6. What percent of the data values fall within 1 standard deviation of the mean?

7. What percent of the data values fall within 2 standard deviations of the mean?

8. What percent of the data values fall within 3 standard deviations of the mean?

9. How do your answers to questions 6, 7, and 8 compare to 68, 95, and 100%, respectively?

10. Does your answer help support the conclusion you reached in question 4? Explain.

(More techniques for assessing normality are explained in Section 6–2.)
See pages 367 and 368 for the answers.

Exercises 6–1

1. What are the characteristics of a normal distribution?

2. Why is the standard normal distribution important in statistical analysis?

3. What is the total area under the standard normal distribution curve?

4. What percentage of the area falls below the mean? Above the mean?

5. About what percentage of the area under the normal distribution curve falls within 1 standard deviation above and below the mean? 2 standard deviations? 3 standard deviations?

6. What are two other names for a normal distribution?

For Exercises 7 through 26, find the area under the standard normal distribution curve.

7. Between $z = 0$ and $z = 0.98$

8. Between $z = 0$ and $z = 1.77$

9. Between $z = 0$ and $z = -2.14$

10. Between $z = 0$ and $z = -0.32$

11. To the right of $z = 0.29$

12. To the right of $z = 2.01$

13. To the left of $z = -1.39$

14. To the left of $z = -0.75$

15. Between $z = 1.09$ and $z = 1.83$

16. Between $z = 1.23$ and $z = 1.90$

17. Between $z = -1.56$ and $z = -1.83$

18. Between $z = -0.96$ and $z = -0.36$

19. Between $z = -1.46$ and $z = -1.98$

20. Between $z = 0.24$ and $z = -1.12$

21. To the left of $z = 2.22$

22. To the left of $z = 1.31$

23. To the right of $z = -0.12$

24. To the right of $z = -1.92$

25. To the right of $z = 1.92$ and to the left of $z = -0.44$

26. To the left of $z = -2.15$ and to the right of $z = 1.62$

In Exercises 27 through 40, find the probabilities for each, using the standard normal distribution.

27. $P(0 < z < 0.92)$

28. $P(0 < z < 1.96)$

29. $P(-1.43 < z < 0)$

30. $P(-1.23 < z < 0)$

31. $P(z > 2.51)$

32. $P(z > 0.82)$

33. $P(z < -1.46)$

34. $P(z < -1.77)$

35. $P(-2.07 < z < 1.88)$

36. $P(-0.20 < z < 1.56)$

37. $P(1.51 < z < 2.17)$

38. $P(1.12 < z < 1.43)$

39. $P(z < 1.42)$

40. $P(z > -1.43)$

For Exercises 41 through 46, find the z value that corresponds to the given area.

41.

42.

43.

44.

45.

46.

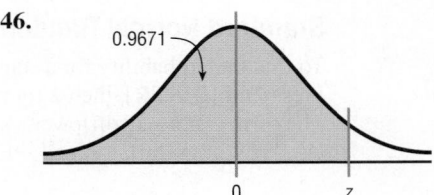

47. Find the z value to the left of the mean so that

    a. 98.87% of the area under the distribution curve lies to the right of it.

    b. 82.12% of the area under the distribution curve lies to the right of it.

    c. 60.64% of the area under the distribution curve lies to the right of it.

48. Find the z value to the right of the mean so that

    a. 54.78% of the area under the distribution curve lies to the left of it.

    b. 69.85% of the area under the distribution curve lies to the left of it.

    c. 88.10% of the area under the distribution curve lies to the left of it.

49. Find two z values, one positive and one negative, that are equidistant from the mean so that the areas in the two tails add to the following values.

a. 5%

b. 10%

c. 1%

50. Find two z values so that 48% of the middle area is bounded by them.

Extending the Concepts

51. Find $P(-1 < z < 1)$, $P(-2 < z < 2)$, and $P(-3 < z < 3)$. How do these values compare with the empirical rule?

52. In the standard normal distribution, find the values of z for the 75th, 80th, and 92nd percentiles.

For Exercises 53–56, z_0 is the statistical notation for an unknown z value. It serves that same function as x does in an algebraic equation.

53. Find z_0 such that $P(-1.2 < z < z_0) = 0.8671$.

54. Find z_0 such that $P(z_0 < z < 2.5) = 0.7672$.

55. Find z_0 such that the area between z_0 and $z = -0.5$ is 0.2345 (two answers).

56. Find z_0 such that $P(-z_0 < z < z_0) = 0.76$.

57. Find the equation for the standard normal distribution by substituting 0 for μ and 1 for σ in the equation

$$y = \frac{e^{-(X-\mu)^2/(2\sigma^2)}}{\sigma\sqrt{2\pi}} \quad \underline{\qquad}$$

58. Graph by hand the standard normal distribution by using the formula derived in Exercise 57. Let $\pi \approx 3.14$ and $e \approx 2.718$. Use X values of -2, -1.5, -1, -0.5, 0, 0.5, 1, 1.5, and 2. (Use a calculator to compute the y values.)

59. Find $P(z < 2.3$ or $z > -1.2)$.

60. Find $P(z > 2.3$ and $z < -1.2)$.

Technology | Step by Step

TI–84 Plus

Step by Step

Standard Normal Random Variables

To find the probability for a standard normal random variable:

Press **2nd [DISTR]**, then **2** for normalcdf(

The form is normalcdf(lower z score, upper z score).

Use E99 for ∞ (infinity) and $-$E99 for $-\infty$ (negative infinity). Press **2nd [EE]** to get E.

Example: Area to the right of $z = 1.11$

normalcdf(1.11,E99)

Example: Area to the left of $z = -1.93$

normalcdf($-$E99,$-$1.93)

Example: Area between $z = 2.00$ and $z = 2.47$
normalcdf(2.00,2.47)

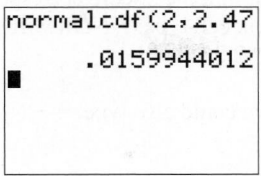

To find the percentile for a standard normal random variable:
Press **2nd [DISTR],** then **3** for the invNorm(
The form is invNorm(area to the left of z score)

Example: Find the z score such that the area under the standard normal curve to the left of it is 0.7123.
invNorm(.7123)

EXCEL
Step by Step

The Standard Normal Distribution
Finding Areas under the Standard Normal Distribution Curve
Example XL6–1

Find the area to the left of $z = 1.99$.
In a blank cell type: =NORMSDIST(1.99)
Answer: 0.976705

Example XL6–2

Find the area to the right of $z = -2.04$.
In a blank cell type: = 1-NORMSDIST(-2.04)
Answer: 0.979325

Example XL6–3

Find the area between $z = -2.04$ and $z = 1.99$.
In a blank cell type: =NORMSDIST(1.99) $-$ NORMSDIST(-2.04)
Answer: 0.956029

Finding a z Value Given an Area Under the Standard Normal Distribution Curve
Example XL6–4

Find a z score given the cumulative area (area to the left of z) is 0.0250.
In a blank cell type: =NORMSINV(.025)
Answer: -1.95996

Example XL6–5

Find a z score, given the area to the right of z is 0.4567.
We must find the z score corresponding to a cumulative area $1 - 0.4567$.
In a blank cell type: =NORMSINV($1 - .4567$)
Answer: 0.108751

Example XL6–6

Find a (positive) z score given the area between $-z$ and z is 0.98.
We must find the z score corresponding to a cumulative area $0.98 + 0.01$ or 0.99
In a blank cell type: =NORMSINV(.99)
Answer: 2.326348

Note: We could also type: $= -$NORMSINV(.01) to find the z score for Example XL6–6.

MINITAB
Step by Step

Normal Distributions with MINITAB

Finding the area above an interval for a normal distribution is synonymous with finding a probability. We never find the probability that X or Z is exactly equal to a value. We always find the probability that the value is some interval, some range of values. These MINITAB instructions will show you how to get the same results that you would by using Table E, Standard Normal Distribution. Five cases follow.

   Open MINITAB. It doesn't matter if something is in the worksheet or not.

Case 1: Find the Probability That *z* Is to the Left of a Given Value

Find the area to the left of $z = -1.96$. This is the same as saying $z < -1.96$, represented by the number line to the left of -1.96.

   1. Select **Graph>Probability Distribution Plot>View Probability,** then click [OK].

   a) The distribution should be Normal with the Mean set to **0.0** and the Standard deviation set to **1.0.**

   b) Choose the button for Shaded Area, then select the ratio button for X Value.

   c) Click the picture for Left Tail.

   d) Type in the Z value of -1.96 and click [OK].

$$P(Z < -1.96) = 0.02500.$$

You can copy and paste the graph into a document if you like. To copy, right-click on the gray area of the graph in MINITAB. Options will be given for copying the graph.

Case 1 $Z < -1.96$

Case 2 $Z > 2.33$

Case 2: Find the Probability That *z* Is to the Right of a Given Value

Use these instructions for positive or negative values of z.
Find the area **to the right of** $z = +2.33$. This is the same as $Z > 2.33$.

   2. Click the icon for **Edit Last Dialog** box or select **Graph>Probability Distribution Plot>View Probability** and click [OK].

   a) The distribution should be normal with the mean set to 0.0 and the standard deviation set to 1.0.

b) Choose the tab for Shaded Area, then select the ratio button for *X* Value.

c) Click the picture for Right Tail.

d) Type in the *Z* value of 2.33 and click [OK].

$$P(X > +2.33) = 0.009903.$$

Case 3: Find the Probability That *Z* Is between Two Values

Find the area if *z* is between −1.11 and +0.24.

3. Click the icon for **Edit Last Dialog** box or select **Graph>Probability Distribution Plot>View Probability** and click [OK].

   a) The distribution should be Normal with the Mean set to **0.0** and the Standard deviation set to **1.0.**

   b) Choose the tab for Shaded Area, then *X* Value.

   c) Click the picture for Middle.

   d) Type in the smaller value −1.11 for *X* value 1 and then the larger value 0.24 for the *X* value 2. Click [OK]. $P(-1.11 < Z < +0.24) = 0.4613$. Remember that smaller values are to the left on the number line.

Case 3

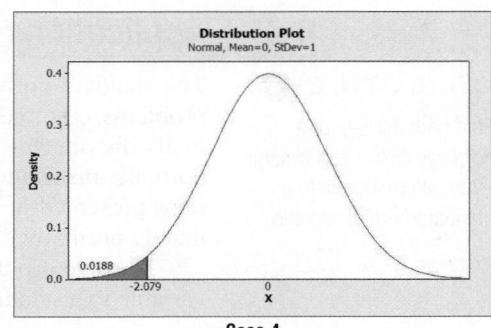

Case 4

Case 4: Find *z* if the Area Is Given

If the area to the left of some *z* value is 0.0188, find the *z* value.

4. Select **Graph>Probability Distribution Plot>View Probability** and click [OK].

   a) The distribution should be Normal with the Mean set to 0.0 and the Standard deviation set to 1.0.

   b) Choose the tab for Shaded Area and then the ratio button for Probability.

   c) Select Left Tail.

   d) Type in 0.0188 for probability and then click [OK]. The *z* value is −2.079.

$$P(Z < -2.079) = 0.0188.$$

Case 5: Find Two *z* Values, One Positive and One Negative (Same Absolute Value), so That the Area in the Middle is 0.95

5. Select **Graph>Probability Distribution Plot>View Probability** or click the **Edit Last Dialog** icon.

   a) The distribution should be Normal with the Mean set to **0.0** and the Standard deviation set to **1.0.**

   b) Choose the tab for Shaded Area, then select the ratio button for Probability.

c) Select Middle. You will need to know the area in each tail of the distribution. Subtract 0.95 from 1, then divide by 2. The area in each tail is 0.025.

d) Type in the first probability of **0.025** and the same for the second probability. Click [OK].

$$P(-1.960 < Z < +1.96) = 0.9500.$$

Case 5 Dialog box

Graph window

6–2   Applications of the Normal Distribution

OBJECTIVE ④

Find probabilities for a normally distributed variable by transforming it into a standard normal variable.

The standard normal distribution curve can be used to solve a wide variety of practical problems. The only requirement is that the variable be normally or approximately normally distributed. There are several mathematical tests to determine whether a variable is normally distributed. See the Critical Thinking Challenges on page 366. For all the problems presented in this chapter, you can assume that the variable is normally or approximately normally distributed.

To solve problems by using the standard normal distribution, transform the original variable to a standard normal distribution variable by using the formula

$$z = \frac{\text{value} - \text{mean}}{\text{standard deviation}} \qquad \text{or} \qquad z = \frac{X - \mu}{\sigma}$$

This is the same formula presented in Section 3–3. This formula transforms the values of the variable into standard units or z values. Once the variable is transformed, then the Procedure Table and Table E in Appendix A can be used to solve problems.

For example, suppose that the scores for a standardized test are normally distributed, have a mean of 100, and have a standard deviation of 15. When the scores are transformed to z values, the two distributions coincide, as shown in Figure 6–17. (Recall that the z distribution has a mean of 0 and a standard deviation of 1.)

FIGURE 6–17

Test Scores and Their Corresponding z Values

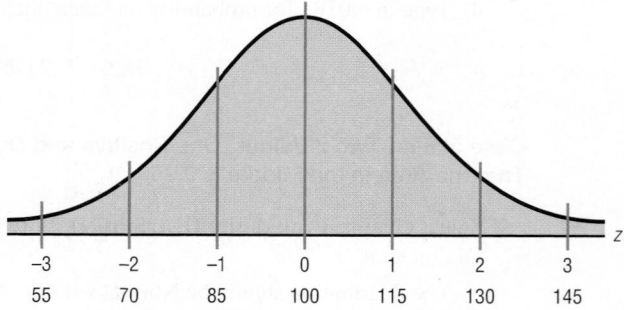

z							
−3	−2	−1	0	1	2	3
55	70	85	100	115	130	145

Note: The z values are rounded to two decimal places because Table E gives the z values to two decimal places.

Since we now have the ability to find the area under the standard curve, we can find the area under any normal curve by transforming the values of the variable to z values, and then we find the areas under the standard normal distribution, as shown in Section 6–1. This procedure is summarized next.

Procedure Table

Finding the Area Under Any Normal Curve

Step 1 Draw a normal curve and shade the desired area.

Step 2 Convert the values of X to z values, using the formula $z = \dfrac{X - \mu}{\sigma}$.

Step 3 Find the corresponding area, using a table, calculator, or software.

EXAMPLE 6–6 Liters of Blood

An adult has on average 5.2 liters of blood. Assume the variable is normally distributed and has a standard deviation of 0.3. Find the percentage of people who have less than 5.4 liters of blood in their system.

SOLUTION

Step 1 Draw a normal curve and shade the desired area. See Figure 6–18.

FIGURE 6–18
Area Under a
Normal Curve for
Example 6–6

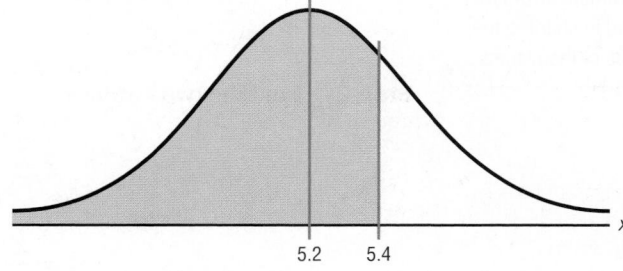

Step 2 Find the z value corresponding to 5.4.

$$z = \frac{X - \mu}{\sigma} = \frac{5.4 - 5.2}{0.3} = \frac{0.2}{0.3} = 0.67$$

Hence, 5.4 is 0.67 of a standard deviation above the mean, as shown in Figure 6–19.

FIGURE 6–19
Area and z Values for
Example 6–6

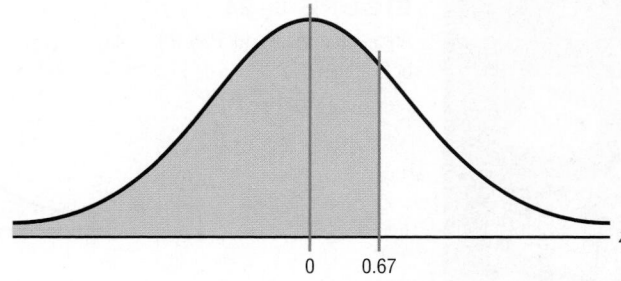

Step 3 Find the corresponding area in Table E. The area under the standard normal curve to the left of $z = 0.67$ is 0.7486.

Therefore, 0.7486, or 74.86%, of adults have less than 5.4 liters of blood in their system.

EXAMPLE 6–7   Monthly Newspaper Recycling

Each month, an American household generates an average of 28 pounds of newspaper for garbage or recycling. Assume the variable is approximately normally distributed and the standard deviation is 2 pounds. If a household is selected at random, find the probability of its generating

    a. Between 27 and 31 pounds per month

    b. More than 30.2 pounds per month

Source: Michael D. Shook and Robert L. Shook, *The Book of Odds.*

SOLUTION *a*

Step 1   Draw a normal curve and shade the desired area. See Figure 6–20.

> **Historical Note**
>
> Astronomers in the late 1700s and the 1800s used the principles underlying the normal distribution to correct measurement errors that occurred in charting the positions of the planets.

FIGURE 6–20
Area Under a Normal Curve for Part *a* of Example 6–7

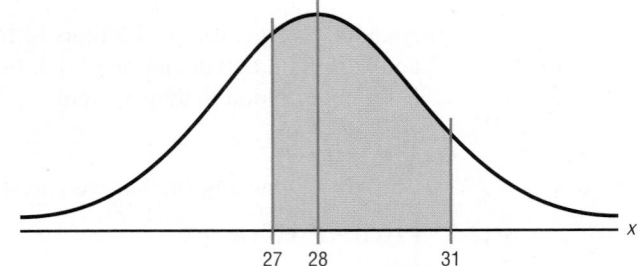

Step 2   Find the two *z* values.

$$z_1 = \frac{X - \mu}{\sigma} = \frac{27 - 28}{2} = -\frac{1}{2} = -0.5$$

$$z_2 = \frac{X - \mu}{\sigma} = \frac{31 - 28}{2} = \frac{3}{2} = 1.5$$

Step 3   Find the appropriate area, using Table E. The area to the left of z_2 is 0.9332, and the area to the left of z_1 is 0.3085. Hence, the area between z_1 and z_2 is 0.9332 − 0.3085 = 0.6247. See Figure 6–21.

FIGURE 6–21
Area and *z* Values for Part *a* of Example 6–7

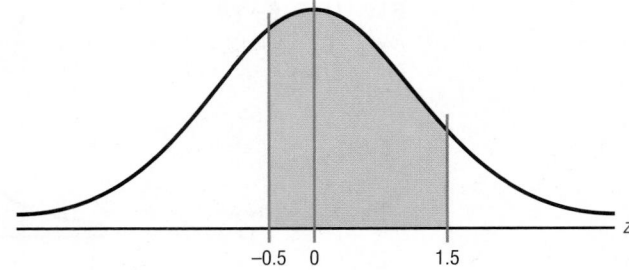

Hence, the probability that a randomly selected household generates between 27 and 31 pounds of newspapers per month is 62.47%.

SOLUTION *b*

Step 1   Draw a normal curve and shade the desired area, as shown in Figure 6–22.

FIGURE 6–22
Area Under a Normal
Curve for Part *b* of
Example 6–7

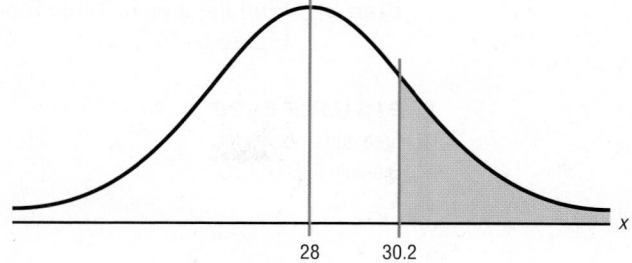

Step 2   Find the *z* value for 30.2.

$$z = \frac{X - \mu}{\sigma} = \frac{30.2 - 28}{2} = \frac{2.2}{2} = 1.1$$

Step 3   Find the appropriate area. The area to the left of $z = 1.1$ is 0.8643. Hence, the area to the right of $z = 1.1$ is $1.0000 - 0.8643 = 0.1357$. See Figure 6–23.

FIGURE 6–23
Area and *z* Values for
Part *b* of Example 6–7

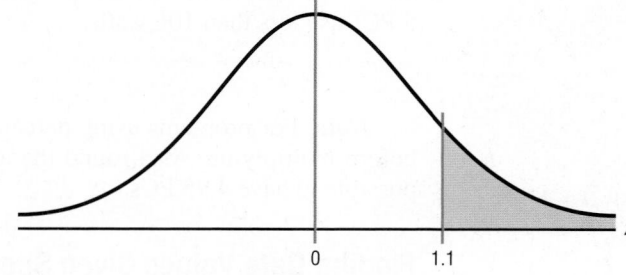

Hence, the probability that a randomly selected household will accumulate more than 30.2 pounds of newspapers is 0.1357, or 13.57%.

A normal distribution can also be used to answer questions of "How many?" This application is shown in Example 6–8.

EXAMPLE 6–8   Amount of Electricity Used by a PC

A desktop PC uses 120 watts of electricity per hour based on 4 hours of use per day. Assume the variable is approximately normally distributed and the standard deviation is 6. If 500 PCs are selected, approximately how many will use less than 106 watts of power?

SOLUTION

Step 1   Draw a normal curve and shade the desired area. See Figure 6–24.

FIGURE 6–24
Area Under a
Normal Curve for
Example 6–8

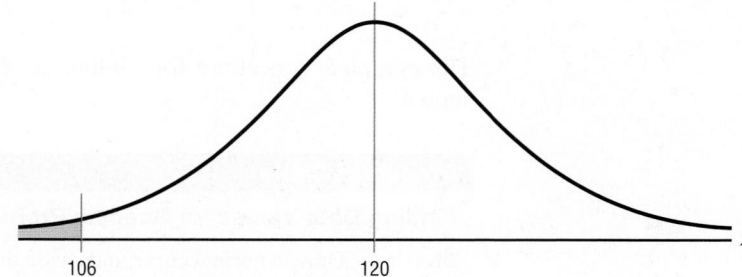

Step 2   Find the *z* value corresponding to 106.

$$z = \frac{X - \mu}{\sigma} = \frac{106 - 120}{6} = -2.33$$

Step 3   Find the area in Table E corresponding to $z = -2.33$. It is 0.0099. See Figure 6–25.

FIGURE 6–25
Area and z Values for
Example 6–8

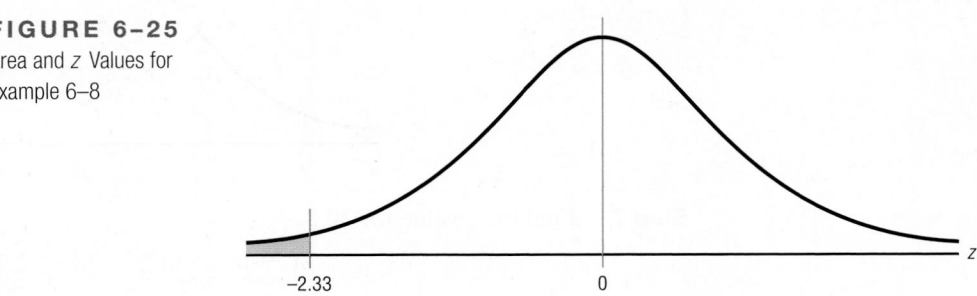

To find the number of PCs that use less than 106 watts per hour, multiply $500 \times 0.0099 = 4.95$. Since we are using PCs, round the answer to 5. Hence, approximately 5 PCs use less than 106 watts.

Note: For problems using percentages, be sure to write the percentage as a decimal before multiplying. Also round the answer to the nearest whole number, since it is not possible to have 4.95 PCs.

Finding Data Values Given Specific Probabilities

A normal distribution can also be used to find specific data values for given percentages. In this case, you are given a probability or percentage and need to find the corresponding data value X. You can use the formula $z = \frac{X - \mu}{\sigma}$. Substitute the values for z, μ, and σ; then solve for X. However, you can transform the formula and solve for X as shown.

$$z = \frac{X - \mu}{\sigma}$$

$z \cdot \sigma = X - \mu$ Multiply both sides by σ.

$z \cdot \sigma + \mu = X - \mu + \mu$ Add μ to both sides.

$X = z \cdot \sigma + \mu$ Exchange both sides of the equation.

Now you can use this new formula and find the value for X.

Formula for Finding the Value of a Normal Variable X

$$X = z \cdot \sigma + \mu$$

The complete procedure for finding an X value is summarized in the Procedure Table shown.

Procedure Table

Finding Data Values for Specific Probabilities

Step 1   Draw a normal curve and shade the desired area that represents the probability, proportion, or percentile.

Step 2   Find the z value from the table that corresponds to the desired area.

Step 3   Calculate the X value by using the formula $X = z\sigma + \mu$.

EXAMPLE 6–9   Police Academy Qualifications

OBJECTIVE **5**

Find specific data values for given percentages, using the standard normal distribution.

To qualify for a police academy, candidates must score in the top 10% on a general abilities test. Assume the test scores are normally distributed and the test has a mean of 200 and a standard deviation of 20. Find the lowest possible score to qualify.

SOLUTION

Step 1   Draw a normal distribution curve and shade the desired area that represents the probability.

Since the test scores are normally distributed, the test value X that cuts off the upper 10% of the area under a normal distribution curve is desired. This area is shown in Figure 6–26.

FIGURE 6–26
Area Under a Normal Curve
for Example 6–9

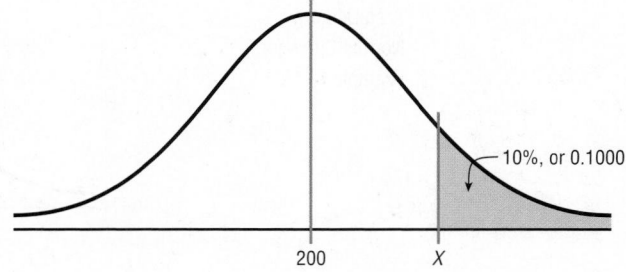

Work backward to solve this problem.

Subtract 0.1000 from 1.0000 to get the area under the normal distribution to the left of x: $1.0000 - 0.1000 = 0.9000$.

Step 2   Find the z value from Table E that corresponds to the desired area.

Find the z value that corresponds to an area of 0.9000 by looking up 0.9000 in the area portion of Table E. If the specific value cannot be found, use the closest value—in this case 0.8997, as shown in Figure 6–27. The corresponding z value is 1.28. (If the area falls exactly halfway between two z values, use the larger of the two z values. For example, the area 0.9500 falls halfway between 0.9495 and 0.9505. In this case use 1.65 rather than 1.64 for the z value.)

FIGURE 6–27
Finding the z Value from
Table E (Example 6–9)

Step 3   Find the X value.

$$X = z \cdot \sigma + \mu = 1.28(20) + 200 = 25.6 + 200$$
$$= 225.6 = 226 \text{ (rounded)}$$

A score of 226 should be used as a cutoff. Anybody scoring 226 or higher qualifies for the academy.

EXAMPLE 6–10   Systolic Blood Pressure

For a medical study, a researcher wishes to select people in the middle 60% of the population based on blood pressure. Assuming that blood pressure readings are normally distributed and the mean systolic blood pressure is 120 and the standard deviation is 8, find the upper and lower readings that would qualify people to participate in the study.

SOLUTION

Step 1   Draw a normal distribution curve and shade the desired area. The cutoff points are shown in Figure 6–28.

Two values are needed, one above the mean and one below the mean.

FIGURE 6–28
Area Under a
Normal Curve for
Example 6–10

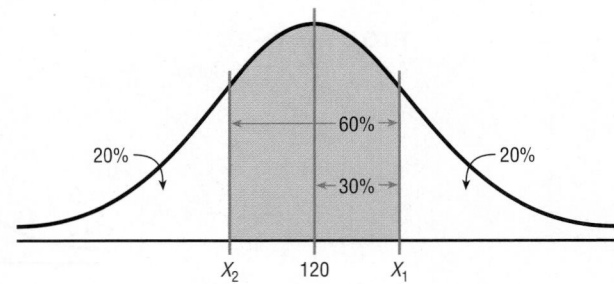

Step 2   Find the z values.

To get the area to the left of the positive z value, add $0.5000 + 0.3000 = 0.8000$ ($30\% = 0.3000$). The z value with area to the left closest to 0.8000 is 0.84.

Step 3   Calculate the X values.

Substituting in the formula $X = z\sigma + \mu$ gives

$$X_1 = z\sigma + \mu = (0.84)(8) + 120 = 126.72$$

The area to the left of the negative z value is 20%, or 0.2000. The area closest to 0.2000 is -0.84.

$$X_2 = (-0.84)(8) + 120 = 113.28$$

Therefore, the middle 60% will have blood pressure readings of $113.28 < X < 126.72$.

As shown in this section, a normal distribution is a useful tool in answering many questions about variables that are normally or approximately normally distributed.

Determining Normality

A normally shaped or bell-shaped distribution is only one of many shapes that a distribution can assume; however, it is very important since many statistical methods require that the distribution of values (shown in subsequent chapters) be normally or approximately normally shaped.

There are several ways statisticians check for normality. The easiest way is to draw a histogram for the data and check its shape. If the histogram is not approximately bell-shaped, then the data are not normally distributed.

Skewness can be checked by using the Pearson coefficient (PC) of skewness also called Pearson's index of skewness. The formula is

$$PC = \frac{3(\overline{X} - \text{median})}{s}$$

If the index is greater than or equal to $+1$ or less than or equal to -1, it can be concluded that the data are significantly skewed.

In addition, the data should be checked for outliers by using the method shown in Chapter 3. Even one or two outliers can have a big effect on normality.

Examples 6–11 and 6–12 show how to check for normality.

EXAMPLE 6–11   Technology Inventories

A survey of 18 high-tech firms showed the number of days' inventory they had on hand. Determine if the data are approximately normally distributed.

5	29	34	44	45	63	68	74	74
81	88	91	97	98	113	118	151	158

Source: *USA TODAY.*

SOLUTION

Step 1   Construct a frequency distribution and draw a histogram for the data, as shown in Figure 6–29.

Class	Frequency
5–29	2
30–54	3
55–79	4
80–104	5
105–129	2
130–154	1
155–179	1

FIGURE 6–29
Histogram for
Example 6–11

Since the histogram is approximately bell-shaped, we can say that the distribution is approximately normal.

Step 2   Check for skewness. For these data, $\overline{X} = 79.5$, median $= 77.5$, and $s = 40.5$. Using the Pearson coefficient of skewness gives

$$PC = \frac{3(79.5 - 77.5)}{40.5}$$

$$= 0.148$$

In this case, PC is not greater than $+1$ or less than -1, so it can be concluded that the distribution is not significantly skewed.

Step 3   Check for outliers. Recall that an outlier is a data value that lies more than 1.5(IQR) units below Q_1 or 1.5(IQR) units above Q_3. In this case, $Q_1 = 45$ and $Q_3 = 98$; hence, IQR $= Q_3 - Q_1 = 98 - 45 = 53$. An outlier would be a data value less than $45 - 1.5(53) = -34.5$ or a data value larger than $98 + 1.5(53) = 177.5$. In this case, there are no outliers.

Since the histogram is approximately bell-shaped, the data are not significantly skewed, and there are no outliers, it can be concluded that the distribution is approximately normally distributed.

EXAMPLE 6–12   Number of Baseball Games Played

The data shown consist of the number of games played each year in the career of Baseball Hall of Famer Bill Mazeroski. Determine if the data are approximately normally distributed.

81	148	152	135	151	152
159	142	34	162	130	162
163	143	67	112	70	

Source: *Greensburg Tribune Review.*

SOLUTION

Step 1   Construct a frequency distribution and draw a histogram for the data. See Figure 6–30.

FIGURE 6–30   Histogram for Example 6–12

Class	Frequency
34–58	1
59–83	3
84–108	0
109–133	2
134–158	7
159–183	4

The histogram shows that the frequency distribution is somewhat negatively skewed.

Step 2   Check for skewness; $\overline{X} = 127.24$, median $= 143$, and $s = 39.87$.

$$PC = \frac{3(\overline{X} - \text{median})}{s}$$

$$= \frac{3(127.24 - 143)}{39.87}$$

$$\approx -1.19$$

Since the PC is less than -1, it can be concluded that the distribution is significantly skewed to the left.

Step 3   Check for outliers. In this case, $Q_1 = 96.5$ and $Q_3 = 155.5$. IQR = $Q_3 - Q_1 = 155.5 - 96.5 = 59$. Any value less than $96.5 - 1.5(59) = 8$ or above $155.5 + 1.5(59) = 244$ is considered an outlier. There are no outliers.

In summary, the distribution is somewhat negatively skewed.

Another method that is used to check normality is to draw a *normal quantile plot.* *Quantiles,* sometimes called *fractiles,* are values that separate the data set into approximately equal groups. Recall that quartiles separate the data set into four approximately equal groups, and deciles separate the data set into 10 approximately equal groups. A normal quantile plot consists of a graph of points using the data values for the *x* coordinates and the *z* values of the quantiles corresponding to the *x* values for the *y* coordinates. (*Note:* The calculations of the *z* values are somewhat complicated, and technology is usually used to draw the graph. The Technology Step by Step section shows how to draw a normal quantile plot.) If the points of the quantile plot do not lie in an approximately straight line, then normality can be rejected.

There are several other methods used to check for normality. A method using normal probability graph paper is shown in the Critical Thinking Challenge section at the end of this chapter, and the chi-square goodness-of-fit test is shown in Chapter 11. Two other tests sometimes used to check normality are the Kolmogorov-Smirnov test and the Lilliefors test. An explanation of these tests can be found in advanced texts.

Applying the Concepts 6–2

Smart People

Assume you are thinking about starting a Mensa chapter in your hometown, which has a population of about 10,000 people. You need to know how many people would qualify for Mensa, which requires an IQ of at least 130. You realize that IQ is normally distributed with a mean of 100 and a standard deviation of 15. Complete the following.

1. Find the approximate number of people in your hometown who are eligible for Mensa.
2. Is it reasonable to continue your quest for a Mensa chapter in your hometown?
3. How could you proceed to find out how many of the eligible people would actually join the new chapter? Be specific about your methods of gathering data.
4. What would be the minimum IQ score needed if you wanted to start an Ultra-Mensa club that included only the top 1% of IQ scores?

See page 368 for the answers.

Exercises 6–2

1. **Admission Charge for Movies** The average early-bird special admission price for a movie is $5.81. If the distribution of movie admission charges is approximately normal with a standard deviation of $0.81, what is the probability that a randomly selected admission charge is less than $3.50?

2. **Teachers' Salaries** The average annual salary for all U.S. teachers is $47,750. Assume that the distribution is normal and the standard deviation is $5680. Find the probability that a randomly selected teacher earns
   a. Between $35,000 and $45,000 a year
   b. More than $40,000 a year

   c. If you were applying for a teaching position and were offered $31,000 a year, how would you feel (based on this information)?

   Source: *New York Times Almanac.*

3. **Population in U.S. Jails** The average daily jail population in the United States is 706,242. If the distribution is normal and the standard deviation is 52,145, find the probability that on a randomly selected day, the jail population is
   a. Greater than 750,000
   b. Between 600,000 and 700,000

   Source: *New York Times Almanac.*

4. **SAT Scores** The national average SAT score (for Verbal and Math) is 1028. If we assume a normal distribution with $\sigma = 92$, what is the 90th percentile score? What is the probability that a randomly selected score exceeds 1200?

   Source: *New York Times Almanac.*

5. **Chocolate Bar Calories** The average number of calories in a 1.5-ounce chocolate bar is 225. Suppose that the distribution of calories is approximately normal with $\sigma = 10$. Find the probability that a randomly selected chocolate bar will have

   a. Between 200 and 220 calories

   b. Less than 200 calories

   Source: *The Doctor's Pocket Calorie, Fat, and Carbohydrate Counter.*

6. **Monthly Mortgage Payments** The average monthly mortgage payment including principal and interest is $982 in the United States. If the standard deviation is approximately $180 and the mortgage payments are approximately normally distributed, find the probability that a randomly selected monthly payment is

   a. More than $1000

   b. More than $1475

   c. Between $800 and $1150

   Source: *World Almanac.*

7. **Professors' Salaries** The average salary for a Queens College full professor is $85,900. If the average salaries are normally distributed with a standard deviation of $11,000, find these probabilities.

   a. The professor makes more than $90,000.

   b. The professor makes more than $75,000.

   Source: AAUP, *Chronicle of Higher Education.*

8. **Doctoral Student Salaries** Full-time Ph.D. students receive an average of $12,837 per year. If the average salaries are normally distributed with a standard deviation of $1500, find these probabilities.

   a. The student makes more than $15,000.

   b. The student makes between $13,000 and $14,000.

   Source: U.S. Education Dept., *Chronicle of Higher Education.*

9. **Miles Driven Annually** The mean number of miles driven per vehicle annually in the United States is 12,494 miles. Choose a randomly selected vehicle, and assume the annual mileage is normally distributed with a standard deviation of 1290 miles. What is the probability that the vehicle was driven more than 15,000 miles? Less than 8000 miles? Would you buy a vehicle if you had been told that it had been driven less than 6000 miles in the past year?

   Source: *World Almanac.*

10. **Commute Time to Work** The average commute to work (one way) is 25 minutes according to the 2005 American Community Survey. If we assume that commuting times are normally distributed and that the standard deviation is

6.1 minutes, what is the probability that a randomly selected commuter spends more than 30 minutes commuting one way? Less than 18 minutes?

Source: www.census.gov

11. **Credit Card Debt** The average credit card debt for college seniors is $3262. If the debt is normally distributed with a standard deviation of $1100, find these probabilities.

    a. The senior owes at least $1000.

    b. The senior owes more than $4000.

    c. The senior owes between $3000 and $4000.

    Source: *USA TODAY.*

12. **Price of Gasoline** The average retail price of gasoline (all types) for the first half of 2009 was 236.5 cents. What would the standard deviation have to be in order for there to be a 15% probability that a gallon of gas costs less than $2.00?

    Source: *World Almanac.*

13. **Paper Use** Each American uses an average of 650 pounds (295 kg) of paper in a year. Suppose that the distribution is approximately normal with a population standard deviation of 153.5 pounds. Assume the variable is normally distributed. Find the probability that a randomly selected American uses

    a. More than 800 pounds of paper in a year

    b. Less than 400 pounds a year

    c. Between 500 and 700 pounds a year

    Source: *Time—Kids Almanac 2012.*

14. **Newborn Elephant Weights** Newborn elephant calves usually weigh between 200 and 250 pounds—until October 2006, that is. An Asian elephant at the Houston (Texas) Zoo gave birth to a male calf weighing in at a whopping 384 pounds! Mack (like the truck) is believed to be the heaviest elephant calf ever born at a facility accredited by the Association of Zoos and Aquariums. If, indeed, the mean weight for newborn elephant calves is 225 pounds with a standard deviation of 45 pounds, what is the probability of a newborn weighing at least 384 pounds? Assume that the weights of newborn elephants are normally distributed.

    Source: www.houstonzoo.org

15. **Jobs for Registered Nurses** The average annual number of jobs available for registered nurses is 103,900. If we assume a normal distribution with a standard deviation of 8040, find the probability that

    a. More than 100,000 jobs are available for RNs

    b. More than 80,000 but less than 95,000 jobs are available for RNs

    c. If the probability is 0.1977 that more than X amount of jobs are available, find the value of X.

    Source: *World Almanac 2012.*

16. **Salary of Full Professors** The average salary of a male full professor at a public four-year institution offering classes at the doctoral level is $99,685. For a

female full professor at the same kind of institution, the salary is $90,330. If the standard deviation for the salaries of both genders is approximately $5200 and the salaries are normally distributed, find the 80th percentile salary for male professors and for female professors.

Source: *World Almanac.*

17. **Professors' Salaries** The average annual professor's salary at a doctoral level at a private, independent institution is $159,964 for men and $147,702 for women. Consider the women's salaries. Assume that they are normally distributed with a standard deviation of $8900. What is the probability that a woman professor makes more than the men's average salary?

Source: *World Almanac 2012.*

18. **Itemized Charitable Contributions** The average charitable contribution itemized per income tax return in Pennsylvania is $792. Suppose that the distribution of contributions is normal with a standard deviation of $103. Find the limits for the middle 50% of contributions.

Source: IRS, *Statistics of Income Bulletin.*

19. **New Home Sizes** A contractor decided to build homes that will include the middle 80% of the market. If the average size of homes built is 1810 square feet, find the maximum and minimum sizes of the homes the contractor should build. Assume that the standard deviation is 92 square feet and the variable is normally distributed.

Source: Michael D. Shook and Robert L. Shook, *The Book of Odds.*

20. **New-Home Prices** If the average price of a new one-family home is $246,300 with a standard deviation of $15,000, find the minimum and maximum prices of the houses that a contractor will build to satisfy the middle 80% of the market. Assume that the variable is normally distributed.

Source: *New York Times Almanac.*

21. **Cost of Personal Computers** The average price of a personal computer (PC) is $949. If the computer prices are approximately normally distributed and $\sigma = \$100$, what is the probability that a randomly selected PC costs more than $1200? The least expensive 10% of personal computers cost less than what amount?

Source: *New York Times Almanac.*

22. **Reading Improvement Program** To help students improve their reading, a school district decides to implement a reading program. It is to be administered to the bottom 5% of the students in the district, based on the scores on a reading achievement exam. If the average score for the students in the district is 122.6, find the cutoff score that will make a student eligible for the program. The standard deviation is 18. Assume the variable is normally distributed.

23. **Used Car Prices** An automobile dealer finds that the average price of a previously owned vehicle is $8256. He decides to sell cars that will appeal to the middle 60% of the market in terms of price. Find the maximum and minimum prices of the cars the dealer will sell. The standard deviation is $1150, and the variable is normally distributed.

24. **Ages of Amtrak Passenger Cars** The average age of Amtrak passenger train cars is 19.4 years. If the distribution of ages is normal and 20% of the cars are older than 22.8 years, find the standard deviation.

Source: *New York Times Almanac.*

25. **Lengths of Hospital Stays** The average length of a hospital stay for all diagnoses is 4.8 days. If we assume that the lengths of hospital stays are normally distributed with a variance of 2.1, then 10% of hospital stays are longer than how many days? Thirty percent of stays are less than how many days?

Source: www.cdc.gov

26. **High School Competency Test** A mandatory competency test for high school sophomores has a normal distribution with a mean of 400 and a standard deviation of 100.

    a. The top 3% of students receive $500. What is the minimum score you would need to receive this award?

    b. The bottom 1.5% of students must go to summer school. What is the minimum score you would need to stay out of this group?

27. **Product Marketing** An advertising company plans to market a product to low-income families. A study states that for a particular area, the average income per family is $24,596 and the standard deviation is $6256. If the company plans to target the bottom 18% of the families based on income, find the cutoff income. Assume the variable is normally distributed.

28. **Bottled Drinking Water** Americans drank an average of 23.2 gallons of bottled water per capita in 2008. If the standard deviation is 2.7 gallons and the variable is normally distributed, find the probability that a randomly selected American drank more than 25 gallons of bottled water. What is the probability that the selected person drank between 22 and 30 gallons?

Source: www.census.gov

29. **Wristwatch Lifetimes** The mean lifetime of a wristwatch is 25 months, with a standard deviation of 5 months. If the distribution is normal, for how many months should a guarantee be made if the manufacturer does not want to exchange more than 10% of the watches? Assume the variable is normally distributed.

30. **Police Academy Acceptance Exams** To qualify for a police academy, applicants are given a test of physical fitness. The scores are normally distributed with a mean of 64 and a standard deviation of 9. If only the top 20% of the applicants are selected, find the cutoff score.

31. In the distributions shown, state the mean and standard deviation for each. *Hint:* See Figures 6–4 and 6–6. Also the vertical lines are 1 standard deviation apart.

a.

b.

c.

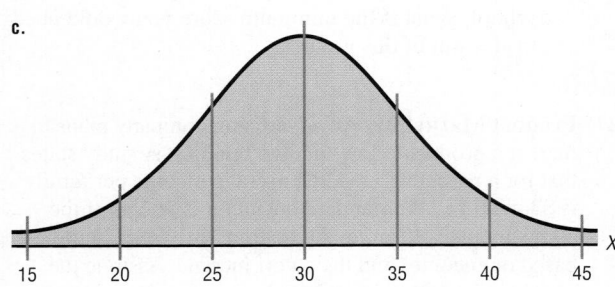

32. SAT Scores Suppose that the mathematics SAT scores for high school seniors for a specific year have a mean of 456 and a standard deviation of 100 and are approximately normally distributed. If a subgroup of these high school seniors, those who are in the National Honor Society, is selected, would you expect the distribution of scores to have the same mean and standard deviation? Explain your answer.

33. Temperatures for Dallas The mean temperature (of daily maximum temperatures) in July for Dallas–Ft. Worth, Texas, is 85 degrees. Assuming a normal distribution, what would the standard deviation have to be if 10% of days have a high of at least 100 degrees?

34. If a distribution of raw scores were plotted and then the scores were transformed to z scores, would the shape of the distribution change? Explain your answer.

35. Social Security Payments Consider the distribution of monthly Social Security (OASDI) payments. Assume a normal distribution with a standard deviation of $120. If

one-fourth of the payments are above $1255.94, what is the mean monthly payment?

Source: *World Almanac 2012.*

36. In a normal distribution, find μ when σ is 6 and 3.75% of the area lies to the left of 85.

37. Internet Users U.S. internet users spend an average of 18.3 hours a week online. If 95% of users spend between 13.1 and 23.5 hours a week, what is the probability that a randomly selected user is online less than 15 hours a week?

Source: *World Almanac 2012.*

38. Exam Scores An instructor gives a 100-point examination in which the grades are normally distributed. The mean is 60 and the standard deviation is 10. If there are 5% A's and 5% F's, 15% B's and 15% D's, and 60% C's, find the scores that divide the distribution into those categories.

39. Drive-in Movies The data shown represent the number of outdoor drive-in movies in the United States for a 14-year period. Check for normality.

2084	1497	1014	910	899	870	837	859
848	826	815	750	637	737		

Source: National Association of Theater Owners.

40. Cigarette Taxes The data shown represent the cigarette tax (in cents) for 50 selected states. Check for normality.

200	160	156	200	30	300	224	346	170	55
160	170	270	60	57	80	37	153	200	60
100	178	302	84	251	125	44	435	79	166
68	37	153	252	300	141	57	42	134	136
200	98	45	118	200	87	103	250	17	62

Source: http://www.tobaccofreekids.org

41. Box Office Revenues The data shown represent the box office total revenue (in millions of dollars) for a randomly selected sample of the top-grossing films in 2009. Check for normality.

37	32	155	277
146	80	66	113
71	29	166	36
28	72	32	32
30	32	52	84
37	402	42	109

Source: http://boxofficemojo.com

42. Number of Runs Made The data shown represent the number of runs made each year during Bill Mazeroski's career. Check for normality.

30	59	69	50	58	71	55	43	66	52	56	62
36	13	29	17	3							

Source: *Greensburg Tribune Review.*

43. Use your calculator to generate 20 random integers from 1–100, and check the set of data for normality. Would you expect these data to be normal? Explain.

≣ Technology

TI-84 Plus
Step by Step

Step by Step

Normal Random Variables

To find the probability for a normal random variable:
Press **2nd [DISTR]**, then **2** for normalcdf(
The form is normalcdf(lower x value, upper x value, μ, σ)
Use E99 for ∞ (infinity) and $-$E99 for $-\infty$ (negative infinity). Press **2nd [EE]** to get E.

Example: Find the probability that x is between 27 and 31 when $\mu = 28$ and $\sigma = 2$.
(Example 6–7a from the text).
normalcdf(27,31,28,2)

To find the percentile for a normal random variable:
Press **2nd [DISTR]**, then **3** for invNorm(
The form is invNorm(area to the left of x value, μ, σ)

Example: Find the 90th percentile when $\mu = 200$ and $\sigma = 20$ (Example 6–9 from text).
invNorm(.9,200,20)

To construct a normal quantile plot:

1. Enter the data values into L_1.

2. Press **2nd [STAT PLOT]** to get the STAT PLOT menu.

3. Press **1** for Plot 1.

4. Turn on the plot by pressing **ENTER** while the cursor is flashing over ON.

5. Move the cursor to the normal quantile plot (6th graph).

6. Make sure L_1 is entered for the Data List and X is highlighted for the Data Axis.

7. Press **WINDOW** for the Window menu. Adjust Xmin and Xmax according to the data values. Adjust Ymin and Ymax as well; Ymin $= -3$ and Ymax $= 3$ usually work fine.

8. Press **GRAPH.**

Example: A data set is given below. Check for normality by constructing a normal quantile plot.

5	29	34	44	45	63	68	74	74
81	88	91	97	98	113	118	151	158

  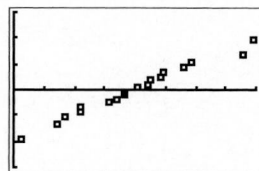

Since the points in the normal quantile plot lie close to a straight line, the distribution is approximately normal.

EXCEL
Step by Step

Normal Quantile Plot

Excel can be used to construct a normal quantile plot in order to examine if a set of data is approximately normally distributed.

1. Enter the data from the MINITAB Example 6–1 (see next page) into column A of a new worksheet. The data should be sorted in ascending order. If the data are not already sorted in ascending order, highlight the data to be sorted and select the Sort & Filter icon from the toolbar. Then select Sort Smallest to Largest.

2. After all the data are entered and sorted in column A, select cell B1. Type: =NORMSINV(1/(2*18)). Since the sample size is 18, each score represents $\frac{1}{18}$, or approximately 5.6%, of the sample. Each data value is assumed to subdivide the data into equal intervals. Each data value corresponds to the midpoint of a particular subinterval. Thus, this procedure will standardize the data by assuming each data value represents the midpoint of a subinterval of width $\frac{1}{18}$.

3. Repeat the procedure from step 2 for each data value in column A. However, for each subsequent value in column A, enter the next odd multiple of $\frac{1}{36}$ in the argument for the NORMSINV function. For example, in cell B2, type: =NORMSINV(3/(2*18)). In cell B3, type: =NORMSINV(5/(2*18)), and so on until all the data values have corresponding z scores.

4. Highlight the data from columns A and B, and select Insert, then Scatter chart. Select the Scatter with only markers (the first Scatter chart).

5. To insert a title to the chart: Left-click on any region of the chart. Select Chart Tools and Layout from the toolbar. Then select Chart Title.

6. To insert a label for the variable on the horizontal axis: Left-click on any region of the chart. Select Chart Tools and Layout from the toolbar. Then select Axis Titles>Primary Horizontal Axis Title.

The points on the chart appear to lie close to a straight line. Thus, we deduce that the data are approximately normally distributed.

MINITAB
Step by Step

Determining Normality

There are several ways in which statisticians test a data set for normality. Four are shown here.

Construct a Histogram

Inspect the histogram for shape.

Data for Example 6–1

5	29	34	44	45
63	68	74	74	81
88	91	97	98	113
118	151	158		

1. Enter the data in the first column of a new worksheet. Name the column Inventory.

2. Use Stat>Basic Statistics>Graphical Summary to create the histogram. Is it symmetric? Is there a single peak? The instructions in Section 2–2 can be used to change the X scale to match the histogram.

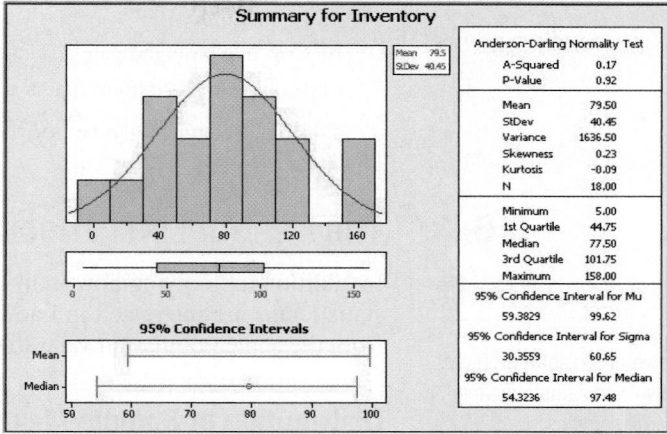

Check for Outliers

Inspect the boxplot for outliers. There are no outliers in this graph. Furthermore, the box is in the middle of the range, and the median is in the middle of the box. Most likely this is not a skewed distribution either.

Calculate the Pearson Coefficient of Skewness

The measure of skewness in the graphical summary is not the same as the Pearson coefficient. Use the calculator and the formula.

$$PC = \frac{3(\overline{X} - \text{median})}{s}$$

3. Select **Calc>Calculator**, then type **PC** in the text box for Store result in:.

4. Enter the expression: **3*(MEAN(C1)MEDIAN(C1))/(STDEV(C1))**. Make sure you get all the parentheses in the right place!

5. Click [OK]. The result, 0.148318, will be stored in the first row of C2 named PC. Since it is smaller than +1, the distribution is not skewed.

Construct a Normal Probability Plot

6. Select **Graph>Probability Plot**, then Single and click [OK].

7. Double-click C1 Inventory to select the data to be graphed.

8. Click [Distribution] and make sure that Normal is selected. Click [OK].

9. Click [Labels] and enter the title for the graph: **Quantile Plot for Inventory.** You may also put **Your Name** in the subtitle.

10. Click [OK] twice. Inspect the graph to see if the graph of the points is linear.

These data are nearly normal.

What do you look for in the plot?

a) An "S curve" indicates a distribution that is too thick in the tails, a uniform distribution, for example.

b) Concave plots indicate a skewed distribution.

c) If one end has a point that is extremely high or low, there may be outliers.

This data set appears to be nearly normal by every one of the four criteria!

6–3   The Central Limit Theorem

OBJECTIVE

Use the central limit theorem to solve problems involving sample means for large samples.

In addition to knowing how individual data values vary about the mean for a population, statisticians are interested in knowing how the means of samples of the same size taken from the same population vary about the population mean.

Distribution of Sample Means

Suppose a researcher selects a sample of 30 adult males and finds the mean of the measure of the triglyceride levels for the sample subjects to be 187 milligrams/deciliter. Then suppose a second sample is selected, and the mean of that sample is found to be 192 milligrams/deciliter. Continue the process for 100 samples. What happens then is that the mean becomes a random variable, and the sample means 187, 192, 184, . . . , 196 constitute a *sampling distribution of sample means.*

> A **sampling distribution of sample means** is a distribution using the means computed from all possible random samples of a specific size taken from a population.

If the samples are randomly selected with replacement, the sample means, for the most part, will be somewhat different from the population mean μ. These differences are caused by sampling error.

> **Sampling error** is the difference between the sample measure and the corresponding population measure due to the fact that the sample is not a perfect representation of the population.

When all possible samples of a specific size are selected with replacement from a population, the distribution of the sample means for a variable has two important properties, which are explained next.

> **Properties of the Distribution of Sample Means**
>
> 1. The mean of the sample means will be the same as the population mean.
> 2. The standard deviation of the sample means will be smaller than the standard deviation of the population, and it will be equal to the population standard deviation divided by the square root of the sample size.

The following example illustrates these two properties. Suppose a professor gave an 8-point quiz to a small class of four students. The results of the quiz were 2, 6, 4, and 8. For the sake of discussion, assume that the four students constitute the population. The mean of the population is

$$\mu = \frac{2 + 6 + 4 + 8}{4} = 5$$

FIGURE 6–31
Distribution of Quiz Scores

The standard deviation of the population is

$$\sigma = \sqrt{\frac{(2-5)^2 + (6-5)^2 + (4-5)^2 + (8-5)^2}{4}} \approx 2.236$$

The graph of the original distribution is shown in Figure 6–31. This is called a *uniform distribution.*

Now, if all samples of size 2 are taken with replacement and the mean of each sample is found, the distribution is as shown.

Sample	Mean	Sample	Mean
2, 2	2	6, 2	4
2, 4	3	6, 4	5
2, 6	4	6, 6	6
2, 8	5	6, 8	7
4, 2	3	8, 2	5
4, 4	4	8, 4	6
4, 6	5	8, 6	7
4, 8	6	8, 8	8

A frequency distribution of sample means is as follows.

$\overline{X}$	f
2	1
3	2
4	3
5	4
6	3
7	2
8	1

For the data from the example just discussed, Figure 6–32 shows the graph of the sample means. The histogram appears to be approximately normal.

The mean of the sample means, denoted by $\mu_{\overline{X}}$, is

$$\mu_{\overline{X}} = \frac{2 + 3 + \cdots + 8}{16} = \frac{80}{16} = 5$$

FIGURE 6–32
Distribution of Sample Means

which is the same as the population mean. Hence,

$$\mu_{\overline{X}} = \mu$$

The standard deviation of sample means, denoted by $\sigma_{\overline{X}}$, is

$$\sigma_{\overline{X}} = \sqrt{\frac{(2 - 5)^2 + (3 - 5)^2 + \cdots + (8 - 5)^2}{16}} \approx 1.581$$

which is the same as the population standard deviation, divided by $\sqrt{2}$:

$$\sigma_{\overline{X}} = \frac{2.236}{\sqrt{2}} \approx 1.581$$

Unusual Stats

Each year a person living in the United States consumes on average 1400 pounds of food.

(*Note:* Rounding rules were not used here in order to show that the answers coincide.)

In summary, if all possible samples of size n are taken with replacement from the same population, the mean of the sample means, denoted by $\mu_{\overline{X}}$, equals the population mean μ; and the standard deviation of the sample means, denoted by $\sigma_{\overline{X}}$, equals $\sigma / \sqrt{n}$. The standard deviation of the sample means is called the **standard error of the mean.** Hence,

$$\sigma_{\overline{X}} = \frac{\sigma}{\sqrt{n}}$$

A third property of the sampling distribution of sample means pertains to the shape of the distribution and is explained by the **central limit theorem.**

The Central Limit Theorem

As the sample size n increases without limit, the shape of the distribution of the sample means taken with replacement from a population with mean μ and standard deviation σ will approach a normal distribution. As previously shown, this distribution will have a mean μ and a standard deviation $\sigma / \sqrt{n}$.

If the sample size is sufficiently large, the central limit theorem can be used to answer questions about sample means in the same manner that a normal distribution can be used to answer questions about individual values. The only difference is that a new formula must be used for the z values. It is

$$z = \frac{\overline{X} - \mu}{\sigma / \sqrt{n}}$$

Notice that $\overline{X}$ is the sample mean, and the denominator must be adjusted since means are being used instead of individual data values. The denominator is the standard deviation of the sample means.

If a large number of samples of a given size are selected from a normally distributed population, or if a large number of samples of a given size that is greater than or equal to 30 are selected from a population that is not normally distributed, and the sample means are computed, then the distribution of sample means will look like the one shown in Figure 6–33. Their percentages indicate the areas of the regions.

It's important to remember two things when you use the central limit theorem:

1. When the original variable is normally distributed, the distribution of the sample means will be normally distributed, for any sample size n.

2. When the distribution of the original variable is not normal, a sample size of 30 or more is needed to use a normal distribution to approximate the distribution of the sample means. The larger the sample, the better the approximation will be.

Examples 6–13 through 6–15 show how the standard normal distribution can be used to answer questions about sample means.

FIGURE 6–33

Distribution of Sample Means for a Large Number of Samples

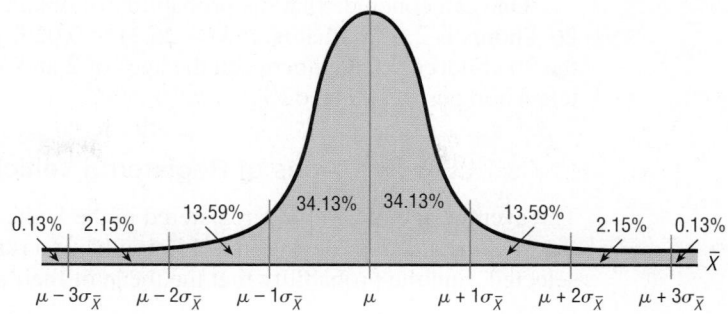

EXAMPLE 6–13   **Hours That Children Watch Television**

A. C. Neilsen reported that children between the ages of 2 and 5 watch an average of 25 hours of television per week. Assume the variable is normally distributed and the standard deviation is 3 hours. If 20 children between the ages of 2 and 5 are randomly selected, find the probability that the mean of the number of hours they watch television will be greater than 26.3 hours.

Source: Michael D. Shook and Robert L. Shook, *The Book of Odds.*

SOLUTION

Since the variable is approximately normally distributed, the distribution of sample means will be approximately normal, with a mean of 25. The standard deviation of the sample means is

$$\sigma_{\overline{X}} = \frac{\sigma}{\sqrt{n}} = \frac{3}{\sqrt{20}} = 0.671$$

Step 1   Draw a normal curve and shade the desired area.

The distribution of the means is shown in Figure 6–34, with the appropriate area shaded.

FIGURE 6–34

Distribution of the Means for Example 6–13

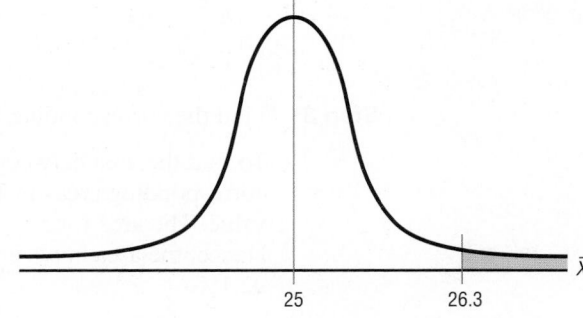

Step 2   Convert the $\overline{X}$ value to a z value.

The z value is

$$z = \frac{\overline{X} - \mu}{\sigma/\sqrt{n}} = \frac{26.3 - 25}{3/\sqrt{20}} = \frac{1.3}{0.671} = 1.94$$

Step 3   Find the corresponding area for the z value.

The area to the right of 1.94 is $1.000 - 0.9738 = 0.0262$, or 2.62%.

One can conclude that the probability of obtaining a sample mean larger than 26.3 hours is 2.62% [that is, $P(\overline{X} > 26.3) = 0.0262$]. Specifically, the probability that the 20 children selected between the ages of 2 and 5 watch more than 26.3 hours of television per week is 2.62%.

EXAMPLE 6–14   Ages of Registered Vehicles

The average age of a vehicle registered in the United States is 8 years, or 96 months. Assume the standard deviation is 16 months. If a random sample of 36 vehicles is selected, find the probability that the mean of their age is between 90 and 100 months.

Source: *Harper's Index.*

SOLUTION

Step 1   Draw a normal curve and shade the desired area.

Since the sample is 30 or larger, the normality assumption is not necessary. The desired area is shown in Figure 6–35.

FIGURE 6–35

Area Under a
Normal Curve for
Example 6–14

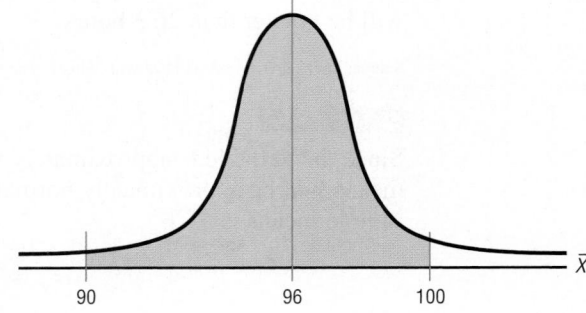

Step 2   Convert the $\overline{X}$ values to z values.

The two z values are

$$z_1 = \frac{90 - 96}{16/\sqrt{36}} = -2.25$$

$$z_2 = \frac{100 - 96}{16/\sqrt{36}} = 1.50$$

Step 3   Find the corresponding area for the z values.

To find the area between the two z values of -2.25 and 1.50, look up the corresponding areas in Table E and subtract the smaller value from the larger value. The area for $z = -2.25$ is 0.0122, and the area for $z = 1.50$ is 0.9332. Hence, the area between the two values is $0.9332 - 0.0122 = 0.9210$, or 92.1%.

Hence, the probability of obtaining a sample mean between 90 and 100 months is 92.1%; that is, $P(90 < \overline{X} < 100) = 0.9210$. Specifically, the probability that the 36 vehicles selected have a mean age between 90 and 100 months is 92.1%.

Students sometimes have difficulty deciding whether to use

$$z = \frac{\overline{X} - \mu}{\sigma/\sqrt{n}} \qquad \text{or} \qquad z = \frac{X - \mu}{\sigma}$$

The formula

$$z = \frac{\overline{X} - \mu}{\sigma/\sqrt{n}}$$

should be used to gain information about a sample mean, as shown in this section. The formula

$$z = \frac{X - \mu}{\sigma}$$

is used to gain information about an individual data value obtained from the population. Notice that the first formula contains $\overline{X}$, the symbol for the sample mean, while the second formula contains X, the symbol for an individual data value. Example 6–15 illustrates the uses of the two formulas.

EXAMPLE 6–15   Working Weekends

The average time spent by construction workers who work on weekends is 7.93 hours (over 2 days). Assume the distribution is approximately normal and has a standard deviation of 0.8 hour.

    a. Find the probability that an individual who works at that trade works fewer than 8 hours on the weekend.

    b. If a sample of 40 construction workers is randomly selected, find the probability that the mean of the sample will be less than 8 hours.

Source: Bureau of Labor Statistics.

SOLUTION *a*

Step 1   Draw a normal distribution and shade the desired area.

        Since the question concerns an individual person, the formula $z = (X - \mu)/\sigma$ is used. The distribution is shown in Figure 6–36.

FIGURE 6–36
Area Under a Normal
Curve for Part *a* of
Example 6–15

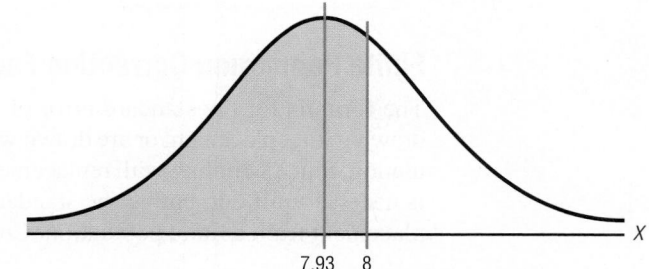

7.93   8
Distribution of individual data values for the population

Step 2   Find the z value.

$$Z = \frac{X - \mu}{\sigma} = \frac{8 - 7.93}{0.8} \approx 0.09$$

Step 3   Find the area to the left of $z = 0.09$.

        It is 0.5359.

Hence, the probability of selecting a construction worker who works less than 8 hours on a weekend is 0.5359, or 53.59%.

Step 1   Draw a normal curve and shade the desired area.

Since the question concerns the mean of a sample with a size of 40, the central limit theorem formula $z = (\overline{X} - \mu)/(\sigma/\sqrt{n})$ is used. The area is shown in Figure 6–37.

FIGURE 6–37
Area Under a Normal
Curve for Part *b* of
Example 6–15

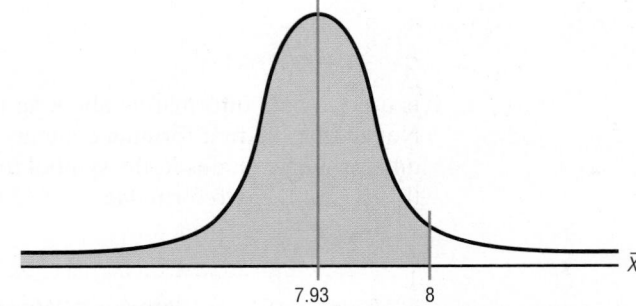

7.93   8 $\overline{X}$
Distribution of means for all samples of size 40 taken from the population

Step 2   Find the z value for a mean of 8 hours and a sample size of 40.

$$z = \frac{\overline{X} - \mu}{\sigma/\sqrt{n}} = \frac{8 - 7.93}{0.8/\sqrt{40}} \approx 0.55$$

Step 3   Find the area corresponding to $z = 0.55$. The area is 0.7088.

Hence, the probability of getting a sample mean of less than 8 hours when the sample size is 40 is 0.7088, or 70.88%.

Comparing the two probabilities, you can see the probability of selecting an individual construction worker who works less than 8 hours on a weekend is 53.59%. The probability of selecting a random sample of 40 construction workers with a mean of less than 8 hours per week is 70.88%. This difference of 17.29% is due to the fact that the distribution of sample means is much less variable than the distribution of individual data values. The reason is that as the sample size increases, the standard deviation of the means decreases.

Finite Population Correction Factor (Optional)

The formula for the standard error of the mean $\sigma/\sqrt{n}$ is accurate when the samples are drawn with replacement or are drawn without replacement from a very large or infinite population. Since sampling with replacement is for the most part unrealistic, a *correction factor* is necessary for computing the standard error of the mean for samples drawn without replacement from a finite population. Compute the correction factor by using the expression

$$\sqrt{\frac{N - n}{N - 1}}$$

where N is the population size and n is the sample size.

This correction factor is necessary if relatively large samples (usually greater than 5% of the population) are taken from a small population, because the sample mean will then more accurately estimate the population mean and there will be less error in the estimation. Therefore, the standard error of the mean must be multiplied by the correction factor to adjust for large samples taken from a small population. That is,

$$\sigma_{\overline{X}} = \frac{\sigma}{\sqrt{n}} \cdot \sqrt{\frac{N - n}{N - 1}}$$

Interesting Fact

The bubonic plague killed more than 25 million people in Europe between 1347 and 1351.

Finally, the formula for the z value becomes

$$z = \frac{\overline{X} - \mu}{\dfrac{\sigma}{\sqrt{n}} \cdot \sqrt{\dfrac{N - n}{N - 1}}}$$

When the population is large and the sample is small, the correction factor is generally not used, since it will be very close to 1.00.

The formulas and their uses are summarized in Table 6–1.

TABLE 6–1	Summary of Formulas and Their Uses
Formula	**Use**
1. $z = \dfrac{X - \mu}{\sigma}$	Used to gain information about an individual data value when the variable is normally distributed
2. $z = \dfrac{\overline{X} - \mu}{\sigma/\sqrt{n}}$	Used to gain information when applying the central limit theorem about a sample mean when the variable is normally distributed or when the sample size is 30 or more

Applying the Concepts 6–3

Central Limit Theorem

Twenty students from a statistics class each collected a random sample of times on how long it took students to get to class from their homes. All the sample sizes were 30. The resulting means are listed.

Student	Mean	Std. Dev.	Student	Mean	Std. Dev.
1	22	3.7	11	27	1.4
2	31	4.6	12	24	2.2
3	18	2.4	13	14	3.1
4	27	1.9	14	29	2.4
5	20	3.0	15	37	2.8
6	17	2.8	16	23	2.7
7	26	1.9	17	26	1.8
8	34	4.2	18	21	2.0
9	23	2.6	19	30	2.2
10	29	2.1	20	29	2.8

1. The students noticed that everyone had different answers. If you randomly sample over and over from any population, with the same sample size, will the results ever be the same?

2. The students wondered whose results were right. How can they find out what the population mean and standard deviation are?

3. Input the means into the computer and check if the distribution is normal.

4. Check the mean and standard deviation of the means. How do these values compare to the students' individual scores?

5. Is the distribution of the means a sampling distribution?

6. Check the sampling error for students 3, 7, and 14.

7. Compare the standard deviation of the sample of the 20 means. Is that equal to the standard deviation from student 3 divided by the square of the sample size? How about for student 7, or 14?

See page 368 for the answers.

☰ Exercises 6–3

1. If samples of a specific size are selected from a population and the means are computed, what is this distribution of means called?

2. Why do most of the sample means differ somewhat from the population mean? What is this difference called?

3. What is the mean of the sample means?

4. What is the standard deviation of the sample means called? What is the formula for this standard deviation?

5. What does the central limit theorem say about the shape of the distribution of sample means?

6. What formula is used to gain information about an individual data value when the variable is normally distributed?

For Exercises 7 through 25, assume that the sample is taken from a large population and the correction factor can be ignored.

7. **Unemployment Benefits** The average weekly unemployment benefit in Montana is $272. Suppose that the benefits are normally distributed with a standard deviation of $43. A random sample of 15 benefits is chosen in Montana. What is the probability that the mean for this sample is greater than the U.S. average, which is $299? Is the normal distribution appropriate here since the sample size is only 15? Explain.

   Source: *World Almanac.*

8. **Glass Garbage Generation** A survey found that the American family generates an average of 17.2 pounds of glass garbage each year. Assume the standard deviation of the distribution is 2.5 pounds. Find the probability that the mean of a sample of 55 families will be between 17 and 18 pounds.

   Source: Michael D. Shook and Robert L. Shook, *The Book of Odds.*

9. **College Costs** The mean undergraduate cost for tuition, fees, room, and board for four-year institutions was $26,489 for a recent academic year. Suppose that $\sigma = \$3204$ and that 36 four-year institutions are randomly selected. Find the probability that the sample mean cost for these 36 schools is

   a. Less than $25,000

   b. Greater than $26,000

   c. Between $24,000 and $26,000

   Source: www.nces.ed.gov

10. **Teachers' Salaries in Connecticut** The average teacher's salary in Connecticut (ranked first among states) is $57,337. Suppose that the distribution of salaries is normal with a standard deviation of $7500.

    a. What is the probability that a randomly selected teacher makes less than $52,000 per year?

    b. If we sample 100 teachers' salaries, what is the probability that the sample mean is less than $56,000?

    Source: *New York Times Almanac.*

11. **Serum Cholesterol Levels** The mean serum cholesterol level of a large population of overweight children is 220 milligrams per deciliter (mg/dl), and the standard deviation is 16.3 mg/dl. If a random sample of 35 overweight children is selected, find the probability that the mean will be between 220 and 222 mg/dl. Assume the serum cholesterol level variable is normally distributed.

12. **Teachers' Salaries in North Dakota** The average teacher's salary in North Dakota is $37,764. Assume a normal distribution with $\sigma = \$5100$.

    a. What is the probability that a randomly selected teacher's salary is greater than $45,000?

    b. For a sample of 75 teachers, what is the probability that the sample mean is greater than $38,000?

    Source: *New York Times Almanac.*

13. **Movie Ticket Prices** In a recent year the average movie ticket cost $7.89. In a random sample of 50 movie tickets from various areas, what is the probability that the mean cost exceeds $8.00, given that the population standard deviation is $1.39?

    Source: *World Almanac.*

14. **SAT Scores** The national average SAT score (for Verbal and Math) is 1028. Suppose that nothing is known about the shape of the distribution and that the standard deviation is 100. If a random sample of 200 scores were selected and the sample mean were calculated to be 1050, would you be surprised? Explain.

    Source: *New York Times Almanac.*

15. **Cost of Overseas Trip** The average overseas trip cost is $2708 per visitor. If we assume a normal distribution with a standard deviation of $405, what is the probability that the cost for a randomly selected trip is more than $3000? If we select a random sample of 30 overseas trips and find the mean of the sample, what is the probability that the mean is greater than $3000?

    Source: *World Almanac.*

16. **Cell Phone Lifetimes** A recent study of the lifetimes of cell phones found the average is 24.3 months. The standard deviation is 2.6 months. If a company provides its 33 employees with a cell phone, find the probability that the mean lifetime of these phones will be less than 23.8 months. Assume cell phone life is a normally distributed variable.

17. **Water Use** The *Old Farmer's Almanac* reports that the average person uses 123 gallons of water daily. If the standard deviation is 21 gallons, find the probability that the mean of a randomly selected sample of 15 people will be between 120 and 126 gallons. Assume the variable is normally distributed.

18. Medicare Hospital Insurance The average yearly Medicare Hospital Insurance benefit per person was $4064 in a recent year. If the benefits are normally distributed with a standard deviation of $460, find the probability that the mean benefit for a random sample of 20 patients is

a. Less than $3800

b. More than $4100

Source: *New York Times Almanac.*

19. Amount of Laundry Washed Each Year Procter & Gamble reported that an American family of four washes an average of 1 ton (2000 pounds) of clothes each year. If the standard deviation of the distribution is 187.5 pounds, find the probability that the mean of a randomly selected sample of 50 families of four will be between 1980 and 1990 pounds.

Source: *The Harper's Index Book.*

20. Per Capita Income of Delaware Residents In a recent year, Delaware had the highest per capita annual income with $51,803. If $\sigma = \$4850$, what is the probability that a random sample of 34 state residents had a mean income greater than $50,000? Less than $48,000?

Source: *New York Times Almanac.*

21. Annual Precipitation The average annual precipitation for a large Midwest city is 30.85 inches with a standard deviation of 3.6 inches. Assume the variable is normally distributed.

a. Find the probability that a randomly selected month will have less than 30 inches.

b. Find the probability that the mean of a random selection of 32 months will have a mean less than 30 inches.

c. Does it seem reasonable that one month could have a rainfall amount less than 30 inches?

d. Does it seem reasonable that the mean of a sample of 32 months could be less than 30 inches?

22. Systolic Blood Pressure Assume that the mean systolic blood pressure of normal adults is 120 millimeters of

mercury (mm Hg) and the standard deviation is 5.6. Assume the variable is normally distributed.

a. If an individual is selected, find the probability that the individual's pressure will be between 120 and 121.8 mm Hg.

b. If a sample of 30 adults is randomly selected, find the probability that the sample mean will be between 120 and 121.8 mm Hg.

c. Why is the answer to part *a* so much smaller than the answer to part *b*?

23. Cholesterol Content The average cholesterol content of a certain brand of eggs is 215 milligrams, and the standard deviation is 15 milligrams. Assume the variable is normally distributed.

a. If a single egg is selected, find the probability that the cholesterol content will be greater than 220 milligrams.

b. If a sample of 25 eggs is selected, find the probability that the mean of the sample will be larger than 220 milligrams.

Source: *Living Fit.*

24. Ages of Proofreaders At a large publishing company, the mean age of proofreaders is 36.2 years, and the standard deviation is 3.7 years. Assume the variable is normally distributed.

a. If a proofreader from the company is randomly selected, find the probability that his or her age will be between 36 and 37.5 years.

b. If a random sample of 15 proofreaders is selected, find the probability that the mean age of the proofreaders in the sample will be between 36 and 37.5 years.

25. TIMSS Test On the Trends in International Mathematics and Science Study (TIMSS) test in a recent year, the United States scored an average of 508 (well below South Korea, 597; Singapore, 593; Hong Kong, 572; and Japan, 570). Suppose that we take a random sample of *n* United States scores and that the population standard deviation is 72. If the probability that the mean of the sample exceeds 520 is 0.0985, what was the sample size?

Source: *World Almanac.*

Extending the Concepts

For Exercises 26 and 27, check to see whether the correction factor should be used. If so, be sure to include it in the calculations.

26. Life Expectancies In a study of the life expectancy of 500 people in a certain geographic region, the mean age at death was 72.0 years, and the standard deviation was 5.3 years. If a sample of 50 people from this region is selected, find the probability that the mean life expectancy will be less than 70 years.

27. Home Values A study of 800 homeowners in a certain area showed that the average value of the homes was $82,000, and the standard deviation was $5000. If 50 homes are for sale, find the probability that the mean of the values of these homes is greater than $83,500.

28. Breaking Strength of Steel Cable The average breaking strength of a certain brand of steel cable is 2000 pounds, with a standard deviation of 100 pounds.

A sample of 20 cables is selected and tested. Find the sample mean that will cut off the upper 95% of all samples of size 20 taken from the population. Assume the variable is normally distributed.

29. The standard deviation of a variable is 15. If a sample of 100 individuals is selected, compute the standard error

of the mean. What size sample is necessary to double the standard error of the mean?

30. In Exercise 29, what size sample is needed to cut the standard error of the mean in half?

6–4   The Normal Approximation to the Binomial Distribution

OBJECTIVE ❼

Use the normal approximation to compute probabilities for a binomial variable.

A normal distribution is often used to solve problems that involve the binomial distribution since when n is large (say, 100), the calculations are too difficult to do by hand using the binomial distribution. Recall from Chapter 5 that a binomial distribution has the following characteristics:

1. There must be a fixed number of trials.
2. The outcome of each trial must be independent.
3. Each experiment can have only two outcomes or outcomes that can be reduced to two outcomes.
4. The probability of a success must remain the same for each trial.

Also, recall that a binomial distribution is determined by n (the number of trials) and p (the probability of a success). When p is approximately 0.5, and as n increases, the shape of the binomial distribution becomes similar to that of a normal distribution. The larger n is and the closer p is to 0.5, the more similar the shape of the binomial distribution is to that of a normal distribution.

But when p is close to 0 or 1 and n is relatively small, a normal approximation is inaccurate. As a rule of thumb, statisticians generally agree that a normal approximation should be used only when $n \cdot p$ and $n \cdot q$ are both greater than or equal to 5. (*Note:* $q = 1 - p$.) For example, if p is 0.3 and n is 10, then $np = (10)(0.3) = 3$, and a normal distribution should not be used as an approximation. On the other hand, if $p = 0.5$ and $n = 10$, then $np = (10)(0.5) = 5$ and $nq = (10)(0.5) = 5$, and a normal distribution can be used as an approximation. See Figure 6–38.

In addition to the previous condition of $np \geq 5$ and $nq \geq 5$, a correction for continuity may be used in the normal approximation.

> A **correction for continuity** is a correction employed when a continuous distribution is used to approximate a discrete distribution.

The continuity correction means that for any specific value of X, say 8, the boundaries of X in the binomial distribution (in this case, 7.5 to 8.5) must be used. (See Section 1–2.) Hence, when you employ a normal distribution to approximate the binomial, you must use the boundaries of any specific value X as they are shown in the binomial distribution. For example, for $P(X = 8)$, the correction is $P(7.5 < X < 8.5)$. For $P(X \leq 7)$, the correction is $P(X < 7.5)$. For $P(X \geq 3)$, the correction is $P(X > 2.5)$.

Students sometimes have difficulty deciding whether to add 0.5 or subtract 0.5 from the data value for the correction factor. Table 6–2 summarizes the different situations.

The formulas for the mean and standard deviation for the binomial distribution are necessary for calculations. They are

$$\mu = n \cdot p \qquad \text{and} \qquad \sigma = \sqrt{n \cdot p \cdot q}$$

Interesting Fact

Of the 12 months, August ranks first in the number of births for Americans.

FIGURE 6–38

Comparison of the Binomial
Distribution and a Normal
Distribution

Binomial probabilities for $n = 10$, $p = 0.3$
$[n \cdot p = 10(0.3) = 3; n \cdot q = 10(0.7) = 7]$

X	P(X)
0	0.028
1	0.121
2	0.233
3	0.267
4	0.200
5	0.103
6	0.037
7	0.009
8	0.001
9	0.000
10	0.000

Binomial probabilities for $n = 10$, $p = 0.5$
$[n \cdot p = 10(0.5) = 5; n \cdot q = 10(0.5) = 5]$

X	P(X)
0	0.001
1	0.010
2	0.044
3	0.117
4	0.205
5	0.246
6	0.205
7	0.117
8	0.044
9	0.010
10	0.001

TABLE 6–2   Summary of the Normal Approximation to the Binomial Distribution

Binomial	Normal
When finding:	Use:
1. $P(X = a)$	$P(a - 0.5 < X < a + 0.5)$
2. $P(X \geq a)$	$P(X > a - 0.5)$
3. $P(X > a)$	$P(X > a + 0.5)$
4. $P(X \leq a)$	$P(X < a + 0.5)$
5. $P(X < a)$	$P(X < a - 0.5)$

For all cases, $\mu = n \cdot p$, $\sigma = \sqrt{n \cdot p \cdot q}$, $n \cdot p \geq 5$, and $n \cdot q \geq 5$.

The steps for using the normal distribution to approximate the binomial distribution are shown in this Procedure Table.

Procedure Table

Procedure for the Normal Approximation to the Binomial Distribution

Step 1   Check to see whether the normal approximation can be used.

Step 2   Find the mean μ and the standard deviation σ.

Step 3   Write the problem in probability notation, using X.

Step 4   Rewrite the problem by using the continuity correction factor, and show the corresponding area under the normal distribution.

Step 5   Find the corresponding z values.

Step 6   Find the solution.

EXAMPLE 6–16   Reading While Driving

A magazine reported that 6% of American drivers read the newspaper while driving. If 300 drivers are selected at random, find the probability that exactly 25 say they read the newspaper while driving.

Source: USA Snapshot, *USA TODAY.*

SOLUTION

Here $p = 0.06$, $q = 0.94$, and $n = 300$.

Step 1   Check to see whether a normal approximation can be used.

$$np = (300)(0.06) = 18 \qquad nq = (300)(0.94) = 282$$

Since $np \geq 5$ and $nq \geq 5$, the normal distribution can be used.

Step 2   Find the mean and standard deviation.

$$\mu = np = (300)(0.06) = 18$$
$$\sigma = \sqrt{npq} = \sqrt{(300)(0.06)(0.94)} = \sqrt{16.92} \approx 4.11$$

Step 3   Write the problem in probability notation: $P(X = 25)$.

Step 4   Rewrite the problem by using the continuity correction factor. See approximation number 1 in Table 6–2: $P(25 - 0.5 < X < 25 + 0.5) = P(24.5 < X < 25.5)$. Show the corresponding area under the normal distribution curve. See Figure 6–39.

FIGURE 6–39
Area Under a Normal Curve and X Values for Example 6–16

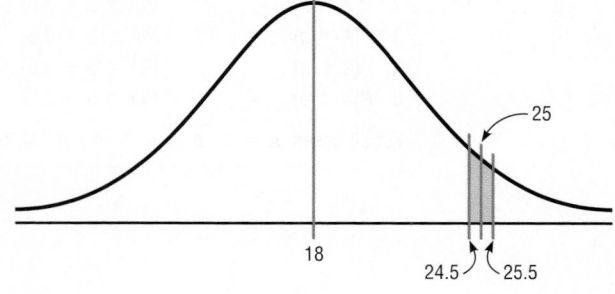

Step 5   Find the corresponding z values. Since 25 represents any value between 24.5 and 25.5, find both z values.

$$z_1 = \frac{25.5 - 18}{4.11} \approx 1.82 \qquad z_2 = \frac{24.5 - 18}{4.11} \approx 1.58$$

Step 6   The area to the left of $z = 1.82$ is 0.9656, and the area to the left of $z = 1.58$ is 0.9429. The area between the two z values is $0.9656 - 0.9429 = 0.0227$, or 2.27%. Hence, the probability that exactly 25 people read the newspaper while driving is 2.27%.

EXAMPLE 6–17   Ragweed Allergies

Ten percent of Americans are allergic to ragweed. If a random sample of 200 people is selected, find the probability that 10 or more will be allergic to ragweed.

SOLUTION

Step 1   Check to see whether the normal approximate can be used.

Here $p = 0.10$, $q = 0.90$, and $n = 200$. Since $np = (200)(0.10) = 20$ and $nq = (200)(0.90) = 180$, the normal approximation can be used.

Step 2   Find the mean and the standard deviation.

$$\mu = np = (200)(0.10) = 20$$
$$\sigma = \sqrt{npq} = \sqrt{(200)(0.10)(0.90)} = \sqrt{18} \approx 4.24$$

Step 3   Write the problem in probability notation, using X.

$$P(X \geq 10)$$

Step 4   Rewrite the problem, using the continuity correction factor, and show the corresponding area under the normal distribution.

See approximation number 2 in Table 6–2: $P(X > 10 - 0.5) = P(X > 9.5)$. The desired area is shown in Figure 6–40.

FIGURE 6–40
Area Under a Normal
Curve and X Value for
Example 6–17

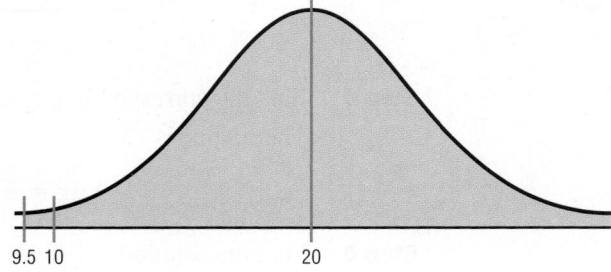

9.5 10   20

Step 5   Find the corresponding z values.

Since the problem is to find the probability of 10 or more positive responses, a normal distribution graph is as shown in Figure 6–40.
The z value is

$$z = \frac{9.5 - 20}{4.24} = -2.48$$

Step 6   Find the solution.

The area to the left of $z = -2.48$ is 0.0066. Hence, the area to the right of $z = -2.48$ is $1.0000 - 0.0066 = 0.9934$, or 99.34%.

It can be concluded, then, that in a random sample of 200 Americans the probability of 10 or more Americans being allergic to ragweed is 99.34%.

EXAMPLE 6–18   Batting Averages

If a baseball player's batting average is 0.320 (32%), find the probability that the player will get at most 26 hits in 100 times at bat.

SOLUTION

Step 1   Check to see whether the normal approximate can be used.

Here, $p = 0.32$, $q = 0.68$, and $n = 100$.

Since $np = (100)(0.320) = 32$ and $nq = (100)(0.680) = 68$, the normal distribution can be used to approximate the binomial distribution.

Step 2   Find the mean and the standard deviation.

$$\mu = np = (100)(0.320) = 32$$

$$\sigma = \sqrt{npq} = \sqrt{(100)(0.32)(0.68)} \approx \sqrt{21.76} \approx 4.66$$

Step 3   Write the problem in probability notation, using X.

$$P(X \le 26)$$

Step 4   Rewrite the problem using the continuity correction factor and show the corresponding area under the normal distribution.

See approximation number 4 in Table 6–2: $P(X < 26 + 0.5) = P(X < 26.5)$. The desired area is shown in Figure 6–41.

FIGURE 6–41

Area Under a
Normal Curve for
Example 6–18

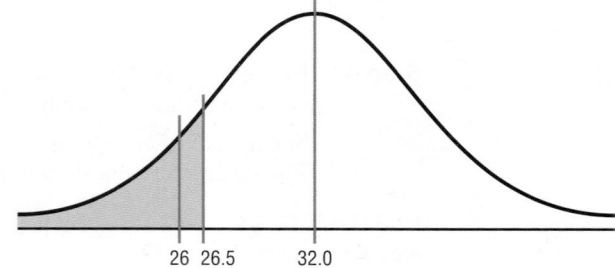

26 26.5   32.0

Step 5   Find the corresponding z values.

The z value is

$$z = \frac{26.5 - 32}{4.66} \approx -1.18$$

Step 6   Find the solution.

The area to the left of $z = -1.18$ is 0.1190. Hence, the probability is 0.1190, or 11.9%.

It can be concluded that the probability of a player getting at most 26 hits in 100 times at bat is 11.9%.

The closeness of the normal approximation is shown in Example 6–19.

EXAMPLE 6–19

When $n = 10$ and $p = 0.5$, use the binomial distribution table (Table B in Appendix A) to find the probability that $X = 6$. Then use the normal approximation to find the probability that $X = 6$.

SOLUTION

From Table B, for $n = 10$, $p = 0.5$, and $X = 6$, the probability is 0.205.

For a normal approximation,

$$\mu = np = (10)(0.5) = 5$$

$$\sigma = \sqrt{npq} = \sqrt{(10)(0.5)(0.5)} \approx 1.58$$

Now, $X = 6$ is represented by the boundaries 5.5 and 6.5. So the z values are

$$z_1 = \frac{6.5 - 5}{1.58} \approx 0.95 \qquad z_2 = \frac{5.5 - 5}{1.58} \approx 0.32$$

The corresponding area for 0.95 is 0.8289, and the corresponding area for 0.32 is 0.6255. The area between the two z values of 0.95 and 0.32 is $0.8289 - 0.6255 = 0.2034$, which is very close to the binomial table value of 0.205. See Figure 6–42.

FIGURE 6–42
Area Under a Normal Curve
for Example 6–19

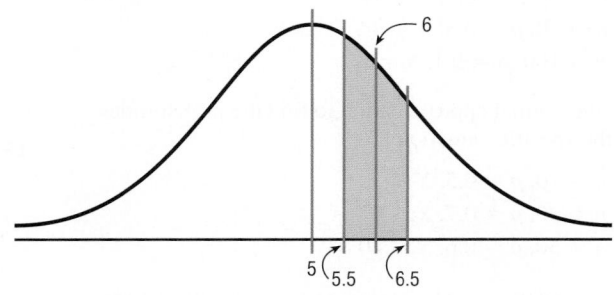

The normal approximation also can be used to approximate other distributions, such as the Poisson distribution (see Table C in Appendix C).

Applying the Concepts 6–4

How Safe Are You?

Assume one of your favorite activities is mountain climbing. When you go mountain climbing, you have several safety devices to keep you from falling. You notice that attached to one of your safety hooks is a reliability rating of 97%. You estimate that throughout the next year you will be using this device about 100 times. Answer the following questions.

1. Does a reliability rating of 97% mean that there is a 97% chance that the device will not fail any of the 100 times?

2. What is the probability of at least one failure?

3. What is the complement of this event?

4. Can this be considered a binomial experiment?

5. Can you use the binomial probability formula? Why or why not?

6. Find the probability of at least two failures.

7. Can you use a normal distribution to accurately approximate the binomial distribution? Explain why or why not.

8. Is correction for continuity needed?

9. How much safer would it be to use a second safety hook independent of the first?

See page 368 for the answers.

Exercises 6–4

1. Explain why a normal distribution can be used as an approximation to a binomial distribution.

2. What conditions must be met to use the normal distribution to approximate the binomial distribution?

3. Why is a correction for continuity necessary?

4. When is the normal distribution not a good approximation for the binomial distribution?

5. Use the normal approximation to the binomial to find the probabilities for the specific value(s) of X.

   a. $n = 30, p = 0.5, X = 18$
   b. $n = 50, p = 0.8, X = 44$
   c. $n = 100, p = 0.1, X = 12$

6. Use the normal approximation to find the probabilities for the specific value(s) of X.

   a. $n = 10, p = 0.5, X \geq 7$
   b. $n = 20, p = 0.7, X \leq 12$
   c. $n = 50, p = 0.6, X \leq 40$

7. Check each binomial distribution to see whether it can be approximated by a normal distribution (i.e., are $np \geq 5$ and $nq \geq 5$?).

   a. $n = 20, p = 0.5$
   b. $n = 10, p = 0.6$
   c. $n = 40, p = 0.9$

8. Check each binomial distribution to see whether it can be approximated by a normal distribution (i.e., are $np \geq 5$ and $nq \geq 5$?).

   a. $n = 50, p = 0.2$
   b. $n = 30, p = 0.8$
   c. $n = 20, p = 0.85$

9. **People Who Smoke** In a recent year, 23.3% of Americans smoked cigarettes. What is the probability that in a random sample of 200 Americans, more than 50 smoke?

   Source: *World Almanac.*

10. **School Enrollment** Of all 3- to 5-year-old children, 56% are enrolled in school. If a sample of 500 such children is randomly selected, find the probability that at least 250 will be enrolled in school.

    Source: *Statistical Abstract of the United States.*

11. **Home Ownership** In a recent year, the rate of U.S. home ownership was 65.9%. Choose a random sample of 120 households across the United States. What is the probability that 65 to 85 (inclusive) of them live in homes that they own?

    Source: *World Almanac.*

12. **Mail Order** A mail order company has an 8% success rate. If it mails advertisements to 600 people, find the probability of getting fewer than 40 sales.

13. **Health Insurance** In a recent year, 56% of employers offered a consumer-directed health plan (CDHP). This type of plan typically combines a high deductible with a health savings plan. Choose 80 employers at random. What is the probability that more than 50 will offer a CDHP?

    Source: *USA TODAY.*

14. **Household Computers** According to recent surveys, 60% of households have personal computers. If a random sample of 180 households is selected, what is the probability that more than 60 but fewer than 100 have a personal computer?

    Source: *New York Times Almanac.*

15. **Youth Smoking** Two out of five adult smokers acquired the habit by age 14. If 400 smokers are randomly selected, find the probability that 170 or fewer acquired the habit by age 14.

    Source: *Harper's Index.*

16. **Population of College Cities** College students often make up a substantial portion of the population of college cities and towns. State College, Pennsylvania, ranks first with 71.1% of its population made up of college students. What is the probability that in a random sample of 150 people from State College, more than 50 are not college students?

    Source: www.infoplease.com

17. **Voter Preference** A political candidate estimates that 30% of the voters in her party favor her proposed tax reform bill. If there are 400 people at a rally, find the probability that at least 100 voters will favor her tax bill. Based on your answer, is it likely that 100 or more people will favor the bill?

18. **Telephone Answering Devices** Seventy-eight percent of U.S. homes have a telephone answering device. In a random sample of 250 homes, what is the probability that fewer than 50 do not have a telephone answering device?

    Source: *New York Times Almanac.*

19. **Female Americans Who Have Completed 4 Years of College** The percentage of female Americans 25 years old and older who have completed 4 years of college or more is 26.1. In a random sample of 200 American women who are at least 25, what is the probability that at most 50 have completed 4 years of college or more?

    Source: *New York Times Almanac.*

20. **Residences of U.S. Citizens** According to the U.S. Census, 67.5% of the U.S. population were born in their state of residence. In a random sample of

200 Americans, what is the probability that fewer than 125 were born in their state of residence?

Source: www.census.gov

21. Elementary School Teachers Women comprise 80.3% of all elementary school teachers. In a random sample of 300 elementary teachers, what is the probability that less than three-fourths are women?

Source: *New York Times Almanac.*

22. Parking Lot Construction The mayor of a small town estimates that 35% of the residents in the town favor the construction of a municipal parking lot. If there are 350 people at a town meeting, find the probability that at least 100 favor construction of the parking lot. Based on your answer, is it likely that 100 or more people would favor the parking lot?

Extending the Concepts

23. Recall that for use of a normal distribution as an approximation to the binomial distribution, the conditions $np \geq 5$ and $nq \geq 5$ must be met. For each given probability, compute the minimum sample size needed for use of the normal approximation.

   a. $p = 0.1$ *d.* $p = 0.8$

   b. $p = 0.3$ *e.* $p = 0.9$

   c. $p = 0.5$

Summary

- A normal distribution can be used to describe a variety of variables, such as heights, weights, and temperatures. A normal distribution is bell-shaped, unimodal, symmetric, and continuous; its mean, median, and mode are equal. Since each normally distributed variable has its own distribution with mean μ and standard deviation σ, mathematicians use the standard normal distribution, which has a mean of 0 and a standard deviation of 1. Other approximately normally distributed variables can be transformed to the standard normal distribution with the formula $z = (X - \mu)/\sigma$. (6–1)

- A normal distribution can be used to solve a variety of problems in which the variables are approximately normally distributed. (6–2)

- A sampling distribution of sample means is a distribution using the means computed from all possible random samples of a specific size taken from a population. The difference between a sample measure and the corresponding population measure is due to what is called *sampling error*. The mean of the sample means will be the same as the population mean. The standard deviation of the sample means will be equal to the population standard deviation divided by the square root of the sample size. The central limit theorem states that as the sample size increases without limit, the shape of the distribution of the sample means taken with replacement from a population will approach that of a normal distribution. (6–3)

- A normal distribution can be used to approximate other distributions, such as a binomial distribution. For a normal distribution to be used as an approximation, the conditions $np \geq 5$ and $nq \geq 5$ must be met. Also, a correction for continuity may be used for more accurate results. (6–4)

Important Terms

central limit theorem 346	normal distribution 313	sampling error 344	symmetric distribution 314
correction for continuity 354	positively or right-skewed distribution 315	standard error of the mean 346	z value (z score) 316
negatively or left-skewed distribution 315	sampling distribution of sample means 344	standard normal distribution 315	

Important Formulas

Formula for the z score (or standard score):

$$z = \frac{X - \mu}{\sigma}$$

Formula for finding a specific data value:

$$X = z \cdot \sigma + \mu$$

Formula for the mean of the sample means:

$$\mu_{\bar{X}} = \mu$$

Formula for the standard error of the mean:

$$\sigma_{\bar{X}} = \frac{\sigma}{\sqrt{n}}$$

Formula for the z value for the central limit theorem:

$$z = \frac{\bar{X} - \mu}{\sigma/\sqrt{n}}$$

Formulas for the mean and standard deviation for the binomial distribution:

$$\mu = n \cdot p \qquad \sigma = \sqrt{n \cdot p \cdot q}$$

Review Exercises

Section 6–1

1. Find the area under the standard normal distribution curve for each.

   a. Between $z = 0$ and $z = 1.95$
   b. Between $z = 0$ and $z = 0.37$
   c. Between $z = 1.32$ and $z = 1.82$
   d. Between $z = -1.05$ and $z = 2.05$
   e. Between $z = -0.03$ and $z = 0.53$

2. Find the area under the standard normal distribution for each.

   a. Between $z = 1.10$ and $z = -1.80$
   b. To the right of $z = 1.99$
   c. To the right of $z = -1.36$
   d. To the left of $z = -2.09$
   e. To the left of $z = 1.68$

3. Using the standard normal distribution, find each probability.

   a. $P(0 < z < 2.07)$
   b. $P(-1.83 < z < 0)$
   c. $P(-1.59 < z < 2.01)$
   d. $P(1.33 < z < 1.88)$
   e. $P(-2.56 < z < 0.37)$

4. Using the standard normal distribution, find each probability.

   a. $P(z > 1.66)$
   b. $P(z < -2.03)$
   c. $P(z > -1.19)$
   d. $P(z < 1.93)$
   e. $P(z > -1.77)$

Section 6–2

5. **Per Capita Spending on Health Care** The average per capita spending on health care in the United States is $5274. If the standard deviation is $600 and the distribution of health care spending is approximately normal, what is the probability that a randomly selected person spends more than $6000? Find the

limits of the middle 50% of individual health care expenditures.

Source: *World Almanac.*

6. **Salaries for Actuaries** The average salary for graduates entering the actuarial field is $40,000. If the salaries are normally distributed with a standard deviation of $5000, find the probability that

   a. An individual graduate will have a salary over $45,000.
   b. A group of nine graduates will have a group average over $45,000.

Source: www.BeAnActuary.org

7. **Commuter Train Passengers** On a certain run of a commuter train, the average number of passengers is 476 and the standard deviation is 22. Assume the variable is normally distributed. If the train makes the run, find the probability that the number of passengers will be

   a. Between 476 and 500 passengers
   b. Less than 450 passengers
   c. More than 510 passengers

8. **Monthly Spending for Paging and Messaging Services** The average individual monthly spending in the United States for paging and messaging services is $10.15. If the standard deviation is $2.45 and the amounts are normally distributed, what is the probability that a randomly selected user of these services pays more than $15.00 per month? Between $12.00 and $14.00 per month?

Source: *New York Times Almanac.*

9. **Cost of iPod Repair** The average cost of repairing an iPod is $120 with a standard deviation of $10.50. The costs are normally distributed. If 15% of the costs are considered excessive, find the cost in dollars that would be considered excessive.

10. **Prices of Homes** The mean home price in Raleigh, North Carolina, is $217,600. Assuming that the home prices are normally distributed with a standard deviation of $36,400, what is the probability that a randomly selected home in Raleigh has a price below $200,000? Below $150,000?

Source: *World Almanac 2012.*

11. **Private Four-Year College Enrollment** A random sample of enrollments in Pennsylvania's private four-year colleges is listed here. Check for normality.

1350	1886	1743	1290	1767
2067	1118	3980	1773	4605
1445	3883	1486	980	1217
3587				

Source: *New York Times Almanac.*

12. **Heights of Active Volcanoes** The heights (in feet above sea level) of a random sample of the world's active volcanoes are shown here. Check for normality.

13,435	5,135	11,339	12,224	7,470
9,482	12,381	7,674	5,223	5,631
3,566	7,113	5,850	5,679	15,584
5,587	8,077	9,550	8,064	2,686
5,250	6,351	4,594	2,621	9,348
6,013	2,398	5,658	2,145	3,038

Source: *New York Times Almanac.*

Section 6–3

13. **Confectionary Products** Americans ate an average of 25.7 pounds of confectionary products each last year and spent an average of $61.50 per person doing so. If the standard deviation for consumption is 3.75 pounds and the standard deviation for the amount spent is $5.89, find the following:

a. The probability that the sample mean confectionary consumption for a random sample of 40 American consumers was greater than 27 pounds

b. The probability that for a random sample of 50, the sample mean for confectionary spending exceeded $60.00

Source: www.census.gov

14. **Average Precipitation** For the first 7 months of the year, the average precipitation in Toledo, Ohio, is 19.32 inches. If the average precipitation is normally distributed with a standard deviation of 2.44 inches, find these probabilities.

a. A randomly selected year will have precipitation greater than 18 inches for the first 7 months.

b. Five randomly selected years will have an average precipitation greater than 18 inches for the first 7 months.

Source: *Toledo Blade.*

15. **Sodium in Frozen Food** The average number of milligrams (mg) of sodium in a certain brand of low-salt microwave frozen dinners is 660 mg, and the standard deviation is 35 mg. Assume the variable is normally distributed.

a. If a single dinner is selected, find the probability that the sodium content will be more than 670 mg.

b. If a sample of 10 dinners is selected, find the probability that the mean of the sample will be larger than 670 mg.

c. Why is the probability for part *a* greater than that for part *b*?

16. **Portable CD Player Lifetimes** A recent study of the life span of portable compact disc players found the average to be 3.7 years with a standard deviation of 0.6 year. If a random sample of 32 people who own CD players is selected, find the probability that the mean lifetime of the sample will be less than 3.4 years. If the sample mean is less than 3.4 years, would you consider that 3.7 years might be incorrect?

Section 6–4

17. **Retirement Income** Of the total population of American households, including older Americans and perhaps some not so old, 17.3% receive retirement income. In a random sample of 120 households, what is the probability that more than 20 households but fewer than 35 households receive a retirement income?

Source: www.bls.gov

18. **Slot Machines** The probability of winning on a slot machine is 5%. If a person plays the machine 500 times, find the probability of winning 30 times. Use the normal approximation to the binomial distribution.

19. **Multiple-Job Holders** According to the government, 5.3% of those employed are multiple-job holders. In a random sample of 150 people who are employed, what is the probability that fewer than 10 hold multiple jobs? What is the probability that more than 50 are not multiple-job holders?

Source: www.bls.gov

20. **Enrollment in Personal Finance Course** In a large university, 30% of the incoming first-year students elect to enroll in a personal finance course offered by the university. Find the probability that of 800 randomly selected incoming first-year students, at least 260 have elected to enroll in the course.

21. **U.S. Population** Of the total population of the United States, 20% live in the northeast. If 200 residents of the United States are selected at random, find the probability that at least 50 live in the northeast.

Source: *Statistical Abstract of the United States.*

22. **Larceny-Thefts** Excluding motor vehicle thefts, 26% of all larceny-thefts involved items taken from motor vehicles. Local police forces are trying to help the situation with their "Put your junk in the trunk!" campaign. Consider a random sample of 60 larceny-thefts. What is the probability that 20 or more were items stolen from motor vehicles?

Source: *World Almanac.*

≡ STATISTICS TODAY

What Is Normal?—Revisited

Many of the variables measured in medical tests—blood pressure, triglyceride level, etc.—are approximately normally distributed for the majority of the population in the United States. Thus, researchers can find the mean and standard deviation of these variables. Then, using these two measures along with the z values, they can find normal intervals for healthy individuals. For example, 95% of the systolic blood pressures of healthy individuals fall within 2 standard deviations of the mean. If an individual's pressure is outside the determined normal range (either above or below), the physician will look for a possible cause and prescribe treatment if necessary.

≡ Chapter Quiz

Determine whether each statement is true or false. If the statement is false, explain why.

1. The total area under a normal distribution is infinite.

2. The standard normal distribution is a continuous distribution.

3. All variables that are approximately normally distributed can be transformed to standard normal variables.

4. The z value corresponding to a number below the mean is always negative.

5. The area under the standard normal distribution to the left of $z = 0$ is negative.

6. The central limit theorem applies to means of samples selected from different populations.

Select the best answer.

7. The mean of the standard normal distribution is

   a. 0   c. 100
   b. 1   d. Variable

8. Approximately what percentage of normally distributed data values will fall within 1 standard deviation above or below the mean?

   a. 68%   c. 99.7%
   b. 95%   d. Variable

9. Which is not a property of the standard normal distribution?

   a. It's symmetric about the mean.
   b. It's uniform.
   c. It's bell-shaped.
   d. It's unimodal.

10. When a distribution is positively skewed, the relationship of the mean, median, and mode from left to right will be

   a. Mean, median, mode   c. Median, mode, mean
   b. Mode, median, mean   d. Mean, mode, median

11. The standard deviation of all possible sample means equals

   a. The population standard deviation
   b. The population standard deviation divided by the population mean
   c. The population standard deviation divided by the square root of the sample size
   d. The square root of the population standard deviation

Complete the following statements with the best answer.

12. When one is using the standard normal distribution, $P(z < 0) =$ _____.

13. The difference between a sample mean and a population mean is due to _____.

14. The mean of the sample means equals _____.

15. The standard deviation of all possible sample means is called the _____.

16. The normal distribution can be used to approximate the binomial distribution when $n \cdot p$ and $n \cdot q$ are both greater than or equal to _____.

17. The correction factor for the central limit theorem should be used when the sample size is greater than _____ of the size of the population.

18. Find the area under the standard normal distribution for each.

   a. Between 0 and 1.50
   b. Between 0 and -1.25
   c. Between 1.56 and 1.96
   d. Between -1.20 and -2.25
   e. Between -0.06 and 0.73
   f. Between 1.10 and -1.80
   g. To the right of $z = 1.75$
   h. To the right of $z = -1.28$
   i. To the left of $z = -2.12$
   j. To the left of $z = 1.36$

19. Using the standard normal distribution, find each probability.

 a. $P(0 < z < 2.16)$

 b. $P(-1.87 < z < 0)$

 c. $P(-1.63 < z < 2.17)$

 d. $P(1.72 < z < 1.98)$

 e. $P(-2.17 < z < 0.71)$

 f. $P(z > 1.77)$

 g. $P(z < -2.37)$

 h. $P(z > -1.73)$

 i. $P(z < 2.03)$

 j. $P(z > -1.02)$

20. Amount of Rain in a City The average amount of rain per year in Greenville is 49 inches. The standard deviation is 8 inches. Find the probability that next year Greenville will receive the following amount of rainfall. Assume the variable is normally distributed.

 a. At most 55 inches of rain

 b. At least 62 inches of rain

 c. Between 46 and 54 inches of rain

 d. How many inches of rain would you consider to be an extremely wet year?

21. Heights of People The average height of a certain age group of people is 53 inches. The standard deviation is 4 inches. If the variable is normally distributed, find the probability that a selected individual's height will be

 a. Greater than 59 inches

 b. Less than 45 inches

 c. Between 50 and 55 inches

 d. Between 58 and 62 inches

22. Lemonade Consumption The average number of gallons of lemonade consumed by the football team during a game is 20, with a standard deviation of 3 gallons. Assume the variable is normally distributed. When a game is played, find the probability of using

 a. Between 20 and 25 gallons

 b. Less than 19 gallons

 c. More than 21 gallons

 d. Between 26 and 28 gallons

23. Years to Complete a Graduate Program The average number of years a person takes to complete a graduate degree program is 3. The standard deviation is 4 months. Assume the variable is normally distributed. If an individual enrolls in the program, find the probability that it will take

 a. More than 4 years to complete the program

 b. Less than 3 years to complete the program

 c. Between 3.8 and 4.5 years to complete the program

 d. Between 2.5 and 3.1 years to complete the program

24. Passengers on a Bus On the daily run of an express bus, the average number of passengers is 48. The standard deviation is 3. Assume the variable is normally distributed. Find the probability that the bus will have

 a. Between 36 and 40 passengers

 b. Fewer than 42 passengers

 c. More than 48 passengers

 d. Between 43 and 47 passengers

25. Thickness of Library Books The average thickness of books on a library shelf is 8.3 centimeters. The standard deviation is 0.6 centimeter. If 20% of the books are oversized, find the minimum thickness of the oversized books on the library shelf. Assume the variable is normally distributed.

26. Membership in an Organization Membership in an elite organization requires a test score in the upper 30% range. If $\mu = 115$ and $\sigma = 12$, find the lowest acceptable score that would enable a candidate to apply for membership. Assume the variable is normally distributed.

27. Repair Cost for Microwave Ovens The average repair cost of a microwave oven is $55, with a standard deviation of $8. The costs are normally distributed. If 12 ovens are repaired, find the probability that the mean of the repair bills will be greater than $60.

28. Electric Bills The average electric bill in a residential area is $72 for the month of April. The standard deviation is $6. If the amounts of the electric bills are normally distributed, find the probability that the mean of the bill for 15 residents will be less than $75.

29. Sleep Survey According to a recent survey, 38% of Americans get 6 hours or less of sleep each night. If 25 people are selected, find the probability that 14 or more people will get 6 hours or less of sleep each night. Does this number seem likely?

Source: *Amazing Almanac.*

30. Unemployment If 8% of all people in a certain geographic region are unemployed, find the probability that in a sample of 200 people, fewer than 10 people are unemployed.

31. Household Online Connection The percentage of U.S. households that have online connections is 44.9%. In a random sample of 420 households, what is the probability that fewer than 200 have online connections?

Source: *New York Times Almanac.*

32. Computer Ownership Fifty-three percent of U.S. households have a personal computer. In a random sample of 250 households, what is the probability that fewer than 120 have a PC?

Source: *New York Times Almanac.*

33. **Calories in Fast-Food Sandwiches** The number of calories contained in a selection of fast-food sandwiches is shown here. Check for normality.

390	405	580	300	320
540	225	720	470	560
535	660	530	290	440
390	675	530	1010	450
320	460	290	340	610
430	530			

Source: *The Doctor's Pocket Calorie, Fat, and Carbohydrate Counter.*

34. **GMAT Scores** The average GMAT scores for the top-30 ranked graduate schools of business are listed here. Check for normality.

718	703	703	703	700	690	695	705	690	688
676	681	689	686	691	669	674	652	680	670
651	651	637	662	641	645	645	642	660	636

Source: *U.S. News & World Report Best Graduate Schools.*

Critical Thinking Challenges

Sometimes a researcher must decide whether a variable is normally distributed. There are several ways to do this. One simple but very subjective method uses special graph paper, which is called *normal probability paper*. For the distribution of systolic blood pressure readings given in Chapter 3 of the text, the following method can be used:

1. Make a table, as shown.

Boundaries	Frequency	Cumulative frequency	Cumulative percent frequency
89.5–104.5	24		
104.5–119.5	62		
119.5–134.5	72		
134.5–149.5	26		
149.5–164.5	12		
164.5–179.5	4		
	200		

2. Find the cumulative frequencies for each class, and place the results in the third column.

3. Find the cumulative percents for each class by dividing each cumulative frequency by 200 (the total frequencies) and multiplying by 100%. (For the first class, it would be $24/200 \times 100\% = 12\%$.) Place these values in the last column.

4. Using the normal probability paper shown in Table 6–3, label the *x* axis with the class boundaries as shown and plot the percents.

5. If the points fall approximately in a straight line, it can be concluded that the distribution is normal. Do you feel that this distribution is approximately normal? Explain your answer.

6. To find an approximation of the mean or median, draw a horizontal line from the 50% point on the *y* axis over

TABLE 6–3 **Normal Probability Paper**

to the curve and then a vertical line down to the *x* axis. Compare this approximation of the mean with the computed mean.

7. To find an approximation of the standard deviation, locate the values on the *x* axis that correspond to the

16 and 84% values on the *y* axis. Subtract these two values and divide the result by 2. Compare this approximate standard deviation to the computed standard deviation.

8. Explain why the method used in step 7 works.

Data Projects

1. **Business and Finance** Use the data collected in data project 1 of Chapter 2 regarding earnings per share to complete this problem. Use the mean and standard deviation computed in data project 1 of Chapter 3 as estimates for the population parameters. What value separates the top 5% of stocks from the others?

2. **Sports and Leisure** Find the mean and standard deviation for the batting average for a player in the most recently completed MLB season. What batting average would separate the top 5% of all hitters from the rest? What is the probability that a randomly selected player bats over 0.300? What is the probability that a team of 25 players has a mean that is above 0.275?

3. **Technology** Use the data collected in data project 3 of Chapter 2 regarding song lengths. If the sample estimates for mean and standard deviation are used as replacements for the population parameters for this data set, what song length separates the bottom 5% and top 5% from the other values?

4. **Health and Wellness** Use the data regarding heart rates collected in data project 6 of Chapter 2 for this problem. Use the sample mean and standard deviation as estimates of the population parameters. For the before-exercise data, what heart rate separates the top

10% from the other values? For the after-exercise data, what heart rate separates the bottom 10% from the other values? If a student were selected at random, what would be the probability of her or his mean heart rate before exercise being less than 72? If 25 students were selected at random, what would be the probability that their mean heart rate before exercise was less than 72?

5. **Politics and Economics** Collect data regarding Math SAT scores to complete this problem. What are the mean and standard deviation for statewide Math SAT scores? What SAT score separates the bottom 10% of states from the others? What is the probability that a randomly selected state has a statewide SAT score above 500?

6. **Formulas** Confirm the two formulas hold true for the central limit theorem for the population containing the elements {1, 5, 10}. First, compute the population mean and standard deviation for the data set. Next, create a list of all 9 of the possible two-element samples that can be created with replacement: {1, 1}, {1, 5}, etc. For each of the 9 compute the sample mean. Now find the mean of the sample means. Does it equal the population mean? Compute the standard deviation of the sample means. Does it equal the population standard deviation, divided by the square root of *n*?

Answers to Applying the Concepts

Section 6–1   Assessing Normality

1. Answers will vary. One possible frequency distribution is the following:

Limits	Frequency
0–9	1
10–19	14
20–29	17
30–39	7
40–49	3
50–59	2
60–69	2
70–79	1
80–89	2
90–99	1

2. Answers will vary according to the frequency distribution in question 1. This histogram matches the frequency distribution in question 1.

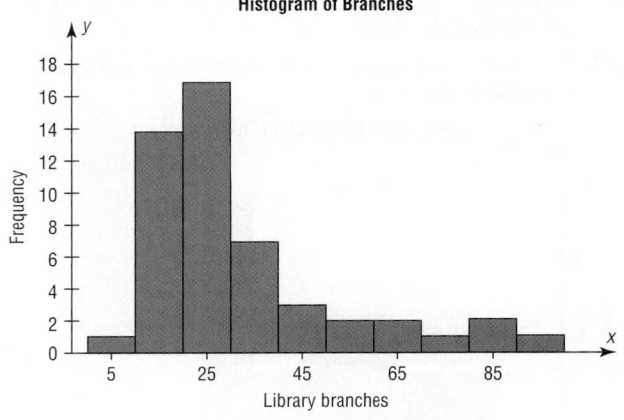

Histogram of Branches

3. The histogram is unimodal and skewed to the right (positively skewed).

4. The distribution does not appear to be normal.

5. The mean number of branches is $\overline{X} = 31.4$, and the standard deviation is $s = 20.6$.

6. Of the data values, 80% fall within 1 standard deviation of the mean (between 10.8 and 52).

7. Of the data values, 92% fall within 2 standard deviations of the mean (between 0 and 72.6).

8. Of the data values, 98% fall within 3 standard deviations of the mean (between 0 and 93.2).

9. My values in questions 6–8 differ from the 68, 95, and 100% that we would see in a normal distribution.

10. These values support the conclusion that the distribution of the variable is not normal.

Section 6–2   Smart People

1. $z = \frac{130 - 100}{15} = 2$. The area to the right of 2 in the standard normal table is about 0.0228, so I would expect about $10,000(0.0228) = 228$ people in my hometown to qualify for Mensa.

2. It does seem reasonable to continue my quest to start a Mensa chapter in my hometown.

3. Answers will vary. One possible answer would be to randomly call telephone numbers (both home and cell phones) in my hometown, ask to speak to an adult, and ask whether the person would be interested in joining Mensa.

4. To have an Ultra-Mensa club, I would need to find the people in my hometown who have IQs that are at least 2.326 standard deviations above average. This means that I would need to recruit those with IQs that are at least 135:

$$2.326 = \frac{x - 100}{15} \Rightarrow x = 100 + 2.326(15) = 134.89$$

Section 6–3   Central Limit Theorem

1. It is very unlikely that we would ever get the same results for any of our random samples. While it is a remote possibility, it is highly unlikely.

2. A good estimate for the population mean would be to find the average of the students' sample means. Similarly, a good estimate for the population standard deviation would be to find the average of the students' sample standard deviations.

3. The distribution appears to be somewhat left-skewed (negatively skewed).

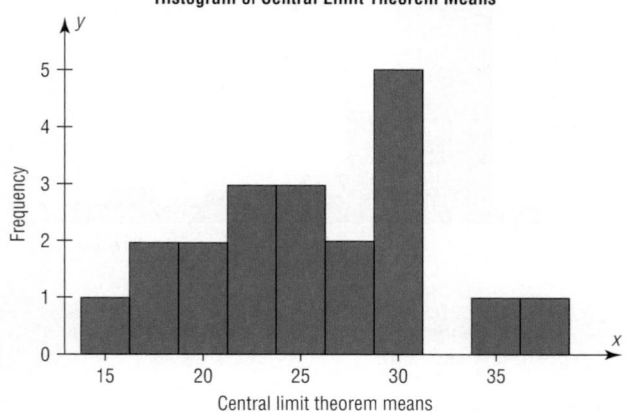

Histogram of Central Limit Theorem Means

Central limit theorem means

4. The mean of the students' means is 25.4, and the standard deviation is 5.8.

5. The distribution of the means is not a sampling distribution, since it represents just 20 of all possible samples of size 30 from the population.

6. The sampling error for student 3 is $18 - 25.4 = -7.4$; the sampling error for student 7 is $26 - 25.4 = +0.6$; the sampling error for student 14 is $29 - 25.4 = +3.6$.

7. The standard deviation for the sample of the 20 means is greater than the standard deviations for each of the individual students. So it is not equal to the standard deviation divided by the square root of the sample size.

Section 6–4   How Safe Are You?

1. A reliability rating of 97% means that, on average, the device will not fail 97% of the time. We do not know how many times it will fail for any particular set of 100 climbs.

2. The probability of at least 1 failure in 100 climbs is $1 - (0.97)^{100} = 1 - 0.0476 = 0.9524$ (about 95%).

3. The complement of the event in question 2 is the event of "no failures in 100 climbs."

4. This can be considered a binomial experiment. We have two outcomes: success and failure. The probability of the equipment working (success) remains constant at 97%. We have 100 independent climbs. And we are counting the number of times the equipment works in these 100 climbs.

5. We could use the binomial probability formula, but it would be very messy computationally.

6. The probability of at least two failures *cannot* be estimated with the normal distribution (see below). So the probability is $1 - [(0.97)^{100} + 100(0.97)^{99}(0.03)] = 1 - 0.1946 = 0.8054$ (about 80.5%).

7. We *should not* use the normal approximation to the binomial since $nq < 10$.

8. If we had used the normal approximation, we would have needed a correction for continuity, since we would have been approximating a discrete distribution with a continuous distribution.

9. Since a second safety hook will be successful or will fail independently of the first safety hook, the probability of failure drops from 3% to $(0.03)(0.03) = 0.0009$, or 0.09%.

Confidence Intervals and Sample Size

▰ STATISTICS TODAY

Stress and the College Student

A recent poll conducted by the mtvU/Associated Press found that 85% of college students reported that they experience stress daily. The study said, "It is clear that being stressed is a fact of life on college campuses today."

The study also reports that 74% of students' stress comes from school work, 71% from grades, and 62% from financial woes. The report stated that 2240 undergraduate students were selected and that the poll has a margin of error of ±3.0%.

In this chapter you will learn how to make a true estimate of a parameter, what is meant by the margin of error, and whether or not the sample size was large enough to represent all college students.

See Statistics Today—Revisited at the end of this chapter for more details.

OUTLINE

Introduction

7–1 Confidence Intervals for the Mean When σ Is Known

7–2 Confidence Intervals for the Mean When σ Is Unknown

7–3 Confidence Intervals and Sample Size for Proportions

7–4 Confidence Intervals for Variances and Standard Deviations

Summary

OBJECTIVES

After completing this chapter, you should be able to

1 Find the confidence interval for the mean when σ is known.

2 Determine the minimum sample size for finding a confidence interval for the mean.

3 Find the confidence interval for the mean when σ is unknown.

4 Find the confidence interval for a proportion.

5 Determine the minimum sample size for finding a confidence interval for a proportion.

6 Find a confidence interval for a variance and a standard deviation.

Introduction

One aspect of inferential statistics is **estimation,** which is the process of estimating the value of a parameter from information obtained from a sample. For example, consider the following statements:

> "For each dollar you pay in county property tax, 22 cents covers the cost of incarcerating prisoners." (*Pittsburgh City Paper*)
>
> "The average amount employees and employers pay for health insurance is $11,664 per year." *(USA TODAY)*
>
> "For people who were asked if they won $5,000 tomorrow, 54% of them said that they would use it to pay off their debts." (ING U.S. Survey)
>
> "The average amount spent by a TV Super Bowl viewer is $63.87." (Retail Advertising and Marketing Association)
>
> "Eight percent of the people surveyed in the United States said that they participate in skiing in the winter time." (IMRE sports)
>
> "Consumers spent an average of $126 for Valentine's Day this year." (National Retail Federation)

Since the populations from which these values were obtained are large, these values are only *estimates* of the true parameters and are derived from data collected from samples.

The statistical procedures for estimating the population mean, proportion, variance, and standard deviation will be explained in this chapter.

An important question in estimation is that of sample size. How large should the sample be in order to make an accurate estimate? This question is not easy to answer since the size of the sample depends on several factors, such as the accuracy desired and the probability of making a correct estimate. The question of sample size will be explained in this chapter also.

Inferential statistical techniques have various **assumptions** that must be met before valid conclusions can be obtained. One common assumption is that the samples must be randomly selected. Chapter 1 explains how to obtain a random sample. The other common assumption is that either the sample size must be greater than or equal to 30 or the population must be normally or approximately normally distributed if the sample size is less than 30.

To check this assumption, you can use the methods explained in Chapter 6. Just for review, the methods are to check the histogram to see if it is approximately bell-shaped, check for outliers, and if possible, generate a normal quantile plot and see whether the points fall close to a straight line. (*Note:* An area of statistics called nonparametric statistics does not require the variable to be normally distributed.)

7–1   Confidence Intervals for the Mean When σ Is Known

OBJECTIVE

Find the confidence interval for the mean when σ is known.

The main objective of this section is to show the procedure of estimating the value of an unknown population mean when the standard deviation of the population is known.

Suppose a college president wishes to estimate the average age of students attending classes this semester. The president could select a random sample of 100 students and find the average age of these students, say, 22.3 years. From the sample mean, the president could infer that the average age of all the students is 22.3 years. This type of estimate is called a *point estimate.*

> A **point estimate** is a specific numerical value estimate of a parameter. The best point estimate of the population mean μ is the sample mean $\bar{X}$.

You might ask why other measures of central tendency, such as the median and mode, are not used to estimate the population mean. The reason is that the means of samples vary less than other statistics (such as medians and modes) when many samples are selected from the same population. Therefore, the sample mean is the best estimate of the population mean.

Sample measures (i.e., statistics) are used to estimate population measures (i.e., parameters). These statistics are called **estimators.** As previously stated, the sample mean is a better estimator of the population mean than the sample median or sample mode.

A good estimator should satisfy the three properties described next.

Three Properties of a Good Estimator

1. The estimator should be an **unbiased estimator.** That is, the expected value or the mean of the estimates obtained from samples of a given size is equal to the parameter being estimated.

2. The estimator should be consistent. For a **consistent estimator,** as sample size increases, the value of the estimator approaches the value of the parameter estimated.

3. The estimator should be a **relatively efficient estimator.** That is, of all the statistics that can be used to estimate a parameter, the relatively efficient estimator has the smallest variance.

Confidence Intervals

As stated in Chapter 6, the sample mean will be, for the most part, somewhat different from the population mean due to sampling error. Therefore, you might ask a second question: How good is a point estimate? The answer is that there is no way of knowing how close a particular point estimate is to the population mean.

This answer creates some doubt about the accuracy of point estimates. For this reason, statisticians prefer another type of estimate, called an *interval estimate.*

An **interval estimate** of a parameter is an interval or a range of values used to estimate the parameter. This estimate may or may not contain the value of the parameter being estimated.

In an interval estimate, the parameter is specified as being between two values. For example, an interval estimate for the average age of all students might be $21.9 < \mu < 22.7$, or 22.3 ± 0.4 years.

Either the interval contains the parameter or it does not. A degree of confidence (usually a percent) must be assigned before an interval estimate is made. For instance, you may wish to be 95% confident that the interval contains the true population mean. Another question then arises. Why 95%? Why not 99 or 99.5%?

If you desire to be more confident, such as 99 or 99.5% confident, then you must make the interval larger. For example, a 99% confidence interval for the mean age of college students might be $21.7 < \mu < 22.9$, or 22.3 ± 0.6. Hence, a tradeoff occurs. To be more confident that the interval contains the true population mean, you must make the interval wider.

The **confidence level** of an interval estimate of a parameter is the probability that the interval estimate will contain the parameter, assuming that a large number of samples are selected and that the estimation process on the same parameter is repeated.

A **confidence interval** is a specific interval estimate of a parameter determined by using data obtained from a sample and by using the specific confidence level of the estimate.

Historical Notes

Point and interval estimates were known as long ago as the late 1700s. However, it wasn't until 1937 that a mathematician, J. Neyman, formulated practical applications for them.

Intervals constructed in this way are called *confidence intervals.* Three common confidence intervals are used: the 90%, the 95%, and the 99% confidence intervals.

The algebraic derivation of the formula for determining a confidence interval for a mean will be shown later. A brief intuitive explanation will be given first.

The central limit theorem states that when the sample size is large, approximately 95% of the sample means of same-size samples taken from a population will fall within ± 1.96 standard errors of the population mean, that is,

$$\mu \pm 1.96\left(\frac{\sigma}{\sqrt{n}}\right)$$

Now, if a specific sample mean is selected, say, $\overline{X}$, there is a 95% probability that the interval $\mu \pm 1.96(\sigma/\sqrt{n})$ contains $\overline{X}$. Likewise, there is a 95% probability that the interval specified by

$$\overline{X} \pm 1.96\left(\frac{\sigma}{\sqrt{n}}\right)$$

will contain μ, as will be shown later. Stated another way,

$$\overline{X} - 1.96\left(\frac{\sigma}{\sqrt{n}}\right) < \mu < \overline{X} + 1.96\left(\frac{\sigma}{\sqrt{n}}\right)$$

Hence, you can be 95% confident that the population mean is contained within that interval when the values of the variable are normally distributed in the population.

The value used for the 95% confidence interval, 1.96, is obtained from Table E in Appendix A. For a 99% confidence interval, the value 2.58 is used instead of 1.96 in the formula. This value is also obtained from Table E and is based on the standard normal distribution. Since other confidence intervals are used in statistics, the symbol $z_{\alpha/2}$ (read "zee sub alpha over two") is used in the general formula for confidence intervals. The Greek letter α (alpha) represents the total area in both tails of the standard normal distribution curve, and $\alpha/2$ represents the area in each one of the tails. The value $z_{\alpha/2}$ is called a *critical value*.

The relationship between α and the confidence level is that the stated confidence level is the percentage equivalent to the decimal value of $1 - \alpha$, and vice versa. When the 95% confidence interval is to be found, $\alpha = 0.05$, since $1 - 0.05 = 0.95$, or 95%. When $\alpha = 0.01$, then $1 - \alpha = 1 - 0.01 = 0.99$, and the 99% confidence interval is being calculated.

> ⌐ **Interesting Fact**
>
> A postal worker who delivers mail walks on average 5.2 miles per day.

Formula for the Confidence Interval of the Mean for a Specific α When σ is Known

$$\overline{X} - z_{\alpha/2}\left(\frac{\sigma}{\sqrt{n}}\right) < \mu < \overline{X} + z_{\alpha/2}\left(\frac{\sigma}{\sqrt{n}}\right)$$

For a 90% confidence interval, $z_{\alpha/2} = 1.65$; for a 95% confidence interval, $z_{\alpha/2} = 1.96$; and for a 99% confidence interval, $z_{\alpha/2} = 2.58$.

The term $z_{\alpha/2}(\sigma/\sqrt{n})$ is called the *margin of error* (also called the *maximum error of the estimate*). For a specific value, say, $\alpha = 0.05$, 95% of the sample means will fall within this error value on either side of the population mean, as previously explained. See Figure 7–1.

When $n \geq 30$, s can be substituted for σ, but a different distribution is used.

The **margin of error**, also called the *maximum error of the estimate,* is the maximum likely difference between the point estimate of a parameter and the actual value of the parameter.

FIGURE 7–1
95% Confidence Interval

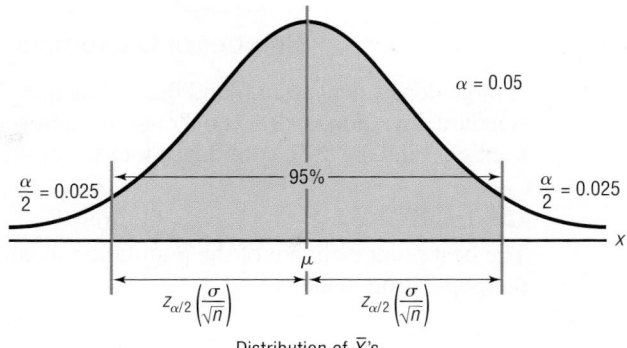

Distribution of $\bar{X}$'s

A more detailed explanation of the margin of error follows Examples 7–1 and 7–2, which illustrate the computation of confidence intervals.

Assumptions for Finding a Confidence Interval for a Mean When σ Is Known

1. The sample is a random sample.
2. Either $n \geq 30$ or the population is normally distributed when $n < 30$.

In this book, the assumptions will be stated in the exercises; however, when encountering statistics in other situations, you must check to see that these assumptions have been met before proceeding.

Some statistical techniques are called **robust.** This means that the distribution of the variable can depart somewhat from normality, and valid conclusions can still be obtained.

Rounding Rule for a Confidence Interval for a Mean   When you are computing a confidence interval for a population mean by using *raw data,* round off to one more decimal place than the number of decimal places in the original data. When you are computing a confidence interval for a population mean by using a sample mean and a standard deviation, round off to the same number of decimal places as given for the mean.

EXAMPLE 7–1   Days It Takes to Sell an Aveo

A researcher wishes to estimate the number of days it takes an automobile dealer to sell a Chevrolet Aveo. A random sample of 50 cars had a mean time on the dealer's lot of 54 days. Assume the population standard deviation to be 6.0 days. Find the best point estimate of the population mean and the 95% confidence interval of the population mean.

Source: Based on information obtained from Power Information Network.

SOLUTION

The best point estimate of the population mean is 54 days. For the 95% confidence interval use $z = 1.96$.

$$\bar{X} - z_{\alpha/2}\left(\frac{\sigma}{\sqrt{n}}\right) < \mu < \bar{X} + z_{\alpha/2}\left(\frac{\sigma}{\sqrt{n}}\right)$$

$$54 - 1.96\left(\frac{6.0}{\sqrt{50}}\right) < \mu < 54 + 1.96\left(\frac{6.0}{\sqrt{50}}\right)$$

$$54 - 1.7 < \mu < 54 + 1.7$$

$$52.3 < \mu < 55.7 \text{ or } 54 \pm 1.7$$

Hence, one can say with 95% confidence that the interval between 52.3 and 55.7 days does contain the population mean, based on a sample of 50 automobiles.

EXAMPLE 7–2 Number of Customers

A large department store found that it averages 362 customers per hour. Assume that the standard deviation is 29.6 and a random sample of 40 hours was used to determine the average. Find the 99% confidence interval of the population mean.

SOLUTION

The best point estimate of the population mean is 362. The 99% confidence interval for the population mean is

$$\bar{X} - z_{\alpha/2}\left(\frac{\sigma}{\sqrt{n}}\right) < \mu < \bar{X} + z_{\alpha/2}\left(\frac{\sigma}{\sqrt{n}}\right)$$

$$362 - 2.58\left(\frac{29.6}{\sqrt{40}}\right) < \mu < 362 + 2.58\left(\frac{29.6}{\sqrt{40}}\right)$$

$$362 - 12.1 < \mu < 362 + 12.1$$

$$349.9 < \mu < 374.1$$

$$350 < \mu < 374$$

Hence, one can be 99% confident (rounded values) that the mean number of customers that the store averages is between 350 and 374 customers per hour.

Source: Based on information from Number Freaking.

Another way of looking at a confidence interval is shown in Figure 7–2. According to the central limit theorem, approximately 95% of the sample means fall within 1.96 standard deviations of the population mean if the sample size is 30 or more, or if σ is known when n is less than 30 and the population is normally distributed. If it were possible to build a confidence interval about each sample mean, as was done in Examples 7–1 and 7–2 for μ, then 95% of these intervals would contain the population mean, as shown in Figure 7–3. Hence, you can be 95% confident that an interval built around a specific sample mean would contain the population mean. If you desire to be 99% confident, you must enlarge the confidence intervals so that 99 out of every 100 intervals contain the population mean.

Since other confidence intervals (besides 90, 95, and 99%) are sometimes used in statistics, an explanation of how to find the values for $z_{\alpha/2}$ is necessary. As stated previously, the Greek letter α represents the total of the areas in both tails of the normal distribution. The value for α is found by subtracting the decimal equivalent for the desired confidence level from 1. For example, if you wanted to find the 98% confidence interval, you would change 98% to 0.98 and find $\alpha = 1 - 0.98$, or 0.02. Then $\alpha/2$ is obtained by dividing α by 2. So $\alpha/2$ is 0.02/2, or 0.01. Finally, $z_{0.01}$ is the z value that will give an area of 0.01 in the right tail of the standard normal distribution curve. See Figure 7–4.

Once $\alpha/2$ is determined, the corresponding $z_{\alpha/2}$ value can be found by using the procedure shown in Chapter 6, which is reviewed here. To get the $z_{\alpha/2}$ value for a 98%

FIGURE 7–2

95% Interval for Sample Means

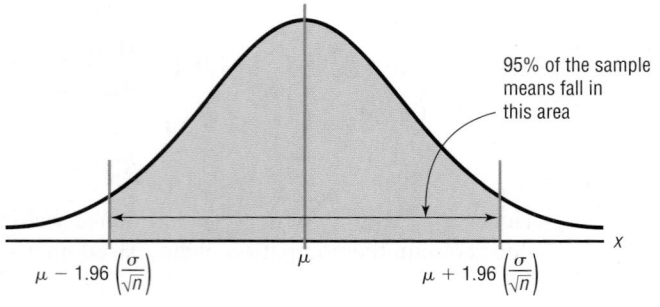

FIGURE 7–3

95% Confidence Intervals for
Each Sample Mean

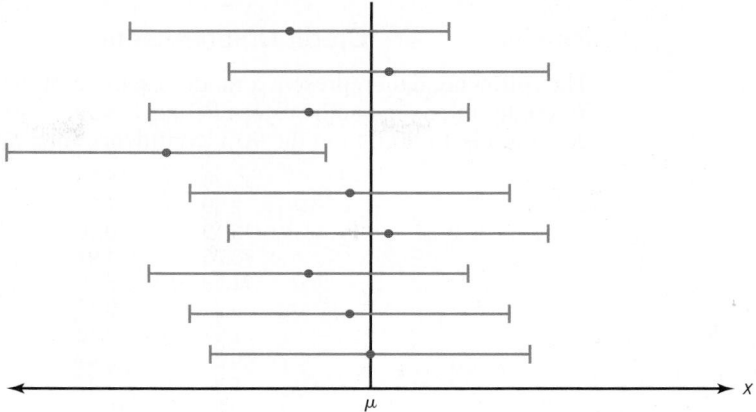

Each • represents a sample mean.
Each ├──┤ represents a 95% confidence interval.

FIGURE 7–4

Finding $\alpha/2$ for a 98%
Confidence Interval

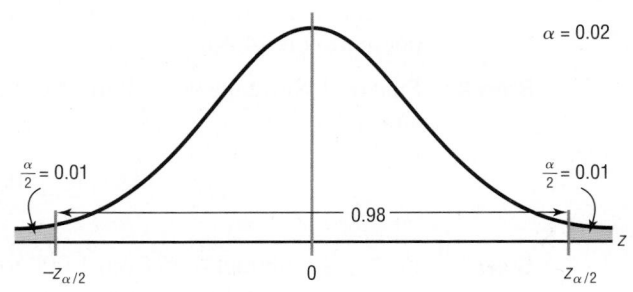

FIGURE 7–5

Finding $z_{\alpha/2}$ for a 98%
Confidence Interval

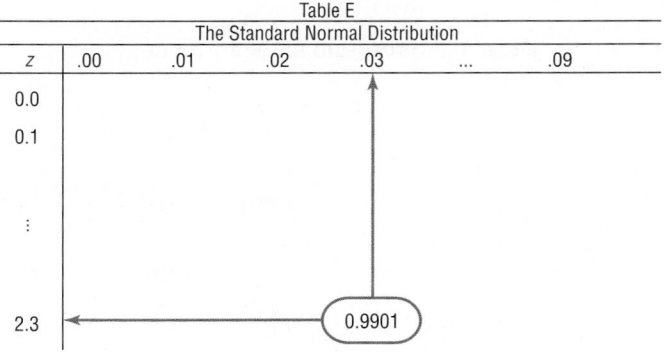

confidence interval, subtract 0.01 from 1.0000 to get 0.9900. Next, locate the area that is closest to 0.9900 (in this case, 0.9901) in Table E, and then find the corresponding z value. In this example, it is 2.33. See Figure 7–5.

For confidence intervals, only the positive z value is used in the formula.

When the original variable is normally distributed and σ is known, the standard normal distribution can be used to find confidence intervals regardless of the size of the sample. When $n \geq 30$, the distribution of means will be approximately normal even if the original distribution of the variable departs from normality.

When σ is unknown, s can be used as an estimate of σ, but a different distribution is used for the critical values. This method is explained in Section 7–2.

EXAMPLE 7–3   Credit Union Assets

The following data represent a random sample of the assets (in millions of dollars) of 30 credit unions in southwestern Pennsylvania. Assume the population standard deviation is 14.405. Find the 90% confidence interval of the mean.

12.23	16.56	4.39
2.89	1.24	2.17
13.19	9.16	1.42
73.25	1.91	14.64
11.59	6.69	1.06
8.74	3.17	18.13
7.92	4.78	16.85
40.22	2.42	21.58
5.01	1.47	12.24
2.27	12.77	2.76

Source: *Pittsburgh Post Gazette.*

SOLUTION

Step 1   Find the mean for the data. Use the formula shown in Chapter 3 or your calculator. The mean $\bar{X} = 11.091$. Assume the standard deviation of the population is 14.405.

Step 2   Find $\alpha/2$. Since the 90% confidence interval is to be used, $\alpha = 1 - 0.90 = 0.10$, and

$$\frac{\alpha}{2} = \frac{0.10}{2} = 0.05$$

Step 3   Find $z_{\alpha/2}$. Subtract 0.05 from 1.000 to get 0.9500. The corresponding z value obtained from Table E is 1.65. (*Note:* This value is found by using the z value for an area between 0.9495 and 0.9505. A more precise z value obtained mathematically is 1.645 and is sometimes used; however, 1.65 will be used in this text.)

Step 4   Substitute in the formula

$$\bar{X} - z_{\alpha/2}\left(\frac{\sigma}{\sqrt{n}}\right) < \mu < \bar{X} + z_{\alpha/2}\left(\frac{\sigma}{\sqrt{n}}\right)$$

$$11.091 - 1.65\left(\frac{14.405}{\sqrt{30}}\right) < \mu < 11.091 + 1.65\left(\frac{14.405}{\sqrt{30}}\right)$$

$$11.091 - 4.339 < \mu < 11.091 + 4.339$$

$$6.752 < \mu < 15.430$$

Hence, one can be 90% confident that the population mean of the assets of all credit unions is between $6.752 million and $15.430 million, based on a sample of 30 credit unions.

Comment to Computer and Statistical Calculator Users

This chapter and subsequent chapters include examples using raw data. If you are using computer or calculator programs to find the solutions, the answers you get may vary somewhat from the ones given in the text. This is so because computers and calculators do not round the answers in the intermediate steps and can use 12 or more decimal places for computation. Also, they use more-exact critical values than those given in the tables in the back of this book.

When you are calculating other statistics, such as the z, t, χ^2, or F values (shown in this chapter and later chapters), it is permissible to carry out the values of means, variances, and standard deviations to more decimal places than specified by the rounding rules in Chapter 3. This will give answers that are closer to the calculator or computer values. These small discrepancies are part of statistics.

Sample Size

OBJECTIVE **2**

Determine the minimum sample size for finding a confidence interval for the mean.

Sample size determination is closely related to statistical estimation. Quite often you ask, How large a sample is necessary to make an accurate estimate? The answer is not simple, since it depends on three things: the margin of error, the population standard deviation, and the degree of confidence. For example, how close to the true mean do you want to be (2 units, 5 units, etc.), and how confident do you wish to be (90, 95, 99%, etc.)? For the purposes of this chapter, it will be assumed that the population standard deviation of the variable is known or has been estimated from a previous study.

The formula for sample size is derived from the margin of error formula

$$E = z_{\alpha/2}\left(\frac{\sigma}{\sqrt{n}}\right)$$

and this formula is solved for n as follows:

$$E\sqrt{n} = z_{\alpha/2}(\sigma)$$

$$\sqrt{n} = \frac{z_{\alpha/2} \cdot \sigma}{E}$$

Hence,

$$n = \left(\frac{z_{\alpha/2} \cdot \sigma}{E}\right)^2$$

Formula for the Minimum Sample Size Needed for an Interval Estimate of the Population Mean

$$n = \left(\frac{z_{\alpha/2} \cdot \sigma}{E}\right)^2$$

where E is the margin of error. If necessary, round the answer up to obtain a whole number. That is, if there is any fraction or decimal portion in the answer, use the next whole number for sample size n.

EXAMPLE 7–4   Depth of a River

A scientist wishes to estimate the average depth of a river. He wants to be 99% confident that the estimate is accurate within 2 feet. From a previous study, the standard deviation of the depths measured was 4.33 feet.

SOLUTION

Since $\alpha = 0.01$ (or $1 - 0.99$), $z_{\alpha/2} = 2.58$ and $E = 2$. Substituting in the formula,

$$n = \left(\frac{z_{\alpha/2} \cdot \sigma}{E}\right)^2 = \left[\frac{(2.58)(4.33)}{2}\right]^2 = 31.2$$

Round the value 31.2 up to 32. Therefore, to be 99% confident that the estimate is within 2 feet of the true mean depth, the scientist needs a sample of at least 32 measurements.

In most cases in statistics, we round off. However, when determining sample size, we always round up to the next whole number.

Notice that when you are finding the sample size, the size of the population is irrelevant when the population is large or infinite or when sampling is done with replacement. In other cases, an adjustment is made in the formula for computing sample size. This adjustment is beyond the scope of this book.

The formula for determining sample size requires the use of the population standard deviation. What happens when σ is unknown? In this case, an attempt is made to estimate σ. One such way is to use the standard deviation s obtained from a sample taken previously as an estimate for σ. The standard deviation can also be estimated by dividing the range by 4.

Sometimes, interval estimates rather than point estimates are reported. For instance, you may read a statement: "On the basis of a sample of 200 families, the survey estimates that an American family of two spends an average of \$84 per week for groceries. One can be 95% confident that this estimate is accurate within \$3 of the true mean." This statement means that the 95% confidence interval of the true mean is

$$\$84 - \$3 < \mu < \$84 + \$3$$
$$\$81 < \mu < \$87$$

The algebraic derivation of the formula for a confidence interval is shown next. As explained in Chapter 6, the sampling distribution of the mean is approximately normal when large samples ($n \geq 30$) are taken from a population. Also,

$$z = \frac{\bar{X} - \mu}{\sigma/\sqrt{n}}$$

Furthermore, there is a probability of $1 - \alpha$ that a z will have a value between $-z_{\alpha/2}$ and $+z_{\alpha/2}$. Hence,

$$-z_{\alpha/2} < \frac{\bar{X} - \mu}{\sigma/\sqrt{n}} < z_{\alpha/2}$$

By using algebra, the formula can be rewritten as

$$-z_{\alpha/2} \cdot \frac{\sigma}{\sqrt{n}} < \bar{X} - \mu < z_{\alpha/2} \cdot \frac{\sigma}{\sqrt{n}}$$

Subtracting $\bar{X}$ from both sides and from the middle gives

$$-\bar{X} - z_{\alpha/2} \cdot \frac{\sigma}{\sqrt{n}} < -\mu < -\bar{X} + z_{\alpha/2} \cdot \frac{\sigma}{\sqrt{n}}$$

Multiplying by -1 gives

$$\bar{X} + z_{\alpha/2} \cdot \frac{\sigma}{\sqrt{n}} > \mu > \bar{X} - z_{\alpha/2} \cdot \frac{\sigma}{\sqrt{n}}$$

Reversing the inequality yields the formula for the confidence interval:

$$\bar{X} - z_{\alpha/2} \cdot \frac{\sigma}{\sqrt{n}} < \mu < \bar{X} + z_{\alpha/2} \cdot \frac{\sigma}{\sqrt{n}}$$

⬛ Applying the Concepts 7–1

Making Decisions with Confidence Intervals

Assume you work for Kimberly Clark Corporation, the makers of Kleenex. The job you are presently working on requires you to decide how many Kleenexes are to be put in the new automobile glove compartment boxes. Complete the following.

1. How will you decide on a reasonable number of Kleenexes to put in the boxes?

2. When do people usually need Kleenexes?

3. What type of data collection technique would you use?

4. Assume you found out that from your sample of 85 people, an average of about 57 Kleenexes are used throughout the duration of a cold, with a population standard deviation of 15. Use a confidence interval to help you decide how many Kleenexes will go in the boxes.

5. Explain how you decided how many Kleenexes will go in the boxes.

See page 411 for the answers.

Exercises 7–1

1. What is the difference between a point estimate and an interval estimate of a parameter? Which is better? Why?

2. What information is necessary to calculate a confidence interval?

3. What is the margin of error?

4. What is meant by the 95% confidence interval of the mean?

5. What are three properties of a good estimator?

6. What statistic best estimates μ?

7. Find each.
   a. $z_{\alpha/2}$ for the 99% confidence interval
   b. $z_{\alpha/2}$ for the 98% confidence interval
   c. $z_{\alpha/2}$ for the 95% confidence interval
   d. $z_{\alpha/2}$ for the 90% confidence interval
   e. $z_{\alpha/2}$ for the 94% confidence interval

8. What is necessary to determine the sample size?

9. **Fuel Efficiency of Cars and Trucks** Since 1975 the average fuel efficiency of U.S. cars and light trucks (SUVs) has increased from 13.5 to 25.8 mpg, an increase of over 90%! A random sample of 40 cars from a large community got a mean mileage of 28.1 mpg per vehicle. The population standard deviation is 4.7 mpg. Estimate the true mean gas mileage with 95% confidence.

   Source: *World Almanac 2012.*

10. **Fast-Food Bills for Drive-Thru Customers** A random sample of 50 cars in the drive-thru of a popular fast food restaurant revealed an average bill of $18.21 per car. The population standard deviation is $5.92. Estimate the mean bill for all cars from the drive-thru with 98% confidence.

11. **Playing Video Games** In a recent study of 35 ninth-grade students, the mean number of hours per week that they played video games was 16.6. The standard deviation of the population was 2.8.
    a. Find the best point estimate of the population mean.

   b. Find the 95% confidence interval of the mean of the time playing video games.
   c. Find the 99% confidence interval of the mean time playing video games.
   d. Which is larger? Explain why.

12. **Number of Jobs** A sociologist found that in a random sample of 50 retired men, the average number of jobs they had during their lifetimes was 7.2. The population standard deviation is 2.1.
    a. Find the best point estimate of the population mean.
    b. Find the 95% confidence interval of the mean number of jobs.
    c. Find the 99% confidence interval of the mean number of jobs.
    d. Which is smaller? Explain why.

13. **Number of Faculty** The numbers of faculty at 32 randomly selected state-controlled colleges and universities with enrollment under 12,000 students are shown below. Use these data to estimate the mean number of faculty at all state-controlled colleges and universities with enrollment under 12,000 with 92% confidence. Assume $\sigma = 165.1$.

211	384	396	211	224	337	395	121	356
621	367	408	515	280	289	180	431	176
318	836	203	374	224	121	412	134	539
471	638	425	159	324				

Source: *World Almanac.*

14. **Freshmen's GPAs** First-semester GPAs for a random selection of freshmen at a large university are shown. Estimate the true mean GPA of the freshman class with 99% confidence. Assume $\sigma = 0.62$.

1.9	3.2	2.0	2.9	2.7	3.3
2.8	3.0	3.8	2.7	2.0	1.9
2.5	2.7	2.8	3.2	3.0	3.8
3.1	2.7	3.5	3.8	3.9	2.7
2.0	2.8	1.9	4.0	2.2	2.8
2.1	2.4	3.0	3.4	2.9	2.1

15. **Carbohydrate Grams in Commercial Subs** The number of grams of carbohydrates in various commercially prepared 7-inch subs is recorded below.

The population standard deviation is 6.46. Estimate the mean number of carbs in all similarly sized subs with 95% confidence.

63	67	61	64	51	42	56	70	61
55	60	55	57	60	60	66	55	58
70	65	49	51	61	54	50	55	56
53	65	68	63	48	54	56	57	

16. Number of Farms A random sample of the number of farms (in thousands) in various states follows. Estimate the mean number of farms per state with 90% confidence. Assume $\sigma = 31.0$.

47	95	54	33	64	4	8	57	9	80
8	90	3	49	4	44	79	80	48	16
68	7	15	21	52	6	78	109	40	50
29									

Source: *New York Times Almanac.*

17. Television Viewing A study of 415 randomly selected kindergarten students showed that they have seen on average 5000 hours of television. If the sample standard deviation of the population is 900, find the 95% confidence interval of the mean for all students. If a father claimed that his children watched 4000 hours, would the claim be believable?

Source: U.S. Department of Education.

18. Day Care Tuition A random sample of 50 four-year-olds attending day care centers provided a yearly tuition average of $3987 and the population standard deviation of $630. Find the 90% confidence interval of the true mean. If a day care center were starting up and wanted to keep tuition low, what would be a reasonable amount to charge?

19. Hospital Noise Levels Noise levels at various area urban hospitals were measured in decibels. The mean of the noise levels in 84 randomly selected corridors was 61.2 decibels, and the standard deviation of the population was 7.9. Find the 95% confidence interval of the true mean.

Source: M. Bayo, A. Garcia, and A. Garcia, "Noise Levels in an Urban Hospital and Workers' Subjective Responses," *Archives of Environmental Health* 50, no. 3, p. 249 (May–June 1995). Reprinted with permission of the Helen Dwight Reid Educational Foundation. Published by Heldref Publications, 1319 Eighteenth St. N.W., Washington, D.C. 20036-1802. Copyright © 1995.

20. Length of Growing Seasons The growing seasons for a random sample of 35 U.S. cities were recorded, yielding a sample mean of 190.7 days and the population standard deviation of 54.2 days. Estimate for all U.S. cities the true mean of the growing season with 95% confidence.

Source: *The Old Farmer's Almanac.*

21. Monthly Gasoline Expenditures How large a sample is needed to estimate the population mean monthly gasoline expenditure within $10 with 95% confidence? The population standard deviation is $59.50.

22. Hospital Noise Levels In the hospital study cited in Exercise 19, the mean noise level in 171 randomly selected ward areas was 58.0 decibels, and the population standard deviation was 4.8. Find the 90% confidence interval of the true mean.

Source: M. Bayo, A. Garcia, and A. Garcia, "Noise Levels in an Urban Hospital and Workers' Subjective Responses," *Archives of Environmental Health* 50, no. 3, p. 249 (May–June 1995). Reprinted with permission of the Helen Dwight Reid Educational Foundation. Published by Heldref Publications, 1319 Eighteenth St. N.W., Washington, D.C. 20036-1802. Copyright © 1995.

23. Birth Weights of Infants A health care professional wishes to estimate the birth weights of infants. How large a sample must be obtained if she desires to be 90% confident that the true mean is within 2 ounces of the sample mean? Assume $\sigma = 8$ ounces.

24. Cost of Pizzas A pizza shop owner wishes to find the 95% confidence interval of the true mean cost of a large plain pizza. How large should the sample be if she wishes to be accurate to within $0.15? A previous study showed that the standard deviation of the price was $0.26.

25. National Accounting Examination If the variance of a national accounting examination is 900, how large a sample is needed to estimate the true mean score within 5 points with 99% confidence?

26. Undergraduate GPAs It is desired to estimate the mean GPA of each undergraduate class at a large university. How large a sample is necessary to estimate the GPA within 0.25 at the 99% confidence level? The population standard deviation is 1.2.

≡Technology   Step by Step

TI-84 Plus
Step by Step

Finding a z Confidence Interval for the Mean (Data)

1. Enter the data into L₁.
2. Press **STAT** and move the cursor to TESTS.
3. Press **7** for ZInterval.
4. Move the cursor to Data and press **ENTER**.
5. Type in the appropriate values.
6. Move the cursor to Calculate and press **ENTER**.

Example TI7–1

For Example 7–3 from the text, find the 90% confidence interval for the population mean, given the data values.

12.23	2.89	13.19	73.25	11.59	8.74	7.92	40.22	5.01	2.27
16.56	1.24	9.16	1.91	6.69	3.17	4.78	2.42	1.47	12.77
4.39	2.17	1.42	14.64	1.06	18.13	16.85	21.58	12.24	2.76

The population standard deviation σ is unknown. Since the sample size is $n = 30$, you can use the sample standard deviation s as an approximation for σ. After the data values are entered in L_1 (step 1 above), press **STAT,** move the cursor to CALC, press **1** for 1-Var Stats, then press **ENTER.** The sample standard deviation of 14.40544747 will be one of the statistics listed. Then continue with step 2. At step 5 on the line for σ, press **VARS** for variables, press **5** for Statistics, press **3** for S_x.

The 90% confidence interval is $6.765 < \mu < 15.417$. The difference between these limits and the ones in Example 7–3 is due to rounding.

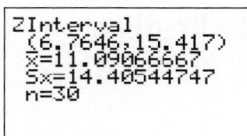

Finding a *z* Confidence Interval for the Mean (Statistics)

1. Press **STAT** and move the cursor to TESTS.
2. Press **7** for ZInterval.
3. Move the cursor to Stats and press **ENTER.**
4. Type in the appropriate values.
5. Move the cursor to Calculate and press **ENTER.**

Example TI7–2

Find the 95% confidence interval for the population mean, given $\sigma = 2$, $\overline{X} = 23.2$, and $n = 50$.

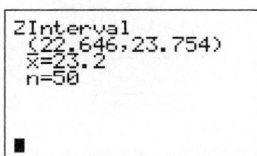

The 95% confidence interval is $22.646 < \mu < 23.754$.

EXCEL
Step by Step

Finding a *z* Confidence Interval for the Mean

Excel has a procedure to compute the margin of error. But it does not compute confidence intervals. However, you may determine confidence intervals for the mean by using the MegaStat Add-in available in your online resources. If you have not installed this add-in, do so, following the instructions from the Chapter 1 Excel Step by Step.

Example XL7–1

Find the 95% confidence interval for the mean if $\sigma = 11$, using this sample:

43	52	18	20	25	45	43	21	42	32	24	32	19	25	26
44	42	41	41	53	22	25	23	21	27	33	36	47	19	20

1. Enter the data into an Excel worksheet.
2. From the toolbar, select Add-Ins, **MegaStat>Confidence Intervals/Sample Size.**
   Note: You may need to open **MegaStat** from the **MegaStat.xls** file on your computer's hard drive.
3. Enter the mean of the data, **32.03.**
4. Select *z* for the standard normal distribution.
5. Enter **11** for the standard deviation and **30** for *n*, the sample size.
6. Either type in or scroll to 95% for the Confidence Level, then click [OK].

The result of the procedure is shown next.

Confidence Interval—Mean

95%	Confidence level
32.03	Mean
11	Standard deviation
30	n
1.960	z
3.936	Half-width
35.966	Upper confidence limit
28.094	Lower confidence limit

MINITAB
Step by Step

Finding a *z* Confidence Interval for the Mean

For Example 7–3, find the 90% confidence interval estimate for the mean amount of assets for credit unions in southwestern Pennsylvania.

1. Maximize the worksheet, then enter the data into C1 of a MINITAB worksheet. Sigma is given as 14.405.

2. Select **Stat>Basic Statistics>1-Sample Z.**

   a) Select C1 Assets for the **Samples in Columns.**

   b) Click in the box for **Standard Deviation** and type 14.405.

3. Click the [Options] button. In the dialog box make sure the **Confidence Level** is 90 and the **Alternative** is not equal. Click [OK].

4. Optional: Click [Graphs], then select **Boxplot of data.** The boxplot of these data will show possible outliers!

5. Click [OK] twice. The results will be displayed in the session window and boxplot.

Boxplot of ASSETS
(with 90% Z-confidence interval for the Mean, and StDev = 14.405)

One-Sample Z: Assets

The assumed standard deviation = 14.405

Variable	N	Mean	StDev	SE Mean	90% CI
Assets	30	11.09	14.41	2.63	(6.76, 15.42)

7–2   Confidence Intervals for the Mean When σ Is Unknown

OBJECTIVE ③

Find the confidence interval for the mean when σ is unknown.

When σ is known and the sample size is 30 or more, or the population is normally distributed if the sample size is less than 30, the confidence interval for the mean can be found by using the z distribution, as shown in Section 7–1. However, most of the time, the value of σ is not known, so it must be estimated by using s, namely, the standard deviation of the sample. When s is used, especially when the sample size is small, critical values greater than the values for $z_{\alpha/2}$ are used in confidence intervals in order to keep the interval at a given level, such as the 95%. These values are taken from the *Student t distribution,* most often called the **t distribution.**

To use this method, the samples must be simple random samples, and the population from which the samples were taken must be normally or approximately normally distributed, or the sample size must be 30 or more.

Some important characteristics of the t distribution are described now.

Characteristics of the *t* Distribution

The t distribution shares some characteristics of the standard normal distribution and differs from it in others. The t distribution is similar to the standard normal distribution in these ways:

1. It is bell-shaped.
2. It is symmetric about the mean.
3. The mean, median, and mode are equal to 0 and are located at the center of the distribution.
4. The curve approaches but never touches the x axis.

The t distribution differs from the standard normal distribution in the following ways:

1. The variance is greater than 1.
2. The t distribution is actually a family of curves based on the concept of *degrees of freedom,* which is related to sample size.
3. As the sample size increases, the t distribution approaches the standard normal distribution. See Figure 7–6.

Many statistical distributions use the concept of degrees of freedom, and the formulas for finding the degrees of freedom vary for different statistical tests. The **degrees of freedom** are the number of values that are free to vary after a sample statistic has been computed, and they tell the researcher which specific curve to use when a distribution consists of a family of curves.

For example, if the mean of 5 values is 10, then 4 of the 5 values are free to vary. But once 4 values are selected, the fifth value must be a specific number to get a sum of 50, since $50 \div 5 = 10$. Hence, the degrees of freedom are $5 - 1 = 4$, and this value tells the researcher which t curve to use.

The symbol d.f. will be used for degrees of freedom. The degrees of freedom for a confidence interval for the mean are found by subtracting 1 from the sample size. That is, d.f. $= n - 1$. *Note:* For some statistical tests used later in this book, the degrees of freedom are not equal to $n - 1$.

FIGURE 7–6
The *t* Family of Curves

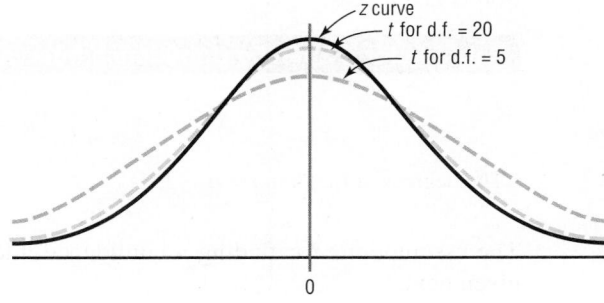

The formula for finding the confidence interval using the t distribution has a critical value $t_{\alpha/2}$.

The values for $t_{\alpha/2}$ are found in Table F in Appendix A. The top row of Table F, labeled Confidence Intervals, is used to get these values. The other two rows, labeled One tail and Two tails, will be explained in Chapter 8 and should not be used here.

Example 7–5 shows how to find the value in Table F for $t_{\alpha/2}$.

EXAMPLE 7–5

Find the $t_{\alpha/2}$ value for a 95% confidence interval when the sample size is 22.

SOLUTION

The d.f. = 22 − 1, or 21. Find 21 in the left column and 95% in the row labeled Confidence Intervals. The intersection where the two meet gives the value for $t_{\alpha/2}$, which is 2.080. See Figure 7–7.

FIGURE 7–7   Finding $t_{\alpha/2}$ for Example 7–5

	Table F The t Distribution					
	Confidence Intervals	80%	90%	95%	98%	99%
d.f.	One tail α	0.10	0.05	0.025	0.01	0.005
	Two tails α	0.20	0.10	0.05	0.02	0.01
1						
2						
3						
⋮						
21				2.080	2.518	2.831
⋮						
$(z)^\infty$		1.282[a]	1.645[b]	1.960	2.326[c]	2.576[d]

When d.f. is greater than 30, it may fall between two table values. For example, if d.f. = 68, it falls between 65 and 70. Many texts say to use the closest value, for example, 68 is closer to 70 than 65; however, in this text a conservative approach is used. In this case, always round down to the nearest table value. In this case, 68 rounds down to 65.

Note: At the bottom of Table F where d.f. is large or ∞, the $z_{\alpha/2}$ values can be found for specific confidence intervals. The reason is that as the degrees of freedom increase, the t distribution approaches the standard normal distribution.

Examples 7–6 and 7–7 show how to find the confidence interval when you are using the t distribution.

The formula for finding a confidence interval about the mean by using the t distribution is given next.

Formula for a Specific Confidence Interval for the Mean When σ Is Unknown

$$\bar{X} - t_{\alpha/2}\left(\frac{s}{\sqrt{n}}\right) < \mu < \bar{X} + t_{\alpha/2}\left(\frac{s}{\sqrt{n}}\right)$$

The degrees of freedom are $n - 1$.

The assumptions for finding a confidence interval for a mean when σ is unknown are given next.

> **Assumptions for Finding a Confidence Interval for a Mean When σ Is Unknown**
>
> 1. The sample is a random sample.
> 2. Either $n \geq 30$ or the population is normally distributed when $n < 30$.

In this text, the assumptions will be stated in the exercises; however, when encountering statistics in other situations, you must check to see that these assumptions have been met before proceeding.

EXAMPLE 7–6   Infant Growth

A random sample of 10 children found that their average growth for the first year was 9.8 inches. Assume the variable is normally distributed and the sample standard deviation is 0.96 inch. Find the 95% confidence interval of the population mean for growth during the first year.

SOLUTION

$$\overline{X} = 9.8 \qquad s = 0.96 \qquad n = 10$$

Since σ is unknown and s must replace it, the t distribution (Table F) must be used for the confidence interval. Hence, with 9 degrees of freedom $t_{\alpha/2} = 2.262$. The 95% confidence interval can be found by substituting in the formula.

$$\overline{X} - t_{\alpha/2}\left(\frac{s}{\sqrt{n}}\right) < \mu < \overline{X} + t_{\alpha/2}\left(\frac{s}{\sqrt{n}}\right)$$

$$9.8 - 2.262\left(\frac{0.96}{\sqrt{10}}\right) < \mu < 9.8 + 2.262\left(\frac{0.96}{\sqrt{10}}\right)$$

$$9.8 - 0.69 < \mu < 9.8 + 0.69$$

$$9.11 < \mu < 10.49$$

Therefore, one can be 95% confident that the population mean of the first-year growth is between 9.11 and 10.49 inches.

EXAMPLE 7–7   Home Fires Started by Candles

The data represent a random sample of the number of home fires started by candles for the past several years. (Data are from the National Fire Protection Association.) Find the 99% confidence interval for the mean number of home fires started by candles each year.

5460	5900	6090	6310	7160	8440	9930

SOLUTION

Step 1   Find the mean and standard deviation for the data. Use the formulas in Chapter 3 or your calculator. The mean $\overline{X} = 7041.4$. The standard deviation $s = 1610.3$.

Step 2   Find $t_{\alpha/2}$ in Table F. Use the 99% confidence interval with d.f. = 6. It is 3.707.

Step 3   Substitute in the formula and solve.

$$\overline{X} - t_{\alpha/2}\left(\frac{s}{\sqrt{n}}\right) < \mu < \overline{X} + t_{\alpha/2}\left(\frac{s}{\sqrt{n}}\right)$$

$$7041.4 - 3.707\left(\frac{1610.3}{\sqrt{7}}\right) < \mu < 7041.4 + 3.707\left(\frac{1610.3}{\sqrt{7}}\right)$$

$$7041.4 - 2256.2 < \mu < 7041.4 + 2256.2$$

$$4785.2 < \mu < 9297.6$$

One can be 99% confident that the population mean number of home fires started by candles each year is between 4785.2 and 9297.6, based on a sample of home fires occurring over a period of 7 years.

FIGURE 7–8

When to Use the *z* or *t* Distribution

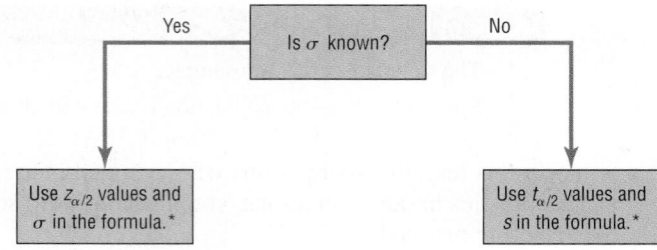

*If *n* < 30, the variable must be normally distributed.

Students sometimes have difficulty deciding whether to use $z_{\alpha/2}$ or $t_{\alpha/2}$ values when finding confidence intervals for the mean. As stated previously, when σ is known, $z_{\alpha/2}$ values can be used *no matter what the sample size is,* as long as the variable is normally distributed or $n \geq 30$. When σ is unknown and $n \geq 30$, then *s* can be used in the formula and $t_{\alpha/2}$ values can be used. Finally, when σ is unknown and $n < 30$, *s* is used in the formula and $t_{\alpha/2}$ values are used, as long as the variable is approximately normally distributed. These rules are summarized in Figure 7–8.

Applying the Concepts 7–2

Sport Drink Decision

Assume you get a new job as a coach for a sports team, and one of your first decisions is to choose the sports drink that the team will use during practices and games. You obtain a *Sports Report* magazine so you can use your statistical background to help you make the best decision. The following table lists the most popular sports drinks and some important information about each. Answer the following questions about the table.

Drink	Calories	Sodium	Potassium	Cost
Gatorade	60	110	25	$1.29
Powerade	68	77	32	1.19
All Sport	75	55	55	0.89
10-K	63	55	35	0.79
Exceed	69	50	44	1.59
1st Ade	58	58	25	1.09
Hydra Fuel	85	23	50	1.89

1. Would this be considered a small sample?

2. Compute the mean cost per container, and create a 90% confidence interval about that mean. Do all the costs per container fall inside the confidence interval? If not, which ones do not?

3. Are there any you would consider outliers?

4. How many degrees of freedom are there?

5. If cost is a major factor influencing your decision, would you consider cost per container or cost per serving?

6. List which drink you would recommend and why.

See page 411 for the answers.

Exercises 7–2

1. What are the properties of the *t* distribution?

2. What is meant by *degrees of freedom?*

3. Find the values for each.

   a. $t_{\alpha/2}$ and $n = 18$ for the 99% confidence interval for the mean

   b. $t_{\alpha/2}$ and $n = 23$ for the 95% confidence interval for the mean

   c. $t_{\alpha/2}$ and $n = 15$ for the 98% confidence interval for the mean

   d. $t_{\alpha/2}$ and $n = 10$ for the 90% confidence interval for the mean

   e. $t_{\alpha/2}$ and $n = 20$ for the 95% confidence interval for the mean

4. When should the *t* distribution be used to find a confidence interval for the mean?

For Exercises 5 through 20, assume that all variables are approximately normally distributed.

5. **High Temperatures for May** The predicted high temperatures for a day in late May for a random sample of U.S. cities are listed here. Estimate the mean population high temperature with 90% confidence.

60	73	103	67	89	76
88	86	79	72	88	87

6. **Digital Camera Prices** The prices (in dollars) for a particular model of digital camera with 6.0 megapixels and an optical 3X zoom lens are shown here for 10 randomly selected online retailers. Estimate the true mean price for this particular model with 95% confidence.

   225 240 215 206 211 210 193 250 225 202

7. **Women Representatives in State Legislature** A state representative wishes to estimate the mean number of women representatives per state legislature. A random sample of 17 states is selected, and the number of women representatives is shown. Based on the sample, what is the point estimate of the mean? Find the 90% confidence interval of the mean population. (*Note:* The population mean is actually 31.72, or about 32.) Compare this value to the point estimate and the confidence interval. There is something unusual about the data. Describe it and state how it would affect the confidence interval.

5	33	35	37	24
31	16	45	19	13
18	29	15	39	18
58	132			

8. **State Gasoline Taxes** A random sample of state gasoline taxes (in cents) is shown here for 12 states. Use the data to estimate the true population mean gasoline tax with 90%

confidence. Does your interval contain the national average of 44.7 cents?

38.4	40.9	67	32.5	51.5	43.4
38	43.4	50.7	35.4	39.3	41.4

Source: http://www.api.org/statistics/fueltaxes/

9. **Calories in Candy Bars** The number of calories per candy bar for a random sample of standard-size candy bars is shown below. Estimate the mean number of calories per candy bar with 98% confidence.

220	220	210	230	275
260	240	260	220	240
240	280	230	280	

10. **Dance Company Students** The number of students who belong to the dance company at each of several randomly selected small universities is shown here. Estimate the true population mean size of a university dance company with 99% confidence.

21	25	32	22	28	30	29	30
47	26	35	26	35	26	28	28
32	27	40					

11. **Distance Traveled to Work** A recent study of 28 randomly selected employees of a company showed that the mean of the distance they traveled to work was 14.3 miles. The standard deviation of the sample mean was 2.0 miles. Find the 95% confidence interval of the true mean. If a manager wanted to be sure that most of his employees would not be late, how much time would he suggest they allow for the commute if the average speed were 30 miles per hour?

12. **Thunderstorm Speeds** A meteorologist who sampled 13 randomly selected thunderstorms found that the average speed at which they traveled across a certain state was 15.0 miles per hour. The standard deviation of the sample was 1.7 miles per hour. Find the 99% confidence interval of the mean. If a meteorologist wanted to use the highest speed to predict the times it would take storms to travel across the state in order to issue warnings, what figure would she likely use?

13. **Students per Teacher in U.S. Public Schools** The national average for the number of students per teacher for all U.S. public schools is 15.9. A random sample of 12 school districts from a moderately populated area showed that the mean number of students per teacher was 19.2 with a variance of 4.41. Estimate the true mean number of students per teacher with 95% confidence. How does your estimate compare with the national average?

    Source: *World Almanac.*

14. **Social Networking Sites** A recent survey of 8 randomly selected social networking sites has a mean of

13.1 million visitors for a specific month. The standard deviation is 4.1 million. Find the 95% confidence interval of the true mean.

Source: ComScore Media Matrix.

15. **Chicago Commuters** A sample of 14 randomly selected commuters in Chicago showed the average of the commuting times was 33.2 minutes. If the standard deviation was 8.3 minutes, find the 95% confidence interval of the true mean.

Source: U.S. Census Bureau.

16. **Hospital Noise Levels** For a random sample of 24 operating rooms taken in the hospital study mentioned in Exercise 19 in Section 7–1, the mean noise level was 41.6 decibels, and the standard deviation was 7.5. Find the 95% confidence interval of the true mean of the noise levels in the operating rooms.

Source: M. Bayo, A. Garcia, and A. Garcia, "Noise Levels in an Urban Hospital and Workers' Subjective Responses," *Archives of Environmental Health* 50, no. 3, p. 249 (May–June 1995). Reprinted with permission of the Helen Dwight Reid Educational Foundation. Published by Heldref Publications, 1319 Eighteenth St. N.W., Washington, D.C. 20036-1802. Copyright © 1995.

17. **Costs for a 30-Second Spot on Cable Television** The approximate costs for 30-second randomly selected spots for various cable networks in a random selection of cities are shown. Estimate the true population mean cost for a 30-second advertisement on cable network with 90% confidence.

| 14 | 55 | 165 | 9 | 15 | 66 | 23 | 30 | 150 |
| 22 | 12 | 13 | 54 | 73 | 55 | 41 | 78 | |

Source: www.spotrunner.com

18. **Indy 500 Qualifier Speeds** The speeds in miles per hour of eight randomly selected qualifiers for the Indianapolis 500 (in 2012) are listed below. Estimate the mean qualifying speed with 95% confidence.

| 224.037 | 226.484 | 222.891 | 222.929 |
| 223.422 | 225.172 | 226.240 | 223.684 |

19. **NYSE Stock Prices** An investing club randomly selects 15 NYSE stocks for consideration, and the prices per share are listed here. Estimate the mean price in dollars of all stocks with 95% confidence.

41.53	19.83	15.18	50.40	29.97
58.42	21.63	121.17	5.49	54.87
13.10	87.78	19.32	54.83	13.89

20. **Unhealthy Days in Cities** The number of unhealthy days based on the AQI (Air Quality Index) for a random sample of metropolitan areas is shown. Construct a 98% confidence interval based on the data.

| 61 | 12 | 6 | 40 | 27 | 38 | 93 | 5 | 13 | 40 |

Source: *New York Times Almanac.*

Extending the Concepts

21. **Parking Meter Revenue** A *one-sided confidence interval* can be found for a mean by using

$$\mu > \bar{X} - t_\alpha \frac{s}{\sqrt{n}} \quad \text{or} \quad \mu < \bar{X} + t_\alpha \frac{s}{\sqrt{n}}$$

where t_α is the value found under the row labeled One tail. Find two one-sided 95% confidence intervals of the population mean for the data shown, and interpret the answers. The data represent the daily revenues in dollars from 20 parking meters in a small municipality.

2.60	1.05	2.45	2.90
1.30	3.10	2.35	2.00
2.40	2.35	2.40	1.95
2.80	2.50	2.10	1.75
1.00	2.75	1.80	1.95

Technology   Step by Step

TI-84 Plus

Step by Step

Finding a *t* Confidence Interval for the Mean (Data)

1. Enter the data into L_1.
2. Press **STAT** and move the cursor to TESTS.
3. Press **8** for TInterval.
4. Move the cursor to Data and press **ENTER**.
5. Type in the appropriate values.
6. Move the cursor to Calculate and press **ENTER**.

Finding a *t* Confidence Interval for the Mean (Statistics)

1. Press **STAT** and move the cursor to TESTS.
2. Press **8** for TInterval.
3. Move the cursor to Stats and press **ENTER**.
4. Type in the appropriate values.
5. Move the cursor to Calculate and press **ENTER**.

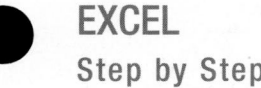

EXCEL
Step by Step

Finding a *t* Confidence Interval for the Mean

Excel has a procedure to compute the margin of error. But it does not compute confidence intervals. However, you may determine confidence intervals for the mean by using the MegaStat Add-in available in your online resources. If you have not installed this add-in, do so, following the instructions from the Chapter 1 Excel Step by Step.

Example XL7–2

Find the 95% confidence interval, using these sample data:

| 625 | 675 | 535 | 406 | 512 | 680 | 483 | 522 | 619 | 575 |

1. Enter the data into an Excel worksheet.

2. From the toolbar, select Add-Ins, **MegaStat>Confidence Intervals/Sample Size.** *Note:* You may need to open **MegaStat** from the **MegaStat.xls** file on your computer's hard drive.

3. Enter the mean of the data, **563.2.**

4. Select *t* for the *t* distribution.

5. Enter **87.9** for the standard deviation and **10** for *n*, the sample size.

6. Either type in or scroll to 95% for the Confidence Level, then click [OK].

The result of the procedure is shown next.

Confidence Interval—Mean

95%	Confidence level
563.2	Mean
87.9	Standard deviation
10	*n*
2.262	*t* (d.f. = 9)
62.880	Half-width
626.080	Upper confidence limit
500.320	Lower confidence limit

MINITAB
Step by Step

Find a *t* Interval for the Mean

For Example 7–7, find the 99% confidence interval for the mean number of home fires started by candles each year.

1. Type the data into C1 of a MINITAB worksheet. Name the column **Home Fires.**

2. Select **Stat>Basic Statistics>1-Sample t.**

3. Double-click C1 Home Fires for the Samples in Columns.

4. Click on [Options] and be sure the Confidence Level is 99 and the Alternative is not equal.

5. Click [OK] twice.

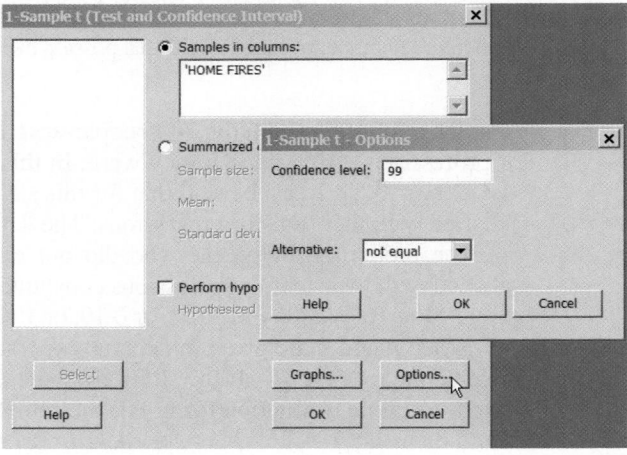

6. Check for normality:

  a) Select **Graph>Probability Plot,** then Single.

  b) Select C1 Home Fires for the variable. The normal plot is concave, a skewed distribution.

In the session window you will see the results. The 99% confidence interval estimate for μ is between 4785 and 9298. The sample size, mean, standard deviation, and standard error of the mean are also shown.

  However, this small sample appears to have a nonnormal population. The interval is less likely to contain the true mean.

One-Sample T: HOME FIRES

Variable	N	Mean	StDev	SE Mean	99% CI
HOME FIRES	7	7041	1610	609	(4785, 9298)

7–3   Confidence Intervals and Sample Size for Proportions

OBJECTIVE ❹

Find the confidence interval for a proportion.

One of the most common types of confidence intervals is one that uses proportions. Many statistical studies involve finding a proportion of the population that has a certain characteristic. In this section, you will learn how to find the confidence interval for a population.

  A *USA TODAY* Snapshots feature stated that 12% of the pleasure boats in the United States were named *Serenity*. The parameter 12% is called a **proportion.** It means that of all the pleasure boats in the United States, 12 out of every 100 are named *Serenity*. A proportion represents a part of a whole. It can be expressed as a fraction, decimal, or percentage. In this case, $12\% = 0.12 = \frac{12}{100}$ or $\frac{3}{25}$. Proportions can also represent probabilities. In this case, if a pleasure boat is selected at random, the probability that it is called *Serenity* is 0.12.

  Proportions can be obtained from samples or populations. The following symbols will be used.

Symbols Used in Proportion Notation

$$p = \text{population proportion}$$

$$\hat{p} \ (\text{read ``}p\text{ hat''}) = \text{sample proportion}$$

For a sample proportion,

$$\hat{p} = \frac{X}{n} \qquad \text{and} \qquad \hat{q} = \frac{n - X}{n} \qquad \text{or} \qquad \hat{q} = 1 - \hat{p}$$

where X = number of sample units that possess the characteristics of interest and n = sample size.

  For example, in a study, 200 people were asked if they were satisfied with their jobs or professions; 162 said that they were. In this case, $n = 200$, $X = 162$, and $\hat{p} = X/n = 162/200 = 0.81$. It can be said that for this sample, 0.81, or 81%, of those surveyed were satisfied with their jobs or professions. The sample proportion is $\hat{p} = 0.81$.

  The proportion of people who did not respond favorably when asked if they were satisfied with their jobs or professions constituted $\hat{q}$, where $\hat{q} = (n - X)/n$. For this survey, $\hat{q} = (200 - 162)/200 = 38/200$, or 0.19, or 19%.

  When $\hat{p}$ and $\hat{q}$ are given in decimals or fractions, $\hat{p} + \hat{q} = 1$. When $\hat{p}$ and $\hat{q}$ are given in percentages, $\hat{p} + \hat{q} = 100\%$. It follows, then, that $\hat{q} = 1 - \hat{p}$, or $\hat{p} = 1 - \hat{q}$, when $\hat{p}$ and $\hat{q}$ are in decimal or fraction form. For the sample survey on job satisfaction, $\hat{q}$ can also be found by using $\hat{q} = 1 - \hat{p}$, or $1 - 0.81 = 0.19$.

Similar reasoning applies to population proportions; that is, $p = 1 - q$, $q = 1 - p$, and $p + q = 1$, when p and q are expressed in decimal or fraction form. When p and q are expressed as percentages, $p + q = 100\%$, $p = 100\% - q$, and $q = 100\% - p$.

EXAMPLE 7–8   Driving to Work

A random sample of 200 workers found that 128 drove to work alone. Find $\hat{p}$ and $\hat{q}$, where $\hat{p}$ is the proportion of workers who drove to work alone.

SOLUTION

In this case, $X = 128$ and $n = 200$.

$$\hat{p} = \frac{X}{n} = \frac{128}{200} = 0.64 = 64\%$$

$$\hat{q} = \frac{n - X}{200} = \frac{200 - 128}{200} = \frac{72}{200} = 0.36 = 36\%$$

Also $\hat{q}$ can be found by using the formula $\hat{q} = 1 - \hat{p}$. In this case, $\hat{q} = 1 - 0.64 = 0.36$. So 64% of the people in the survey drive to work alone, and 36% drive with others.

As with means, the statistician, given the sample proportion, tries to estimate the population proportion. Point and interval estimates for a population proportion can be made by using the sample proportion. For a point estimate of p (the population proportion), $\hat{p}$ (the sample proportion) is used. On the basis of the three properties of a good estimator, $\hat{p}$ is unbiased, consistent, and relatively efficient. But as with means, one is not able to decide how good the point estimate of p is. Therefore, statisticians also use an interval estimate for a proportion, and they can assign a probability that the interval will contain the population proportion.

The confidence interval for a particular p is based on the sampling distribution of $\hat{p}$. When the sample size n is no more than 5% of the population size, the sampling distribution of $\hat{p}$ is approximately normal with a mean of p and a standard deviation of $\sqrt{pq/n}$, where $q = 1 - p$.

Confidence Intervals

To construct a confidence interval about a proportion, you must use the margin of error, which is

$$E = z_{\alpha/2}\sqrt{\frac{\hat{p}\hat{q}}{n}}$$

Confidence intervals about proportions must meet the criteria that $n\hat{p} \geq 5$ and $n\hat{q} \geq 5$.

Formula for a Specific Confidence Interval for a Proportion

$$\hat{p} - z_{\alpha/2}\sqrt{\frac{\hat{p}\hat{q}}{n}} < p < \hat{p} + z_{\alpha/2}\sqrt{\frac{\hat{p}\hat{q}}{n}}$$

when $n\hat{p}$ and $n\hat{q}$ are each greater than or equal to 5.

Assumptions for Finding a Confidence Interval for a Population Proportion

1. The sample is a random sample.
2. The conditions for a binomial experiment are satisfied (see Chapter 5).

In this book, the assumptions will be stated in the exercises; however, when encountering statistics in other situations, you must check to see that these assumptions have been met before proceeding.

Rounding Rule for a Confidence Interval for a Proportion Round off to three decimal places.

EXAMPLE 7–9 Covering College Costs

A survey conducted by Sallie Mae and Gallup of 1404 respondents found that 323 students paid for their education by student loans. Find the 90% confidence interval of the true proportion of students who paid for their education by student loans.

SOLUTION

Step 1 Determine $\hat{p}$ and $\hat{q}$.

$$\hat{p} = \frac{X}{n} = \frac{323}{1404} = 0.23$$

$$\hat{q} = 1 - \hat{p} = 1.00 - 0.23 = 0.77$$

Step 2 Determine the critical value.

$$\alpha = 1 - 0.90 = 0.10$$

$$\frac{\alpha}{2} = \frac{0.10}{2} = 0.05$$

$$z_{\alpha/2} = 1.65$$

Step 3 Substitute in the formula

$$\hat{p} - z_{\alpha/2}\sqrt{\frac{\hat{p}\hat{q}}{n}} < p < \hat{p} + z_{\alpha/2}\sqrt{\frac{\hat{p}\hat{q}}{n}}$$

$$0.23 - 1.65\sqrt{\frac{(0.23)(0.77)}{1404}} < p < 0.23 + 1.65\sqrt{\frac{(0.23)(0.77)}{1404}}$$

$$0.23 - 0.019 < p < 0.23 + 0.019$$

$$0.211 < p < 0.249$$

or

$$21.1\% < p < 24.9\%$$

Hence, you can be 90% confident that the percentage of students who pay for their college education by student loans is between 21.1 and 24.9%.

When a specific percentage is given, the percentage becomes $\hat{p}$ when it is changed to a decimal. For example, if the problem states that 12% of the applicants were men, then $\hat{p} = 0.12$.

EXAMPLE 7–10 Lawn Weeds

A survey of 1898 adults with lawns conducted by Harris Interactive Poll found that 45% of the adults said that dandelions were the toughest weeds to control in their yards. Find the 95% confidence interval of the true proportion who said that dandelions were the toughest weeds to control in their yards.

SOLUTION

Step 1 Determine $\hat{p}$ and $\hat{q}$.

In this case, $\hat{p}$ is already given. It is 45%, or 0.45.

$$\hat{q} = 1 - \hat{p} = 1.00 - 0.45 = 0.55$$

Step 2   Determine the critical value.

$$\alpha = 1 - 0.95 = 0.05$$

$$\frac{\alpha}{2} = \frac{0.05}{2} = 0.025$$

$$z_{\alpha/2} = 1.96$$

Step 3   Substitute in the formula.

$$\hat{p} - z_{\alpha/2}\sqrt{\frac{\hat{p}\hat{q}}{n}} < p < \hat{p} + z_{\alpha/2}\sqrt{\frac{\hat{p}\hat{q}}{n}}$$

$$0.45 - 1.96\sqrt{\frac{(0.45)(0.55)}{1898}} < p < 0.45 + 1.96\sqrt{\frac{(0.45)(0.55)}{1898}}$$

$$0.45 - 0.022 < p < 0.45 + 0.022$$

$$0.428 < p < 0.472$$

$$42.8\% < p < 47.2\%$$

Hence, you can say with 95% confidence that the true percentage of adults who consider dandelions the toughest weeds to control in their lawns is between 42.8% and 47.2%.

Sample Size for Proportions

To find the sample size needed to determine a confidence interval about a proportion, use this formula:

OBJECTIVE 5

Determine the minimum sample size for finding a confidence interval for a proportion.

> **Formula for Minimum Sample Size Needed for Interval Estimate of a Population Proportion**
>
> $$n = \hat{p}\hat{q}\left(\frac{z_{\alpha/2}}{E}\right)^2$$
>
> If necessary, round up to obtain a whole number.

This formula can be found by solving the margin of error value for n in the formula

$$E = z_{\alpha/2}\sqrt{\frac{\hat{p}\hat{q}}{n}}$$

There are two situations to consider. First, if some approximation of $\hat{p}$ is known (e.g., from a previous study), that value can be used in the formula.

Second, if no approximation of $\hat{p}$ is known, you should use $\hat{p} = 0.5$. This value will give a sample size sufficiently large to guarantee an accurate prediction, given the confidence interval and the error of estimate. The reason is that when $\hat{p}$ and $\hat{q}$ are each 0.5, the product $\hat{p}\hat{q}$ is at maximum, as shown here.

$\hat{p}$	$\hat{q}$	$\hat{p}\hat{q}$
0.1	0.9	0.09
0.2	0.8	0.16
0.3	0.7	0.21
0.4	0.6	0.24
0.5	**0.5**	**0.25**
0.6	0.4	0.24
0.7	0.3	0.21
0.8	0.2	0.16
0.9	0.1	0.09

Using the maximum value yields the largest possible value of n for a given margin of error and for a given confidence interval.

The disadvantage of this method is that it can lead to a larger sample size than is necessary.

W. C. Fields said, "Start every day off with a smile and get it over with."

Do you think people are happy because they are successful, or are they successful because they are happy people? A recent survey conducted by *Money* magazine showed that 34% of the people surveyed said that they were happy because they were successful; however, 63% said that they were successful because they were happy individuals. The people surveyed had an average household income of $75,000 or more. The margin of error was ±2.5%. Based on the information in this article, what would be the confidence interval for each percent?

EXAMPLE 7–11   Home Computers

A researcher wishes to estimate, with 95% confidence, the proportion of people who own a home computer. A previous study shows that 40% of those interviewed had a computer at home. The researcher wishes to be accurate within 2% of the true proportion. Find the minimum sample size necessary.

SOLUTION

Since $z_{\alpha/2} = 1.96$, $E = 0.02$, $\hat{p} = 0.40$, and $\hat{p} = 0.60$, then

$$n = \hat{p}\hat{q}\left(\frac{z_{\alpha/2}}{E}\right)^2 = (0.40)(0.60)\left(\frac{1.96}{0.02}\right)^2 = 2304.96$$

which, when rounded up, is 2305 people to interview. So the researcher must interview 2305 people.

EXAMPLE 7–12   Home Computers

In Example 7–11 assume that no previous study was done. Find the minimum sample size necessary to be accurate within 2% of the true population.

SOLUTION

Here we do not know the values of $\hat{p}$ and $\hat{q}$. So we use $\hat{p} = 0.5$ and $\hat{q} = 0.5$.

$$E = 0.02 \quad \text{and} \quad z_{\alpha/2} = 1.96$$

$$n = \hat{p}\hat{q}\left(\frac{z_{\alpha/2}}{E}\right)^2$$

$$= (0.5)(0.5)\left(\frac{1.96}{0.02}\right)^2$$

$$= 2401$$

Hence, 2401 people must be interviewed when $\hat{p}$ is unknown. This is 96 more people than needed if $\hat{p}$ is known.

In determining the sample size, the size of the population is irrelevant. Only the degree of confidence and the margin of error are necessary to make the determination.

Applying the Concepts 7–3

Contracting Influenza

To answer the questions, use the following table describing the percentage of people who reported contracting influenza by gender and race/ethnicity.

Influenza		
Characteristic	**Percent**	**(95% CI)**
Gender		
Men	48.8	(47.1–50.5%)
Women	51.5	(50.2–52.8%)
Race/ethnicity		
Caucasian	52.2	(51.1–53.3%)
African American	33.1	(29.5–36.7%)
Hispanic	47.6	(40.9–54.3%)
Other	39.7	(30.8–48.5%)
Total	50.4	(49.3–51.5%)

Forty-nine states and the District of Columbia participated in the study. Weighted means were used. The sample size was 19,774. There were 12,774 women and 7000 men.

1. Explain what (95% CI) means.
2. How large is the margin of error for men reporting influenza?
3. What is the sample size?
4. How does the sample size affect the size of the confidence interval?
5. Would the confidence intervals be larger or smaller for a 90% CI, using the same data?
6. Where does the 51.5% influenza for women fit into its associated 95% CI?

See pages 411–412 for the answers.

Exercises 7–3

1. In each case, find $\hat{p}$ and $\hat{q}$.
   a. $n = 80$ and $X = 40$
   b. $n = 200$ and $X = 90$
   c. $n = 130$ and $X = 60$
   d. 25%
   e. 42%

2. Find $\hat{p}$ and $\hat{q}$ for each percentage.
   a. $n = 60$ and $X = 35$
   b. $n = 95$ and $X = 43$
   c. 68%
   d. 55%
   e. 12%

3. **Perry Como Fans** Fifty-six percent of respondents to an online poll said that they were Perry Como fans. If 982 randomly selected people responded to this poll, what is the true proportion of all local residents who are Perry Como fans? Estimate at the 95% confidence level.

   Source: *Washington Observer-Reporter.*

4. **Manual Transmission Automobiles** In 1980 more than 35% of cars purchased had a manual transmission (i.e. stick shift). By 2007 the proportion had decreased to 7.7%. A random sample of college students who owned cars revealed the following: out of 122 cars, 26 had stick shifts. Estimate the proportion of college students who drive sticks with 90% confidence.

   Source: pollingreport.com

5. **Private Schools** The proportion of students in private schools is around 11%. A random sample of 450 students from a wide geographic area indicated that 55 attended private schools. Estimate the true proportion of students attending private schools with 95% confidence. How does your estimate compare to 11%?

   Source: National Center for Education Statistics (www.nces.ed.gov).

6. **Belief in Haunted Places** A random sample of 205 college students was asked if they believed that places could be haunted, and 65 responded yes. Estimate the true proportion of college students who believe in the

possibility of haunted places with 99% confidence. According to *Time* magazine, 37% of all Americans believe that places can be haunted.

Source: *Time* magazine, Oct. 2006.

7. Work Interruptions A survey found that out of a random sample of 200 workers, 168 said they were interrupted three or more times an hour by phone messages, faxes, etc. Find the 90% confidence interval of the population proportion of workers who are interrupted three or more times an hour.

Source: Based on information from *USA TODAY* Snapshot.

8. Travel to Outer Space A CBS News/*New York Times* poll found that 329 out of 763 randomly selected adults said they would travel to outer space in their lifetime, given the chance. Estimate the true proportion of adults who would like to travel to outer space with 92% confidence.

Source: www.pollingreport.com

9. High School Graduates Who Take the SAT The national average for the percentage of high school graduates taking the SAT is 49%, but the state averages vary from a low of 4% to a high of 92%. A random sample of 300 graduating high school seniors was polled across a particular tristate area, and it was found that 195 had taken the SAT. Estimate the true proportion of high school graduates in this region who take the SAT with 95% confidence.

Source: *World Almanac.*

10. Educational Television In a random sample of 200 people, 154 said that they watched educational television. Find the 90% confidence interval of the true proportion of people who watched educational television. If the television company wanted to publicize the proportion of viewers, do you think it should use the 90% confidence interval?

11. Fruit Consumption A nutritionist found that in a random sample of 80 families, 25% indicated that they ate fruit at least 3 times a week. Find the 99% confidence interval of the true proportion of families who said that they ate fruit at least 3 times a week. Would a proportion of families equal to 28% be considered large?

12. Students Who Major in Business It has been reported that 20.4% of incoming freshmen indicate that they will major in business or a related field. A random sample of 400 incoming college freshmen was asked their preference, and 95 replied that they were considering business as a major. Estimate the true proportion of freshman business majors with 98% confidence. Does your interval contain 20.4?

Source: *New York Times Almanac.*

13. Home Security Systems In 2008, 17% of American homes were protected by a home security system. A marketing firm wanted to estimate the proportion of

protected homes today. It chose a random sample of 200 homes and discovered that 53 had home security systems. Estimate the true proportion of homes with security systems with 99% confidence.

Source: pollingreport.com

14. Home Broadband Internet Access According to a study, 76% of adults ages 18–29 years had broadband Internet access at home in 2011. A researcher wanted to estimate the proportion of undergraduate college students (18–23 years) with access, so she randomly sampled 180 undergraduates and found that 157 had access. Estimate the true proportion with 90% confidence.

Source: *World Almanac 2012.*

15. Overseas Travel A researcher wishes to be 95% confident that her estimate of the true proportion of individuals who travel overseas is within 4% of the true proportion. Find the sample necessary if, in a prior study, a sample of 200 people showed that 40 traveled overseas last year. If no estimate of the sample proportion is available, how large should the sample be?

16. Widows A recent study indicated that 29% of the 100 women over age 55 in the study were widows.

   a. How large a sample must you take to be 90% confident that the estimate is within 0.05 of the true proportion of women over age 55 who are widows?

   b. If no estimate of the sample proportion is available, how large should the sample be?

17. Direct Satellite Television It is believed that 25% of U.S. homes have a direct satellite television receiver. How large a sample is necessary to estimate the true population of homes that do with 95% confidence and within 3 percentage points? How large a sample is necessary if nothing is known about the proportion?

Source: *New York Times Almanac.*

18. Obesity Obesity is defined as a *body mass index* (BMI) of 30 kg/m^2 or more. A 95% confidence interval for the percentage of U.S. adults aged 20 years and over who were obese was found to be 22.4 to 23.5%. What was the sample size?

Source: National Center for Health Statistics (www.cdc.gov/nchs).

19. Unmarried Americans Nearly one-half of Americans aged 25 to 29 are unmarried. How large a sample is necessary to estimate the true proportion of unmarried Americans in this age group within 2½ percentage points with 90% confidence?

Source: *Time* magazine, Oct. 2006.

20. Diet Habits A federal report indicated that 27% of children ages 2 to 5 years had a good diet—an increase over previous years. How large a sample is needed to estimate the true proportion of children with good diets within 2% with 95% confidence?

Source: Federal Interagency Forum on Child and Family Statistics, *Washington Observer-Reporter.*

≡ Extending the Concepts

21. Gun Control If a random sample of 600 people is selected and the researcher decides to have a margin of error of 4% on the specific proportion who favor gun control, find the degree of confidence. A recent study showed that 50% were in favor of some form of gun control.

22. Survey on Politics In a study, 68% of 1015 randomly selected adults said that they believe the Republicans favor the rich. If the margin of error was 3 percentage points, what was the confidence level used for the proportion?
Source: *USA TODAY.*

≡ Technology   Step by Step

TI-84 Plus
Step by Step

Finding a Confidence Interval for a Proportion

1. Press **STAT** and move the cursor to TESTS.
2. Press **A (ALPHA, MATH)** for 1-PropZInt.
3. Type in the appropriate values.
4. Move the cursor to Calculate and press **ENTER**.

Example TI7–3

Find the 95% confidence interval of p when $X = 60$ and $n = 500$.
    The 95% confidence level for p is $0.09152 < p < 0.14848$.
Also $\hat{p}$ is given.

EXCEL
Step by Step

Finding a Confidence Interval for a Proportion

Excel has a procedure to compute the margin of error. But it does not compute confidence intervals. However, you may determine confidence intervals for a proportion by using the MegaStat Add-in available in your online resources. If you have not installed this add-in, do so, following the instructions from the Chapter 1 Excel Step by Step.

Example XL7–3

There were 500 nursing applications in a sample, including 60 from men. Find the 90% confidence interval for the true proportion of male applicants.

1. From the toolbar, select Add-Ins, **MegaStat>Confidence Intervals/Sample Size**. *Note:* You may need to open **MegaStat** from the **MegaStat.xls** file on your computer's hard drive.
2. In the dialog box, select Confidence interval—p.
3. Enter **60** in the box labeled p; p will automatically change to x.
4. Enter **500** in the box labeled n.
5. Either type in or scroll to 90% for the Confidence Level, then click [OK].

The result of the procedure is shown next.

Confidence Interval—Proportion

90%	Confidence level
0.12	Proportion
500	n
1.645	z
0.024	Half-width
0.144	Upper confidence limit
0.096	Lower confidence limit

Here is a survey about college students' credit card usage. Suggest several ways that the study could have been more meaningful if confidence intervals had been used.

OTHER PEOPLE'S MONEY

Undergrads love their plastic. That means—you guessed it—students are learning to become debtors. According to the Public Interest Research Groups, only half of all students pay off card balances in full each month, 36% sometimes do and 14% never do. Meanwhile, 48% have paid a late fee. Here's how undergrads stack up, according to Nellie Mae, a provider of college loans:

Undergrads with a credit card **78%**

Average number of cards owned **3**

Average student card debt **$1236**

Students with 4 or more cards. **32%**

Balances of $3000 to $7000 . . . .**13%**

Balances over $7000 . . . .**9%**

MINITAB
Step by Step

Find a Confidence Interval for a Proportion

MINITAB will calculate a confidence interval, given the statistics from a sample *or* given the raw data. From Example 7–9 covering college costs, 323 out of 1404 respondents paid for their education by student loans. Find the 90% confidence interval of the true proportion of students who paid for their education by student loans.

1. Select **Stat>Basic Statistics>1 Proportion.**
2. Click on the button for Summarized data. No data will be entered in the worksheet.
3. Click in the box for Number of trials and enter **1404.**
4. In the Number of events box, enter **323.**
5. Click on [Options].
6. Type **90** for the confidence level.

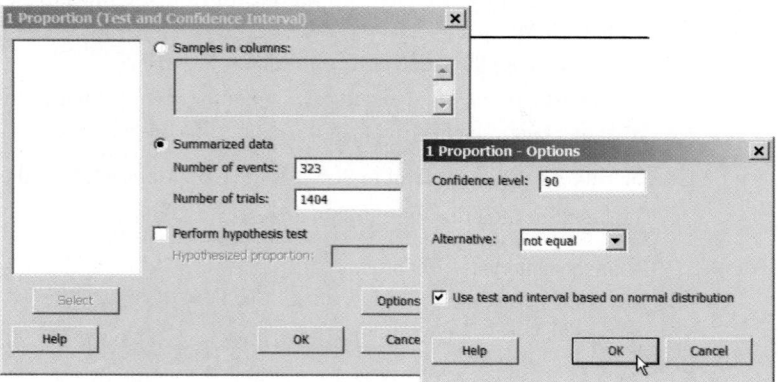

7. Check the box for Use test and interval based on normal distribution.
8. Click [OK] twice.

The results for the confidence interval will be displayed in the session window.

Test and CI for One Proportion

Sample	X	N	Sample p	90% CI
1	323	1404	0.230057	(0.211582, 0.248532)

Using the normal approximation.

7–4   Confidence Intervals for Variances and Standard Deviations

OBJECTIVE ⑥

Find a confidence interval for a variance and a standard deviation.

In Sections 7–1 through 7–3 confidence intervals were calculated for means and proportions. This section will explain how to find confidence intervals for variances and standard deviations. In statistics, the variance and standard deviation of a variable are as important as the mean. For example, when products that fit together (such as pipes) are manufactured, it is important to keep the variations of the diameters of the products as small as possible; otherwise, they will not fit together properly and will have to be scrapped. In the manufacture of medicines, the variance and standard deviation of the medication in the pills play an important role in making sure patients receive the proper dosage. For these reasons, confidence intervals for variances and standard deviations are necessary.

To calculate these confidence intervals, a new statistical distribution is needed. It is called the **chi-square distribution.**

The chi-square variable is similar to the t variable in that its distribution is a family of curves based on the number of degrees of freedom. The symbol for chi-square is χ^2 (Greek letter chi, pronounced "ki"). Several of the distributions are shown in Figure 7–9, along with the corresponding degrees of freedom. The chi-square distribution is obtained from the values of $(n - 1)s^2/\sigma^2$ when random samples are selected from a normally distributed population whose variance is σ^2.

A chi-square variable cannot be negative, and the distributions are skewed to the right. At about 100 degrees of freedom, the chi-square distribution becomes somewhat symmetric. The area under each chi-square distribution is equal to 1.00, or 100%.

⌐Historical Note

The χ^2 distribution with 2 degrees of freedom was formulated by a mathematician named Hershel in 1869 while he was studying the accuracy of shooting arrows at a target. Many other mathematicians have since contributed to its development.

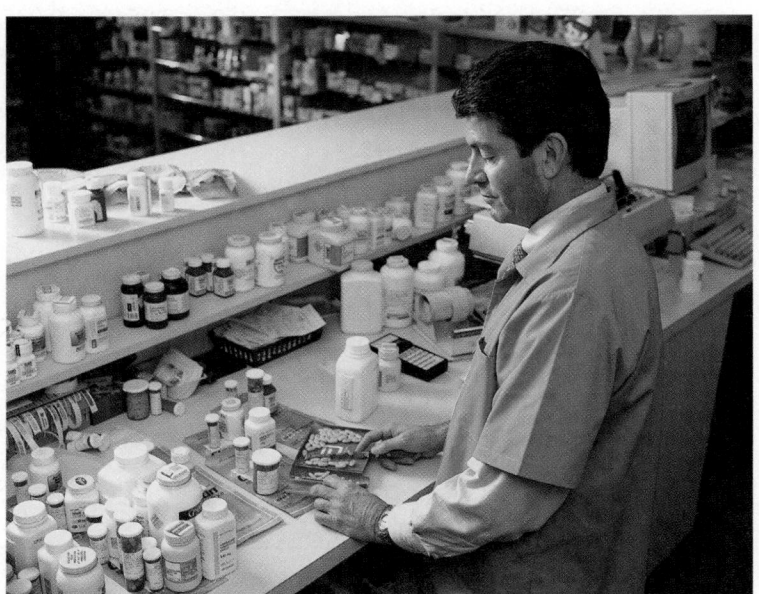

FIGURE 7–9
The Chi-Square Family of
Curves

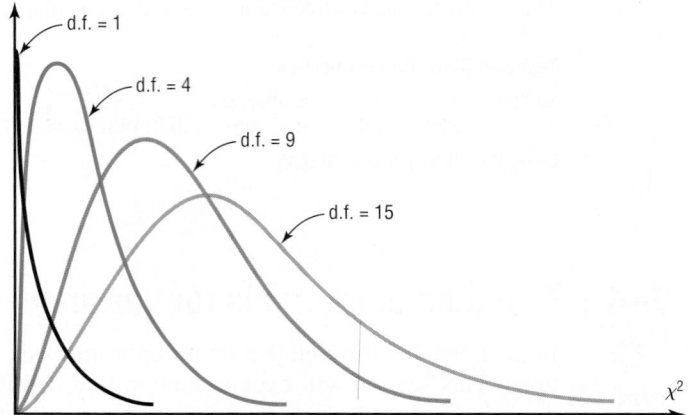

A summary of the characteristics of the chi-square distribution is given next.

> ### Characteristics of the Chi-Square Distribution
>
> 1. All chi-square values are greater than or equal to 0.
> 2. The chi-square distribution is a family of curves based on the degrees of freedom.
> 3. The area under each chi-square distribution curve is equal to 1.
> 4. The chi-square distributions are positively skewed.

Table G in Appendix A gives the values for the chi-square distribution. These values are used in the denominators of the formulas for confidence intervals. Two different values are used in the formula because the distribution is not symmetric. One value is found on the left side of the table, and the other is on the right. See Figure 7–10.

Table G is set up similarly to the table used for the t distribution. The left column denotes the degrees of freedom, and the top row represents the area to the *right* of the critical value. For example, to find the table values corresponding to the 95% confidence interval, you must first change 95% to a decimal and subtract it from 1 ($1 - 0.95 = 0.05$). Then divide the answer by 2 ($\alpha/2 = 0.05/2 = 0.025$). This is the column on the right side of the table, used to get the values for χ^2_{right}. To get the value for χ^2_{left}, subtract the value of $\alpha/2$ from 1 ($1 - 0.05/2 = 0.975$). Finally, find the appropriate row corresponding to the degrees of freedom $n - 1$. A similar procedure is used to find the values for a 90 or 99% confidence interval.

FIGURE 7–10
Chi-Square Distribution for
d.f. $= n - 1$

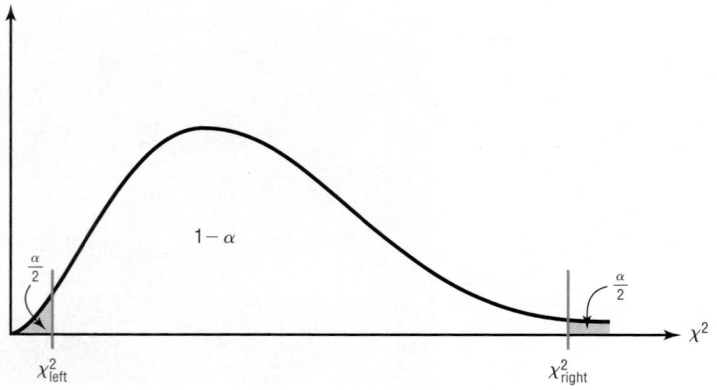

EXAMPLE 7–13

Find the values for χ^2_{right} and χ^2_{left} for a 90% confidence interval when $n = 25$.

SOLUTION

To find χ^2_{right}, subtract $1 - 0.90 = 0.10$; then divide 0.10 by 2 to get 0.05.
To find χ^2_{left}, subtract $1 - 0.05 = 0.95$.
Then use the 0.95 and 0.05 columns with d.f. $= n - 1 = 25 - 1 = 24$. See Figure 7–11.

FIGURE 7–11 χ^2 Table for Example 7–13

					Table G					
				The Chi-square Distribution						
Degrees of freedom					α					
	0.995	0.99	0.975	0.95	0.90	0.10	0.05	0.025	0.01	0.005
1										
2										
⋮										
24				13.848			36.415			
				χ^2_{left}			χ^2_{right}			

The values are

$$\chi^2_{\text{right}} = 36.415$$

$$\chi^2_{\text{left}} = 13.848$$

See Figure 7–12.

FIGURE 7–12 χ^2 Distribution for Example 7–13

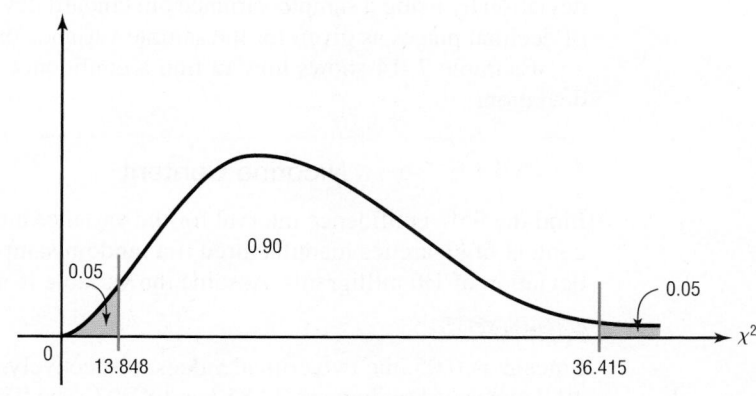

If the number for the degrees of freedom is not given in the table, use the closest lower value in the table. For example, for d.f. = 53, use d.f. = 50. This is a conservative approach.

Useful estimates for σ^2 and σ are s^2 and s, respectively.

To find confidence intervals for variances and standard deviations, you must assume that the variable is normally distributed.

The formulas for the confidence intervals are shown here.

Formula for the Confidence Interval for a Variance

$$\frac{(n-1)s^2}{\chi^2_{\text{right}}} < \sigma^2 < \frac{(n-1)s^2}{\chi^2_{\text{left}}}$$

$$\text{d.f.} = n - 1$$

Formula for the Confidence Interval for a Standard Deviation

$$\sqrt{\frac{(n-1)s^2}{\chi^2_{\text{right}}}} < \sigma < \sqrt{\frac{(n-1)s^2}{\chi^2_{\text{left}}}}$$

$$\text{d.f.} = n - 1$$

Recall that s^2 is the symbol for the sample variance and s is the symbol for the sample standard deviation. If the problem gives the sample standard deviation s, be sure to *square* it when you are using the formula. But if the problem gives the sample variance s^2, *do not square it* when you are using the formula, since the variance is already in square units.

Assumptions for Finding a Confidence Interval for a Variance or Standard Deviation

1. The sample is a random sample.
2. The population must be normally distributed.

In this text, the assumptions will be stated in the exercises; however, when encountering statistics in other situations, you must check to see that these assumptions have been met before proceeding.

Rounding Rule for a Confidence Interval for a Variance or Standard Deviation
When you are computing a confidence interval for a population variance or standard deviation by using raw data, round off to one more decimal place than the number of decimal places in the original data.

When you are computing a confidence interval for a population variance or standard deviation by using a sample variance or standard deviation, round off to the same number of decimal places as given for the sample variance or standard deviation.

Example 7–14 shows how to find a confidence interval for a variance and standard deviation.

EXAMPLE 7–14 Nicotine Content

Find the 95% confidence interval for the variance and standard deviation of the nicotine content of cigarettes manufactured if a random sample of 20 cigarettes has a standard deviation of 1.6 milligrams. Assume the variable is normally distributed.

SOLUTION

Since $\alpha = 0.05$, the two critical values, respectively, for the 0.025 and 0.975 levels for 19 degrees of freedom are 32.852 and 8.907. The 95% confidence interval for the variance is found by substituting in the formula.

$$\frac{(n-1)s^2}{\chi^2_{\text{right}}} < \sigma^2 < \frac{(n-1)s^2}{\chi^2_{\text{left}}}$$

$$\frac{(20-1)(1.6)^2}{32.852} < \sigma^2 < \frac{(20-1)(1.6)^2}{8.907}$$

$$1.5 < \sigma^2 < 5.5$$

Hence, you can be 95% confident that the true variance for the nicotine content is between 1.5 and 5.5.

For the standard deviation, the confidence interval is

$$\sqrt{1.5} < \sigma < \sqrt{5.5}$$
$$1.2 < \sigma < 2.3$$

Hence, you can be 95% confident that the true standard deviation for the nicotine content of all cigarettes manufactured is between 1.2 and 2.3 milligrams based on a sample of 20 cigarettes.

EXAMPLE 7–15   Named Storms

Find the 90% confidence interval for the variance and standard deviation for the number of named storms per year in the Atlantic basin. A random sample of 10 years has been used. Assume the distribution is approximately normal.

| 10 | 5 | 12 | 11 | 13 |
| 15 | 19 | 18 | 14 | 16 |

Source: Atlantic Oceanographic and Meteorological Laboratory.

SOLUTION

Step 1   Find the variance for the data. Use the formulas in Chapter 3 or your calculator. The variance $s^2 = 16.9$.

Step 2   Find χ^2_{right} and χ^2_{left} from Table G in Appendix A, using $10 - 1 = 9$ degrees of freedom.

In this case, use $\alpha = 0.05$ and 0.95; $\chi^2_{\text{right}} = 3.325$; $\chi^2_{\text{left}} = 16.919$.

Step 3   Substitute in the formula.

$$\frac{(n-1)s^2}{\chi^2_{\text{right}}} < \sigma^2 < \frac{(n-1)s^2}{\chi^2_{\text{left}}}$$

$$\frac{(10-1)(16.9)}{16.919} < \sigma^2 < \frac{(10-1)(16.9)}{3.325}$$

$$8.99 < \sigma^2 < 45.74$$

$$\sqrt{8.99} < \sigma < \sqrt{45.74}$$

$$3.0 < \sigma < 6.8$$

Hence, you can be 90% confident that the standard deviation for the number of named storms is between 3.0 and 6.8 based on a random sample of 10 years.

Note: If you are using the standard deviation instead (as in Example 7–14) of the variance, be sure to square the standard deviation when substituting in the formula.

Applying the Concepts 7–4

Confidence Interval for Standard Deviation

Shown are the ages (in years) of the Presidents at the times of their deaths.

67	90	83	85	73	80	78	79
68	71	53	65	74	64	77	56
66	63	70	49	57	71	67	71
58	60	72	67	57	60	90	63
88	78	46	64	81	93	93	

1. Do the data represent a population or a sample?

2. Select a random sample of 12 ages and find the variance and standard deviation.

3. Find the 95% confidence interval of the standard deviation.

4. Find the standard deviation of all the data values.

5. Does the confidence interval calculated in question 3 contain the standard deviation?

6. If it does not, give a reason why.

7. What assumption(s) must be considered for constructing the confidence interval in step 3?

See page 412 for the answers.

Exercises 7–4

1. What distribution must be used when computing confidence intervals for variances and standard deviations?

2. What assumption must be made when computing confidence intervals for variances and standard deviations?

3. Using Table G, find the values for χ^2_{left} and χ^2_{right}.

    a. $\alpha = 0.05, n = 12$
    b. $\alpha = 0.10, n = 20$
    c. $\alpha = 0.05, n = 27$
    d. $\alpha = 0.01, n = 6$
    e. $\alpha = 0.10, n = 41$

4. **Lifetimes of Wristwatches** Find the 90% confidence interval for the variance and standard deviation for the lifetimes of inexpensive wristwatches if a random sample of 24 watches has a standard deviation of 4.8 months. Assume the variable is normally distributed. Do you feel that the lifetimes are relatively consistent?

5. **Carbohydrates in Yogurt** The number of carbohydrates (in grams) per 8-ounce serving of yogurt for each of a random selection of brands is listed below. Estimate the true population variance and standard deviation for the number of carbohydrates per 8-ounce serving of yogurt with 95% confidence. Assume the variable is normally distributed.

    17 42 41 20 39 41 35 15 43
    25 38 33 42 23 17 25 34

6. **Carbon Monoxide Deaths** A study of generation-related carbon monoxide deaths showed that a random sample of 6 recent years had a standard deviation of 4.1 deaths per year. Find the 99% confidence interval of the variance and standard deviation. Assume the variable is normally distributed.

    Source: Based on information from Consumer Protection Safety Commission.

7. **Cost of Knee Replacement Surgery** U.S. insurers' costs for knee replacement surgery range from $17,627 to $25,462. Estimate the population variance (standard deviation) in cost with 98% confidence based on a random sample of 10 persons who have had this surgery. The retail costs (for uninsured persons) for the same procedure range from $40,640 to $58,702. Estimate the population variance and standard deviation in cost with 98% confidence based on a sample of 10 persons, and compare your two intervals. Assume the variable is normally distributed.

    Source: Time Almanac.

8. **Age of College Students** Find the 90% confidence interval for the variance and standard deviation of the ages of seniors at Oak Park College if a random sample of 24 students has a standard deviation of 2.3 years. Assume the variable is normally distributed.

9. **New-Car Lease Fees** A new-car dealer is leasing various brand-new randomly selected models for the monthly rates (in dollars) listed below. Estimate the true population variance (and standard deviation) in leasing rates with 90% confidence. Assume the variable is normally distributed.

    169   169   199   239   239   249

10. **Stock Prices** A random sample of stock prices per share (in dollars) is shown. Find the 90% confidence interval for the variance and standard deviation for the prices. Assume the variable is normally distributed.

26.69	13.88	28.37	12.00
75.37	7.50	47.50	43.00
3.81	53.81	13.62	45.12
6.94	28.25	28.00	60.50
40.25	10.87	46.12	14.75

    Source: Pittsburgh Tribune Review.

11. **Number of Homeless Individuals** A researcher wishes to find the confidence interval of the population standard deviation for the number of homeless people in a large city. A random sample of 25 months had a standard deviation of 462. Find the 95% confidence interval. Assume the variable is normally distributed.

12. **Home Ownership Rates** The percentage rates of home ownership for 8 randomly selected states are listed below. Estimate the population variance and standard deviation for the percentage rate of home ownership with 99% confidence. Assume the variable is normally distributed.

    66.0   75.8   70.9   73.9   63.4   68.5   73.3   65.9

    Source: *World Almanac.*

13. **Calories in a Standard Size Candy Bar** Estimate the standard deviation in calories for these randomly selected standard-size candy bars with 95% confidence. (The number of calories is listed for each.) Assume the variable is normally distributed.

220	220	210	230	275	260	240
220	240	240	280	230	280	260

14. **SAT Scores** Estimate the variance in mean mathematics SAT scores by state, using the randomly selected scores listed below. Estimate with 99% confidence. Assume the variable is normally distributed.

490	502	211	209	499	565
469	543	572	550	515	500

    Source: *World Almanac 2012.*

15. **Daily Cholesterol Intake** The American Heart Association recommends a daily cholesterol intake of less than 300 mg. Here are the cholesterol amounts in a random sample of single servings of grilled meats. Estimate the standard deviation in cholesterol with 95% confidence. Assume the variable is normally distributed.

90	200	80	105	95
85	70	105	115	110
100	225	125	130	145

≡ Extending the Concepts

16. **Calculator Battery Lifetimes** A confidence interval for a standard deviation for large samples taken from a normally distributed population can be approximated by

    $$s - z_{\alpha/2} \frac{s}{\sqrt{2n}} < \sigma < s + z_{\alpha/2} \frac{s}{\sqrt{2n}}$$

    Find the 95% confidence interval for the population standard deviation of calculator batteries. A random sample of 200 calculator batteries has a standard deviation of 18 months.

≡ Technology   Step by Step

TI-84 Plus
Step by Step

The TI-84 Plus does not have a built-in confidence interval for the variance or standard deviation. However, the downloadable program named SDINT is available in your online resources. Follow the instructions online for downloading the program.

Finding a Confidence Interval for the Variance and Standard Deviation (Data)

1. Enter the data values into L_1.
2. Press **PRGM,** move the cursor to the program named SDINT, and press **ENTER** twice.
3. Press **1** for Data.
4. Type L_1 for the list and press **ENTER.**
5. Type the confidence level and press **ENTER.**
6. Press **ENTER** to clear the screen.

Example TI7–4

Find the 90% confidence interval for the variance and standard deviation for the data:

59   54   53   52   51   39   49   46   49   48

```
LIST ?L₁
```

```
ENTER CONF LEVEL
(0 < CL <1)


CONF LEVEL=.9
```

```
CONF LEVEL .9      ⋮
S= 5.31   n=10

CONF INT FOR σx²
(15.01,76.39)
CONF INT FOR σx
(3.87,8.74)
ENTER TO CLEAR
```

Finding a Confidence Interval for the Variance and Standard Deviation (Statistics)

1. Press **PRGM,** move the cursor to the program named SDINT, and press **ENTER** twice.

2. Press **2** for Stats.

3. Type the sample standard deviation and press **ENTER.**

4. Type the sample size and press **ENTER.**

5. Type the confidence level and press **ENTER.**

6. Press **ENTER** to clear the screen.

Example TI7–5

This refers to Example 7–14 in the text. Find the 95% confidence interval for the variance and standard deviation, given $n = 20$ and $s = 1.6$.

```
S= 1.6
N= 20
```

```
ENTER CONF LEVEL
(0 < CL <1)

CONF LEVEL=.95■
```

```
CONF LEVEL .95  :
S= 1.6    n=20

CONF INT FOR σx²
(1.48,5.46)
CONF INT FOR σx
(1.22,2.34)
ENTER TO CLEAR
```

≡ Summary

- An important aspect of inferential statistics is estimation. Estimations of parameters of populations are accomplished by selecting a random sample from that population and choosing and computing a statistic that is the best estimator of the parameter. A good estimator must be unbiased, consistent, and relatively efficient. The best estimate of μ is $\overline{X}$. (7–1)

- There are two types of estimates of a parameter: point estimates and interval estimates. A point estimate is a specific value. For example, if a researcher wishes to estimate the average length of a certain adult fish, a sample of the fish is selected and measured. The mean of this sample is computed, for example, 3.2 centimeters. From this sample mean, the researcher estimates the population mean to be 3.2 centimeters. The problem with point estimates is that the accuracy of the estimate cannot be determined. For this reason, statisticians prefer to use the interval estimate. By computing an interval about the sample value, statisticians can be 95 or 99% (or some other percentage) confident that their estimate contains the true parameter. The confidence level is determined by the researcher. The higher the confidence level, the wider the interval of the estimate must be. For example, a 95% confidence interval of the true mean length of a certain species of fish might be

$$3.17 < \mu < 3.23$$

whereas the 99% confidence interval might be

$$3.15 < \mu < 3.25 \quad (7–1)$$

- When the population standard deviation is known, the z value is used to compute the confidence interval. (7–1)

- Closely related to computing confidence intervals is the determination of the sample size to make an estimate of the mean. This information is needed to determine the minimum sample size necessary.

  1. The degree of confidence must be stated.

  2. The population standard deviation must be known or be able to be estimated.

  3. The margin of error must be stated. (7–1)

- If the population standard deviation is unknown, the t value is used. When the sample size is less than 30, the population must be normally distributed. (7–2)

- Confidence intervals and sample sizes can also be computed for proportions by using the normal distribution. (7–3)

- Finally, confidence intervals for variances and standard deviations can be computed by using the chi-square distribution. (7–4)

Important Terms

assumptions 370	degrees of freedom 383	margin of error 372	robust 373
chi-square distribution 399	estimation 370	point estimate 370	t distribution 383
confidence interval 371	estimator 371	proportion 390	unbiased estimator 371
confidence level 371	interval estimate 371	relatively efficient estimator 371	
consistent estimator 371			

Important Formulas

Formula for the confidence interval of the mean when σ is known (when $n \geq 30$, s can be used if σ is unknown):

$$\overline{X} - z_{\alpha/2}\left(\frac{\sigma}{\sqrt{n}}\right) < \mu < \overline{X} + z_{\alpha/2}\left(\frac{\sigma}{\sqrt{n}}\right)$$

Formula for the sample size for means:

$$n = \left(\frac{z_{\alpha/2} \cdot \sigma}{E}\right)^2$$

where E is the margin of error.

Formula for the confidence interval of the mean when σ is unknown:

$$\overline{X} - t_{\alpha/2}\left(\frac{s}{\sqrt{n}}\right) < \mu < \overline{X} + t_{\alpha/2}\left(\frac{s}{\sqrt{n}}\right)$$

Formula for the confidence interval for a proportion:

$$\hat{p} - z_{\alpha/2}\sqrt{\frac{\hat{p}\hat{q}}{n}} < p < \hat{p} + z_{\alpha/2}\sqrt{\frac{\hat{p}\hat{q}}{n}}$$

where $\hat{p} = X/n$ and $\hat{q} = 1 - \hat{p}$.

Formula for the sample size for proportions:

$$n = \hat{p}\hat{q}\left(\frac{z_{\alpha/2}}{E}\right)^2$$

Formula for the confidence interval for a variance:

$$\frac{(n-1)s^2}{\chi^2_{\text{right}}} < \sigma^2 < \frac{(n-1)s^2}{\chi^2_{\text{left}}}$$

Formula for the confidence interval for a standard deviation:

$$\sqrt{\frac{(n-1)s^2}{\chi^2_{\text{right}}}} < \sigma < \sqrt{\frac{(n-1)s^2}{\chi^2_{\text{left}}}}$$

Review Exercises

Section 7–1

1. **Isotopes** Eight chemical elements do not have isotopes (different forms of the same element having the same atomic number but different atomic weights). A random sample of 30 of the elements that do have isotopes showed a mean number of 19.63 isotopes per element, and the population has a standard deviation of 18.73. Estimate the true mean number of isotopes for all elements with isotopes with 90% confidence.

   Source: Time Almanac.

2. **Vacation Days** A U.S. Travel Data Center survey reported that Americans stayed an average of 7.5 nights when they went on vacation. The sample size was 1500. Find a point estimate of the population mean. Find the 95% confidence interval of the true mean. Assume the population standard deviation was 0.8.

   Source: USA TODAY.

3. **Spending for Postage** A researcher wishes to estimate within $25 the average cost of postage a community college spends in one year. If she wishes to be 90% confident, how large of a sample will be necessary if the population standard deviation is $80.

4. **Shopping Survey** A random sample of 49 shoppers showed that they spend an average of $23.45 per visit at the Saturday Mornings Bookstore. The standard deviation of the population is $2.80. Find a point estimate of the population mean. Find the 90% confidence interval of the true mean.

Section 7–2

5. **Lengths of Children's Animated Films** The lengths (in minutes) of a random selection of popular children's animated films are listed below. Estimate the true mean length of all children's animated films with 95% confidence. Assume the variable is normally distributed.

   93   83   76   92   77   81   78   100   78   76   75

6. **Dog Bites to Postal Workers** For a certain urban area, in a random sample of 5 months, an average of 28 mail carriers were bitten by dogs each month. The standard deviation of the sample was 3. Find the 90% confidence interval of the true mean number of mail carriers who are bitten by dogs each month. Assume the variable is normally distributed.

Section 7–3

7. **Presidential Travel** In a survey of 1004 randomly selected individuals, 442 felt that President George W. Bush spent too much time away from Washington. Find a 95% confidence interval for the true population proportion.

Source: *USA TODAY*/CNN/Gallup Poll.

8. **Vacation Sites** A U.S. Travel Data Center's survey of 1500 randomly selected adults found that 42% of respondents stated that they favor historical sites as vacations. Find the 95% confidence interval of the true proportion of all adults who favor visiting historical sites for vacations.

Source: *USA TODAY*.

9. **Marriages in the United States** In 1960, 67.6% of the U.S. population (aged 14 and over) was married. A random sample of 600 Americans in 2011 indicated that 312 were married. Estimate the true proportion of married Americans with 99% confidence. Assume the variable is normally distributed.

Source: *World Almanac 2012.*

10. **Adult Educational Activities** A local county has a very active adult education venue. A random sample of the population showed that 189 out of 400 persons 16 years old or older participated in some type of formal adult education activities, such as basic skills training, apprenticeships, personal interest courses, and part-time college or university degree programs. Estimate the true proportion of adults participating in some kind of formal education program with 98% confidence. Assume the variable is normally distributed.

11. **Pet Owners** It is believed that slightly over 60% of Americans own pets. How large a sample is necessary to estimate the true proportion within 0.02 with 90% confidence?

12. **Child Care Programs** A study found that 73% of randomly selected prekindergarten children ages 3 to 5 whose mothers had a bachelor's degree or higher were enrolled in center-based early childhood care and education programs. How large a sample is needed to estimate the true proportion within 3 percentage points with 95% confidence? How large a sample is needed if you had no prior knowledge of the proportion?

Section 7–4

13. **Baseball Diameters** The standard deviation of the diameter of 18 randomly selected baseballs was 0.29 cm. Find the 95% confidence interval of the true standard deviation of the diameters of the baseballs. Do you think the manufacturing process should be checked for inconsistency? Assume the variable is normally distributed.

14. **MPG for Lawn Mowers** A random sample of 22 lawn mowers was selected, and the motors were tested to see how many miles per gallon of gasoline each one obtained. The variance of the measurements was 2.6. Find the 95% confidence interval of the true variance. Assume the variable is normally distributed.

15. **Lifetimes of Snowmobiles** A random sample of 15 snowmobiles was selected, and the lifetime (in months) of the batteries was measured. The variance of the sample was 8.6. Find the 90% confidence interval of the true variance. Assume the variable is normally distributed.

16. **Length of Children's Animated Films** Use the data from Exercise 5 to estimate the population variance and standard deviation in length of children's animated films with 99% confidence. Assume the variable is normally distributed.

≡ STATISTICS TODAY

Stress and the College Student —Revisited

The estimates given in the survey were point estimates; however, since the margin of error was 3 percentage points, a confidence interval can be constructed. For example, a confidence interval for the 85% figure would be 82% < p < 88%. We don't know whether this is a 90%, 95%, 99%, or some other confidence level because this was not specified in the report.

Using the formula in Section 7–3, a minimum sample size could be found. We can take $\hat{p}$ and $\hat{q}$ as 0.5 since no value for $\hat{p}$ is known, and $z_{\alpha/2} = 1.96$ for a 95% confidence interval.

$$n = \hat{p}\hat{q}\left(\frac{z_{\alpha/2}}{E}\right)$$

$$= (0.5)(0.5)\left(\frac{1.96}{0.03}\right)^2 = 1067.1$$

For a 95% confidence interval, then, the minimum sample size would be 1068 people (rounded up). Since the survey used 2240 students, it can be said that we are at least 95% confident that the true proportion of students who experience stress in college is somewhere between 82 and 88%.

Data Analysis

The Data Bank is found in Appendix B, or on the World Wide Web by following links from www.mhhe.com/math/stat/bluman/.

1. From the Data Bank choose a variable, find the mean, and construct the 95 and 99% confidence intervals of the population mean. Use a sample of at least 30 subjects. Find the mean of the population, and determine whether it falls within the confidence interval.

2. Repeat Exercise 1, using a different variable and a sample of 15.

3. Repeat Exercise 1, using a proportion. For example, construct a confidence interval for the proportion of individuals who did not complete high school.

4. From Data Set III in Appendix B, select a sample of 30 values and construct the 95 and 99% confidence intervals of the mean length in miles of major North American rivers. Find the mean of all the values, and determine if the confidence intervals contain the mean.

5. From Data Set VI in Appendix B, select a sample of 20 values and find the 90% confidence interval of the mean of the number of acres. Find the mean of all the values, and determine if the confidence interval contains the mean.

6. Select a random sample of 20 of the record high temperatures in the United States, found in Data Set I in Appendix B. Find the proportion of temperatures below 110°. Construct a 95% confidence interval for this proportion. Then find the true proportion of temperatures below 110°, using all the data. Is the true proportion contained in the confidence interval? Explain.

Chapter Quiz

Determine whether each statement is true or false. If the statement is false, explain why.

1. Interval estimates are preferred over point estimates since a confidence level can be specified.

2. For a specific confidence interval, the larger the sample size, the smaller the margin of error will be.

3. An estimator is consistent if as the sample size decreases, the value of the estimator approaches the value of the parameter estimated.

4. To determine the sample size needed to estimate a parameter, you must know the margin of error.

Select the best answer.

5. When a 99% confidence interval is calculated instead of a 95% confidence interval with n being the same, the margin of error will be

   a. Smaller   *c.* The same
   b. Larger   *d.* It cannot be determined.

6. The best point estimate of the population mean is

   a. The sample mean
   b. The sample median
   c. The sample mode
   d. The sample midrange

7. When the population standard deviation is unknown and the sample size is less than 30, what table value should be used in computing a confidence interval for a mean?

   a. z
   b. t
   c. Chi-square
   d. None of the above

Complete the following statements with the best answer.

8. A good estimator should be _____, _____, and _____.

9. The maximum likely difference between the point estimate of a parameter and the actual value of the parameter is called the _____.

10. The statement "The average height of an adult male is 5 feet 10 inches" is an example of a(n) _____ estimate.

11. The three confidence levels used most often are the _____%, _____%, and _____%.

12. **Cost of Texts** An irate student complained that the cost of textbooks was too high. He randomly surveyed 36 other students and found that the mean amount of money spent for texts was $121.60. If the standard deviation of the population was $6.36, find the best point estimate and the 90% confidence interval of the true mean.

13. **Doctor Visit Costs** An irate patient complained that the cost of a doctor's visit was too high. She randomly surveyed 20 other patients and found that the mean amount of money they spent on each doctor's visit was $44.80. The standard deviation of the sample was $3.53. Find a point estimate of the population mean. Find the 95% confidence interval of the population mean. Assume the variable is normally distributed.

14. **Weights of Minivans** The average weight of 40 randomly selected minivans was 4150 pounds. The population standard deviation was 480 pounds. Find a point estimate of the population mean. Find the 99% confidence interval of the true mean weight of the minivans.

15. **Ages of Insurance Representatives** In a study of 10 randomly selected insurance sales representatives from a certain large city, the average age of the group was 48.6 years and the standard deviation was 4.1 years. Assume the variable is normally distributed. Find the 95% confidence interval of the population mean age of all insurance sales representatives in that city.

16. **Patients Treated in Hospital Emergency Rooms** In a hospital, a random sample of 8 weeks was selected, and it was found that an average of 438 patients were treated in the emergency room each week. The standard deviation was 16. Find the 99% confidence interval of the true mean. Assume the variable is normally distributed.

17. **Burglaries** For a certain urban area, it was found that in a random sample of 4 months, an average of 31 burglaries occurred each month. The standard deviation was 4. Assume the variable is normally distributed. Find the 90% confidence interval of the true mean number of burglaries each month.

18. **Hours Spent Studying** A university dean wishes to estimate the average number of hours that freshmen study each week. The standard deviation from a previous study is 2.6 hours. How large a sample must be selected if he wants to be 99% confident of finding whether the true mean differs from the sample mean by 0.5 hour?

19. **Money Spent on Road Repairs** A researcher wishes to estimate within $300 the true average amount of money a county spends on road repairs each year. If she wants to be 90% confident, how large a sample is necessary? The standard deviation is known to be $900.

20. **Political Survey** A political analyst found that 43% of 300 randomly selected Republican voters feel that the federal government has too much power. Find the 95% confidence interval of the population proportion of Republican voters who feel this way.

21. **Emergency Room Accidents** In a study of 150 randomly selected accidents that required treatment in an emergency room, 36% involved children under 6 years of age. Find the 90% confidence interval of the true proportion of accidents that involve children under the age of 6.

22. **Television Set Ownership** A survey of 90 randomly selected families showed that 40 owned at least one television set. Find the 95% confidence interval of the true proportion of families who own at least one television set.

23. **Skipping Lunch** A nutritionist wishes to determine, within 3%, the true proportion of adults who do not eat any lunch. If he wishes to be 95% confident that his estimate contains the population proportion, how large a sample will be necessary? A previous study found that 15% of the 125 people surveyed said they did not eat lunch.

24. **Novel Pages** A random sample of 25 novels has a standard deviation of 9 pages. Find the 95% confidence interval of the population standard deviation. Assume the variable is normally distributed.

25. **Truck Safety Check** Find the 90% confidence interval for the variance and standard deviation for the time it takes a state police inspector to check a truck for safety if a random sample of 27 trucks has a standard deviation of 6.8 minutes. Assume the variable is normally distributed.

26. **Automobile Pollution** A random sample of 20 automobiles has a pollution by-product release standard deviation of 2.3 ounces when 1 gallon of gasoline is used. Find the 90% confidence interval of the population standard deviation. Assume the variable is normally distributed.

⬛ Critical Thinking Challenges

A confidence interval for a median can be found by using these formulas

$$U = \frac{n+1}{2} + \frac{z_{\alpha/2}\sqrt{n}}{2} \qquad \text{(round up)}$$

$$L = n - U + 1$$

to define positions in the set of ordered data values.

Suppose a data set has 30 values, and you want to find the 95% confidence interval for the median. Substituting in the formulas, you get

$$U = \frac{30+1}{2} + \frac{1.96\sqrt{30}}{2} = 21 \qquad \text{(rounded up)}$$

$$L = 30 - 21 + 1 = 10$$

when $n = 30$ and $z_{\alpha/2} = 1.96$.

Arrange the data in order from smallest to largest, and then select the 10th and 21st values of the data array; hence, $X_{10} < \text{median} < X_{21}$.

Using the previous information, find the 90% confidence interval for the median for the given data.

84	49	3	133	85	4340	461	60	28	97
14	252	18	16	24	346	254	29	254	6
31	104	72	29	391	19	125	10	6	17
72	31	23	225	72	5	61	366	77	8
26	8	55	138	158	846	123	47	21	82

⬛ Data Projects

1. **Business and Finance** Use 30 stocks classified as the Dow Jones industrials as the sample. Note the amount each stock has gained or lost in the last quarter. Compute the mean and standard deviation for the data set. Compute the 95% confidence interval for the mean and the 95% confidence interval for the standard deviation. Compute the percentage of stocks that had a gain in the last quarter. Find a 95% confidence interval for the percentage of stocks with a gain.

2. **Sports and Leisure** Use the top home run hitter from each major league baseball team as the data set. Find the mean and the standard deviation for the number of home runs hit by the top hitter on each team. Find a 95% confidence interval for the mean number of home runs hit.

3. **Technology** Use the data collected in data project 3 of Chapter 2 regarding song lengths. Select a specific genre, and compute the percentage of songs in the sample that are of that genre. Create a 95% confidence interval for the true percentage. Use the entire music library, and find the population percentage of the library with that genre. Does the population percentage fall within the confidence interval?

4. **Health and Wellness** Use your class as the sample. Have each student take her or his temperature on a day when he or she is healthy. Compute the mean and standard deviation for the sample. Create a 95% confidence interval for the mean temperature. Does the confidence interval obtained support the long-held belief that the average body temperature is 98.6°F?

5. **Politics and Economics** Select five political polls and note the margin of error, sample size, and percentage favoring the candidate for each. For each poll, determine the level of confidence that must have been used to obtain the margin of error given, knowing the percentage favoring the candidate and number of participants. Is there a pattern that emerges?

6. **Your Class** Have each student compute his or her body mass index (BMI) (703 times weight in pounds, divided by the square of the height in inches). Find the mean and standard deviation for the data set. Compute a 95% confidence interval for the mean BMI of a student. A BMI score over 30 is considered obese. Does the confidence interval indicate that the mean for BMI could be in the obese range?

⬛ Answers to Applying the Concepts

Section 7–1   Making Decisions with Confidence Intervals

1. Answers will vary. One possible answer is to find out the average number of Kleenexes that a group of randomly selected individuals use in a 2-week period.

2. People usually need Kleenexes when they have colds or when their allergies are acting up.

3. If we want to concentrate on the number of Kleenexes used when people have colds, we select a random sample of people with colds and have them keep a record of how many Kleenexes they use during their colds.

4. Answers may vary. I will use a 95% confidence interval:

$$\bar{x} \pm 1.96 \frac{\sigma}{\sqrt{n}} = 57 \pm 1.96 \frac{15}{\sqrt{85}} = 57 \pm 3$$

I am 95% confident that the interval 54–60 contains the true mean number of Kleenexes used by people when they have colds. It seems reasonable to put 60 Kleenexes in the new automobile glove compartment boxes.

5. Answers will vary. Since I am 95% confident that the interval contains the true average, any number of Kleenexes between 54 and 60 would be reasonable. Sixty seemed to be the most reasonable answer, since it is close to 2 standard deviations above the sample mean.

Section 7–2   Sport Drink Decision

1. Answers will vary. One possible answer is that this is a small sample since I am only looking at seven popular sport drinks.

2. The mean cost per container is $1.25, with standard deviation of $0.39. The 90% confidence interval is

$$\bar{X} \pm t_{\alpha/2} \frac{s}{\sqrt{n}} = 1.25 \pm 1.943 \frac{0.39}{\sqrt{7}} = 1.25 \pm 0.29$$

or $0.96 < \mu < 1.54$

The 10-K, All Sport, Exceed, and Hydra Fuel all fall outside of the confidence interval.

3. None of the values appear to be outliers.

4. There are $7 - 1 = 6$ degrees of freedom.

5. Cost per serving would impact my decision on purchasing a sport drink, since this would allow me to compare the costs on an equal scale.

6. Answers will vary.

Section 7–3   Contracting Influenza

1. (95% CI) means that these are the 95% confidence intervals constructed from the data.

2. The margin of error for men reporting influenza is $(50.5 - 47.1)/2 = 1.7\%$.

3. The total sample size was 19,774.

4. The larger the sample size, the smaller the margin of error and the narrower the confidence interval (all other things being held constant).

5. A 90% confidence interval would be narrower (smaller) than a 95% confidence interval, since we need to include fewer values in the interval.

6. The 51.5% is the middle of the confidence interval, since it is the point estimate for the confidence interval.

Section 7–4   Confidence Interval for Standard Deviation

1. The data represent a population, since we have the age at death for all deceased Presidents (at the time of the writing of this book).

2. Answers will vary. One possible sample is 56, 67, 53, 46, 63, 77, 63, 57, 71, 57, 80, 65, which results in a standard deviation of 9.9 years and a variance of 98.0.

3. Answers will vary. The 95% confidence interval for the standard deviation is $\sqrt{\frac{(n-1)s^2}{\chi^2_{\text{right}}}}$ to $\sqrt{\frac{(n-1)s^2}{\chi^2_{\text{left}}}}$. In this case we have $\sqrt{\frac{(12-1)9.9^2}{21.920}} = \sqrt{49.1839} = 7.0$ to $\sqrt{\frac{(12-1)9.9^2}{3.816}} = \sqrt{282.524} = 16.8$, or 7.0 to 16.8 years.

4. The standard deviation for all the data values is 11.9 years.

5. Answers will vary. Yes, the confidence interval does contain the population standard deviation.

6. Answers will vary.

7. We need to assume that the distribution of ages at death is normal.

Hypothesis Testing

8

⊿ STATISTICS TODAY

How Much Better Is Better?

Suppose a school superintendent reads an article which states that the overall mean score for the SAT is 910. Furthermore, suppose that, for a sample of students, the average of the SAT scores in the superintendent's school district is 960. Can the superintendent conclude that the students in his school district scored higher on average? At first glance, you might be inclined to say yes, since 960 is higher than 910. But recall that the means of samples vary about the population mean when samples are selected from a specific population. So the question arises, Is there a real difference in the means, or is the difference simply due to chance (i.e., sampling error)? In this chapter, you will learn how to answer that question by using statistics that explain hypothesis testing. See Statistics Today—Revisited at the end of the chapter for the answer. In this chapter, you will learn how to answer many questions of this type by using statistics that are explained in the theory of hypothesis testing.

OUTLINE

Introduction

8–1 Steps in Hypothesis Testing—Traditional Method

8–2 *z* Test for a Mean

8–3 *t* Test for a Mean

8–4 *z* Test for a Proportion

8–5 χ^2 Test for a Variance or Standard Deviation

8–6 Additional Topics Regarding Hypothesis Testing

Summary

OBJECTIVES

After completing this chapter, you should be able to

1 Understand the definitions used in hypothesis testing.

2 State the null and alternative hypotheses.

3 Find critical values for the *z* test.

4 State the five steps used in hypothesis testing.

5 Test means when σ is known, using the *z* test.

6 Test means when σ is unknown, using the *t* test.

7 Test proportions, using the *z* test.

8 Test variances or standard deviations, using the chi-square test.

9 Test hypotheses, using confidence intervals.

10 Explain the relationship between type I and type II errors and the power of a test.

Introduction

Researchers are interested in answering many types of questions. For example, a scientist might want to know whether there is evidence of global warming. A physician might want to know whether a new medication will lower a person's blood pressure. An educator might wish to see whether a new teaching technique is better than a traditional one. A retail merchant might want to know whether the public prefers a certain color in a new line of fashion. Automobile manufacturers are interested in determining whether a new type of seat belt will reduce the severity of injuries caused by accidents. These types of questions can be addressed through statistical **hypothesis testing,** which is a decision-making process for evaluating claims about a population. In hypothesis testing, the researcher must define the population under study, state the particular hypotheses that will be investigated, give the significance level, select a sample from the population, collect the data, perform the calculations required for the statistical test, and reach a conclusion.

Hypotheses concerning parameters such as means and proportions can be investigated. There are two specific statistical tests used for hypotheses concerning means: the *z test* and the *t test.* This chapter will explain in detail the hypothesis-testing procedure along with the *z* test and the *t* test. In addition, a hypothesis-testing procedure for testing a single variance or standard deviation using the chi-square distribution is explained in Section 8–5.

The three methods used to test hypotheses are

1. The traditional method
2. The *P*-value method
3. The confidence interval method

The *traditional method* will be explained first. It has been used since the hypothesis-testing method was formulated. A newer method, called the *P-value method,* has become popular with the advent of modern computers and high-powered statistical calculators. It will be explained at the end of Section 8–2. The third method, the *confidence interval method,* is explained in Section 8–6 and illustrates the relationship between hypothesis testing and confidence intervals.

8–1   Steps in Hypothesis Testing—Traditional Method

Every hypothesis-testing situation begins with the statement of a hypothesis.

> A **statistical hypothesis** is a conjecture about a population parameter. This conjecture may or may not be true.

OBJECTIVE

Understand the definitions used in hypothesis testing.

There are two types of statistical hypotheses for each situation: the null hypothesis and the alternative hypothesis.

> The **null hypothesis,** symbolized by H_0, is a statistical hypothesis that states that there is no difference between a parameter and a specific value, or that there is no difference between two parameters.
>
> The **alternative hypothesis,** symbolized by H_1, is a statistical hypothesis that states the existence of a difference between a parameter and a specific value, or states that there is a difference between two parameters.

(*Note:* Although the definitions of null and alternative hypotheses given here use the word *parameter,* these definitions can be extended to include other terms such as *distributions* and *randomness.* This is explained in later chapters.)

As an illustration of how hypotheses should be stated, three different statistical studies will be used as examples.

Situation A   A medical researcher is interested in finding out whether a new medication will have any undesirable side effects. The researcher is particularly concerned with the pulse rate of the patients who take the medication. Will the pulse rate increase, decrease, or remain unchanged after a patient takes the medication?

Since the researcher knows that the mean pulse rate for the population under study is 82 beats per minute, the hypotheses for this situation are

$$H_0: \mu = 82 \qquad \text{and} \qquad H_1: \mu \neq 82$$

The null hypothesis specifies that the mean will remain unchanged, and the alternative hypothesis states that it will be different. This test is called a *two-tailed test* (a term that will be formally defined later in this section), since the possible side effects of the medicine could be to raise or lower the pulse rate.

Situation B   A chemist invents an additive to increase the life of an automobile battery. If the mean lifetime of the automobile battery without the additive is 36 months, then her hypotheses are

$$H_0: \mu = 36 \qquad \text{and} \qquad H_1: \mu > 36$$

In this situation, the chemist is interested only in increasing the lifetime of the batteries, so her alternative hypothesis is that the mean is greater than 36 months. The null hypothesis is that the mean is equal to 36 months. This test is called *right-tailed,* since the interest is in an increase only.

Situation C   A contractor wishes to lower heating bills by using a special type of insulation in houses. If the average of the monthly heating bills is $78, her hypotheses about heating costs with the use of insulation are

$$H_0: \mu = \$78 \qquad \text{and} \qquad H_1: \mu < \$78$$

This test is a *left-tailed test,* since the contractor is interested only in lowering heating costs.

To state hypotheses correctly, researchers must translate the *conjecture* or *claim* from words into mathematical symbols. The basic symbols used are as follows:

Equal to	$=$	Greater than	$>$
Not equal to	$\neq$	Less than	$<$

The null and alternative hypotheses are stated together, and the null hypothesis contains the equals sign, as shown (where k represents a specified number).

Also notice that in a right-tailed test, the inequality sign points to the right; and in a left-tailed test, the inequality sign points to the left. Right- and left-tailed tests are also called one-tailed tests.

Two-tailed test	Right-tailed test	Left-tailed test
$H_0: \mu = k$	$H_0: \mu = k$	$H_0: \mu = k$
$H_1: \mu \neq k$	$H_1: \mu > k$	$H_1: \mu < k$

The formal definitions of the different types of tests are given later in this section.

In this book, the null hypothesis is always stated using the equals sign. This is done because in most professional journals, and when we test the null hypothesis, the assumption is that the mean, proportion, or standard deviation is equal to a given specific value. Also, when a researcher conducts a study, he or she is generally looking for evidence to support a claim. Therefore, the claim should be stated as the alternative hypothesis, i.e., using $<$ or $>$ or $\neq$. Because of this, the alternative hypothesis is sometimes called the **research hypothesis.**

TABLE 8-1 Hypothesis-Testing Common Phrases	
>	**<**
Is greater than	Is less than
Is above	Is below
Is higher than	Is lower than
Is longer than	Is shorter than
Is bigger than	Is smaller than
Is increased	Is decreased or reduced from
=	**≠**
Is equal to	Is not equal to
Is the same as	Is different from
Has not changed from	Has changed from
Is the same as	Is not the same as

A claim, however, can be stated as either the null hypothesis or the alternative hypothesis; but the statistical evidence can only *support* the claim if it is the alternative hypothesis. Statistical evidence can be used to *reject* the claim if the claim is the null hypothesis. These facts are important when you are stating the conclusion of a statistical study.

Table 8–1 shows some common phrases that are used in hypotheses and conjectures, and the corresponding symbols. This table should be helpful in translating verbal conjectures into mathematical symbols.

EXAMPLE 8–1

State the null and alternative hypotheses for each conjecture.

a. A researcher thinks that if expectant mothers use vitamin pills, the birth weight of the babies will increase. The average birth weight of the population is 8.6 pounds.

b. An engineer hypothesizes that the mean number of defects can be decreased in a manufacturing process of USB drives by using robots instead of humans for certain tasks. The mean number of defective drives per 1000 is 18.

c. A psychologist feels that playing soft music during a test will change the results of the test. The psychologist is not sure whether the grades will be higher or lower. In the past, the mean of the scores was 73.

SOLUTION

a. H_0: $\mu = 8.6$ and H_1: $\mu > 8.6$

b. H_0: $\mu = 18$ and H_1: $\mu < 18$

c. H_0: $\mu = 73$ and H_1: $\mu \neq 73$

After stating the hypothesis, the researcher designs the study. The researcher selects the correct *statistical test,* chooses an appropriate *level of significance,* and formulates a plan for conducting the study. In situation A, for instance, the researcher will select a sample of patients who will be given the drug. After allowing a suitable time for the drug to be absorbed, the researcher will measure each person's pulse rate.

Recall that when samples of a specific size are selected from a population, the means of these samples will vary about the population mean, and the distribution of the sample means will be approximately normal when the sample size is 30 or more. (See Section 6–3.) So even if the null hypothesis is true, the mean of the pulse rates of the sample of patients will not, in most cases, be exactly equal to the population mean of 82 beats per minute. There are

FIGURE 8–1
Situations in
Hypothesis Testing

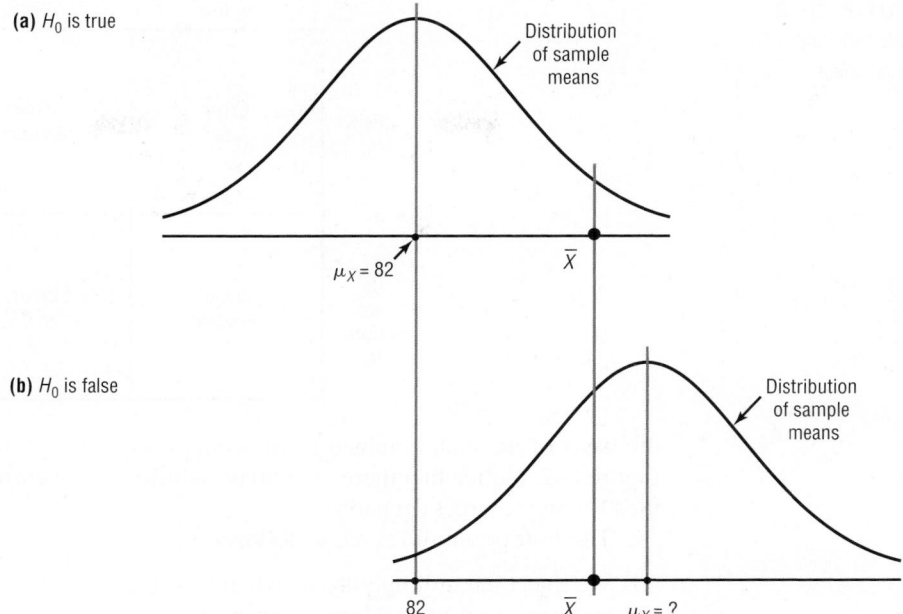

(a) H_0 is true

Distribution of sample means

$\mu_{\bar{X}} = 82$ $\bar{X}$

(b) H_0 is false

Distribution of sample means

82     $\bar{X}$ $\mu_{\bar{X}} = ?$

two possibilities. Either the null hypothesis is true, and the difference between the sample mean and the population mean is due to chance; *or* the null hypothesis is false, and the sample came from a population whose mean is not 82 beats per minute but is some other value that is not known. These situations are shown in Figure 8–1.

The farther away the sample mean is from the population mean, the more evidence there would be for rejecting the null hypothesis. The probability that the sample came from a population whose mean is 82 decreases as the distance or absolute value of the difference between the means increases.

If the mean pulse rate of the sample were, say, 83, the researcher would probably conclude that this difference was due to chance and would not reject the null hypothesis. But if the sample mean were, say, 90, then in all likelihood the researcher would conclude that the medication increased the pulse rate of the users and would reject the null hypothesis. The question is, Where does the researcher draw the line? This decision is not made on feelings or intuition; it is made statistically. That is, the difference must be significant and in all likelihood not due to chance. Here is where the concepts of statistical test and level of significance are used.

> A **statistical test** uses the data obtained from a sample to make a decision about whether the null hypothesis should be rejected.
>
> The numerical value obtained from a statistical test is called the **test value.**

In this type of statistical test, the mean is computed for the data obtained from the sample and is compared with the population mean. Then a decision is made to reject or not reject the null hypothesis on the basis of the value obtained from the statistical test. If the difference is significant, the null hypothesis is rejected. If it is not, then the null hypothesis is not rejected.

As previously stated, sample data are used to determine if a null hypothesis should be rejected. Because this decision is based on sample data, there is a possibility that an incorrect decision can be made.

In the hypothesis-testing situation, there are four possible outcomes. In reality, the null hypothesis may or may not be true, and a decision is made to reject or not reject it on

FIGURE 8–2
Possible Outcomes of a
Hypothesis Test

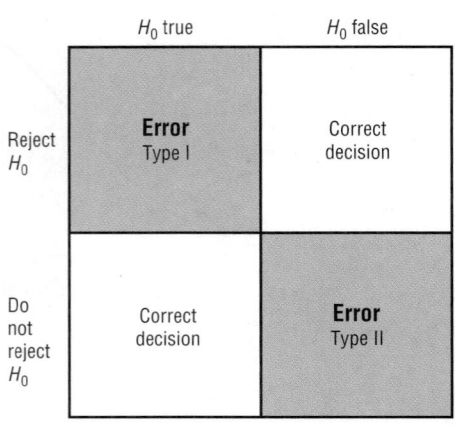

the basis of the data obtained from a sample. The four possible outcomes are shown in Figure 8–2. Notice that there are two possibilities for a correct decision and two possibilities for an incorrect decision.

The four possibilities are as follows:

1. We reject the null hypothesis when it is true. This would be an incorrect decision and would result in a **type I error.**
2. We reject the null hypothesis when it is false. This would be a correct decision.
3. We do not reject the null hypothesis when it is true. This would be a correct decision.
4. We do not reject the null hypothesis when it is false. This would be an incorrect decision and would result in a **type II error.**

> A **type I error** occurs if you reject the null hypothesis when it is true.
>
> A **type II error** occurs if you do not reject the null hypothesis when it is false.

If a null hypothesis is true and it is rejected, then a *type I error* is made. In situation A, for instance, the medication might not significantly change the pulse rate of all the users in the population; but it might change the rate, by chance, of the subjects in the sample. In this case, the researcher will reject the null hypothesis when it is really true, thus committing a type I error.

On the other hand, the medication might not change the pulse rate of the subjects in the sample; but when it is given to the general population, it might cause a significant increase or decrease in the pulse rate of users. The researcher, on the basis of the data obtained from the sample, will not reject the null hypothesis, thus committing a *type II error.*

In situation B, the additive might not significantly increase the lifetimes of automobile batteries in the population, but it might increase the lifetimes of the batteries in the sample. In this case, the null hypothesis would be rejected when it was really true. This would be a type I error. On the other hand, the additive might not work on the batteries selected for the sample, but if it were to be used in the general population of batteries, it might significantly increase their lifetimes. The researcher, on the basis of information obtained from the sample, would not reject the null hypothesis, thus committing a type II error.

The hypothesis-testing situation can be likened to a jury trial. In a jury trial, there are four possible outcomes. The defendant is either guilty or innocent, and he or she will be convicted or acquitted. See Figure 8–3.

Now the hypotheses are

H_0: The defendant is innocent.

H_1: The defendant is not innocent (i.e., guilty).

FIGURE 8–3

Hypothesis Testing and a Jury Trial

H_0: The defendant is innocent.
H_1: The defendant is not innocent.

The results of a trial can be shown as follows:

	H_0 true (innocent)	H_0 false (not innocent)
Reject H_0 (convict)	Type I error 1.	Correct decision 2.
Do not reject H_0 (acquit)	Correct decision 3.	Type II error 4.

Next, the evidence is presented in court by the prosecutor, and based on this evidence, the jury decides the verdict, innocent or guilty.

If the defendant is convicted but he or she did not commit the crime, then a type I error has been committed. See block 1 of Figure 8–3. In other words, a type I error means an innocent person is put in jail. On the other hand, if the defendant is convicted and he or she has committed the crime, then a correct decision has been made. See block 2.

If the defendant is acquitted and he or she did not commit the crime, a correct decision has been made by the jury. See block 3. However, if the defendant is acquitted and he or she did commit the crime, then a type II error has been made. See block 4. In other words, a type II error is letting a guilty person go free.

The decision of the jury does not prove that the defendant did or did not commit the crime. The decision is based on the evidence presented. If the evidence is strong enough, the defendant will be convicted in most cases. If the evidence is weak, the defendant will be acquitted in most cases. Nothing is proved absolutely. Likewise, the decision to reject or not reject the null hypothesis does not prove anything. *The only way to prove anything statistically is to use the entire population,* which, in most cases, is not possible. The decision, then, is made on the basis of probabilities. That is, when there is a large difference between the mean obtained from the sample and the hypothesized mean, the null hypothesis is probably not true. The question is, How large a difference is necessary to reject the null hypothesis? Here is where the level of significance is used.

Unusual Stats

Of workers in the United States, 64% drive to work alone and 6% of workers walk to work.

The **level of significance** is the maximum probability of committing a type I error. This probability is symbolized by α (Greek letter **alpha**). That is, $P(\text{type I error}) = \alpha$.

The probability of a type II error is symbolized by β, the Greek letter **beta**. That is, $P(\text{type II error}) = \beta$. In most hypothesis-testing situations, β cannot be easily computed; however, α and β are related in that decreasing one increases the other.

Statisticians generally agree on using three arbitrary significance levels: the 0.10, 0.05, and 0.01 levels. That is, if the null hypothesis is rejected, the probability of a type I error will be 10, 5, or 1%, depending on which level of significance is used. Here is another way of putting it: When $\alpha = 0.10$, there is a 10% chance of rejecting a true null hypothesis; when $\alpha = 0.05$, there is a 5% chance of rejecting a true null hypothesis; and when $\alpha = 0.01$, there is a 1% chance of rejecting a true null hypothesis.

In a hypothesis-testing situation, the researcher decides what level of significance to use. It does not have to be the 0.10, 0.05, or 0.01 level. It can be any level, depending on the seriousness of the type I error. After a significance level is chosen, a *critical value* is selected from a table for the appropriate test. If a z test is used, for example, the z table

(Table E in Appendix A) is consulted to find the critical value. The critical value determines the critical and noncritical regions.

> The **critical** or **rejection region** is the range of test values that indicates that there is a significant difference and that the null hypothesis should be rejected.
>
> The **noncritical** or **nonrejection region** is the range of test values that indicates that the difference was probably due to chance and that the null hypothesis should not be rejected.
>
> The **critical value** separates the critical region from the noncritical region. The symbol for critical value is C.V.

The critical value can be on the right side of the mean or on the left side of the mean for a one-tailed test. Its location depends on the inequality sign of the alternative hypothesis. For example, in situation B, where the chemist is interested in increasing the average lifetime of automobile batteries, the alternative hypothesis is H_1: $\mu > 36$. Since the inequality sign is $>$, the null hypothesis will be rejected only when the sample mean is significantly greater than 36. Hence, the critical value must be on the right side of the mean. Therefore, this test is called a right-tailed test.

> A **one-tailed test** indicates that the null hypothesis should be rejected when the test value is in the critical region on one side of the mean. A one-tailed test is either a **right-tailed test** or a **left-tailed test,** depending on the direction of the inequality of the alternative hypothesis.

OBJECTIVE 3

Find critical values for the z test.

To obtain the critical value, the researcher must choose an alpha level. In situation B, suppose the researcher chose $\alpha = 0.01$. Then the researcher must find a z value such that 1% of the area falls to the right of the z value and 99% falls to the left of the z value, as shown in Figure 8–4(a).

Next, the researcher must find the area value in Table E closest to 0.9900. The critical z value is 2.33, since that value gives the area closest to 0.9900 (that is, 0.9901), as shown in Figure 8–4(b).

The critical and noncritical regions and the critical value are shown in Figure 8–5.

FIGURE 8–4   Finding the Critical Value for $\alpha = 0.01$ (Right-Tailed Test)

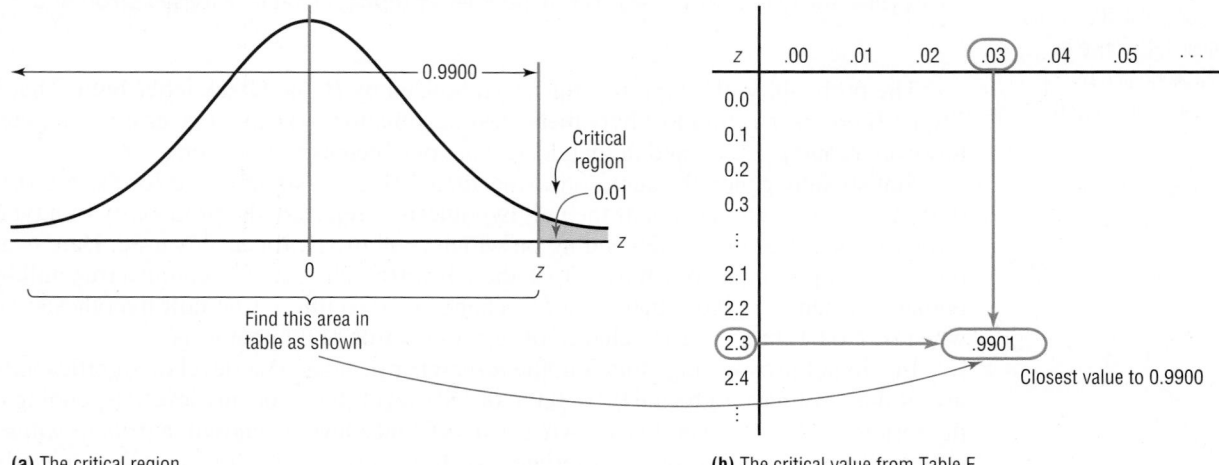

(a) The critical region

(b) The critical value from Table E

FIGURE 8–5

Critical and Noncritical Regions for $\alpha = 0.01$ (Right-Tailed Test)

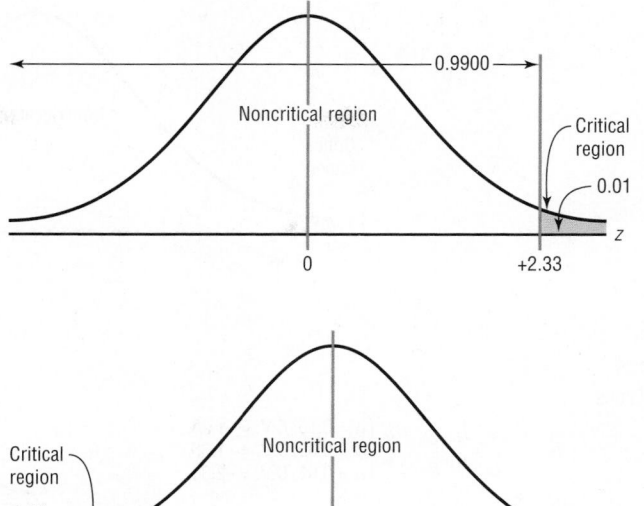

FIGURE 8–6

Critical and Noncritical Regions for $\alpha = 0.01$ (Left-Tailed Test)

Now, move on to situation C, where the contractor is interested in lowering the heating bills. The alternative hypothesis is H_1: $\mu <$ \$78. Hence, the critical value falls to the left of the mean. This test is thus a left-tailed test. At $\alpha = 0.01$, the critical value is -2.33, since 0.0099 is the closest value to 0.01. This is shown in Figure 8–6.

When a researcher conducts a two-tailed test, as in situation A, the null hypothesis can be rejected when there is a significant difference in either direction, above or below the mean.

> In a **two-tailed test,** the null hypothesis should be rejected when the test value is in either of the two critical regions.

For a two-tailed test, then, the critical region must be split into two equal parts. If $\alpha = 0.01$, then one-half of the area, or 0.005, must be to the right of the mean and one-half must be to the left of the mean, as shown in Figure 8–7.

In this case, the z value on the left side is found by looking up the z value corresponding to an area of 0.0050. The z value falls about halfway between -2.57 and -2.58 corresponding to the areas 0.0051 and 0.0049. The average of -2.57 and -2.58 is $[(-2.57) + (-2.58)] \div 2 = -2.575$ so if the z value is needed to three decimal places, -2.575 is used; however, if the z value is rounded to two decimal places, -2.58 is used.

On the right side, it is necessary to find the z value corresponding to $0.99 + 0.005$, or 0.9950. Again, the value falls between 0.9949 and 0.9951, so $+2.575$ or 2.58 can be used. See Figure 8–7.

FIGURE 8–7

Finding the Critical Values for $\alpha = 0.01$ (Two-Tailed Test)

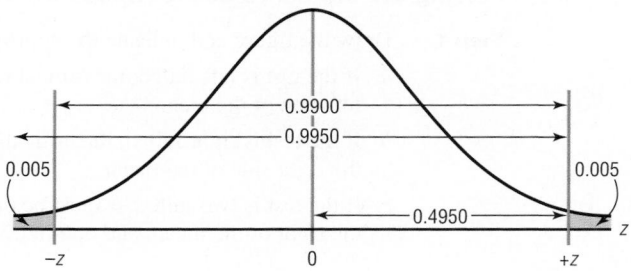

FIGURE 8–8

Critical and Noncritical
Regions for $\alpha = 0.01$
(Two-Tailed Test)

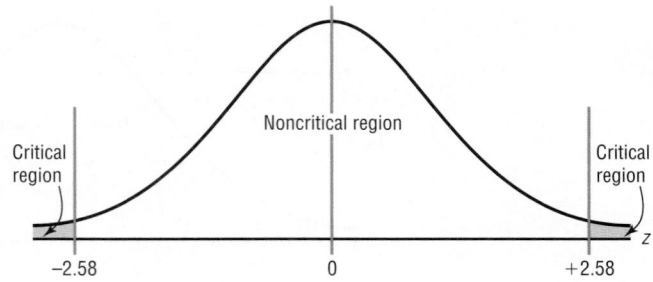

FIGURE 8–9

Summary of Hypothesis
Testing and Critical Values

$H_0: \mu = k$ $\begin{cases} \alpha = 0.10, \text{C.V.} = -1.28 \\ \alpha = 0.05, \text{C.V.} = -1.65 \\ \alpha = 0.01, \text{C.V.} = -2.33 \end{cases}$
$H_1: \mu < k$

(a) Left-tailed

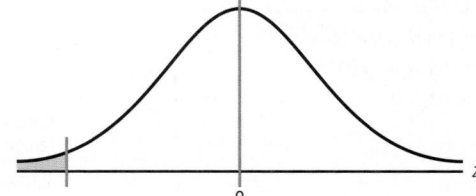

$H_0: \mu = k$ $\begin{cases} \alpha = 0.10, \text{C.V.} = +1.28 \\ \alpha = 0.05, \text{C.V.} = +1.65 \\ \alpha = 0.01, \text{C.V.} = +2.33 \end{cases}$
$H_1: \mu > k$

(b) Right-tailed

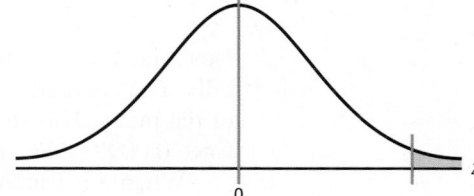

$H_0: \mu = k$ $\begin{cases} \alpha = 0.10, \text{C.V.} = \pm1.65 \\ \alpha = 0.05, \text{C.V.} = \pm1.96 \\ \alpha = 0.01, \text{C.V.} = \pm2.58 \end{cases}$
$H_1: \mu \neq k$

(c) Two-tailed

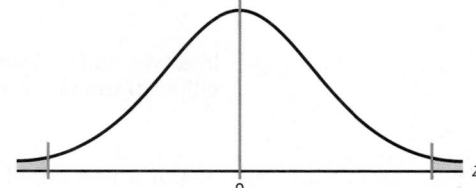

The critical values are $+2.58$ and -2.58, as shown in Figure 8–8.

Similar procedures are used to find other values of α.

Figure 8–9 with rejection regions shaded shows the critical values (C.V.) for the three situations discussed in this section for $\alpha = 0.10$, $\alpha = 0.05$, and $\alpha = 0.01$. The procedure for finding critical values is outlined next (where k is a specified number).

Procedure Table

Finding the Critical Values for Specific α Values, Using Table E

Step 1   Draw the figure and indicate the appropriate area.

  a. If the test is left-tailed, the critical region, with an area equal to α, will be on the left side of the mean.

  b. If the test is right-tailed, the critical region, with an area equal to α, will be on the right side of the mean.

  c. If the test is two-tailed, α must be divided by 2; one-half of the area will be to the right of the mean, and one-half will be to the left of the mean.

Step 2   a. For a left-tailed test, use the z value that corresponds to the area equivalent to α in Table E.

b. For a right-tailed test, use the z value that corresponds to the area equivalent to $1 - \alpha$.

c. For a two-tailed test, use the z value that corresponds to $\alpha/2$ for the left value. It will be negative. For the right value, use the z value that corresponds to the area equivalent to $1 - \alpha/2$. It will be positive.

EXAMPLE 8–2

Using Table E in Appendix A, find the critical value(s) for each situation and draw the appropriate figure, showing the critical region.

a. A left-tailed test with $\alpha = 0.10$.

b. A two-tailed test with $\alpha = 0.02$.

c. A right-tailed test with $\alpha = 0.005$.

SOLUTION *a*

Step 1   Draw the figure and indicate the appropriate area. Since this is a left-tailed test, the area of 0.10 is located in the left tail, as shown in Figure 8–10.

Step 2   Find the area closest to 0.1000 in Table E. In this case, it is 0.1003. Find the z value that corresponds to the area 0.1003. It is -1.28. See Figure 8–10.

FIGURE 8–10
Critical Value and Critical
Region for part *a* of
Example 8–2

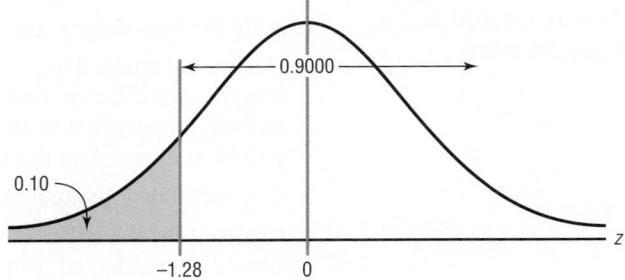

SOLUTION *b*

Step 1   Draw the figure and indicate the appropriate area. In this case, there are two areas equivalent to $\alpha/2$, or $0.02/2 = 0.01$.

Step 2   For the left z critical value, find the area closest to $\alpha/2$, or $0.02/2 = 0.01$. In this case, it is 0.0099.

For the right z critical value, find the area closest to $1 - \alpha/2$, or $1 - 0.02/2 = 0.9900$. In this case, it is 0.9901.

Find the z values for each of the areas. For 0.0099, $z = -2.33$. For the area of 0.9901, $z = +2.33$. See Figure 8–11.

FIGURE 8–11
Critical Values and Critical
Regions for part *b* of
Example 8–2

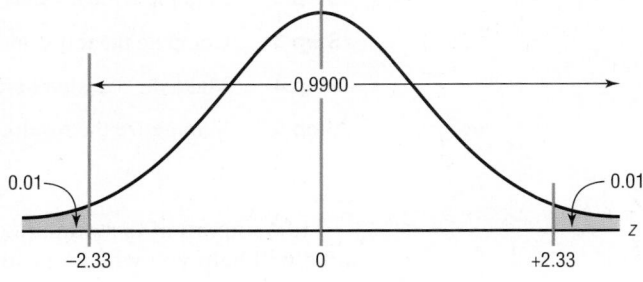

SOLUTION *c*

Step 1   Draw the figure and indicate the appropriate area. Since this is a right-tailed test, the area 0.005 is located in the right tail, as shown in Figure 8–12.

FIGURE 8–12
Critical Value and Critical
Region for part *c* of
Example 8–2

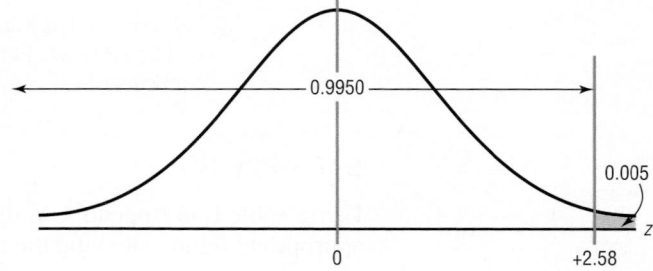

Step 2   Find the area closest to $1 - \alpha$, or $1 - 0.005 = 0.9950$. In this case, it is 0.9949 or 0.9951.

The two *z* values corresponding to areas 0.9949 and 0.9951 are +2.57 and +2.58 respectively. Since 0.9500 is halfway between these two *z* values, find the average of the two *z* values $(+2.57 + 2.58) \div 2 = +2.575$. However, 2.58 is most often used. See Figure 8–12.

OBJECTIVE ❹

State the five steps used in hypothesis testing.

In hypothesis testing, the following steps are recommended.

1. State the hypotheses. Be sure to state both the null and alternative hypotheses.
2. Design the study. This step includes selecting the correct statistical test, choosing a level of significance, and formulating a plan to carry out the study. The plan should include information such as the definition of the population, the way the sample will be selected, and the methods that will be used to collect the data.
3. Conduct the study and collect the data.
4. Evaluate the data. The data should be tabulated in this step, and the statistical test should be conducted. Finally, decide whether to reject or not reject the null hypothesis.
5. Summarize the results.

For the purposes of this chapter, a simplified version of the hypothesis-testing procedure will be used, since designing the study and collecting the data will be omitted. The steps are summarized in the Procedure Table.

Procedure Table
Solving Hypothesis-Testing Problems (Traditional Method)
Step 1   State the hypotheses and identify the claim.
Step 2   Find the critical value(s) from the appropriate table in Appendix A.
Step 3   Compute the test value.
Step 4   Make the decision to reject or not reject the null hypothesis.
Step 5   Summarize the results.

It is important to summarize the results of a statistical study correctly. The following table will help you when you summarize the results.

Decision	Claim	
	Claim is H_0	**Claim is H_1**
Reject H_0	There is enough evidence to reject the claim.	There is enough evidence to support the claim.
Do not reject H_0	There is not enough evidence to reject the claim.	There is not enough evidence to support the claim.

To further illustrate, the claim can be either the null or alternative hypothesis, and one should identify which it is. After the study is completed, the null hypothesis is either rejected or not rejected. From these two facts, the decision can be identified in the appropriate block.

For example, suppose a researcher claims that the mean weight of an adult animal of a particular species is 42 pounds. In this case, the claim would be the null hypothesis, H_0: $\mu = 42$, since the researcher is asserting that the parameter is a specific value. If the null hypothesis is rejected, the conclusion would be that there is enough evidence to reject the claim that the mean weight of the adult animal is 42 pounds.

On the other hand, suppose the researcher claims that the mean weight of the adult animals is not 42 pounds. The claim would be the alternative hypothesis H_1: $\mu \neq 42$. Furthermore, suppose that the null hypothesis is not rejected. The conclusion, then, would be that there is not enough evidence to support the claim that the mean weight of the adult animals is not 42 pounds.

Again, remember that nothing is being proved true or false. The statistician is only stating that there is or is not enough evidence to say that a claim is *probably* true or false. As noted previously, the only way to prove something would be to use the entire population under study, and usually this cannot be done, especially when the population is large.

Applying the Concepts 8–1

Eggs and Your Health

The Incredible Edible Egg company recently found that eating eggs does not increase a person's blood serum cholesterol. Five hundred subjects participated in a study that lasted for 2 years. The participants were randomly assigned to either a no-egg group or a moderate-egg group. The blood serum cholesterol levels were checked at the beginning and at the end of the study. Overall, the groups' levels were not significantly different. The company reminds us that eating eggs is healthy if done in moderation. Many of the previous studies relating eggs and high blood serum cholesterol jumped to improper conclusions.

Using this information, answer these questions.

1. What prompted the study?

2. What is the population under study?

3. Was a sample collected?

4. What was the hypothesis?

5. Were data collected?

6. Were any statistical tests run?

7. What was the conclusion?

See page 485 for the answers.

⊒ Exercises 8–1

1. Define *null* and *alternative hypotheses,* and give an example of each.

2. What is meant by a type I error? A type II error? How are they related?

3. What is meant by a statistical test?

4. Explain the difference between a one-tailed and a two-tailed test.

5. What is meant by the critical region? The *noncritical* region?

6. What symbols are used to represent the null hypothesis and the alternative hypothesis?

7. What symbols are used to represent the probabilities of type I and type II errors?

8. Explain what is meant by a significant difference.

9. When should a one-tailed test be used? A two-tailed test?

10. In hypothesis testing, why can't the hypothesis be proved true?

11. Using the z table (Table E), find the critical value (or values) for each.
    a. $\alpha = 0.05$, two-tailed test
    b. $\alpha = 0.01$, left-tailed test
    c. $\alpha = 0.005$, right-tailed test
    d. $\alpha = 0.01$, right-tailed test
    e. $\alpha = 0.05$, left-tailed test

12. Using the z table (Table E), find the critical value (or values) for each.
    a. $\alpha = 0.02$, left-tailed test
    b. $\alpha = 0.05$, right-tailed test
    c. $\alpha = 0.01$, two-tailed test
    d. $\alpha = 0.04$, left-tailed test
    e. $\alpha = 0.02$, right-tailed test

13. For each conjecture, state the null and alternative hypotheses.
    a. The average age of community college students is 24.6 years.
    b. The average income of accountants is $51,497.
    c. The average age of attorneys is greater than 25.4 years.
    d. The average score of high school basketball games is less than 88.
    e. The average resting pulse rate of male marathon runners is less than 70 beats per minute.

14. For each conjecture, state the null and alternative hypotheses.
    a. The average age of first-year medical school students is at least 27 years.
    b. The average experience (in seasons) for an NBA player is 4.71.
    c. The average number of monthly visits/sessions on the Internet by a person at home has increased from 36 in 2009.
    d. The average cost of a DVD player is $79.95.
    e. The average weight loss for a sample of people who exercise 30 minutes per day for 6 weeks is 8.2 pounds.

8–2   *z* Test for a Mean

OBJECTIVE ❺

Test means when σ is known, using the z test.

In this chapter, two statistical tests will be explained: the z test is used when σ is known, and the t test is used when σ is unknown. This section explains the z test, and Section 8–3 explains the t test.

Many hypotheses are tested using a statistical test based on the following general formula:

$$\text{Test value} = \frac{(\text{observed value}) - (\text{expected value})}{\text{standard error}}$$

The observed value is the statistic (such as the sample mean) that is computed from the sample data. The expected value is the parameter (such as the population mean) that you would expect to obtain if the null hypothesis were true—in other words, the hypothesized value. The denominator is the standard error of the statistic being tested (in this case, the standard error of the mean).

The *z* test is defined formally as follows.

> The **z test** is a statistical test for the mean of a population. It can be used either when $n \geq 30$ or when the population is normally distributed and σ is known.
>   The formula for the *z* test is
>
> $$z = \frac{\overline{X} - \mu}{\sigma/\sqrt{n}}$$
>
> where $\overline{X}$ = sample mean
> μ = hypothesized population mean
> σ = population standard deviation
> n = sample size

For the *z* test, the observed value is the value of the sample mean. The expected value is the value of the population mean, assuming that the null hypothesis is true. The denominator $\sigma/\sqrt{n}$ is the standard error of the mean.

The formula for the *z* test is the same formula shown in Chapter 6 for the situation where you are using a distribution of sample means. Recall that the central limit theorem allows you to use the standard normal distribution to approximate the distribution of sample means when $n \geq 30$.

The assumptions for the *z* test when σ is known are given next.

> **Assumptions for the z Test for a Mean When σ Is Known**
>
> 1. The sample is a random sample.
> 2. Either $n \geq 30$ or the population is normally distributed when $n < 30$.

In this text, the assumptions will be stated in the exercises; however, when encountering statistics in other situations, you must check to see that these assumptions have been met before proceeding.

As stated in Section 8–1, there are five steps for solving *hypothesis-testing* problems:

Step 1   State the hypotheses and identify the claim.

Step 2   Find the critical value(s).

Step 3   Compute the test value.

Step 4   Make the decision to reject or not reject the null hypothesis.

Step 5   Summarize the results.

Note: Your first encounter with hypothesis testing can be somewhat challenging and confusing, since there are many new concepts being introduced at the same time. *To understand all the concepts, you must carefully follow each step in the examples and try each exercise that is assigned.* Only after careful study and patience will these concepts become clear.

Again, *z* values are rounded to two decimal places because they are given to two decimal places in Table E.

EXAMPLE 8–3   Intelligence Tests

In Pennsylvania the average IQ score is 101.5. The variable is normally distributed, and the population standard deviation is 15. A school superintendent claims that the students in her school district have an IQ higher than the average of 101.5. She selects a random sample of 30 students and finds the mean of the test scores is 106.4. Test the claim at $\alpha = 0.05$.

Source: top50states.com

This study found that people who used pedometers reported having increased energy, mood improvement, and weight loss. State possible null and alternative hypotheses for the study. What would be a likely population? What is the sample size? Comment on the sample size.

RD HEALTH

Step to It

IT FITS in your hand, costs less than $30, and will make you feel great. Give up? A pedometer. Brenda Rooney, an epidemiologist at Gundersen Lutheran Medical Center in LaCrosse, Wis., gave 500 people pedometers and asked them to take 10,000 steps—about five miles—a day. (Office workers typically average about 4000 steps a day.) By the end of eight weeks, 56 percent reported having more energy, 47 percent improved their mood and 50 percent lost weight. The subjects reported that seeing their total step-count motivated them to take more.

— JENNIFER BRAUNSCHWEIGER

SOLUTION

Step 1 State the hypotheses and identify the claim.

H_0: $\mu = 101.5$ and H_1: $\mu > 101.5$ (claim)

Step 2 Find the critical value. Since $\alpha = 0.05$ and the test is a right-tailed test, the critical value is $z = +1.65$.

Step 3 Compute the test value.

$$z = \frac{\overline{X} - \mu}{\sigma/\sqrt{n}} = \frac{106.4 - 101.5}{15/\sqrt{30}} = 1.79$$

Step 4 Make the decision. Since the test value 1.79 is greater than the critical value 1.65, the decision is to reject the null hypothesis. This is summarized in Figure 8–13.

FIGURE 8–13
Summary of the z Test of Example 8–3

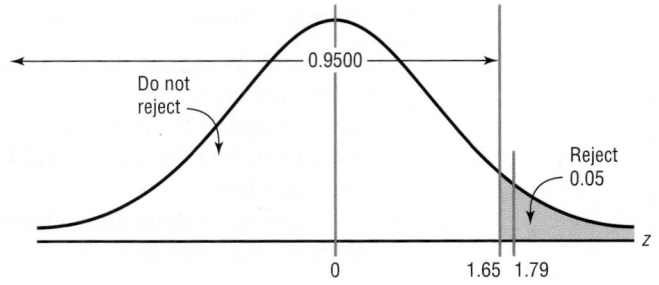

Step 5 Summarize the results. There is enough evidence to support the claim that the IQ of the students is higher than the state average IQ.

Comment: In Example 8–3, the difference is said to be statistically significant. However, when the null hypothesis is rejected, there is always a chance of a type I error. In this case, the probability of a type I error is at most 0.05, or 5%.

EXAMPLE 8–4 SAT Tests

For a specific year, the average score on the SAT Math test was 515.* The variable is normally distributed, and the population standard deviation is 100. The same superintendent in the previous example wishes to see if her students scored significantly below the national average on the test. She randomly selected 36 student scores, as shown. At $\alpha = 0.10$, is there enough evidence to support the claim?

*Source: www.chacha.com

496	506	507	505	438	499
505	522	531	762	513	493
522	668	543	519	349	506
519	516	714	517	511	551
287	523	576	516	515	500
243	509	523	503	414	504

SOLUTION

Step 1 State the hypotheses and identify the claim.

$$H_0: \mu = 515 \qquad \text{and} \qquad H_1: \mu < 515 \text{ (claim)}$$

Step 2 Find the critical value. Since $\alpha = 0.10$ and the test is a left-tailed test, the critical value is -1.28.

Step 3 Compute the test value. Since the exercise gives raw data, it is necessary to find the mean of the data.

$$\overline{X} = \frac{496 + 505 + 522 + \cdots + 504}{36} = \frac{18{,}325}{36} = 509.028$$

$$z = \frac{\overline{X} - \mu}{\sigma/\sqrt{n}} = \frac{509.028 - 515}{100/\sqrt{36}} = -0.36$$

Step 4 Make the decision. Since the test value, -0.36, falls in a noncritical region, the decision is to not reject the null hypothesis. See Figure 8–14.

FIGURE 8–14
Critical and Test Values for
Example 8–4

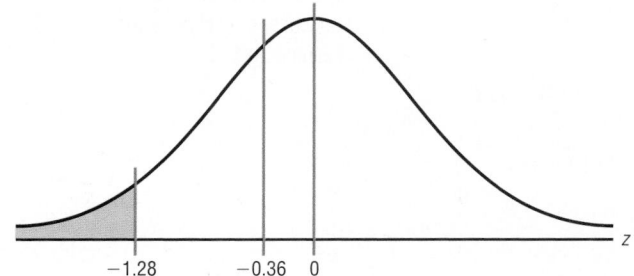

Step 5 Summarize the results. There is not enough evidence to support the claim that the students scored below the national average.

Comment: Even though in Example 8–4 the sample mean of 509.028 is lower than the hypothesized population mean of 515, it is not *significantly* lower. Hence, the difference may be due to chance. When the null hypothesis is not rejected, there is still a probability of a type II error, i.e., of not rejecting the null hypothesis when it is false.

The probability of a type II error is not easily ascertained. Further explanation about the type II error is given in Section 8–6. For now, it is only necessary to realize that the probability of type II error exists when the decision is to not reject the null hypothesis.

Also note that when the null hypothesis is not rejected, it cannot be accepted as true. There is merely not enough evidence to say that it is false. This guideline may sound a little confusing, but the situation is analogous to a jury trial. The verdict is either guilty or not guilty and is based on the evidence presented. If a person is judged not guilty, it does not mean that the person is proved innocent; it only means that there was not enough evidence to reach the guilty verdict.

EXAMPLE 8–5   Cost of Rehabilitation

The Medical Rehabilitation Education Foundation reports that the average cost of rehabilitation for stroke victims is \$24,672. To see if the average cost of rehabilitation is different at a particular hospital, a researcher selects a random sample of 35 stroke victims at the hospital and finds that the average cost of their rehabilitation is \$26,343. The standard deviation of the population is \$3251. At $\alpha = 0.01$, can it be concluded that the average cost of stroke rehabilitation at a particular hospital is different from \$24,672?

Source: Snapshot, *USA TODAY.*

SOLUTION

Step 1   State the hypotheses and identify the claim.

$$H_0: \mu = \$24{,}672 \qquad \text{and} \qquad H_1: \mu \neq \$24{,}672 \text{ (claim)}$$

Step 2   Find the critical values. Since $\alpha = 0.01$ and the test is a two-tailed test, the critical values are $+2.58$ and -2.58.

Step 3   Compute the test value.

$$z = \frac{\overline{X} - \mu}{\sigma/\sqrt{n}} = \frac{26{,}343 - 24{,}672}{3251/\sqrt{35}} = 3.04$$

Step 4   Make the decision. Reject the null hypothesis, since the test value falls in the critical region, as shown in Figure 8–15.

FIGURE 8–15
Critical and Test Values for
Example 8–5

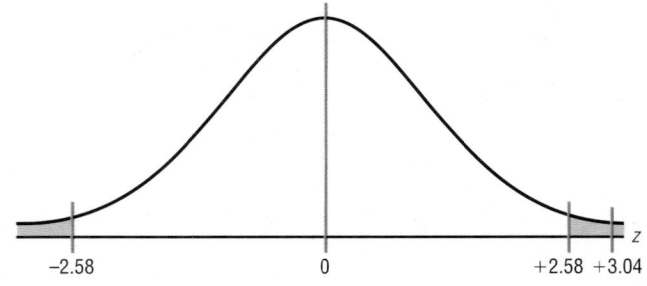

Step 5   Summarize the results. There is enough evidence to support the claim that the average cost of rehabilitation at the particular hospital is different from \$24,672.

P-Value Method for Hypothesis Testing

Statisticians usually test hypotheses at the common α levels of 0.05 or 0.01 and sometimes at 0.10. Recall that the choice of the level depends on the seriousness of the type I error. Besides listing an α value, many computer statistical packages give a *P*-value for hypothesis tests.

FIGURE 8–16

Comparison of α Values and *P*-Values

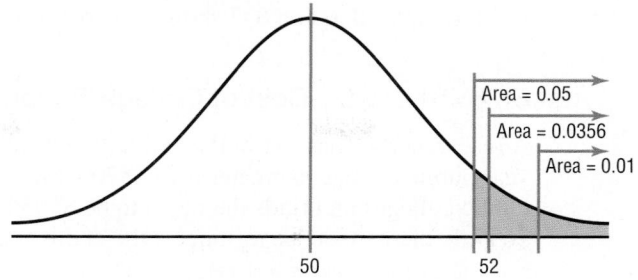

Area = 0.05

Area = 0.0356

Area = 0.01

50   52

> The ***P*-value** (or probability value) is the probability of getting a sample statistic (such as the mean) or a more extreme sample statistic in the direction of the alternative hypothesis when the null hypothesis is true.

In other words, the *P*-value is the actual area under the standard normal distribution curve (or other curve, depending on what statistical test is being used) representing the probability of a particular sample statistic or a more extreme sample statistic occurring if the null hypothesis is true.

For example, suppose that an alternative hypothesis is H_1: $\mu > 50$ and the mean of a sample is $\overline{X} = 52$. If the computer printed a *P*-value of 0.0356 for a statistical test, then the probability of getting a sample mean of 52 or greater is 0.0356 if the true population mean is 50 (for the given sample size and standard deviation). The relationship between the *P*-value and the α value can be explained in this manner. For $P = 0.0356$, the null hypothesis would be rejected at $\alpha = 0.05$ but not at $\alpha = 0.01$. See Figure 8–16.

When the hypothesis test is two-tailed, the area in one tail must be doubled. For a two-tailed test, if α is 0.05 and the area in one tail is 0.0356, the *P*-value will be $2(0.0356) = 0.0712$. That is, the null hypothesis should not be rejected at $\alpha = 0.05$, since 0.0712 is greater than 0.05. In summary, then, if the *P*-value is less than α, reject the null hypothesis. If the *P*-value is greater than α, do not reject the null hypothesis.

Decision Rule When Using a *P*-Value

If *P*-value $\leq \alpha$, reject the null hypothesis.

If *P*-value $> \alpha$, do not reject the null hypothesis.

The *P*-values for the *z* test can be found by using Table E in Appendix A. First find the area under the standard normal distribution curve corresponding to the *z* test value. For a left-tailed test, use the area given in the table; for a right-tailed test, use 1.0000 minus the area given in the table. To get the *P*-value for a two-tailed test, double the area you found in the tail. This procedure is shown in step 3 of Examples 8–6 and 8–7.

The *P*-value method for testing hypotheses differs from the traditional method somewhat. The steps for the *P*-value method are summarized next.

Procedure Table

Solving Hypothesis-Testing Problems (*P*-Value Method)

Step 1   State the hypotheses and identify the claim.

Step 2   Compute the test value.

Step 3   Find the *P*-value.

Step 4   Make the decision.

Step 5   Summarize the results.

Examples 8–6 and 8–7 show how to use the *P*-value method to test hypotheses.

EXAMPLE 8–6   Cost of College Tuition

A researcher wishes to test the claim that the average cost of tuition and fees at a four-year public college is greater than $5700. She selects a random sample of 36 four-year public colleges and finds the mean to be $5950. The population standard deviation is $659. Is there evidence to support the claim at $\alpha = 0.05$? Use the *P*-value method.

Source: Based on information from the College Board.

SOLUTION

Step 1   State the hypotheses and identify the claim.

$$H_0: \mu = \$5700 \qquad \text{and} \qquad H_1: \mu > \$5700 \text{ (claim)}.$$

Step 2   Compute the test value.

$$z = \frac{\overline{X} - \mu}{\sigma/\sqrt{n}} = \frac{5950 - 5700}{659/\sqrt{36}} = 2.28$$

Step 3   Find the *P*-value. Using Table E in Appendix A, find the corresponding area under the normal distribution for $z = 2.28$. It is 0.9887. Subtract this value for the area from 1.0000 to find the area in the right tail.

$$1.0000 - 0.9887 = 0.0113$$

Hence, the *P*-value is 0.0113.

Step 4   Make the decision. Since the *P*-value is less than 0.05, the decision is to reject the null hypothesis. See Figure 8–17.

FIGURE 8–17
P-Value and α Value for
Example 8–6

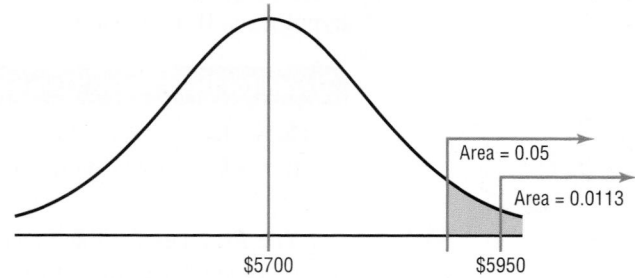

Step 5   Summarize the results. There is enough evidence to support the claim that the tuition and fees at four-year public colleges are greater than $5700.
Note: Had the researcher chosen $\alpha = 0.01$, the null hypothesis would not have been rejected since the *P*-value (0.0113) is greater than 0.01.

EXAMPLE 8–7   Wind Speed

A researcher claims that the average wind speed in a certain city is 8 miles per hour. A sample of 32 days has an average wind speed of 8.2 miles per hour. The standard deviation of the population is 0.6 mile per hour. At $\alpha = 0.05$, is there enough evidence to reject the claim? Use the *P*-value method.

SOLUTION

Step 1   State the hypotheses and identify the claim.

$$H_0: \mu = 8 \text{ (claim)} \qquad \text{and} \qquad H_1: \mu \neq 8$$

Step 2   Compute the test value.

$$z = \frac{8.2 - 8}{0.6/\sqrt{32}} = 1.89$$

Step 3   Find the *P*-value. Using Table E, find the corresponding area for *z* = 1.89. It is 0.9706. Subtract the value from 1.0000.

$$1.0000 - 0.9706 = 0.0294$$

Since this is a two-tailed test, the area of 0.0294 must be doubled to get the *P*-value.

$$2(0.0294) = 0.0588$$

Step 4   Make the decision. The decision is to not reject the null hypothesis, since the *P*-value is greater than 0.05. See Figure 8–18.

FIGURE 8–18
P-Values and *α* Values
for Example 8–7

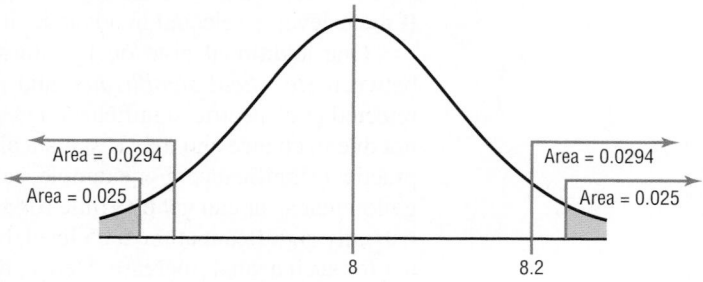

Step 5   Summarize the results. There is not enough evidence to reject the claim that the average wind speed is 8 miles per hour.

In Examples 8–6 and 8–7, the *P*-value and the *α* value were shown on a normal distribution curve to illustrate the relationship between the two values; however, it is not necessary to draw the normal distribution curve to make the decision whether to reject the null hypothesis. You can use the following rule:

> **Decision Rule When Using a *P*-Value**
>
> If *P*-value $\leq$ *α*, reject the null hypothesis.
> If *P*-value $>$ *α*, do not reject the null hypothesis.

In Example 8–6, *P*-value = 0.0113 and *α* = 0.05. Since *P*-value $\leq$ *α*, the null hypothesis was rejected. In Example 8–7, *P*-value = 0.0588 and *α* = 0.05. Since *P*-value $>$ *α*, the null hypothesis was not rejected.

The *P*-values given on calculators and computers are slightly different from those found with Table E. This is so because *z* values and the values in Table E have been rounded. *Also, most calculators and computers give the exact P-value for two-tailed tests, so it should not be doubled (as it should when the area found in Table E is used).*

A clear distinction between the *α* value and the *P*-value should be made. The *α* value is chosen by the researcher *before* the statistical test is conducted. The *P*-value is computed after the sample mean has been found.

There are two schools of thought on *P*-values. Some researchers do not choose an *α* value but report the *P*-value and allow the reader to decide whether the null hypothesis should be rejected.

In this case, the following guidelines can be used, but be advised that these guidelines are not written in stone, and some statisticians may have other opinions.

Guidelines for P-Values

If P-value ≤ 0.01, reject the null hypothesis. The difference is highly significant.

If P-value > 0.01 but P-value ≤ 0.05, reject the null hypothesis. The difference is significant.

If P-value > 0.05 but P-value ≤ 0.10, consider the consequences of type I error before rejecting the null hypothesis.

If P-value > 0.10, do not reject the null hypothesis. The difference is not significant.

Others decide on the α value in advance and use the P-value to make the decision, as shown in Examples 8–6 and 8–7. A note of caution is needed here: If a researcher selects $\alpha = 0.01$ and the P-value is 0.03, the researcher may decide to change the α value from 0.01 to 0.05 so that the null hypothesis will be rejected. This, of course, should not be done. If the α level is selected in advance, it should be used in making the decision.

One additional note on hypothesis testing is that the researcher should distinguish between *statistical significance* and *practical significance*. When the null hypothesis is rejected at a specific significance level, it can be concluded that the difference is probably not due to chance and thus is statistically significant. However, the results may not have any practical significance. For example, suppose that a new fuel additive increases the miles per gallon that a car can get by $\frac{1}{4}$ mile for a sample of 1000 automobiles. The results may be statistically significant at the 0.05 level, but it would hardly be worthwhile to market the product for such a small increase. Hence, there is no practical significance to the results. It is up to the researcher to use common sense when interpreting the results of a statistical test.

Applying the Concepts 8–2

Car Thefts

You recently received a job with a company that manufactures an automobile antitheft device. To conduct an advertising campaign for the product, you need to make a claim about the number of automobile thefts per year. Since the population of various cities in the United States varies, you decide to use rates per 10,000 people. (The rates are based on the number of people living in the cities.) Your boss said that last year the theft rate per 10,000 people was 44 vehicles. You want to see if it has changed. The following are rates per 10,000 people for 36 randomly selected locations in the United States. Assume $\sigma = 30.3$.

55	42	125	62	134	73
39	69	23	94	73	24
51	55	26	66	41	67
15	53	56	91	20	78
70	25	62	115	17	36
58	56	33	75	20	16

Source: Based on information from the National Insurance Crime Bureau.

Using this information, answer these questions.

1. What hypotheses would you use?

2. Is the sample considered small or large?

3. What assumption must be met before the hypothesis test can be conducted?

4. Which probability distribution would you use?

5. Would you select a one- or two-tailed test? Why?

6. What critical value(s) would you use?

7. Conduct a hypothesis test.

8. What is your decision?

9. What is your conclusion?

10. Write a brief statement summarizing your conclusion.

11. If you lived in a city whose population was about 50,000, how many automobile thefts per year would you expect to occur?

See pages 485–486 for the answers.

Exercises 8–2

For Exercises 1 through 25, perform each of the following steps.

   a. State the hypotheses and identify the claim.

   b. Find the critical value(s).

   c. Compute the test value.

   d. Make the decision.

   e. Summarize the results.

Use diagrams to show the critical region (or regions), and use the traditional method of hypothesis testing unless otherwise specified.

1. Warming and Ice Melt The average depth of the Hudson Bay is 305 feet. Climatologists were interested in seeing if warming and ice melt were affecting the water level. Fifty-five measurements over a period of randomly selected weeks yielded a sample mean of 306.2 feet. The population variance is known to be 3.6. Can it be concluded at the 0.05 level of significance that the average depth has increased? Is there evidence of what caused this to happen?

Source: *World Almanac and Book of Facts 2010.*

2. Facebook Friends Many people believe that the average number of Facebook friends is 130. The population standard deviation is 38.2. A random sample of 50 high school students in a particular county revealed that the average number of Facebook friends was 162. At $\alpha = 0.05$, is there sufficient evidence to conclude that the mean number of friends is greater than 130?

3. Revenue of Large Businesses A researcher estimates that the average revenue of the largest businesses in the United States is greater than $24 billion. A random sample of 50 companies is selected, and the revenues (in billions of dollars) are shown. At $\alpha = 0.05$, is there enough evidence to support the researcher's claim? Assume $\sigma = 28.7$.

178	122	91	44	35
61	56	46	20	32
30	28	28	20	27
29	16	16	19	15
41	38	36	15	25
31	30	19	19	19
24	16	15	15	19
25	25	18	14	15
24	23	17	17	22
22	21	20	17	20

Source: *New York Times Almanac.*

4. Moviegoers The average "moviegoer" sees 8.5 movies a year. A *moviegoer* is defined as a person who sees at least one movie in a theater in a 12-month period. A random sample of 40 moviegoers from a large university revealed that the average number of movies seen per person was 9.6. The population standard deviation is 3.2 movies. At the 0.05 level of significance, can it be concluded that this represents a difference from the national average?

Source: *MPAA Study.*

5. Nonparental Care According to the *Digest of Educational Statistics,* a certain group of preschool children under the age of one year each spends an average of 30.9 hours per week in nonparental care. A study of state university center-based programs indicated that a random sample of 32 infants spent an average of 32.1 hours per week in their care. The standard deviation of the population is 3.6 hours. At $\alpha = 0.01$, is there sufficient evidence to conclude that the sample mean differs from the national mean?

Source: www.nces.ed.gov

6. Cost of Building a Home According to the National Association of Home Builders, the average cost of building a home in the Northeast is $117.91 per square foot. A random sample of 36 new homes indicated that the mean cost was $122.57 and the standard deviation was $20. Can it be concluded that the mean cost differs from $117.91, using the 0.10 level of significance?

7. **Heights of 1-Year-Olds** The average 1-year-old (both genders) is 29 inches tall. A random sample of 30 1-year-olds in a large day care franchise resulted in the following heights. At $\alpha = 0.05$, can it be concluded that the average height differs from 29 inches? Assume $\sigma = 2.61$.

25	32	35	25	30	26.5	26	25.5	29.5	32
30	28.5	30	32	28	31.5	29	29.5	30	34
29	32	27	28	33	28	27	32	29	29.5

Source: www.healthepic.com

8. **Salaries of Government Employees** The mean salary of federal government employees on the General Schedule is $59,593. The average salary of 30 randomly selected state employees who do similar work is $58,800 with $\sigma = \$1500$. At the 0.01 level of significance, can it be concluded that state employees earn on average less than federal employees?

Source: *New York Times Almanac.*

9. **Operating Costs of an Automobile** The average cost of owning and operating an automobile is $8121 per 15,000 miles including fixed and variable costs. A random survey of 40 automobile owners revealed an average cost of $8350 with a population standard deviation of $750. Is there sufficient evidence to conclude that the average is greater than $8121? Use $\alpha = 0.01$.

Source: *New York Times Almanac 2010.*

10. **Heights of NBA Players** The average height of an NBA player is 6.698 feet. A random sample of 30 players' heights from a major college basketball program found the mean height was 6.75 feet with a standard deviation of 5.5 inches. At $\alpha = 0.05$, is there sufficient evidence to conclude that the mean height differs from 6.698 feet?

11. **Speeding Ticket Costs** The average cost of a speeding ticket plus court fees is approximately $150. A random sample of 38 speeding ticket court cases showed that the mean cost was $152.59. At the 0.01 level of significance, is that greater than $150? The population standard deviation is $10.78.

12. **Student Expenditures** The average expenditure per student (based on average daily attendance) for a certain school year was $10,337 with a population standard deviation of $1560. A survey for the next school year of 150 randomly selected students resulted in a sample mean of $10,798. Do these results indicate that the average expenditure has changed? Choose your own level of significance.

Source: *World Almanac.*

13. **Ages of U.S. Senators** The mean age of Senators in the 109th Congress was 60.35 years. A random sample of 40 senators from various state senates had an average age of 55.4 years, and the population standard deviation is 6.5 years. At $\alpha = 0.05$, is there sufficient evidence that state senators are on average younger than the Senators in Washington?

Source: *CG Today.*

14. **Prison Sentences** The average length of prison term in the United States for white collar crime is 34.9 months. A random sample of 40 prison terms indicated a mean stay of 28.5 months with a standard deviation of 8.9 months. At $\alpha = 0.04$, is there sufficient evidence to conclude that the average stay differs from 34.9 months?

Source: californiawatch.org

15. State whether the null hypothesis should be rejected on the basis of the given P-value.

   a. P-value = 0.258, $\alpha = 0.05$, one-tailed test

   b. P-value = 0.0684, $\alpha = 0.10$, two-tailed test

   c. P-value = 0.0153, $\alpha = 0.01$, one-tailed test

   d. P-value = 0.0232, $\alpha = 0.05$, two-tailed test

   e. P-value = 0.002, $\alpha = 0.01$, one-tailed test

16. **Soft Drink Consumption** A researcher claims that the yearly consumption of soft drinks per person is 52 gallons. In a sample of 50 randomly selected people, the mean of the yearly consumption was 56.3 gallons. The standard deviation of the population is 3.5 gallons. Find the P-value for the test. On the basis of the P-value, is the researcher's claim valid?

Source: U.S. Department of Agriculture.

17. **Stopping Distances** A study found that the average stopping distance of a school bus traveling 50 miles per hour was 264 feet. A group of automotive engineers decided to conduct a study of its school buses and found that for 20 randomly selected buses, the average stopping distance of buses traveling 50 miles per hour was 262.3 feet. The standard deviation of the population was 3 feet. Test the claim that the average stopping distance of the company's buses is actually less than 264 feet. Find the P-value. On the basis of the P-value, should the null hypothesis be rejected at $\alpha = 0.01$? Assume that the variable is normally distributed.

Source: Snapshot, *USA TODAY.*

18. **Copy Machine Use** A store manager hypothesizes that the average number of pages a person copies on the store's copy machine is less than 40. A random sample of 50 customers' orders is selected. At $\alpha = 0.01$, is there enough evidence to support the claim? Use the P-value hypothesis-testing method. Assume $\sigma = 30.9$.

2	2	2	5	32
5	29	8	2	49
21	1	24	72	70
21	85	61	8	42
3	15	27	113	36
37	5	3	58	82
9	2	1	6	9
80	9	51	2	122
21	49	36	43	61
3	17	17	4	1

19. Burning Calories by Playing Tennis A health researcher read that a 200-pound male can burn an average of 546 calories per hour playing tennis. Thirty-six males were randomly selected and tested. The mean of the number of calories burned per hour was 544.8. Test the claim that the average number of calories burned is actually less than 546, and find the *P*-value. On the basis of the *P*-value, should the null hypothesis be rejected at $\alpha = 0.01$? The standard deviation of the population is 3. Can it be concluded that the average number of calories burned is less than originally thought?

20. Breaking Strength of Cable A special cable has a breaking strength of 800 pounds. The standard deviation of the population is 12 pounds. A researcher selects a random sample of 20 cables and finds that the average breaking strength is 793 pounds. Can he reject the claim that the breaking strength is 800 pounds? Find the *P*-value. Should the null hypothesis be rejected at $\alpha = 0.01$? Assume that the variable is normally distributed.

21. Farm Sizes The average farm size in the United States is 444 acres. A random sample of 40 farms in Oregon indicated a mean size of 430 acres, and the population standard deviation is 52 acres. At $\alpha = 0.05$, can it be concluded that the average farm in Oregon differs from the national mean? Use the *P*-value method.

Source: *New York Times Almanac.*

22. Farm Sizes Ten years ago, the average acreage of farms in a certain geographic region was 65 acres. The standard deviation of the population was 7 acres. A recent study consisting of 22 randomly selected farms showed that the average was 63.2 acres per farm. Test the claim, at $\alpha = 0.10$, that the average has not changed by finding the *P*-value for the test. Assume that σ has not changed and the variable is normally distributed.

23. Transmission Service A car dealer recommends that transmissions be serviced at 30,000 miles. To see whether her customers are adhering to this recommendation, the dealer selects a random sample of 40 customers and finds that the average mileage of the automobiles serviced is 30,456. The standard deviation of the population is 1684 miles. By finding the *P*-value, determine whether the owners are having their transmissions serviced at 30,000 miles. Use $\alpha = 0.10$. Do you think the α value of 0.10 is an appropriate significance level?

24. Speeding Tickets A motorist claims that the South Boro Police issue an average of 60 speeding tickets per day. These data show the number of speeding tickets issued each day for a randomly selected period of 30 days. Assume σ is 13.42. Is there enough evidence to reject the motorist's claim at $\alpha = 0.05$? Use the *P*-value method.

72	45	36	68	69	71	57	60
83	26	60	72	58	87	48	59
60	56	64	68	42	57	57	
58	63	49	73	75	42	63	

25. Sick Days A manager states that in his factory, the average number of days per year missed by the employees due to illness is less than the national average of 10. The following data show the number of days missed by 40 randomly selected employees last year. Is there sufficient evidence to believe the manager's statement at $\alpha = 0.05$? $\sigma = 3.63$. Use the *P*-value method.

0	6	12	3	3	5	4	1
3	9	6	0	7	6	3	4
7	4	7	1	0	8	12	3
2	5	10	5	15	3	2	5
3	11	8	2	2	4	1	9

Extending the Concepts

26. Suppose a statistician chose to test a hypothesis at $\alpha = 0.01$. The critical value for a right-tailed test is +2.33. If the test value were 1.97, what would the decision be? What would happen if, after seeing the test value, she decided to choose $\alpha = 0.05$? What would the decision be? Explain the contradiction, if there is one.

27. Hourly Wage The president of a company states that the average hourly wage of her employees is $8.65. A random sample of 50 employees has the distribution shown. At $\alpha = 0.05$, is the president's statement believable? Assume $\sigma = 0.105$.

Class	Frequency
8.35–8.43	2
8.44–8.52	6
8.53–8.61	12
8.62–8.70	18
8.71–8.79	10
8.80–8.88	2

Technology   Step by Step

TI-84 Plus

Step by Step

Hypothesis Test for the Mean and the *z* Distribution (Data)

1. Enter the data values into L₁.
2. Press **STAT** and move the cursor to TESTS.
3. Press **1** for ZTest.

4. Move the cursor to Data and press **ENTER**.

5. Type in the appropriate values.

6. Move the cursor to the appropriate alternative hypothesis and press **ENTER**.

7. Move the cursor to Calculate and press **ENTER**.

Example TI8–1

This relates to Example 8–4 from the text. At the 10% significance level, test the claim that $\mu < 515$, given the data values.

496	506	507	505	438	499	505	522	531	762	513	493
522	668	543	519	349	506	519	516	714	517	511	551
287	523	576	516	515	500	243	509	523	503	414	504

The test statistic is $z = -0.3583333333$, and the P-value is 0.3600469966.

Hypothesis Test for the Mean and the *z* Distribution (Statistics)

1. Press **STAT** and move the cursor to TESTS.

2. Press **1** for ZTest.

3. Move the cursor to Stats and press **ENTER**.

4. Type in the appropriate values.

5. Move the cursor to the appropriate alternative hypothesis and press **ENTER**.

6. Move the cursor to Calculate and press **ENTER**.

Example TI8–2

At the 5% significance level, test the claim that $\mu > 42{,}000$ given $\sigma = 5230$, $\overline{X} = 43{,}260$, and $n = 30$.

The test statistic is $z = 1.319561037$, and the P-value is 0.0934908728.

EXCEL
Step by Step

Hypothesis Test for the Mean: *z* Test

Excel does not have a procedure to conduct a hypothesis test for a single population mean. However, you may conduct the test of the mean by using the MegaStat Add-in available in your online resources. If you have not installed this add-in, do so, following the instructions from the Chapter 1 Excel Step by Step.

Example XL8–1

This example relates to Example 8–4 from the text. At the 10% level of significance, test the claim that $\mu < 515$. The MegaStat z test uses the P-value method. Therefore, it is not necessary to enter a significance level.

1. Enter the data from Example 8–4 into column A of a new Excel worksheet.

2. From the Toolbar, select Add-Ins, **MegaStat>Hypothesis Tests>Mean vs. Hypothesized Value.** *Note:* You may need to open MegaStat from the MegaStat.xls file on your computer's hard drive.

Menu Commands									
A37			*f*_x						
	A	B	C	D	E	F	G	H	I
1	496								
2	506								
3	507								
4	505								
5	438								
6	499								
7	505								
8	522								
9	531								

3. Select data input and type **A1:A36** as the Input Range.

4. Type **515** for the Hypothesized mean and select the Alternative "less than."

5. Select *z* test and click **[OK]**.

The result of the procedure is shown next.

Hypothesis Test: Mean vs. Hypothesized Value

515.000	Hypothesized value
509.028	Mean data
92.703	Std. dev.
15.450	Std. error
36	*n*
−0.39	*z*
0.3495	*P*-value (one-tailed, lower)

MINITAB
Step by Step

Hypothesis Test for the Mean: *z* Test

MINITAB can be used to calculate the test statistic and the *P*-value. Although the *P*-value approach does not require a critical value from the table, MINITAB can also calculate a critical value as in Example 8–2.

Example 8–2

Find the critical value(s) for each situation and draw the appropriate figure.

Step 1 To find the critical value of *z* for a left-tailed test with $\alpha = 0.10$, select **Graph>Probability Distribution Plot,** then **View Probability,** and then click **[OK].**

Step 2 The Distribution should be set for Normal with a mean of 0 and a standard deviation of 1.

Step 3 Click the tab for **Shaded Area.**

   a) Select **Left Tail.**

   b) Select the ratio button for **Probability.**

   c) Type in the value of alpha for probability, **0.10.**

   d) Click **[OK].** The critical value of *z* to three decimal places is −1.282.

You may click the Edit Last Dialog button and then change the settings for additional critical values.

Example 8–3 Intelligence Tests

MINITAB will calculate the test statistic and *P*-value from the summary statistics. There are no data for this example.

Step 1   Select **Stat>Basic Statistics> 1-sample z.** This is the same menu item used to obtain a *z* interval in Chapter 7.

Step 2   Click on the ratio button for **Summarized Data.**

    a) Type in the sample size of **30.**

    b) Type in the sample mean of **106.4.**

    c) Type in the population standard deviation of **15.**

Step 3   Check the box for Perform hypothesis test, then type in the Hypothesized value of **101.5.**

Step 4   Click the button for **[Options].**

    a) Type the percentage for the Confidence level, **95.**

    b) Click the drop-down menu for the Alternative hypothesis, "greater than."

Step 5   Click **[OK]** twice.

In the session window you will see the results including a confidence interval estimate. The test statistic $z = 1.79$ with a *P*-value of 0.037. Since the *P*-value is smaller than α, the null hypothesis is rejected.

In the session window you will see the results.

One-Sample z

Test of mu = 101.5 vs > 101.5
The assumed standard deviation = 15

N	Mean	SE Mean	95% Lower Bound	Z	P
30	106.40	2.74	101.90	1.79	0.037

Example 8–4 SAT Tests

MINITAB will calculate the test statistic and *P*-value.

Step 1   Type the data into a new MINITAB worksheet.
All 36 values must be in C1. The label SAT Test
must be above the first row of data.

Step 2   Select **Stat>Basic Statistics> 1-sample z.** Press the F3
key to reset the information in the dialog box left over from
the previous example.

Step 3   Click on the ratio button for **Samples in Columns.**
To select the data, click inside the dialog box for Samples
in columns; then select C1 SAT Test from the list.

Step 4   Type in the population standard deviation of **100.**

Step 5   Select the box for Perform hypothesis test, then type in the
Hypothesized value of **515.**

Step 6   Click the button for **[Options].**

a) Type the default confidence level that is $1 - \alpha$, **0.90** or **90.**

b) Click the drop-down menu for the Alternative hypothesis, 'less than'.

c) Click **[OK].**

Optional: Since there are data, select the **[Graphs]** button; then choose one or more
of the three graphs such as the boxplot.

Step 7   Click **[OK]** twice.

	C1	C
	SAT Test	
1	496	
2	505	
3	522	
4	519	
5	287	
6	243	
7	506	
8	522	
9	668	
10	516	
11	523	
12	509	
13	507	
14	531	
15	543	
16	714	

Example 8-4.MTW ***

One-Sample Z: SAT Test

Test of mu = 515 vs < 515
The assumed standard deviation = 100

Variable	N	Mean	StDev	SE Mean	90% Upper Bound	Z	P
SAT Test	36	509.0	92.7	16.7	530.4	−0.36	0.360

The test statistic *z* is equal to −0.36. The null hypothesis cannot be rejected since the *P*-value of
0.360 is larger than 0.10.

8–3   *t* Test for a Mean

OBJECTIVE ❻

Test means when σ is unknown, using the *t* test.

When the population standard deviation is unknown, the *z* test is not typically used for testing hypotheses involving means. A different test, called the *t test,* is used. The distribution of the variable should be approximately normal.

As stated in Chapter 7, the *t* distribution is similar to the standard normal distribution in the following ways.

1. It is bell-shaped.

2. It is symmetric about the mean.

3. The mean, median, and mode are equal to 0 and are located at the center of the distribution.

4. The curve approaches but never touches the *x* axis.

The *t* distribution differs from the standard normal distribution in the following ways.

1. The variance is greater than 1.

2. The *t* distribution is a family of curves based on the *degrees of freedom,* which is a number related to sample size. (Recall that the symbol for degrees of freedom is d.f. See Section 7–2 for an explanation of degrees of freedom.)

3. As the sample size increases, the *t* distribution approaches the normal distribution.

The *t* test is defined next.

> The **_t_ test** is a statistical test for the mean of a population and is used when the population is normally or approximately normally distributed and σ is unknown.
> The formula for the *t* test is
>
> $$t = \frac{\overline{X} - \mu}{s/\sqrt{n}}$$
>
> The degrees of freedom are d.f. $= n - 1$.

The formula for the *t* test is similar to the formula for the *z* test. But since the population standard deviation σ is unknown, the sample standard deviation *s* is used instead.

The critical values for the *t* test are given in Table F in Appendix A. For a one-tailed test, find the α level by looking at the top row of the table and finding the appropriate column. Find the degrees of freedom by looking down the left-hand column.

Notice that the degrees of freedom are given for values from 1 through 30, then at intervals above 30. When the degrees of freedom are above 30, some texts will tell you to use the nearest table value; however, in this text, you should always round down to the nearest table value. For example, if d.f. = 59, use d.f. = 55 to find the critical value or values. This is a conservative approach.

As the degrees of freedom get larger, the critical values approach the *z* values. Hence, the bottom values (large sample size) are the same as the *z* values that were used in the last section.

EXAMPLE 8–8

Find the critical *t* value for $\alpha = 0.05$ with d.f. $= 16$ for a right-tailed *t* test.

SOLUTION

Find the 0.05 column in the top row labeled One tail and 16 in the left-hand column. Where the row and column meet, the appropriate critical value is found; it is $+1.746$. See Figure 8–19.

FIGURE 8–19

Finding the Critical Value
for the *t* Test in Table F
(Example 8–8)

d.f.	One tail, α	0.10	0.05	0.025	0.01	0.005
	Two tails, α	0.20	0.10	0.05	0.02	0.01
1						
2						
3						
4						
5						
⋮						
14						
15						
16		1.746				
17						
18						
⋮						

EXAMPLE 8–9

Find the critical *t* value for $\alpha = 0.01$ with d.f. = 22 for a left-tailed *t* test.

SOLUTION

Find the 0.01 column in the row labeled One tail, and find 22 in the left column. The critical value is -2.508 since the test is a one-tailed left test.

EXAMPLE 8–10

Find the critical values for $\alpha = 0.10$ with d.f. = 18 for a two-tailed *t* test.

SOLUTION

Find the 0.10 column in the row labeled Two tails, and find 18 in the column labeled d.f. The critical values are $+1.734$ and -1.734.

EXAMPLE 8–11

Find the critical value for $\alpha = 0.05$ with d.f. = 28 for a right-tailed *t* test.

SOLUTION

Find the 0.05 column in the One-tail row and 28 in the left column. The critical value is $+1.701$.

In order to test hypotheses regarding the population mean when the standard deviation is unknown, these assumptions should be verified first.

Assumptions for the *t* Test for a Mean When σ Is Unknown

1. The sample is a random sample.
2. Either $n \geq 30$ or the population is normally distributed when $n < 30$.

In this text, the assumptions will be stated in the exercises; however, when encountering statistics in other situations, you must check to see that these assumptions have been met before proceeding.

When you test hypotheses by using the t test (traditional method), follow the same procedure as for the z test, except use Table F.

Step 1   State the hypotheses and identify the claim.

Step 2   Find the critical value(s) from Table F.

Step 3   Compute the test value.

Step 4   Make the decision to reject or not reject the null hypothesis.

Step 5   Summarize the results.

Remember that the t test should be used when the population is approximately normally distributed and the population standard deviation is unknown.
    Examples 8–12 and 8–13 illustrate the application of the t test, using the traditional approach.

EXAMPLE 8–12   Hospital Infections

A medical investigation claims that the average number of infections per week at a hospital in southwestern Pennsylvania is 16.3. A random sample of 10 weeks had a mean number of 17.7 infections. The sample standard deviation is 1.8. Is there enough evidence to reject the investigator's claim at $\alpha = 0.05$? Assume the variable is normally distributed.

Source: Based on information obtained from Pennsylvania Health Care Cost Containment Council.

SOLUTION

Step 1 H_0: $\mu = 16.3$ (claim) and H_1: $\mu \neq 16.3$.

Step 2   The critical values are $+2.262$ and -2.262 for $\alpha = 0.05$ and d.f. $= 9$.

Step 3   The test value is

$$t = \frac{\overline{X} - \mu}{s/\sqrt{n}} = \frac{17.7 - 16.3}{1.8/\sqrt{10}} = 2.460$$

Step 4   Reject the null hypothesis since $2.460 > 2.262$. See Figure 8–20.

FIGURE 8–20
Summary of the t Test of
Example 8–12

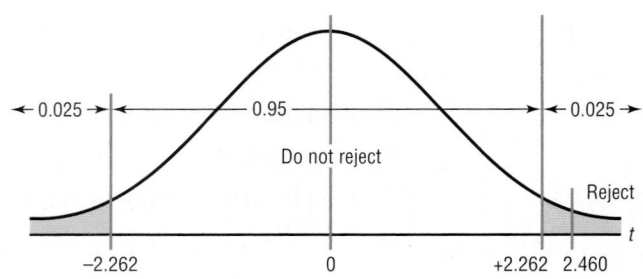

Step 5   There is enough evidence to reject the claim that the average number of infections is 16.3.

EXAMPLE 8–13   Starting Salary for Nurse Practitioners

According to payscale.com, the average starting salary for a nurse practitioner is $79,500. A researcher wishes to test the claim that the starting salary is less than $79,500. A random sample of 8 starting nurse practitioners is selected, and their starting salaries (in dollars) are shown. Is there enough evidence to support the researcher's claim at $\alpha = 0.10$? Assume the variable is normally distributed.

82,000	68,000	70,200	75,600
83,500	64,300	78,600	79,000

SOLUTION

Step 1   State the hypothesis and identify the claim.

$$H_0: \mu = \$79{,}500 \quad \text{and} \quad H_1: \mu < \$79{,}500 \text{ (claim)}$$

Step 2   Find the critical value. At $\alpha = 0.10$ and d.f. $= 7$, the critical value is -1.415.

Step 3   Compute the test value. In this case, the mean and standard deviation must be found. Use the formulas in Chapter 3 or your calculator.

$$\overline{X} = \$75{,}150 \qquad s = \$6{,}937.68$$

$$t = \frac{\overline{X} - \mu}{s/\sqrt{n}} = \frac{75{,}150 - 79{,}500}{6937.68/\sqrt{8}} = -1.773$$

Step 4   Make the decision. Reject the null hypothesis since -1.773 falls in the critical region. See Figure 8–21.

FIGURE 8–21
Critical Value and
Test Value for
Example 8–13

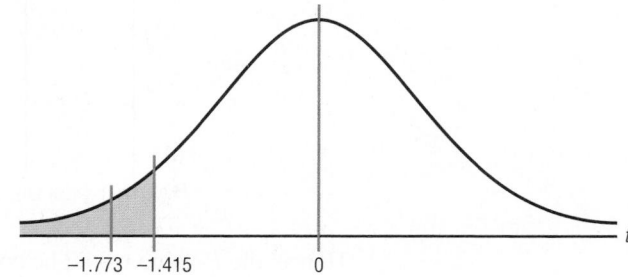

Step 5   Summarize the results. There is enough evidence to support the claim that the average starting salary for nurse practitioners is less than $79,500.

The *P*-values for the *t* test can be found by using Table F; however, specific *P*-values for *t* tests cannot be obtained from the table since only selected values of α (for example, 0.01, 0.05) are given. To find specific *P*-values for *t* tests, you would need a table similar to Table E for each degree of freedom. Since this is not practical, only *intervals* can be found for *P*-values. Examples 8–14 to 8–16 show how to use Table F to determine intervals for *P*-values for the *t* test.

EXAMPLE 8–14

Find the *P*-value when the *t* test value is 2.056, the sample size is 11, and the test is right-tailed.

SOLUTION

To get the *P*-value, look across the row with 10 degrees of freedom (d.f. $= n - 1$) in Table F and find the two values that 2.056 falls between. They are 1.812 and 2.228. Since this is a right-tailed test, look up to the row labeled One tail, α and find the two α values corresponding to 1.812 and 2.228. They are 0.05 and 0.025, respectively. See Figure 8–22.

FIGURE 8–22

Finding the *P*-Value for Example 8–14

Confidence intervals	80%	90%	95%	98%	99%
One tail, α	0.10	(0.05)	(0.025)	0.01	0.005
d.f.	Two tails, α	0.20	0.10	0.05	0.02	0.01
1		3.078	6.314	12.706	31.821	63.657
2		1.886	2.920	4.303	6.965	9.925
3		1.638	2.353	3.182	4.541	5.841
4		1.533	2.132	2.776	3.747	4.604
5		1.476	2.015	2.571	3.365	4.032
6		1.440	1.943	2.447	3.143	3.707
7		1.415	1.895	2.365	2.998	3.499
8		1.397	1.860	2.306	2.896	3.355
9		1.383	1.833	2.262	2.821	3.250
(10)		1.372	(1.812) *	(2.228)	2.764	3.169
11		1.363	1.796	2.201	2.718	3.106
12		1.356	1.782	2.179	2.681	3.055
13		1.350	1.771	2.160	2.650	3.012
14		1.345	1.761	2.145	2.624	2.977
15		1.341	1.753	2.131	2.602	2.947
⋮		⋮	⋮	⋮	⋮	⋮
(z) ∞		1.282	1.645	1.960	2.326	2.576

*2.056 falls between 1.812 and 2.228.

Hence, the *P*-value would be contained in the interval $0.025 < P\text{-value} < 0.05$. This means that the *P*-value is between 0.025 and 0.05. If α were 0.05, you would reject the null hypothesis since the *P*-value is less than 0.05. But if α were 0.01, you would not reject the null hypothesis since the *P*-value is greater than 0.01. (Actually, it is greater than 0.025.)

EXAMPLE 8–15

Find the *P*-value when the *t* test value is 2.983, the sample size is 6, and the test is two-tailed.

SOLUTION

To get the *P*-value, look across the row with d.f. = 5 in Table F and find the two values that 2.983 falls between. They are 2.571 and 3.365. Then look up the row labeled Two tails, α to find the corresponding α values.

In this case, they are 0.05 and 0.02. Hence, the *P*-value is contained in the interval $0.02 < P\text{-value} < 0.05$. This means that the *P*-value is between 0.02 and 0.05. In this case, if $\alpha = 0.05$, the null hypothesis can be rejected since *P*-value < 0.05; but if $\alpha = 0.01$, the null hypothesis cannot be rejected since *P*-value > 0.01 (actually *P*-value > 0.02).

Note: **Since many of you will be using calculators or computer programs that give the specific *P*-value for the *t* test and other tests presented later in this textbook, these specific values, in addition to the intervals, will be given for the answers to the examples and exercises.**

The *P*-value obtained from a calculator for Example 8–14 is 0.033. The *P*-value obtained from a calculator for Example 8–15 is 0.031.

To test hypotheses using the *P*-value method, follow the same steps as explained in Section 8–2. These steps are repeated here.

Step 1   State the hypotheses and identify the claim.

Step 2   Compute the test value.

Step 3   Find the *P*-value.

Step 4   Make the decision.

Step 5   Summarize the results.

This method is shown in Example 8–16.

EXAMPLE 8–16   Jogger's Oxygen Uptake

A physician claims that joggers' maximal volume oxygen uptake is greater than the average of all adults. A random sample of 15 joggers has a mean of 40.6 milliliters per kilogram (ml/kg) and a standard deviation of 6 ml/kg. If the average of all adults is 36.7 ml/kg, is there enough evidence to support the physician's claim at $\alpha = 0.05$? Assume the variable is normally distributed.

SOLUTION

Step 1   State the hypotheses and identify the claim.

$$H_0: \mu = 36.7 \qquad \text{and} \qquad H_1: \mu > 36.7 \text{ (claim)}$$

Step 2   Compute the test value. The test value is

$$t = \frac{\overline{X} - \mu}{s/\sqrt{n}} = \frac{40.6 - 36.7}{6/\sqrt{15}} = 2.517$$

Step 3   Find the *P*-value. Looking across the row with d.f. = 14 in Table F, you see that 2.517 falls between 2.145 and 2.624, corresponding to $\alpha = 0.025$ and $\alpha = 0.01$ since this is a right-tailed test. Hence, *P*-value > 0.01 and *P*-value < 0.025, or $0.01 < P\text{-value} < 0.025$. That is, the *P*-value is somewhere between 0.01 and 0.025. (The *P*-value obtained from a calculator is 0.012.)

> **Interesting Fact**
>
> The area of Alaska contains $\frac{1}{6}$ of the total area of the United States.

Step 4   Reject the null hypothesis since *P*-value < 0.05 (that is, *P*-value $< \alpha$).

Step 5   There is enough evidence to support the claim that the joggers' maximal volume oxygen uptake is greater than 36.7 ml/kg.

Students sometimes have difficulty deciding whether to use the *z* test or *t* test. The rules are the same as those pertaining to confidence intervals.

1. If σ is known, use the *z* test. The variable must be normally distributed if $n < 30$.

2. If σ is unknown but $n \geq 30$, use the *t* test.

3. If σ is unknown and $n < 30$, use the *t* test. (The population must be approximately normally distributed.)

These rules are summarized in Figure 8–23.

A study conducted at the University of Pittsburgh showed that hospital patients in rooms with lots of sunlight required less pain medication the day after surgery and during their total stay in the hospital than patients who were in darker rooms.

Patients in the sunny rooms averaged 3.2 milligrams of pain reliever per hour for their total stay as opposed to 4.1 milligrams per hour for those in darker rooms. This study compared two groups of patients. Although no statistical tests were mentioned in the article, what statistical test do you think the researchers used to compare the groups?

FIGURE 8–23

Using the *z* or *t* Test

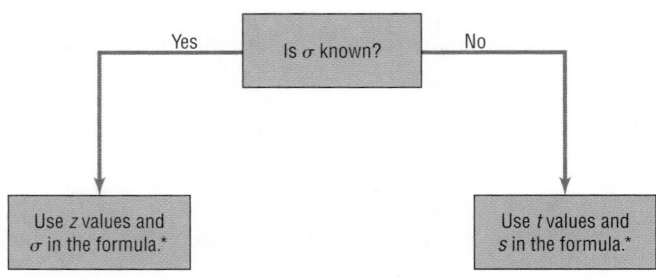

*If *n* < 30, the variable must be normally distributed.

≝ Applying the Concepts 8–3

How Much Nicotine Is in Those Cigarettes?

A tobacco company claims that its best-selling cigarettes contain at most 40 mg of nicotine. This claim is tested at the 1% significance level by using the results of 15 randomly selected cigarettes. The mean is 42.6 mg and the standard deviation is 3.7 mg. Evidence suggests that nicotine is normally distributed. Information from a computer output of the hypothesis test is listed.

Sample mean = 42.6　　　　　　　　　　P-value = 0.008
Sample standard deviation = 3.7　　　　Significance level = 0.01
Sample size = 15　　　　　　　　　　　Test statistic t = 2.72155
Degrees of freedom = 14　　　　　　　 Critical value t = 2.62449

1. What are the degrees of freedom?

2. Is this a *z* or *t* test?

3. Is this a comparison of one or two samples?

4. Is this a right-tailed, left-tailed, or two-tailed test?

5. From observing the *P*-value, what would you conclude?

6. By comparing the test statistic to the critical value, what would you conclude?

7. Is there a conflict in this output? Explain.

8. What has been proved in this study?

See page 486 for the answers.

≡ Exercises 8–3

1. In what ways is the *t* distribution similar to the standard normal distribution? In what ways is the *t* distribution different from the standard normal distribution?

2. What are the degrees of freedom for the *t* test?

3. Find the critical value (or values) for the *t* test for each.
  a. $n = 10$, $\alpha = 0.05$, right-tailed
  b. $n = 18$, $\alpha = 0.10$, two-tailed
  c. $n = 6$, $\alpha = 0.01$, left-tailed
  d. $n = 9$, $\alpha = 0.025$, right-tailed

4. Find the critical value (or values) for the *t* test for each.
  a. $n = 15$, $\alpha = 0.05$, right-tailed
  b. $n = 23$, $\alpha = 0.005$, left-tailed
  c. $n = 28$, $\alpha = 0.01$, two-tailed
  d. $n = 17$, $\alpha = 0.02$, two-tailed

5. Using Table F, find the *P*-value interval for each test value.
  a. $t = 2.321$, $n = 15$, right-tailed
  b. $t = 1.945$, $n = 28$, two-tailed
  c. $t = -1.267$, $n = 8$, left-tailed
  d. $t = 1.562$, $n = 17$, two-tailed

6. Using Table F, find the *P*-value interval for each test value.
  a. $t = 3.025$, $n = 24$, right-tailed
  b. $t = -1.145$, $n = 5$, left-tailed
  c. $t = 2.179$, $n = 13$, two-tailed
  d. $t = 0.665$, $n = 10$, right-tailed

For Exercises 7 through 23, perform each of the following steps.
  a. State the hypotheses and identify the claim.
  b. Find the critical value(s).
  c. Find the test value.
  d. Make the decision.
  e. Summarize the results.

Use the traditional method of hypothesis testing unless otherwise specified.

Assume that the population is approximately normally distributed.

7. Strawberry Seeds The average strawberry has approximately 200 seeds. A very patient student selected a random sample of 10 strawberries and found a sample mean of 185.2 seeds with a standard deviation of 10. At the 0.05 level of significance, can it be concluded that the mean is less than 200?

8. Cost of Braces The average cost for teeth straightening with metal braces is approximately $5400. A nationwide franchise thinks that its cost is below that figure. A random sample of 28 patients across the country had an average cost of $5250 with a standard deviation of $629. At $\alpha = 0.025$, can it be concluded that the mean is less than $5400?

9. Heights of Tall Buildings A researcher estimates that the average height of the buildings of 30 or more stories in a large city is at least 700 feet. A random sample of 10 buildings is selected, and the heights in feet are shown. At $\alpha = 0.025$, is there enough evidence to reject the claim?

485	511	841	725	615
520	535	635	616	582

Source: *Pittsburgh Tribune-Review.*

10. Number of Words in a Novel The National Novel Writing Association states that the average novel is at least 50,000 words. A particularly ambitious writing club at a college-preparatory high school had randomly selected members with works of the following lengths. At $\alpha = 0.10$, is there sufficient evidence to conclude that the mean length is greater than 50,000 words?

48,972	50,100	51,560
49,800	50,020	49,900
52,193		

11. Television Viewing by Teens Teens are reported to watch the fewest total hours of television per week of all the demographic groups. The average television viewing for teens on Sunday from 1:00 to 7:00 P.M. is 1 hour 13 minutes. A random sample of local teens disclosed the following times for Sunday afternoon television viewing. At $\alpha = 0.01$, can it be concluded that the average is greater than the national viewing time? (*Note:* Change all times to minutes.)

2:30	2:00	1:30	3:20
1:00	2:15	1:50	2:10
1:30	2:30		

Source: *World Almanac.*

12. Chocolate Chip Cookie Calories The average 1-ounce chocolate chip cookie contains 110 calories. A random sample of 15 different brands of 1-ounce chocolate chip cookies resulted in the following calorie amounts. At the $\alpha = 0.01$ level, is there sufficient evidence that the average calorie content is greater than 110 calories?

100	125	150	160	185	125	155	145	160
100	150	140	135	120	110			

Source: *The Doctor's Pocket Calorie, Fat, and Carbohydrate Counter.*

13. Cost of Making a Movie During a recent year the average cost of making a movie was $54.8 million. This year, a random sample of 15 recent action movies had an average production cost of $62.3 million with a variance of $90.25 million. At the 0.05 level of significance, can it be concluded that it costs more than average to produce an action movie?

Source: *New York Times Almanac.*

14. Internet Visits A U.S. Web Usage Snapshot indicated a monthly average of 36 Internet visits per user from home. A random sample of 24 Internet users yielded a sample mean of 42.1 visits with a standard deviation of 5.3. At the 0.01 level of significance, can it be concluded that this differs from the national average?

Source: *New York Times Almanac.*

15. Cell Phone Bills The average monthly cell phone bill was reported to be $50.07 by the U.S. Wireless Industry. Random sampling of a large cell phone company found the following monthly cell phone charges (in dollars):

55.83	49.88	62.98	70.42
60.47	52.45	49.20	50.02
58.60	51.29		

At the 0.05 level of significance, can it be concluded that the average phone bill has increased?

Source: *World Almanac.*

16. Teaching Assistants' Stipends A random sample of stipends of teaching assistants in economics is listed. Is there sufficient evidence at the $\alpha = 0.05$ level to conclude that the average stipend differs from $15,000? The stipends listed (in dollars) are for the academic year.

14,000	18,000	12,000	14,356	13,185
13,419	14,000	11,981	17,604	12,283
16,338	15,000			

Source: *Chronicle of Higher Education.*

17. Cost of a Movie Ticket The average movie ticket in 2010 cost $7.89. A random sample of 15 movie tickets from the suburbs of a large U.S. city indicated that the mean cost was $11.09 with a standard deviation of $4.86. At the 0.01 level of significance, can it be concluded that the mean is higher than the national average?

18. Cell Phone Call Lengths The average local cell phone call length was reported to be 2.27 minutes. A random sample of 20 phone calls showed an average of 2.98 minutes in length with a standard deviation of 0.98 minute. At $\alpha = 0.05$, can it be concluded that the average differs from the population average?

Source: *World Almanac.*

19. Commute Time to Work A survey of 15 large U.S. cities finds that the average commute time one way is 25.4 minutes. A chamber of commerce executive feels that the commute in his city is less and wants to

publicize this. He randomly selects 25 commuters and finds the average is 22.1 minutes with a standard deviation of 5.3 minutes. At $\alpha = 0.10$, is he correct?

Source: *New York Times Almanac.*

20. Average Family Size The average family size was reported as 3.18. A random sample of families in a particular school district resulted in the following family sizes:

5	4	5	4	4	3	6	4	3	3	5
6	3	3	2	7	4	5	2	2	2	3
5	2									

At $\alpha = 0.05$, does the average family size differ from the national average?

Source: *New York Times Almanac.*

21. Doctor Visits A report by the Gallup Poll stated that on average a woman visits her physician 5.8 times a year. A researcher randomly selects 20 women and obtained these data.

3	2	1	3	7	2	9	4	6	6
8	0	5	6	4	2	1	3	4	1

At $\alpha = 0.05$, can it be concluded that the average is still 5.8 visits per year? Use the *P*-value method.

22. Number of Jobs The U.S. Bureau of Labor and Statistics reported that a person between the ages of 18 and 34 has had an average of 9.2 jobs. To see if this average is correct, a researcher selected a random sample of 8 workers between the ages of 18 and 34 and asked how many different places they had worked. The results were as follows:

8	12	15	6	1	9	13	2

At $\alpha = 0.05$, can it be concluded that the mean is 9.2? Use the *P*-value method. Give one reason why the respondents might not have given the exact number of jobs that they have worked.

23. Water Consumption The *Old Farmer's Almanac* stated that the average consumption of water per person per day was 123 gallons. To test the hypothesis that this figure may no longer be true, a researcher randomly selected 16 people and found that they used on average 119 gallons per day and $s = 5.3$. At $\alpha = 0.05$, is there enough evidence to say that the *Old Farmer's Almanac* figure might no longer be correct? Use the *P*-value method.

≡Technology   Step by Step

TI-84 Plus

Step by Step

Hypothesis Test for the Mean and the *t* Distribution (Data)

1. Enter the data values into L_1.
2. Press **STAT** and move the cursor to TESTS.
3. Press **2** for T-Test.
4. Move the cursor to Data and press **ENTER.**
5. Type in the appropriate values.

6. Move the cursor to the appropriate alternative hypothesis and press **ENTER.**

7. Move the cursor to Calculate and press **ENTER.**

Hypothesis Test for the Mean and the *t* Distribution (Statistics)

1. Press **STAT** and move the cursor to TESTS.

2. Press **2** for T-Test.

3. Move the cursor to Stats and press **ENTER.**

4. Type in the appropriate values.

5. Move the cursor to the appropriate alternative hypothesis and press **ENTER.**

6. Move the cursor to Calculate and press **ENTER.**

EXCEL
Step by Step

Hypothesis Test for the Mean: *t* Test

Excel does not have a procedure to conduct a hypothesis test for the mean. However, you may conduct the test of the mean using the MegaStat Add-in available in your online resources. If you have not installed this add-in, do so, following the instructions from the Chapter 1 Excel Step by Step.

Substitute Teachers' Salaries

An educator claims that the average salary of substitute teachers in school districts in Allegheny County, Pennsylvania, is less than $60 per day. A random sample of eight school districts is selected, and the daily salaries (in dollars) are shown. Is there enough evidence to support the educator's claim at $\alpha = 0.10$? Assume the variable is normally distributed.

$$60 \quad 56 \quad 60 \quad 55 \quad 70 \quad 55 \quad 60 \quad 55$$

Source: *Pittsburgh Tribune-Review.*

The MegaStat *t* test uses the *P*-value method. Therefore, it is not necessary to enter a significance level.

1. Enter the data into column A of a new worksheet.

2. From the toolbar, select Add-Ins, **MegaStat>Hypothesis Tests>Mean vs. Hypothesized Value.** *Note:* You may need to open MegaStat from the MegaStat.xls file on your computer's hard drive.

3. Select data input and type **A1:A8** as the Input Range.

4. Type **60** for the Hypothesized mean and select the "less than" Alternative.

5. Select *t* test and click [OK].

The result of the procedure is shown next.

Hypothesis Test: Mean vs. Hypothesized Value

60.000	Hypothesized value
58.875	Mean data
5.083	Standard deviation
1.797	Standard error
8	*n*
7	d.f.
−0.63	*t*
0.2756	*P*-value (one-tailed, lower)

MINITAB
Step by Step

Hypothesis Test for the Mean and the *t* Distribution

MINITAB can be used to look up a critical value of *t*.

Example 8–8

Find the critical *t* value for $\alpha = 0.05$ with d.f. $= 16$ for a right-tailed *t* test.

Step 1 To find the critical value of *t* for a right-tailed test, select **Graph>Probability Distribution Plot,** then **View Probability,** and then click [OK].

Step 2   Change the Distribution to a *t* distribution with Degrees of freedom equal to **16.**

Step 3   Click the tab for **Shaded Area.**

    a) Select the ratio button for **Probability.**

    b) Select **Right Tail.**

    c) Type in the value of alpha for Probability, **0.05.**

    d) Click **[OK].**

The critical value of *t* to three decimal places is 1.746.

    You may click the Edit Last Dialog button and then change the settings for additional critical values.

Example 8–13 Starting Salaries

MINITAB will calculate the test statistic and *P*-value from the data.

Step 1   Type the data into a new MINITAB worksheet. All 8 values must be in C1. The label must be above the first row of data. Do not type the commas in large numbers.

Step 2   Select **Stat>Basic Statistics> 1-sample t.**

Step 3   Click on the ratio button for **Samples in Columns.**

    To select the data, click inside the dialog box for Samples in columns, and then select C1 Starting Salaries from the list.

Step 4   Select the box for Perform hypothesis test, and then type in the Hypothesized value of **79500.**

Step 5   Click the button for **[Options].**

    a) Type the default confidence level that is $1 - \alpha = 0.90$ or 90.

    b) Click the drop down menu for the Alternative hypothesis, 'less than'.

    c) Click **[OK].**

        Optional: Since there are data, select the **[Graphs]** button and then choose one or more of the three graphs such as the boxplot.

Step 6   Click **[OK]** twice.

One-Sample t: Starting Salaries

Test of mu = 79500 vs < 79500

Variable	N	Mean	StDev	SE Mean	90% Upper Bound	T	P
Starting Salaries	8	75150	6938	2453	78621	−1.77	0.060

The test statistic is −1.77. Since the *P*-value of 0.060 is less than alpha, the null hypothesis is rejected.

8–4   *z* Test for a Proportion

OBJECTIVE 7

Test proportions, using the *z* test.

Many hypothesis-testing situations involve proportions. Recall from Chapter 7 that a *proportion* is the same as a percentage of the population.

These data were obtained from *The Book of Odds* by Michael D. Shook and Robert L. Shook (New York: Penguin Putnam, Inc.):

- 59% of consumers purchase gifts for their fathers.
- 85% of people over 21 said they have entered a sweepstakes.
- 51% of Americans buy generic products.
- 35% of Americans go out for dinner once a week.

A hypothesis test involving a population proportion can be considered as a binomial experiment when there are only two outcomes and the probability of a success does not change from trial to trial. Recall from Section 5–3 that the mean is $\mu = np$ and the standard deviation is $\sigma = \sqrt{npq}$ for the binomial distribution.

Since a normal distribution can be used to approximate the binomial distribution when $np \geq 5$ and $nq \geq 5$, the standard normal distribution can be used to test hypotheses for proportions.

Formula for the *z* Test for Proportions

$$z = \frac{\hat{p} - p}{\sqrt{pq/n}}$$

where $\hat{p} = \dfrac{X}{n}$ sample proportion

p = population proportion
n = sample size

The formula is derived from the normal approximation to the binomial and follows the general formula

$$\text{Test value} = \frac{(\text{observed value}) - (\text{expected value})}{\text{standard error}}$$

We obtain $\hat{p}$ from the sample (i.e., observed value), p is the expected value (i.e., hypothesized population proportion), and $\sqrt{pq/n}$ is the standard error.

The formula $z = \dfrac{\hat{p} - p}{\sqrt{pq/n}}$ can be derived from the formula $z = \dfrac{X - \mu}{\sigma}$ by substituting $\mu = np$ and $\sigma = \sqrt{npq}$ and then dividing both numerator and denominator by n. Some algebra is used. See Exercise 23 in this section.

The assumptions for testing a proportion are given next.

Assumptions for Testing a Proportion

1. The sample is a random sample.
2. The conditions for a binomial experiment are satisfied. (See Chapter 5.)
3. $np \geq 5$ and $nq \geq 5$.

In this book, the assumptions will be stated in the exercises; however, when encountering statistics in other situations, you must check to see that these assumptions have been met before proceeding.

The steps for hypothesis testing are the same as those shown in Section 8–3. Table E is used to find critical values and *P*-values.

Chapter 8 Hypothesis Testing

Examples 8–17 to 8–19 show the traditional method of hypothesis testing. Example 8–20 shows the *P*-value method.

Sometimes it is necessary to find $\hat{p}$, as shown in Examples 8–17, 8–19, and 8–20, and sometimes $\hat{p}$ is given in the exercise. See Example 8–18.

EXAMPLE 8–17 Obese Young People

A researcher claims that based on the information obtained from the Centers for Disease Control and Prevention, 17% of young people ages 2–19 are obese. To test this claim, she randomly selected 200 people ages 2–19 and found that 42 were obese. At $\alpha = 0.05$, is there enough evidence to reject the claim?

SOLUTION

Step 1   State the hypotheses and identify the claim.

$$H_0\colon p = 0.17 \text{ (claim)} \qquad \text{and} \qquad H_1\colon p \neq 0.17$$

Step 2   Find the critical values. Since $\alpha = 0.05$ and the test is two-tailed, the critical values are ± 1.96.

Step 3   Compute the test value. First, it is necessary to find $\hat{p}$.

$$\hat{p} = \frac{X}{n} = \frac{42}{200} = 0.21 \qquad p = 0.17 \qquad q = 1 - p = 1 - 0.17 = 0.83$$

Substitute in the formula.

$$z = \frac{\hat{p} - p}{\sqrt{pq/n}} = \frac{0.21 - 0.17}{\sqrt{(0.17)(0.83)/200}} = 1.51$$

Step 4   Make the decision. Do not reject the null hypothesis since the test value falls in the noncritical region. See Figure 8–24.

FIGURE 8–24
Critical and Test Values for
Example 8–17

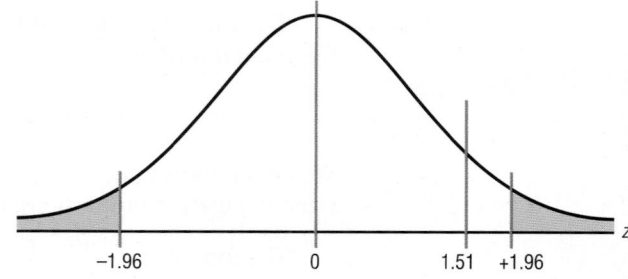

Step 5   Summarize the results. There is not enough evidence to reject the claim that 17% of young people ages 2–19 are obese.

EXAMPLE 8–18 Female Gun Owners

The Gallup Crime Survey stated that 23% of gun owners are women. A researcher believes that in the area where he lives, the percentage is less than 23%. He randomly selects a sample of 100 gun owners and finds that 11% of the gun owners are women. At $\alpha = 0.01$, is the percentage of female gun owners in his area less than 23%.

SOLUTION

Step 1   State the hypotheses and identify the claim.

$$H_0\colon p = 0.23 \qquad \text{and} \qquad H_1\colon p < 0.23 \text{ (claim)}$$

Step 2   Find the critical value. Since $\alpha = 0.01$ and the test is one-tailed, the critical value is -2.33.

Step 3   Compute the test value. In this case, $\hat{p}$ is given.

$$p = 0.23 \qquad q = 1 - p = 1 - 0.23 = 0.77 \qquad \hat{p} = 0.11$$

$$z = \frac{\hat{p} - p}{\sqrt{pq/n}} = \frac{0.11 - 0.23}{\sqrt{(0.23)(0.77)/100}} = -2.85$$

Step 4   Make the decision. Reject the null hypothesis since the test value falls in the critical region. See Figure 8–25.

FIGURE 8–25

Critical and Test Values for
Example 8–18

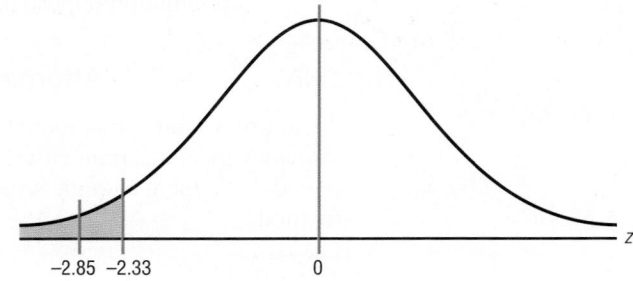

Step 5   Summarize the results. There is enough evidence to support the claim that the percentage of female gun owners in that area is less than 23%.

EXAMPLE 8–19   Replacing $1 Bills with $1 Coins

A statistician read that at least 77% of the population oppose replacing $1 bills with $1 coins. To see if this claim is valid, the statistician selected a random sample of 80 people and found that 55 were opposed to replacing the $1 bills. At $\alpha = 0.01$, test the claim that at least 77% of the population are opposed to the change.

Source: *USA TODAY.*

SOLUTION

Step 1   State the hypotheses and identify the claim.

$$H_0: p = 0.77 \text{ (claim)} \qquad \text{and} \qquad H_1: p < 0.77$$

Step 2   Find the critical value(s). Since $\alpha = 0.01$ and the test is left-tailed, the critical value is -2.33.

Step 3   Compute the test value.

$$\hat{p} = \frac{X}{n} = \frac{55}{80} = 0.6875$$

$$p = 0.77 \qquad \text{and} \qquad q = 1 - 0.77 = 0.23$$

$$z = \frac{\hat{p} - p}{\sqrt{pq/n}} = \frac{0.6875 - 0.77}{\sqrt{(0.77)(0.23)/80}} = -1.75$$

Step 4   Do not reject the null hypothesis, since the test value does not fall in the critical region, as shown in Figure 8–26.

FIGURE 8–26
Critical and Test Values for
Example 8–19

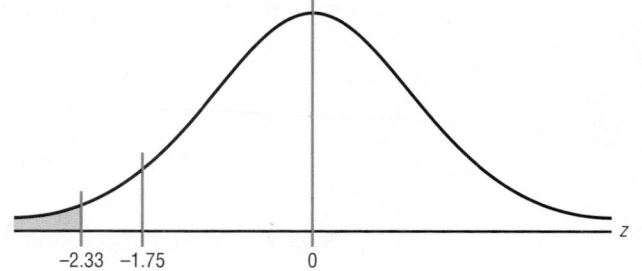

Step 5   There is not enough evidence to reject the claim that at least 77% of the population oppose replacing $1 bills with $1 coins.

EXAMPLE 8–20   Attorney Advertisements

An attorney claims that more than 25% of all lawyers advertise. A random sample of 200 lawyers in a certain city showed that 63 had used some form of advertising. At $\alpha = 0.05$, is there enough evidence to support the attorney's claim? Use the P-value method.

SOLUTION

Step 1   State the hypotheses and identify the claim.

$$H_0: p = 0.25 \qquad \text{and} \qquad H_1: p > 0.25 \text{ (claim)}$$

Step 2   Compute the test value.

$$\hat{p} = \frac{X}{n} = \frac{63}{200} = 0.315$$

$$p = 0.25 \qquad \text{and} \qquad q = 1 - 0.25 = 0.75$$

$$z = \frac{\hat{p} - p}{\sqrt{pq/n}} = \frac{0.315 - 0.25}{\sqrt{(0.25)(0.75)/200}} = 2.12$$

Step 3   Find the P-value. The area under the curve in Table E for $z = 2.12$ is 0.9830. Subtracting the area from 1.0000, you get $1.0000 - 0.9830 = 0.0170$. The P-value is 0.0170.

Step 4   Reject the null hypothesis, since $0.0170 < 0.05$ (that is, P-value $< \alpha$). See Figure 8–27.

> **Interesting Facts**
>
> Lightning is the second most common killer among storm-related hazards. On average, 73 people are killed each year by lightning. Of people who are struck by lightning, 90% do survive; however, they usually have lasting medical problems or disabilities.

FIGURE 8–27
P-Value and α Value for
Example 8–20

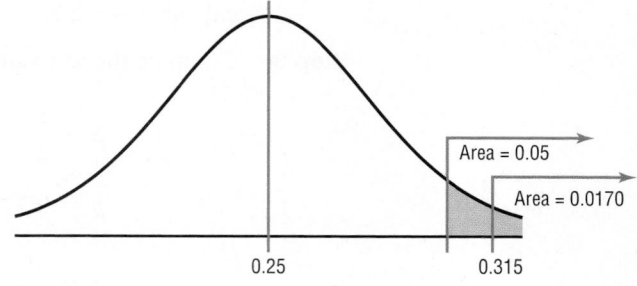

Step 5   There is enough evidence to support the attorney's claim that more than 25% of the lawyers use some form of advertising.

≡ Applying the Concepts 8–4

Quitting Smoking

Assume you are part of a research team that compares products designed to help people quit smoking. Condor Consumer Products Company would like more specific details about the study to be made available to the scientific community. Review the following and then answer the questions about how you would have conducted the study.

New StopSmoke

No method has been proved more effective. StopSmoke provides significant advantages over all other methods. StopSmoke is simpler to use, and it requires no weaning. StopSmoke is also significantly less expensive than the leading brands. StopSmoke's superiority has been proved in two independent studies.

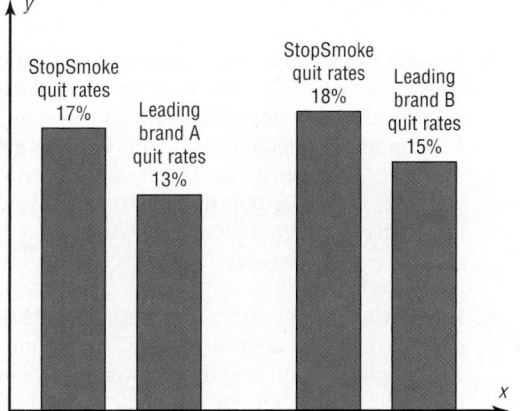

1. What were the statistical hypotheses?

2. What were the null hypotheses?

3. What were the alternative hypotheses?

4. Were any statistical tests run?

5. Were one- or two-tailed tests run?

6. What were the levels of significance?

7. If a type I error was committed, explain what it would have been.

8. If a type II error was committed, explain what it would have been.

9. What did the studies prove?

10. Two statements are made about significance. One states that StopSmoke provides significant advantages, and the other states that StopSmoke is significantly less expensive than other leading brands. Are they referring to statistical significance? What other type of significance is there?

See page 486 for the answers.

≡ Exercises 8–4

1. Give three examples of proportions.

2. Why is a proportion considered a binomial variable?

3. When you are testing hypotheses by using proportions, what are the necessary requirements?

4. What are the mean and the standard deviation of a proportion?

For Exercises 5 through 20, perform each of the following steps.

    a. State the hypotheses and identify the claim.

    b. Find the critical value(s).

    c. Compute the test value.

    d. Make the decision.

    e. Summarize the results.

Use the traditional method of hypothesis testing unless otherwise specified.

5. **Improper Driving** In 2009, 45.6% of motor vehicle accidents involved no improper driving. In an area comprised of six adjoining counties, it was found that out of 110 randomly selected accidents, 60 involved improper driving in some way. At the 0.10 level of significance, is there sufficient evidence to conclude that the proportion of accidents involving improper driving differs from the 2009 proportion?

Source: *World Almanac 2012.*

6. **Stocks and Mutual Fund Ownership** It has been found that 50.3% of U.S. households own stocks and mutual funds. A random sample of 300 heads of

households indicated that 171 owned some type of stock. At what level of significance would you conclude that this was a significant difference?

Source: www.census.gov

7. **Fans of Professional Baseball** According to a professional polling company, an unbelievably low percentage—36%—of Americans said that they were fans of professional baseball. A random sample of 200 people in southwestern Pennsylvania indicated that 88 were baseball fans. At $\alpha = 0.02$, is the proportion greater than 36%?

8. **Female Physicians** The percentage of physicians who are women is 27.9%. In a survey of physicians employed by a large university health system, 45 of 120 randomly selected physicians were women. Is there sufficient evidence at the 0.05 level of significance to conclude that the proportion of women physicians at the university health system exceeds 27.9%?

Source: New York Times Almanac.

9. **Burglaries** About 30% of all burglaries are through an open or unlocked door or window. A random sample of 130 burglaries indicated that 85 were not via an open or unlocked door or window. At the 0.05 level of significance, can it be concluded that this differs from the stated proportion?

Source: polling report.com

10. **Undergraduate Enrollment** It has been found that 85.6% of all enrolled college and university students in the United States are undergraduates. A random sample of 500 enrolled college students in a particular state revealed that 420 of them were undergraduates. Is there sufficient evidence to conclude that the proportion differs from the national percentage? Use $\alpha = 0.05$.

Source: Time Almanac.

11. **Moviegoers** The largest group of moviegoers by age is the 40- to 59-year-old age group. This group constitutes 32% of the movie-going population. A theater complex randomly surveyed the customers over a three-week period and found that out of 423 surveyed, 170 were 40 to 59 years of age. At the 0.01 level of significance, does this differ from the stated proportion?

Source: MPAA Study.

12. **Television Set Ownership** According to Nielsen Media Research, of all the U.S. households that owned at least one television set, 83% had two or more sets. A local cable company canvassing the town to promote a new cable service found that of the 300 randomly selected households visited, 240 had two or more television sets. At $\alpha = 0.05$, is there sufficient evidence to conclude that the proportion is less than the one in the report?

Source: World Almanac.

13. **After-School Snacks** In the Journal of the American Dietetic Association, it was reported that 54% of kids said that they had a snack after school. A random sample of 60 kids was selected, and 36 said that they had a snack after school. Use $\alpha = 0.01$ and the P-value method to test the claim. On the basis of the results, should parents be concerned about their children eating a healthy snack?

14. **Natural Gas Heat** The Energy Information Administration reported that 51.7% of homes in the United States were heated by natural gas. A random sample of 200 homes found that 115 were heated by natural gas. Does the evidence support the claim, or has the percentage changed? Use $\alpha = 0.05$ and the P-value method. What could be different if the sample were taken in a different geographic area?

15. **Youth Smoking** Researchers suspect that 18% of all high school students smoke at least one pack of cigarettes a day. At Wilson High School, a randomly selected sample of 300 students found that 50 students smoked at least one pack of cigarettes a day. At $\alpha = 0.05$, test the claim that less than 18% of all high school students smoke at least one pack of cigarettes a day. Use the P-value method.

16. **Exercise to Reduce Stress** A survey by Men's Health magazine stated that 14% of men said they used exercise to reduce stress. Use $\alpha = 0.10$. A random sample of 100 men was selected, and 10 said that they used exercise to relieve stress. Use the P-value method to test the claim. Could the results be generalized to all adult Americans?

17. **Borrowing Library Books** For Americans using library services, the American Library Association (ALA) claims that 67% borrow books. A library director feels that this is not true so he randomly selects 100 borrowers and finds that 82 borrowed books. Can he show that the ALA claim is incorrect? Use $\alpha = 0.05$.

Source: American Library Association; USA TODAY.

18. **Doctoral Students' Salaries** Nationally, at least 60% of Ph.D. students have paid assistantships. A college dean feels that this is not true in his state, so he randomly selects 50 Ph.D. students and finds that 26 have assistantships. At $\alpha = 0.05$, is the dean correct?

Source: U.S. Department of Education, Chronicle of Higher Education.

19. **Football Injuries** A report by the NCAA states that 57.6% of football injuries occur during practices. A head trainer claims that this is too high for his conference, so he randomly selects 36 injuries and finds that 17 occurred during practices. Is his claim correct, at $\alpha = 0.05$?

Source: NCAA Sports Medicine Handbook.

20. **Recycling** Approximately 70% of the U.S. population recycles. According to a green survey of a random sample of 250 college students, 204 said that they recycled. At $\alpha = 0.01$, is there sufficient evidence to conclude that the proportion of college students who recycle is greater than 70%?

≡ Extending the Concepts

When np *or* nq *is not 5 or more, the binomial table (Table B in Appendix A) must be used to find critical values in hypothesis tests involving proportions.*

21. Coin Tossing A coin is tossed 9 times and 3 heads appear. Can you conclude that the coin is not balanced? Use $\alpha = 0.10$. [*Hint:* Use the binomial table and find $2P(X \le 3)$ with $p = 0.5$ and $n = 9$.]

22. First-Class Airline Passengers In the past, 20% of all airline passengers flew first class. In a sample of 15 passengers, 5 flew first class. At $\alpha = 0.10$, can you conclude that the proportions have changed?

23. Show that $z = \dfrac{\hat{p} - p}{\sqrt{pq/n}}$ can be derived from $z = \dfrac{X - \mu}{\sigma}$ by substituting $\mu = np$ and $\sigma = \sqrt{npq}$ and dividing both numerator and denominator by n.

≡ Technology   Step by Step

TI-84 Plus
Step by Step

Hypothesis Test for the Proportion

1. Press **STAT** and move the cursor to TESTS.
2. Press **5** for 1-PropZTest.
3. Type in the appropriate values.
4. Move the cursor to the appropriate alternative hypothesis and press **ENTER.**
5. Move the cursor to Calculate and press **ENTER.**

Example TI8–3

Test the claim that 40% of all telephone customers have call-waiting service, when $n = 100$ and $\hat{p} = 37\%$. Use $\alpha = 0.01$.

The test statistic is $z = -0.6123724357$, and the *P*-value is 0.5402912598.

EXCEL
Step by Step

Hypothesis Test for the Proportion: *z* Test

Excel does not have a procedure to conduct a hypothesis test for a single population proportion. However, you may conduct the test of the proportion, using the MegaStat Add-in available in your online resources. If you have not installed this add-in, do so, following the instructions from the Chapter 1 Excel Step by Step.

Example XL8–2

This example relates to the previous example. At the 1% significance level, test the claim that $p = 0.40$. The MegaStat test of the population proportion uses the *P*-value method. Therefore, it is not necessary to enter a significance level.

1. From the toolbar, select Add-Ins, **MegaStat>Hypothesis Tests>Proportion vs. Hypothesized Value.** *Note:* You may need to open MegaStat from the MegaStat.xls file on your computer's hard drive.
2. Type **0.37** for the Observed proportion, p.
3. Type **0.40** for the Hypothesized proportion, p.
4. Type **100** for the sample size, n.
5. Select the "not equal" Alternative.
6. Click [OK].

The result of the procedure is shown next.

Hypothesis Test for Proportion vs. Hypothesized Value

Observed	Hypothesized	
0.37	0.4	p (as decimal)
37/100	40/100	p (as fraction)
37.	40.	X
100	100	n
	0.049	standard error
	−0.61	z
	0.5403	p-value (two-tailed)

MINITAB
Step by Step

Hypothesis Test for One Proportion and the *z* Distribution

MINITAB can be used to find a critical value of chi-square.

Example 8–17

Test the claim that 17% of young people between the ages of 2 and 19 are obese.
MINITAB will calculate the test statistic and *P*-value based on the normal distribution. There are no data for this example. It doesn't matter what is in the worksheet.

Step 1   Select **Stat>Basic Statistics> 1-proportion.**

Step 2   Check the ratio button for Summarized data.

    a) In the dialog box for Number of events, type in the number of successes in the sample, **42.**

    b) In the dialog box for Number of trials, type in the sample size, **200.**

Step 3   Select the box for **Perform hypothesis test,** then type the decimal form of the Hypothesized proportion, **0.17.**

Step 4   Click the button for **[Options].**

    a) Type in the confidence level, **95.**

    b) The Alternative hypothesis should match the condition in H_1, not equal.

    c) Check the box for Use test and interval based on normal distribution.

    d) Click [OK] twice.

In the Session Window the output will include the test statistics, $t = 1.51$ and its *P*-value 0.132. The null hypothesis cannot be rejected.

Test and CI for One Proportion
Test of p = 0.17 vs p not = 0.17

Sample	X	N	Sample p	95% CI	Z-Value	P-Value
1	42	200	0.210000	(0.153551, 0.266449)	1.51	0.132

Using the normal approximation.

8–5 χ^2 Test for a Variance or Standard Deviation

In Chapter 7, the chi-square distribution was used to construct a confidence interval for a single variance or standard deviation. This distribution is also used to test a claim about a single variance or standard deviation.

Recall from Chapter 7 the characteristics of the chi-square distribution:

1. All chi-square values are greater than or equal to 0.

2. The chi-square distribution is a family of curves based on the degrees of freedom.

3. The area under each chi-square distribution is equal to 1.

4. The chi-square distributions are positively skewed.

To find the area under the chi-square distribution, use Table G in Appendix A. There are three cases to consider:

1. Finding the chi-square critical value for a specific α when the hypothesis test is right-tailed

2. Finding the chi-square critical value for a specific α when the hypothesis test is left-tailed

3. Finding the chi-square critical values for a specific α when the hypothesis test is two-tailed

Table G is set up so it gives the areas to the right of the critical value; so if the test is right-tailed, just use the area under the α value for the specific degrees of freedom. If the test is left-tailed, subtract the α value from 1; then use the area in the table for that value for a specific d.f. If the test is two-tailed, divide the α value by 2; then use the area under that value for a specific d.f. for the right critical value and the area for the $1 - \alpha/2$ value for the d.f. for the left critical value.

EXAMPLE 8–21

Find the critical chi-square value for 15 degrees of freedom when $\alpha = 0.05$ and the test is right-tailed.

SOLUTION

The distribution is shown in Figure 8–28.

FIGURE 8–28
Chi-Square Distribution for
Example 8–21

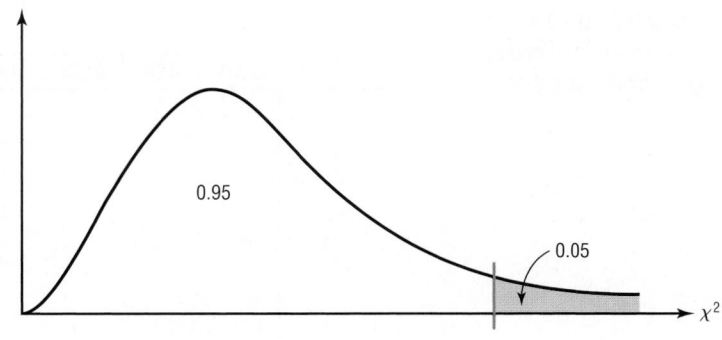

Find the α value at the top of Table G, and find the corresponding degrees of freedom in the left column. The critical value is located where the two columns meet—in this case, 24.996. See Figure 8–29.

FIGURE 8–29

Locating the Critical Value in
Table G for Example 8–21

EXAMPLE 8–22

Find the critical chi-square value for 10 degrees of freedom when $\alpha = 0.05$ and the test is left-tailed.

SOLUTION

This distribution is shown in Figure 8–30.

FIGURE 8–30

Chi-Square Distribution for
Example 8–22

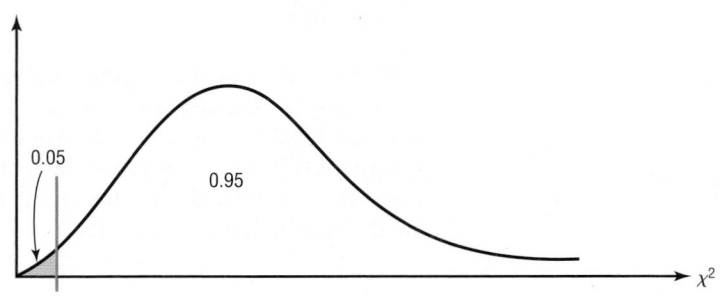

When the test is left-tailed, the α value must be subtracted from 1, that is, $1 - 0.05 = 0.95$. The left side of the table is used, because the chi-square table gives the area to the right of the critical value, and the chi-square statistic cannot be negative. The table is set up so that it gives the values for the area to the right of the critical value. In this case, 95% of the area will be to the right of the value.

For 0.95 and 10 degrees of freedom, the critical value is 3.940. See Figure 8–31.

FIGURE 8–31

Locating the Critical Value in
Table G for Example 8–22

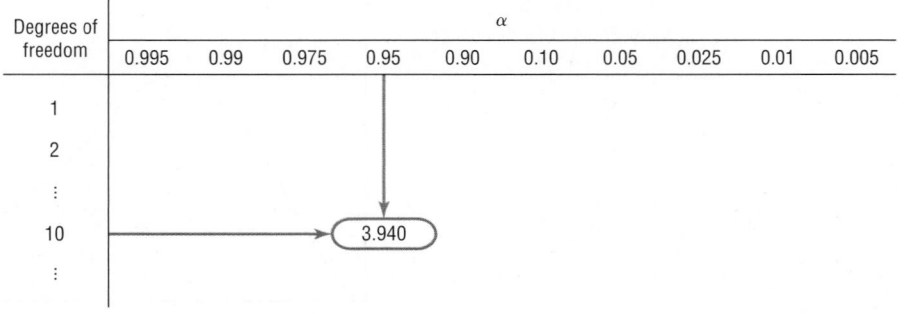

EXAMPLE 8–23

Find the critical chi-square values for 22 degrees of freedom when $\alpha = 0.05$ and a two-tailed test is conducted.

SOLUTION

When a two-tailed test is conducted, the area must be split, as shown in Figure 8–32. Note that the area to the right of the larger value is 0.025 (0.05/2 or $\alpha/2$), and the area to the right of the smaller value is 0.975 (1.00 − 0.05/2 or 1 − $\alpha/2$).

FIGURE 8–32
Chi-Square Distribution for
Example 8–23

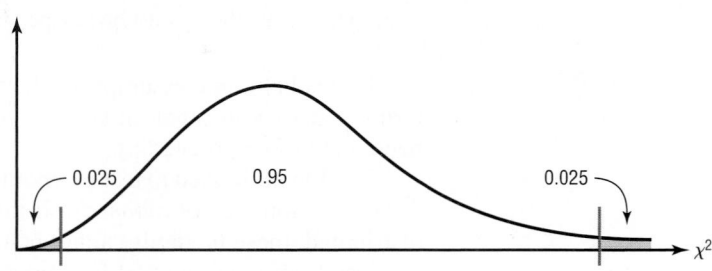

Remember that chi-square values cannot be negative. Hence, you must use α values in the table of 0.025 and 0.975. With 22 degrees of freedom, the critical values are 36.781 and 10.982, respectively.

After the degrees of freedom reach 30, Table G gives values only for multiples of 10 (40, 50, 60, etc.). When the exact degrees of freedom sought are not specified in the table, the closest smaller value should be used. For example, if the given degrees of freedom are 36, use the table value for 30 degrees of freedom. This guideline keeps the type I error equal to or below the α value.

When you are testing a claim about a single variance using the **chi-square test,** there are three possible test situations: right-tailed test, left-tailed test, and two-tailed test.

If a researcher believes the variance of a population to be greater than some specific value, say, 225, then the researcher states the hypotheses as

$$H_0: \sigma^2 = 225 \qquad \text{and} \qquad H_1: \sigma^2 > 225$$

and conducts a right-tailed test.

If the researcher believes the variance of a population to be less than 225, then the researcher states the hypotheses as

$$H_0: \sigma^2 = 225 \qquad \text{and} \qquad H_1: \sigma^2 < 225$$

and conducts a left-tailed test.

Finally, if a researcher does not wish to specify a direction, she or he states the hypotheses as

$$H_0: \sigma^2 = 225 \qquad \text{and} \qquad H_1: \sigma^2 \neq 225$$

and conducts a two-tailed test.

Formula for the Chi-Square Test for a Single Variance

$$\chi^2 = \frac{(n-1)s^2}{\sigma^2}$$

with degrees of freedom equal to $n - 1$ and where
$\quad n$ = sample size
$\quad s^2$ = sample variance
$\quad \sigma^2$ = population variance

Three assumptions are made for the chi-square test, as outlined here.

Assumptions for the Chi-Square Test for a Single Variance
1. The sample must be randomly selected from the population.
2. The population must be normally distributed for the variable under study.
3. The observations must be independent of one another.

In this book, the assumptions will be stated in the exercises; however, when encountering statistics in other situations, you must check to see that these assumptions have been met before proceeding.

The methods used to test a hypothesis about a population variance or population standard deviation are not robust. So if the data come from a population that is not normally distributed, these methods cannot be used.

The traditional method for hypothesis testing follows the same five steps listed earlier. They are repeated here.

Step 1   State the hypotheses and identify the claim.

Step 2   Find the critical value(s).

Step 3   Compute the test value.

Step 4   Make the decision.

Step 5   Summarize the results.

Examples 8–24 through 8–26 illustrate the traditional hypothesis-testing procedure for variances.

You might ask, Why is it important to test variances? There are several reasons. First, in any situation where consistency is required, such as in manufacturing, you would like to have the smallest variation possible in the products. For example, when bolts are manufactured, the variation in diameters due to the process must be kept to a minimum, or else the nuts will not fit them properly. In education, consistency is required on a test. That is, if the same students take the same test several times, they should get approximately the same grades, and the variance of each of the student's grades should be small. On the other hand, if the test is to be used to judge learning, the overall standard deviation of all the grades should be large so that you can differentiate those who have learned the subject from those who have not learned it.

EXAMPLE 8–24   Math SAT Test

The standard deviation for the Math SAT test is 100. The variance is 10,000. An instructor wishes to see if the variance of the 23 randomly selected students in her school is less than 10,000. The variance for the 23 test scores is 7225. Is there enough evidence to support the claim that the variance of the students in her school is less than 10,000 at $\alpha = 0.05$? Assume that the scores are normally distributed.

SOLUTION

Step 1   State the hypotheses and identify the claim.

$$H_0: \sigma^2 = 10,000 \qquad \text{and} \qquad H_1: \sigma^2 < 10,000 \text{ (claim)}$$

Step 2   Find the critical value. Since this test is left-tailed and $\alpha = 0.05$, use the value $1 - 0.05 = 0.95$. The degrees of freedom are $n - 1 = 23 - 1 = 22$. Hence, the critical value is 12.338. Note that the critical region is on the left, as shown in Figure 8–33.

Step 3   Compute the test value.

$$\chi^2 = \frac{(n-1)s^2}{\sigma^2} = \frac{(23-1)7225}{10,000} = 15.895$$

Step 4   Make the decision. Since 15.895 falls in the noncritical region, do not reject the null hypothesis. See Figure 8–33.

FIGURE 8–33
Critical and Test Values for
Example 8–24

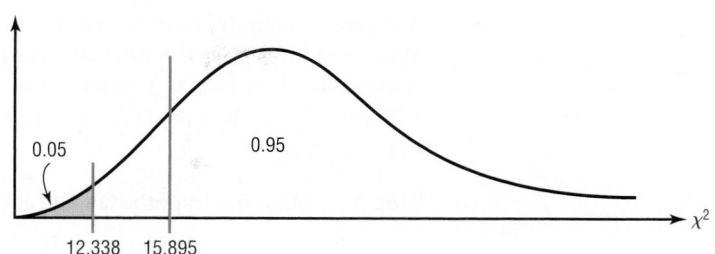

0.05   0.95

12.338 15.895

Step 5   Summarize the results. There is not enough evidence to support the claim that the variation of the students' test scores is less than the population variance.

EXAMPLE 8–25   Outpatient Surgery

A hospital administrator believes that the standard deviation of the number of people using outpatient surgery per day is greater than 8. A random sample of 15 days is selected. The data are shown. At $\alpha = 0.10$, is there enough evidence to support the administrator's claim? Assume the variable is normally distributed.

25	30	5	15	18
42	16	9	10	12
12	38	8	14	27

SOLUTION

Step 1   State the hypotheses and identify the claim.

$$H_0: \sigma = 8 \qquad \text{and} \qquad H_1: \sigma > 8 \text{ (claim)}$$

Since the standard deviation is given, it should be squared to get the variance.

Step 2   Find the critical value. Since this test is right-tailed with d.f. of $15 - 1 = 14$ and $\alpha = 0.10$, the critical value is 21.064.

Step 3   Compute the test value. Since raw data are given, the standard deviation of the sample must be found by using the formula in Chapter 3 or your calculator. It is $s = 11.2$.

$$\chi^2 = \frac{(n - 1)s^2}{\sigma^2} = \frac{(15 - 1)(11.2)^2}{64} = 27.44$$

Step 4   Make the decision. The decision is to reject the null hypothesis since the test value, 27.44, is greater than the critical value, 21.064, and falls in the critical region. See Figure 8–34.

FIGURE 8–34
Critical and Test Value for
Example 8–25

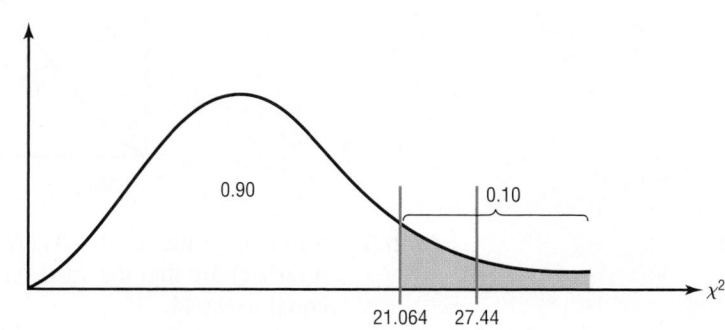

0.90   0.10

21.064 27.44

Step 5   Summarize the results. There is enough evidence to support the claim that the standard deviation is greater than 8.

EXAMPLE 8–26   Nicotine Content of Cigarettes

A cigarette manufacturer wishes to test the claim that the variance of the nicotine content of its cigarettes is 0.644. Nicotine content is measured in milligrams, and assume that it is normally distributed. A random sample of 20 cigarettes has a standard deviation of 1.00 milligram. At $\alpha = 0.05$, is there enough evidence to reject the manufacturer's claim?

SOLUTION

Step 1   State the hypotheses and identify the claim.

$$H_0: \sigma^2 = 0.644 \text{ (claim)} \quad \text{and} \quad H_1: \sigma^2 \neq 0.644$$

Step 2   Find the critical values. Since this test is a two-tailed test at $\alpha = 0.05$, the critical values for 0.025 and 0.975 must be found. The degrees of freedom are 19; hence, the critical values are 32.852 and 8.907, respectively. The critical or rejection regions are shown in Figure 8–35.

FIGURE 8–35
Critical Values for
Example 8–26

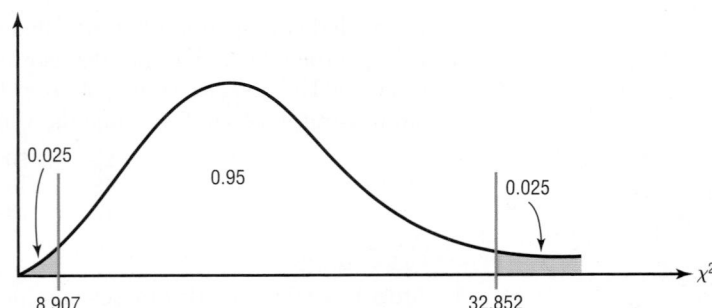

Step 3   Compute the test value.

$$\chi^2 = \frac{(n-1)s^2}{\sigma^2} = \frac{(20-1)(1.0)^2}{0.644} = 29.5$$

Since the sample standard deviation s is given in the problem, it must be squared for the formula.

Step 4   Make the decision. Do not reject the null hypothesis, since the test value falls between the critical values ($8.907 < 29.5 < 32.852$) and in the noncritical region, as shown in Figure 8–36.

FIGURE 8–36
Critical and Test Values for
Example 8–26

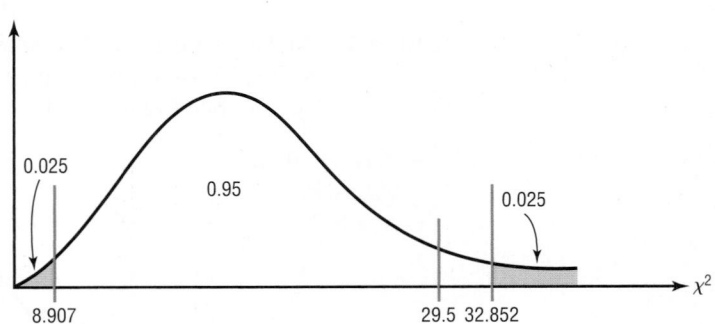

Step 5   Summarize the results. There is not enough evidence to reject the manufacturer's claim that the variance of the nicotine content of the cigarettes is equal to 0.644.

Approximate *P*-values for the chi-square test can be found by using Table G in Appendix A. The procedure is somewhat more complicated than the previous procedures for finding *P*-values for the *z* and *t* tests since the chi-square distribution is not exactly symmetric and χ^2 values cannot be negative. As we did for the *t* test, we will determine an *interval* for the *P*-value based on the table. Examples 8–27 through 8–29 show the procedure.

EXAMPLE 8–27

Find the *P*-value when $\chi^2 = 19.274$, $n = 8$, and the test is right-tailed.

SOLUTION

To get the *P*-value, look across the row with d.f. = 7 in Table G and find the two values that 19.274 falls between. They are 18.475 and 20.278. Look up to the top row and find the α values corresponding to 18.475 and 20.278. They are 0.01 and 0.005, respectively. See Figure 8–37. Hence, the *P*-value is contained in the interval $0.005 < P\text{-value} < 0.01$. (The *P*-value obtained from a calculator is 0.007.)

FIGURE 8–37   *P*-Value Interval for Example 8–27

Degrees of freedom	α									
	0.995	0.99	0.975	0.95	0.90	0.10	0.05	0.025	0.01	0.005
1	—	—	0.001	0.004	0.016	2.706	3.841	5.024	6.635	7.879
2	0.010	0.020	0.051	0.103	0.211	4.605	5.991	7.378	9.210	10.597
3	0.072	0.115	0.216	0.352	0.584	6.251	7.815	9.348	11.345	12.838
4	0.207	0.297	0.484	0.711	1.064	7.779	9.488	11.143	13.277	14.860
5	0.412	0.554	0.831	1.145	1.610	9.236	11.071	12.833	15.086	16.750
6	0.676	0.872	1.237	1.635	2.204	10.645	12.592	14.449	16.812	18.548
7	0.989	1.239	1.690	2.167	2.833	12.017	14.067	16.013	18.475	20.278
8	1.344	1.646	2.180	2.733	3.490	13.362	15.507	17.535	20.090	21.955
9	1.735	2.088	2.700	3.325	4.168	14.684	16.919	19.023	21.666	23.589
10	2.156	2.558	3.247	3.940	4.865	15.987	18.307	20.483	23.209	25.188
⋮	⋮	⋮	⋮	⋮	⋮	⋮	⋮	⋮	⋮	⋮
100	67.328	70.065	74.222	77.929	82.358	118.498	124.342	129.561	135.807	140.169

*19.274 falls between 18.475 and 20.278

EXAMPLE 8–28

Find the *P*-value when $\chi^2 = 3.823$, $n = 13$, and the test is left-tailed.

SOLUTION

To get the *P*-value, look across the row with d.f. = 12 and find the two values that 3.823 falls between. They are 3.571 and 4.404. Look up to the top row and find the values corresponding to 3.571 and 4.404. They are 0.99 and 0.975, respectively. When the χ^2 test value falls on the left side, each of the values must be subtracted from 1 to get the interval that *P*-value falls between.

$$1 - 0.99 = 0.01 \qquad \text{and} \qquad 1 - 0.975 = 0.025$$

Hence, the *P*-value falls in the interval

$$0.01 < P\text{-value} < 0.025$$

(The *P*-value obtained from a calculator is 0.014.)

When the χ^2 test is two-tailed, both interval values must be doubled. If a two-tailed test were being used in Example 8–28, then the interval would be $2(0.01) <$ P-value $< 2(0.025)$, or $0.02 <$ P-value < 0.05.

The P-value method for hypothesis testing for a variance or standard deviation follows the same steps shown in the preceding sections.

Step 1   State the hypotheses and identify the claim.

Step 2   Compute the test value.

Step 3   Find the P-value.

Step 4   Make the decision.

Step 5   Summarize the results.

Example 8–29 shows the P-value method for variances or standard deviations.

EXAMPLE 8–29   Car Inspection Times

A researcher knows from past studies that the standard deviation of the time it takes to inspect a car is 16.8 minutes. A random sample of 24 cars is selected and inspected. The standard deviation is 12.5 minutes. At $\alpha = 0.05$, can it be concluded that the standard deviation has changed? Use the P-value method. Assume the variable is normally distributed.

SOLUTION

Step 1   State the hypotheses and identify the claim.

$$H_0\colon \sigma = 16.8 \qquad \text{and} \qquad H_1\colon \sigma \neq 16.8 \text{ (claim)}$$

Step 2   Compute the test value.

$$\chi^2 = \frac{(n-1)s^2}{\sigma^2} = \frac{(24-1)(12.5)^2}{(16.8)^2} = 12.733$$

Step 3   Find the P-value. Using Table G with d.f. = 23, the value 12.733 falls between 11.689 and 13.091, corresponding to 0.975 and 0.95, respectively. Since these values are found on the left side of the distribution, each value must be subtracted from 1. Hence, $1 - 0.975 = 0.025$ and $1 - 0.95 = 0.05$. Since this is a two-tailed test, the area must be doubled to obtain the P-value interval. Hence, $0.05 <$ P-value < 0.10, or somewhere between 0.05 and 0.10. (The P-value obtained from a calculator is 0.085.)

Step 4   Make the decision. Since $\alpha = 0.05$ and the P-value is between 0.05 and 0.10, the decision is to not reject the null hypothesis since P-value $> \alpha$.

Step 5   Summarize the results. There is not enough evidence to support the claim that the standard deviation of the time it takes to inspect a car has changed.

▤ Applying the Concepts 8–5

Testing Gas Mileage Claims

Assume that you are working for the Consumer Protection Agency and have recently been getting complaints about the highway gas mileage of the new Dodge Caravans. Chrysler Corporation agrees to allow you to randomly select 40 of its new Dodge Caravans to test the highway mileage.

Chrysler claims that the Caravans get 28 mpg on the highway. Your results show a mean of 26.7 and a standard deviation of 4.2. You support Chrysler's claim.

1. Show whether or not you support Chrysler's claim by listing the *P*-value from your output. After more complaints, you decide to test the variability of the miles per gallon on the highway. From further questioning of Chrysler's quality control engineers, you find they are claiming a standard deviation of no more than 2.1. Use a one-tailed test.

2. Test the claim about the standard deviation.

3. Write a short summary of your results and any necessary action that Chrysler must take to remedy customer complaints.

4. State your position about the necessity to perform tests of variability along with tests of the means.

See page 486 for the answers.

Exercises 8–5

1. Using Table G, find the critical value(s) for each. Show the critical and noncritical regions, and state the appropriate null and alternative hypotheses. Use $\sigma^2 = 225$.

   a. $\alpha = 0.05$, $n = 18$, right-tailed
   b. $\alpha = 0.10$, $n = 23$, left-tailed
   c. $\alpha = 0.05$, $n = 15$, two-tailed
   d. $\alpha = 0.10$, $n = 8$, two-tailed

2. Using Table G, find the critical value(s) for each. Show the critical and noncritical regions, and state the appropriate null and alternative hypotheses. Use $\sigma^2 = 225$.

   a. $\alpha = 0.01$, $n = 17$, right-tailed
   b. $\alpha = 0.025$, $n = 20$, left-tailed
   c. $\alpha = 0.01$, $n = 13$, two-tailed
   d. $\alpha = 0.025$, $n = 29$, left-tailed

3. Using Table G, find the *P*-value interval for each χ^2 test value.

   a. $\chi^2 = 29.321$, $n = 16$, right-tailed
   b. $\chi^2 = 10.215$, $n = 25$, left-tailed
   c. $\chi^2 = 24.672$, $n = 11$, two-tailed
   d. $\chi^2 = 23.722$, $n = 9$, right-tailed

4. Using Table G, find the *P*-value interval for each χ^2 test value.

   a. $\chi^2 = 13.974$, $n = 28$, two-tailed
   b. $\chi^2 = 10.571$, $n = 19$, left-tailed
   c. $\chi^2 = 12.144$, $n = 6$, two-tailed
   d. $\chi^2 = 8.201$, $n = 23$, two-tailed

For Exercises 5 through 20, assume that the variables are normally or approximately normally distributed. Use the traditional method of hypothesis testing unless otherwise specified.

5. **Stolen Aircraft** Test the claim that the standard deviation of the number of aircraft stolen each year in the United States is less than 15 if a random sample of 12 years had a standard deviation of 13.6. Use $\alpha = 0.05$.

   Source: Aviation Crime Prevention Institute.

6. **Carbohydrates in Fast Foods** The number of carbohydrates found in a random sample of fast-food entrees is listed. Is there sufficient evidence to conclude that the variance differs from 100? Use the 0.05 level of significance.

53	46	39	39	30
47	38	73	43	41

   Source: Fast Food Explorer (www.fatcalories.com).

7. **Transferring Phone Calls** The manager of a large company claims that the standard deviation of the time (in minutes) that it takes a telephone call to be transferred to the correct office in her company is 1.2 minutes or less. A random sample of 15 calls is selected, and the calls are timed. The standard deviation of the sample is 1.8 minutes. At $\alpha = 0.01$, test the claim that the standard deviation is less than or equal to 1.2 minutes. Use the *P*-value method.

8. **Soda Bottle Content** A machine fills 12-ounce bottles with soda. For the machine to function properly, the standard deviation of the sample must be less than or equal to 0.03 ounce. A random sample of 8 bottles is selected, and the number of ounces of soda in each bottle is given. At $\alpha = 0.05$, can we reject the claim that the machine is functioning properly? Use the *P*-value method.

12.03	12.10	12.02	11.98
12.00	12.05	11.97	11.99

9. **High-Potassium Foods** Potassium is important to good health in keeping fluids and minerals balanced and blood pressure low. High-potassium foods are those that contain more than 200 mg per serving. The amounts of potassium for a random sample are shown. At $\alpha = 0.10$,

is the standard deviation of the potassium content greater than 100?

| 781 | 467 | 508 | 530 |
| 707 | 535 | 498 | 400 |

Source: www.drugs.com

10. **Exam Grades** A statistics professor is used to having a variance in his class grades of no more than 100. He feels that his current group of students is different, and so he examines a random sample of midterm grades as shown. At $\alpha = 0.05$, can it be concluded that the variance in grades exceeds 100?

92.3	89.4	76.9	65.2	49.1
96.7	69.5	72.8	67.5	52.8
88.5	79.2	72.9	68.7	75.8

11. **Tornado Deaths** A researcher claims that the standard deviation of the number of deaths annually from tornadoes in the United States is less than 35. If a random sample of 11 years had a standard deviation of 32, is the claim believable? Use $\alpha = 0.05$.

Source: National Oceanic and Atmospheric Administration.

12. **Interstate Speeds** It has been reported that the standard deviation of the speeds of drivers on Interstate 75 near Findlay, Ohio, is 8 miles per hour for all vehicles. A driver feels from experience that this is very low. A survey is conducted, and for 50 randomly selected drivers the standard deviation is 10.5 miles per hour. At $\alpha = 0.05$, is the driver correct?

13. **Sodium Amounts in Food** Healthier diets generally involve lower sodium amounts. The American Heart Association recommends less than 2300 mg of sodium daily. (One teaspoon of table salt contains 2400 mg of sodium!) A random sample of prepared foods has the sodium amounts listed below. Is there sufficient evidence to conclude at $\alpha = 0.05$ that the standard deviation in sodium amounts in prepared foods exceeds 150 mg?

| 640 | 580 | 450 | 480 | 570 | 900 | 900 |
| 600 | 540 | 500 | 350 | 500 | 700 | |

14. **Vitamin C in Fruits and Vegetables** The amounts of vitamin C (in milligrams) for 100 g (3.57 ounces) of various randomly selected fruits and vegetables are listed. Is there sufficient evidence to conclude that the standard deviation differs from 12 mg? Use $\alpha = 0.10$.

| 7.9 | 16.3 | 12.8 | 13.0 | 32.2 | 28.1 | 34.4 |
| 46.4 | 53.0 | 15.4 | 18.2 | 25.0 | 5.2 | |

Source: Time Almanac 2012.

15. **Manufactured Machine Parts** A manufacturing process produces machine parts with measurements the standard deviation of which must be no more than 0.52 mm. A random sample of 20 parts in a given lot revealed a standard deviation in measurement of 0.568 mm. Is there sufficient evidence at $\alpha = 0.05$ to

conclude that the standard deviation of the parts is outside the required guidelines?

16. **Golf Scores** A random sample of second-round golf scores from a major tournament is listed below. At $\alpha = 0.10$, is there sufficient evidence to conclude that the population variance exceeds 9?

| 75 | 67 | 69 | 72 | 70 |
| 66 | 74 | 69 | 74 | 71 |

17. **Calories in Pancake Syrup** A nutritionist claims that the standard deviation of the number of calories in 1 tablespoon of the major brands of pancake syrup is 60. A random sample of major brands of syrup is selected, and the number of calories is shown. At $\alpha = 0.10$, can the claim be rejected?

53	210	100	200	100	220
210	100	240	200	100	210
100	210	100	210	100	60

Source: Based on information from *The Complete Book of Food Counts* by Corrine T. Netzer, Dell Publishers, New York.

18. **High Temperatures in January** Daily weather observations for southwestern Pennsylvania for the first three weeks of January for randomly selected years show daily high temperatures as follows: 55, 44, 51, 59, 62, 60, 46, 51, 37, 30, 46, 51, 53, 57, 57, 39, 28, 37, 35, and 28 degrees Fahrenheit. The normal standard deviation in high temperatures for this time period is usually no more than 8 degrees. A meteorologist believes that with the unusual trend in temperatures the standard deviation is greater. At $\alpha = 0.05$, can we conclude that the standard deviation is greater than 8 degrees?

Source: www.wunderground.com

19. **College Room and Board Costs** Room and board fees for a random sample of independent religious colleges are shown.

7460	7959	7650	8120	7220
8768	7650	8400	7860	6782
8754	7443	9500	9100	

Estimate the standard deviation in costs based on $s \approx R/4$. Is there sufficient evidence to conclude that the sample standard deviation differs from this estimated amount? Use $\alpha = 0.05$.

Source: *World Almanac.*

20. **Heights of Volcanoes** A random sample of heights (in feet) of active volcanoes in North America, outside of Alaska, is shown. Is there sufficient evidence that the standard deviation in heights of volcanoes outside Alaska is less than the standard deviation in heights of Alaskan volcanoes, which is 2385.9 feet? Use $\alpha = 0.05$.

| 10,777 | 8159 | 11,240 | 10,456 |
| 14,163 | 8363 | | |

Source: *Time Almanac.*

≡ Technology Step by Step

TI-84 Plus
Step by Step

The TI-84 Plus does not have a built-in hypothesis test for the variance or standard deviation. However, the downloadable program named SDHYP is available in your online resources. Follow the instructions online for downloading the program.

Performing a Hypothesis Test for the Variance and Standard Deviation (Data)

1. Enter the values into L_1.
2. Press **PRGM,** move the cursor to the program named SDHYP, and press **ENTER** twice.
3. Press **1** for Data.
4. Type L_1 for the list and press **ENTER.**
5. Type the number corresponding to the type of alternative hypothesis.
6. Type the value of the hypothesized variance and press **ENTER.**
7. Press **ENTER** to clear the screen.

Example TI8–4

This pertains to Example 8–25 in the text. Test the claim that $\sigma > 8$ for these data.

$$25 \quad 30 \quad 5 \quad 15 \quad 18 \quad 42 \quad 16 \quad 9 \quad 10 \quad 12 \quad 12 \quad 38 \quad 8 \quad 14 \quad 27$$

Since P-value $= 0.017 < 0.1$, we reject H_0 and conclude H_1. Therefore, there is enough evidence to support the claim that the standard deviation of the number of people using outpatient surgery is greater than 8.

Performing a Hypothesis Test for the Variance and Standard Deviation (Statistics)

1. Press **PRGM,** move the cursor to the program named SDHYP, and press **ENTER** twice.
2. Press **2** for Stats.
3. Type the sample standard deviation and press **ENTER.**
4. Type the sample size and press **ENTER.**
5. Type the number corresponding to the type of alternative hypothesis.
6. Type the value of the hypothesized variance and press **ENTER.**
7. Press **ENTER** to clear the screen.

Example TI8–5

This pertains to Example 8–26 in the text. Test the claim that $\sigma^2 = 0.644$, given $n = 20$ and $s = 1$.

Since P-value $= 0.117 > 0.05$, we do not reject H_0 and do not conclude H_1. Therefore, there is not enough evidence to reject the manufacturer's claim that the variance of the nicotine content of the cigarettes is equal to 0.644.

EXCEL
Step by Step

Hypothesis Test for the Variance: Chi-Square Test

Excel does not have a procedure to conduct a hypothesis test for a single population variance. However, you may conduct the test of the variance using the MegaStat Add-in available in your online resources. If you have not installed this add-in, do so, following the instructions from the Chapter 1 Excel Step by Step.

Example XL8–3

This example relates to Example 8–26 from the text. At the 5% significance level, test the claim that $\sigma^2 = 0.644$. The MegaStat chi-square test of the population variance uses the P-value method. Therefore, it is not necessary to enter a significance level.

1. Type a label for the variable: Nicotine in cell A1.
2. Type the observed variance: **1** in cell A2.
3. Type the sample size: **20** in cell A3.
4. From the toolbar, select Add-Ins, **MegaStat>Hypothesis Tests>Chi-Square Variance Test.** *Note:* You may need to open MegaStat from the MegaStat.xls file on your computer's hard drive.
5. Select summary input.
6. Type **A1:A3** for the Input Range.
7. Type **0.644** for the Hypothesized variance and select the Alternative not equal.
8. Click [OK].

The result of the procedure is shown next.

Chi-Square Variance Test

0.64	Hypothesized variance
1.00	Observed variance of nicotine
20	*n*
19	d.f.
29.50	Chi-square

0.1169   *P*-value (two-tailed)

MINITAB
Step by Step

Hypothesis Test for Standard Deviation or Variance

MINITAB can be used to find a critical value of chi-square. It can also calculate the test statistic and P-value for a chi-square test of variance.

Example 8–22

Find the critical χ^2 value for $\alpha = 0.05$ for a left-tailed test with d.f. = 10.

Step 1   To find the critical value of t for a right-tailed test, select **Graph>Probability Distribution Plot,** then **View Probability,** then click **[OK].**

Step 2   Change the Distribution to a Chi-square distribution and type in the degrees of freedom, **10.**

Step 3   Click the tab for **Shaded Area.**

  a) Select the ratio button for **Probability.**
  b) Select **Left Tail.**
  c) Type in the value of alpha for probability, **0.05.**
  d) Click **[OK].**

The critical value of χ^2 to three decimal places is 3.940.
You may click the Edit Last Dialog button and then change the settings for additional critical values.

Example 8–25 Outpatient Surgery

MINITAB will calculate the test statistic and *P*-value. There are data for this example.

Step 1   Type the data into a new MINITAB worksheet. All 15 values must be in C1. Type the label Surgeries above the first row of data.

Step 2   Select **Stat>Basic Statistics> 1-variance.**

Step 3   In the box for Data select **Samples in columns** from the drop-down list.

Step 4   To select the data, click inside the dialog box for Columns; then select C1 Surgeries from the list.

Step 5   Select the box for Perform hypothesis test.

    a)   Select Hypothesized standard deviation from the drop-down list.

    b)   Type in the hypothesized value of **8.**

Step 6   Click the button for **[Options].**

    a)   Type the default confidence level, that is, **90.**

    b)   Click the drop-down menu for the Alternative hypothesis, greater than.

Step 7   Click **[OK]** twice.

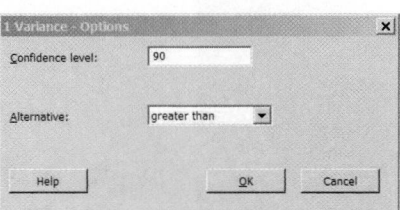

In the Session Window scroll down to the output labeled Statistics and further to the output labeled Tests. You should see the test statistic and P-value for the chi-square test. Since the P-value is less than 0.10, the null hypothesis will be rejected. The standard deviation, $s = 11.2$ is significantly greater than 8.

Statistics

Variable	N	StDev	Variance
Surgeries	15	11.2	125

Tests

Variable	Method	Test Statistic	DF	P-Value
Surgeries	Chi-Square	27.45	14	0.017

Although the text shows how to calculate a P-value, these are included in the MINITAB output of all hypothesis tests. The Alternative hypothesis in the Options dialog box must match your Alternative hypothesis.

8–6 Additional Topics Regarding Hypothesis Testing

In hypothesis testing, there are several other concepts that might be of interest to students in elementary statistics. These topics include the relationship between hypothesis testing and confidence intervals, and some additional information about the type II error.

OBJECTIVE ⑨

Test hypotheses, using confidence intervals.

Confidence Intervals and Hypothesis Testing

There is a relationship between confidence intervals and hypothesis testing. When the null hypothesis is rejected in a hypothesis-testing situation, the confidence interval for the mean using the same level of significance *will not* contain the hypothesized mean. Likewise, when the null hypothesis is not rejected, the confidence interval computed using the same level of significance *will* contain the hypothesized mean. Examples 8–30 and 8–31 show this concept for two-tailed tests.

EXAMPLE 8–30 Sugar Packaging

Sugar is packed in 5-pound bags. An inspector suspects the bags may not contain 5 pounds. A random sample of 50 bags produces a mean of 4.6 pounds and a standard deviation of 0.7 pound. Is there enough evidence to conclude that the bags do not contain 5 pounds as stated at $\alpha = 0.05$? Also, find the 95% confidence interval of the true mean. Assume the variable is normally distributed.

SOLUTION

Step 1   State the hypotheses and identify the claim.

$$H_0\colon \mu = 5 \qquad \text{and} \qquad H_1\colon \mu \neq 5 \text{ (claim)}$$

Step 2   At $\alpha = 0.05$ and d.f. $= 49$ (use d.f. $= 45$), the critical values are $+2.014$ and -2.014.

Step 3   Compute the test value.

$$t = \frac{\overline{X} - \mu}{s/\sqrt{n}} = \frac{4.6 - 5.0}{0.7/\sqrt{50}} = \frac{-0.4}{0.099} = -4.04$$

Step 4   Make the decision. Reject the null hypothesis since $-4.04 < -2.014$. See Figure 8–38.

FIGURE 8–38

Critical Values and Test
Value for Example 8–30

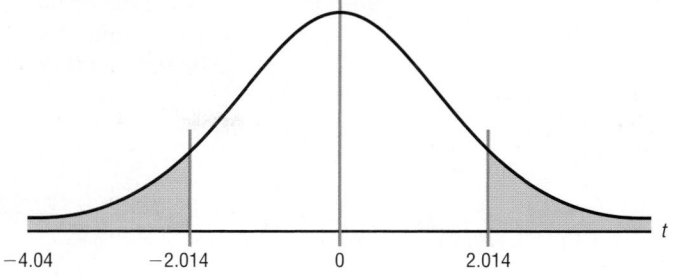

Step 5   Summarize the results. There is enough evidence to support the claim that
the bags do not weigh 5 pounds.
The 95% confidence for the mean is given by

$$\overline{X} - t_{\alpha/2}\frac{s}{\sqrt{n}} < \mu < \overline{X} + t_{\alpha/2}\frac{s}{\sqrt{n}}$$

$$4.6 - (2.014)\left(\frac{0.7}{\sqrt{50}}\right) < \mu < 4.6 + (2.014)\left(\frac{0.7}{\sqrt{50}}\right)$$

$$4.4 < \mu < 4.8$$

Notice that the 95% confidence interval of μ does *not* contain the hypothesized value $\mu = 5$. Hence, there is agreement between the hypothesis test and
the confidence interval.

EXAMPLE 8–31   Hog Weights

A researcher claims that adult hogs fed a special diet will have an average weight of
200 pounds. A random sample of 10 hogs has an average weight of 198.2 pounds and a
standard deviation of 3.3 pounds. At $\alpha = 0.05$, can the claim be rejected? Also, find the
95% confidence interval of the true mean. Assume the variable is normally distributed.

SOLUTION

Step 1   State the hypotheses and identify the claim.

$$H_0: \mu = 200 \text{ lb (claim)} \qquad \text{and} \qquad H_1: \mu \neq 200 \text{ lb}$$

Step 2   Find the critical values. At $\alpha = 0.05$ and d.f. $= 9$, the critical values are
$+2.262$ and -2.262.

Step 3   Compute the test value.

$$t = \frac{\overline{X} - \mu}{s/\sqrt{n}} = \frac{198.2 - 200}{3.3/\sqrt{10}} = \frac{-1.8}{1.0436} = -1.72$$

Step 4   Make the decision. Do not reject the null hypothesis. See Figure 8–39.

FIGURE 8–39

Critical Values and Test Value
for Example 8–31

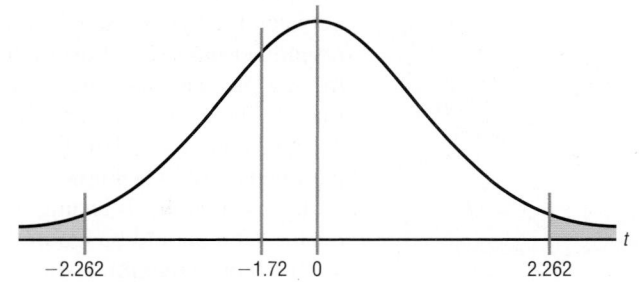

Step 5   Summarize the results. There is not enough evidence to reject the claim that the mean weight of adult hogs is 200 lb.

The 95% confidence interval of the mean is

$$\overline{X} - t_{\alpha/2}\frac{s}{\sqrt{n}} < \mu < \overline{X} + t_{\alpha/2}\frac{s}{\sqrt{n}}$$

$$198.2 - (2.262)\left(\frac{3.3}{\sqrt{10}}\right) < \mu < 198.2 + (2.262)\left(\frac{3.3}{\sqrt{10}}\right)$$

$$198.2 - 2.361 < \mu < 198.2 + 2.361$$

$$195.8 < \mu < 200.6$$

The 95% confidence interval does contain the hypothesized mean $\mu = 200$. Again there is agreement between the hypothesis test and the confidence interval.

In summary, then, when the null hypothesis is rejected at a significance level of α, the confidence interval computed at the $1 - \alpha$ level will not contain the value of the mean that is stated in the null hypothesis. On the other hand, when the null hypothesis is not rejected, the confidence interval computed at the same significance level will contain the value of the mean stated in the null hypothesis. These results are true for other hypothesis-testing situations and are not limited to means tests.

The relationship between confidence intervals and hypothesis testing presented here is valid for two-tailed tests. The relationship between one-tailed hypothesis tests and one-sided or one-tailed confidence intervals is also valid; however, this technique is beyond the scope of this text.

Type II Error and the Power of a Test

Recall that in hypothesis testing, there are two possibilities: Either the null hypothesis H_0 is true, or it is false. Furthermore, on the basis of the statistical test, the null hypothesis is either rejected or not rejected. These results give rise to four possibilities, as shown in Figure 8–40. This figure is similar to Figure 8–2.

OBJECTIVE ❿

Explain the relationship between type I and type II errors and the power of a test.

As stated previously, there are two types of errors: type I and type II. A type I error can occur only when the null hypothesis is rejected. By choosing a level of significance, say, of 0.05 or 0.01, the researcher can determine the probability of committing a type I error. For example, suppose that the null hypothesis was H_0: $\mu = 50$, and it was rejected. At the 0.05 level (one tail), the researcher has only a 5% chance of being wrong, i.e., of rejecting a true null hypothesis.

On the other hand, if the null hypothesis is not rejected, then either it is true or a type II error has been committed. A type II error occurs when the null hypothesis is indeed false, but is not rejected. The probability of committing a type II error is denoted as β.

The value of β is not easy to compute. It depends on several things, including the value of α, the size of the sample, the population standard deviation, and the actual difference between the hypothesized value of the parameter being tested and the true parameter. The researcher has control over two of these factors, namely, the selection of α and the size of the sample. The standard deviation of the population is sometimes known or can be estimated. The major problem, then, lies in knowing the actual difference between the hypothesized parameter and the true parameter. If this difference were known, then the value of the parameter would be known; and if the parameter were known, then there would be no need to do any hypothesis testing. Hence, the value of β cannot be computed. But this does not mean that it should be ignored. What the researcher usually does is to try to minimize the size of β or to maximize the size of $1 - \beta$, which is called the **power of a test.**

FIGURE 8–40

Possibilities in
Hypothesis Testing

	H_0 true	H_0 false
Reject H_0	**Type I** error α	Correct decision $1 - \beta$
Do not reject H_0	Correct decision $1 - \alpha$	**Type II** error β

The power of a statistical test measures the sensitivity of the test to detect a real difference in parameters if one actually exists. The power of a test is a probability and, like all probabilities, can have values ranging from 0 to 1. The higher the power, the more sensitive the test is to detecting a real difference between parameters if there is a difference. In other words, the closer the power of a test is to 1, the better the test is for rejecting the null hypothesis if the null hypothesis is, in fact, false.

The power of a test is equal to $1 - \beta$, that is, 1 minus the probability of committing a type II error. The power of the test is shown in the upper right-hand block of Figure 8–40. If somehow it were known that $\beta = 0.04$, then the power of a test would be $1 - 0.04 = 0.96$, or 96%. In this case, the probability of rejecting the null hypothesis when it is false is 96%.

As stated previously, the power of a test depends on the probability of committing a type II error, and since β is not easily computed, the power of a test cannot be easily computed. (See the Critical Thinking Challenges on pages 484 and 485.)

However, there are some guidelines that can be used when you are conducting a statistical study concerning the power of a test. In that case, use the test that has the highest power for the data. There are times when the researcher has a choice of two or more statistical tests to test the hypotheses. The tests with the highest power should be used. It is important, however, to remember that statistical tests have assumptions that need to be considered.

If these assumptions cannot be met, then another test with lower power should be used. The power of a test can be increased by increasing the value of α. For example, instead of using $\alpha = 0.01$, use $\alpha = 0.05$. Recall that as α increases, β decreases. So if β is decreased, then $1 - \beta$ will increase, thus increasing the power of the test.

Another way to increase the power of a test is to select a larger sample size. A larger sample size would make the standard error of the mean smaller and consequently reduce β. (The derivation is omitted.)

These two methods should not be used at the whim of the researcher. Before α can be increased, the researcher must consider the consequences of committing a type I error. If these consequences are more serious than the consequences of committing a type II error, then α should not be increased.

Likewise, there are consequences to increasing the sample size. These consequences might include an increase in the amount of money required to do the study and an increase in the time needed to tabulate the data. When these consequences result, increasing the sample size may not be practical.

There are several other methods a researcher can use to increase the power of a statistical test, but these methods are beyond the scope of this text.

One final comment is necessary. When the researcher fails to reject the null hypothesis, this does not mean that there is not enough evidence to support alternative hypotheses. It may be that the null hypothesis is false, but the statistical test has too low a power to detect the real difference; hence, one can conclude only that in this study, there is not enough evidence to reject the null hypothesis.

The relationship among α, β, and the power of a test can be analyzed in greater detail than the explanation given here. However, it is hoped that this explanation will show you that there is no magic formula or statistical test that can guarantee foolproof results when a decision is made about the validity of H_0. Whether the decision is to reject H_0 or not to reject H_0, there is in either case a chance of being wrong. The goal, then, is to try to keep the probabilities of type I and type II errors as small as possible.

≡ Applying the Concepts 8–6

Consumer Protection Agency Complaints

Hypothesis testing and testing claims with confidence intervals are two different approaches that lead to the same conclusion. In the following activities, you will compare and contrast those two approaches.

Assume you are working for the Consumer Protection Agency and have recently been getting complaints about the highway gas mileage of the new Dodge Caravans. Chrysler Corporation agrees to allow you to randomly select 40 of its new Dodge Caravans to test the highway mileage. Chrysler claims that the vans get 28 mpg on the highway. Your results show a mean of 26.7 and a standard deviation of 4.2. You are not certain if you should create a confidence interval or run a hypothesis test. You decide to do both at the same time.

1. Draw a normal curve, labeling the critical values, critical regions, test statistic, and population mean. List the significance level and the null and alternative hypotheses.

2. Draw a confidence interval directly below the normal distribution, labeling the sample mean, error, and boundary values.

3. Explain which parts from each approach are the same and which parts are different.

4. Draw a picture of a normal curve and confidence interval where the sample and hypothesized means are equal.

5. Draw a picture of a normal curve and confidence interval where the lower boundary of the confidence interval is equal to the hypothesized mean.

6. Draw a picture of a normal curve and confidence interval where the sample mean falls in the left critical region of the normal curve.

See page 486 for the answers.

≡ Exercises 8–6

1. **First-Time Births** According to the almanac, the mean age for a woman giving birth for the first time is 25.2 years. A random sample of ages of 35 professional women giving birth for the first time had a mean of 28.7 years and a standard deviation of 4.6 years. Use both a confidence interval and a hypothesis test at the 0.05 level of significance to test if the mean age of professional woman is different from 25.2 years at the time of their first birth.

2. **One-Way Airfares** The average one-way airfare from Pittsburgh to Washington, D.C., is $236. A random sample of 20 one-way fares during a particular month had a mean of $210 with a standard deviation of $43. At $\alpha = 0.02$, is there sufficient evidence to conclude a difference from the stated mean? Use the sample statistics to construct a 98% confidence interval for the true mean one-way airfare from Pittsburgh to Washington, D.C., and compare your interval to the results of the test. Do they support or contradict one another?

Source: www.fedstats.gov

3. **IRS Audits** The IRS examined approximately 1% of individual tax returns for a specific year, and the average recommended additional tax per return was $19,150. Based on a random sample of 50 returns, the mean additional tax was $17,020. If the population standard deviation is $4080, is there sufficient evidence to conclude that the mean differs from $19,150 at $\alpha = 0.05$? Does a 95% confidence interval support this result?

Source: *New York Times Almanac.*

4. Prison Time According to a public service website, 69.4% of white collar criminals get prison time. A randomly selected sample of 165 white collar criminals revealed that 120 were serving or had served prison time. Using $\alpha = 0.05$, test the conjecture that the proportion of white collar criminals serving prison time differs from 69.4% in two different ways.

5. Working at Home Workers with a formal arrangement with their employer to be paid for time worked at home worked an average of 19 hours per week. A random sample of 15 mortgage brokers indicated that they worked a mean of 21.3 hours per week at home with a standard deviation of 6.5 hours. At $\alpha = 0.05$, is there sufficient evidence to conclude a difference? Construct a 95% confidence interval for the true mean number of paid working hours at home. Compare the results of your confidence interval to the conclusion of your hypothesis test and discuss the implications.
Source: www.bls.gov

6. Newspaper Reading Times A survey taken several years ago found that the average time a person spent reading the local daily newspaper was 10.8 minutes. The standard deviation of the population was 3 minutes. To see whether the average time had changed since the newspaper's format was revised, the newspaper editor surveyed 36 individuals. The average time that these 36 randomly selected people spent reading the paper was 12.2 minutes. At $\alpha = 0.02$, is there a change in the average time an individual spends reading the newspaper? Find the 98% confidence interval of the mean. Do the results agree? Explain.

7. What is meant by the power of a test?

8. How is the power of a test related to the type II error?

9. How can the power of a test be increased?

Summary

This chapter introduces the basic concepts of hypothesis testing. A statistical hypothesis is a conjecture about a population. There are two types of statistical hypotheses: the null and the alternative hypotheses. The null hypothesis states that there is no difference, and the alternative hypothesis specifies a difference. To test the null hypothesis, researchers use a statistical test. Many test values are computed by using

$$\text{Test value} = \frac{(\text{observed value}) - (\text{expected value})}{\text{standard error}}$$

- Researchers compute a test value from the sample data to decide whether the null hypothesis should be rejected. Statistical tests can be one-tailed or two-tailed, depending on the hypotheses.

    The null hypothesis is rejected when the difference between the population parameter and the sample statistic is said to be significant. The difference is significant when the test value falls in the critical region of the distribution. The critical region is determined by α, the level of significance of the test. The level is the probability of committing a type I error. This error occurs when the null hypothesis is rejected when it is true. Three generally agreed upon significance levels are 0.10, 0.05, and 0.01. A second kind of error, the type II error, can occur when the null hypothesis is not rejected when it is false. (8–1)

- There are two common methods used to test hypotheses; they are the traditional method and the P-value method. (8–2)

- All hypothesis-testing situations using the traditional method should include the following steps:

    1. State the null and alternative hypotheses and identify the claim.

    2. State an alpha level and find the critical value(s).

    3. Compute the test value.

    4. Make the decision to reject or not reject the null hypothesis.

    5. Summarize the results.

- All hypothesis-testing situations using the P-value method should include the following steps:

    1. State the hypotheses and identify the claim.

    2. Compute the test value.

    3. Find the P-value.

    4. Make the decision.

    5. Summarize the results.

- The z test is used to test a mean when the population standard deviation is known. When the sample size is less than 30, the population values need to be normally distributed. (8–2)

- When the population standard deviation is not known, researchers use a t test to test a claim about a mean. If the sample size is less than 30, the population values need to be normally or approximately normally distributed. (8–3)

- The z test can be used to test a claim about a population when $np \geq 5$ and $nq \geq 5$. (8–4)
- A single variance can be tested by using the chi-square test. (8–5)
- There is a relationship between confidence intervals and hypothesis testing. When the null hypothesis is rejected, the confidence interval for the mean using the same level of significance will not contain the hypothesized mean. When the null hypothesis is not rejected, the confidence interval, using the same level of significance, will contain the hypothesized mean. (8–6)

- The power of a statistical test measures the sensitivity of the test to detect a real difference in parameters if one actually exists; $1 - \beta$ is called the power of a test. (8–6)

Important Terms

α (alpha) 419	critical value 420	one-tailed test 420	test value 417
alternative hypothesis 414	hypothesis testing 414	power of a test 476	t test 442
β (beta) 419	left-tailed test 420	P-value 431	two-tailed test 421
chi-square test 463	level of significance 419	research hypothesis 415	type I error 418
critical or rejection region 420	noncritical or nonrejection region 420	right-tailed test 420	type II error 418
	null hypothesis 414	statistical hypothesis 414	z test 427
		statistical test 417	

Important Formulas

Formula for the z test for means:

$$z = \frac{\overline{X} - \mu}{\sigma/\sqrt{n}} \quad \text{if } n < 30, \text{ variable must be normally distributed}$$

Formula for the t test for means:

$$t = \frac{\overline{X} - \mu}{s/\sqrt{n}} \quad \text{if } n < 30, \text{ variable must be normally distributed}$$

Formula for the z test for proportions:

$$z = \frac{\hat{p} - p}{\sqrt{pq/n}}$$

Formula for the chi-square test for variance or standard deviation:

$$\chi^2 = \frac{(n-1)s^2}{\sigma^2}$$

Review Exercises

For Exercises 1 through 20, perform each of the following steps.

a. State the hypotheses and identify the claim.

b. Find the critical value(s).

c. Compute the test value.

d. Make the decision.

e. Summarize the results.

Use the traditional method of hypothesis testing unless otherwise specified.

Section 8–2

1. **Time Online** It has been found that the average time Internet users spend online per week is 18.3 hours. A random sample of 48 teenagers indicated that their mean amount of Internet time per week was 20.9 hours with a population variance of 32.49. At the 0.02 level of significance, can it be concluded that the mean time differs from 18.3 hours per week?

2. **Travel Times to Work** Based on information from the U.S. Census Bureau, the mean travel time to work in minutes for all workers 16 years old and older was 25.3 minutes. A large company with offices in several states randomly sampled 100 of its workers to ascertain their commuting times. The sample mean was 23.9 minutes, and the population standard deviation is 6.39 minutes. At the 0.01 level of significance, can it be concluded that the mean commuting time is less for this particular company?

Source: factfinder.census.gov

3. **Debt of College Graduates** A random sample of the average debt (in dollars) at graduation from 30 of the top 100 public colleges and universities is listed below. Is there sufficient evidence at $\alpha = 0.01$ to conclude that the population mean debt at graduation is less than $18,000? Assume $\sigma = \$2605$.

16,012	15,784	16,597	18,105	12,665	14,734
17,225	16,953	15,309	15,297	14,437	14,835
13,607	13,374	19,410	18,385	22,312	16,656
20,142	17,821	12,701	22,400	15,730	17,673
18,978	13,661	12,580	14,392	16,000	15,176

Source: www.Kiplinger.com

4. **Time Until Indigestion Relief** An advertisement claims that Fasto Stomach Calm will provide relief from indigestion in less than 10 minutes. For a test of the claim, 35 randomly selected individuals were given the product; the average time until relief was 9.25 minutes. From past studies, the standard deviation of the population is known to be 2 minutes. Can you conclude that the claim is justified? Find the P-value and let $\alpha = 0.05$.

5. **Monthly Home Rent** The average monthly rent for a one-bedroom home in San Francisco is $1229. A random sample of 15 one-bedroom homes about 15 miles outside of San Francisco had a mean rent of $1350. The population standard deviation is $250. At $\alpha = 0.05$, can we conclude that the monthly rent outside San Francisco differs from that in the city? Assume the variable is normally distributed.

Source: *New York Times Almanac.*

Section 8–3

6. **Trifecta Winnings** A random sample of $1 Trifecta tickets at a local racetrack paid the following amounts (in dollars and cents). Is there sufficient evidence to conclude that the average Trifecta winnings exceed $50? Use $\alpha = 0.10$. Assume the variable is normally distributed.

8.90	141.00	72.70	32.40
70.20	48.60	75.30	19.00
15.00	83.00	59.20	190.10
29.10			

7. **Weights of Men's Soccer Shoes** Is lighter better? A random sample of men's soccer shoes from an international catalog had the following weights (in ounces).

10.8	9.8	8.8	9.6	9.9
10	8.4	9.6	10	9.4
9.8	9.4	9.8		

At $\alpha = 0.05$, can it be concluded that the average weight is less than 10 ounces? Assume the variable is normally distributed.

8. **Whooping Crane Eggs** Once down to about 15, the world's only wild flock of whooping cranes now numbers a record 237 birds in its Texas Coastal Bend wintering ground (www.SunHerald.com). The average whooping crane egg weighs 208 grams. A new batch of randomly selected eggs was recently weighed, and their weights are listed. At $\alpha = 0.01$, is there sufficient evidence to conclude that the weight is greater than 208 grams? Assume the variable is normally distributed.

210	208.5	211.6	212	210.3
210.2	209	206.4	209.7	

Source: http://www.pwrc.usgs.gov/cranes.htm

Section 8–4

9. **Home Security Systems** In 2008, 17% of U.S. homes were protected by a home security system. A random sample of 220 homes across several neighborhoods indicated that 28% were protected. At $\alpha = 0.05$, is there sufficient evidence to conclude that the proportion is actually greater?

10. **Federal Prison Populations** Nationally 60.2% of federal prisoners are serving time for drug offenses. A warden feels that in his prison the percentage is even higher. He surveys 400 randomly selected inmates' records and finds that 260 of the inmates are drug offenders. At $\alpha = 0.05$, is he correct?

Source: *New York Times Almanac.*

11. **Free School Lunches** It has been reported that 59.3% of U.S. school lunches served are free or at a reduced price. A random sample of 300 children in a large metropolitan area indicated that 156 of them received lunch free or at a reduced price. At the 0.01 level of significance, is there sufficient evidence to conclude that the proportion is less than 59.3%?

Source: www.fns.usda.gov

12. **MP3 Ownership** An MP3 manufacturer claims that 65% of teenagers 13 to 16 years old have their own MP3 players. A researcher wishes to test the claim and selects a random sample of 80 teenagers. She finds that 57 have their own MP3 players. At $\alpha = 0.05$, should the claim be rejected? Use the P-value method.

13. **Alcohol and Tobacco Use by High School Students** The use of both alcohol and tobacco by high school seniors has declined in the last 30 years. Alcohol use is down from 68.2 to 43.1%, and the use of cigarettes by high school seniors has decreased from 36.7 to 20.4%. A random sample of 300 high school seniors from a large region indicated that 18% had used cigarettes during the 30 days prior to the survey. At the 0.05 level of significance, does this differ from the national proportion?

Source: *New York Times Almanac.*

14. **Men Aged 65 and Over in the Labor Force** Of men aged 65 and over 20.5% are still in the U.S. labor force. A random sample of 120 retired male teachers indicated that 38 were still working. Use both a confidence interval and a hypothesis test. Test the claim that the proportion is greater than 20.5% at $\alpha = 0.10$.

Section 8–5

15. **Fuel Consumption** The standard deviation of the fuel consumption of a certain automobile is hypothesized to be greater than or equal to 4.3 miles per gallon. A random sample of 20 automobiles produced a standard deviation of 2.6 miles per gallon. Is the standard deviation really less than previously thought? Use $\alpha = 0.05$ and the P-value method. Assume the variable is normally distributed.

16. **Movie Admission Prices** The average movie admission price for a recent year was $7.18. The population variance was 3.81. A random sample of 15 theater

admission prices had a mean of $8.02 with a standard deviation of $2.08. At $\alpha = 0.05$, is there sufficient evidence to conclude a difference from the population variance? Assume the variable is normally distributed.

Source: *New York Times Almanac.*

17. Games Played by NBA Scoring Leaders A random sample of the number of games played by individual NBA scoring leaders is shown. Is there sufficient evidence to conclude that the variance in games played differs from 40? Use $\alpha = 0.05$. Assume the variable is normally distributed.

72	79	80	74	82
79	82	78	60	75

Source: *Time Almanac.*

18. Times of Videos A film editor feels that the standard deviation for the number of minutes in a video is 3.4 minutes. A random sample of 24 videos has a standard deviation of 4.2 minutes. At $\alpha = 0.05$, is the sample standard deviation different from what the editor hypothesized? Assume the variable is normally distributed.

Section 8–6

19. Plant Leaf Lengths A biologist knows that the average length of a leaf of a certain full-grown plant is 4 inches. The standard deviation of the population is 0.6 inch. A random sample of 20 leaves of that type of plant given a new type of plant food had an average length of 4.2 inches. Is there reason to believe that the new food is responsible for a change in the growth of the leaves? Use $\alpha = 0.01$. Find the 99% confidence interval of the mean. Do the results concur? Explain. Assume that the variable is approximately normally distributed.

20. Tire Inflation To see whether people are keeping their car tires inflated to the correct level of 35 pounds per square inch (psi), a tire company manager selects a random sample of 36 tires and checks the pressure. The mean of the sample is 33.5 psi, and the population standard deviation is 3 psi. Are the tires properly inflated? Use $\alpha = 0.10$. Find the 90% confidence interval of the mean. Do the results agree? Explain.

STATISTICS TODAY

How Much Better Is Better? —Revisited

Now that you have learned the techniques of hypothesis testing presented in this chapter, you realize that the difference between the sample mean and the population mean must be *significant* before you can conclude that the students really scored above average. The superintendent should follow the steps in the hypothesis-testing procedure and be able to reject the null hypothesis before announcing that his students scored higher than average.

Data Analysis

The Data Bank is found in Appendix B, or on the World Wide Web by following links from www.mhhe.com/math/stats/bluman/

1. From the Data Bank, select a random sample of at least 30 individuals, and test one or more of the following hypotheses by using the z test. Use $\alpha = 0.05$.

   a. For serum cholesterol, H_0: $\mu = 220$ milligram percent (mg%). Use $\sigma = 5$.

   b. For systolic pressure, H_0: $\mu = 120$ millimeters of mercury (mm Hg). Use $\sigma = 13$.

   c. For IQ, H_0: $\mu = 100$. Use $\sigma = 15$.

   d. For sodium level, H_0: $\mu = 140$ milliequivalents per liter (mEq/l). Use $\sigma = 6$.

2. Select a random sample of 15 individuals and test one or more of the hypotheses in Exercise 1 by using the t test. Use $\alpha = 0.05$.

3. Select a random sample of at least 30 individuals, and using the z test for proportions, test one or more of the following hypotheses. Use $\alpha = 0.05$.

   a. For educational level, H_0: $p = 0.50$ for level 2.

   b. For smoking status, H_0: $p = 0.20$ for level 1.

   c. For exercise level, H_0: $p = 0.10$ for level 1.

   d. For gender, H_0: $p = 0.50$ for males.

4. Select a sample of 20 individuals and test the hypothesis H_0: $\sigma^2 = 225$ for IQ level. Use $\alpha = 0.05$. Assume the variable is normally distributed.

5. Using the data from Data Set XIII, select a sample of 10 hospitals, and test H_0: $\mu = 250$ and H_1: $\mu < 250$ for the number of beds. Use $\alpha = 0.05$. Assume the variable is normally distributed.

6. Using the data obtained in Exercise 5, test the hypothesis H_0: $\sigma \geq 150$. Use $\alpha = 0.05$. Assume the variable is normally distributed.

☰ Chapter Quiz

Determine whether each statement is true or false. If the statement is false, explain why.

1. No error is committed when the null hypothesis is rejected when it is false.

2. When you are conducting the t test, the population must be approximately normally distributed.

3. The test value separates the critical region from the noncritical region.

4. The values of a chi-square test cannot be negative.

5. The chi-square test for variances is always one-tailed.

Select the best answer.

6. When the value of α is increased, the probability of committing a type I error is

   a. Decreased
   b. Increased
   c. The same
   d. None of the above

7. If you wish to test the claim that the mean of the population is 100, the appropriate null hypothesis is

   a. $\bar{X} = 100$
   b. $\mu \geq 100$
   c. $\mu \leq 100$
   d. $\mu = 100$

8. The degrees of freedom for the chi-square test for variances or standard deviations are

   a. 1
   b. n
   c. $n - 1$
   d. None of the above

9. For the t test, one uses _____ instead of σ.

   a. n
   b. s
   c. χ^2
   d. t

Complete the following statements with the best answer.

10. Rejecting the null hypothesis when it is true is called a(n) _____ error.

11. The probability of a type II error is referred to as _____.

12. A conjecture about a population parameter is called a(n) _____.

13. To test the claim that the mean is greater than 87, you would use a(n) _____-tailed test.

    The degrees of freedom for the t test are _____.

For the following exercises where applicable:

   a. State the hypotheses and identify the claim.
   b. Find the critical value(s).
   c. Compute the test value.
   d. Make the decision.
   e. Summarize the results.

Use the traditional method of hypothesis testing unless otherwise specified. Assume all variables are normally distributed.

15. **Ages of Professional Women** A sociologist wishes to see if it is true that for a certain group of professional women, the average age at which they have their first child is 28.6 years. A random sample of 36 women is selected, and their ages at the birth of their first child are recorded. At $\alpha = 0.05$, does the evidence refute the sociologist's assertion? Assume $\sigma = 4.18$.

32	28	26	33	35	34
29	24	22	25	26	28
28	34	33	32	30	29
30	27	33	34	28	25
24	33	25	37	35	33
34	36	38	27	29	26

16. **Home Closing Costs** A real estate agent believes that the average closing cost of purchasing a new home is $6500 over the purchase price. She selects 40 new home sales at random and finds that the average closing costs are $6600. The standard deviation of the population is $120. Test her belief at $\alpha = 0.05$.

17. **Chewing Gum Use** A recent study stated that if a person chewed gum, the average number of sticks of gum he or she chewed daily was 8. To test the claim, a researcher selected a random sample of 36 gum chewers and found the mean number of sticks of gum chewed per day was 9. The standard deviation of the population is 1. At $\alpha = 0.05$, is the number of sticks of gum a person chews per day actually greater than 8?

18. **Hotel Rooms** A travel agent claims that the average of the number of rooms in hotels in a large city is 500. At $\alpha = 0.01$, is the claim realistic? The data for a random sample of seven hotels are shown.

713	300	292	311	598	401	618

Give a reason why the claim might be deceptive.

19. **Heights of Models** In a New York modeling agency, a researcher wishes to see if the average height of female models is really less than 67 inches, as the chief claims. A random sample of 20 models has an average height of 65.8 inches. The standard deviation of the sample is 1.7 inches. At $\alpha = 0.05$, is the average height of the models really less than 67 inches? Use the P-value method.

20. **Experience of Taxi Drivers** A taxi company claims that its drivers have an average of at least 12.4 years' experience. In a study of 15 randomly selected taxi drivers, the average experience was 11.2 years. The standard deviation was 2. At $\alpha = 0.10$, is the number of years' experience of the taxi drivers really less than the taxi company claimed?

21. **Ages of Robbery Victims** A recent study in a small city stated that the average age of robbery victims was 63.5 years. A random sample of 20 recent victims had a mean of 63.7 years and a standard deviation of 1.9 years. At $\alpha = 0.05$, is the average age higher than originally believed? Use the P-value method.

22. **First-Time Marriages** A magazine article stated that the average age of women who are getting married for the first time is 26 years. A researcher decided to test this hypothesis at $\alpha = 0.02$. She selected a random sample of 25 women who were recently married for the first time and found the average was 25.1 years. The standard deviation was 3 years. Should the null hypothesis be rejected on the basis of the sample?

23. **Survey on Vitamin Usage** A survey in *Men's Health* magazine reported that 39% of cardiologists said that they took vitamin E supplements. To see if this is still true, a researcher randomly selected 100 cardiologists and found that 36 said that they took vitamin E supplements. At $\alpha = 0.05$, test the claim that 39% of the cardiologists took vitamin E supplements.

24. **Breakfast Survey** A dietitian read in a survey that at least 55% of adults do not eat breakfast at least 3 days a week. To verify this, she selected a random sample of 80 adults and asked them how many days a week they skipped breakfast. A total of 50% responded that they skipped breakfast at least 3 days a week. At $\alpha = 0.10$, test the claim.

25. **Caffeinated Beverage Survey** A Harris Poll found that 35% of people said that they drink a caffeinated beverage to combat midday drowsiness. A recent survey found that 19 out of 48 randomly selected people stated that they drank a caffeinated beverage to combat midday

drowsiness. At $\alpha = 0.02$, is the claim of the percentage found in the Harris Poll believable?

26. **Radio Ownership** A magazine claims that 75% of all teenage boys have their own radios. A researcher wished to test the claim and selected a random sample of 60 teenage boys. She found that 54 had their own radios. At $\alpha = 0.01$, should the claim be rejected?

27. Find the P-value for the z test in Exercise 15.

28. Find the P-value for the z test in Exercise 16.

29. **Pages in Romance Novels** A copyeditor thinks the standard deviation for the number of pages in a romance novel is greater than 6. A random sample of 25 novels has a standard deviation of 9 pages. At $\alpha = 0.05$, is it higher, as the editor hypothesized?

30. **Seed Germination Times** It has been hypothesized that the standard deviation of the germination time of radish seeds is 8 days. The standard deviation of a random sample of 60 radish plants' germination times was 6 days. At $\alpha = 0.01$, test the claim.

31. **Pollution By-products** The standard deviation of the pollution by-products released in the burning of 1 gallon of gas is 2.3 ounces. A random sample of 20 automobiles tested produced a standard deviation of 1.9 ounces. Is the standard deviation really less than previously thought? Use $\alpha = 0.05$.

32. **Strength of Wrapping Cord** A manufacturer claims that the standard deviation of the strength of wrapping cord is 9 pounds. A random sample of 10 wrapping cords produced a standard deviation of 11 pounds. At $\alpha = 0.05$, test the claim. Use the P-value method.

33. Find the 90% confidence interval of the mean in Exercise 15. Is μ contained in the interval?

34. Find the 95% confidence interval for the mean in Exercise 16. Is μ contained in the interval?

≜ Critical Thinking Challenges

The power of a test $(1 - \beta)$ can be calculated when a specific value of the mean is hypothesized in the alternative hypothesis; for example, let H_0: $\mu = 50$ and let H_1: $\mu = 52$. To find the power of a test, it is necessary to find the value of β. This can be done by the following steps:

Step 1 For a specific value of α find the corresponding value of $\overline{X}$, using $z = \dfrac{\overline{X} - \mu}{\sigma / \sqrt{n}}$, where μ is the hypothesized value given in H_0. Use a right-tailed test.

Step 2 Using the value of $\overline{X}$ found in step 1 and the value of μ in the alternative hypothesis, find the area corresponding to z in the formula $z = \dfrac{\overline{X} - \mu}{\sigma / \sqrt{n}}$.

Step 3 Subtract this area from (lue of β.

Step 4 Subtract the value of β fr   the power of a test. See Fig

1. Find the power of a test, using the hypotheses given previously and $\alpha = 0.05$, $\sigma = 3$, and $n = 30$.

2. Select several other values for μ in H_1 and compute the power of the test. Generalize the results.

FIGURE 8–41
Relationship Among α, β, and the Power of a Test

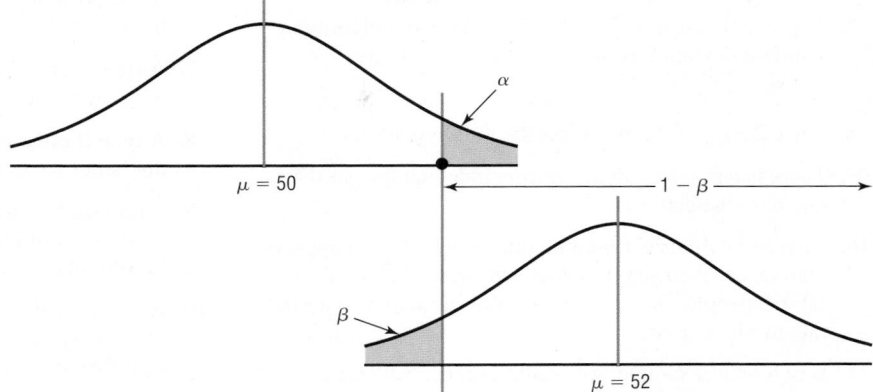

Data Projects

Use a significance level of 0.05 for all tests below.

1. **Business and Finance** Use the Dow Jones Industrial stocks in data project 1 of Chapter 7 as your data set. Find the gain or loss for each stock over the last quarter. Test the claim that the mean is that the stocks broke even (no gain or loss indicates a mean of 0).

2. **Sports and Leisure** Use the most recent NFL season for your data. For each team, find the quarterback rating for the number one quarterback. Test the claim that the mean quarterback rating for a number one quarterback is more than 80.

3. **Technology** Use your last month's itemized cell phone bill for your data. Determine the percentage of your text messages that were outgoing. Test the claim that a majority of your text messages were outgoing. Determine the mean, median, and standard deviation for the length of a call. Test the claim that the mean length

of a call is longer than the value you found for the median length.

4. **Health and Wellness** Use the data collected in data project 4 of Chapter 7 for this exercise. Test the claim that the mean body temperature is less than 98.6 degrees Fahrenheit.

5. **Politics and Economics** Use the most recent results of the Presidential primary elections for both parties. Determine what percentage of voters in your state voted for the eventual Democratic nominee for President and what percentage voted for the eventual Republican nominee. Test the claim that a majority of your state favored the candidate who won the nomination for each party.

6. **Your Class** Use the data collected in data project 6 of Chapter 7 for this exercise. Test the claim that the mean BMI for a student is more than 25.

Answers to Applying the Concepts

Section 8–1   Eggs and Your Health

1. The study was prompted by claims that linked eating eggs to high blood serum cholesterol.

2. The population under study is people in general.

3. A sample of 500 subjects was collected.

4. The hypothesis was that eating eggs did not increase blood serum cholesterol.

5. Blood serum cholesterol levels were collected.

6. Most likely, but we are not told which test.

7. The conclusion was that eating a moderate amount of eggs will not significantly increase blood serum cholesterol level.

Section 8–2   Car Thefts

1. The hypotheses are H_0: $\mu = 44$ and H_1: $\mu \neq 44$.

2. This sample can be considered large for our purposes.

3. The variable needs to be normally distributed.

4. We will use a z distribution.

5. Since we are interested in whether the car theft rate has changed, we use a two-tailed test.

6. Answers may vary. At the $\alpha = 0.05$ significance level, the critical values are $z = \pm 1.96$.

7. The sample mean is $\overline{X} = 55.97$, and the population standard deviation is 30.30. Our test statistic is
$z = \frac{55.97 - 44}{30.30/\sqrt{36}} = 2.37$.

8. Since $2.37 > 1.96$, we reject the null hypothesis.

9. There is enough evidence to conclude that the car theft rate has changed.

10. Answers will vary. Based on our sample data, it appears that the car theft rate has changed from 44 vehicles per 10,000 people. In fact, the data indicate that the car theft rate has increased.

11. Based on our sample, we would expect 55.97 car thefts per 10,000 people, so we would expect $(55.97)(5) = 279.85$, or about 280, car thefts in the city.

Section 8–3   How Much Nicotine Is in Those Cigarettes?

1. We have $15 - 1 = 14$ degrees of freedom.

2. This is a t test.

3. We are only testing one sample.

4. This is a right-tailed test, since the hypotheses of the tobacco company are H_0: $\mu = 40$ and H_1: $\mu > 40$.

5. The P-value is 0.008, which is less than the significance level of 0.01. We reject the tobacco company's claim.

6. Since the test statistic (2.72) is greater than the critical value (2.62), we reject the tobacco company's claim.

7. There is no conflict in this output, since the results based on the P-value and the test statistic value agree.

8. Answers will vary. It appears that the company's claim is false and that there is more than 40 mg of nicotine in its cigarettes.

Section 8–4   Quitting Smoking

1. The statistical hypotheses were that StopSmoke helps more people quit smoking than the other leading brands.

2. The null hypotheses were that StopSmoke has the same effectiveness as or is not as effective as the other leading brands.

3. The alternative hypotheses were that StopSmoke helps more people quit smoking than the other leading brands. (The alternative hypotheses are the statistical hypotheses.)

4. No statistical tests were run that we know of.

5. Had tests been run, they would have been one-tailed tests.

6. Some possible significance levels are 0.01, 0.05, and 0.10.

7. A type I error would be to conclude that StopSmoke is better when it really is not.

8. A type II error would be to conclude that StopSmoke is not better when it really is.

9. These studies proved nothing. Had statistical tests been used, we could have tested the effectiveness of StopSmoke.

10. Answers will vary. One possible answer is that more than likely the statements are talking about practical significance and not statistical significance, since we have no indication that any statistical tests were conducted.

Section 8–5   Testing Gas Mileage Claims

1. The hypotheses are H_0: $\mu = 28$ and H_1: $\mu < 28$. The value of our test statistic is $t = -1.96$, and the associated P-value is 0.0287. We would reject Chrysler's claim at $\alpha = 0.05$ that the Dodge Caravans are getting 28 mpg.

2. The hypotheses are H_0: $\sigma = 2.1$ and H_1: $\sigma > 2.1$. The value of our test statistic is $\chi^2 = \frac{(n-1)s^2}{\sigma^2} = \frac{(39)4.2^2}{2.1^2} = 156$, and the associated P-value is approximately zero. We would reject Chrysler's claim that the standard deviation is no more than 2.1 mpg.

3. Answers will vary. It is recommended that Chrysler lower its claim about the highway miles per gallon of the Dodge Caravans. Chrysler should also try to reduce variability in miles per gallon and provide confidence intervals for the highway miles per gallon.

4. Answers will vary. There are cases when a mean may be fine, but if there is a lot of variability about the mean, there will be complaints (due to the lack of consistency).

Section 8–6   Consumer Protection Agency Complaints

1. Answers will vary.

2. Answers will vary.

3. Answers will vary.

4. Answers will vary.

5. Answers will vary.

6. Answers will vary.

Testing the Difference Between Two Means, Two Proportions, and Two Variances

⊟ STATISTICS TODAY

To Vaccinate or Not to Vaccinate? Small versus Large Nursing Homes

Influenza is a serious disease among the elderly, especially those living in nursing homes. Those residents are more susceptible to influenza than elderly persons living in the community because the former are usually older and more debilitated, and they live in a closed environment where they are exposed more so than community residents to the virus if it is introduced into the home. Three researchers decided to investigate the use of vaccine and its value in determining outbreaks of influenza in small nursing homes.

These researchers surveyed 83 randomly selected licensed homes in seven counties in Michigan. Part of the study consisted of comparing the number of people being vaccinated in small nursing homes (100 or fewer beds) with the number in larger nursing homes (more than 100 beds). Unlike the statistical methods presented in Chapter 8, these researchers used the techniques explained in this chapter to compare two sample proportions to see if there was a significant difference in the vaccination rates of patients in small nursing homes compared to those in large nursing homes. See Statistics Today—Revisited at the end of the chapter.

Source: Nancy Arden, Arnold S. Monto, and Suzanne E. Ohmit, "Vaccine Use and the Risk of Outbreaks in a Sample of Nursing Homes During an Influenza Epidemic," *American Journal of Public Health* 85, no. 3, pp. 399–401. Copyright by the American Public Health Association.

OUTLINE

Introduction

9–1 Testing the Difference Between Two Means: Using the *z* Test

9–2 Testing the Difference Between Two Means of Independent Samples: Using the *t* Test

9–3 Testing the Difference Between Two Means: Dependent Samples

9–4 Testing the Difference Between Proportions

9–5 Testing the Difference Between Two Variances

Summary

OBJECTIVES

After completing this chapter, you should be able to

1 Test the difference between sample means, using the *z* test.

2 Test the difference between two means for independent samples, using the *t* test.

3 Test the difference between two means for dependent samples.

4 Test the difference between two proportions.

5 Test the difference between two variances or standard deviations.

Introduction

The basic concepts of hypothesis testing were explained in Chapter 8. With the z, t, and χ^2 tests, a sample mean, variance, or proportion can be compared to a specific population mean, variance, or proportion to determine whether the null hypothesis should be rejected.

There are, however, many instances when researchers wish to compare two sample means, using experimental and control groups. For example, the average lifetimes of two different brands of bus tires might be compared to see whether there is any difference in tread wear. Two different brands of fertilizer might be tested to see whether one is better than the other for growing plants. Or two brands of cough syrup might be tested to see whether one brand is more effective than the other.

In the comparison of two means, the same basic steps for hypothesis testing shown in Chapter 8 are used, and the z and t tests are also used. When comparing two means by using the t test, the researcher must decide if the two samples are *independent* or *dependent*. The concepts of independent and dependent samples will be explained in Sections 9–2 and 9–3.

The z test can be used to compare two proportions, as shown in Section 9–4. Finally, two variances can be compared by using an F test as shown in Section 9–5.

9–1   Testing the Difference Between Two Means: Using the z Test

OBJECTIVE

Test the difference between sample means, using the z test.

Suppose a researcher wishes to determine whether there is a difference in the average age of nursing students who enroll in a nursing program at a community college and those who enroll in a nursing program at a university. In this case, the researcher is not interested in the average age of all beginning nursing students; instead, he is interested in *comparing* the means of the two groups. His research question is, Does the mean age of nursing students who enroll at a community college differ from the mean age of nursing students who enroll at a university? Here, the hypotheses are

$$H_0: \mu_1 = \mu_2$$
$$H_1: \mu_1 \neq \mu_2$$

where

μ_1 = mean age of all beginning nursing students at a community college
μ_2 = mean age of all beginning nursing students at a university

Another way of stating the hypotheses for this situation is

$$H_0: \mu_1 - \mu_2 = 0$$
$$H_1: \mu_1 - \mu_2 \neq 0$$

If there is no difference in population means, subtracting them will give a difference of zero. If they are different, subtracting will give a number other than zero. Both methods of stating hypotheses are correct; however, the first method will be used in this text.

If two samples are *independent* of each other, the subjects selected for the first sample in no way influence the way the subjects are selected in the second sample. For example, if a group of 50 people were randomly divided into two groups of 25 in order to test the effectiveness of a new drug, where one group gets the drug and the other group gets a placebo, the samples would be independent of each other.

On the other hand, two samples would be *dependent* if the selection of subjects for the first group in some way influenced the selection of subjects for the second group. For example, suppose you wanted to determine if a person's right foot was larger than his or her left foot. In this case, the samples are dependent because

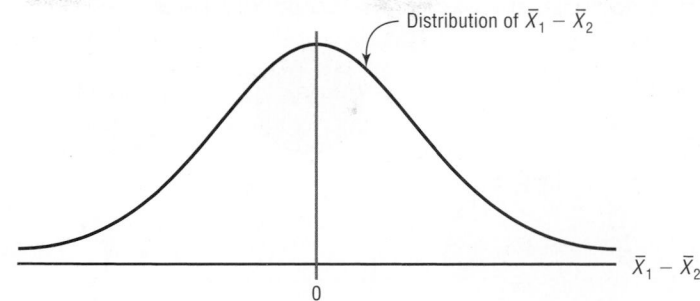

FIGURE 9–1

Differences of Means of Pairs of Samples

Distribution of $\bar{X}_1 - \bar{X}_2$

$\bar{X}_1 - \bar{X}_2$

0

person's right foot for sample 1, you must select his or her left foot for sample 2 because you are using the same person for both feet.

Before you can use the z test to test the difference between two independent sample means, you must make sure that the following assumptions are met.

Assumptions for the z Test to Determine the Difference Between Two Means

1. Both samples are random samples.
2. The samples must be independent of each other. That is, there can be no relationship between the subjects in each sample.
3. The standard deviations of both populations must be known; and if the sample sizes are less than 30, the populations must be normally or approximately normally distributed.

In this book, the assumptions will be stated in the exercises; however, when encountering statistics in other situations, you must check to see that these assumptions have been met before proceeding.

The theory behind testing the difference between two means is based on selecting pairs of samples and comparing the means of the pairs. The population means need not be known.

All possible pairs of samples are taken from populations. The means for each pair of samples are computed and then subtracted, and the differences are plotted. If both populations have the same mean, then most of the differences will be zero or close to zero. Occasionally, there will be a few large differences due to chance alone, some positive and others negative. If the differences are plotted, the curve will be shaped like a normal distribution and have a mean of zero, as shown in Figure 9–1.

The variance of the difference $\bar{X}_1 - \bar{X}_2$ is equal to the sum of the individual variances of $\bar{X}_1$ and $\bar{X}_2$. That is,

$$\sigma^2_{\bar{X}_1 - \bar{X}_2} = \sigma^2_{\bar{X}_1} + \sigma^2_{\bar{X}_2}$$

where

$$\sigma^2_{\bar{X}_1} = \frac{\sigma^2_1}{n_1} \qquad \text{and} \qquad \sigma^2_{\bar{X}_2} = \frac{\sigma^2_2}{n_2}$$

So the standard deviation of $\bar{X}_1 - \bar{X}_2$ is

$$\sqrt{\frac{\sigma^2_1}{n_1} + \frac{\sigma^2_2}{n_2}}$$

Unusual Stats

Adult children who live with their parents spend more than 2 hours a day doing household chores. According to a study, daughters contribute about 17 hours a week and sons about 14.4 hours.

Formula for the z Test for Comparing Two Means from Independent Populations

$$z = \frac{(\bar{X}_1 - \bar{X}_2) - (\mu_1 - \mu_2)}{\sqrt{\dfrac{\sigma^2_1}{n_1} + \dfrac{\sigma^2_2}{n_2}}}$$

FIGURE 9–2   Hypothesis-Testing Situations in the Comparison of Means

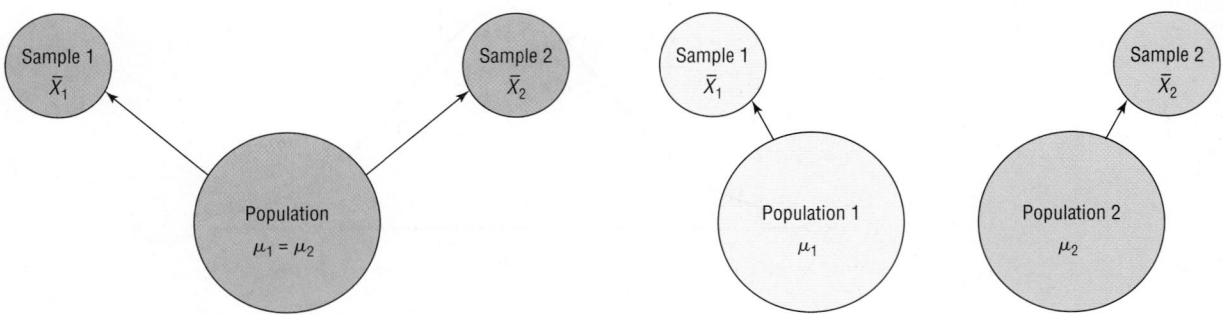

(a) Difference is not significant. The means of the populations are the same.

Do not reject H_0: $\mu_1 = \mu_2$ since $\bar{X}_1 - \bar{X}_2$ is not significant.

(b) Difference is significant. The means of the populations are different.

Reject H_0: $\mu_1 = \mu_2$ since $\bar{X}_1 - \bar{X}_2$ is significant.

This formula is based on the general format of

$$\text{Test value} = \frac{(\text{observed value}) - (\text{expected value})}{\text{standard error}}$$

where $\bar{X}_1 - \bar{X}_2$ is the observed difference, and the expected difference $\mu_1 - \mu_2$ is zero when the null hypothesis is $\mu_1 = \mu_2$, since that is equivalent to $\mu_1 - \mu_2 = 0$. Finally, the standard error of the difference is

$$\sqrt{\frac{\sigma_1^2}{n_1} + \frac{\sigma_2^2}{n_2}}$$

In the comparison of two sample means, the difference may be due to chance, in which case the null hypothesis will not be rejected and the researcher can assume that the means of the populations are basically the same. The difference in this case is not significant. See Figure 9–2(a). On the other hand, if the difference is significant, the null hypothesis is rejected and the researcher can conclude that the population means are different. See Figure 9–2(b).

These tests can also be one-tailed, using the following hypotheses:

Right-tailed			Left-tailed		
H_0: $\mu_1 = \mu_2$	or	H_0: $\mu_1 - \mu_2 = 0$	H_0: $\mu_1 = \mu_2$	or	H_0: $\mu_1 - \mu_2 = 0$
H_1: $\mu_1 > \mu_2$		H_1: $\mu_1 - \mu_2 > 0$	H_1: $\mu_1 < \mu_2$		H_1: $\mu_1 - \mu_2 < 0$

The same critical values used in Section 8–2 are used here. They can be obtained from Table E in Appendix A.

The basic format for hypothesis testing using the traditional method is reviewed here.

Step 1   State the hypotheses and identify the claim.

Step 2   Find the critical value(s).

Step 3   Compute the test value.

Step 4   Make the decision.

Step 5   Summarize the results.

EXAMPLE 9–1   Leisure Time

A study using two random samples of 35 people each found that the average amount of time those in the age group of 26–35 years spent per week on leisure activities was 39.6 hours, and those in the age group of 46–55 years spent 35.4 hours. Assume that the population standard deviation for those in the first age group found by previous studies is 6.3 hours, and the population standard deviation of those in the second group found by previous studies was 5.8 hours. At $\alpha = 0.05$, can it be concluded that there is a significant difference in the average times each group spends on leisure activities?

SOLUTION

Step 1   State the hypotheses and identify the claim.

$$H_0: \mu_1 = \mu_2 \quad \text{and} \quad H_1: \mu_1 \neq \mu_2 \text{ (claim)}$$

Step 2   Find the critical values. Since $\alpha = 0.05$, the critical values are $+1.96$ and -1.96.

Step 3   Compute the test value.

$$z = \frac{(\overline{X}_1 - \overline{X}_2) - (\mu_1 - \mu_2)}{\sqrt{\dfrac{\sigma_1^2}{n_1} + \dfrac{\sigma_2^2}{n_2}}} = \frac{(39.6 - 35.4) - 0}{\sqrt{\dfrac{6.3^2}{35} + \dfrac{5.8^2}{35}}} = \frac{4.2}{1.447} = 2.90$$

Step 4   Make the decision. Reject the null hypothesis at $\alpha = 0.05$ since $2.90 > 1.96$. See Figure 9–3.

FIGURE 9–3   Critical and Test Values for Example 9–1

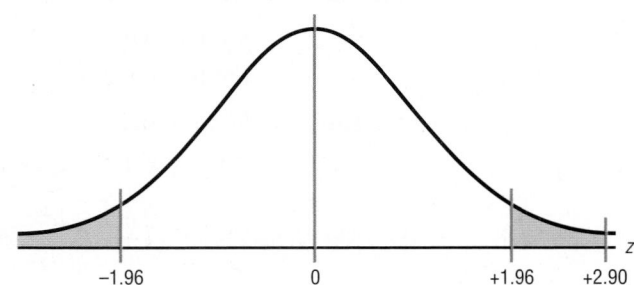

Step 5   Summarize the results. There is enough evidence to support the claim that the means are not equal. That is, the average of the times spent on leisure activities is different for the groups.

The P-values for this test can be determined by using the same procedure shown in Section 8–2. For example, if the test value for a two-tailed test is 2.90, then the P-value obtained from Table E is 0.0038. This value is obtained by looking up the area for $z = 2.90$, which is 0.9981. Then 0.9981 is subtracted from 1.0000 to get 0.0019. Finally, this value is doubled to get 0.0038 since the test is two-tailed. If $\alpha = 0.05$, the decision would be to reject the null hypothesis, since P-value $< \alpha$ (that is, $0.0038 < 0.05$). *Note:* The P-value obtained on the TI-84 is 0.0037.

The P-value method for hypothesis testing for this chapter also follows the same format as stated in Chapter 8. The steps are reviewed here.

Step 1   State the hypotheses and identify the claim.

Step 2   Compute the test value.

Step 3   Find the P-value.

Step 4   Make the decision.

Step 5   Summarize the results.

Example 9–2 illustrates these steps.

EXAMPLE 9–2   College Sports Offerings

A researcher hypothesizes that the average number of sports that colleges offer for males is greater than the average number of sports that colleges offer for females. A random sample of the number of sports offered by colleges for males and females is shown. At $\alpha = 0.10$, is there enough evidence to support the claim? Assume σ_1 and $\sigma_2 = 3.3$.

Males					Females				
6	11	11	8	15	6	8	11	13	8
6	14	8	12	18	7	5	13	14	6
6	9	5	6	9	6	5	5	7	6
6	9	18	7	6	10	7	6	5	5
15	6	11	5	5	16	10	7	8	5
9	9	5	5	8	7	5	5	6	5
8	9	6	11	6	9	18	13	7	10
9	5	11	5	8	7	8	5	7	6
7	7	5	10	7	11	4	6	8	7
10	7	10	8	11	14	12	5	8	5

Source: *USA TODAY.*

SOLUTION

Step 1   State the hypotheses and identify the claim.

$$H_0: \mu_1 = \mu_2 \quad \text{and} \quad H_1: \mu_1 > \mu_2 \text{ (claim)}$$

Step 2   Compute the test value. Using a calculator or the formula in Chapter 3, find the mean for each data set.

$$\text{For the males} \quad \overline{X}_1 = 8.6 \quad \text{and} \quad \sigma_1 = 3.3$$
$$\text{For the females} \quad \overline{X}_2 = 7.9 \quad \text{and} \quad \sigma_2 = 3.3$$

Substitute in the formula.

$$z = \frac{(\overline{X}_1 - \overline{X}_2) - (\mu_1 - \mu_2)}{\sqrt{\dfrac{\sigma_1^2}{n_1} + \dfrac{\sigma_2^2}{n_2}}} = \frac{(8.6 - 7.9) - 0}{\sqrt{\dfrac{3.3^2}{50} + \dfrac{3.3^2}{50}}} = 1.06*$$

Step 3   Find the P-value from Table E. For $z = 1.06$, the area is 0.8554, and $1.0000 - 0.8554 = 0.1446$, or a P-value of 0.1446.

Step 4   Make the decision. Since the P-value is larger than α (that is, $0.1446 > 0.10$), the decision is to not reject the null hypothesis. See Figure 9–4.

Step 5   Summarize the results. There is not enough evidence to support the claim that colleges offer more sports for males than they do for females at the 0.10 level of significance.

FIGURE 9–4   *P-Value and α Value for Example 9–2*

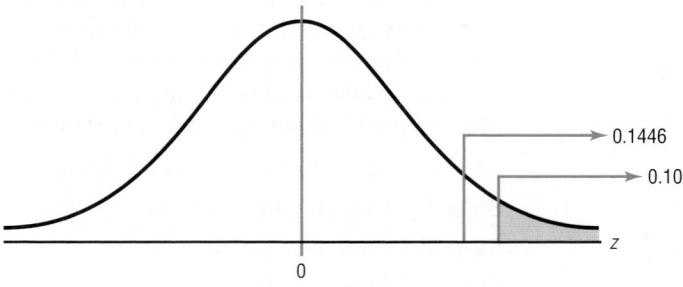

→ 0.1446

→ 0.10

0

Note: Calculator results may differ due to rounding.

Sometimes, the researcher is interested in testing a specific difference in means other than zero. For example, he or she might hypothesize that the nursing students at a community college are, on average, 3.2 years older than those at a university. In this case, the hypotheses are

$$H_0: \mu_1 - \mu_2 = 3.2 \qquad \text{and} \qquad H_1: \mu_1 - \mu_2 > 3.2$$

The formula for the z test is still

$$z = \frac{(\bar{X}_1 - \bar{X}_2) - (\mu_1 - \mu_2)}{\sqrt{\dfrac{\sigma_1^2}{n_1} + \dfrac{\sigma_2^2}{n_2}}}$$

where $\mu_1 - \mu_2$ is the hypothesized difference or expected value. In this case, $\mu_1 - \mu_2 = 3.2$.

Confidence intervals for the difference between two means can also be found. When you are hypothesizing a difference of zero, if the confidence interval contains zero, the null hypothesis is not rejected. If the confidence interval does not contain zero, the null hypothesis is rejected.

Confidence intervals for the difference between two means can be found by using this formula:

Formula for the z Confidence Interval for Difference Between Two Means

$$(\bar{X}_1 - \bar{X}_2) - z_{\alpha/2}\sqrt{\frac{\sigma_1^2}{n_1} + \frac{\sigma_2^2}{n_2}} < \mu_1 - \mu_2 < (\bar{X}_1 - \bar{X}_2) + z_{\alpha/2}\sqrt{\frac{\sigma_1^2}{n_1} + \frac{\sigma_2^2}{n_2}}$$

EXAMPLE 9–3   Leisure Time

Find the 95% confidence interval for the difference between the means in Example 9–1.

SOLUTION

Substitute in the formula, using $z_{\alpha/2} = 1.96$.

$$(\bar{X}_1 - \bar{X}_2) - z_{\alpha/2}\sqrt{\frac{\sigma_1^2}{n_1} + \frac{\sigma_2^2}{n_2}} < \mu_1 - \mu_2 < (\bar{X}_1 - \bar{X}_2) + z_{\alpha/2}\sqrt{\frac{\sigma_1^2}{n_1} + \frac{\sigma_2^2}{n_2}}$$

$$(39.6 - 35.4) - 1.96\sqrt{\frac{6.3^2}{35} + \frac{5.8^2}{35}} < \mu_1 - \mu_2 < (39.6 - 35.4) + 1.96\sqrt{\frac{6.3^2}{35} + \frac{5.8^2}{35}}$$

$$4.2 - 2.8 < \mu_1 - \mu_2 < 4.2 + 2.8$$

$$1.4 < \mu_1 - \mu_2 < 7.0$$

(The confidence interval obtained from the TI-84 is $1.363 < \mu_1 - \mu_2 < 7.037$.)

Since the confidence interval does not contain zero, the decision is to reject the null hypothesis, which agrees with the previous result.

Applying the Concepts 9–1

Home Runs

For a sports radio talk show, you are asked to research the question whether more home runs are hit by players in the National League or by players in the American League. You decide to use the home run leaders from each league for a 40-year period as your data. The numbers are shown.

National League									
47	49	73	50	65	70	49	47	40	43
46	35	38	40	47	39	49	37	37	36
40	37	31	48	48	45	52	38	38	36
44	40	48	45	45	36	39	44	52	47

American League									
47	57	52	47	48	56	56	52	50	40
46	43	44	51	36	42	49	49	40	43
39	39	22	41	45	46	39	32	36	32
32	32	37	33	44	49	44	44	49	32

Using the data given, answer the following questions.

1. Define a population.

2. What kind of sample was used?

3. Do you feel that the samples are representative?

4. What are your hypotheses?

5. What significance level will you use?

6. What statistical test will you use?

7. What are the test results? (Assume $\sigma_1 = 8.8$ and $\sigma_2 = 7.8$.)

8. What is your decision?

9. What can you conclude?

10. Do you feel that using the data given really answers the original question asked?

11. What other data might be used to answer the question?

See pages 545 and 546 for the answers.

Exercises 9–1

1. Explain the difference between testing a single mean and testing the difference between two means.

2. When a researcher selects all possible pairs of samples from a population in order to find the difference between the means of each pair, what will be the shape of the distribution of the differences when the original distributions are normally distributed? What will be the mean of the distribution? What will be the standard deviation of the distribution?

3. What three assumptions must be met when you are using the z test to test differences between two means when σ_1 and σ_2 are known?

4. Show two different ways to state that the means of two populations are equal.

For Exercises 5 through 16, perform each of the following steps.

    a. State the hypotheses and identify the claim.

    b. Find the critical value(s).

    c. Compute the test value.

    d. Make the decision.

    e. Summarize the results.

Use the traditional method of hypothesis testing unless otherwise specified.

5. **Lengths of Major Rivers** A researcher wishes to see if the average length of the major rivers in the United States is the same as the average length of the major rivers in Europe. The data (in miles) of a random sample of rivers are shown. At $\alpha = 0.01$, is there enough evidence to reject the claim? Assume $\sigma_1 = 450$ and $\sigma_2 = 474$.

United States			Europe		
729	560	434	481	724	820
329	332	360	532	357	505
450	2315	865	1776	1122	496
330	410	1036	1224	634	230
329	800	447	1420	326	626
600	1310	652	877	580	210
1243	605	360	447	567	252
525	926	722	824	932	600
850	310	430	634	1124	1575
532	375	1979	565	405	2290
710	545	259	675	454	
300	470	425			

Source: *The World Almanac and Book of Facts.*

6. **Teachers' Salaries** California and New York lead the list of average teachers' salaries. The California yearly average is $64,421 while teachers in New York make an average annual salary of $62,332. Random samples of 45 teachers from each state yielded the following.

	California	New York
Sample mean	64,510	62,900
Population standard deviation	8,200	7,800

At $\alpha = 0.10$, is there a difference in means of the salaries?

Source: *World Almanac.*

7. **Commuting Times** The U.S. Census Bureau reports that the average commuting time for citizens of both Baltimore, Maryland, and Miami, Florida, is approximately 29 minutes. To see if their commuting times appear to be any different in the winter, random samples of 40 drivers were surveyed in each city and the average commuting time for the month of January was calculated for both cities. The results are shown. At the 0.05 level of significance, can it be concluded that the commuting times are different in the winter?

	Miami	Baltimore
Sample size	40	40
Sample mean	28.5 min	35.2 min
Population standard deviation	7.2 min	9.1 min

Source: www.census.gov

8. **Heights of 9-Year-Olds** At age 9 the average weight (21.3 kg) and the average height (124.5 cm) for both boys and girls are exactly the same. A random sample of 9-year-olds yielded these results. At $\alpha = 0.05$, do the data support the given claim that there is a difference in heights?

	Boys	Girls
Sample size	60	50
Mean height, cm	123.5	126.2
Population variance	98	120

Source: www.healthepic.com

9. **Length of Hospital Stays** The average length of "short hospital stays" for men is slightly longer than that for women, 5.2 days versus 4.5 days. A random sample of recent hospital stays for both men and women revealed the following. At $\alpha = 0.01$, is there sufficient evidence to conclude that the average hospital stay for men is longer than the average hospital stay for women?

	Men	Women
Sample size	32	30
Sample mean	5.5 days	4.2 days
Population standard deviation	1.2 days	1.5 days

Source: www.cdc.gov/nchs

10. **Home Prices** A real estate agent compares the selling prices of randomly selected homes in two municipalities in southwestern Pennsylvania to see if there is a difference. The results of the study are shown. Is there enough evidence to reject the claim that the average cost of a home in both locations is the same? Use $\alpha = 0.01$.

Scott	Ligonier
$\overline{X}_1 = \$93,430*$	$\overline{X}_2 = \$98,043*$
$\sigma_1 = \$5602$	$\sigma_2 = \$4731$
$n_1 = 35$	$n_2 = 40$

*Based on information from RealSTATs.

11. **Women Science Majors** In a study of randomly selected women science majors, the following data were obtained on two groups, those who left their profession within a few months after graduation (leavers) and those who remained in their profession after they graduated (stayers). Test the claim that those who stayed had a higher science grade point average than those who left. Use $\alpha = 0.05$.

Leavers	Stayers
$\overline{X}_1 = 3.16$	$\overline{X}_2 = 3.28$
$\sigma_1 = 0.52$	$\sigma_2 = 0.46$
$n_1 = 103$	$n_2 = 225$

Source: Paula Rayman and Belle Brett, "Women Science Majors: What Makes a Difference in Persistence after Graduation?" *The Journal of Higher Education.*

12. **ACT Scores** A random survey of 1000 students nationwide showed a mean ACT score of 21.4. Ohio was not used. A survey of 500 randomly selected Ohio scores showed a mean of 20.8. If the population standard deviation in each case is 3, can we conclude that Ohio is below the national average? Use $\alpha = 0.05$.

Source: Report of WFIN radio.

13. **Per Capita Income** The average per capita income for Wisconsin is reported to be $37,314, and for South Dakota it is $37,375—almost the same thing. A random sample of 50 workers from each state indicated the following sample statistics.

	Wisconsin	South Dakota
Size	50	50
Mean	$40,275	$38,750
Population standard deviation	$10,500	$12,500

At $\alpha = 0.05$, can we conclude a difference in means of the personal incomes?

Source: *New York Times Almanac.*

14. **Monthly Social Security Benefits** The average monthly Social Security benefit for a specific year for retired workers was $954.90 and for disabled workers was $894.10. Researchers used data from the Social Security records to test the claim that the difference in monthly benefits between the two groups was greater

than $30. Based on the following information, can the researchers' claim be supported at the 0.05 level of significance?

	Retired	Disabled
Sample size	60	60
Mean benefit	$960.50	$902.89
Population standard deviation	$98	$101

Source: *New York Times Almanac.*

15. Self-Esteem Scores In the study cited in Exercise 11, the researchers collected the data shown here on a self-esteem questionnaire. At $\alpha = 0.05$, can it be concluded that there is a difference in the self-esteem scores of the two groups? Use the *P*-value method.

Leavers	Stayers
$\overline{X}_1 = 3.05$	$\overline{X}_2 = 2.96$
$\sigma_1 = 0.75$	$\sigma_2 = 0.75$
$n_1 = 103$	$n_2 = 225$

Source: Paula Rayman and Belle Brett, "Women Science Majors: What Makes a Difference in Persistence after Graduation?" *The Journal of Higher Education.*

16. Ages of College Students The dean of students wants to see whether there is a significant difference in ages of resident students and commuting students. She selects a random sample of 50 students from each group. The ages are shown here. At $\alpha = 0.05$, decide if there is enough evidence to reject the claim of no difference in the ages of the two groups. Use the *P*-value method. Assume $\sigma_1 = 3.68$ and $\sigma_2 = 4.7$.

Resident students

22	25	27	23	26	28	26	24
25	20	26	24	27	26	18	19
18	30	26	18	18	19	32	23
19	19	18	29	19	22	18	22
26	19	19	21	23	18	20	18
22	21	19	21	21	22	18	20
19	23						

Commuter students

18	20	19	18	22	25	24	35
23	18	23	22	28	25	20	24
26	30	22	22	22	21	18	20
19	26	35	19	19	18	19	32
29	23	21	19	36	27	27	20
20	21	18	19	23	20	19	19
20	25						

17. Problem-Solving Ability Two groups of students are given a problem-solving test, and the results are compared. Find the 90% confidence interval of the true difference in means.

Mathematics majors	Computer science majors
$\overline{X}_1 = 83.6$	$\overline{X}_2 = 79.2$
$\sigma_1 = 4.3$	$\sigma_2 = 3.8$
$n_1 = 36$	$n_2 = 36$

18. Credit Card Debt The average credit card debt for a recent year was $9205. Five years earlier the average credit card debt was $6618. Assume sample sizes of 35 were used and the population standard deviations of both samples were $1928. Find the 95% confidence interval of the difference in means.

Source: CardWeb.com

19. Literacy Scores Adults aged 16 or older were assessed in three types of literacy: prose, document, and quantitative. The scores in document literacy were the same for 19- to 24-year-olds and for 40- to 49-year-olds. A random sample of scores from a later year showed the following statistics.

Age group	Mean score	Population standard deviation	Sample size
19–24	280	56.2	40
40–49	315	52.1	35

Construct a 95% confidence interval for the true difference in mean scores for these two groups. What does your interval say about the claim that there is no difference in mean scores?

Source: www.nces.ed.gov

20. Battery Voltage Two brands of batteries are tested, and their voltages are compared. The summary statistics follow. Find the 95% confidence interval of the true difference in the means. Assume that both variables are normally distributed.

Brand X	Brand Y
$\overline{X}_1 = 9.2$ volts	$\overline{X}_2 = 8.8$ volts
$\sigma_1 = 0.3$ volt	$\sigma_2 = 0.1$ volt
$n_1 = 27$	$n_2 = 30$

21. Television Watching The average number of hours of television watched per week by women over age 55 is 48 hours. Men over age 55 watch an average of 43 hours of television per week. Random samples of 40 men and 40 women from a large retirement community yielded the following results. At the 0.01 level of significance, can it be concluded that women watch more television per week than men?

	Sample size	Mean	Population standard deviation
Women	40	48.2	5.6
Men	40	44.3	4.5

Source: *World Almanac 2012.*

22. Commuting Times for College Students The mean travel time to work for Americans is 25.3 minutes. An employment agency wanted to test the mean commuting times for college graduates and those with only some college. Thirty-five college graduates spent a mean time of 40.5 minutes commuting to work with a population variance of 67.24. Thirty workers who had completed some college had a mean commuting time of 34.8 minutes with a population variance of 39.69. At the 0.05 level of significance, can a difference in means be concluded?

Source: *World Almanac 2012.*

23. Store Sales A company owned two small Bath and Body Goods stores in different cities. It was desired to see if there was a difference in their mean daily sales. The following results were obtained from a random sample of daily sales over a six-week period. At $\alpha = 0.01$, can a difference in sales be concluded? Use the *P*-value method.

Store	Mean	Population standard deviation	Sample size
A	$995	$120	30
B	1120	250	30

24. Home Prices According to the almanac, the average sales price of a single-family home in the metropolitan Dallas/Ft. Worth/Irving, Texas, area is $143,800. The average home price in Orlando, Florida, is $134,700. The mean of a random sample of 45 homes in the Texas metroplex was $156,500 with a population standard deviation of $30,000. In the Orlando, Florida, area a sample of 40 homes had a mean price of $142,000 with a population standard deviation of $32,500. At the 0.05 level of significance, can it be concluded that the mean price in Dallas exceeds the mean price in Orlando? Use the *P*-value method.

Source: *World Almanac 2012.*

Extending the Concepts

25. Exam Scores at Private and Public Schools A researcher claims that students in a private school have exam scores that are at most 8 points higher than those of students in public schools. Random samples of 60 students from each type of school are selected and given an exam. The results are shown. At $\alpha = 0.05$, test the claim.

Private school	Public school
$\overline{X}_1 = 110$	$\overline{X}_2 = 104$
$\sigma_1 = 15$	$\sigma_2 = 15$
$n_1 = 60$	$n_2 = 60$

26. Sale Prices for Houses The average sales price of new one-family houses in the Midwest is $250,000 and in the South is $253,400. A random sample of 40 houses in each region was examined with the following results. At the 0.05 level of significance, can it be concluded that the difference in mean sales price for the two regions is greater than $3400?

	South	Midwest
Sample size	40	40
Sample mean	$261,500	$248,200
Population standard deviation	$10,500	$12,000

Source: *New York Times Almanac.*

27. Average Earnings for College Graduates The average earnings of year-round full-time workers with bachelor's degrees or more is $88,641 for men and $58,000 for women—a difference of slightly over $30,000 a year. One hundred of each were randomly sampled, resulting in a sample mean of $90,200 for men, and the population standard deviation is $15,000; and a mean of $57,800 for women, and the population standard deviation is $12,800. At the 0.01 level of significance, can it be concluded that the difference in means is not $30,000?

Source: *New York Times Almanac.*

Technology   Step by Step

TI-84 Plus
Step by Step

Hypothesis Test for the Difference Between Two Means and *z* Distribution (Data)

This refers to Example 9–2 in the text.

Example TI9–1

1. Enter the data values into L₁ and L₂.
2. Press **STAT** and move the cursor to TESTS.
3. Press **3** for 2-SampZTest.
4. Move the cursor to Data and press **ENTER**.
5. Type in the appropriate values.
6. Move the cursor to the appropriate alternative hypothesis and press **ENTER**.
7. Move the cursor to Calculate and press **ENTER**.

Hypothesis Test for the Difference Between Two Means and *z* Distribution (Statistics)

This refers to Example 9–1 in the text.

Example TI9–2

1. Press **STAT** and move the cursor to TESTS.
2. Press **3** for 2-SampZTest.
3. Move the cursor to Stats and press **ENTER**.
4. Type in the appropriate values.
5. Move the cursor to the appropriate alternative hypothesis and press **ENTER**.
6. Move the cursor to Calculate and press **ENTER**.

Confidence Interval for the Difference Between Two Means and *z* Distribution (Data)

1. Enter the data values into L_1 and L_2.
2. Press **STAT** and move the cursor to TESTS.
3. Press **9** for 2-SampZInt.
4. Move the cursor to Data and press **ENTER**.
5. Type in the appropriate values.
6. Move the cursor to Calculate and press **ENTER**.

Confidence Interval for the Difference Between Two Means and *z* Distribution (Statistics)

This refers to Example 9–3 in the text.

Example TI9–3

1. Press **STAT** and move the cursor to TESTS.
2. Press **9** for 2-SampZInt.
3. Move the cursor to Stats and press **ENTER**.
4. Type in the appropriate values.
5. Move the cursor to Calculate and press **ENTER**.

EXCEL
Step by Step

z Test for the Difference Between Two Means

Excel has a two-sample *z* test included in the Data Analysis Add-in. To perform a *z* test for the difference between the means of two populations, given two independent samples, do this:

1. Enter the first sample data set into column A.
2. Enter the second sample data set into column B.
3. If the population variances are not known but $n \geq 30$ for both samples, use the formulas =VAR(A1:A*n*) and =VAR(B1:B*n*), where A*n* and B*n* are the last cells with data in each column, to find the variances of the sample data sets.
4. Select the Data tab from the toolbar. Then select Data Analysis.
5. In the Analysis Tools box, select *z* test: Two sample for Means.
6. Type the ranges for the data in columns A and B and type a value (usually 0) for the Hypothesized Mean Difference.
7. If the population variances are known, type them for Variable 1 and Variable 2. Otherwise, use the sample variances obtained in step 3.
8. Specify the confidence level Alpha.
9. Specify a location for the output, and click [OK].

Example XL9–1

Test the claim that the two population means are equal, using the sample data provided here, at $\alpha = 0.05$. Assume the population variances are $\sigma_A^2 = 10.067$ and $\sigma_B^2 = 7.067$.

Set A	10	2	15	18	13	15	16	14	18	12	15	15	14	18	16
Set B	5	8	10	9	9	11	12	16	8	8	9	10	11	7	6

The two-sample *z* test dialog box is shown (before the variances are entered); the results appear in the table that Excel generates. Note that the *P*-value and critical *z* value are provided for both the one-tailed test and the two-tailed test. The *P*-values here are expressed in scientific notation: $7.09045E\text{-}06 = 7.09045 \times 10^{-6} = 0.00000709045$. Because this value is less than 0.05, we reject the null hypothesis and conclude that the population means are not equal.

Two-Sample *z* Test Dialog Box

z-Test: Two Sample for Means		
	Variable 1	*Variable 2*
Mean	14.06666667	9.266666667
Known Variance	10.067	7.067
Observations	15	15
Hypothesized Mean Difference	0	
z	4.491149228	
P(Z<=z) one-tail	3.54522E-06	
z Critical one-tail	1.644853	
P(Z<=z) two-tail	7.09045E-06	
z Critical two-tail	1.959961082	

9–2   Testing the Difference Between Two Means of Independent Samples: Using the *t* Test

OBJECTIVE ❷

Test the difference between two means for independent samples, using the *t* test.

In Section 9–1, the *z* test was used to test the difference between two means when the population standard deviations were known and the variables were normally or approximately normally distributed, or when both sample sizes were greater than or equal to 30. In many situations, however, these conditions cannot be met—that is, the population standard deviations are not known. In these cases, a *t* test is used to test the difference between means when the two samples are independent and when the samples are taken from two normally or approximately normally distributed populations. Samples are independent samples when they are not related. Also it will be assumed that the variances are not equal.

Formula for the *t* Test for Testing the Difference Between Two Means, Independent Samples

Variances are assumed to be unequal:

$$t = \frac{(\bar{X}_1 - \bar{X}_2) - (\mu_1 - \mu_2)}{\sqrt{\dfrac{s_1^2}{n_1} + \dfrac{s_2^2}{n_2}}}$$

where the degrees of freedom are equal to the smaller of $n_1 - 1$ or $n_2 - 1$.

The formula

$$t = \frac{(\bar{X}_1 - \bar{X}_2) - (\mu_1 - \mu_2)}{\sqrt{\dfrac{s_1^2}{n_1} + \dfrac{s_2^2}{n_2}}}$$

follows the format of

$$\text{Test value} = \frac{(\text{observed value}) - (\text{expected value})}{\text{standard error}}$$

where $\bar{X}_1 - \bar{X}_2$ is the observed difference between sample means and where the expected value $\mu_1 - \mu_2$ is equal to zero when no difference between population means is hypothesized. The denominator $\sqrt{s_1^2/n_1 + s_2^2/n_2}$ is the standard error of the difference between two means. This formula is similar to the one used when σ_1 and σ_2 are known; but when we use this t test, σ_1 and σ_2 are unknown, so s_1 and s_2 are used in the formula in place of σ_1 and σ_2. Since mathematical derivation of the standard error is somewhat complicated, it will be omitted here.

Before you can use the testing methods to determine whether two independent sample means differ when σ_1 and σ_2 are unknown, the following assumptions must be met.

Assumptions for the t Test for Two Independent Means When σ_1 and σ_2 Are Unknown

1. The samples are random samples.
2. The sample data are independent of one another.
3. When the sample sizes are less than 30, the populations must be normally or approximately normally distributed.

In this book, the assumptions will be stated in the exercises; however, when encountering statistics in other situations, you must check to see that these assumptions have been met before proceeding.

Again the hypothesis test here follows the same steps as those in Section 9–1; however, the formula uses s_1 and s_2 and Table F to get the critical values.

EXAMPLE 9–4   Weights of Newborn Infants

A researcher wishes to see if the average weights of newborn male infants are different from the average weights of newborn female infants. She selects a random sample of 10 male infants and finds the mean weight is 7 pounds 11 ounces and the standard deviation of the sample is 8 ounces. She selects a random sample of 8 female infants and finds that the mean weight is 7 pounds 4 ounces and the standard deviation of the sample is 5 ounces. Can it be concluded at $\alpha = 0.05$ that the mean weight of the males is different from the mean weight of the females? Assume that the variables are normally distributed.

SOLUTION

Step 1   State the hypotheses and identify the claim for the means.

$$H_0: \mu_1 = \mu_2 \quad \text{and} \quad H_1: \mu_1 \neq \mu_2 \text{ (claim)}$$

Step 2   Find the critical values. Since the test is two-tailed and $\alpha = 0.05$, the degrees of freedom are the smaller of $n_1 - 1$ or $n_2 - 1$. In this case, $n_1 - 1 = 10 - 1 = 9$ and $n_2 - 1 = 8 - 1 = 7$. From Table F, the critical values are $+2.365$ and -2.365.

Step 3   Compute the test value. Change the means to ounces (1 lb = 16 oz):

$$7 \text{ lb } 11 \text{ oz } = 7 \times 16 + 11 = 123 \text{ oz}$$

$$7 \text{ lb } 4 \text{ oz } = 7 \times 16 + 4 = 116 \text{ oz}$$

$$t = \frac{(\bar{X}_1 - \bar{X}_2) - (\mu_1 - \mu_2)}{\sqrt{\dfrac{s_1^2}{n_1} + \dfrac{s_2^2}{n_2}}} = \frac{(123 - 116) - 0}{\sqrt{\dfrac{8^2}{10} + \dfrac{5^2}{8}}} = \frac{7}{3.086} = 2.268$$

Step 4   Make the decision. Do not reject the null hypothesis, since $2.268 < 2.365$. See Figure 9–5.

FIGURE 9–5   Critical and Test Values for Example 9–4

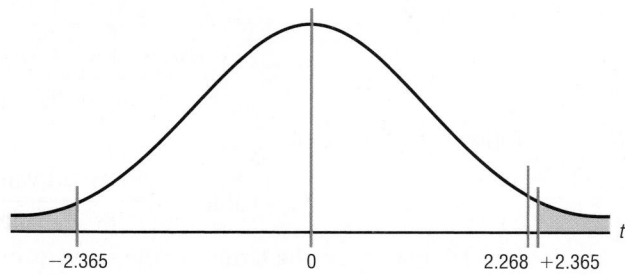

−2.365	0	2.268 +2.365

Step 5   Summarize the results.

There is not enough evidence to support the claim that the mean of the weights of the male infants is different from the mean of the weights of the female infants.

When raw data are given in the exercises, use your calculator or the formulas in Chapter 3 to find the means and variances for the data sets. Then follow the procedures shown in this section to test the hypotheses.

Confidence intervals can also be found for the difference of two means with this formula:

Confidence Intervals for the Difference of Two Means: Independent Samples

Variances assumed to be unequal:

$$(\bar{X}_1 - \bar{X}_2) - t_{\alpha/2}\sqrt{\frac{s_1^2}{n_1} + \frac{s_2^2}{n_2}} < \mu_1 - \mu_2 < (\bar{X}_1 - \bar{X}_2) + t_{\alpha/2}\sqrt{\frac{s_1^2}{n_1} + \frac{s_2^2}{n_2}}$$

d.f. = smaller value of $n_1 - 1$ or $n_2 - 1$

EXAMPLE 9–5   Find the 95% confidence interval for the data in Example 9–4.

SOLUTION

Substitute in the formula.

$$(\bar{X}_1 - \bar{X}_2) - t_{\alpha/2}\sqrt{\frac{s_1^2}{n_1} + \frac{s_2^2}{n_2}} < \mu_1 - \mu_2 < (\bar{X}_1 - \bar{X}_2) + t_{\alpha/2}\sqrt{\frac{s_1^2}{n_1} + \frac{s_2^2}{n_2}}$$

$$(123 - 116) - 2.365\sqrt{\frac{8^2}{10} + \frac{5^2}{8}} < \mu_1 - \mu_2 < (123 - 116) + 2.365\sqrt{\frac{8^2}{10} + \frac{5^2}{8}}$$

$$7 - 7.3 < \mu_1 - \mu_2 < 7 + 7.3$$

$$-0.3 < \mu_1 - \mu_2 < 14.3$$

Since 0 is contained in the interval, there is not enough evidence to support the claim that the mean weights are different.

In many statistical software packages, a different method is used to compute the degrees of freedom for this t test. They are determined by the formula

$$\text{d.f.} = \frac{(s_1^2/n_1 + s_2^2/n_2)^2}{(s_1^2/n_1)^2/(n_1 - 1) + (s_2^2/n_2)^2/(n_2 - 1)}$$

This formula will not be used in this textbook.

There are actually two different options for the use of t tests. *One option is used when the variances of the populations are not equal, and the other option is used when the variances are equal.* To determine whether two sample variances are equal, the researcher can use an F test, as shown in Section 9–5.

When the variances are assumed to be equal, this formula is used and

$$t = \frac{(\bar{X}_1 - \bar{X}_2) - (\mu_1 - \mu_2)}{\sqrt{\dfrac{(n_1 - 1)s_1^2 + (n_2 - 1)s_2^2}{n_1 + n_2 - 2}}\sqrt{\dfrac{1}{n_1} + \dfrac{1}{n_2}}}$$

follows the format of

$$\text{Test value} = \frac{(\text{observed value}) - (\text{expected value})}{\text{standard error}}$$

For the numerator, the terms are the same as in the previously given formula. However, a note of explanation is needed for the denominator of the second test statistic. Since both populations are assumed to have the same variance, the standard error is computed with what is called a pooled estimate of the variance. A **pooled estimate of the variance** is a weighted average of the variance using the two sample variances and the *degrees of freedom* of each variance as the weights. Again, since the algebraic derivation of the standard error is somewhat complicated, it is omitted.

Note, however, that not all statisticians are in agreement about using the F test before using the t test. Some believe that conducting the F and t tests at the same level of significance will change the overall level of significance of the t test. Their reasons are beyond the scope of this text. Because of this, we will assume that $\sigma_1 \neq \sigma_2$ in this text.

Applying the Concepts 9–2

Too Long on the Telephone

A company collects data on the lengths of telephone calls made by employees in two different divisions. The sample mean and the sample standard deviation for the sales division are 10.26 and 8.56, respectively. The sample mean and sample standard deviation for the shipping and receiving division are 6.93 and 4.93, respectively. A hypothesis test was run, and the computer output follows.

> Degrees of freedom = 56
> Confidence interval limits = −0.18979, 6.84979
> Test statistic $t = 1.89566$
> Critical value $t = -2.0037, 2.0037$
> P-value = 0.06317
> Significance level = 0.05

1. Are the samples independent or dependent?

2. Which number from the output is compared to the significance level to check if the null hypothesis should be rejected?

3. Which number from the output gives the probability of a type I error that is calculated from the sample data?

4. Was a right-, left-, or two-tailed test done? Why?

5. What are your conclusions?

6. What would your conclusions be if the level of significance were initially set at 0.10?

See page 546 for the answers.

≡ Exercises 9–2

For these exercises, perform each of these steps. Assume that all variables are normally or approximately normally distributed.

    a. State the hypotheses and identify the claim.
    b. Find the critical value(s).
    c. Compute the test value.
    d. Make the decision.
    e. Summarize the results.

Use the traditional method of hypothesis testing unless otherwise specified and assume the variances are unequal.

1. **Bestseller Books** The mean for the number of weeks 15 *New York Times* hard-cover fiction books spent on the bestseller list is 22 weeks. The standard deviation is 6.17 weeks. The mean for the number of weeks 15 *New York Times* hard-cover nonfiction books spent on the list is 28 weeks. The standard deviation is 13.2 weeks. At $\alpha = 0.10$, can we conclude that there is a difference in the mean times for the number of weeks the books were on the bestseller lists?

2. **Tax-Exempt Properties** A tax collector wishes to see if the mean values of the tax-exempt properties are different for two cities. The values of the tax-exempt properties for the two random samples are shown. The data are given in millions of dollars. At $\alpha = 0.05$, is there enough evidence to support the tax collector's claim that the means are different?

City A				City B			
113	22	14	8	82	11	5	15
25	23	23	30	295	50	12	9
44	11	19	7	12	68	81	2
31	19	5	2	20	16	4	5

3. **Noise Levels in Hospitals** The mean noise level of 20 randomly selected areas designated as "casualty doors" was 63.1 dBA, and the sample standard deviation is 4.1 dBA. The mean noise level for 24 randomly selected areas designated as operating theaters was 56.3 dBA, and the sample standard deviation was 7.5 dBA. At $\alpha = 0.05$, can it be concluded that there is a difference in the means?

4. **Ages of Gamblers** The mean age of a random sample of 25 people who were playing the slot machines is 48.7 years, and the standard deviation is 6.8 years. The mean age of a random sample of 35 people who were playing roulette is 55.3 with a standard deviation of 3.2 years. Can it be concluded at $\alpha = 0.05$ that the mean age of those playing the slot machines is less than those playing roulette?

5. **Carbohydrates in Candies** The number of grams of carbohydrates contained in 1-ounce servings of randomly selected chocolate and nonchocolate candy is listed here. Is there sufficient evidence to conclude that the difference in the means is statistically significant? Use $\alpha = 0.10$.

Chocolate:	29	25	17	36	41	25	32	29
	38	34	24	27	29			

Nonchocolate:	41	41	37	29	30	38	39	10
	29	55	29					

Source: *The Doctor's Pocket Calorie, Fat, and Carbohydrate Counter.*

6. **Weights of Vacuum Cleaners** Upright vacuum cleaners have either a hard body type or a soft body type. Shown are the weights in pounds of a random sample of each type. At $\alpha = 0.05$, can it be concluded that the means of the weights are different?

Hard body types				Soft body types		
21	17	17	20	24	13	11	13
16	17	15	20	12	15		
23	16	17	17				
13	15	16	18				
18							

7. **Weights of Running Shoes** The weights in ounces of a sample of running shoes for men and women are shown. Test the claim that the means are different. Use the *P*-value method with $\alpha = 0.05$.

Men		Women		
10.4	12.6	10.6	10.2	8.8
11.1	14.7	9.6	9.5	9.5
10.8	12.9	10.1	11.2	9.3
11.7	13.3	9.4	10.3	9.5
12.8	14.5	9.8	10.3	11.0

8. **Teacher Salaries** A researcher claims that the mean of the salaries of elementary school teachers is greater than the mean of the salaries of secondary school teachers in a large school district. The mean of the salaries of a random sample of 26 elementary school teachers is $48,256, and the sample standard deviation is $3,912.40. The mean of the salaries of a random sample of 24 secondary school teachers is $45,633. The sample standard deviation is $5533. At $\alpha = 0.05$, can it be concluded that the mean of the salaries of the elementary school teachers is greater than the mean of the salaries of the secondary school teachers? Use the *P*-value method.

9. Find the 95% confidence interval for the difference of the means in Exercise 3 of this section.

10. Find the 95% confidence interval for the difference of the means in Exercise 6 of this section.

11. **Hours Spent Watching Television** According to Nielsen Media Research, children (ages 2–11) spend an average of 21 hours 30 minutes watching television per week while teens (ages 12–17) spend an average of

20 hours 40 minutes. Based on the sample statistics shown, is there sufficient evidence to conclude a difference in average television watching times between the two groups? Use $\alpha = 0.01$.

	Children	Teens
Sample mean	22.45	18.50
Sample variance	16.4	18.2
Sample size	15	15

Source: *Time Almanac.*

12. NFL Salaries An agent claims that there is no difference between the pay of safeties and linebackers in the NFL. A survey of 15 randomly selected safeties found an average salary of $501,580, and a survey of 15 randomly selected linebackers found an average salary of $513,360. If the standard deviation in the first sample is $20,000 and the standard deviation in the second sample is $18,000, is the agent correct? Use $\alpha = 0.05$.

Source: *NFL Players Assn./USA TODAY.*

13. Cyber School Enrollment The data show the number of students attending cyber charter schools in Allegheny County and the number of students attending cyber schools in counties surrounding Allegheny County. At $\alpha = 0.01$, is there enough evidence to support the claim that the average number of students in school districts in Allegheny County who attend cyber schools is greater than those who attend cyber schools in school districts outside Allegheny County? Give a factor that should be considered in interpreting this answer.

Allegheny County						Outside Allegheny County					
25	75	38	41	27	32	57	25	38	14	10	29

Source: *Pittsburgh Tribune-Review.*

14. Hockey's Highest Scorers The number of points held by random samples of the NHL's highest scorers for both the Eastern Conference and the Western Conference is shown. At $\alpha = 0.05$, can it be concluded that there is a difference in means based on these data?

Eastern Conference				Western Conference			
83	60	75	58	77	59	72	58
78	59	70	58	37	57	66	55
62	61	59		61			

Source: www.foxsports.com

15. Hospital Stays for Maternity Patients Health Care Knowledge Systems reported that an insured woman spends on average 2.3 days in the hospital for a routine childbirth, while an uninsured woman spends on average 1.9 days. Assume two random samples of 16 women each were used in both samples. The standard deviation of the first sample is equal to 0.6 day, and the standard deviation of the second sample is 0.3 day. At $\alpha = 0.01$, test the claim that the means are equal. Find the 99% confidence interval for the differences of the means. Use the *P*-value method.

Source: Michael D. Shook and Robert L. Shook, *The Book of Odds.*

16. Ages of Homes Whiting, Indiana, leads the "Top 100 Cities with the Oldest Houses" list with the average age of houses being 66.4 years. Farther down the list resides Franklin, Pennsylvania, with an average house age of 59.4 years. Researchers selected a random sample of 20 houses in each city and obtained the following statistics. At $\alpha = 0.05$, can it be concluded that the houses in Whiting are older? Use the *P*-value method.

	Whiting	Franklin
Mean age	62.1 years	55.6 years
Standard deviation	5.4 years	3.9 years

Source: www.city-data.com

17. Medical School Enrollments A random sample of enrollments from medical schools that specialize in research and from those that are noted for primary care is listed. Find the 90% confidence interval for the difference in the means.

Research				Primary care			
474	577	605	663	783	605	427	728
783	467	670	414	546	474	371	107
813	443	565	696	442	587	293	277
692	694	277	419	662	555	527	320
884							

Source: *U.S. News & World Report Best Graduate Schools.*

18. Out-of-State Tuitions The out-of-state tuitions (in dollars) for random samples of both public and private four-year colleges in a New England state are listed. Find the 95% confidence interval for the difference in the means.

Private		Public	
13,600	13,495	7,050	9,000
16,590	17,300	6,450	9,758
23,400	12,500	7,050	7,871
		16,100	

Source: *New York Times Almanac.*

19. Gasoline Prices A random sample of monthly gasoline prices was taken from 2005 and from 2011. The samples are shown. Using $\alpha = 0.01$, can it be concluded that gasoline cost less in 2005? Use the *P*-value method.

2005	2.017	2.468	2.502	2.701	3.130	2.560	
2011	3.345	3.807	4.074	3.972	3.553	4.192	3.424

20. Miniature Golf Scores A large group of friends went miniature golfing together at a par 54 course and decided to play on two teams. A random sample of scores from each of the two teams is shown. At $\alpha = 0.05$, is there a difference in mean scores between the two teams? Use the *P*-value method.

Team 1	61	44	52	47	56	63	62	55
Team 2	56	40	42	58	48	52	51	

21. Random Numbers Two sets of 15 random integers from 1 to 100 were generated by a calculator. They are shown below. At the 0.10 level of significance, can it be concluded that the means differ? What would you expect? Why?

Set 1	80	43	60	41	16	39	29	12	12	13	54	24	9	46	25
Set 2	94	53	28	83	26	86	72	2	85	36	23	81	15	1	100

22. Batting Averages Random samples of batting averages from the leaders in both leagues prior to the All-Star break are shown. At the 0.05 level of significance, can a difference be concluded?

National	.360	.654	.652	.338	.313	.309
American	.340	.332	.317	.316	.314	.306

Technology   Step by Step

TI-84 Plus
Step by Step

Hypothesis Test for the Difference Between Two Means and *t* Distribution (Statistics)

This refers to Example 9–4 in the text.

Example TI9–4

1. Press **STAT** and move the cursor to TESTS.
2. Press **4** for 2-SampTTest.
3. Move the cursor to Stats and press **ENTER**.
4. Type in the appropriate values.
5. Move the cursor to the appropriate alternative hypothesis and press **ENTER**.
6. On the line for Pooled, move the cursor to No (standard deviations are assumed not equal) and press **ENTER**.
7. Move the cursor to Calculate and press **ENTER**.

Confidence Interval for the Difference Between Two Means and *t* Distribution (Data)

1. Enter the data values into L₁ and L₂.
2. Press **STAT** and move the cursor to TESTS.
3. Press **0** for 2-SampTInt.
4. Move the cursor to Data and press **ENTER**.
5. Type in the appropriate values.
6. On the line for Pooled, move the cursor to No (standard deviations are assumed not equal) and press **ENTER**.
7. Move the cursor to Calculate and press **ENTER**.

Confidence Interval for the Difference Between Two Means and *t* Distribution (Statistics)

This refers to Example 9–5 in the text.

Example TI9–5

1. Press **STAT** and move the cursor to TESTS.
2. Press **0** for 2-SampTInt.
3. Move the cursor to Stats and press **ENTER**.
4. Type in the appropriate values.
5. On the line for Pooled, move the cursor to No (standard deviations are assumed not equal) and press **ENTER**.
6. Move the cursor to Calculate and press **ENTER**.

EXCEL
Step by Step

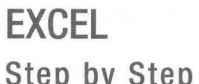

Testing the Difference Between Two Means: Independent Samples

Excel has a two-sample *t* test included in the Data Analysis Add-in. The following example shows how to perform a *t* test for the difference between two means.

Example XL9–2

Test the claim that there is no difference between population means based on these sample data. Assume the population variances are not equal. Use $\alpha = 0.05$.

Set A	32	38	37	36	36	34	39	36	37	42
Set B	30	36	35	36	31	34	37	33	32	

1. Enter the 10-number data set A into column A.
2. Enter the 9-number data set B into column B.
3. Select the **Data tab** from the toolbar. Then select **Data Analysis**.
4. In the **Data Analysis** box, under **Analysis Tools** select *t*-test: Two-Sample Assuming Unequal Variances, and click [OK].
5. In **Input**, type in the Variable 1 Range: **A1:A10** and the Variable 2 Range: **B1:B9**.
6. Type **0** for the **Hypothesized Mean Difference.**
7. Type **0.05** for Alpha.
8. In **Output** options, type D7 for the **Output Range**, then click [OK].

Two-Sample *t* Test
in Excel

t-Test: Two-Sample Assuming Unequal Variances

	Variable 1	Variable 2
Mean	36.7	33.77777778
Variance	7.344444444	5.944444444
Observations	10	9
Hypothesized Mean Difference	0	
df	17	
t Stat	2.474205364	
P(T<=t) one-tail	0.012095	
t Critical one-tail	1.739606716	
P(T<=t) two-tail	0.024189999	
t Critical two-tail	2.109815559	

Note: You may need to increase the column width to see all the results. To do this:

1. Highlight the columns D, E, and F.
2. Select **Format>AutoFit** Column Width.

The output reports both one- and two-tailed *P*-values.

MINITAB
Step by Step

Test the Difference Between Two Means: Independent Samples*

MINITAB will calculate the test statistic and *P*-value for differences between the means for two populations when the population standard deviations are unknown.

For Example 9–2, is the average number of sports for men higher than the average number for women?

1. Enter the data for Example 9–2 into C1 and C2. Name the columns **MaleS** and **FemaleS.**
2. Select **Stat>Basic Statistics>2-Sample t.**
3. Click the button for **Samples in different columns.**

*MINITAB does not calculate a *z* test statistic. This statistic can be used instead.

There is one sample in each column.

4. Click in the box for First:. Double-click C1 MaleS in the list.

5. Click in the box for Second:, then double-click C2 FemaleS in the list. Do not check the box for Assume equal variances. MINITAB will use the large sample formula. The completed dialog box is shown.

6. Click [Options].

a) Type in **90** for the Confidence level and **0** for the Test mean.

b) Select greater than for the Alternative. This option affects the *P*-value. It must be correct.

7. Click [OK] twice. Since the *P*-value is greater than the significance level, $0.172 > 0.1$, do not reject the null hypothesis.

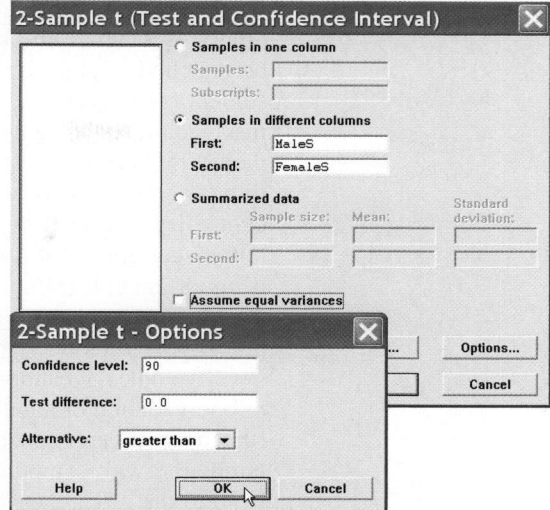

Two-Sample t-Test and CI: MaleS, FemaleS

Two-sample t for MaleS vs FemaleS

	N	Mean	StDev	SE Mean
MaleS	50	8.56	3.26	0.46
FemaleS	50	7.94	3.27	0.46

Difference = mu (MaleS) − mu (FemaleS)
Estimate for difference: 0.620000
90% lower bound for difference: −0.221962
t-Test of difference = 0 (vs >): t-Value = 0.95 P-Value = 0.172 DF = 97

9–3 Testing the Difference Between Two Means: Dependent Samples

OBJECTIVE 3

Test the difference between two means for dependent samples.

In Section 9–1, the *z* test was used to compare two sample means when the samples were independent and σ_1 and σ_2 were known. In Section 9–2, the *t* test was used to compare two sample means when the samples were independent. In this section, a different version of the *t* test is explained. This version is used when the samples are dependent. Samples are considered to be dependent samples when the subjects are paired or matched in some way. Dependent samples are sometimes called matched-pair samples.

For example, suppose a medical researcher wants to see whether a drug will affect the reaction time of its users. To test this hypothesis, the researcher must pretest the subjects in the sample. That is, they are given a test to ascertain their normal reaction times. Then after taking the drug, the subjects are tested again, using a posttest. Finally, the means of the two tests are compared to see whether there is a difference. Since the same subjects are used in both cases, the samples are *related;* subjects scoring high on the pretest will generally score high on the posttest, even after consuming the drug. Likewise, those scoring lower on the pretest will tend to score lower on the posttest. To take this effect into account, the researcher employs a *t* test, using the differences between the pretest values and the posttest values. Thus, only the gain or loss in values is compared.

Here are some other examples of dependent samples. A researcher may want to design an SAT preparation course to help students raise their test scores the second time they take the SAT. Hence, the differences between the two exams are compared. A medical specialist may want to see whether a new counseling program will help subjects lose weight. Therefore, the preweights of the subjects will be compared with the postweights.

Besides samples in which the same subjects are used in a pre-post situation, there are other cases where the samples are considered dependent. For example, students might be matched or paired according to some variable that is pertinent to the study; then one student is assigned to one group, and the other student is assigned to a second group. For instance, in a study involving learning, students can be selected and paired according to their IQs. That is, two students with the same IQ will be paired. Then one will be assigned to one sample group (which might receive instruction by computers), and the other student will be assigned to another sample group (which might receive instruction by the lecture discussion method). These assignments will be done randomly. Since a student's IQ is important to learning, it is a variable that should be controlled. By matching subjects on IQ, the researcher can eliminate the variable's influence, for the most part. Matching, then, helps to reduce type II error by eliminating extraneous variables.

Two notes of caution should be mentioned. First, when subjects are matched according to one variable, the matching process does not eliminate the influence of other variables. Matching students according to IQ does not account for their mathematical ability or their familiarity with computers. Since not all variables influencing a study can be controlled, it is up to the researcher to determine which variables should be used in matching. Second, when the same subjects are used for a pre-post study, sometimes the knowledge that they are participating in a study can influence the results. For example, if people are placed in a special program, they may be more highly motivated to succeed simply because they have been selected to participate; the program itself may have little effect on their success.

When the samples are dependent, a special t test for dependent means is used. This test employs the difference in values of the matched pairs. The hypotheses are as follows:

Two-tailed	Left-tailed	Right-tailed
$H_0: \mu_D = 0$	$H_0: \mu_D = 0$	$H_0: \mu_D = 0$
$H_1: \mu_D \neq 0$	$H_1: \mu_D < 0$	$H_1: \mu_D > 0$

Here, μ_D is the symbol for the expected mean of the difference of the matched pairs. The general procedure for finding the test value involves several steps.

First, find the differences of the values of the pairs of data.

$$D = X_1 - X_2$$

Second, find the mean $\overline{D}$ of the differences, using the formula

$$\overline{D} = \frac{\Sigma D}{n}$$

where n is the number of data pairs. Third, find the standard deviation s_D of the differences, using the formula

$$s_D = \sqrt{\frac{n\Sigma D^2 - (\Sigma D)^2}{n(n-1)}}$$

Fourth, find the estimated standard error $s_{\overline{D}}$ of the differences, which is

$$s_{\overline{D}} = \frac{s_D}{\sqrt{n}}$$

Finally, find the test value, using the formula

$$t = \frac{\overline{D} - \mu_D}{s_D/\sqrt{n}} \quad \text{with d.f.} = n - 1$$

The formula in the final step follows the basic format of

$$\text{Test value} = \frac{(\text{observed value}) - (\text{expected value})}{\text{standard error}}$$

where the observed value is the mean of the differences. The expected value μ_D is zero if the hypothesis is $\mu_D = 0$. The standard error of the difference is the standard deviation of the difference, divided by the square root of the sample size. Both populations must be normally or approximately normally distributed.

Before you can use the testing method presented in this section, the following assumptions must be met.

Assumptions for the *t* Test for Two Means When the Samples Are Dependent

1. The sample or samples are random.
2. The sample data are dependent.
3. When the sample size or sample sizes are less than 30, the population or populations must be normally or approximately normally distributed.

In this book, the assumptions will be stated in the exercises; however, when encountering statistics in other situations, you must check to see that these assumptions have been met before proceeding.

The formulas for this *t* test are given next.

Formulas for the *t* Test for Dependent Samples

$$t = \frac{\bar{D} - \mu_D}{s_D/\sqrt{n}}$$

with d.f. $= n - 1$ and where

$$\bar{D} = \frac{\Sigma D}{n} \quad \text{and} \quad s_D = \sqrt{\frac{n\Sigma D^2 - (\Sigma D)^2}{n(n - 1)}}$$

The steps for this *t* test are summarized in the Procedure Table.

Procedure Table

Testing the Difference Between Means for Dependent Samples

Step 1 State the hypotheses and identify the claim.

Step 2 Find the critical value(s).

Step 3 Compute the test value.

    a. Make a table, as shown.

X_1	X_2	A $D = X_1 - X_2$	B $D^2 = (X_1 - X_2)^2$
$\vdots$	$\vdots$		
		$\Sigma D =$ _____	$\Sigma D^2 =$ _____

    b. Find the differences and place the results in column A.
$$D = X_1 - X_2$$

    c. Find the mean of the differences.
$$\bar{D} = \frac{\Sigma D}{n}$$

    d. Square the differences and place the results in column B. Complete the table.
$$D^2 = (X_1 - X_2)^2$$

    e. Find the standard deviation of the differences.
$$s_D = \sqrt{\frac{n\Sigma D^2 - (\Sigma D)^2}{n(n - 1)}}$$

    f. Find the test value.
$$t = \frac{\bar{D} - \mu_D}{s_D/\sqrt{n}} \quad \text{with d.f.} = n - 1$$

Step 4 Make the decision.

Step 5 Summarize the results.

Unusual Stat

About 4% of Americans spend at least one night in jail each year.

EXAMPLE 9–6   Bank Deposits

A random sample of nine local banks shows their deposits (in billions of dollars) 3 years ago and their deposits (in billions of dollars) today. At $\alpha = 0.05$, can it be concluded that the average in deposits for the banks is greater today than it was 3 years ago? Use $\alpha = 0.05$. Assume the variable is normally distributed.

Source: SNL Financial.

Bank	1	2	3	4	5	6	7	8	9
3 years ago	11.42	8.41	3.98	7.37	2.28	1.10	1.00	0.9	1.35
Today	16.69	9.44	6.53	5.58	2.92	1.88	1.78	1.5	1.22

SOLUTION

Step 1 State the hypothesis and identify the claim. Since we are interested to see if there has been an increase in deposits, the deposits 3 years ago must be less than the deposits today; hence, the deposits must be significantly less 3 years ago than they are today. Hence, the mean of the differences must be less than zero.

$$H_0: \mu_D = 0 \quad \text{and} \quad H_1: \mu_D < 0 \text{ (claim)}$$

Step 2 Find the critical value. The degrees of freedom are $n - 1$, or $9 - 1 = 8$. Using Table F, the critical value for a left-tailed test with $\alpha = 0.05$ is -1.860.

Step 3 Compute the test value.

a. Make a table.

3 years ago (X_1)	Today (X_2)	A $D = X_1 - X_2$	B $D^2 = (X_1 - X_2)^2$
11.42	16.69		
8.41	9.44		
3.98	6.53		
7.37	5.58		
2.28	2.92		
1.10	1.88		
1.00	1.78		
0.90	1.50		
1.35	1.22		

b. Find the differences and place the results in column A.

$$11.42 - 16.69 = -5.27$$
$$8.41 - 9.44 = -1.03$$
$$3.98 - 6.53 = -2.55$$
$$7.37 - 5.58 = +1.79$$
$$2.28 - 2.92 = -0.64$$
$$1.10 - 1.88 = -0.78$$
$$1.00 - 1.78 = -0.78$$
$$0.9 - 1.50 = -0.60$$
$$1.35 - 1.22 = +0.13$$
$$\Sigma D = \overline{-9.73}$$

c. Find the means of the differences.

$$\overline{D} = \frac{\Sigma D}{n} = \frac{-9.73}{9} = -1.081$$

d. Square the differences and place the results in column B.

$$(-5.27)^2 = 27.7729$$
$$(-1.03)^2 = 1.0609$$
$$(-2.55)^2 = 6.5025$$
$$(+1.79)^2 = 3.2041$$
$$(-0.64)^2 = 0.4096$$
$$(-0.78)^2 = 0.6084$$
$$(-0.78)^2 = 0.6084$$
$$(-0.60)^2 = 0.3600$$
$$(+0.13)^2 = 0.0169$$
$$\Sigma D^2 = 40.5437$$

The completed table is shown next.

3 years ago (X_1)	Today (X_2)	A $D = X_1 - X_2$	B $D^2 = (X_1 - X_2)^2$
11.42	16.69	−5.27	27.7729
8.41	9.44	−1.03	1.0609
3.98	6.53	−2.55	6.5025
7.37	5.58	+1.79	3.2041
2.28	2.92	−0.64	0.4096
1.10	1.88	−0.78	0.6084
1.00	1.78	−0.78	0.6084
0.90	1.50	−0.60	0.3600
1.35	1.22	+0.13	0.0169
		$\Sigma D = -9.73$	$\Sigma D^2 = 40.5437$

e. Find the standard deviation of the differences.

$$s_D = \sqrt{\frac{n\Sigma D^2 - (\Sigma D)^2}{n(n-1)}}$$

$$= \sqrt{\frac{9(40.5437) - (-9.73)^2}{9(9-1)}}$$

$$= \sqrt{\frac{270.2204}{72}}$$

$$= 1.937$$

f. Find the test value.

$$t = \frac{\overline{D} - \mu_D}{s_D/\sqrt{n}} = \frac{-1.081 - 0}{1.937/\sqrt{9}} = -1.674$$

Step 4 Make the decision. Do not reject the null hypothesis since the test value, −1.674, is greater than the critical value, −1.860. See Figure 9–6.

FIGURE 9–6 Critical and Test Values for Example 9–6

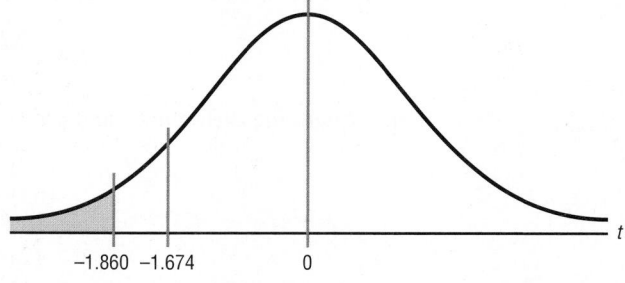

Step 5 Summarize the results. There is not enough evidence to show that the deposits have increased over the last 3 years.

EXAMPLE 9–7   Cholesterol Levels

A dietitian wishes to see if a person's cholesterol level will change if the diet is supplemented by a certain mineral. Six randomly selected subjects were pretested, and then they took the mineral supplement for a 6-week period. The results are shown in the table. (Cholesterol level is measured in milligrams per deciliter.) Can it be concluded that the cholesterol level has been changed at $\alpha = 0.10$? Assume the variable is approximately normally distributed.

Subject	1	2	3	4	5	6
Before (X_1)	210	235	208	190	172	244
After (X_2)	190	170	210	188	173	228

SOLUTION

Step 1 State the hypotheses and identify the claim. If the diet is effective, the before cholesterol levels should be different from the after levels.

$$H_0: \mu_D = 0 \quad \text{and} \quad H_1: \mu_D \neq 0 \text{ (claim)}$$

Step 2 Find the critical value. The degrees of freedom are $6 - 1 = 5$. At $\alpha = 0.10$, the critical values are ± 2.015.

Step 3 Compute the test value.

a. Make a table.

Before (X_1)	After (X_2)	A $D = X_1 - X_2$	B $D^2 = (X_1 - X_2)^2$
210	190		
235	170		
208	210		
190	188		
172	173		
244	228		

b. Find the differences and place the results in column A.

$$210 - 190 = 20$$
$$235 - 170 = 65$$
$$208 - 210 = -2$$
$$190 - 188 = 2$$
$$172 - 173 = -1$$
$$244 - 228 = \underline{16}$$
$$\Sigma D = 100$$

c. Find the mean of the differences.

$$\overline{D} = \frac{\Sigma D}{n} = \frac{100}{6} = 16.7$$

d. Square the differences and place the results in column B.

$$(20)^2 = 400$$
$$(65)^2 = 4225$$
$$(-2)^2 = 4$$
$$(2)^2 = 4$$
$$(-1)^2 = 1$$
$$(16)^2 = \underline{256}$$
$$\Sigma D^2 = 4890$$

Then complete the table as shown.

Before (X_1)	After (X_2)	A $D = X_1 - X_2$	B $D^2 = (X_1 - X_2)^2$
210	190	20	400
235	170	65	4225
208	210	−2	4
190	188	2	4
172	173	−1	1
244	228	16	256
		$\Sigma D = 100$	$\Sigma D^2 = 4890$

e. Find the standard deviation of the differences.

$$s_D = \sqrt{\frac{n\Sigma D^2 - (\Sigma D)^2}{n(n-1)}}$$

$$= \sqrt{\frac{6 \cdot 4890 - 100^2}{6(6-1)}}$$

$$= \sqrt{\frac{29{,}340 - 10{,}000}{30}}$$

$$= 25.4$$

f. Find the test value.

$$t = \frac{\overline{D} - \mu_D}{s_D/\sqrt{n}} = \frac{16.7 - 0}{25.4/\sqrt{6}} = 1.610$$

Step 4 Make the decision. The decision is to not reject the null hypothesis, since the test value 1.610 is in the noncritical region, as shown in Figure 9–7.

FIGURE 9–7 Critical and Test Values for Example 9–7

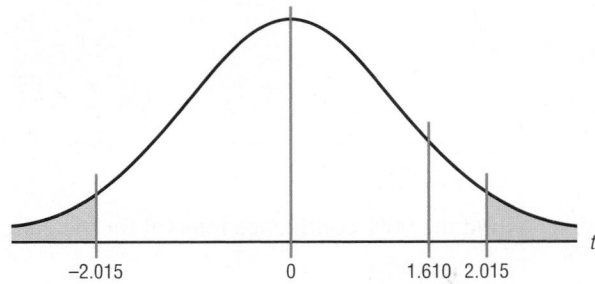

Step 5 Summarize the results. There is not enough evidence to support the claim that the mineral changes a person's cholesterol level.

The P-values for the t test are found in Table F. For a two-tailed test with d.f. = 5 and $t = 1.610$, the P-value is found between 1.476 and 2.015; hence, $0.10 < P$-value < 0.20. Thus, the null hypothesis cannot be rejected at $\alpha = 0.10$.

If a specific difference is hypothesized, this formula should be used

$$t = \frac{\overline{D} - \mu_D}{s_D/\sqrt{n}}$$

where μ_D is the hypothesized difference.

SPEAKING OF STATISTICS Can Video Games Save Lives?

Can playing video games help doctors perform surgery? The answer is yes. A study showed that surgeons who played video games for at least 3 hours each week made about 37% fewer mistakes and finished operations 27% faster than those who did not play video games.

The type of surgery that they performed is called *laparoscopic* surgery, where the surgeon inserts a tiny video camera into the body and uses a joystick to maneuver the surgical instruments while watching the results on a television monitor. This study compares two groups and uses proportions. What statistical test do you think was used to compare the percentages? (See Section 9–4.)

For example, if a dietitian claims that people on a specific diet will lose an average of 3 pounds in a week, the hypotheses are

$$H_0: \mu_D = 3 \quad \text{and} \quad H_1: \mu_D \neq 3$$

The value 3 will be substituted in the test statistic formula for μ_D.

Confidence intervals can be found for the mean differences with this formula.

Confidence Interval for the Mean Difference

$$\overline{D} - t_{\alpha/2}\frac{s_D}{\sqrt{n}} < \mu_D < \overline{D} + t_{\alpha/2}\frac{s_D}{\sqrt{n}}$$

$$\text{d.f.} = n - 1$$

EXAMPLE 9–8

Find the 90% confidence interval for the data in Example 9–7.

SOLUTION

Substitute in the formula.

$$\overline{D} - t_{\alpha/2}\frac{s_D}{\sqrt{n}} < \mu_D < \overline{D} + t_{\alpha/2}\frac{s_D}{\sqrt{n}}$$

$$16.7 - 2.015 \cdot \frac{25.4}{\sqrt{6}} < \mu_D < 16.7 + 2.015 \cdot \frac{25.4}{\sqrt{6}}$$

$$16.7 - 20.89 < \mu_D < 16.7 + 20.89$$

$$-4.19 < \mu_D < 37.59$$

$$-4.2 < \mu_D < 37.6$$

Since 0 is contained in the interval, the decision is to not reject the null hypothesis $H_0: \mu_D = 0$. Hence, there is not enough evidence to support the claim that the mineral changes a person's cholesterol, as previously shown.

Applying the Concepts 9–3

Air Quality

As a researcher for the EPA, you have been asked to determine if the air quality in the United States has changed over the past 2 years. You select a random sample of 10 metropolitan areas and find the number of days each year that the areas failed to meet acceptable air quality standards. The data are shown.

Year 1	18	125	9	22	138	29	1	19	17	31
Year 2	24	152	13	21	152	23	6	31	34	20

Source: *The World Almanac and Book of Facts.*

Based on the data, answer the following questions.

1. What is the purpose of the study?
2. Are the samples independent or dependent?
3. What hypotheses would you use?
4. What is (are) the critical value(s) that you would use?
5. What statistical test would you use?
6. How many degrees of freedom are there?
7. What is your conclusion?
8. Could an independent means test have been used?
9. Do you think this was a good way to answer the original question?

See page 546 for the answers.

Exercises 9–3

1. Classify each as independent or dependent samples.

   a. Heights of identical twins

   b. Test scores of the same students in English and psychology

   c. The effectiveness of two different brands of aspirin on two different groups of people

   d. Effects of a drug on reaction time of two different groups of people, measured by a before-and-after test

   e. The effectiveness of two different diets on two different groups of individuals

For Exercises 2 through 12, perform each of these steps. Assume that all variables are normally or approximately normally distributed.

   a. State the hypotheses and identify the claim.

   b. Find the critical value(s).

   c. Compute the test value.

   d. Make the decision.

   e. Summarize the results.

Use the traditional method of hypothesis testing unless otherwise specified.

2. **Retention Test Scores** A random sample of non-English majors at a selected college was used in a study to see if the student retained more from reading a 19th-century novel or by watching it in DVD form. Each student was assigned one novel to read and a different one to watch, and then they were given a 100-point written quiz on each novel. The test results are shown. At $\alpha = 0.05$, can it be concluded that the book scores are higher than the DVD scores?

Book	90	80	90	75	80	90	84
DVD	85	72	80	80	70	75	80

3. **Improving Study Habits** As an aid for improving students' study habits, nine students were randomly selected to attend a seminar on the importance of education in life. The table shows the number of hours each student studied per week before and after the seminar. At $\alpha = 0.10$, did attending the seminar

increase the number of hours the students studied per week?

Before	9	12	6	15	3	18	10	13	7
After	9	17	9	20	2	21	15	22	6

4. Obstacle Course Times An obstacle course was set up on a campus, and 8 randomly selected volunteers were given a chance to complete it while they were being timed. They then sampled a new energy drink and were given the opportunity to run the course again. The "before" and "after" times in seconds are shown. Is there sufficient evidence at $\alpha = 0.05$ to conclude that the students did better the second time? Discuss possible reasons for your results.

Student	1	2	3	4	5	6	7	8
Before	67	72	80	70	78	82	69	75
After	68	70	76	65	75	78	65	68

5. Sleep Report Randomly selected students in a statistics class were asked to report the number of hours they slept on weeknights and on weekends. At $\alpha = 0.05$, is there sufficient evidence that there is a difference in the mean number of hours slept?

Student	1	2	3	4	5	6	7	8
Hours, Sun.–Thurs.	8	5.5	7.5	8	7	6	6	8
Hours, Fri.–Sat.	4	7	10.5	12	11	9	6	9

6. PGA Golf Scores At a recent PGA tournament (the Honda Classic at Palm Beach Gardens, Florida) the following scores were posted for eight randomly selected golfers for two consecutive days. At $\alpha = 0.05$, is there evidence of a difference in mean scores for the two days?

Golfer	1	2	3	4	5	6	7	8
Thursday	67	65	68	68	68	70	69	70
Friday	68	70	69	71	72	69	70	70

Source: *Washington Observer-Reporter.*

7. Reducing Errors in Grammar A composition teacher wishes to see whether a new grammar program will reduce the number of grammatical errors her students make when writing a two-page essay. She randomly selects six students, and the data are shown. At $\alpha = 0.025$, can it be concluded that the number of errors has been reduced?

Student	1	2	3	4	5	6
Errors before	12	9	0	5	4	3
Errors after	9	6	1	3	2	3

8. Overweight Dogs A veterinary nutritionist developed a diet for overweight dogs. The total volume of food consumed remains the same, but one-half of the dog food is replaced with a low-calorie "filler" such as canned green beans. Six overweight dogs were randomly selected from her practice and were put on this program. Their initial weights were recorded, and they were weighed again after 4 weeks. At the 0.05 level of significance, can it be concluded that the dogs lost weight?

Before	42	53	48	65	40	52
After	39	45	40	58	42	47

9. Pulse Rates of Identical Twins A researcher wanted to compare the pulse rates of identical twins to see whether there was any difference. Eight sets of twins were randomly selected. The rates are given in the table as number of beats per minute. At $\alpha = 0.01$, is there a significant difference in the average pulse rates of twins? Use the *P*-value method. Find the 99% confidence interval for the difference of the two.

Twin A	87	92	78	83	88	90	84	93
Twin B	83	95	79	83	86	93	80	86

10. Toy Assembly Test An educational researcher devised a wooden toy assembly project to test learning in 6-year-olds. The time in seconds to assemble the project was noted, and the toy was disassembled out of the child's sight. Then the child was given the task to repeat. The researcher would conclude that learning occurred if the mean of the second assembly times was less than the mean of the first assembly times. At $\alpha = 0.01$, can it be concluded that learning took place? Use the *P*-value method, and find the 99% confidence interval of the difference in means.

Child	1	2	3	4	5	6	7
Trial 1	100	150	150	110	130	120	118
Trial 2	90	130	150	90	105	110	120

11. Golf Scores A researcher hypothesized that scores differed between the first and last rounds of major U.S. golf tournaments. Here are the paired data for randomly selected golfers from the 2012 U.S. Open. At the 0.05 level of significance, is there a difference?

Golfer	1	2	3	4	5	6	7	8
Round 1	72	73	72	72	72	70	73	70
Round 2	72	69	75	76	75	73	75	74

12. Mistakes in a Song A random sample of six music students played a short song, and the number of mistakes in music each student made was recorded. After they practiced the song 5 times, the number of mistakes each student made was recorded. The data are shown. At $\alpha = 0.05$, can it be concluded that there was a decrease in the mean number of mistakes?

Student	A	B	C	D	E	F
Before	10	6	8	8	13	8
After	4	2	2	7	8	9

Extending the Concepts

13. Instead of finding the mean of the differences between X_1 and X_2 by subtracting $X_1 - X_2$, you can find it by finding the means of X_1 and X_2 and then subtracting the means. Show that these two procedures will yield the same results.

Technology   Step by Step

TI-84 Plus
Step by Step

Hypothesis Test for the Difference Between Two Means: Dependent Samples

This refers to Example 9–7 in the text.

Example TI9–6

1. Enter the data values into L_1 and L_2.

2. Move the cursor to the top of the L_3 column so that L_3 is highlighted.

3. Type $L_1 - L_2$, then press **ENTER**.

4. Press **STAT** and move the cursor to TESTS.

5. Press **2** for TTest.

6. Move the cursor to Data and press **ENTER**.

7. Type in the appropriate values, using **0** for μ_0 and L_3 for the list.

8. Move the cursor to the appropriate alternative hypothesis and press **ENTER**.

9. Move the cursor to Calculate and press **ENTER**.

Confidence Interval for the Difference Between Two Means: Dependent Samples

This refers to Example 9–8 in the text.

Example TI9–7

1. Enter the data values into L_1 and L_2.

2. Move the cursor to the top of the L_3 column so that L_3 is highlighted.

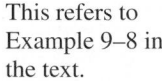

3. Type $L_1 - L_2$, then press **ENTER**.

4. Press **STAT** and move the cursor to TESTS.

5. Press **8** for TInterval.

6. Move the cursor to Data and press **ENTER**.

7. Type in the appropriate values, using L_3 for the list.

8. Move the cursor to Calculate and press **ENTER**.

EXCEL
Step by Step

Testing the Difference Between Two Means: Dependent Samples

Example XL9–3

Test the claim that there is no difference between population means based on these sample paired data. Use $\alpha = 0.05$.

Set A	33	35	28	29	32	34	30	34
Set B	27	29	36	34	30	29	28	24

1. Enter the 8-number data set A into column A.

2. Enter the 8-number data set B into column B.

3. Select the Data tab from the toolbar. Then select Data Analysis.

4. In the Data Analysis box, under Analysis Tools select *t*-test: Paired Two Sample for Means, and click [OK].

5. In Input, type in the Variable 1 Range: **A1:A8** and the Variable 2 Range: **B1:B8.**

6. Type **0** for the Hypothesized Mean Difference.

7. Type **0.05** for Alpha.

8. In Output options, type **D5** for the Output Range, then click [OK].

t-Test: Paired Two Sample for Means		
	Variable 1	Variable 2
Mean	31.875	29.625
Variance	6.696428571	14.55357143
Observations	8	8
Pearson Correlation	-0.757913399	
Hypothesized Mean Difference	0	
df	7	
t Stat	1.057517468	
P(T<=t) one-tail	0.1626994	
t Critical one-tail	1.894578604	
P(T<=t) two-tail	0.3253988	
t Critical two-tail	2.364624251	

Note: You may need to increase the column width to see all the results. To do this:

1. Highlight the columns D, E, and F.

2. Select **Format>AutoFit** Column Width.

The output shows a *P*-value of 0.3253988 for the two-tailed case. This value is greater than the alpha level of 0.05, so we fail to reject the null hypothesis.

MINITAB
Step by Step

Test the Difference Between Two Means: Dependent Samples

A physical education director claims by taking a special vitamin, a weight lifter can increase his strength. Eight athletes are selected and given a test of strength, using the standard bench press. After 2 weeks of regular training, supplemented with the vitamin, they are tested again. Test the effectiveness of the vitamin regimen at $\alpha = 0.05$. Each value in these data represents the maximum number of pounds the athlete can bench-press. Assume that the variable is approximately normally distributed.

Athlete	1	2	3	4	5	6	7	8
Before (X_1)	210	230	182	205	262	253	219	216
After (X_2)	219	236	179	204	270	250	222	216

1. Enter the data into C1 and C2. Name the columns **Before** and **After.**

2. Select **Stat>Basic Statistics>Paired t.**

3. Double-click C1 Before for First sample.

4. Double-click C2 After for Second sample. The second sample will be subtracted from the first. The differences are not stored or displayed.

5. Click [Options].

6. Change the Alternative to less than.

7. Click [OK] twice.

Paired t (Test and Confidence Inte... ✕

⊙ Samples in columns
First sample: │BEFORE
Second sample: │AFTER

◌ Summarized data (differences)
Sample size:

Paired t - Options ✕

Confidence level: │95.0

Test mean: │0.0

Alternative: │less than ▾│

Help   OK   Cancel

Paired t-Test and CI: BEFORE, AFTER

Paired t for BEFORE - AFTER

	N	Mean	StDev	SE Mean
BEFORE	8	222.125	25.920	9.164
AFTER	8	224.500	27.908	9.867
Difference	8	−2.37500	4.83846	1.71065

95% upper bound for mean difference: 0.86597
t-Test of mean difference = 0 (vs < 0) : t-Value = −1.39 P-Value = 0.104.

Since the *P*-value is 0.104, do not reject the null hypothesis. The sample difference of −2.38 in the strength measurement is not statistically significant. ▬

9–4 Testing the Difference Between Proportions

OBJECTIVE ❹

Test the difference between two proportions.

In Chapter 8, an inference about a single proportion was explained. In this section, testing the difference between two sample proportions will be explained.

The *z* test with some modifications can be used to test the equality of two proportions. For example, a researcher might ask, Is the proportion of men who exercise regularly less than the proportion of women who exercise regularly? Is there a difference in the percentage of students who own a personal computer and the percentage of nonstudents who own one? Is there a difference in the proportion of college graduates who pay cash for purchases and the proportion of non-college graduates who pay cash?

Recall from Chapter 7 that the symbol $\hat{p}$ ("*p* hat") is the sample proportion used to estimate the population proportion, denoted by *p*. For example, if in a sample of 30 college students, 9 are on probation, then the sample proportion is $\hat{p} = \frac{9}{30}$, or 0.3. The population proportion *p* is the number of all students who are on probation, divided by the number of students who attend the college. The formula for the sample proportion $\hat{p}$ is

$$\hat{p} = \frac{X}{n}$$

where

X = number of units that possess the characteristic of interest
n = sample size

When you are testing the difference between two population proportions p_1 and p_2, the hypotheses can be stated thus, if no specific difference between the proportions is hypothesized.

$$H_0: p_1 = p_2 \qquad H_0: p_1 - p_2 = 0$$
$$\text{or}$$
$$H_1: p_1 \neq p_2 \qquad H_1: p_1 - p_2 \neq 0$$

Similar statements using < or > in the alternate hypothesis can be formed for one-tailed tests.

For two proportions, $\hat{p}_1 = X_1/n_1$ is used to estimate p_1 and $\hat{p}_2 = X_2/n_2$ is used to estimate p_2. The standard error of the difference is

$$\sigma_{\hat{p}_1 - \hat{p}_2} = \sqrt{\sigma_{p_1}^2 + \sigma_{p_2}^2} = \sqrt{\frac{p_1 q_1}{n_1} + \frac{p_2 q_2}{n_2}}$$

where $\sigma_{p_1}^2$ and $\sigma_{p_2}^2$ are the variances of the proportions, $q_1 = 1 - p_1$, $q_2 = 1 - p_2$, and n_1 and n_2 are the respective sample sizes.

Since p_1 and p_2 are unknown, a weighted estimate of p can be computed by using the formula

$$\bar{p} = \frac{n_1 \hat{p}_1 + n_2 \hat{p}_2}{n_1 + n_2}$$

and $\bar{q} = 1 - \bar{p}$. This weighted estimate is based on the hypothesis that $p_1 = p_2$. Hence, $\bar{p}$ is a better estimate than either $\hat{p}_1$ or $\hat{p}_2$, since it is a combined average using both $\hat{p}_1$ and $\hat{p}_2$.

Since $\hat{p}_1 = X_1/n_1$ and $\hat{p}_2 = X_2/n_2$, $\bar{p}$ can be simplified to

$$\bar{p} = \frac{X_1 + X_2}{n_1 + n_2}$$

Finally, the standard error of the difference in terms of the weighted estimate is

$$\sigma_{\hat{p}_1 - \hat{p}_2} = \sqrt{\bar{p}\,\bar{q}\left(\frac{1}{n_1} + \frac{1}{n_2}\right)}$$

The formula for the test value is shown next.

Formula for the *z* Test Value for Comparing Two Proportions

$$z = \frac{(\hat{p}_1 - \hat{p}_2) - (p_1 - p_2)}{\sqrt{\bar{p}\,\bar{q}\left(\dfrac{1}{n_1} + \dfrac{1}{n_2}\right)}}$$

where

$$\bar{p} = \frac{X_1 + X_2}{n_1 + n_2} \qquad \hat{p}_1 = \frac{X_1}{n_1}$$

$$\bar{q} = 1 - \bar{p} \qquad \hat{p}_2 = \frac{X_2}{n_2}$$

This formula follows the format

$$\text{Test value} = \frac{(\text{observed value}) - (\text{expected value})}{\text{standard error}}$$

Before you can test the difference between two sample proportions, the following assumptions must be met.

Assumptions for the *z* Test for Two Proportions

1. The samples must be random samples.
2. The sample data are independent of one another.
3. For both samples $np \geq 5$ and $nq \geq 5$.

In this book, the assumptions will be stated in the exercises; however, when encountering statistics in other situations, you must check to see that these assumptions have been met before proceeding.

The hypothesis-testing procedure used here follows the five-step procedure presented previously except that $\hat{p}_1$, $\hat{p}_2$, $\bar{p}$, and $\bar{q}$ must be computed.

EXAMPLE 9–9   Vaccination Rates in Nursing Homes

In the nursing home study mentioned in the chapter-opening Statistics Today, the researchers found that 12 out of 34 randomly selected small nursing homes had a resident vaccination rate of less than 80%, while 17 out of 24 randomly selected large nursing homes had a vaccination rate of less than 80%. At $\alpha = 0.05$, test the claim that there is no difference in the proportions of the small and large nursing homes with a resident vaccination rate of less than 80%.

Source: Nancy Arden, Arnold S. Monto, and Suzanne E. Ohmit, "Vaccine Use and the Risk of Outbreaks in a Sample of Nursing Homes During an Influenza Epidemic," *American Journal of Public Health*.

SOLUTION

Step 1   State the hypotheses and identify the claim.

$$H_0: p_1 = p_2 \text{ (claim)} \qquad \text{and} \qquad H_1: p_1 \neq p_2$$

Step 2   Find the critical values. Since $\alpha = 0.05$, the critical values are $+1.96$ and -1.96.

Step 3   Compute the test value. First compute $\hat{p}_1, \hat{p}_2, \bar{p}$, and $\bar{q}$. Then substitute in the formula.

Let $\hat{p}_1$ be the proportion of the small nursing homes with a vaccination rate of less than 80% and $\hat{p}_2$ be the proportion of the large nursing homes with a vaccination rate of less than 80%. Then

$$\hat{p}_1 = \frac{X_1}{n_1} = \frac{12}{34} = 0.35 \qquad \text{and} \qquad \hat{p}_2 = \frac{X_2}{n_2} = \frac{17}{24} = 0.71$$

$$\bar{p} = \frac{X_1 + X_2}{n_1 + n_2} = \frac{12 + 17}{34 + 24} = \frac{29}{58} = 0.5$$

$$\bar{q} = 1 - \bar{p} = 1 - 0.5 = 0.5$$

$$z = \frac{(\hat{p}_1 - \hat{p}_2) - (p_1 - p_2)}{\sqrt{\bar{p}\,\bar{q}\left(\dfrac{1}{n_1} + \dfrac{1}{n_2}\right)}}$$

$$= \frac{(0.35 - 0.71) - 0}{\sqrt{(0.5)(0.5)\left(\dfrac{1}{34} + \dfrac{1}{24}\right)}} = \frac{-0.36}{0.1333} = -2.70$$

Step 4   Make the decision. Reject the null hypothesis, since $-2.70 < -1.96$. See Figure 9–8.

FIGURE 9–8   Critical and Test Values for Example 9–9

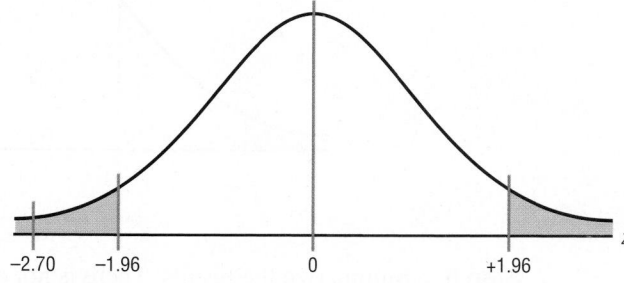

Step 5   Summarize the results. There is enough evidence to reject the claim that there is no difference in the proportions of small and large nursing homes with a resident vaccination rate of less than 80%.

EXAMPLE 9–10   Male and Female Workers

A survey of 200 randomly selected male and female workers (100 in each group) found that 7% of the male workers said that they worked more than 5 days per week while 11% of the female workers said that they worked more than 5 days per week. At $\alpha = 0.01$, can it be concluded that the percentage of males who work more than 5 days per week is less than the percentage of female workers who work more than 5 days per week?

Source: Based on a study by the Fit survey of workers.

SOLUTION

Step 1   State the hypotheses and identify the claim.

$$H_0: p_1 = p_2 \qquad \text{and} \qquad H_1: p_1 < p_2 \text{ (claim)}$$

Step 2   Find the critical value. Using Table E and $\alpha = 0.01$, the critical value is -2.33.

Step 3   Compute the test value. You are given the percentages $\hat{p}_1 = 7\%$, or 0.07, and $\hat{p}_2 = 11\%$, or 0.11. To compute $\bar{p}$ and $\bar{q}$, you must find X_1 and X_2.

$$X_1 = \hat{p}_1 n_1 = 0.07\,(100) = 7$$

$$X_2 = \hat{p}_2 n_2 = 0.11\,(100) = 11$$

$$\bar{p} = \frac{\overline{X}_1 + \overline{X}_2}{n_1 + n_2} = \frac{7 + 11}{100 + 100} = \frac{18}{200} = 0.09$$

$$\bar{q} = 1 - \bar{p} = 1 - 0.09 = 0.91$$

$$z = \frac{(\hat{p}_1 - \hat{p}_2) - (p_1 - p_2)}{\sqrt{\bar{p}\,\bar{q}\left(\dfrac{1}{n_1} + \dfrac{1}{n_2}\right)}} = \frac{(0.07 - 0.11) - 0}{\sqrt{(0.09)(0.91)\left(\dfrac{1}{100} + \dfrac{1}{100}\right)}} = \frac{-0.04}{0.0404} = -0.99$$

Step 4   Make the decision. Do not reject the null hypothesis since $-0.99 > -2.33$. That is, -0.99 is in the noncritical region. See Figure 9–9.

FIGURE 9–9   Critical and Test Values for Example 9–10

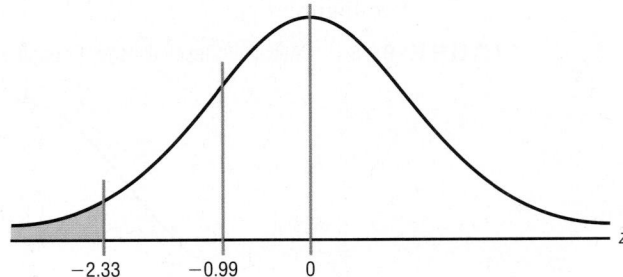

Step 5   Summarize the results. There is not enough evidence to support the claim that the proportion of men who say that they work more than 5 days a week is less than the proportion of women who say that they work more than 5 days a week.

An article in the *Journal of the American Medical Association* explained a study done on placebo pain pills. Researchers randomly assigned 82 healthy people to two groups. The individuals in the first group were given sugar pills, but they were told that the pills were a new, fast-acting opioid pain reliever similar to codeine and that they were listed at $2.50 each. The individuals in the other group received the same sugar pills but were told that the pills had been marked down to 10¢ each.

Each group received electrical shocks before and after taking the pills. They were then asked if the pills reduced the pain. Eighty-five percent of the group who were told that the pain pills cost $2.50 said that they were effective, while 61% of the group who received the supposedly discounted pills said that they were effective.

State possible null and alternative hypotheses for this study. What statistical test could be used in this study? What might be the conclusion of the study?

The *P*-value for the difference of proportions can be found from Table E as shown in Section 9–1. For Example 9–10, the table value for -0.99 is 0.1611. Hence, $0.1611 > 0.01$; thus the decision is to not reject the null hypothesis.

The sampling distribution of the difference of two proportions can be used to construct a confidence interval for the difference of two proportions. The formula for the confidence interval for the difference between two proportions is shown next.

Confidence Interval for the Difference Between Two Proportions

$$(\hat{p}_1 - \hat{p}_2) - z_{\alpha/2}\sqrt{\frac{\hat{p}_1\hat{q}_1}{n_1} + \frac{\hat{p}_2\hat{q}_2}{n_2}} < p_1 - p_2 < (\hat{p}_1 - \hat{p}_2) + z_{\alpha/2}\sqrt{\frac{\hat{p}_1\hat{q}_1}{n_1} + \frac{\hat{p}_2\hat{q}_2}{n_2}}$$

Here, the confidence interval uses a standard deviation based on estimated values of the population proportions, but the hypothesis test uses a standard deviation based on the assumption that the two population proportions are equal. As a result, you may obtain different conclusions when using a confidence interval or a hypothesis test. So when testing for a difference of two proportions, you use the *z* test rather than the confidence interval.

EXAMPLE 9–11

Find the 95% confidence interval for the difference of proportions for the data in Example 9–9.

SOLUTION

$$\hat{p}_1 = \frac{12}{34} = 0.35 \qquad \hat{q}_1 = 0.65$$

$$\hat{p}_2 = \frac{17}{24} = 0.71 \qquad \hat{q}_2 = 0.29$$

Substitute in the formula.

$$(\hat{p}_1 - \hat{p}_2) - z_{\alpha/2}\sqrt{\frac{\hat{p}_1\hat{q}_1}{n_1} + \frac{\hat{p}_2\hat{q}_2}{n_2}} < p_1 - p_2$$

$$< (\hat{p}_1 - \hat{p}_2) + z_{\alpha/2}\sqrt{\frac{\hat{p}_1\hat{q}_1}{n_1} + \frac{\hat{p}_2\hat{q}_2}{n_2}}$$

$$(0.35 - 0.71) - 1.96\sqrt{\frac{(0.35)(0.65)}{34} + \frac{(0.71)(0.29)}{24}}$$

$$< p_1 - p_2 < (0.35 - 0.71) + 1.96\sqrt{\frac{(0.35)(0.65)}{34} + \frac{(0.71)(0.29)}{24}}$$

$$-0.36 - 0.242 < p_1 - p_2 < -0.36 + 0.242$$

$$-0.602 < p_1 - p_2 < -0.118$$

Applying the Concepts 9–4

Smoking and Education

You are researching the hypothesis that there is no difference in the percent of public school students who smoke and the percent of private school students who smoke. You find these results from a recent survey.

School	Percent who smoke
Public	32.3
Private	14.5

Based on these figures, answer the following questions.

1. What hypotheses would you use if you wanted to compare percentages of the public school students who smoke with the private school students who smoke?
2. What critical value(s) would you use?
3. What statistical test would you use to compare the two percentages?
4. What information would you need to complete the statistical test?
5. Suppose you found that 1000 randomly selected individuals in each group were surveyed. Could you perform the statistical test?
6. If so, complete the test and summarize the results.

See page 546 for the answers.

Exercises 9–4

1. Find the proportions $\hat{p}$ and $\hat{q}$ for each.
   a. $n = 48, X = 34$
   b. $n = 75, X = 28$
   c. $n = 100, X = 50$
   d. $n = 24, X = 6$
   e. $n = 144, X = 12$

2. Find $\hat{p}$ and $\hat{q}$ for each.
   a. $n = 36, X = 20$
   b. $n = 50, X = 35$
   c. $n = 64, X = 16$
   d. $n = 200, X = 175$
   e. $n = 148, X = 16$

3. Find each X, given $\hat{p}$.

    a. $\hat{p} = 0.16, n = 100$

    b. $\hat{p} = 0.08, n = 50$

    c. $\hat{p} = 6\%, n = 800$

    d. $\hat{p} = 52\%, n = 200$

    e. $\hat{p} = 20\%, n = 150$

4. Find each X, given $\hat{p}$.

    a. $\hat{p} = 0.24, n = 300$

    b. $\hat{p} = 0.09, n = 200$

    c. $\hat{p} = 88\%, n = 500$

    d. $\hat{p} = 40\%, n = 480$

    e. $\hat{p} = 32\%, n = 700$

5. Find $\bar{p}$ and $\bar{q}$ for each.

    a. $X_1 = 60, n_1 = 100, X_2 = 40, n_2 = 100$

    b. $X_1 = 22, n_1 = 50, X_2 = 18, n_2 = 30$

    c. $X_1 = 18, n_1 = 60, X_2 = 20, n_2 = 80$

    d. $X_1 = 5, n_1 = 32, X_2 = 12, n_2 = 48$

    e. $X_1 = 12, n_1 = 75, X_2 = 15, n_2 = 50$

6. Find $\bar{p}$ and $\bar{q}$.

    a. $X_1 = 6, n_1 = 15, X_2 = 9, n_2 = 15$

    b. $X_1 = 21, n_1 = 100, X_2 = 43, n_2 = 150$

    c. $X_1 = 20, n_1 = 80, X_2 = 65, n_2 = 120$

    d. $X_1 = 15, n_1 = 50, X_2 = 3, n_2 = 12$

    e. $X_1 = 24, n_1 = 40, X_2 = 18, n_2 = 36$

For Exercises 7 through 27, perform these steps.

    a. State the hypotheses and identify the claim.

    b. Find the critical value(s).

    c. Compute the test value.

    d. Make the decision.

    e. Summarize the results.

Use the traditional method of hypothesis testing unless otherwise specified.

7. Lecture versus Computer-Assisted Instruction A survey found that 83% of the men questioned preferred computer-assisted instruction to lecture and 75% of the women preferred computer-assisted instruction to lecture. There were 100 randomly selected individuals in each sample. At $\alpha = 0.05$, test the claim that there is no difference in the proportion of men and the proportion of women who favor computer-assisted instruction over lecture. Find the 95% confidence interval for the difference of the two proportions.

8. Leisure Time In a sample of 50 men, 44 said that they had less leisure time today than they had 10 years ago. In a random sample of 50 women, 48 women said that they had less leisure time than they had 10 years ago. At $\alpha = 0.10$, is there a difference in the proportions? Find the 90% confidence interval for the difference of the

two proportions. Does the confidence interval contain 0? Give a reason why this information would be of interest to a researcher.

Source: Based on statistics from Market Directory.

9. Desire to Be Rich In a random sample of 80 Americans, 44 wished that they were rich. In a random sample of 90 Europeans, 41 wished that they were rich. At $\alpha = 0.01$, is there a difference in the proportions? Find the 99% confidence interval for the difference of the two proportions.

10. Animal Bites of Postal Workers In Cleveland, a random sample of 73 mail carriers showed that 10 had been bitten by an animal during one week. In Philadelphia, in a random sample of 80 mail carriers, 16 had received animal bites. Is there a significant difference in the proportions? Use $\alpha = 0.05$. Find the 95% confidence interval for the difference of the two proportions.

11. Dog Ownership A survey found that in a random sample of 75 families, 26 owned dogs. A survey done 15 years ago found that in a random sample of 60 families, 26 owned dogs. At $\alpha = 0.05$, has the proportion of dog owners changed over the 15-year period? Use the P-value method.

Source: Based on statistics from the American Veterinary Medical Association.

12. Seat Belt Use In a random sample of 200 men, 130 said they used seat belts. In a random sample of 300 women, 63 said they used seat belts. Test the claim that men are more safety-conscious than women, at $\alpha = 0.01$. Use the P-value method.

13. Survey on Inevitability of War A random sample of 200 teenagers shows that 50 believe that war is inevitable, and a random sample of 300 people over age 60 shows that 93 believe war is inevitable. Is the proportion of teenagers who believe war is inevitable different from the proportion of people over age 60 who do? Use $\alpha = 0.01$. Find the 99% confidence interval for the difference of the two proportions.

14. Hypertension It has been found that 26% of men 20 years and older suffer from hypertension (high blood pressure) and 31.5% of women are hypertensive. A random sample of 150 of each gender was selected from recent hospital records, and the following results were obtained. Can you conclude that a higher percentage of women have high blood pressure? Use $\alpha = 0.05$.

Men   43 patients had high blood pressure
Women   52 patients had high blood pressure

Source: www.nchs.gov

15. Partisan Support of Salary Increase Bill Find the 99% confidence interval for the difference in the population proportions for the data of a study in which 80% of the 150 randomly selected Republicans surveyed favored the bill for a salary increase and 60% of the

200 randomly selected Democrats surveyed favored the bill for a salary increase.

16. **Smoking Survey** National statistics show that 23% of men smoke and 18.5% of women smoke. A random sample of 180 men indicated that 50 were smokers, and a random sample of 150 women surveyed indicated that 39 smoked. Construct a 98% confidence interval for the true difference in proportions of male and female smokers. Comment on your interval—does it support the claim that there is a difference?

Source: www.nchs.gov

17. **Senior Workers** It seems that people are choosing or finding it necessary to work later in life. Random samples of 200 men and 200 women age 65 or older were selected, and 80 men and 59 women were found to be working. At $\alpha = 0.01$, can it be concluded that the proportions are different?

Source: Based on www.census.gov

18. **Airlines On-Time Arrivals** The percentages of on-time arrivals for major U.S. airlines range from 68.6 to 91.1. Two regional airlines were surveyed with the following results. At $\alpha = 0.01$, is there a difference in proportions?

	Airline A	Airline B
No. of flights	300	250
No. of on-time flights	213	185

Source: *New York Times Almanac.*

19. **College Education** The percentages of adults 25 years of age and older who have completed 4 or more years of college are 23.6% for females and 27.8% for males. A random sample of women and men who were 25 years old or older was surveyed with these results. Estimate the true difference in proportions with 95% confidence, and compare your interval with the *Almanac* statistics.

	Women	Men
Sample size	350	400
No. who completed 4 or more years	100	115

Source: *New York Times Almanac.*

20. **Married People** In a specific year 53.7% of men in the United States were married and 50.3% of women were married. Random samples of 300 men and 300 women found that 178 men and 139 women were married (not necessarily to each other). At the 0.05 level of significance, can it be concluded that the proportion of men who were married is greater than the proportion of women who were married?

Source: *New York Times Almanac.*

21. **Undergraduate Financial Aid** A study is conducted to determine if the percent of women who receive financial aid in undergraduate school is different from the percent of men who receive financial aid in undergraduate

school. A random sample of undergraduates revealed these results. At $\alpha = 0.01$, is there significant evidence to reject the null hypothesis?

	Women	Men
Sample size	250	300
Number receiving aid	200	180

Source: U.S. Department of Education, National Center for Education Statistics.

22. **High School Graduation Rates** The overall U.S. public high school graduation rate is 73.4%. For Pennsylvania it is 83.5% and for Idaho 80.5%—a difference of 3%. Random samples of 1200 students from each state indicated that 980 graduated in Pennsylvania and 940 graduated in Idaho. At the 0.05 level of significance, can it be concluded that there is a difference in the proportions of graduating students between the states?

Source: *World Almanac.*

23. **Interview Errors** It has been found that many first-time interviewees commit errors that could very well affect the outcome of the interview. An astounding 77% are guilty of using their cell phones or texting during the interview! A researcher wanted to see if the proportion of male offenders differed from the proportion of female ones. Out of 120 males, 72 used their cell phone and 80 of 150 females did so. At the 0.01 level of significance is there a difference?

Source: Careerbuilder.com

24. **Medical Supply Sales** According to the U.S. Bureau of Labor Statistics, approximately equal numbers of men and women are engaged in sales and related occupations. Although that may be true for total numbers, perhaps the proportions differ by industry. A random sample of 200 salespersons from the industrial sector indicated that 114 were men, and in the medical supply sector, 80 of 200 were men. At the 0.05 level of significance, can we conclude that the proportion of men in industrial sales differs from the proportion of men in medical supply sales?

25. **Coupon Use** In today's economy, everyone has become savings savvy. It is still believed, though, that a higher percentage of women than men clip coupons. A random survey of 180 female shoppers indicated that 132 clipped coupons while 56 out of 100 men did so. At $\alpha = 0.01$, is there sufficient evidence that the proportion of couponing women is higher than the proportion of couponing men? Use the *P*-value method.

26. **Never Married People** The percentage of males 18 years and older who have never married is 30.4. For females the percentage is 23.6. Looking at the records in a particular populous county, a random sample of 250 men showed that 78 had never married and 58 of 200 women had never married. At the 0.05 level of significance, is the proportion of men greater than the proportion of women? Use the *P*-value method.

27. Bullying Bullying is a problem at any age but especially for students aged 12 to 18. A study showed that 7.2% of all students in this age bracket reported being bullied at school during the past six months with 6th grade having the highest incidence at 13.9% and 12th grade the lowest at 2.2%. To see if there is a difference between public and private schools, 200 students were randomly selected from each. At the 0.05 level of significance, can a difference be concluded?

	Private	Public
Sample size	200	200
No. bullied	13	16

Source: www.nces.ed.gov

Extending the Concepts

28. If there is a significant difference between p_1 and p_2 and between p_2 and p_3, can you conclude that there is a significant difference between p_1 and p_3?

Technology

Step by Step

TI-84 Plus
Step by Step

Hypothesis Test for the Difference Between Two Proportions

Example TI9–8

1. Press **STAT** and move the cursor to TESTS.
2. Press **6** for 2-PropZTEST.
3. Type in the appropriate values.
4. Move the cursor to the appropriate alternative hypothesis and press **ENTER**.
5. Move the cursor to Calculate and press **ENTER**.

This refers to Example 9–9 in the text.

Confidence Interval for the Difference Between Two Proportions

Example TI9–9

1. Press **STAT** and move the cursor to TESTS.
2. Press **B (ALPHA APPS)** for 2-PropZInt.
3. Type in the appropriate values.
4. Move the cursor to Calculate and press **ENTER**.

This refers to Example 9–11 in the text.

EXCEL
Step by Step

Testing the Difference Between Two Proportions

Excel does not have a procedure to test the difference between two population proportions. However, you may conduct this test using the MegaStat Add-in available in your online resources. If you have not installed this add-in, do so, following the instructions from the Chapter 1 Excel Step by Step.

We will use the summary information from Example 9–9.

1. From the toolbar, select Add-Ins, **MegaStat>Hypothesis Tests>Compare Two Independent Proportions**. *Note:* You may need to open MegaStat from the MegaStat.xls file on your computer's hard drive.

2. Under Group 1, type **12** for p and **34** for n. Under Group 2, type **17** for p and **24** for n. MegaStat automatically changes p to X unless a decimal value less than 1 is typed in for these.

3. Type **0** for the Hypothesized difference, select the not equal Alternative, and click [OK].

Hypothesis Test for Two Independent Proportions

p_1	p_2		p_c	
0.3529	0.7083		0.5	p (as decimal)
12/34	17/24		29/58	p (as fraction)
12.	17.		29.	X
34	24		58	n
	−0.3554	Difference		
	0.	Hypothesized difference		
	0.1333	Standard error		
	−2.67	z		
	0.0077	P-value (two-tailed)		

MINITAB
Step by Step

Test the Difference Between Two Proportions

For Example 9–9, test for a difference in the resident vaccination rates between small and large nursing homes.

1. This test does not require data. It doesn't matter what is in the worksheet.
2. Select **Stat>Basic Statistics>2 Proportions**.
3. Click the button for Summarized data.
4. Press **TAB** to move cursor to the first sample box for Trials.
    a) Enter **34, TAB,** then enter **12.**
    b) Press **TAB** or click in the second sample text box for Trials.
    c) Enter **24, TAB,** then enter **17.**
5. Click on [Options]. Check the box for Use pooled estimate of p for test. The Confidence level should be 95%, and the Test difference should be 0.
6. Click [OK] twice. The results are shown in the session window.

Test and CI for Two Proportions

Sample	X	N	Sample p
1	12	34	0.352941
2	17	24	0.708333

Difference = p (1) − p (2)
Estimate for difference: −0.355392
95% CI for difference: (−0.598025, −0.112759)
Test for difference = 0 (vs not = 0): Z = −2.67 P-Value = 0.008

The *P*-value of the test is 0.008. Reject the null hypothesis. The difference is statistically significant. Of all small nursing homes 35%, compared to 71% of all large nursing homes, have an immunization rate of less than 80%. We can't tell why, only that there is a difference.

9–5   Testing the Difference Between Two Variances

OBJECTIVE 5

Test the difference between two variances or standard deviations.

In addition to comparing two means, statisticians are interested in comparing two variances or standard deviations. For example, is the variation in the temperatures for a certain month for two cities different?

In another situation, a researcher may be interested in comparing the variance of the cholesterol of men with the variance of the cholesterol of women. For the comparison of two variances or standard deviations, an *F* **test** is used. The *F* test should not be confused with the chi-square test, which compares a single sample variance to a specific population variance, as shown in Chapter 8.

FIGURE 9–10
The *F* Family of Curves

Figure 9–10 shows the shapes of several curves for the *F* distribution.

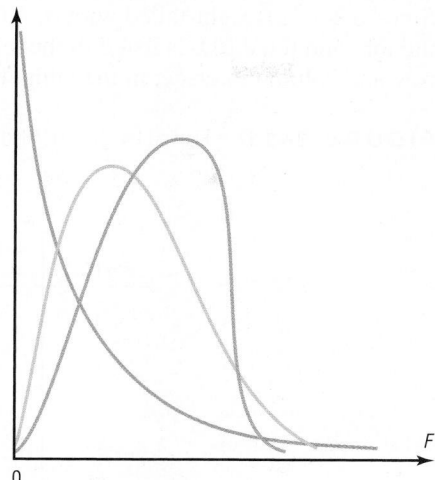

If two independent samples are selected from two normally distributed populations in which the population variances are equal ($\sigma_1^2 = \sigma_2^2$) and if the sample variances s_1^2 and s_2^2 are compared as $\dfrac{s_1^2}{s_2^2}$, the sampling distribution of the variances is called the ***F* distribution.**

Characteristics of the *F* Distribution

1. The values of *F* cannot be negative, because variances are always positive or zero.
2. The distribution is positively skewed.
3. The mean value of *F* is approximately equal to 1.
4. The *F* distribution is a family of curves based on the degrees of freedom of the variance of the numerator and the degrees of freedom of the variance of the denominator.

Formula for the *F* Test

$$F = \frac{s_1^2}{s_2^2}$$

where the larger of the two variances is placed in the numerator regardless of the subscripts. (See note on page 534.)

The *F* test has two values for the degrees of freedom: that of the numerator, $n_1 - 1$, and that of the denominator, $n_2 - 1$, where n_1 is the sample size from which the larger variance was obtained.

When you are finding the *F* test value, *the larger of the variances is placed in the numerator of the F formula;* this is not necessarily the variance of the larger of the two sample sizes.

Table H in Appendix A gives the *F* critical values for $\alpha = 0.005, 0.01, 0.025, 0.05,$ and 0.10 (each α value involves a separate table in Table H). These are one-tailed values; if a two-tailed test is being conducted, then the $\alpha/2$ value must be used. For example, if a two-tailed test with $\alpha = 0.05$ is being conducted, then the $0.05/2 = 0.025$ table of Table H should be used.

EXAMPLE 9–12

Find the critical value for a right-tailed *F* test when $\alpha = 0.05$, the degrees of freedom for the numerator (abbreviated d.f.N.) are 15, and the degrees of freedom for the denominator (d.f.D.) are 21.

SOLUTION

Since this test is right-tailed with $\alpha = 0.05$, use the 0.05 table. The d.f.N. is listed across the top, and the d.f.D. is listed in the left column. The critical value is found where the row and column intersect in the table. In this case, it is 2.18. See Figure 9–11.

FIGURE 9–11   Finding the Critical Value in Table H for Example 9–12

$\alpha = \mathbf{0.05}$

	d.f.N.				
d.f.D.	1	2	···	14	15
1					
2					
⋮					
20					
21					2.18
22					
⋮					

As noted previously, when the F test is used, the larger variance is always placed in the numerator of the formula. When you are conducting a two-tailed test, α is split; and even though there are two values, only the right tail is used. The reason is that the F test value is always greater than or equal to 1.

EXAMPLE 9–13

Find the critical value for a two-tailed F test with $\alpha = 0.05$ when the sample size from which the variance for the numerator was obtained was 21 and the sample size from which the variance for the denominator was obtained was 12.

SOLUTION

Since this is a two-tailed test with $\alpha = 0.05$, the $0.05/2 = 0.025$ table must be used. Here, d.f.N. $= 21 - 1 = 20$, and d.f.D. $= 12 - 1 = 11$; hence, the critical value is 3.23. See Figure 9–12.

FIGURE 9–12   Finding the Critical Value in Table H for Example 9–13

$\alpha = \mathbf{0.025}$

	d.f.N.			
d.f.D.	1	2	···	20
1				
2				
⋮				
10				
11				3.23
12				
⋮				

If the exact degrees of freedom are not specified in Table H, the closest smaller value should be used. For example, if $\alpha = 0.05$ (right-tailed test), d.f.N. = 18, and d.f.D. = 20, use the column d.f.N. = 15 and the row d.f.D. = 20 to get $F = 2.20$. Using the smaller value is the more conservative approach.

When you are testing the equality of two variances, these hypotheses are used:

Right-tailed	Left-tailed	Two-tailed
$H_0: \sigma_1^2 = \sigma_2^2$	$H_0: \sigma_1^2 = \sigma_2^2$	$H_0: \sigma_1^2 = \sigma_2^2$
$H_1: \sigma_1^2 > \sigma_2^2$	$H_1: \sigma_1^2 < \sigma_2^2$	$H_1: \sigma_1^2 \neq \sigma_2^2$

There are four key points to keep in mind when you are using the F test.

Unusual Stat

Of all U.S. births, 2% are twins.

Notes for the Use of the F Test

1. The larger variance should always be placed in the numerator of the formula regardless of the subscripts. (See note on page 534.)

$$F = \frac{s_1^2}{s_2^2}$$

2. For a two-tailed test, the α value must be divided by 2 and the critical value placed on the right side of the F curve.
3. If the standard deviations instead of the variances are given in the problem, they must be squared for the formula for the F test.
4. When the degrees of freedom cannot be found in Table H, the closest value on the smaller side should be used.

Before you can use the testing method to determine the difference between two variances, the following assumptions must be met.

Assumptions for Testing the Difference Between Two Variances

1. The samples must be random samples.
2. The populations from which the samples were obtained must be normally distributed. (*Note:* The test should not be used when the distributions depart from normality.)
3. The samples must be independent of one another.

In this book, the assumptions will be stated in the exercises; however, when encountering statistics in other situations, you must check to see that these assumptions have been met before proceeding.

Remember also that in tests of hypotheses using the traditional method, these five steps should be taken:

Step 1 State the hypotheses and identify the claim.

Step 2 Find the critical value.

Step 3 Compute the test value.

Step 4 Make the decision.

Step 5 Summarize the results.

This procedure is not robust, so minor departures from normality will affect the results of the test. So this test should not be used when the distributions depart from normality because standard deviations are not a good measure of the spread in nonsymmetrical distributions. The reason is that the standard deviation is not resistant to outliers or extreme values. These values increase the value of the standard deviation when the distribution is skewed.

EXAMPLE 9–14   Heart Rates of Smokers

A medical researcher wishes to see whether the variance of the heart rates (in beats per minute) of smokers is different from the variance of heart rates of people who do not smoke. Two samples are selected, and the data are shown. Using $\alpha = 0.05$, is there enough evidence to support the claim? Assume the variable is normally distributed.

Smokers	Nonsmokers
$n_1 = 26$	$n_2 = 18$
$s_1^2 = 36$	$s_2^2 = 10$

SOLUTION

Step 1   State the hypotheses and identify the claim.

$$H_0: \sigma_1^2 = \sigma_2^2 \quad \text{and} \quad H_1: \sigma_1^2 \neq \sigma_2^2 \text{ (claim)}$$

Step 2   Find the critical value. Use the 0.025 table in Table H since $\alpha = 0.05$ and this is a two-tailed test. Here, d.f.N. $= 26 - 1 = 25$, and d.f.D. $= 18 - 1 = 17$. The critical value is 2.56 (d.f.N. $= 24$ was used). See Figure 9–13.

FIGURE 9–13   Critical Value for Example 9–14

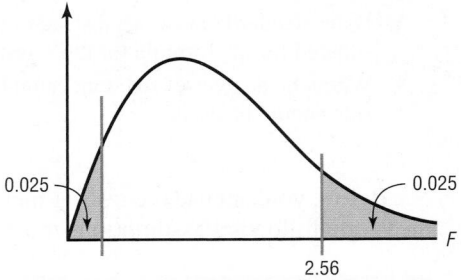

Step 3   Compute the test value.

$$F = \frac{s_1^2}{s_2^2} = \frac{36}{10} = 3.6$$

Step 4   Make the decision. Reject the null hypothesis, since $3.6 > 2.56$.

Step 5   Summarize the results. There is enough evidence to support the claim that the variance of the heart rates of smokers and nonsmokers is different.

EXAMPLE 9–15   Noise Levels of Power Mowers

The mean noise level of a random sample of 16 riding power mowers is 93.2 decibels, and the standard deviation is 4.3 decibels, while the mean noise level of a random sample of 12 push power mowers is 89.5 decibels and the standard deviation is 3.6 decibels. Is there enough evidence at $\alpha = 0.01$ to conclude that the variance of the noise levels of the riding power mowers is greater than the variance of the noise levels of the push power mowers? Assume the noise levels of both types of power mowers are normally distributed.

SOLUTION

Step 1   State the hypotheses and identify the claim.

$$H_0: \sigma_1^2 = \sigma_2^2 \quad \text{and} \quad H_1: \sigma_1^2 > \sigma_2^2 \text{ (claim)}$$

Step 2   Find the critical value. Here, d.f.N. $= 16 - 1 = 15$, and d.f.D. $= 12 - 1 = 11$. From Table H at $\alpha = 0.01$, the critical value is 4.25.

Step 3   Compute the test value.

$$F = \frac{s_1^2}{s_2^2} = \frac{4.3^2}{3.6^2} = 1.43$$

Step 4   Make the decision. Do not reject the null hypothesis since 1.43 does not fall in the critical region, so $1.43 < 4.25$. See Figure 9–14.

FIGURE 9–14   Critical Value and Test Value for Example 9–15.

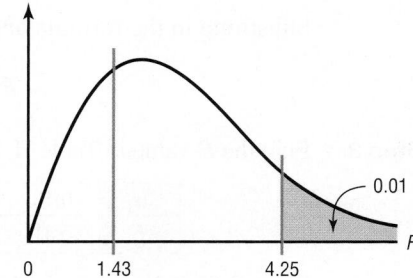

Step 5   Summarize the results. There is not enough evidence to support the claim that the variance of the noise levels of the riding power mowers is greater than the variance of the noise levels of the push power mowers.

Finding P-values for the F test statistic is somewhat more complicated since it requires looking through all the F tables (Table H in Appendix A) using the specific d.f.N. and d.f.D. values. For example, suppose that a certain test has $F = 3.58$, d.f.N. $= 5$, and d.f.D. $= 10$. To find the P-value interval for $F = 3.58$, you must first find the corresponding F values for d.f.N. $= 5$ and d.f.D. $= 10$ for α equal to 0.005, 0.01, 0.025, 0.05, and 0.10 in Table H. Then make a table as shown.

α	0.10	0.05	0.025	0.01	0.005
F	2.52	3.33	4.24	5.64	6.87

Now locate the two F values that the test value 3.58 falls between. In this case, 3.58 falls between 3.33 and 4.24, corresponding to 0.05 and 0.025. Hence, the P-value for a right-tailed test for $F = 3.58$ falls between 0.025 and 0.05 (that is, $0.025 < P$-value < 0.05). For a right-tailed test, then, you would reject the null hypothesis at $\alpha = 0.05$, but not at $\alpha = 0.01$. The P-value obtained from a calculator is 0.0408. Remember that for a two-tailed test the values found in Table H for α must be doubled. In this case, $0.05 < P$-value < 0.10 for $F = 3.58$. Once again, if the P-value is less than α, we reject the null hypothesis.

Once you understand the concept, you can dispense with making a table as shown and find the P-value directly from Table H.

EXAMPLE 9–16   Airport Passengers

The CEO of an airport hypothesizes that the variance in the number of passengers for American airports is greater than the variance in the number of passengers for foreign airports. At $\alpha = 0.10$, is there enough evidence to support the hypothesis? The data in millions of passengers per year are shown for selected airports. Use the P-value method. Assume the variable is normally distributed and the samples are random and independent.

American airports		Foreign airports	
36.8	73.5	60.7	51.2
72.4	61.2	42.7	38.6
60.5	40.1		

Source: Airports Council International.

SOLUTION

Step 1 State the hypotheses and identify the claim.

$$H_0: \sigma_1^2 = \sigma_2^2 \qquad \text{and} \qquad H_1: \sigma_1^2 > \sigma_2^2 \text{ (claim)}$$

Step 2 Compute the test value. Using the formula in Chapter 3 or a calculator, find the variance for each group.

$$s_1^2 = 246.38 \qquad \text{and} \qquad s_2^2 = 95.87$$

Substitute in the formula and solve.

$$F = \frac{s_1^2}{s_2^2} = \frac{246.38}{95.87} = 2.57$$

Step 3 Find the P-value in Table H, using d.f.N. = 6 − 1 = 5 and d.f.D. = 4 − 1 = 3.

α	0.10	0.05	0.025	0.01	0.005
F	5.31	9.01	14.88	28.24	45.39

Since 2.57 is less than 5.31, the P-value is greater than 0.10. (The P-value obtained from a calculator is 0.234.)

Step 4 Make the decision. The decision is to not reject the null hypothesis since P-value > 0.10.

Step 5 Summarize the results. There is not enough evidence to support the claim that the variance in the number of passengers for American airports is greater than the variance in the number of passengers for foreign airports.

Note: It is not absolutely necessary to place the larger variance in the numerator when you are performing the F test. Critical values for left-tailed hypotheses tests can be found by interchanging the degrees of freedom and taking the reciprocal of the value found in Table H.

Also, you should use caution when performing the F test since the data can run contrary to the hypotheses on rare occasions. For example, if the hypotheses are $H_0: \sigma_1^2 \leq \sigma_2^2$ (written $H_0: \sigma_1^2 = \sigma_2^2$) and $H_1: \sigma_1^2 > \sigma_2^2$, but if $s_1^2 < s_2^2$, then the F test should not be performed and you would not reject the null hypothesis.

≡ Applying the Concepts 9–5

Automatic Transmissions

Assume the following data values are from the June 1996 issue of *Automotive Magazine*. An article compared various parameters of U.S.- and Japanese-made sports cars. This report centers on the price of an optional automatic transmission. Which country has the greater variability in the price of automatic transmissions? Answer the following questions.

Japanese cars		U.S. cars	
Nissan 300ZX	$1940	Dodge Stealth	$2363
Mazda RX7	1810	Saturn	1230
Mazda MX6	1871	Mercury Cougar	1332
Nissan NX	1822	Ford Probe	932
Mazda Miata	1920	Eagle Talon	1790
Honda Prelude	1730	Chevy Lumina	1833

1. What is the null hypothesis?
2. What test statistic is used to test for any significant differences in the variances?

3. Is there a significant difference in the variability in the prices between the Japanese cars and the U.S. cars?

4. What effect does a small sample size have on the standard deviations?

5. What degrees of freedom are used for the statistical test?

6. Could two sets of data have significantly different variances without having significantly different means?

See page 546 for the answers.

Exercises 9–5

1. When one is computing the F test value, what condition is placed on the variance that is in the numerator?

2. Why is the critical region always on the right side in the use of the F test?

3. What are the two different degrees of freedom associated with the F distribution?

4. What are the characteristics of the F distribution?

5. Using Table H, find the critical value for each.

   a. Sample 1: $s_1^2 = 128$, $n_1 = 23$
   Sample 2: $s_2^2 = 162$, $n_2 = 16$
   Two-tailed, $\alpha = 0.01$

   b. Sample 1: $s_1^2 = 37$, $n_1 = 14$
   Sample 2: $s_2^2 = 89$, $n_2 = 25$
   Right-tailed, $\alpha = 0.01$

   c. Sample 1: $s_1^2 = 232$, $n_1 = 30$
   Sample 2: $s_2^2 = 387$, $n_2 = 46$
   Two-tailed, $\alpha = 0.05$

6. Using Table H, find the critical value for each.

   a. Sample 1: $s_1^2 = 27.3$, $n_1 = 5$
   Sample 2: $s_2^2 = 38.6$, $n_2 = 9$
   Right-tailed, $\alpha = 0.01$

   b. Sample 1: $s_1^2 = 164$, $n_1 = 21$
   Sample 2: $s_2^2 = 53$, $n_2 = 17$
   Two-tailed, $\alpha = 0.10$

   c. Sample 1: $s_1^2 = 92.8$, $n_1 = 11$
   Sample 2: $s_2^2 = 43.6$, $n_2 = 11$
   Right-tailed, $\alpha = 0.05$

7. Using Table H, find the P-value interval for each F test value.

   a. $F = 2.97$, d.f.N. $= 9$, d.f.D. $= 14$, right-tailed

   b. $F = 3.32$, d.f.N. $= 6$, d.f.D. $= 12$, two-tailed

   c. $F = 2.28$, d.f.N. $= 12$, d.f.D. $= 20$, right-tailed

   d. $F = 3.51$, d.f.N. $= 12$, d.f.D. $= 21$, right-tailed

8. Using Table H, find the P-value interval for each F test value.

   a. $F = 4.07$, d.f.N. $= 6$, d.f.D. $= 10$, two-tailed

   b. $F = 1.65$, d.f.N. $= 19$, d.f.D. $= 28$, right-tailed

   c. $F = 1.77$, d.f.N. $= 28$, d.f.D. $= 28$, right-tailed

   d. $F = 7.29$, d.f.N. $= 5$, d.f.D. $= 8$, two-tailed

For Exercises 9 through 24, perform the following steps. Assume that all variables are normally distributed.

   a. State the hypotheses and identify the claim.

   b. Find the critical value.

   c. Compute the test value.

   d. Make the decision.

   e. Summarize the results.

Use the traditional method of hypothesis testing unless otherwise specified.

9. **Wolf Pack Pups** Does the variance in the number of pups per pack differ between Montana and Idaho wolf packs? Random samples of packs were selected for each area, and the numbers of pups per pack were recorded. At the 0.05 level of significance, can a difference in variances be concluded?

Montana wolf packs	4	3	5	6	1	2	8	2
	3	1	7	6	5			
Idaho wolf packs	2	4	5	4	2	4	6	3
	1	4	2	1				

Source: www.fws.gov

10. **Noise Levels in Hospitals** In a hospital study, it was found that the standard deviation of the sound levels from 20 randomly selected areas designated as "casualty doors" was 4.1 dBA and the standard deviation of 24 randomly selected areas designated as operating theaters was 7.5 dBA. At $\alpha = 0.05$, can you substantiate the claim that there is a difference in the standard deviations?

Source: M. Bayo, A. Garcia, and A. Garcia, "Noise Levels in an Urban Hospital and Workers' Subjective Responses," *Archives of Environmental Health.*

11. Calories in Ice Cream The numbers of calories contained in $\frac{1}{2}$-cup servings of randomly selected flavors of ice cream from two national brands are listed. At the 0.05 level of significance, is there sufficient evidence to conclude that the variance in the number of calories differs between the two brands?

Brand A		Brand B	
330	300	280	310
310	350	300	370
270	380	250	300
310	300	290	310

Source: *The Doctor's Pocket Calorie, Fat and Carbohydrate Counter.*

12. Winter Temperatures A random sample of daily high temperatures in January and February is listed. At $\alpha = 0.05$, can it be concluded that there is a difference in variances in high temperature between the two months?

Jan.	31	31	38	24	24	42	22	43	35	42
Feb.	31	29	24	30	28	24	27	34	27	

13. Population and Area Cities were randomly selected from the list of the 50 largest cities in the United States (based on population). The areas of each in square miles are shown. Is there sufficient evidence to conclude that the variance in area is greater for eastern cities than for western cities at $\alpha = 0.05$? At $\alpha = 0.01$?

Eastern		Western	
Atlanta, GA	132	Albuquerque, NM	181
Columbus, OH	210	Denver, CO	155
Louisville, KY	385	Fresno, CA	104
New York, NY	303	Las Vegas, NV	113
Philadelphia, PA	135	Portland, OR	134
Washington, DC	61	Seattle, WA	84
Charlotte, NC	242		

Source: *New York Times Almanac.*

14. Carbohydrates in Candy The number of grams of carbohydrates contained in 1-ounce servings of randomly selected chocolate and nonchocolate candy is shown. Is there sufficient evidence to conclude that there is a difference between the variation in carbohydrate content for chocolate and nonchocolate candy? Use $\alpha = 0.10$.

Chocolate	29	25	17	36	41	25	32	29
	38	34	24	27	29			
Nonchocolate	41	41	37	29	30	38	39	10
	29	55	29					

Source: *The Doctor's Pocket Calorie, Fat and Carbohydrate Counter.*

15. Tuition Costs for Medical School The yearly tuition costs in dollars for random samples of medical schools that specialize in research and in primary care are listed. At $\alpha = 0.05$, can it be concluded that

a difference between the variances of the two groups exists?

Research			Primary care		
30,897	34,280	31,943	26,068	21,044	30,897
34,294	31,275	29,590	34,208	20,877	29,691
20,618	20,500	29,310	33,783	33,065	35,000
21,274			27,297		

Source: *U.S. News & World Report Best Graduate Schools.*

16. County Size in Indiana and Iowa A researcher wishes to see if the variance of the areas in square miles for counties in Indiana is less than the variance of the areas for counties in Iowa. A random sample of counties is selected, and the data are shown. At $\alpha = 0.01$, can it be concluded that the variance of the areas for counties in Indiana is less than the variance of the areas for counties in Iowa?

Indiana				Iowa			
406	393	396	485	640	580	431	416
431	430	369	408	443	569	779	381
305	215	489	293	717	568	714	731
373	148	306	509	571	577	503	501
560	384	320	407	568	434	615	402

Source: *The World Almanac and Book of Facts.*

17. Heights of Tall Buildings Test the claim that the variance of heights of randomly selected tall buildings in Denver is equal to the variance in heights of randomly selected tall buildings in Detroit at $\alpha = 0.10$. The data are given in feet.

Denver			Detroit		
714	698	544	620	472	430
504	438	408	562	448	420
404			534	436	

Source: *The World Almanac and Book of Facts.*

18. Reading Program Summer reading programs are very popular with children. At the Citizens Library, Team Ramona read an average of 23.2 books with a standard deviation of 6.1. There were 21 members on this team. Team Beezus read an average of 26.1 books with a standard deviation of 2.3. There were 23 members on this team. Did the variances of the two teams differ? Use $\alpha = 0.05$.

19. Weights of Running Shoes The weights in ounces of a random sample of running shoes for men and women are shown. Calculate the variances for each sample, and test the claim that the variances are equal at $\alpha = 0.05$. Use the *P*-value method.

Men			Women		
11.9	10.4	12.6	10.6	10.2	8.8
12.3	11.1	14.7	9.6	9.5	9.5
9.2	10.8	12.9	10.1	11.2	9.3
11.2	11.7	13.3	9.4	10.3	9.5
13.8	12.8	14.5	9.8	10.3	11.0

20. School Teachers' Salaries A researcher claims that the variation in the salaries of elementary school teachers is greater than the variation in the salaries of secondary school teachers. A random sample of the salaries of 30 elementary school teachers has a variance of $8324, and a random sample of the salaries of 30 secondary school teachers has a variance of $2862. At $\alpha = 0.05$, can the researcher conclude that the variation in the elementary school teachers' salaries is greater than the variation in the secondary school teachers' salaries? Use the P-value method.

21. **Numismatist Meeting** At a local county collectors' meeting, fourteen numismatists presented an average of 12.7 items with a standard deviation of 2.4. Nine philatelists presented an average of 10.9 items each with a standard deviation of 4.6. At the 0.05 level of significance, can a difference in variances be concluded?

22. **Daily Stock Prices** Two portfolios were randomly assembled from the New York Stock Exchange, and the daily stock prices are shown. At the 0.05 level of significance, can it be concluded that a difference in variance in price exists between the two portfolios?

Portfolio A	36.44	44.21	12.21	59.60	55.44	39.42	51.29	48.68	41.59	19.49
Portfolio B	32.69	47.25	49.35	36.17	63.04	17.74	4.23	34.98	37.02	31.48

Source: *Washington Observer-Reporter.*

23. **Ages of Hospital Patients** The average age of hospital inpatients has gradually increased to 52.5 years. Studies of two major health care systems found the following information. At the 0.05 level of significance, is there sufficient evidence to conclude a difference between the two variances?

	System 1	System 2
Sample size	60	60
Sample mean	49.8	50.2
Sample standard deviation	5.4	7.6

Source: *New York Times Almanac.*

24. **Museum Attendance** A metropolitan children's museum open year-round wants to see if the variance in daily attendance differs between the summer and winter months. Random samples of 30 days each were selected and showed that in the winter months, the sample mean daily attendance was 300 with a standard deviation of 52, and the sample mean daily attendance for the summer months was 280 with a standard deviation of 65. At $\alpha = 0.05$, can we conclude a difference in variances?

≣Technology Step by Step

TI-84 Plus
Step by Step

Hypothesis Test for the Difference Between Two Variances (Data)

1. Enter the data values into L₁ and L₂.
2. Press **STAT** and move the cursor to TESTS.
3. Press **E (ALPHA SIN)** for 2-SampFTest.
4. Move the cursor to Data and press **ENTER**.
5. Type in the appropriate values.
6. Move the cursor to the appropriate Alternative hypothesis and press **ENTER**.
7. Move the cursor to Calculate and press **ENTER**.

Hypothesis Test for the Difference Between Two Variances (Statistics)

Example TI9–10

1. Press **STAT** and move the cursor to TESTS.
2. Press **E (ALPHA SIN)** for 2-SampFTest.
3. Move the cursor to Stats and press **ENTER**.
4. Type in the appropriate values.
5. Move the cursor to the appropriate Alternative hypothesis and press **ENTER**.
6. Move the cursor to Calculate and press **ENTER**.

This refers to Example 9–14 in the text.

EXCEL
Step by Step

F Test for the Difference Between Two Variances

Excel has a two-sample *F* test included in the Data Analysis Add-in. To perform an *F* test for the difference between the variances of two populations, given two independent samples, do this:

1. Enter the first sample data set into column A.
2. Enter the second sample data set into column B.
3. Select the Data tab from the toolbar. Then select Data Analysis.
4. In the Analysis Tools box, select F-test: Two-sample for Variances.
5. Type the ranges for the data in columns A and B.
6. Specify the confidence level Alpha.
7. Specify a location for the output, and click [OK].

Example XL9–4

At $\alpha = 0.05$, test the hypothesis that the two population variances are equal, using the sample data provided here.

Set A	63	73	80	60	86	83	70	72	82
Set B	86	93	64	82	81	75	88	63	63

The results appear in the table that Excel generates, shown here. For this example, the output shows that the null hypothesis cannot be rejected at an α level of 0.05.

F-Test Two-Sample for Variances		
	Variable 1	*Variable 2*
Mean	74.33333333	77.22222222
Variance	82.75	132.9444444
Observations	9	9
df	8	8
F	0.622440451	
P(F<=f) one-tail	0.258814151	
F Critical one-tail	0.290858004	

MINITAB
Step by Step

Test for the Difference Between Two Variances

For Example 9–16, test the hypothesis that the variance in the number of passengers for American and foreign airports is different. Use the *P*-value approach.

American airports	Foreign airports
36.8	60.7
72.4	42.7
60.5	51.2
73.5	38.6
61.2	
40.1	

1. Enter the data into two columns of MINITAB.

2. Name the columns American and Foreign.

   a) Select **Stat>Basic Statistics>2-Variances.**

   b) Click the button for **Samples in different columns.**

   c) Click in the text box for **First**, then double-click **C1 American.**

   d) Double-click **C2 Foreign**, then click on [Options]. The dialog box is shown. Change the confidence level to **90** and type an appropriate title. In this dialog, we cannot specify a left- or right-tailed test.

3. Click [OK] twice. A graph window will open that includes a small window that says $F = 2.57$ and the P-value is 0.467. Divide this two-tailed P-value by 2 for a one-tailed test.

There is not enough evidence in the sample to conclude there is greater variance in the number of passengers in American airports compared to foreign airports.

Summary

Many times researchers are interested in comparing two parameters such as two means, two proportions, or two variances. These measures are obtained from two samples, then compared using a z test, t test, or an F test.

- If two sample means are compared, when the samples are independent and the population standard deviations are known, a z test is used. If the sample sizes are less than 30, the populations should be normally distributed. (9–1)

- If two means are compared when the samples are independent and the sample standard deviations are used, then a t test is used. The two variances are assumed to be unequal. (9–2)

- When the two samples are dependent or related, such as using the same subjects and comparing the means of before-and-after tests, then the t test for dependent samples is used. (9–3)

- Two proportions can be compared by using the z test for proportions. In this case, each of $n_1 p_1$, $n_1 q_1$, $n_2 p_2$, and $n_2 q_2$ must all be 5 or more. (9–4)

- Two variances can be compared by using an F test. The critical values for the F test are obtained from the F distribution. (9–5)

- Confidence intervals for differences between two parameters can also be found.

Important Terms

dependent samples 507

F distribution 529

F test 528

independent samples 499

pooled estimate of the variance 502

▤ Important Formulas

Formula for the z test for comparing two means from independent populations; σ_1 and σ_2 are known:

$$z = \frac{(\bar{X}_1 - \bar{X}_2) - (\mu_1 - \mu_2)}{\sqrt{\dfrac{\sigma_1^2}{n_1} + \dfrac{\sigma_2^2}{n_2}}}$$

Formula for the confidence interval for difference of two means when σ_1 and σ_2 are known:

$$(\bar{X}_1 - \bar{X}_2) - z_{\alpha/2}\sqrt{\dfrac{\sigma_1^2}{n_1} + \dfrac{\sigma_2^2}{n_2}} < \mu_1 - \mu_2$$
$$< (\bar{X}_1 - \bar{X}_2) + z_{\alpha/2}\sqrt{\dfrac{\sigma_1^2}{n_1} + \dfrac{\sigma_2^2}{n_2}}$$

Formula for the t test for comparing two means (independent samples, variances not equal), σ_1 and σ_2 unknown:

$$t = \frac{(\bar{X}_1 - \bar{X}_2) - (\mu_1 - \mu_2)}{\sqrt{\dfrac{s_1^2}{n_1} + \dfrac{s_2^2}{n_2}}}$$

and d.f. = the smaller of $n_1 - 1$ or $n_2 - 1$.

Formula for the confidence interval for the difference of two means (independent samples, variances unequal), σ_1 and σ_2 unknown:

$$(\bar{X}_1 - \bar{X}_2) - t_{\alpha/2}\sqrt{\dfrac{s_1^2}{n_1} + \dfrac{s_2^2}{n_2}} < \mu_1 - \mu_2$$
$$< (\bar{X}_1 - \bar{X}_2) + t_{\alpha/2}\sqrt{\dfrac{s_1^2}{n_1} + \dfrac{s_2^2}{n_2}}$$

and d.f. = smaller of $n_1 - 1$ and $n_2 - 1$.

Formula for the t test for comparing two means from dependent samples:

$$t = \frac{\bar{D} - \mu_D}{s_D/\sqrt{n}}$$

where $\bar{D}$ is the mean of the differences

$$\bar{D} = \frac{\Sigma D}{n}$$

and s_D is the standard deviation of the differences

$$s_D = \sqrt{\frac{n\Sigma D^2 - (\Sigma D)^2}{n(n - 1)}}$$

Formula for confidence interval for the mean of the difference for dependent samples:

$$\bar{D} - t_{\alpha/2}\frac{s_D}{\sqrt{n}} < \mu_D < \bar{D} + t_{\alpha/2}\frac{s_D}{\sqrt{n}}$$

and d.f. = $n - 1$.

Formula for the z test for comparing two proportions:

$$z = \frac{(\hat{p}_1 - \hat{p}_2) - (p_1 - p_2)}{\sqrt{\bar{p}\,\bar{q}\left(\dfrac{1}{n_1} + \dfrac{1}{n_2}\right)}}$$

where

$$\bar{p} = \frac{X_1 + X_2}{n_1 + n_2} \qquad \hat{p}_1 = \frac{X_1}{n_1}$$
$$\bar{q} = 1 - \bar{p} \qquad \hat{p}_2 = \frac{X_2}{n_2}$$

Formula for confidence interval for the difference of two proportions:

$$(\hat{p}_1 - \hat{p}_2) - z_{\alpha/2}\sqrt{\dfrac{\hat{p}_1\hat{q}_1}{n_1} + \dfrac{\hat{p}_2\hat{q}_2}{n_2}} < p_1 - p_2$$
$$< (\hat{p}_1 - \hat{p}_2) + z_{\alpha/2}\sqrt{\dfrac{\hat{p}_1\hat{q}_1}{n_1} + \dfrac{\hat{p}_2\hat{q}_2}{n_2}}$$

Formula for the F test for comparing two variances:

$$F = \frac{s_1^2}{s_2^2} \qquad \begin{array}{l} \text{d.f.N.} = n_1 - 1 \\ \text{d.f.D.} = n_2 - 1 \end{array}$$

The larger variance is placed in the numerator.

▤ Review Exercises

For each exercise, perform these steps. Assume that all variables are normally or approximately normally distributed.

    a. State the hypotheses and identify the claim.
    b. Find the critical value(s).
    c. Compute the test value.
    d. Make the decision.
    e. Summarize the results.

Use the traditional method of hypothesis testing unless otherwise specified.

Section 9–1

1. Driving for Pleasure Two groups of randomly selected drivers are surveyed to see how many miles per week they drive for pleasure trips. The data are shown. At $\alpha = 0.01$, can it be concluded that single drivers do more driving for pleasure trips on average than married drivers? Assume $\sigma_1 = 16.7$ and $\sigma_2 = 16.1$.

Single drivers					Married drivers				
106	110	115	121	132	97	104	138	102	115
119	97	118	122	135	133	120	119	136	96
110	117	116	138	142	139	108	117	145	114
115	114	103	98	99	140	136	113	113	150
108	117	152	147	117	101	114	116	113	135
154	86	115	116	104	115	109	147	106	88
107	133	138	142	140	113	119	99	108	105

2. Average Earnings of College Graduates The average yearly earnings of male college graduates (with at least a bachelor's degree) are $58,500 for men aged 25 to 34. The average yearly earnings of female college graduates with the same qualifications are $49,339. Based on the results below, can it be concluded that there is a difference in mean earnings between male and female college graduates? Use the 0.01 level of significance.

	Male	Female
Sample mean	$59,235	$52,487
Population standard deviation	$8,945	$10,125
Sample size	40	35

Source: *New York Times Almanac.*

Section 9–2

3. Hospital Volunteers At a large local hospital 20 teen volunteers worked a total of 172 hours with a standard deviation of 3.6. Thirty senior citizen volunteers worked a total of 366 hours with a standard deviation of 4.2. At $\alpha = 0.01$, can a difference in means be concluded?

4. Average Temperatures The average temperatures for a 25-day period for Birmingham, Alabama, and Chicago, Illinois, are shown. Based on the samples, at $\alpha = 0.10$, can it be concluded that it is warmer in Birmingham?

Birmingham					Chicago				
78	82	68	67	68	70	74	73	60	77
75	73	75	64	68	71	72	71	74	76
62	73	77	78	79	71	80	65	70	83
74	72	73	78	68	67	76	75	62	65
73	79	82	71	66	66	65	77	66	64

5. Teachers' Salaries A random sample of 15 teachers from Rhode Island has an average salary of $35,270, with a standard deviation of $3256. A random sample of 30 teachers from New York has an average salary of $29,512, with a standard deviation of $1432. Is there a significant difference in teachers' salaries between the two states? Use $\alpha = 0.02$. Find the 98% confidence interval for the difference of the two means.

6. Soft Drinks in School The data show the amounts (in thousands of dollars) of the contracts for soft drinks in randomly selected local school districts. At $\alpha = 0.10$, can it be concluded that there is a difference in the averages? Use the *P*-value method. Give a reason why the result would be of concern to a cafeteria manager.

Pepsi						Coca-Cola		
46	120	80	500	100	59	420	285	57

Source: Local school districts.

Section 9–3

7. High and Low Temperatures March is a month of variable weather in the Northeast. The chart shows records of the actual high and low temperatures for a selection of days in March from the weather report for Pittsburgh, Pennsylvania. At the 0.01 level of significance, is there sufficient evidence to conclude that there is more than a 10° difference between average highs and lows?

Maximum	44	46	46	36	34	36	57	62	73	53
Minimum	27	34	24	19	19	26	33	57	46	26

Source: www.wunderground.com

8. Testing After Review A statistics class was given a pretest on probability (since many had previous experience in some other class). Then the class was given a six-page review handout to study for two days. At the next class they were given another test. Is there sufficient evidence that the scores improved? Use $\alpha = 0.05$.

Student	1	2	3	4	5	6
Pretest	52	50	40	58	60	52
Posttest	62	65	50	65	68	63

Section 9–4

9. Lay Teachers in Religious Schools A study found a slightly lower percentage of lay teachers in religious secondary schools than in elementary schools. A random sample of 200 elementary school and 200 secondary school teachers from religious schools in a large diocese found the following. At the 0.05 level of significance, is there sufficient evidence to conclude a difference in proportions?

	Elementary	Secondary
Sample size	200	200
Lay teachers	49	62

Source: *New York Times Almanac.*

10. Cell Phones In 2010, 91% of households had at least one cell phone. A random sample of 300 households in each of two different counties indicated the following. At the 0.01 level of significance, can it be concluded that a difference in proportions exists?

	n	X
County X	300	255
County Y	300	278

Source: *World Almanac 2012.*

Section 9–5

11. Noise Levels in Hospitals In the hospital study cited previously, the standard deviation of the noise levels of the 11 intensive care units was 4.1 dBA, and the standard deviation of the noise levels of 24 nonmedical care areas, such as kitchens and machine rooms, was 13.2 dBA. At $\alpha = 0.10$, is there a significant difference between the standard deviations of these two areas?

Source: M. Bayo, A. Garcia, and A. Garcia, "Noise Levels in an Urban Hospital and Workers' Subjective Responses," *Archives of Environmental Health.*

12. Heights of World Famous Cathedrals The heights (in feet) for a random sample of world famous cathedrals are listed. In addition, the heights for a random sample of the tallest buildings in the world are listed. Is there sufficient evidence at $\alpha = 0.05$ to conclude that there is a difference in the variances in height between the two groups?

Cathedrals	72 114 157 56 83 108 90 151
Tallest buildings	452 442 415 391 355 344 310 302 209

Source: www.infoplease.com

13. Paint Prices Two large home improvement stores advertise that they sell their paint at the same average price per gallon. A random sample of 25 cans from store Y had a standard deviation of $5.21, and store Z had a standard deviation of $4.08 based on a random sample of 20 cans. At $\alpha = 0.05$, can we conclude that the variances are different? How much less would store Z's standard deviation have to be in order to conclude a difference?

≡ STATISTICS TODAY

To Vaccinate or Not to Vaccinate? Small or Large? —Revisited

Using a z test to compare two proportions, the researchers found that the proportion of residents in smaller nursing homes who were vaccinated (80.8%) was statistically greater than that of residents in large nursing homes who were vaccinated (68.7%). Using statistical methods presented in later chapters, they also found that the larger size of the nursing home and the lower frequency of vaccination were significant predictions of influenza outbreaks in nursing homes.

≡ Data Analysis

The Data Bank is found in Appendix B, or on the World Wide Web by following links from www.mhhe.com/math/stat/bluman/

1. From the Data Bank, select a variable and compare the mean of the variable for a random sample of at least 30 men with the mean of the variable for the random sample of at least 30 women. Use a z test.

2. Repeat the experiment in Exercise 1, using a different variable and two samples of size 15. Compare the means by using a t test.

3. Compare the proportion of men who are smokers with the proportion of women who are smokers. Use the data in the Data Bank. Choose random samples of size 30 or more. Use the z test for proportions.

4. Select two samples of 20 values from the data in Data Set IV in Appendix B. Test the hypothesis that the mean heights of the buildings are equal.

5. Using the same data obtained in Exercise 4, test the hypothesis that the variances are equal.

≡ Chapter Quiz

Determine whether each statement is true or false. If the statement is false, explain why.

1. When you are testing the difference between two means, it is not important to distinguish whether the samples are independent of each other.

2. If the same diet is given to two groups of randomly selected individuals, the samples are considered to be dependent.

3. When computing the F test value, you should place the larger variance in the numerator of the fraction.

4. Tests for variances are always two-tailed.

Select the best answer.

5. To test the equality of two variances, you would use a(n) _____ test.

   a. z *c.* Chi-square
   b. t *d.* F

6. To test the equality of two proportions, you would use a(n) _____ test.

   a. z *c.* Chi-square
   b. t *d.* F

7. The mean value of F is approximately equal to

   a. 0   *c.* 1
   b. 0.5   *d.* It cannot be determined.

8. What test can be used to test the difference between two sample means when the population variances are known?

   a. z *c.* Chi-square
   b. t *d.* F

Complete these statements with the best answer.

9. If you hypothesize that there is no difference between means, this is represented as H_0: _____.

10. When you are testing the difference between two means, the _____ test is used when the population variances are not known.

11. When the t test is used for testing the equality of two means, the populations must be _____.

12. The values of F cannot be _____.

13. The formula for the F test for variances is _____.

For each of these problems, perform the following steps.

    a. State the hypotheses and identify the claim.

    b. Find the critical value(s).

    c. Compute the test value.

    d. Make the decision.

    e. Summarize the results.

Use the traditional method of hypothesis testing unless otherwise specified.

14. Cholesterol Levels A researcher wishes to see if there is a difference in the cholesterol levels of two groups of men. A random sample of 30 men between the ages of 25 and 40 is selected and tested. The average level is 223. A second random sample of 25 men between the ages of 41 and 56 is selected and tested. The average of this group is 229. The population standard deviation for both groups is 6. At $\alpha = 0.01$, is there a difference in the cholesterol levels between the two groups? Find the 99% confidence interval for the difference of the two means.

15. Apartment Rental Fees The data shown are the rental fees (in dollars) for two random samples of apartments in a large city. At $\alpha = 0.10$, can it be concluded that the average rental fee for apartments in the east is greater than the average rental fee in the west? Assume $\sigma_1 = 119$ and $\sigma_2 = 103$.

East					West				
495	390	540	445	420	525	400	310	375	750
410	550	499	500	550	390	795	554	450	370
389	350	450	530	350	385	395	425	500	550
375	690	325	350	799	380	400	450	365	425
475	295	350	485	625	375	360	425	400	475
275	450	440	425	675	400	475	430	410	450
625	390	485	550	650	425	450	620	500	400
685	385	450	550	425	295	350	300	360	400

Source: *Pittsburgh Post-Gazette.*

16. Prices of Low-Calorie Foods The average price of a random sample of 12 bottles of diet salad dressing taken from different stores is $1.43. The standard deviation is $0.09. The average price of a random sample of 16 low-calorie frozen desserts is $1.03. The standard deviation is $0.10. At $\alpha = 0.01$, is there a significant difference in price? Find the 99% confidence interval of the difference in the means.

17. Jet Ski Accidents The data shown represent the number of accidents people had when using jet skis and other types of wet bikes. At $\alpha = 0.05$, can it be concluded that the average number of accidents per year has increased from one period to the next?

Earlier period			Later period		
376	650	844	1650	2236	3002
1162	1513		4028	4010	

Source: *USA TODAY.*

18. Salaries of Chemists A random sample of 12 chemists from Washington state shows an average salary of $39,420 with a standard deviation of $1659, while a random sample of 26 chemists from New Mexico has an average salary of $30,215 with a standard deviation of $4116. Is there a significant difference between the two states in chemists' salaries at $\alpha = 0.02$? Find the 98% confidence interval of the difference in the means.

19. Family Incomes The average income of 15 randomly selected families who reside in a large metropolitan East Coast city is $62,456. The standard deviation is $9652. The average income of 11 randomly selected families who reside in a rural area of the Midwest is $60,213, with a standard deviation of $2009. At $\alpha = 0.05$, can it be concluded that the families who live in the cities have a higher income than those who live in the rural areas? Use the *P*-value method.

20. Mathematical Skills In an effort to improve the mathematical skills of 10 students, a teacher provides a weekly 1-hour tutoring session for the students. A pretest is given before the sessions, and a posttest is given after. The results are shown here. At $\alpha = 0.01$, can it be concluded that the sessions help to improve the students' mathematical skills?

Student	1	2	3	4	5	6	7	8	9	10
Pretest	82	76	91	62	81	67	71	69	80	85
Posttest	88	80	98	80	80	73	74	78	85	93

21. Egg Production To increase egg production, a farmer decided to increase the amount of time the lights in his hen house were on. Ten hens were randomly selected, and the number of eggs each produced was recorded. After one week of lengthened light time, the same hens were monitored again. The data are given here. At $\alpha = 0.05$, can it be concluded that the increased light time increased egg production?

Hen	1	2	3	4	5	6	7	8	9	10
Before	4	3	8	7	6	4	9	7	6	5
After	6	5	9	7	4	5	10	6	9	6

22. Factory Worker Literacy Rates In a random sample of 80 workers from a factory in city A, it was found that 5% were unable to read, while in a random sample of 50 workers in city B, 8% were unable to read. Can it be concluded that there is a difference in the proportions of nonreaders in the two cities? Use $\alpha = 0.10$. Find the 90% confidence interval for the difference of the two proportions.

23. Male Head of Household A recent survey of 200 randomly selected households showed that 8 had a single male as the head of household. Forty years ago, a survey of 200 randomly selected households showed that 6 had a single male as the head of household. At $\alpha = 0.05$, can it be concluded that the proportion has changed? Find the 95% confidence interval of the difference of the two proportions. Does the confidence interval contain 0? Why is this important to know?

Source: Based on data from the U.S. Census Bureau.

24. Money Spent on Road Repair A politician wishes to compare the variances of the amount of money spent for road repair in two different counties. The data are given here. At $\alpha = 0.05$, is there a significant difference in the

variances of the amounts spent in the two counties? Use the P-value method.

County A	County B
$s_1 = \$11,596$	$s_2 = \$14,837$
$n_1 = 15$	$n_2 = 18$

25. Heights of Basketball Players A researcher wants to compare the variances of the heights (in inches) of four-year college basketball players with those of players in junior colleges. A random sample of 30 players from each type of school is selected, and the variances of the heights for each type are 2.43 and 3.15, respectively. At $\alpha = 0.10$, is there a significant difference between the variances of the heights in the two types of schools?

Critical Thinking Challenges

1. The study cited in the article entitled "Only the Timid Die Young" stated that "Timid rats were 60% more likely to die at any given time than were their outgoing brothers." Based on the results, answer the following questions.

a. Why were rats used in the study?

b. What are the variables in the study?

c. Why were infants included in the article?

d. What is wrong with extrapolating the results to humans?

e. Suggest some ways humans might be used in a study of this type.

ONLY THE TIMID DIE YOUNG
DO OVERACTIVE STRESS HORMONES DAMAGE HEALTH?
ABOUT 15 OUT OF 100 CHILDREN ARE BORN SHY, BUT ONLY THREE WILL BE SHY AS ADULTS.

FEARFUL TYPES MAY MEET THEIR maker sooner, at least among rats. Researchers have for the first time connected a personality trait—fear of novelty—to an early death.

Sonia Cavigelli and Martha McClintock, psychologists at the University of Chicago, presented unfamiliar bowls, tunnels and bricks to a group of young male rats. Those hesitant to explore the mystery objects were classified as "neophobic."

The researchers found that the neophobic rats produced high levels of stress hormones, called glucocorticoids—typically involved in the fight-or-flight stress response—when faced with strange situations. Those rats continued to have high levels of the hormones at random times throughout their lives, indicating that timidity is a fixed and stable trait. The team then set out to examine the cumulative effects of this personality trait on the rats' health.

Timid rats were 60 percent more likely to die at any given time than were their outgoing brothers. The causes of death were similar for both groups. "One hypothesis as to why the

neophobic rats died earlier is that the stress hormones negatively affected their immune system," Cavigelli says. Neophobes died, on average, three months before their rat brothers, a significant gap, considering that most rats lived only two years.

Shyness—the human equivalent of neophobia—can be detected in infants as young as 14 months. Shy people also produce more stress hormones than "average," or thrill-seeking humans. But introverts don't necessarily stay shy for life, as rats apparently do. Jerome Kagan, a professor of psychology at Harvard University, has found that while 15 out of every 100 children will be born with a shy temperament, only three will appear shy as adults. None, however, will be extroverts.

Extrapolating from the doomed fate of neophobic rats to their human counterparts is difficult. "But it means that something as simple as a personality trait could have physiological consequences," Cavigelli says.

—Carlin Flora

2. Based on the study presented in the article entitled "Sleeping Brain, Not at Rest," answer these questions.

 a. What were the variables used in the study?

 b. How were they measured?

 c. Suggest a statistical test that might have been used to arrive at the conclusion.

 d. Based on the results, what would you suggest for students preparing for an exam?

SLEEPING BRAIN, NOT AT REST

Regions of the brain that have spent the day learning sleep more heavily at night.

In a study published in the journal *Nature*, Giulio Tononi, a psychiatrist at the University of Wisconsin–Madison, had subjects perform a simple point-and-click task with a computer adjusted so that its cursor didn't track in the right direction. Afterward, the subjects' brain waves were recorded while they slept, then examined for "slow wave" activity, a kind of deep sleep.

Compared with people who'd completed the same task with normal cursors, Tononi's subjects showed elevated slow wave activity in brain areas associated with spatial orientation, indicating that their brains were adjusting to the day's learning by making cellular-level changes. In the morning, Tononi's subjects performed their tasks better than they had before going to sleep.

—*Richard A. Love*

Reprinted with permission from *Psychology Today Magazine* (Copyright © 2004, Sussex Publishers, LLC).

Data Projects

Use a significance level of 0.05 for all tests below.

1. **Business and Finance** Use the data collected in data project 1 of Chapter 2 to complete this problem. Test the claim that the mean earnings per share for Dow Jones stocks are greater than for NASDAQ stocks.

2. **Sports and Leisure** Use the data collected in data project 2 of Chapter 7 regarding home runs for this problem. Test the claim that the mean number of home runs hit by the American League sluggers is the same as the mean for the National League.

3. **Technology** Use the cell phone data collected for data project 2 in Chapter 8 to complete this problem. Test the claim that the mean length for outgoing calls is the same as that for incoming calls. Test the claim that the standard deviation for outgoing calls is more than that for incoming calls.

4. **Health and Wellness** Use the data regarding BMI that were collected in data project 6 of Chapter 7 to complete this problem. Test the claim that the mean BMI for males is the same as that for females. Test the claim that the standard deviation for males is the same as that for females.

5. **Politics and Economics** Using data from the Internet for the last Presidential election to categorize the 50 states as "red" or "blue" based on who was supported for President in that state, the Democratic or Republican candidate, test the claim that the mean incomes for red states and blue states are equal.

6. **Your Class** Use the data collected in data project 6 of Chapter 2 regarding heart rates. Test the claim that the heart rates after exercise are more variable than the heart rates before exercise.

Answers to Applying the Concepts

Section 9–1   Home Runs

1. The population of all home runs hit by major league baseball players.

2. A cluster sample was used.

3. Answers will vary. While this sample is not representative of all major league baseball players per se, it does allow us to compare the leaders in each league.

4. H_0: $\mu_1 = \mu_2$ and H_1: $\mu_1 \neq \mu_2$

5. Answers will vary. Possible answers include the 0.05 and 0.01 significance levels.

6. We will use the z test for the difference in means.

7. Our test statistic is $z = \dfrac{44.75 - 42.88}{\sqrt{\dfrac{8.8^2}{40} + \dfrac{7.8^2}{40}}} = 1.01$, and our

 P-value is 0.3124.

8. We fail to reject the null hypothesis.

9. There is not enough evidence to conclude that there is a difference in the number of home runs hit by National League versus American League baseball players.

10. Answers will vary. One possible answer is that since we do not have a random sample of data from each league, we cannot answer the original question asked.

11. Answers will vary. One possible answer is that we could get a random sample of data from each league from a recent season.

Section 9–2   Too Long on the Telephone

1. These samples are independent.

2. We compare the P-value of 0.06317 to the significance level to check if the null hypothesis should be rejected.

3. The P-value of 0.06317 also gives the probability of a type I error.

4. Since two critical values are shown, we know that a two-tailed test was done.

5. Since the P-value of 0.06317 is greater than the significance value of 0.05, we fail to reject the null hypothesis and find that we do not have enough evidence to conclude that there is a difference in the lengths of telephone calls made by employees in the two divisions of the company.

6. If the significance level had been 0.10, we would have rejected the null hypothesis, since the P-value would have been less than the significance level.

Section 9–3   Air Quality

1. The purpose of the study is to determine if the air quality in the United States has changed over the past 2 years.

2. These are dependent samples, since we have two readings from each of 10 metropolitan areas.

3. The hypotheses we will test are $H_0: \mu_D = 0$ and $H_1: \mu_D \neq 0$.

4. We will use the 0.05 significance level and critical values of $t = \pm 2.262$.

5. We will use the t test for dependent samples.

6. There are $10 - 1 = 9$ degrees of freedom.

7. Our test statistic is $t = \dfrac{-6.7 - 0}{11.27/\sqrt{10}} = -1.879$. We fail to reject the null hypothesis and find that there is not

enough evidence to conclude that the air quality in the United States has changed over the past 2 years.

8. No, we could not use an independent means test since we have two readings from each metropolitan area.

9. Answers will vary. One possible answer is that there are other measures of air quality that we could have examined to answer the question.

Section 9–4   Smoking and Education

1. Our hypotheses are $H_0: p_1 = p_2$ and $H_1: p_1 \neq p_2$.

2. At the 0.05 significance level, our critical values are $z = \pm 1.96$.

3. We will use the z test for the difference between proportions.

4. To complete the statistical test, we would need the sample sizes.

5. Knowing the sample sizes were 1000, we can now complete the test.

6. Our test statistic is

$$z = \frac{0.323 - 0.145}{\sqrt{(0.234)(0.766)\left(\dfrac{1}{1000} + \dfrac{1}{1000}\right)}} = 9.40,$$

and our P-value is very close to zero. We reject the null hypothesis and find that there is enough evidence to conclude that there is a difference in the proportions of public school students and private school students who smoke.

Section 9–5   Variability and Automatic Transmissions

1. The null hypothesis is that the variances are the same: $H_0: \sigma_1^2 = \sigma_2^2$ ($H_1: \sigma_1^2 \neq \sigma_2^2$).

2. We will use an F test.

3. The value of the test statistic is $F = \dfrac{s_1^2}{s_2^2} = \dfrac{514.8^2}{77.7^2} = 43.90$,

and the P-value < 0.005 (0.0008). There is a significant difference in the variability of the prices between the two countries.

4. Small sample sizes are highly impacted by outliers.

5. The degrees of freedom for the numerator and denominator are both 5.

6. Yes, two sets of data can center on the same mean but have very different standard deviations.

⏚ Hypothesis-Testing Summary 1

1. Comparison of a sample mean with a specific population mean.

   Example: $H_0: \mu = 100$

   a. Use the z test when σ is known:

   $$z = \frac{\bar{X} - \mu}{\sigma/\sqrt{n}}$$

b. Use the t test when σ is unknown:

$$t = \frac{\overline{X} - \mu}{s/\sqrt{n}} \quad \text{with d.f.} = n - 1$$

2. Comparison of a sample variance or standard deviation with a specific population variance or standard deviation.

Example: H_0: $\sigma^2 = 225$

Use the chi-square test:

$$\chi^2 = \frac{(n - 1)s^2}{\sigma^2} \quad \text{with d.f.} = n - 1$$

3. Comparison of two sample means.

Example: H_0: $\mu_1 = \mu_2$

a. Use the z test when the population variances are known:

$$z = \frac{(\overline{X}_1 - \overline{X}_2) - (\mu_1 - \mu_2)}{\sqrt{\dfrac{\sigma_1^2}{n_1} + \dfrac{\sigma_2^2}{n_2}}}$$

b. Use the t test for independent samples when the population variances are unknown and assume the sample variances are unequal:

$$t = \frac{(\overline{X}_1 - \overline{X}_2) - (\mu_1 - \mu_2)}{\sqrt{\dfrac{s_1^2}{n_1} + \dfrac{s_2^2}{n_2}}}$$

with d.f. = the smaller of $n_1 - 1$ or $n_2 - 1$.

c. Use the t test for means for dependent samples:

Example: H_0: $\mu_D = 0$

$$t = \frac{\overline{D} - \mu_D}{s_D/\sqrt{n}} \quad \text{with d.f.} = n - 1$$

where n = number of pairs.

4. Comparison of a sample proportion with a specific population proportion.

Example: H_0: $p = 0.32$

Use the z test:

$$z = \frac{X - \mu}{\sigma} \quad \text{or} \quad z = \frac{\hat{p} - p}{\sqrt{pq/n}}$$

5. Comparison of two sample proportions.

Example: H_0: $p_1 = p_2$

Use the z test:

$$z = \frac{(\hat{p}_1 - \hat{p}_2) - (p_1 - p_2)}{\sqrt{\overline{p}\,\overline{q}\left(\dfrac{1}{n_1} + \dfrac{1}{n_2}\right)}}$$

where

$$\overline{p} = \frac{X_1 + X_2}{n_1 + n_2} \qquad \hat{p}_1 = \frac{X_1}{n_1}$$

$$\overline{q} = 1 - \overline{p} \qquad \hat{p}_2 = \frac{X_2}{n_2}$$

6. Comparison of two sample variances or standard deviations.

Example: H_0: $\sigma_1^2 = \sigma_2^2$

Use the F test:

$$F = \frac{s_1^2}{s_2^2}$$

where

s_1^2 = larger variance   d.f.N. = $n_1 - 1$

s_2^2 = smaller variance   d.f.D. = $n_2 - 1$

Correlation and Regression

OUTLINE

Introduction

10–1 Scatter Plots and Correlation

10–2 Regression

10–3 Coefficient of Determination and Standard Error of the Estimate

10–4 Multiple Regression (Optional)

Summary

OBJECTIVES

After completing this chapter, you should be able to

1 Draw a scatter plot for a set of ordered pairs.

2 Compute the correlation coefficient.

3 Test the hypothesis H_0: $\rho = 0$.

4 Compute the equation of the regression line.

5 Compute the coefficient of determination.

6 Compute the standard error of the estimate.

7 Find a prediction interval.

8 Be familiar with the concept of multiple regression.

STATISTICS TODAY

Can Temperature Predict Crime?

Over the last years, researchers have been interested in the relationship between increasing temperatures and increasing crime rates. To test this relationship, the author selected a city on the East Coast and obtained the average monthly temperatures for that city as well as the number of crimes committed each month for the year 2011. The data are shown.

Month	Average temperature	Total offenses
January	36	83
February	35	82
March	42	81
April	52	102
May	60.5	122
June	71.5	117
July	77	126
August	77.5	115
September	73	84
October	63	123
November	53	82
December	45	102

Source: City of Annapolis, Maryland, Police Department and www.average-temperature.com

Using the statistical methods described in this chapter, you will be able to answer these questions:

1. Is there a linear relationship between the monthly average temperatures and the number of crimes committed during the month?

2. If so, how strong is the relationship between the average monthly temperature and the number of crimes committed?

3. If a relationship exists, can it be said that an increase in temperatures will cause an increase in the number of crimes occurring in that city?

See Statistics Today—Revisited at the end of the chapter for the answers to these questions.

Introduction

In Chapters 7 and 8, two areas of inferential statistics—confidence intervals and hypothesis testing—were explained. Another area of inferential statistics involves determining whether a relationship exists between two or more numerical or quantitative variables. For example, a businessperson may want to know whether the volume of sales for a given month is related to the amount of advertising the firm does that month. Educators are interested in determining whether the number of hours a student studies is related to the student's score on a particular exam. Medical researchers are interested in questions such as, Is caffeine related to heart damage? or Is there a relationship between a person's age and his or her blood pressure? A zoologist may want to know whether the birth weight of a certain animal is related to its life span. These are only some of the many questions that can be answered by using the techniques of correlation and regression analysis.

The purpose of this chapter then is to answer these questions statistically:

1. Are two or more variables linearly related?

2. If so, what is the strength of the relationship?

3. What type of relationship exists?

4. What kind of predictions can be made from the relationship?

Unusual Stat

A person walks on average 100,000 miles in his or her lifetime. This is about 3.4 miles per day.

10–1 Scatter Plots and Correlation

OBJECTIVE ①

Draw a scatter plot for a set of ordered pairs.

In simple correlation and regression studies, the researcher collects data on two numerical or quantitative variables to see whether a relationship exists between the variables. For example, if a researcher wishes to see whether there is a relationship between number of hours of study and test scores on an exam, she must select a random sample of students, determine the number of hours each studied, and obtain their grades on the exam. A table can be made for the data, as shown here.

Student	Hours of study x	Grade y (%)
A	6	82
B	2	63
C	1	57
D	5	88
E	2	68
F	3	75

The two variables for this study are called the **independent variable** and the **dependent variable.** The independent variable is the variable in regression that can be controlled or manipulated. In this case, the number of hours of study is the independent variable and is designated as the x variable. The dependent variable is the variable in regression that cannot be controlled or manipulated. The grade the student received on the exam is the dependent variable, designated as the y variable. The reason for this distinction between the variables is that you assume that the grade the student earns *depends* on the number of hours the student studied. Also, you assume that, to some extent, the student can regulate or *control* the number of hours he or she studies for the exam. The independent variable is also known as the *explanatory variable,* and the dependent variable is also called the *response variable*.

The determination of the x and y variables is not always clear-cut and is sometimes an arbitrary decision. For example, if a researcher studies the effects of age on a person's blood pressure, the researcher can generally assume that age affects blood pressure. Hence, the variable *age* can be called the *independent variable,* and the variable *blood pressure* can be called the *dependent variable.* On the other hand, if a researcher is studying the attitudes of husbands on a certain issue and the attitudes of their wives on the same issue, it is difficult to say which variable is the independent variable and which is the dependent variable. In this study, the researcher can arbitrarily designate the variables as independent and dependent.

FIGURE 10–1

Types of Relationships

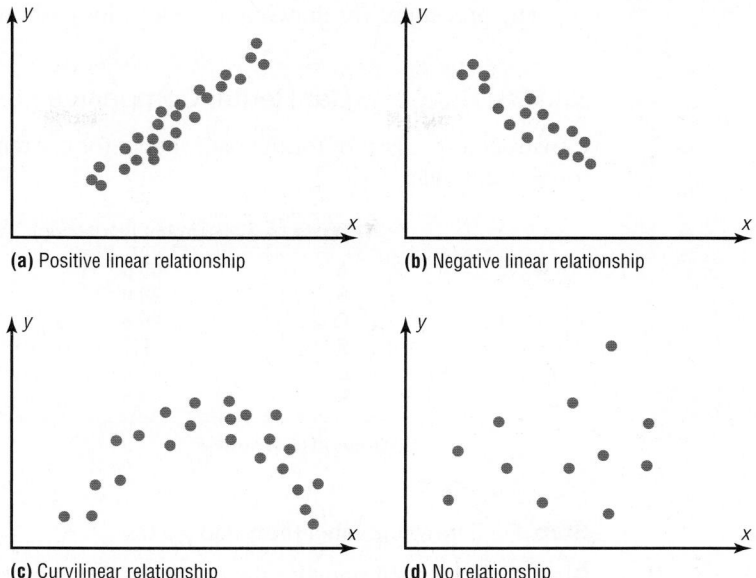

(a) Positive linear relationship

(b) Negative linear relationship

(c) Curvilinear relationship

(d) No relationship

The independent and dependent variables can be plotted on a graph called a *scatter plot*. The independent variable x is plotted on the horizontal axis, and the dependent variable y is plotted on the vertical axis.

> A **scatter plot** is a graph of the ordered pairs (x, y) of numbers consisting of the independent variable x and the dependent variable y.

The scatter plot is a visual way to describe the nature of the relationship between the independent and dependent variables. The scales of the variables can be different, and the coordinates of the axes are determined by the smallest and largest data values of the variables.

Researchers look for various types of patterns in scatter plots. For example, in Figure 10–1(a), the pattern in the points of the scatter plot shows a *positive linear relationship*. Here, as the values of the independent variable (x variable) increase, the values of the dependent variable (y variable) increase. Also, the points form somewhat of a straight line going in an upward direction from left to right.

The pattern of the points of the scatter plot shown in Figure 10–1(b) shows a *negative linear relationship*. In this case, as the values of the independent variable increase, the values of the dependent variable decrease. Also, the points show a somewhat straight line going in a downward direction from left to right.

The pattern of the points of the scatter plot shown in Figure 10–1(c) shows some type of a nonlinear relationship or a curvilinear relationship.

Finally, the scatter plot shown in Figure 10–1(d) shows basically no relationship between the independent variable and the dependent variable since no pattern (line or curve) can be seen.

The procedure table for drawing a scatter plot is given next.

Procedure Table
Drawing a Scatter Plot
Step 1   Draw and label the x and y axes.
Step 2   Plot each point on the graph.
Step 3   Determine the type of relationship (if any) that exists for the variables.

The procedure for drawing a scatter plot is shown in Examples 10–1 through 10–3.

EXAMPLE 10–1 Car Rental Companies

Construct a scatter plot for the data shown for car rental companies in the United States for a recent year.

Company	Cars (in ten thousands)	Revenue (in billions)
A	63.0	$7.0
B	29.0	3.9
C	20.8	2.1
D	19.1	2.8
E	13.4	1.4
F	8.5	1.5

Source: *Auto Rental News.*

SOLUTION

Step 1   Draw and label the *x* and *y* axes.

Step 2   Plot each point on the graph, as shown in Figure 10–2.

FIGURE 10–2   Scatter Plot for Example 10–1

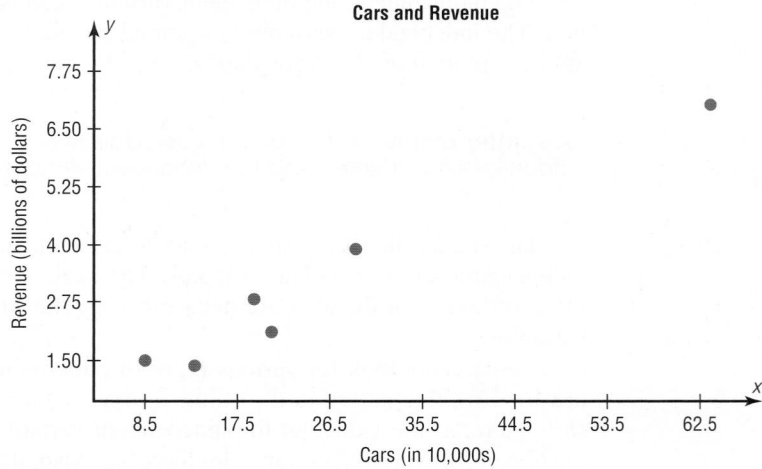

Step 3   Determine the type of relationship (if any) that exists.

In this example, it looks as if a positive linear relationship exists between the number of cars that an agency owns and the total revenue that is made by the company.

EXAMPLE 10–2 Absences and Final Grades

Construct a scatter plot for the data obtained in a study on the number of absences and the final grades of seven randomly selected students from a statistics class. The data are shown here.

Student	Number of absences *x*	Final grade *y* (%)
A	6	82
B	2	86
C	15	43
D	9	74
E	12	58
F	5	90
G	8	78

Step 1   Draw and label the x and y axes.

Step 2   Plot each point on the graph, as shown in Figure 10–3.

FIGURE 10–3   Scatter Plot for Example 10–2

Step 3   Determine the type of relationship (if any) that exists.

In this example, it looks as if a negative linear relationship exists between the number of student absences and the final grade of the students.

EXAMPLE 10–3   Age and Wealth

A researcher wishes to see if there is a relationship between the ages of the wealthiest people in the world and their net worth. A random sample of 10 persons was selected from the *Forbes* list of the 400 richest people for a recent year. The data are shown. Draw a scatter plot for the data.

Person	Age x	Net worth y (in billions of dollars)
A	60	11
B	72	69
C	56	11.9
D	55	30
E	83	12.2
F	67	36
G	38	18.7
H	62	10.2
I	62	23.3
J	46	10.6

Source: *Forbes* magazine.

Step 1   Draw and label the x and y axes.

Step 2   Plot each point on the graph, as shown in Figure 10–4.

FIGURE 10–4 Scatter Plot for Example 10–3

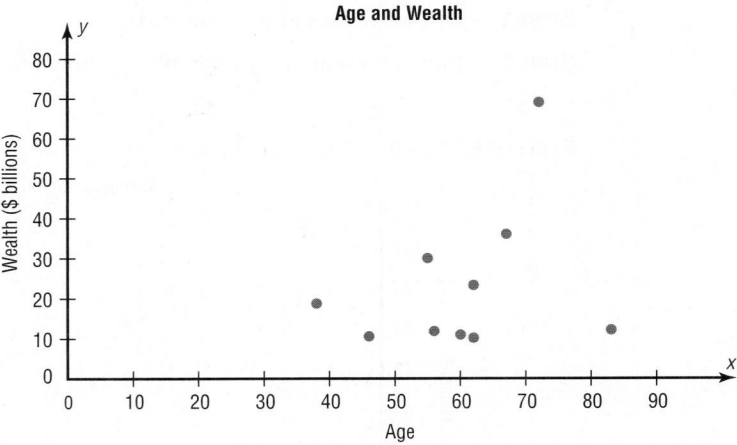

Step 3 Determine the type of relationship (if any) that exists.

In this example, there is no type of a strong linear or curvilinear relationship between a person's age and his or her net worth.

Correlation

OBJECTIVE ❷

Compute the correlation coefficient.

Correlation Coefficient Statisticians use a measure called the *correlation coefficient* to determine the strength of the linear relationship between two variables. There are several types of correlation coefficients.

> The **population correlation coefficient** denoted by the Greek letter ρ is the correlation computed by using all possible pairs of data values (x, y) taken from a population.

> The **linear correlation coefficient** computed from the sample data measures the strength and direction of a linear relationship between two quantitative variables. The symbol for the sample correlation coefficient is r.

The linear correlation coefficient explained in this section is called the **Pearson product moment correlation coefficient (PPMC),** named after statistician Karl Pearson, who pioneered the research in this area.

The *range of the linear correlation coefficient* is from -1 to $+1$. If there is a *strong positive linear relationship* between the variables, the value of r will be close to $+1$. If there is a *strong negative linear relationship* between the variables, the value of r will be close to -1. When there is no linear relationship between the variables or only a weak relationship, the value of r will be close to 0. See Figure 10–5. When the value of r is 0 or close to zero, it implies only that there is no linear relationship between the variables. The data may be related in some other nonlinear way.

FIGURE 10–5

Range of Values for the Correlation Coefficient

FIGURE 10–6

Relationship Between the
Correlation Coefficient and
the Scatter Plot

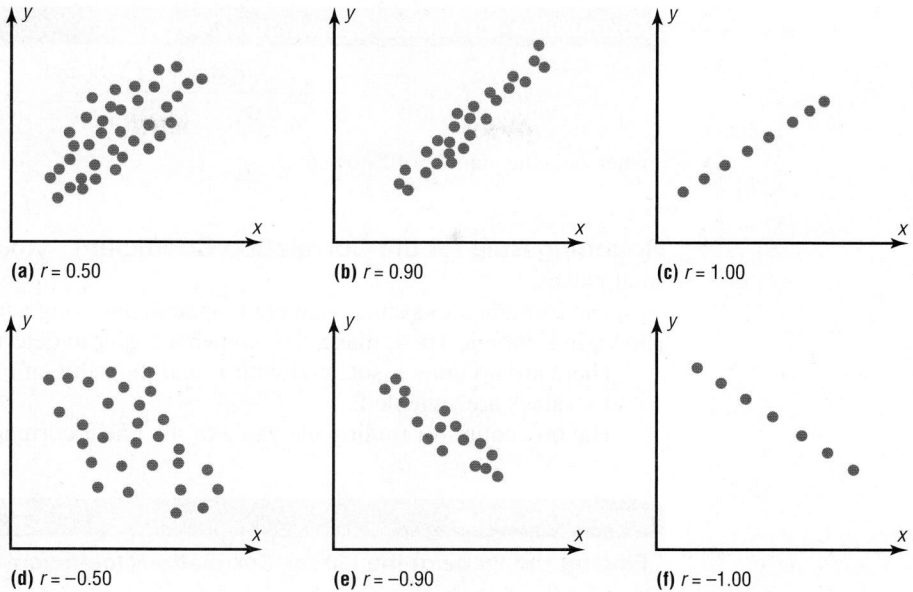

(a) $r = 0.50$ **(b)** $r = 0.90$ **(c)** $r = 1.00$

(d) $r = -0.50$ **(e)** $r = -0.90$ **(f)** $r = -1.00$

Properties of the Linear Correlation Coefficient

1. The correlation coefficient is a unitless measure.
2. The value of r will always be between -1 and $+1$ inclusively. That is, $-1 \leq r \leq 1$.
3. If the values of x and y are interchanged, the value of r will be unchanged.
4. If the values of x and/or y are converted to a different scale, the value of r will be unchanged.
5. The value of r is sensitive to outliers and can change dramatically if they are present in the data.

The graphs in Figure 10–6 show the relationship between the correlation coefficients and their corresponding scatter plots. Notice that as the value of the correlation coefficient increases from 0 to $+1$ (parts a, b, and c), data values become closer to a straight line and to an increasingly strong relationship. As the value of the correlation coefficient decreases from 0 to -1 (parts d, e, and f), the data values also become closer to a straight line. Again this suggests a stronger relationship.

Assumptions for the Correlation Coefficient

1. The sample is a random sample.
2. The data pairs fall approximately on a straight line and are measured at the interval or ratio level.
3. The variables have a bivariate normal distribution. (This means that given any specific value of x, the y values are normally distributed; and given any specific value of y, the x values are normally distributed.)

In this book, the assumptions will be stated in the exercises; however, when encountering statistics in other situations, you must check to see that these assumptions have been met before proceeding.

There are several ways to compute the value of the correlation coefficient. One method is to use the formula shown here.

Formula for the Linear Correlation Coefficient r

$$r = \frac{n(\Sigma xy) - (\Sigma x)(\Sigma y)}{\sqrt{[n(\Sigma x^2) - (\Sigma x)^2][n(\Sigma y^2) - (\Sigma y)^2]}}$$

where n is the number of data pairs.

Rounding Rule for the Correlation Coefficient   Round the value of r to three decimal places.

The formula looks somewhat complicated, but using a table to compute the values, as shown in Example 10–4, makes it somewhat easier to determine the value of r.

There are no units associated with r, and the value of r will remain unchanged if the x and y values are switched.

The procedure for finding the value of the linear correlation coefficient is given next.

Procedure Table

Finding the Value of the Linear Correlation Coefficient

Step 1   Make a table as shown.

x	y	xy	x^2	y^2

Step 2   Place the values of x in the x column and the values of y in the y column.
Multiply each x value by the corresponding y value, and place the products in the xy column.
Square each x value and place the squares in the x^2 column.
Square each y value and place the squares in the y^2 column.
Find the sum of each column.

Step 3   Substitute in the formula and find the value for r.

$$r = \frac{n(\Sigma xy) - (\Sigma x)(\Sigma y)}{\sqrt{[n(\Sigma x^2) - (\Sigma x)^2][n(\Sigma y^2) - (\Sigma y)^2]}}$$

where n is the number of data pairs.

EXAMPLE 10–4   **Car Rental Companies**

Compute the linear correlation coefficient for the data in Example 10–1.

SOLUTION

Step 1   Make a table as shown here.

Company	Cars x (in ten thousands)	Revenue y (in billions)	xy	x^2	y^2
A	63.0	$7.0			
B	29.0	3.9			
C	20.8	2.1			
D	19.1	2.8			
E	13.4	1.4			
F	8.5	1.5			

Step 2   Find the values of xy, x^2, and y^2, and place these values in the corresponding columns of the table.

The completed table is shown.

Company	Cars x (in 10,000s)	Revenue y (in billions of dollars)	xy	x²	y²
A	63.0	7.0	441.00	3969.00	49.00
B	29.0	3.9	113.10	841.00	15.21
C	20.8	2.1	43.68	432.64	4.41
D	19.1	2.8	53.48	364.81	7.84
E	13.4	1.4	18.76	179.56	1.96
F	8.5	1.5	12.75	72.25	2.25
	$\Sigma x = 153.8$	$\Sigma y = 18.7$	$\Sigma xy = 682.77$	$\Sigma x^2 = 5859.26$	$\Sigma y^2 = 80.67$

Step 3   Substitute in the formula and solve for r.

$$r = \frac{n(\Sigma xy) - (\Sigma x)(\Sigma y)}{\sqrt{[n(\Sigma x^2) - (\Sigma x)^2][n(\Sigma y^2) - (\Sigma y)^2]}}$$

$$= \frac{(6)(682.77) - (153.8)(18.7)}{\sqrt{[(6)(5859.26) - (153.8)^2][(6)(80.67) - (18.7)^2]}} = 0.982$$

The linear correlation coefficient suggests a strong positive linear relationship between the number of cars a rental agency has and its annual revenue. That is, the more cars a rental agency has, the more annual revenue the company will have.

EXAMPLE 10–5   **Absences and Final Grades**

Compute the value of the linear correlation coefficient for the data obtained in the study of the number of absences and the final grade of the seven students in the statistics class given in Example 10–2.

SOLUTION

Step 1   Make a table.

Step 2   Find the values of xy, x^2, and y^2; place these values in the corresponding columns of the table.

Student	Number of absences x	Final grade y (%)	xy	x²	y²
A	6	82	492	36	6,724
B	2	86	172	4	7,396
C	15	43	645	225	1,849
D	9	74	666	81	5,476
E	12	58	696	144	3,364
F	5	90	450	25	8,100
G	8	78	624	64	6,084
	$\Sigma x = 57$	$\Sigma y = 511$	$\Sigma xy = 3745$	$\Sigma x^2 = 579$	$\Sigma y^2 = 38,993$

Step 3   Substitute in the formula and solve for r.

$$r = \frac{n(\Sigma xy) - (\Sigma x)(\Sigma y)}{\sqrt{[n(\Sigma x^2) - (\Sigma x)^2][n(\Sigma y^2) - (\Sigma y)^2]}}$$

$$= \frac{(7)(3745) - (57)(511)}{\sqrt{[(7)(579) - (57)^2][(7)(38,993) - (511)^2]}} = -0.944$$

The value of r suggests a strong negative linear relationship between a student's final grade and the number of absences a student has. That is, the more absences a student has, the lower is his or her grade.

EXAMPLE 10–6   Age and Wealth

Compute the value of the linear correlation coefficient for the data given in Example 10–3 for the age and wealth of the richest persons in the world.

SOLUTION

Step 1   Make a table.

Step 2   Find the values of xy, x^2, and y^2; place these values in the corresponding columns of the table.

Person	Age x	Net wealth y	xy	x^2	y^2
A	60	11	660	3,600	121
B	72	69	4,968	5,184	4,761
C	56	11.9	666.4	3,136	141.61
D	55	30	1,650	3,025	900
E	83	12.2	1,012.6	6,889	148.84
F	67	36	2,412	4,489	1,296
G	38	18.7	710.6	1,444	349.69
H	62	10.2	632.4	3,844	104.04
I	62	23.3	1,444.6	3,844	542.89
J	46	10.6	487.6	2,116	112.36
	$\Sigma x = 601$	$\Sigma y = 232.9$	$\Sigma xy = 14{,}644.2$	$\Sigma x^2 = 37{,}571$	$\Sigma y^2 = 8{,}477.43$

Step 3   Substitute in the formula and solve for r:

$$r = \frac{n(\Sigma xy) - (\Sigma x)(\Sigma y)}{\sqrt{[n(\Sigma x^2) - (\Sigma x)^2][n(\Sigma y^2) - (\Sigma y)^2]}}$$

$$= \frac{10(14{,}644.2) - (601)(232.9)}{\sqrt{[10(37{,}571) - (601)^2][10(8477.43) - (232.9)^2]}}$$

$$= \frac{6469.1}{\sqrt{(14{,}509)(30{,}531.89)}} = \frac{6469.1}{21{,}047.26091} = 0.307$$

The value of r indicates a weak positive linear relationship between age and wealth of the richest people in the world.

In Example 10–4, the value of r was high (close to 1.00); in Example 10–6, the value of r was much lower (close to 0). This question then arises, When is the value of r due to chance, and when does it suggest a significant linear relationship between the variables? This question will be answered next.

OBJECTIVE ③

Test the hypothesis
$H_0: \rho = 0$.

The Significance of the Correlation Coefficient   As stated before, the range of the correlation coefficient is between -1 and $+1$. When the value of r is near $+1$ or -1, there is a strong linear relationship. When the value of r is near 0, the linear relationship is weak or nonexistent. Since the value of r is computed from data obtained from samples, there are two possibilities when r is not equal to zero: either the value of r is high enough to conclude that there is a significant linear relationship between the variables, or the value of r is due to chance.

To make this decision, you use a hypothesis-testing procedure. The traditional method is similar to the one used in previous chapters.

Step 1   State the hypotheses.

Step 2   Find the critical values.

Step 3   Compute the test value.

Step 4   Make the decision.

Step 5   Summarize the results.

The sample correlation coefficient can then be used as an estimator of ρ if the following assumptions are valid.

Assumptions for Testing the Significance of the Linear Correlation Coefficient

1. The data are quantitative and are obtained from a simple random sample.
2. The scatter plot shows that the data are approximately linearly related.
3. There are no outliers in the data.
4. The variables x and y must come from normally distributed populations.

In this book, the assumptions will be stated in the exercises; however, when encountering statistics in other situations, you must check to see that these assumptions have been met before proceeding.

In hypothesis testing, one of these is true:

H_0: $\rho = 0$ This null hypothesis means that there is no correlation between the x and y variables in the population.

H_1: $\rho \neq 0$ This alternative hypothesis means that there is a significant correlation between the variables in the population.

When the null hypothesis is rejected at a specific level, it means that there is a significant difference between the value of r and 0. When the null hypothesis is not rejected, it means that the value of r is not significantly different from 0 (zero) and is probably due to chance.

Several methods can be used to test the significance of the correlation coefficient. Three methods will be shown in this section. The first uses the t test.

Interesting Fact

Scientists think that a person is never more than 3 feet away from a spider at any given time!

Historical Notes

A mathematician named Karl Pearson (1857–1936) became interested in Francis Galton's work and saw that his correlation and regression theory could be applied to other areas besides heredity. Pearson developed the correlation coefficient that bears his name.

Formula for the t Test for the Correlation Coefficient

$$t = r\sqrt{\frac{n-2}{1-r^2}}$$

with degrees of freedom equal to $n - 2$, where n is the number of ordered pairs (x, y).

You do not have to identify the claim here, since the question will always be whether there is a significant linear relationship between the variables.

The two-tailed critical values are used. These values are found in Table F in Appendix A. Also, when you are testing the significance of a correlation coefficient, both variables x and y must come from normally distributed populations.

EXAMPLE 10–7

Test the significance of the correlation coefficient found in Example 10–4. Use $\alpha = 0.05$ and $r = 0.982$.

SOLUTION

Step 1   State the hypotheses.

$$H_0: \rho = 0 \qquad \text{and} \qquad H_1: \rho \neq 0$$

Step 2   Find the critical values. Since $\alpha = 0.05$ and there are $6 - 2 = 4$ degrees of freedom, the critical values obtained from Table F are ± 2.776, as shown in Figure 10–7.

FIGURE 10–7
Critical Values for
Example 10–7

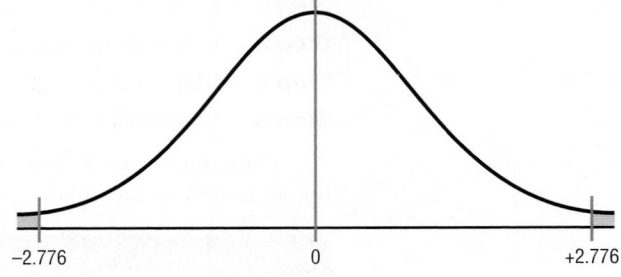

$-2.776 \qquad 0 \qquad +2.776$

Step 3   Compute the test value.

$$t = r\sqrt{\frac{n - 2}{1 - r^2}} = 0.982\sqrt{\frac{6 - 2}{1 - (0.982)^2}} = 10.398$$

Step 4   Make the decision. Reject the null hypothesis, since the test value falls in the critical region, as shown in Figure 10–8.

FIGURE 10–8
Test Value for
Example 10–7

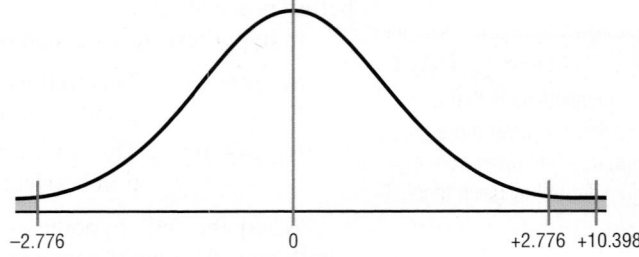

$-2.776 \qquad 0 \qquad +2.776 \ +10.398$

Step 5   Summarize the results. There is a significant relationship between the number of cars a rental agency owns and its annual income.

The second method that can be used to test the significance of r is the P-value method. The method is the same as that shown in Chapters 8 and 9. It uses the following steps.

Step 1   State the hypotheses.

Step 2   Find the test value. (In this case, use the t test.)

Step 3   Find the P-value. (In this case, use Table F.)

Step 4   Make the decision.

Step 5   Summarize the results.

Consider an example where $t = 4.059$, d.f. $= 4$, and $\alpha = 0.05$. Using Table F with d.f. $= 4$ and the row Two tails, the value 4.059 falls between 3.747 and 4.604; hence, $0.01 < P\text{-value} < 0.02$. (The P-value obtained from a calculator is 0.015.) That is, the P-value falls between 0.01 and 0.02. The decision, then, is to reject the null hypothesis since $P\text{-value} < 0.05$.

The third method of testing the significance of r is to use Table I in Appendix A. This table shows the values of the correlation coefficient that are significant for a specific α level and a specific number of degrees of freedom. For example, for 7 degrees of freedom and $\alpha = 0.05$, the table gives a critical value of 0.666. Any value of r greater than $+0.666$ or less than -0.666 will be significant, and the null hypothesis will be rejected. See Figure 10–9. When Table I is used, you need not compute the t test value. Table I is for two-tailed tests only.

FIGURE 10–9

Finding the Critical Value from Table I

d.f.	$\alpha = 0.05$	$\alpha = 0.01$
1		
2		
3		
4		
5		
6		
7	(0.666)	

EXAMPLE 10–8

Using Table I, test the significance at $\alpha = 0.01$ of the correlation coefficient $r = 0.307$, obtained in Example 10–6.

SOLUTION

$$H_0: \rho = 0 \quad \text{and} \quad H_1: \rho \neq 0$$

Since the sample size is 10, there are $n - 2 = 10 - 2 = 8$ degrees of freedom. The critical values obtained from Table I at $\alpha = 0.01$ and 8 degrees of freedom are ± 0.765. Since $0.307 < 0.765$, the decision is to not reject the null hypothesis. Hence, there is not enough evidence to say that there is a significant linear relationship between age and wealth of the richest people in the world. See Figure 10–10.

FIGURE 10–10

Rejection and Nonrejection Regions for Example 10–8

Generally, significance tests for correlation coefficients are two-tailed; however, they can be one-tailed. For example, if a researcher hypothesized a positive linear relationship between two variables, the hypotheses would be

$$H_0: \rho = 0$$
$$H_1: \rho > 0$$

If the researcher hypothesized a negative linear relationship between two variables, the hypotheses would be

$$H_0: \rho = 0$$
$$H_1: \rho < 0$$

In these cases, the t tests and the P-value tests would be one-tailed. Also, tables such as Table I are available for one-tailed tests. In this book, the examples and exercises will involve two-tailed tests.

Correlation and Causation Researchers must understand the nature of the linear relationship between the independent variable x and the dependent variable y. When a hypothesis test indicates that a significant linear relationship exists between the variables, researchers must consider the possibilities outlined next.

When two variables are highly correlated, item 3 in the box states that there exists a possibility that the correlation is due to a third variable. If this is the case and the

Possible Relationships Between Variables

When the null hypothesis has been rejected for a specific α value, any of the following five possibilities can exist.

1. *There is a direct cause-and-effect relationship between the variables.* That is, x causes y. For example, water causes plants to grow, poison causes death, and heat causes ice to melt.

2. *There is a reverse cause-and-effect relationship between the variables.* That is, y causes x. For example, suppose a researcher believes excessive coffee consumption causes nervousness, but the researcher fails to consider that the reverse situation may occur. That is, it may be that an extremely nervous person craves coffee to calm his or her nerves.

3. *The relationship between the variables may be caused by a third variable.* For example, if a statistician correlated the number of deaths due to drowning and the number of cans of soft drink consumed daily during the summer, he or she would probably find a significant relationship. However, the soft drink is not necessarily responsible for the deaths, since both variables may be related to heat and humidity.

4. *There may be a complexity of interrelationships among many variables.* For example, a researcher may find a significant relationship between students' high school grades and college grades. But there probably are many other variables involved, such as IQ, hours of study, influence of parents, motivation, age, and instructors.

5. *The relationship may be coincidental.* For example, a researcher may be able to find a significant relationship between the increase in the number of people who are exercising and the increase in the number of people who are committing crimes. But common sense dictates that any relationship between these two values must be due to coincidence.

third variable is unknown to the researcher or not accounted for in the study, it is called a **lurking variable.** An attempt should be made by the researcher to identify such variables and to use methods to control their influence.

It is important to restate the fact that even if the correlation between two variables is high, it does not necessarily mean causation. There are other possibilities, such as lurking variables or just a coincidental relationship. See the Speaking of Statistics article on page 563.

Also, you should be cautious when the data for one or both of the variables involve averages rather than individual data. It is not wrong to use averages, but the results cannot be generalized to individuals since averaging tends to smooth out the variability among individual data values. The result could be a higher correlation than actually exists.

Thus, when the null hypothesis is rejected, the researcher must consider all possibilities and select the appropriate one as determined by the study. Remember, correlation does not necessarily imply causation.

≡ Applying the Concepts 10–1

Stopping Distances

In a study on speed control, it was found that the main reasons for regulations were to make traffic flow more efficient and to minimize the risk of danger. An area that was focused on in the study was the distance required to completely stop a vehicle at various speeds. Use the following table to answer the questions.

MPH	Braking distance (feet)
20	20
30	45
40	81
50	133
60	205
80	411

In correlation and regression studies, it is difficult to control all variables. This study shows some of the consequences when researchers overlook certain aspects in studies. Suggest ways that the lurking variables might be controlled in future studies.

Coffee Not Disease Culprit, Study Says

NEW YORK (AP)—Two new studies suggest that coffee drinking, even up to 5½ cups per day, does not increase the risk of heart disease, and other studies that claim to have found increased risks might have missed the true culprits, a researcher says.

"It might not be the coffee cup in one hand, it might be the cigarette or coffee roll in the other," said Dr. Peter W. F. Wilson, the author of one of the new studies.

He noted in a telephone interview Thursday that many coffee drinkers, particularly heavy coffee drinkers, are smokers. And one of the new studies found that coffee drinkers had excess fat in their diets.

The findings of the new studies conflict sharply with a study reported in November 1985 by Johns Hopkins University scientists in Baltimore.

The Hopkins scientists found that coffee drinkers who consumed five or more cups of coffee per day had three times the heart-disease risk of non-coffee drinkers.

The reason for the discrepancy appears to be that many of the coffee drinkers in the Hopkins study also smoked—and it was the smoking that increased their heart-disease risk, said Wilson.

Wilson, director of laboratories for the Framingham Heart Study in Framingham, Mass., said Thursday at a conference sponsored by the American Heart Association in Charleston, S.C., that he had examined the coffee intake of 3937 participants in the Framingham study during 1956–66 and an additional 2277 during the years 1972–1982.

In contrast to the subjects in the Hopkins study, most of these coffee drinkers consumed two or three cups per day, Wilson said. Only 10 percent drank six or more cups per day.

He then looked at blood cholesterol levels and heart and blood vessel disease in the two groups. "We ran these analyses for coronary heart disease, heart attack, sudden death and stroke and in absolutely every analysis, we found no link with coffee," Wilson said.

He found that coffee consumption was linked to a significant decrease in total blood cholesterol in men, and to a moderate increase in total cholesterol in women.

Source: Reprinted with permission of the Associated Press.

Assume MPH is going to be used to predict stopping distance.

1. Which of the two variables is the independent variable?
2. Which is the dependent variable?
3. What type of variable is the independent variable?
4. What type of variable is the dependent variable?
5. Construct a scatter plot for the data.
6. Is there a linear relationship between the two variables?
7. Redraw the scatter plot, and change the distances between the independent-variable numbers. Does the relationship look different?
8. Is the relationship positive or negative?
9. Can braking distance be accurately predicted from MPH?
10. List some other variables that affect braking distance.
11. Compute the value of r.
12. Is r significant at $\alpha = 0.05$?

See page 607 for the answers.

⚏ Exercises 10–1

1. What is meant by the statement that two variables are related?

2. How is a linear relationship between two variables measured in statistics? Explain.

3. What is the symbol for the sample correlation coefficient? The population correlation coefficient?

4. What is the range of values for the correlation coefficient?

5. What is meant when the relationship between the two variables is called positive? Negative?

6. Give examples of two variables that are positively correlated and two that are negatively correlated.

7. What is the diagram of the independent and dependent variables called? Why is drawing this diagram important?

8. What is the name of the correlation coefficient used in this section?

9. What statistical test is used to test the significance of the correlation coefficient?

10. When two variables are correlated, can the researcher be sure that one variable causes the other? Why or why not?

For Exercises 11 through 27, perform the following steps.

   a. Draw the scatter plot for the variables.

   b. Compute the value of the correlation coefficient.

   c. State the hypotheses.

   d. Test the significance of the correlation coefficient at $\alpha = 0.05$, using Table I.

   e. Give a brief explanation of the type of relationship. Assume all assumptions have been met.

11. **Crimes** The number of murders and robberies per 100,000 population for a random selection of states is shown. Is there a linear relationship between the variables?

Murders	2.4	2.7	5.6	2.6	2.1	3.3	6.6	5.7
Robberies	25.3	14.3	151.6	91.1	80	49	173	95.8

Source: *Time Almanac.*

12. **Oil and Gas Prices** The average gasoline price per gallon (in cities) and the cost of a barrel of oil are shown for a random selection of weeks from 2009–2010. Is there a linear relationship between the variables?

Oil ($)	46.25	37.51	78.00	75.39	84.88	73.78
Gasoline ($)	2.197	2.182	2.987	3.015	3.109	3.000

(The information in this exercise will be used for Exercise 12 in Section 10–2.)

Source: *World Almanac.*

13. **Commercial Movie Releases** The yearly data have been published showing the number of releases for each of the commercial movie studios and the gross receipts for those studios thus far. Based on these data, can it be concluded that there is a linear relationship between the number of releases and the gross receipts?

No. of releases *x*	361	270	306	22	35	10	8	12	21
Gross receipts *y* (million $)	3844	1962	1371	1064	334	241	188	154	125

(The information in this exercise will be used for Exercises 13 and 36 in Section 10–2 and Exercises 15 and 19 in Section 10–3.)

Source: www.showbizdata.com

14. **Forest Fires and Acres Burned** An environmentalist wants to determine the relationships between the numbers (in thousands) of forest fires over the year and the number (in hundred thousands) of acres burned. The data for 8 recent years are shown. Describe the relationship.

Number of fires *x*	72	69	58	47	84	62	57	45
Number of acres burned *y*	62	42	19	26	51	15	30	15

Source: National Interagency Fire Center.

(The information in this exercise will be used for Exercise 14 in Section 10–2 and Exercises 16 and 20 in Section 10–3.)

15. **Alumni Contributions** The director of an alumni association for a small college wants to determine whether there is any type of relationship between the amount of an alumnus's contribution (in dollars) and the number of years the alumnus has been out of school. The data follow. (The information is used for Exercises 15, 36, and 37 in Section 10–2 and Exercises 17 and 21 in Section 10–3.)

Years *x*	1	5	3	10	7	6
Contribution *y*	500	100	300	50	75	80

16. **State Debt and Per Capita Tax** An economics student wishes to see if there is a relationship between the amount of state debt per capita and the amount of tax per capita at the state level. Based on the following data, can she or he conclude that per capita state debt and per capita state taxes are related? Both amounts are in dollars and represent five randomly selected states. (The information in this exercise will be used for Exercises 16 and 37 in Section 10–2 and Exercises 18 and 22 in Section 10–3.)

Per capita debt *x*	1924	907	1445	1608	661
Per capita tax *y*	1685	1838	1734	1842	1317

Source: *World Almanac.*

17. **Energy Consumption** The annual energy consumption in billions of Btu for both natural gas and coal is shown for a random selection of states. Is there a linear relationship between the variables?

Gas	223	474	377	289	747	146
Coal	478	631	413	356	736	474

Source: *Time Almanac.*

18. **Triples and Home Runs** The data below show the number of triples (three-base hits) and the number of home runs hit during the season by a random sample of MLB teams. Is there a significant relationship between the data?

Triples	25	23	51	19	20	43
Home runs	212	199	144	160	149	122

Source: *New York Times Almanac.*

(The information in this exercise will be used in Exercises 18 and 38 in Section 10–2.)

19. **Carbohydrates and Kilocalories** There are many interesting relationships among the various nutrients found in fruits and vegetables. Listed below are the number of grams of carbohydrates and the number of kilocalories for a 100-gram sample of various raw foods. Is there a linear relationship between the variables? (The information in this exercise will be used in Exercise 19 in Section 10–2.)

Carbs	15.25	16.55	11.10	13.01	14.13	15.11
kcal	59	72	43	55	56	59

Source: *Time Almanac.*

20. **Water and Carbohydrates** Continuing the theme of fruits and vegetables, here are the number of grams of water and the number of grams of carbohydrates for a random selection of raw foods (100 g each). Is there a linear relationship between the variables? (The information in this exercise will be used for Exercises 20 and 38 in Section 10–2.)

Water	83.93	80.76	87.66	85.20	72.85	84.61	83.81
Carbs	15.25	16.55	11.10	13.01	24.27	14.13	15.11

Source: *Time Almanac.*

21. **Faculty and Students** The number of faculty and the number of students are shown for a random selection of small colleges. Is there a significant relationship between the two variables? Switch x and y and repeat the process. Which do you think is really the independent variable?

Faculty	99	110	113	116	138	174	220
Students	1353	1290	1091	1213	1384	1283	2075

Source: *World Almanac.*

(The information in this exercise will be used for Exercises 21 and 36 in Section 10–2.)

22. **Life Expectancies** Is there a relationship between the life expectancy for men and the life expectancy for women in a given country? A random sample of nonindustrialized countries was selected, and the life expectancy in years is listed for both men and women. Are the variables linearly related?

Men	59.7	72.9	41.9	46.2	50.3	43.2
Women	63.8	77.8	44.5	48.3	54.0	43.5

Source: *World Almanac.*

(The information in this exercise will be used for Exercise 22 in Section 10–2.)

23. **Literacy Rates** For the same countries used in Exercise 22, the literacy rates (in percents) for both men and women are listed. Is there a linear relationship between the variables? (The information in this exercise will be used for Exercise 23 in Section 10–2.)

Men (%)	43.1	92.6	65.7	27.9	61.5	76.7
Women (%)	12.6	86.4	45.9	15.4	46.3	96.1

Source: *World Almanac.*

24. **NHL Assists and Total Points** A random sample of scoring leaders from the NHL showed the following numbers of assists and total points. Based on these data, can it be concluded that there is a significant relationship between the two?

Assists	26	29	32	34	36	37	40
Total points	48	68	66	69	76	67	84

Source: *Associated Press.*

(The information in this exercise will be used for Exercise 24 in Section 10–2.)

25. **Bowling Scores** Men's and women's winning national championship bowling series scores are shown for a random selection of years. Is there a linear relationship between the variables?

Men	823	858	812	832	833	826
Women	752	754	771	736	792	763

(The information in this exercise will be used in Exercise 25 in Section 10–2.)

26. **Tall Buildings** An architect wants to determine the relationship between the heights (in feet) of a building and the number of stories in the building. The data for a sample of 10 buildings in Pittsburgh are shown. Explain the relationship.

Stories x	64	54	40	31	45	38	42	41	37	40
Height y	841	725	635	616	615	582	535	520	511	485

Source: *World Almanac Book of Facts.*

(The information in this exercise will be used for Exercise 26 in Section 10–2.)

27. **Class Size and Grades** School administrators wondered whether class size and grade achievement (in percent) were related. A random sample of classes revealed the following data. Are the variables linearly related?

No. of students	15	10	8	20	18	6
Avg. grade (%)	85	90	82	80	84	92

(The information in this exercise will be used for Exercise 28 of this section and Exercise 27 in Section 10–2.)

⊟ Extending the Concepts

28. One of the formulas for computing r is

$$r = \frac{\Sigma(x - \bar{x})(y - \bar{y})}{(n - 1)(s_x)(s_y)}$$

Using the data in Exercise 27, compute r with this formula. Compare the results.

29. Compute r for the data set shown. Explain the reason for this value of r. Now, interchange the values of x and y and

compute r again. Compare this value with the previous one. Explain the results of the comparison.

x	1	2	3	4	5
y	3	5	7	9	11

30. Compute r for the following data and test the hypothesis $H_0: \rho = 0$. Draw the scatter plot; then explain the results.

x	−3	−2	−1	0	1	2	3
y	9	4	1	0	1	4	9

10–2 Regression

OBJECTIVE ④

Compute the equation of the regression line.

In studying relationships between two variables, collect the data and then construct a scatter plot. The purpose of the scatter plot, as indicated previously, is to determine the nature of the relationship between the variables. The possibilities include a positive linear relationship, a negative linear relationship, a curvilinear relationship, or no discernible relationship. After the scatter plot is drawn and a linear relationship is determined, the next steps are to compute the value of the correlation coefficient and to test the significance of the relationship. If the value of the correlation coefficient is significant, the next step is to determine the equation of the **regression line,** which is the data's line of best fit. (*Note:* Determining the regression line when r is not significant and then making predictions using the regression line are meaningless.) The purpose of the regression line is to enable the researcher to see the trend and make predictions on the basis of the data.

Line of Best Fit

Figure 10–11 shows a scatter plot for the data of two variables. It shows that several lines can be drawn on the graph near the points. Given a scatter plot, you must be able to draw the *line of best fit*. *Best fit* means that the sum of the squares of the vertical distances from each point to the line is at a minimum.

FIGURE 10–11
Scatter Plot with Three Lines Fit to the Data

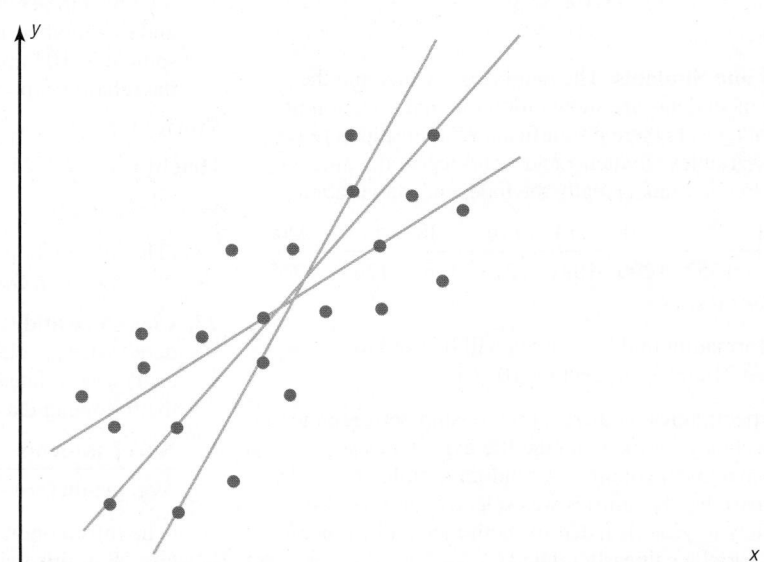

FIGURE 10–12

Line of Best Fit for a Set of Data Points

The difference between the actual value y and the predicted value y' (that is, the vertical distance) is called a **residual** or a predicted error. Residuals are used to determine the line that best describes the relationship between the two variables.

The method used for making the residuals as small as possible is called the *method of least squares*. As a result of this method, the regression line is also called the *least squares regression line*.

The reason you need a line of best fit is that the values of y will be predicted from the values of x; hence, the closer the points are to the line, the better the fit and the prediction will be. See Figure 10–12. When r is positive, the line slopes upward and to the right. When r is negative, the line slopes downward from left to right.

Determination of the Regression Line Equation

In algebra, the equation of a line is usually given as $y = mx + b$, where m is the slope of the line and b is the y intercept. (Students who need an algebraic review of the properties of a line should refer to the online resources, before studying this section.) In statistics, the equation of the regression line is written as $y' = a + bx$, where a is the y' intercept and b is the slope of the line. See Figure 10–13.

There are several methods for finding the equation of the regression line. Two formulas are given here. *These formulas use the same values that are used in computing the value of the correlation coefficient.* The mathematical development of these formulas is beyond the scope of this book.

Historical Notes

Francis Galton drew the line of best fit visually. An assistant of Karl Pearson's named G. Yule devised the mathematical solution using the least-squares method, employing a mathematical technique developed by Adrien-Marie Legendre about 100 years earlier.

FIGURE 10–13   A Line as Represented in Algebra and in Statistics

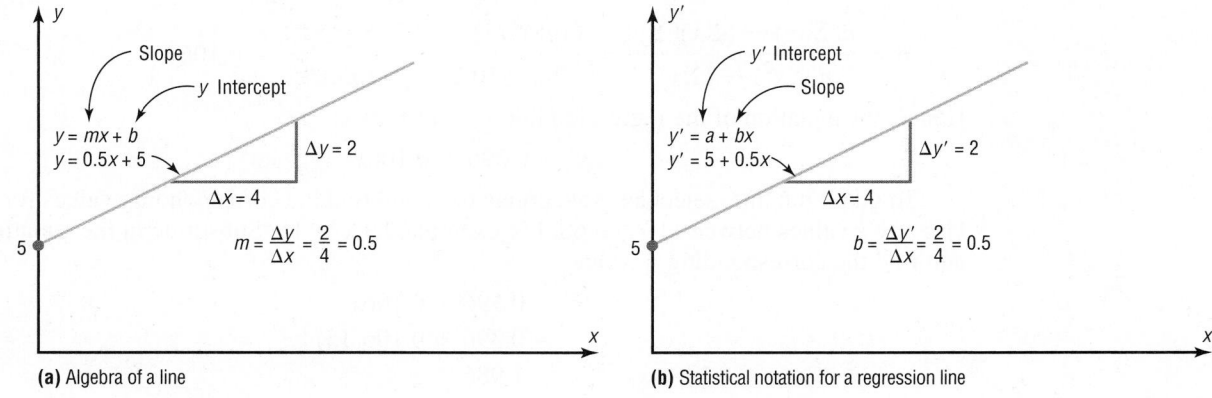

(a) Algebra of a line

(b) Statistical notation for a regression line

Formulas for the Regression Line $y' = a + bx$

$$a = \frac{(\Sigma y)(\Sigma x^2) - (\Sigma x)(\Sigma xy)}{n(\Sigma x^2) - (\Sigma x)^2}$$

$$b = \frac{n(\Sigma xy) - (\Sigma x)(\Sigma y)}{n(\Sigma x^2) - (\Sigma x)^2}$$

where a is the y' intercept and b is the slope of the line.

Rounding Rule for the Intercept and Slope   Round the values of a and b to three decimal places.

The steps for finding the regression line equation are summarized in this Procedure Table:

Procedure Table

Finding the Regression Line Equation

Step 1   Make a table, as shown in step 2.

Step 2   Find the values of xy, x^2, and y^2. Place them in the appropriate columns and sum each column.

x	y	xy	x^2	y^2
.	.	.	.	.
.	.	.	.	.
.	.	.	.	.
$\Sigma x =$	$\Sigma y =$	$\Sigma xy =$	$\Sigma x^2 =$	$\Sigma y^2 =$

Step 3   When r is significant, substitute in the formulas to find the values of a and b for the regression line equation $y' = a + bx$.

$$a = \frac{(\Sigma y)(\Sigma x^2) - (\Sigma x)(\Sigma xy)}{n(\Sigma x^2) - (\Sigma x)^2} \qquad b = \frac{n(\Sigma xy) - (\Sigma x)(\Sigma y)}{n(\Sigma x^2) - (\Sigma x)^2}$$

EXAMPLE 10–9   Car Rental Companies

Find the equation of the regression line for the data in Example 10–4, and graph the line on the scatter plot of the data.

SOLUTION

The values needed for the equation are $n = 6$, $\Sigma x = 153.8$, $\Sigma y = 18.7$, $\Sigma xy = 682.77$, and $\Sigma x^2 = 5859.26$. Substituting in the formulas, you get

$$a = \frac{(\Sigma y)(\Sigma x^2) - (\Sigma x)(\Sigma xy)}{n(\Sigma x^2) - (\Sigma x)^2} = \frac{(18.7)(5859.26) - (153.8)(682.77)}{(6)(5859.26) - (153.8)^2} = 0.396$$

$$b = \frac{n(\Sigma xy) - (\Sigma x)(\Sigma y)}{n(\Sigma x^2) - (\Sigma x)^2} = \frac{6(682.77) - (153.8)(18.7)}{(6)(5859.26) - (153.8)^2} = 0.106$$

Hence, the equation of the regression line $y' = a + bx$ is

$$y' = 0.396 + 0.106x$$

To graph the line, select any two points for x and find the corresponding values for y. Use any x values between 10 and 60. For example, let $x = 15$. Substitute in the equation and find the corresponding y' value.

$$y' = 0.396 + 0.106x$$
$$= 0.396 + 0.106(15)$$
$$= 1.986$$

Let $x = 40$; then

$$y' = 0.396 + 0.106x$$
$$= 0.396 + 0.106(40)$$
$$= 4.636$$

Then plot the two points $(15, 1.986)$ and $(40, 4.636)$ and draw a line connecting the two points. See Figure 10–14.

FIGURE 10–14   Regression Line for Example 10–9

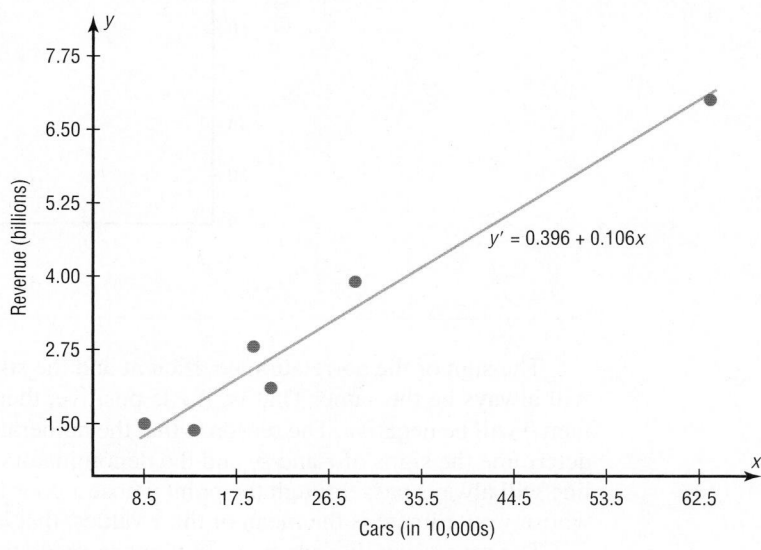

Note: When you draw the regression line, it is sometimes necessary to *truncate* the graph (see Chapter 2). This is done when the distance between the origin and the first labeled coordinate on the x axis is not the same as the distance between the rest of the labeled x coordinates or the distance between the origin and the first labeled y' coordinate is not the same as the distance between the other labeled y' coordinates. When the x axis or the y axis has been truncated, do not use the y' intercept value to graph the line. When you graph the regression line, always select x values between the smallest x data value and the largest x data value.

EXAMPLE 10–10   Absences and Final Grades

Find the equation of the regression line for the data in Example 10–5, and graph the line on the scatter plot.

SOLUTION

The values needed for the equation are $n = 7$, $\Sigma x = 57$, $\Sigma y = 511$, $\Sigma xy = 3745$, and $\Sigma x^2 = 579$. Substituting in the formulas, you get

$$a = \frac{(\Sigma y)(\Sigma x^2) - (\Sigma x)(\Sigma xy)}{n(\Sigma x^2) - (\Sigma x)^2} = \frac{(511)(579) - (57)(3745)}{(7)(579) - (57)^2} = 102.493$$

$$b = \frac{n(\Sigma xy) - (\Sigma x)(\Sigma y)}{n(\Sigma x^2) - (\Sigma x)^2} = \frac{(7)(3745) - (57)(511)}{(7)(579) - (57)^2} = -3.622$$

Hence, the equation of the regression line $y' = a + bx$ is

$$y' = 102.493 - 3.622x$$

Historical Note

In 1795, Adrien-Marie Legendre (1752–1833) measured the meridian arc on the earth's surface from Barcelona, Spain, to Dunkirk, England. This measure was used as the basis for the measure of the meter. Legendre developed the least-squares method around the year 1805.

The graph of the line is shown in Figure 10–15.

FIGURE 10–15

Regression Line for
Example 10–10

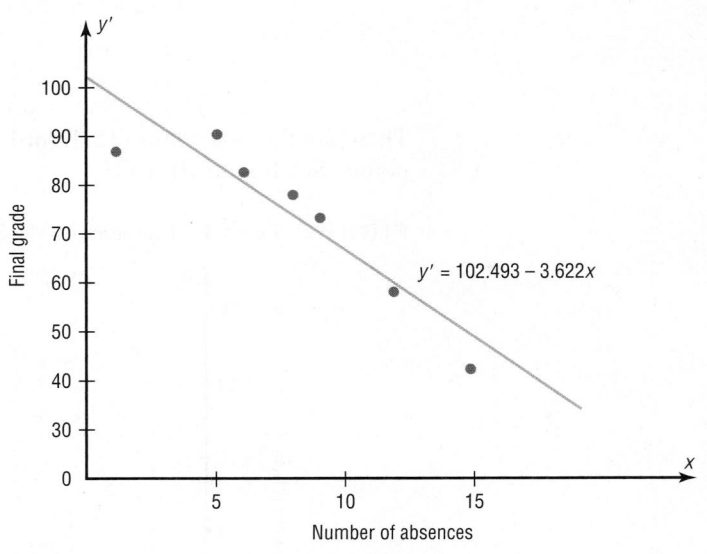

$y' = 102.493 - 3.622x$

The sign of the correlation coefficient and the sign of the slope of the regression line will always be the same. That is, if r is positive, then b will be positive; if r is negative, then b will be negative. The reason is that the numerators of the formulas are the same and determine the signs of r and b, and the denominators are always positive. The regression line will always pass through the point whose x coordinate is the mean of the x values and whose y coordinate is the mean of the y values, that is, $(\bar{x}, \bar{y})$.

The regression line can be used to make predictions for the dependent variable. You should use these guidelines when you are making predictions.

1. The points of the scatter plot fit the linear regression line reasonably well.
2. The value of r is significant.
3. The value of a specific x is not much beyond the observed values (x values) in the original data.
4. If r is not significant, then the best predicted value for a specific x value is the mean of the y value in the original data.

Assumptions for Valid Predictions in Regression

1. The sample is a random sample.
2. For any specific value of the independent variable x, the value of the dependent variable y must be normally distributed about the regression line. See Figure 10–16(a).
3. The standard deviation of each of the dependent variables must be the same for each value of the independent variable. See Figure 10–16(b).

FIGURE 10–16   Assumptions for Predictions

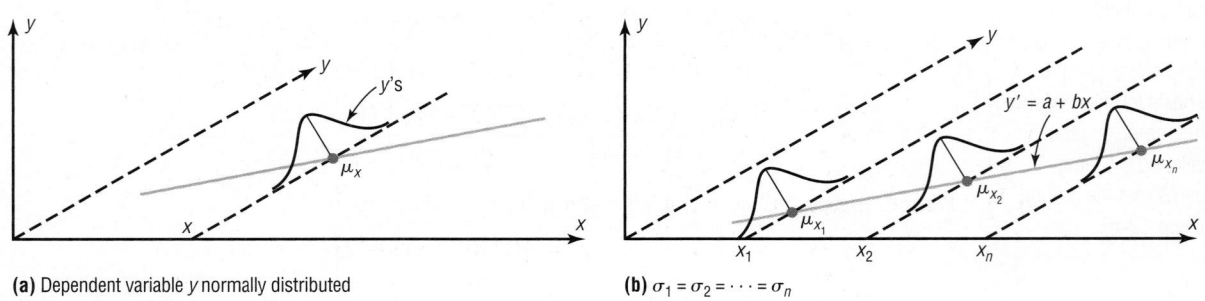

(a) Dependent variable y normally distributed

(b) $\sigma_1 = \sigma_2 = \cdots = \sigma_n$

In this book, the assumptions will be stated in the exercises; however, when encountering statistics in other situations, you must check to see that these assumptions have been met before proceeding.

The method for making predictions is shown in Example 10–11.

EXAMPLE 10–11   Car Rental Companies

Use the equation of the regression line to predict the income of a car rental agency that has 200,000 automobiles.

SOLUTION

Since the x values are in 10,000s, divide 200,000 by 10,000 to get 20, and then substitute 20 for x in the equation.

$$y' = 0.396 + 0.106x$$
$$= 0.396 + 0.106(20)$$
$$= 2.516$$

Hence, when a rental agency has 200,000 automobiles, its revenue will be approximately $2.516 billion.

The value obtained in Example 10–11 is a point prediction, and with point predictions, no degree of accuracy or confidence can be determined. More information on prediction is given in Section 10–3.

The magnitude of the change in one variable when the other variable changes exactly 1 unit is called a **marginal change.** The value of slope b of the regression line equation represents the marginal change. For example, in Example 10–9 the slope of the regression line is 0.106, which means for each additional increase of 10,000 cars, the value of y changes 0.106 unit ($106 million) on average.

Extrapolation, or making predictions beyond the bounds of the data, must be interpreted cautiously. For example, in 1979, some experts predicted that the United States would run out of oil by the year 2003. This prediction was based on the current consumption and on known oil reserves at that time. However, since then, the automobile industry has produced many new fuel-efficient vehicles. Also, there are many as yet undiscovered oil fields. Finally, science may someday discover a way to run a car on something as unlikely but as common as peanut oil. In addition, the price of a gallon of gasoline was predicted to reach $10 a few years later. Fortunately this has not come to pass. *Remember that when predictions are made, they are based on present conditions or on the premise that present trends will continue.* This assumption may or may not prove true in the future.

A scatter plot should be checked for outliers. An outlier is a point that seems out of place when compared with the other points (see Chapter 3). Some of these points can affect the equation of the regression line. When this happens, the points are called **influential points** or **influential observations.**

When a point on the scatter plot appears to be an outlier, it should be checked to see if it is an influential point. An influential point tends to "pull" the regression line toward the point itself. To check for an influential point, the regression line should be graphed with the point included in the data set. Then a second regression line should be graphed that excludes the point from the data set. If the position of the second line is changed considerably, the point is said to be an influential point. Points that are outliers in the x direction tend to be influential points.

Researchers should use their judgment as to whether to include influential observations in the final analysis of the data. If the researcher feels that the observation is not necessary, then it should be excluded so that it does not influence the results of the study. However, if the researcher feels that it is necessary, then he or she may want to obtain additional data values whose x values are near the x value of the influential point and then include them in the study.

Interesting Fact

It is estimated that wearing a motorcycle helmet reduces the risk of a fatal accident by 30%.

"Explain that to me."

© Dave Carpenter. King Features Syndicate.

Applying the Concepts 10–2

Stopping Distances Revisited

In a study on speed and braking distance, researchers looked for a method to estimate how fast a person was traveling before an accident by measuring the length of the skid marks. An area that was focused on in the study was the distance required to completely stop a vehicle at various speeds. Use the following table to answer the questions.

MPH	Braking distance (feet)
20	20
30	45
40	81
50	133
60	205
80	411

Assume MPH is going to be used to predict stopping distance.

1. Find the linear regression equation.
2. What does the slope tell you about MPH and the braking distance? How about the y' intercept?
3. Find the braking distance when MPH = 45.
4. Find the braking distance when MPH = 100.
5. Comment on predicting beyond the given data values.

See page 607 for the answers.

Exercises 10–2

1. What two things should be done before one performs a regression analysis?

2. What are the assumptions for regression analysis?

3. What is the general form for the regression line used in statistics?

4. What is the symbol for the slope? For the y' intercept?

5. What is meant by the *line of best fit?*

6. When all the points fall on the regression line, what is the value of the correlation coefficient?

7. What is the relationship between the sign of the correlation coefficient and the sign of the slope of the regression line?

8. As the value of the correlation coefficient increases from 0 to 1, or decreases from 0 to −1, how do the points of the scatter plot fit the regression line?

9. How is the value of the correlation coefficient related to the accuracy of the predicted value for a specific value of x?

10. When the value of r is not significant, what value should be used to predict y?

For Exercises 11 through 27, use the same data as for the corresponding exercises in Section 10–1. For each exercise, find the equation of the regression line and find the y' value for the specified x value. Remember that no regression should be done when r is not significant.

11. **Crimes** The number of murders and robberies per 100,000 population for a random selection of states are shown.

Murders	2.4	2.7	5.6	2.6	2.1	3.3	6.6	5.7
Robberies	25.3	14.3	151.6	91.1	80	49	173	95.8

Find y' when $x = 4.5$ murders.

12. **Oil and Gas Prices** The average gasoline price per gallon (in cities) and the cost of a barrel of oil are shown below for a random selection of weeks from 2009–2010.

Oil ($)	46.25	37.51	78.00	75.39	84.88	73.78
Gasoline ($)	2.197	2.182	2.987	3.015	3.109	3.000

Find the cost of gasoline when oil is $60 a barrel.

13. **Commercial Movie Releases** New movie releases per studio and gross receipts are as follows:

No. of releases	361	270	306	22	35	10	8	12	21
Gross receipts (million $)	3844	1962	1371	1064	334	241	188	154	125

Find y' when $x = 200$ new releases.

14. Forest Fires and Acres Burned Number of fires and number of acres burned are as follows:

Fires x	72	69	58	47	84	62	57	45
Acres y	62	42	19	26	51	15	30	15

Find y' when $x = 60$ fires.

15. Alumni Contributions Years and contribution data are as follows:

Years x	1	5	3	10	7	6
Contribution y, $	500	100	300	50	75	80

Find y' when $x = 4$ years.

16. State Debt and Per Capita Taxes Data for per capita state debt and per capita state tax are as follows:

Per capita debt	1924	907	1445	1608	661
Per capita tax	1685	1838	1734	1842	1317

Find y' when $x = \$1500$ in per capita debt.

17. Energy Consumption The annual energy consumption in billions of Btu for both natural gas and coal is shown for a random selection of states.

Gas	223	474	377	289	747	146
Coal	478	631	413	356	736	474

Find the amount of coal used when 500 Btu of natural gas is used.

18. Triples and Home Runs The number of triples and the number of home runs obtained by a selected sample of MLB players are shown.

Triples	25	23	51	19	20	43
Home runs	212	199	144	160	149	122

Find y' when $x = 33$.

19. Carbohydrates and Kilograms There are many interesting relationships among the various nutrients found in fruits and vegetables. Listed below are the number of grams of carbohydrates and the number of kilocalories for a 100-gram sample of various raw foods.

Carbs	15.25	16.55	11.10	13.01	14.13	15.11
kcal	59	72	43	55	56	59

Find the number of calories in 100 g of a fruit with 12 g of carbs.

20. Water and Carbohydrates Continuing the theme of fruits and vegetables, here are the number of grams of water and the number of grams of carbohydrates for a random selection of raw foods (100 g each).

Water	83.93	80.76	87.66	85.20	72.85	84.61	83.81
Carbs	15.25	16.55	11.10	13.01	24.27	14.13	15.11

Find y' for $x = 75$.

21. Faculty and Students The number of faculty and the number of students in a random selection of small colleges are shown.

Faculty	99	110	113	116	138	174	220
Students	1353	1290	1091	1213	1384	1283	2075

Now find the equation of the regression line when x is the variable of the number of students.

22. Life Expectancies A random sample of nonindustrialized countries was selected, and the life expectancy in years is listed for both men and women.

Men	59.7	72.9	41.9	46.2	50.3	43.2
Women	63.8	77.8	44.5	48.3	54.0	43.5

Find women's life expectancy in a country where men's life expectancy = 60 years.

23. Literacy Rates For the same countries used in Exercise 22, the literacy rates (in percents) for both men and women are listed.

Men	43.1	92.6	65.7	27.9	61.5	76.7
Women	12.6	86.4	45.9	15.4	46.3	96.1

Find y' when $x = 80$.

24. NHL Assists and Total Points The number of assists and the total number of points for a sample of NHL scoring leaders are shown.

Assists	26	29	32	34	36	37	40
Total points	48	68	66	69	76	67	84

Find y' when $x = 30$ assists.

25. Bowling Scores Men's and women's winning national championship bowling series scores are shown for a random selection of years.

Men	823	858	812	832	833	826
Women	752	754	771	736	792	763

Find y' when $x = 810$.

26. Tall Buildings Stories and heights of buildings data follow:

Stories x	64	54	40	31	45	38	42	41	37	40
Heights y	841	725	635	616	615	582	535	520	511	485

Find y' when $x = 44$.

27. Class Size and Grades School administrators wondered whether class size and grade achievement (in percent) were related. A random sample of classes revealed the following data.

No. of students	15	10	8	20	18	6
Avg. grade (%)	85	90	82	80	84	92

Find y' when $x = 12$.

For Exercises 28 through 33, do a complete regression analysis by performing these steps.

    a. Draw a scatter plot.

    b. Compute the correlation coefficient.

    c. State the hypotheses.

d. Test the hypotheses at $\alpha = 0.05$. Use Table I.

e. Determine the regression line equation if r is significant.

f. Plot the regression line on the scatter plot, if appropriate.

g. Summarize the results.

28. **Fireworks and Injuries** These data were obtained for the years 1993 through 1998 and indicate the number of fireworks (in millions) used and the related injuries. Predict the number of injuries if 100 million fireworks are used during a given year.

Fireworks in use x	67.6	87.1	117	115	118	113
Related injuries y	12,100	12,600	12,500	10,900	7800	7000

Source: National Council of Fireworks Safety, American Pyrotechnic Assoc.

29. **Farm Acreage** Is there a relationship between the number of farms in a state and the acreage per farm? A random selection of states across the country, both eastern and western, produced the following results. Can a relationship between these two variables be concluded?

No. of farms (thousands) x	77	52	20.8	49	28	58.2
Acreage per farm y	347	173	173	218	246	132

Source: *World Almanac.*

30. **SAT Scores** Educational researchers desired to find out if a relationship exists between the average SAT verbal score and the average SAT mathematical score. Several states were randomly selected, and their SAT average scores are recorded below. Is there sufficient evidence to conclude a relationship between the two scores?

Verbal x	526	504	594	585	503	589
Math y	530	522	606	588	517	589

Source: *World Almanac.*

31. **Coal Production** These data were obtained from a sample of counties in southwestern Pennsylvania and indicate the number (in thousands) of tons of bituminous coal produced in each county and the number of employees working in coal production in each county.

Predict the amount of coal produced for a county that has 500 employees.

No. of employees x	110	731	1031	20	118	1162	103	752
Tons y	227	5410	5328	147	729	8095	635	6157

32. **Television Viewers** A television executive selects 10 television shows and compares the average number of viewers the show had last year with the average number of viewers this year. The data (in millions) are shown. Describe the relationship.

Viewers last year x	26.6	17.85	20.3	16.8	20.8
Viewers this year y	28.9	19.2	26.4	13.7	20.2
Viewers last year x	16.7	19.1	18.9	16.0	15.8
Viewers this year y	18.8	25.0	21.0	16.8	15.3

Source: Nielsen Media Research.

33. **Absences and Final Grades** An educator wants to see how the number of absences for a student in her class affects the student's final grade. The data obtained from a sample are shown.

No. of absences x	10	12	2	0	8	5
Final grade y	70	65	96	94	75	82

For Exercises 34 and 35, do a complete regression analysis and test the significance of r at $\alpha = 0.05$, using the P-value method.

34. **Father's and Son's Weights** A physician wishes to know whether there is a relationship between a father's weight (in pounds) and his newborn son's weight (in pounds). The data are given here.

Father's weight x	176	160	187	210	196	142	205	215
Son's weight y	6.6	8.2	9.2	7.1	8.8	9.3	7.4	8.6

35. **Age and Net Worth** Is a person's age related to his or her net worth? A sample of 10 billionaires is selected, and the person's age and net worth are compared. The data are given here.

Age x	56	39	42	60	84	37	68	66	73	55
Net worth y (billion $)	18	14	12	14	11	10	10	7	7	5

Source: The Associated Press.

Extending the Concepts

36. For Exercises 13, 15, and 21 in Section 10–1, find the mean of the x and y variables. Then substitute the mean of the x variable into the corresponding regression line equations found in Exercises 13, 15, and 21 in this section and find y'. Compare the value of y' with $\bar{y}$ for each exercise. Generalize the results.

37. The y intercept value a can also be found by using the equation

$$a = \bar{y} - b\bar{x}$$

Verify this result by using the data in Exercises 15 and 16 of Sections 10–1 and 10–2.

38. The value of the correlation coefficient can also be found by using the formula

$$r = \frac{b s_x}{s_y}$$

where s_x is the standard deviation of the x values and s_y is the standard deviation of the y values. Verify this result for Exercises 18 and 20 of Section 10–1.

▲ Technology

TI-84 Plus

Step by Step

Step by Step

Correlation and Regression

To graph a scatter plot:

1. Enter the x values in L_1 and the y values in L_2.

2. Make sure the Window values are appropriate. Select an Xmin slightly less than the smallest x data value and an Xmax slightly larger than the largest x data value. Do the same for Ymin and Ymax. Also, you may need to change the Xscl and Yscl values, depending on the data.

3. Press **2nd [STAT PLOT] 1** for Plot 1. The other y functions should be turned off.

4. Move the cursor to On and press **ENTER** on the Plot 1 menu.

5. Move the cursor to the graphic that looks like a scatter plot next to Type (first graph), and press **ENTER.** Make sure the X list is L_1 and the Y list is L_2.

6. Press **GRAPH.**

Example TI10–1

Draw a scatter plot for the following data.

x	43	48	56	61	67	70
y	128	120	135	143	141	152

The input and output screens are shown.

Input	Input	Output

  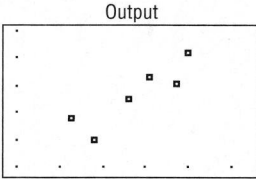

To find the equation of the regression line:

1. Press **STAT** and move the cursor to Calc.

2. Press **8** for LinReg(a+bx) then **ENTER.** The values for a and b will be displayed.

To have the calculator compute and display the correlation coefficient and coefficient of determination as well as the equation of the line, you must set the diagnostics display mode to on. Follow these steps:

1. Press **2nd [CATALOG].**

2. Use the arrow keys to scroll down to DiagnosticOn.

3. Press **ENTER** to copy the command to the home screen.

4. Press **ENTER** to execute the command.

You will have to do this only once. Diagnostic display mode will remain on until you perform a similar set of steps to turn it off.

Example TI10–2

Find the equation of the regression line for the data in Example TI10–1. The input and output screens are shown.

Input	Output

The equation of the regression line is $y' = 81.04808549 + 0.964381122x$.

To plot the regression line on the scatter plot:

1. Press **Y=** and **CLEAR** to clear any previous equations.

2. Press **VARS** and then **5** for Statistics.

3. Move the cursor to EQ and press **1** for RegEQ. The line will be in the Y= screen.

4. Press **GRAPH.**

Example TI10–3

Draw the regression line found in Example TI10–2 on the scatter plot.

The output screens are shown.

Output   Output

To test the significance of b and ρ:

1. Press **STAT** and move the cursor to TESTS.

2. Press **F (ALPHA COS)** for LinRegTTest. Make sure the Xlist is L_1, the Ylist is L_2, and the Freq is 1.

3. Select the appropriate Alternative hypothesis.

4. Move the cursor to Calculate and press **ENTER.**

Example TI10–4

Test the hypothesis H_0: $\rho = 0$ for the data in Example TI 10–1. Use $\alpha = 0.05$.

Input   Output   Output

In this case, the t test value is 4.050983638. The P-value is 0.0154631742, which is significant. The decision is to reject the null hypothesis at $\alpha = 0.05$, since $0.0154631742 < 0.05$; $r = 0.8966728145$, $r^2 = 0.8040221364$.

There are two other ways to store the equation for the regression line in Y_1 for graphing.

1. Type Y_1 after the LinReg(a+bx) command.

2. Type Y_1 in the RegEQ: spot in the LinRegTTest.

To get Y_1 do this:

Press **VARS** for variables, move cursor to Y-VARS, press **1** for Function, and press **1** for Y_1.

EXCEL
Step by Step

Example XL10–1

Use the following data to create a **Scatter Plot,** calculate a **Correlation Coefficient,** and perform a simple linear **Regression Analysis.**

x	43	48	56	61	67	70
y	128	120	135	143	141	152

Enter the data from the example above in a new worksheet. Enter the six values for the x variable in column A and the corresponding y variable in column B.

Scatter Plot

1. Select the Insert tab from the toolbar.

2. Highlight the cells containing the data by holding the left mouse key over the first cell and dragging over the other cells.

3. Select the Scatter Chart type and choose the Scatter plot type in the upper left-hand corner.

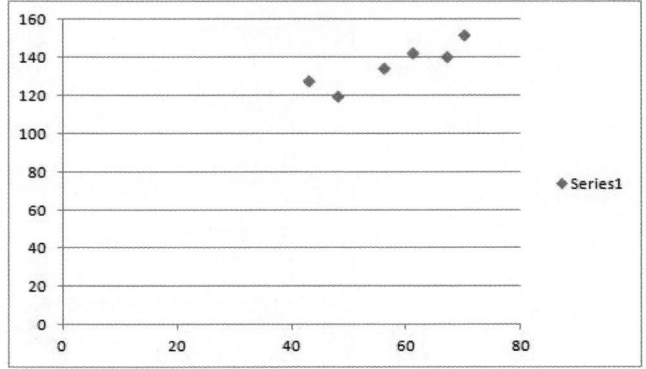

Correlation Coefficient

1. Select any blank cell in the worksheet and then select the insert Function tab from the toolbar.

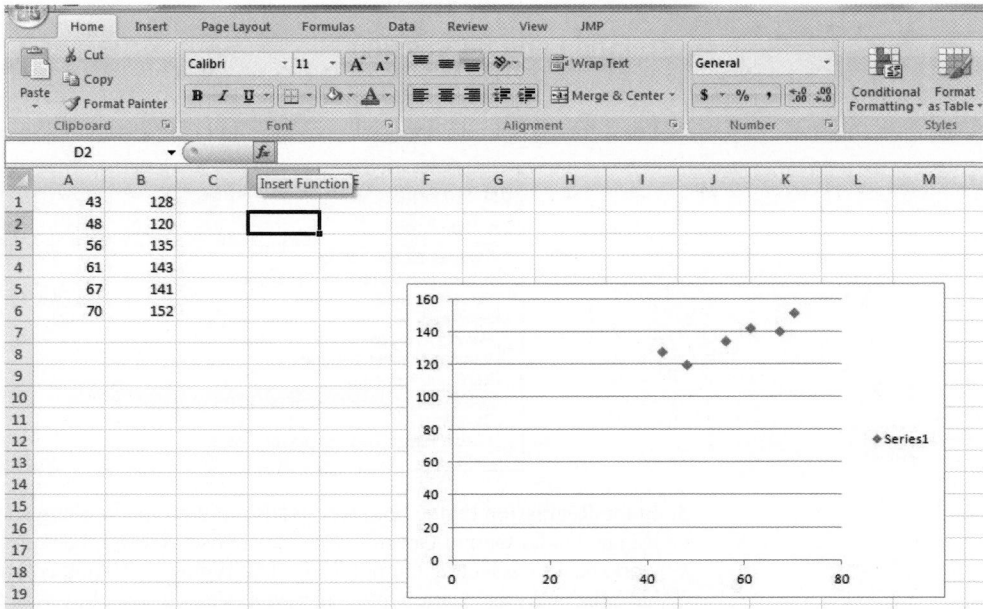

2. From the Insert Function dialog box, select the Statistical category and scroll to the CORREL function (this function will produce the Pearson-Product Moment Correlation Coefficient for the data).

3. Enter the data range A1:A6 for the *x* variable in Array 1 and B1:B6 for the *y* variable in Array 2.

4. Click OK.

Correlation and Regression

1. Select the Data tab from the toolbar, then select the Data Analysis add-in.
2. From Analysis Tools, choose Regression and then click OK.

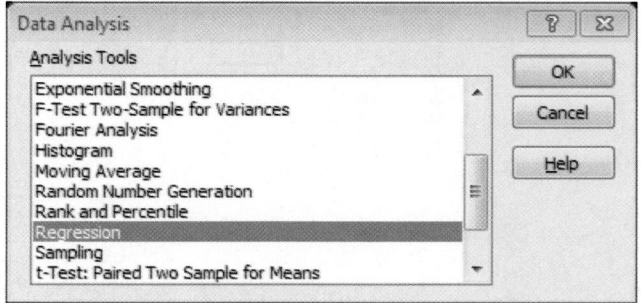

3. In the Regression dialog box, type B1:B6 in the Input Y Range and A1:A6 in the Input X Range. Under Output Options, you can choose to insert the regression analysis in the current worksheet by selecting Output Range and typing in a blank cell name. Or you can choose to have the analysis inserted into a new worksheet in Excel by selecting New Worksheet Ply.

4. Click OK.

5. Once you have the output in a worksheet, you can adjust the cell widths to accommodate the numbers. Then you can see all the decimal places in the output by choosing the Home tab on the Toolbar, highlighting the output, then selecting Format>AutoFit Column Width.

SUMMARY OUTPUT								
Regression Statistics								
Multiple R	0.896672815							
R Square	0.804022136							
Adjusted R Square	0.75502767							
Standard Error	5.641090817							
Observations	6							
ANOVA								
	df	*SS*	*MS*	*F*	*Significance F*			
Regression	1	522.2123776	522.2123776	16.41046844	0.015463174			
Residual	4	127.2876224	31.82190561					
Total	5	649.5						
	Coefficients	*Standard Error*	*t Stat*	*P-value*	*Lower 95%*	*Upper 95%*	*Lower 95.0%*	*Upper 95.0%*
Intercept	81.04808549	13.88088081	5.838828717	0.004289034	42.50858191	119.5875891	42.50858191	119.5875891
X Variable 1	0.964381122	0.238060977	4.050983638	0.015463174	0.303417888	1.625344356	0.303417888	1.625344356

MINITAB
Step by Step

Use these data from Examples 10–2, 10–5, and 10–10 concerning final grades versus absences.

C1 Subject	C2 Absences	C3 Final Grade
A	6	82
B	2	86
C	15	43
D	9	74
E	12	58
F	5	90
G	8	78

Create a Scatter Plot

1. Enter these data into the first three columns of a MINITAB worksheet.

2. Select Graph>Scatterplot, then choose **Simple with Regression** and click [OK].

   a) Double-click C3 Final grade for the Y variable

   b) Double-click C2 Absences for the X variable.

   c) Click the button for [Labels].

      i) Type in a title for the graph such as Final Grade vs Number of Absences.

      ii) Type your name in the box for Footnote 1.

      iii) Optional: Click the tab for Data Labels then the ratio button for Use labels from column; select C1 Student. You may need to click in the dialog box before you see the list of columns.

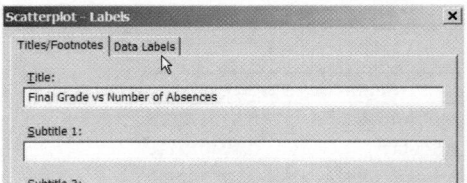

d) Click **[OK]** twice. The graph will open in a new window. MINITAB shows the regression line.

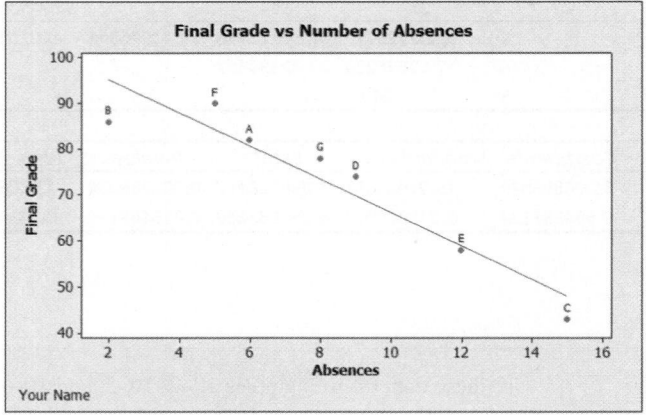

Calculate the Correlation Coefficient, *r*

3. Select **Stat>Basic Statistics>Correlation**.

a) Double-click C3 Final Grade then C2 Absences. Put Y, the dependent variable, first.

b) Click [OK].

The correlation coefficient $r = -0.944$ and the *P*-value $= 0.001$ for the test will be displayed in the Session Window.

Determine the Line of Best Fit

4. Select **Stat>Regression>Regression**.

a) Double-click C3 Final Grade for the Response variable Y.

b) Double-click C2 Absences for the Predictor variable.

c) Click the button for [Storage], then select Residuals and Fits, and click [OK] twice.

5. Select **Data>Data Display**.

a) Drag your mouse over all five columns; then click the [Select] button and [OK].

b) The data in the worksheet will be copied into the Session Window.

Create a Report and Print It

6. Click on the Project Manager icon or select **Window>Project Manager** on the menu bar.

a) Click on the date.

b) Hold down the Shift key while you click on the last item, Data Display.

c) Right-click over the highlighted items, then select **Send to Microsoft Word**®. Alternately you may send it to a presentation instead of a document.

Caution: If a Word document is open, the content will be inserted into the open document.

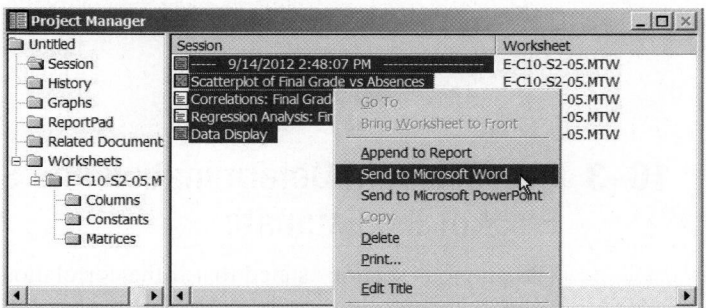

Here is a copy of the report.

Correlations: Final Grade, Absences
Pearson correlation of Final Grade and Absences $= -0.944$
P-Value $= 0.001$

Regression Analysis: Final Grade versus Absences
The regression equation is
Final Grade $= 102 - 3.62$ Absences

Predictor	Coef	SE Coef	T	P
Constant	102.493	5.138	19.95	0.000
Absences	-3.6219	0.5649	-6.41	0.001

$S = 6.05464$ $R-Sq = 89.2\%$ $R-Sq(adj) = 87.0\%$

Analysis of Variance

Source	DF	SS	MS	F	P
Regression	1	1506.7	1506.7	41.10	0.001
Residual Error	5	183.3	36.7		
Total	6	1690.0			

Unusual Observations

Obs	Absences	Final Grade	Fit	SE Fit	Residual	St Resid
2	2.0	86.00	95.25	4.16	-9.25	-2.10R

R denotes an observation with a large standardized residual.

Data Display

Row	Student	Absences	Final Grade	RESI1	FITS1
1	A	6	82	1.23881	80.7612
2	B	2	86	−9.24876	95.2488
3	C	15	43	−5.16418	48.1642
4	D	9	74	4.10448	69.8955
5	E	12	58	−1.02985	59.0299
6	F	5	90	5.61692	84.3831
7	G	8	78	4.48259	73.5174

10–3 Coefficient of Determination and Standard Error of the Estimate

The previous sections stated that if the correlation coefficient is significant, the equation of the regression line can be determined. Also, for various values of the independent variable x, the corresponding values of the dependent variable y can be predicted. Several other measures are associated with the correlation and regression techniques. They include the coefficient of determination, the standard error of the estimate, and the prediction interval. But before these concepts can be explained, the different types of variation associated with the regression model must be defined.

Types of Variation for the Regression Model

Consider the following hypothetical regression model.

x	1	2	3	4	5
y	10	8	12	16	20

The equation of the regression line is $y' = 4.8 + 2.8x$, and $r = 0.919$. The sample y values are 10, 8, 12, 16, and 20. The predicted values, designated by y', for each x can be found by substituting each x value into the regression equation and finding y'. For example, when $x = 1$,

$$y' = 4.8 + 2.8x = 4.8 + (2.8)(1) = 7.6$$

Now, for each x, there is an observed y value and a predicted y' value; for example, when $x = 1$, $y = 10$ and $y' = 7.6$. Recall that the closer the observed values are to the predicted values, the better the fit is and the closer r is to $+1$ or -1.

The *total variation* $\Sigma(y - \bar{y})^2$ is the sum of the squares of the vertical distances each point is from the mean. The total variation can be divided into two parts: that which is attributed to the relationship of x and y and that which is due to chance. The variation obtained from the relationship (i.e., from the predicted y' values) is $\Sigma(y' - \bar{y})^2$ and is called the *explained variation*.

In other words, the explained variation is the vertical distance $y' - \bar{y}$, which is the distance between the predicted value y' and the mean value $\bar{y}$. Most of the variations can be explained by the relationship. The closer the value r is to $+1$ or -1, the better the points fit the line and the closer $\Sigma(y' - \bar{y})^2$ is to $\Sigma(y - \bar{y})^2$. In fact, if all points fall on the regression line, $\Sigma(y' - \bar{y})^2$ will equal $\Sigma(y - \bar{y})^2$, since y' is equal to y in each case.

On the other hand, the variation due to chance, found by $\Sigma(y - y')^2$, is called the *unexplained variation*. In other words, the unexplained variation is the vertical distance $y - y'$, which is the distance between the observed value, y, and the predicted value y'. This variation cannot be attributed to the relationship. When the unexplained variation is small, the value of r is close to $+1$ or -1. If all points fall on the regression line, the unexplained variation $\Sigma(y - y')^2$ will be 0. Hence, the *total variation* is equal to the sum of the explained variation and the unexplained variation. That is,

$$\Sigma(y - \bar{y})^2 = \Sigma(y' - \bar{y})^2 + \Sigma(y - y')^2$$

These values are shown in Figure 10–17. For a single point, the differences are called *deviations*. For the hypothetical regression model given earlier, for $x = 1$ and $y = 10$, you get $y' = 7.6$ and $\bar{y} = 13.2$.

FIGURE 10–17
Deviations for the Regression Equation

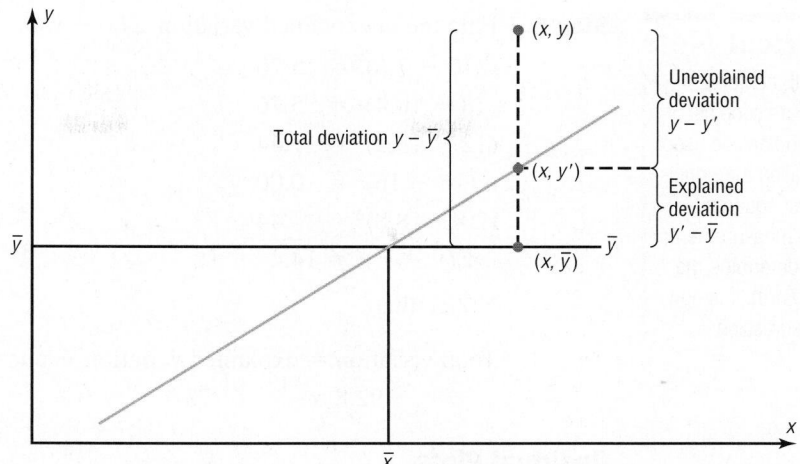

The procedure for finding the three types of variation is illustrated next.

Step 1   Find the predicted y' values.

For $x = 1$ $y' = 4.8 + 2.8x = 4.8 + (2.8)(1) = 7.6$

For $x = 2$ $y' = 4.8 + (2.8)(2) = 10.4$

For $x = 3$ $y' = 4.8 + (2.8)(3) = 13.2$

For $x = 4$ $y' = 4.8 + (2.8)(4) = 16.0$

For $x = 5$ $y' = 4.8 + (2.8)(5) = 18.8$

Hence, the values for this example are as follows:

x	y	y'
1	10	7.6
2	8	10.4
3	12	13.2
4	16	16.0
5	20	18.8

Step 2   Find the mean of the y values.

$$\bar{y} = \frac{10 + 8 + 12 + 16 + 20}{5} = 13.2$$

Step 3   Find the total variation $\Sigma(y - \bar{y})^2$.

$(10 - 13.2)^2 = 10.24$

$(8 - 13.2)^2 = 27.04$

$(12 - 13.2)^2 = 1.44$

$(16 - 13.2)^2 = 7.84$

$(20 - 13.2)^2 = \underline{46.24}$

$\Sigma(y - \bar{y})^2 = 92.8$

Step 4   Find the explained variation $\Sigma(y' - \bar{y})^2$.

$(7.6 - 13.2)^2 = 31.36$

$(10.4 - 13.2)^2 = 7.84$

$(13.2 - 13.2)^2 = 0.00$

$(16 - 13.2)^2 = 7.84$

$(18.8 - 13.2)^2 = \underline{31.36}$

$\Sigma(y' - \bar{y})^2 = 78.4$

Unusual Stat

There are 1,929,770, 126,028,800 different color combinations for Rubik's cube and only one correct solution in which all the colors of the squares on each face are the same.

Step 5   Find the unexplained variation $\Sigma(y - y')^2$.

$$(10 - 7.6)^2 = 5.76$$
$$(8 - 10.4)^2 = 5.76$$
$$(12 - 13.2)^2 = 1.44$$
$$(16 - 16)^2 = 0.00$$
$$(20 - 18.8)^2 = \underline{1.44}$$
$$\Sigma(y - y')^2 = 14.4$$

Notice that

Total variation = explained variation + unexplained variation
92.8 =   78.4   +   14.4

Residual Plots

As previously stated, the values $y - y'$ are called *residuals* (sometimes called the *prediction errors*). These values can be plotted with the x values, and the plot, called a **residual plot,** can be used to determine how well the regression line can be used to make predictions.

The residuals for the previous example are calculated as shown.

x	y	y′	y − y′ = residual
1	10	7.6	10 − 7.6 = 2.4
2	8	10.4	8 − 10.4 = −2.4
3	12	13.2	12 − 13.2 = −1.2
4	16	16	16 − 16 = 0
5	20	18.8	20 − 18.8 = 1.2

The x values are plotted using the horizontal axis, and the residuals are plotted using the vertical axis. Since the mean of the residuals is always zero, a horizontal line with a y coordinate of zero is placed on the y axis as shown in Figure 10–18.

Plot the x and residual values as shown in Figure 10–18.

x	1	2	3	4	5
y − y′	2.4	−2.4	−1.2	0	1.2

To interpret a residual plot, you need to determine if the residuals form a pattern. Figure 10–19 shows four examples of residual plots. If the residual values are more or less evenly distributed about the line, as shown in Figure 10–19(a), then the relationship

FIGURE 10–18
Residual Plot

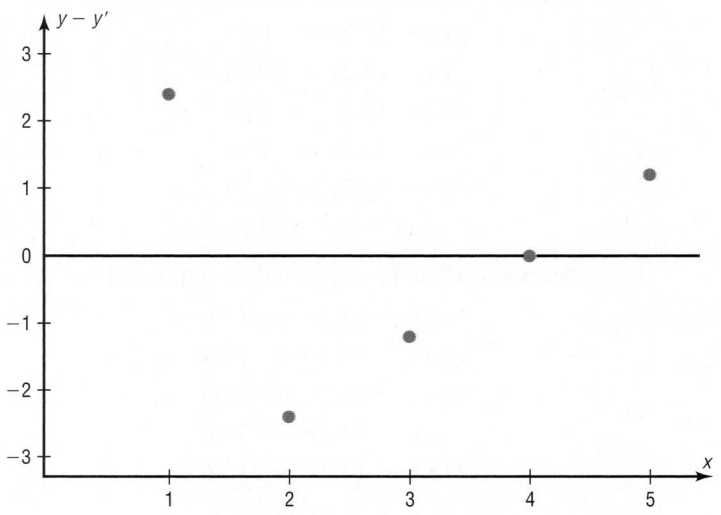

FIGURE 10–19

Examples of
Residual Plots

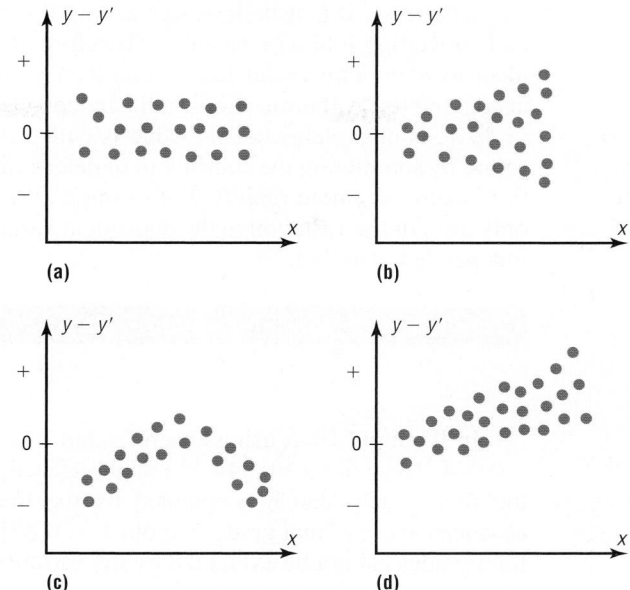

between x and y is linear and the regression line can be used to make predictions. This means that the standard deviations of each of the dependent variables must be the same for each value of the independent variable. This is called the *homoscedasticity assumption*. See assumption 3 on page 570.

Figure 10–19(b) shows that the variance of the residuals increases as the values of x increase. This means that the regression line is not suitable for predictions.

Figure 10–19(c) shows a curvilinear relationship between the x values and the residual values; hence, the regression line is not suitable for making predictions.

Figure 10–19(d) shows that as the x values increase, the residuals increase and become more dispersed. This means that the regression line is not suitable for making predictions.

The residual plot in Figure 10–18 shows that the regression line $y' = 4.8 + 2.8x$ is somewhat questionable for making predictions due to a small sample size.

OBJECTIVE ⑤

Compute the coefficient of
determination.

Coefficient of Determination

The *coefficient of determination* is the ratio of the explained variation to the total variation and is denoted by r^2. That is,

$$r^2 = \frac{\text{explained variation}}{\text{total variation}}$$

> The **coefficient of determination** is a measure of the variation of the dependent variable that is explained by the regression line and the independent variable. The symbol for the coefficient of determination is r^2.

Historical Note

Karl Pearson recommended in 1897 that the French government close all its casinos and turn the gambling devices over to the academic community to use in the study of probability.

The coefficient of determination is a number between 0 and 1 inclusive, or $0 \le r^2 \le 1$. If $r^2 = 0$, then the least squares regression line cannot explain any of the variation. If $r^2 = 1$, the least squares regression line explains 100% of the variation in the dependent variable.

For the example, $r^2 = 78.4/92.8 = 0.845$. The term r^2 is usually expressed as a percentage. So in this case, 84.5% of the total variation is explained by the regression line using the independent variable.

Another way to arrive at the value for r^2 is to square the correlation coefficient. In this case, $r = 0.919$ and $r^2 = 0.845$, which is the same value found by using the variation ratio.

Of course, it is usually easier to find the coefficient of determination by squaring r and converting it to a percentage. Therefore, if $r = 0.90$, then $r^2 = 0.81$, which is equivalent to 81%. This result means that 81% of the variation in the dependent variable is accounted for by the variations in the independent variable. The rest of the variation, 0.19, or 19%, is unexplained. This value is called the *coefficient of nondetermination* and is found by subtracting the coefficient of determination from 1. As the value of r approaches 0, r^2 decreases more rapidly. For example, if $r = 0.6$, then $r^2 = 0.36$, which means that only 36% of the variation in the dependent variable can be attributed to the variation in the independent variable.

> **Coefficient of Nondetermination**
>
> $$1.00 - r^2$$

In Example 10–5 using absences and final grades, the correlation coefficient is $r = -0.944$. Then $r^2 = (-0.944)^2 = 0.891$. Hence, about 0.891, or 89.1%, of the variation in the final grades can be explained by the linear relationship between the number of absences and the final grades. About $1 - 0.891$ or 0.109 or 10.9% of the variation of the final grades cannot be explained by the variation of the absences.

Standard Error of the Estimate

OBJECTIVE **6**

Compute the standard error of the estimate.

When a y' value is predicted for a specific x value, the prediction is a point prediction. The disadvantage of a point prediction is that it doesn't give us any information about how accurate the point prediction is. In previous chapters, we developed confidence interval estimates to overcome this disadvantage. In this section, we will use what is called a **prediction interval,** which is an interval estimate of a variable.

Recall in previous chapters an interval estimate of a parameter, such as the mean or standard deviation, is called a confidence interval.

> A **prediction interval** is an interval estimate of a predicted value of y when the regression equation is used and a specific value of x is given.

A prediction interval about the y' value can be constructed, just as a confidence interval was constructed for an estimate of the population mean. The prediction interval uses a statistic called the *standard error of the estimate.*

> The **standard error of the estimate,** denoted by s_{est}, is the standard deviation of the observed y values about the predicted y' values. The formula for the standard error of the estimate is
>
> $$s_{est} = \sqrt{\frac{\Sigma(y - y')^2}{n - 2}}$$

The standard error of the estimate is similar to the standard deviation, but the mean is not used. Recall that the standard deviation measures how the values deviate from the mean. The standard error of the estimate measures how the data points deviate from the regression line.

As can be seen from the formula, the standard error of the estimate is the square root of the unexplained variation—that is, the variation due to the difference of the observed values and the expected values—divided by $n - 2$. So the closer the observed values are to the predicted values, the smaller the standard error of the estimate will be.

A Procedure Table for finding the standard error of the estimate is shown here.

Procedure Table

Finding the Standard Error of the Estimate

Step 1   Make a table using the column headings shown.

x	y	y'	$y - y'$	$(y - y')^2$

Step 2   Find the predicted values y' for each x value, and place these values under y' in the table.

Step 3   Subtract each y' value from each y value, and place these answers in the $y - y'$ column in the table.

Step 4   Square each of the values in step 3, and place these values in the column $(y - y')^2$.

Step 5   Find the sum of the values in the $(y - y')^2$ column.

Step 6   Substitute in the formula and find s_{est}.

$$s_{est} = \sqrt{\frac{\Sigma(y - y')^2}{n - 2}}$$

Example 10–12 shows how to compute the standard error of the estimate.

EXAMPLE 10–12   Copy Machine Maintenance Costs

A researcher collects the following data and determines that there is a significant relationship between the age of a copy machine and its monthly maintenance cost. The regression equation is $y' = 55.57 + 8.13x$. Find the standard error of the estimate.

Machine	Age x (years)	Monthly cost y
A	1	$ 62
B	2	78
C	3	70
D	4	90
E	4	93
F	6	103

SOLUTION

Step 1   Make a table, as shown.

x	y	y'	$y - y'$	$(y - y')^2$
1	62			
2	78			
3	70			
4	90			
4	93			
6	103			

Step 2   Using the regression line equation $y' = 55.57 + 8.13x$, compute the predicted values y' for each x, and place the results in the column labeled y'.

$$x = 1 \quad y' = 55.57 + (8.13)(1) = \;\;63.70$$
$$x = 2 \quad y' = 55.57 + (8.13)(2) = \;\;71.83$$
$$x = 3 \quad y' = 55.57 + (8.13)(3) = \;\;79.96$$
$$x = 4 \quad y' = 55.57 + (8.13)(4) = \;\;88.09$$
$$x = 6 \quad y' = 55.57 + (8.13)(6) = 104.35$$

Step 3   For each y, subtract y' and place the answer in the column labeled $y - y'$.

$$62 - 63.70 = -1.70 \qquad 90 - 88.09 = 1.91$$
$$78 - 71.83 = 6.17 \qquad 93 - 88.09 = 4.91$$
$$70 - 79.96 = -9.96 \qquad 103 - 104.35 = -1.35$$

Step 4   Square the numbers found in step 3 and place the squares in the column labeled $(y - y')^2$.

Step 5   Find the sum of the numbers in the last column. The completed table is shown.

x	y	y'	$y - y'$	$(y - y')^2$
1	62	63.70	−1.70	2.89
2	78	71.83	6.17	38.0689
3	70	79.96	−9.96	99.2016
4	90	88.09	1.91	3.6481
4	93	88.09	4.91	24.1081
6	103	104.35	−1.35	1.8225
			$\Sigma(y - y')^2 =$	169.7392

Step 6   Substitute in the formula and find s_{est}.

$$s_{\text{est}} = \sqrt{\frac{\Sigma(y - y')^2}{n - 2}} = \sqrt{\frac{169.7392}{6 - 2}} = 6.514$$

In this case, the standard deviation of observed values about the predicted values is 6.514.

The standard error of the estimate can also be found by using the formula

$$s_{\text{est}} = \sqrt{\frac{\Sigma y^2 - a\,\Sigma y - b\,\Sigma xy}{n - 2}}$$

This Procedure Table shows the alternate method for finding the standard error of the estimate.

Procedure Table

Alternative Method for Finding the Standard Error of Estimate

Step 1   Make a table using the column headings shown.

x	y	xy	y^2

Step 2   Place the x values in the first column (the x column), and place the y values in the second column (the y column). Find the products of the x and y values and place them in the third column (the xy column). Square the y values and place them in the fourth column (the y^2 column).

Step 3   Find the sum of the values in the y, xy, and y^2 columns.

Step 4   Identify a and b from the regression equation, substitute in the formula, and evaluate.

$$s_{\text{est}} = \sqrt{\frac{\Sigma y^2 - a\Sigma y - b\Sigma xy}{n - 2}}$$

EXAMPLE 10–13   Find the standard error of the estimate for the data for Example 10–12 by using the preceding formula. The equation of the regression line is $y' = 55.57 + 8.13x$.

SOLUTION

Step 1   Make a table as shown in the Procedure Table.

Step 2   Place the x values in the first column (the x column), and place the y values in the second column (the y column). Find the product of x and y values, and place the results in the third column. Square the y values, and place the results in the y^2 column.

Step 3   Find the sums of the y, xy, and y^2 columns. The completed table is shown here.

x	y	xy	y²
1	62	62	3,844
2	78	156	6,084
3	70	210	4,900
4	90	360	8,100
4	93	372	8,649
6	103	618	10,609
	$\Sigma y = 496$	$\Sigma xy = 1778$	$\Sigma y^2 = 42{,}186$

Step 4   From the regression equation $y' = 55.57 + 8.13x$, $a = 55.57$, and $b = 8.13$. Substitute in the formula and solve for s_{est}.

$$s_{\text{est}} = \sqrt{\frac{\Sigma y^2 - a\,\Sigma y - b\,\Sigma xy}{n - 2}}$$

$$= \sqrt{\frac{42{,}186 - (55.57)(496) - (8.13)(1778)}{6 - 2}} = 6.483$$

This value is close to the value found in Example 10–12. The difference is due to rounding.

OBJECTIVE ❼

Find a prediction interval.

Prediction Interval

The standard error of the estimate can be used for constructing a prediction interval (similar to a confidence interval) about a y' value.

Recall that when a specific value x is substituted into the regression equation, the predicted value y' that you get is a point estimate for y. For example, if the regression line equation for the age of a machine and the monthly maintenance cost is $y' = 55.57 + 8.13x$ (Example 10–12), then the predicted maintenance cost for a 3-year-old machine would be $y' = 55.57 + 8.13(3)$, or \$79.96. Since this is a point estimate obtained from the regression equation, you have no idea how accurate it is because there are possible sources of prediction errors in finding the regression line equation. One source occurs when finding the standard error of the estimate s_{est}. Two others are errors made in estimating the slope and the y' intercept, since the equation of the regression line will change somewhat if different random samples are used when calculating the equation. However, you can construct a prediction interval about the estimate. By selecting an α value, you can achieve $(1 - \alpha) \cdot 100\%$ confidence that the interval contains the actual mean of the y values that correspond to the given value of x.

Formula for the Prediction Interval about a Value y'

$$y' - t_{\alpha/2}s_{est}\sqrt{1 + \frac{1}{n} + \frac{n(x - \overline{X})^2}{n\,\Sigma x^2 - (\Sigma x)^2}} < y < y' + t_{\alpha/2}s_{est}\sqrt{1 + \frac{1}{n} + \frac{n(x - \overline{X})^2}{n\,\Sigma x^2 - (\Sigma x)^2}}$$

with d.f. = $n - 2$.

The next Procedure Table can be used to find the prediction.

Procedure Table

Finding a Prediction Interval for a Specific Independent Data Value

Step 1   Find Σx, Σx^2, and $\overline{x}$.

Step 2   Find y' for the specific x value.

Step 3   Find s_{est}.

Step 4   Substitute in the formula and evaluate.

$$y' - t_{\alpha/2}s_{est}\sqrt{1 + \frac{1}{n} + \frac{n(x - \overline{X})^2}{n\,\Sigma x^2 - (\Sigma x)^2}} < y < y' + t_{\alpha/2}s_{est}\sqrt{1 + \frac{1}{n} + \frac{n(x - \overline{X})^2}{n\,\Sigma x^2 - (\Sigma x)^2}}$$

with d.f. = $n - 2$.

EXAMPLE 10–14   For the data in Example 10–12, find the 95% prediction interval for the monthly maintenance cost of a machine that is 3 years old.

SOLUTION

Step 1   Find Σx, Σx^2, and $\overline{X}$.

$$\Sigma x = 20 \qquad \Sigma x^2 = 82 \qquad \overline{X} = \frac{20}{6} = 3.3$$

Step 2   Find y' for $x = 3$.

$$y' = 55.57 + 8.13x$$
$$= 55.57 + 8.13(3) = 79.96$$

Step 3   Find s_{est}.

$$s_{est} = 6.48$$

as shown in Example 10–13.

Step 4   Substitute in the formula and solve: $t_{\alpha/2} = 2.776$, d.f. = $6 - 2 = 4$ for 95%.

$$y' - t_{\alpha/2}s_{est}\sqrt{1 + \frac{1}{n} + \frac{n(x - \overline{X})^2}{n\,\Sigma x^2 - (\Sigma x)^2}} < y < y'$$

$$+ t_{\alpha/2}s_{est}\sqrt{1 + \frac{1}{n} + \frac{n(x - \overline{X})^2}{n\,\Sigma x^2 - (\Sigma x)^2}}$$

$$79.96 - (2.776)(6.48)\sqrt{1 + \frac{1}{6} + \frac{6(3 - 3.3)^2}{6(82) - (20)^2}} < y < 79.96$$

$$+ (2.776)(6.48)\sqrt{1 + \frac{1}{6} + \frac{6(3 - 3.3)^2}{6(82) - (20)^2}}$$

$$79.96 - (2.776)(6.48)(1.08) < y < 79.96 + (2.776)(6.48)(1.08)$$
$$79.96 - 19.43 < y < 79.96 + 19.43$$
$$60.53 < y < 99.39$$

Hence, you can be 95% confident that the interval $60.53 < y < 99.39$ contains the actual value of y.

That is, if a copy machine is 3 years old, we can be 95% confident that the maintenance cost would be between \$60.53 and \$99.39. This range is large because the sample size is small, $n = 6$, and the standard error of estimate is 6.48.

Applying the Concepts 10–3

Interpreting Simple Linear Regression

Answer the questions about the following computer-generated information.

Linear correlation coefficient $r = 0.794556$
Coefficient of determination $= 0.631319$
Standard error of estimate $= 12.9668$
Explained variation $= 5182.41$
Unexplained variation $= 3026.49$
Total variation $= 8208.90$
Equation of regression line $y' = 0.725983X + 16.5523$
Level of significance $= 0.1$
Test statistic $= 0.794556$
Critical value $= 0.378419$

1. Are both variables moving in the same direction?
2. Which number measures the distances from the prediction line to the actual values?
3. Which number is the slope of the regression line?
4. Which number is the y intercept of the regression line?
5. Which number can be found in a table?
6. Which number is the allowable risk of making a type I error?
7. Which number measures the variation explained by the regression?
8. Which number measures the scatter of points about the regression line?
9. What is the null hypothesis?
10. Which number is compared to the critical value to see if the null hypothesis should be rejected?
11. Should the null hypothesis be rejected?

See page 607 for the answers.

Exercises 10–3

1. What is meant by the *explained variation?* How is it computed?

2. What is meant by the *unexplained variation?* How is it computed?

3. What is meant by the *total variation?* How is it computed?

4. Define the coefficient of determination.

5. How is the coefficient of determination found?

6. Define the coefficient of nondetermination.

7. How is the coefficient of nondetermination found?

For Exercises 8 through 13, find the coefficients of determination and nondetermination and explain the meaning of each.

8. $r = 0.80$

9. $r = 0.75$

10. $r = 0.35$

11. $r = 0.42$

12. $r = 0.18$

13. $r = 0.91$

14. Define the standard error of the estimate for regression. When can the standard error of the estimate be used to construct a prediction interval about a value y'?

15. Compute the standard error of the estimate for Exercise 13 in Section 10–1. The regression line equation was found in Exercise 13 in Section 10–2.

16. Compute the standard error of the estimate for Exercise 14 in Section 10–1. The regression line equation was found in Exercise 14 in Section 10–2.

17. Compute the standard error of the estimate for Exercise 15 in Section 10–1. The regression line equation was found in Exercise 15 in Section 10–2.

18. Compute the standard error of the estimate for Exercise 16 in Section 10–1. The regression line equation was found in Exercise 16 in Section 10–2.

19. For the data in Exercises 13 in Sections 10–1 and 10–2 and 15 in Section 10–3, find the 90% prediction interval when $x = 200$ new releases.

20. For the data in Exercises 14 in Sections 10–1 and 10–2 and 16 in Section 10–3, find the 95% prediction interval when $x = 60$.

21. For the data in Exercises 15 in Sections 10–1 and 10–2 and 17 in Section 10–3, find the 90% prediction interval when $x = 4$ years.

22. For the data in Exercises 16 in Sections 10–1 and 10–2 and 18 in Section 10–3, find the 98% prediction interval when $x = 47$ years.

10–4 Multiple Regression (Optional)

OBJECTIVE

Be familiar with the concept of multiple regression.

The previous sections explained the concepts of simple linear regression and correlation. In simple linear regression, the regression equation contains one independent variable x and one dependent variable y' and is written as

$$y' = a + bx$$

where a is the y' intercept and b is the slope of the regression line.

In **multiple regression,** there are several independent variables and one dependent variable, and the equation is

$$y' = a + b_1x_1 + b_2x_2 + \cdots + b_kx_k$$

where $x_1, x_2, \ldots, x_k$ are the independent variables.

For example, suppose a nursing instructor wishes to see whether there is a relationship between a student's grade point average, age, and score on the state board nursing examination. The two independent variables are GPA (denoted by x_1) and age (denoted by x_2). The instructor will collect the data for all three variables for a sample of nursing students. Rather than conduct two separate simple regression studies, one using the GPA

Unusual Stats

The most popular single-digit number played by people who purchase lottery tickets is 7.

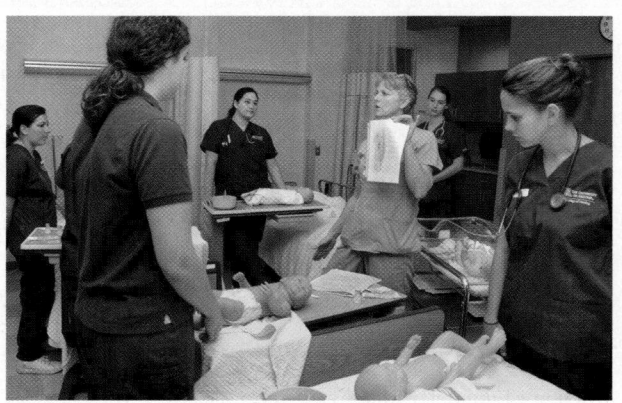

In this study, researchers found a correlation between the cleanliness of the homes children are raised in and the years of schooling completed and earning potential for those children. What interfering variables were controlled? How might these have been controlled? Summarize the conclusions of the study.

SUCCESS

HOME SMART HOME

KIDS WHO GROW UP IN A CLEAN HOUSE FARE BETTER AS ADULTS

Good-bye, GPA. So long, SATs. New research suggests that we may be able to predict children's future success from the level of cleanliness in their homes.

A University of Michigan study presented at the annual meeting of the American Economic Association uncovered a surprising correlation: children raised in clean homes were later found to have completed more school and to have higher earning potential than those raised in dirty homes. The clean homes may indicate a family that values organization and similarly helpful skills at school and work, researchers say.

Cleanliness ratings for about 5,000 households were assessed between 1968 and 1972, and respondents were interviewed 25 years later to determine educational achievement and professional earnings of the young adults who had grown up there,

controlling for variables such as race, socioeconomic status and level of parental education. The data showed that those raised in homes rated "clean" to "very clean" had completed an average of 1.6 more years of school than those raised in "not very clean" or "dirty" homes. Plus, the first group's annual wages averaged about $3,100 more than the second's.

But don't buy stock in Mr. Clean and Pine Sol just yet. "We're not advocating that everyone go out and clean their homes right this minute," explains Rachel Dunifon, a University of Michigan doctoral candidate and a researcher on the study. Rather, the main implication of the study, Dunifon says, is that there is significant evidence that non-cognitive factors, such as organization and efficiency, play a role in determining academic and financial success.

— *Jackie Fisherman*

and state board scores and another using ages and state board scores, the instructor can conduct one study using multiple regression analysis with two independent variables—GPA and ages—and one dependent variable—state board scores.

A multiple regression correlation R can also be computed to determine if a significant relationship exists between the independent variables and the dependent variable. Multiple regression analysis is used when a statistician thinks there are several independent variables contributing to the variation of the dependent variable. This analysis then can be used to increase the accuracy of predictions for the dependent variable over one independent variable alone.

Two other examples for multiple regression analysis are when a store manager wants to see whether the amount spent on advertising and the amount of floor space used for a display affect the amount of sales of a product, and when a sociologist wants to see whether the amount of time children spend watching television and playing video games is related to their weight. Multiple regression analysis can also be conducted by using more than two independent variables, denoted by $x_1, x_2, x_3, \ldots, x_k$. Since these computations are quite complicated and for the most part would be done on a computer, this chapter will show the computations for two independent variables only.

If a multiple regression equation fits the data well, it can be used to make predictions.

For example, the nursing instructor wishes to see whether a student's grade point average and age are related to the student's score on the state board nursing examination. She selects five students and obtains the following data.

Student	GPA x_1	Age x_2	State board score y
A	3.2	22	550
B	2.7	27	570
C	2.5	24	525
D	3.4	28	670
E	2.2	23	490

The multiple regression equation obtained from the data using technology is

$$y' = -44.81 + 87.64x_1 + 14.533x_2$$

If a student has a GPA of 3.0 and is 25 years old, her predicted state board score can be computed by substituting these values in the equation for x_1 and x_2, respectively, as shown.

$$y' = -44.81 + 87.64(3.0) + 14.533(25)$$
$$= 581.44 \text{ or } 581$$

Hence, if a student has a GPA of 3.0 and is 25 years old, the student's predicted state board score is 581.

The Multiple Regression Equation

A multiple regression equation with two independent variables (x_1 and x_2) and one dependent variable has the form

$$y' = a + b_1x_1 + b_2x_2$$

A multiple regression equation with three independent variables (x_1, x_2, and x_3) and one dependent variable has the form

$$y' = a + b_1x_1 + b_2x_2 + b_3x_3$$

General Form of the Multiple Regression Equation

The general form of the multiple regression equation with k independent variables is

$$y' = a + b_1x_1 + b_2x_2 + \cdots + b_kx_k$$

The x's are the independent variables. The value for a is more or less an intercept, although a multiple regression equation with two independent variables constitutes a plane rather than a line. The b's are called *partial regression coefficients*. Each b represents the amount of change in y' for one unit of change in the corresponding x value when the other x values are held constant. In the example just shown, the regression equation was $y' = -44.81 + 87.64x_1 + 14.533x_2$. In this case, for each unit of change in the student's GPA, there is a change of 87.64 units in the state board score with the student's age x_2 being held constant. And for each unit of change in x_2 (the student's age), there is a change of 14.533 units in the state board score with the GPA held constant.

The assumptions for multiple regression are as follows.

Assumptions for Multiple Regression

The assumptions for multiple regression are similar to those for simple regression.

1. For any specific value of the independent variable, the values of the y variable are normally distributed. (This is called the *normality* assumption.)
2. The variances (or standard deviations) for the y variables are the same for each value of the independent variable. (This is called the *equal-variance* assumption.)
3. There is a linear relationship between the dependent variable and the independent variables. (This is called the *linearity* assumption.)
4. The independent variables are not correlated. (This is called the *nonmulticollinearity* assumption.)
5. The values for the y variables are independent. (This is called the *independence* assumption.)

Since these assumptions are somewhat difficult to verify, we will assume throughout this section that they are satisfied.

In multiple regression, as in simple regression, the strength of the relationship between the independent variables and the dependent variable is measured by a correlation coefficient. This **multiple correlation coefficient** is symbolized by R. The value of R can range from 0 to $+1$; R can never be negative. The closer to $+1$, the stronger the relationship; the closer to 0, the weaker the relationship. The value of R takes into account all the independent variables and can be computed by using the values of the individual correlation coefficients. The multiple correlation coefficient is always higher than the individual correlation coefficients. The formula for the multiple correlation coefficient when there are two independent variables is shown next.

Formula for the Multiple Correlation Coefficient

The formula for R is

$$R = \sqrt{\frac{r_{yx_1}^2 + r_{yx_2}^2 - 2r_{yx_1} \cdot r_{yx_2} \cdot r_{x_1x_2}}{1 - r_{x_1x_2}^2}}$$

where r_{yx_1} is the value of the correlation coefficient for variables y and x_1; r_{yx_2} is the value of the correlation coefficient for variables y and x_2; and $r_{x_1x_2}$ is the value of the correlation coefficient for variables x_1 and x_2.

In this case regarding the state board nursing examination scores, R is 0.989, as shown in Example 10–15. The multiple correlation coefficient is always higher than the individual correlation coefficients. For this specific example, the multiple correlation coefficient is higher than the two individual correlation coefficients computed by using grade point average and state board scores ($r_{yx_1} = 0.845$) or age and state board scores ($r_{yx_2} = 0.791$). *Note:* $r_{x_1x_2} = 0.371$.

EXAMPLE 10–15   State Board Scores

For the data regarding nursing state board scores, find the value of R.

SOLUTION

The values of the correlation coefficients are

$$r_{yx_1} = 0.845$$

$$r_{yx_2} = 0.791$$

$$r_{x_1x_2} = 0.371$$

Substituting in the formula, you get

$$R = \sqrt{\frac{r_{yx_1}^2 + r_{yx_2}^2 - 2r_{yx_1} \cdot r_{yx_2} \cdot r_{x_1x_2}}{1 - r_{x_1x_2}^2}}$$

$$= \sqrt{\frac{(0.845)^2 + (0.791)^2 - 2(0.845)(0.791)(0.371)}{1 - 0.371^2}}$$

$$= \sqrt{\frac{0.8437569}{0.862359}} = \sqrt{0.9784288} = 0.989$$

Hence, the correlation between a student's grade point average and age with the student's score on the nursing state board examination is 0.989. In this case, there is a strong relationship among the variables; the value of R is close to 1.00.

As with simple regression, R^2 is the **coefficient of multiple determination,** and it is the amount of variation explained by the regression model. The expression $1 - R^2$ represents the amount of unexplained variation, called the *error* or *residual variation*. In Example 10–15, since $R = 0.989$, $R^2 = 0.978$ and $1 - R^2 = 1 - 0.978 = 0.022$.

Testing the Significance of R

An F test is used to test the significance of R. The hypotheses are

$$H_0: \rho = 0 \quad \text{and} \quad H_1: \rho \neq 0$$

where ρ represents the population correlation coefficient for multiple correlation.

F Test for Significance of R

The formula for the F test is

$$F = \frac{R^2/k}{(1 - R^2)/(n - k - 1)}$$

where n is the number of data groups $(x_1, x_2, \dots, y)$ and k is the number of independent variables.

The degrees of freedom are d.f.N. $= n - k$ and d.f.D. $= n - k - 1$.

EXAMPLE 10–16 State Board Scores

Test the significance of the R obtained in Example 10–15 at $\alpha = 0.05$.

SOLUTION

$$F = \frac{R^2/k}{(1 - R^2)/(n - k - 1)}$$

$$= \frac{0.978/2}{(1 - 0.978)/(5 - 2 - 1)} = \frac{0.489}{0.011} = 44.45$$

The critical value obtained from Table H with $\alpha = 0.05$, d.f.N. $= 3$, and d.f.D. $= 5 - 2 - 1 = 2$ is 19.16. Hence, the decision is to reject the null hypothesis and conclude that there is a significant relationship among the student's GPA, age, and score on the nursing state board examination.

Adjusted R^2

Since the value of R^2 is dependent on n (the number of data pairs) and k (the number of variables), statisticians also calculate what is called an **adjusted R^2,** denoted by R^2_{adj}. This is based on the number of degrees of freedom.

> ### Formula for the Adjusted R^2
>
> The formula for the adjusted R^2 is
>
> $$R^2_{adj} = 1 - \frac{(1 - R^2)(n - 1)}{n - k - 1}$$

The adjusted R^2 is smaller than R^2 and takes into account the fact that when n and k are approximately equal, the value of R may be artificially high, due to sampling error rather than a true relationship among the variables. This occurs because the chance variations of all the variables are used in conjunction with one another to derive the regression equation. Even if the individual correlation coefficients for each independent variable and the dependent variable were all zero, the multiple correlation coefficient due to sampling error could be higher than zero.

Hence, both R^2 and R^2_{adj} are usually reported in a multiple regression analysis.

EXAMPLE 10–17   State Board Scores

Calculate the adjusted R^2 for the data in Example 10–15. The value for R is 0.989.

SOLUTION

$$R^2_{adj} = 1 - \frac{(1 - R^2)(n - 1)}{n - k - 1}$$

$$= 1 - \frac{(1 - 0.989^2)(5 - 1)}{5 - 2 - 1}$$

$$= 1 - 0.043758$$

$$= 0.956$$

In this case, when the number of data pairs and the number of independent variables are accounted for, the adjusted multiple coefficient of determination is 0.956.

≡ Applying the Concepts 10–4

More Math Means More Money

In a study to determine a person's yearly income 10 years after high school, it was found that the two biggest predictors are number of math and science courses taken and number of hours worked per week during a person's senior year of high school. The multiple regression equation generated from a sample of 20 individuals is

$$y' = 6000 + 4540x_1 + 1290x_2$$

Let x_1 represent the number of math and science courses taken and x_2 represent hours worked during senior year. The correlation between income and math and science courses is 0.63. The correlation between income and hours worked is 0.84, and the correlation between math and science courses and hours worked is 0.31. Use this information to answer the following questions.

1. What is the dependent variable?

2. What are the independent variables?

3. What are the multiple regression assumptions?

4. Explain what 4540 and 1290 in the equation tell us.

5. What is the predicted income if a person took 8 math and science classes and worked 20 hours per week during her or his senior year in high school?

6. What does a multiple correlation coefficient of 0.926 mean?

7. Compute R^2.

8. Compute the adjusted R^2.

9. Would the equation be considered a good predictor of income?

10. What are your conclusions about the relationship among courses taken, hours worked, and yearly income?

See pages 607–608 for the answers.

Exercises 10–4

1. Explain the similarities and differences between simple linear regression and multiple regression.

2. What is the general form of the multiple regression equation? What does a represent? What do the b's represent?

3. Why would a researcher prefer to conduct a multiple regression study rather than separate regression studies using one independent variable and the dependent variable?

4. What are the assumptions for multiple regression?

5. How do the values of the individual correlation coefficients compare to the value of the multiple correlation coefficient?

6. **Age, GPA, and Income** A researcher has determined that a significant relationship exists among an employee's age x_1, grade point average x_2, and income y. The multiple regression equation is $y' = -34,127 + 132x_1 + 20,805x_2$. Predict the income of a person who is 32 years old and has a GPA of 3.4.

7. **Fruit Nutrients** As we have seen in previous exercises, there are relationships between various nutrient components in foods. It is far more likely that rather than a linear relationship between any two, there is a complex relationship among many variables. The equation shows the relationship between the number of kilocalories in 100 grams of a fruit or vegetable and the number of milligrams of vitamin C (x_1), grams of carbohydrates (x_2), and grams of water (x_3).

$Y \text{(kcal)} = 442.4 - 0.019834x_1 - 0.51418x_2 - 4.4784x_3$

Find the number of kilocalories in 100 g of a fruit with 12 mg of vitamin C, 15 g of carbohydrates, and 75 g of water.

8. **Special Occasion Cakes** A pastry chef who specializes in special occasion cakes uses the following equation to help calculate the price of a cake:

$y = -26.279 + 14.855x_1 + 3.1035x_2 + 0.73079x_3$, where x_1 is the number of layers desired, x_2 the number of servings needed, and x_3 the amount of filling mix used. Calculate the price of a three-layer cake using 40 ounces of filling to serve 48 people.

9. **Aspects of Students' Academic Behavior** A college statistics professor is interested in the relationship among various aspects of students' academic behavior and their final grade in the class. She found a significant relationship between the number of hours spent studying statistics per week, the number of classes attended per semester, the number of assignments turned in during the semester, and the student's final grade. This relationship is described by the multiple regression equation $y' = -14.9 + 0.93359x_1 + 0.99847x_2 + 5.3844x_3$. Predict the final grade for a student who studies statistics 8 hours per week (x_1), attends 34 classes (x_2), and turns in 11 assignments (x_3).

10. **Age, Cholesterol, and Sodium** A medical researcher found a significant relationship among a person's age x_1, cholesterol level x_2, sodium level of the blood x_3, and systolic blood pressure y. The regression equation is $y' = 97.7 + 0.691x_1 + 219x_2 - 299x_3$. Predict the systolic blood pressure of a person who is 35 years old and has a cholesterol level of 194 milligrams per deciliter (mg/dl) and a sodium blood level of 142 milliequivalents per liter (mEq/l).

11. Explain the meaning of the multiple correlation coefficient R.

12. What is the range of values R can assume?

13. Define R^2 and R^2_{adj}.

14. What are the hypotheses used to test the significance of R?

15. What test is used to test the significance of R?

16. What is the meaning of the adjusted R^2? Why is it computed?

≡ Technology

TI-84 Plus
Step by Step

Step by Step

The TI-84 Plus does not have a built-in function for multiple regression. However, the downloadable program named MULREG is available in your online resources. Follow the instructions online for downloading the program.

Finding a Multiple Regression Equation

1. Enter the sets of data values into L_1, L_2, L_3, etc. Make note of which lists contain the independent variables and which list contains the dependent variable as well as how many data values are in each list.
2. Press **PRGM,** move the cursor to the program named MULREG, and press **ENTER** twice.
3. Type the number of independent variables and press **ENTER.**
4. Type the number of cases for each variable and press **ENTER.**
5. Type the name of the list that contains the data values for the first independent variable and press **ENTER.** Repeat this for all independent variables and the dependent variable.
6. The program will show the regression coefficients.
7. Press **ENTER** to see the values of R^2 and adjusted R^2.
8. Press **ENTER** to see the values of the F test statistics and the P-value.

Find the multiple regression equation for these data used in this section:

Student	GPA x_1	Age x_2	State board score y
A	3.2	22	550
B	2.7	27	570
C	2.5	24	525
D	3.4	28	670
E	2.2	23	490

EXCEL
Step by Step

Multiple Regression

These instructions use data from the nursing examination example discussed at the beginning of Section 10–4.

1. Enter the data from the example into four separate columns of a new worksheet—student in cells A2:A6, GPA in cells B2:B6, age in cells C2:C6, and score in cells D2:D6. Labels can be typed into the first cells of each column.

	A	B	C	D
1	Student	GPA	Age	y
2	A	3.2	22	550
3	B	2.7	27	570
4	C	2.5	24	525
5	D	3.4	28	670
6	E	2.2	23	490

2. Select the Data tab on the toolbar, then **Data Analysis>Regression.**

3. In the Regression dialog box, type D1:D6 for the input Y Range and type B1:C6 for the Input X Range. Check the Labels option if you include labels in the worksheet.

4. Select the Output Range and click OK.

5. To expand the Regression Output to accommodate the decimal places, highlight the output, then select the Home tab, and choose Format>AutoFit Column Width.

SUMMARY OUTPUT

Regression Statistics	
Multiple R	0.989288203
R Square	0.978691148
Adjusted R Square	0.957382297
Standard Error	14.00908721
Observations	5

ANOVA

	df	SS	MS	F	Significance F
Regression	2	18027.49095	9013.745475	45.92885435	0.021308852
Residual	2	392.5090492	196.2545246		
Total	4	18420			

	Coefficients	Standard Error	t Stat	P-value	Lower 95%	Upper 95%	Lower 95.0%	Upper 95.0%
Intercept	-44.81018805	69.24686663	-0.647107808	0.583915745	-342.7554078	253.1350317	-342.7554078	253.1350317
GPA	87.64015185	15.23718666	5.751727913	0.028922601	22.07982905	153.2004746	22.07982905	153.2004746
Age	14.53297431	2.913737536	4.987743106	0.037924877	1.996173545	27.06977507	1.996173545	27.06977507

MINITAB
Step by Step

Multiple Regression

In Example 10–15, is there a correlation between a student's score and her or his age and grade point average?

1. Enter the data for the example into three columns of MINITAB. Name the columns **GPA, AGE,** and **SCORE.**

2. Click **Stat>Regression>Regression.**

3. Double-click on C3 SCORE, the response variable.

4. Double-click C1 GPA, then C2 AGE.

5. Click on [Storage].

   a) Check the box for Residuals.

   b) Check the box for Fits.

6. Click [OK] twice.

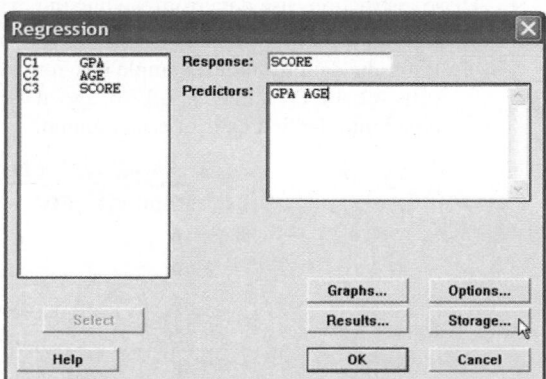

Regression Analysis: SCORE versus GPA, AGE

The regression equation is
SCORE = −44.8 + 87.6 GPA + 14.5 Age

Predictor	Coef	SE Coef	T	P
Constant	−44.81	69.25	−0.65	0.584
GPA	87.64	15.24	5.75	0.029
AGE	14.533	2.914	4.99	0.038

S = 14.0091   R-Sq = 97.9%   R-Sq(adj) = 95.7%

Analysis of Variance

Source	DF	SS	MS	F	P
Regression	2	18027.5	9013.7	45.93	0.021
Residual Error	2	392.5	196.3		
Total	4	18420.0			

The test statistic and *P*-value are 45.93 and 0.021, respectively. Since the *P*-value is less than α, reject the null hypothesis. There is enough evidence in the sample to conclude the scores are related to age and grade point average.

Summary

- Many relationships among variables exist in the real world. One way to determine whether a linear relationship exists is to use the statistical techniques known as correlation and regression. The strength and direction of a linear relationship are measured by the value of the correlation coefficient. It can assume values between and including +1 and −1. The closer the value of the correlation coefficient is to +1 or −1, the stronger the linear relationship is between the variables. A value of +1 or −1 indicates a perfect linear relationship. A positive relationship between two variables means that for small values of the independent variable, the values of the dependent variable will be small; and that for large values of the independent variable, the values of the dependent variable will be large. A negative relationship between two variables means that for small values of the independent variable, the values of the dependent variable will be large; and that for large values of the independent variable, the values of the dependent variable will be small. (10–1)

- Remember that a significant relationship between two variables does not necessarily mean that one variable is a direct cause of the other variable. In some cases this is true, but other possibilities that should be considered include a complex relationship involving other (perhaps unknown) variables, a third variable interacting with both variables, or a relationship due solely to chance. (10–1)

- Relationships can be linear or curvilinear. To determine the shape, you draw a scatter plot of the variables. If the relationship is linear, the data can be approximated by a straight line, called the *least-squares regression line*, or the *line of best fit*. The closer the value of *r* is to +1 or −1, the more closely the points will fit the line. (10–2)

- A residual plot can be used to determine if the regression line equation can be used for predictions. (10–3)

- The coefficient of determination is a better indicator of the strength of a linear relationship than the correlation coefficient. It is better because it identifies the percentage of variation of the dependent variable that is directly attributable to the variation of the independent variable.

"At this point in my report, I'll ask all of you to follow me to the conference room directly below us!"

Source: Cartoon by Bradford Veley, Marquette, Michigan. Reprinted with permission.

The coefficient of determination is obtained by squaring the correlation coefficient and converting the result to a percentage. (10–3)

- Another statistic used in correlation and regression is the standard error of the estimate, which is an estimate of the standard deviation of the y values about the predicted y' values. The standard error of the estimate can be used to construct a prediction interval about a specific value

point estimate y' of the mean of the y values for a given value of x. (10–3)

- In addition, relationships can be multiple. That is, there can be two or more independent variables and one dependent variable. A coefficient of correlation and a regression equation can be found for multiple relationships, just as they can be found for simple relationships. (10–4)

Important Terms

adjusted R^2 597

coefficient of determination 585

correlation 554

correlation coefficient 554

dependent variable 550

extrapolation 571

independent variable 550

influential point or observation 571

lurking variable 562

marginal change 571

multiple correlation coefficient 595

multiple regression 592

negative linear relationship 551

Pearson product moment correlation coefficient (PPMC) 554

population correlation coefficient 554

positive linear relationship 551

prediction interval 586

regression 566

regression line 566

residual 567

residual plot 584

scatter plot 551

standard error of the estimate 586

Important Formulas

Formula for the correlation coefficient:

$$r = \frac{n(\Sigma xy) - (\Sigma x)(\Sigma y)}{\sqrt{[n(\Sigma x^2) - (\Sigma x)^2][n(\Sigma y^2) - (\Sigma y)^2]}}$$

Formula for the t test for the correlation coefficient:

$$t = r\sqrt{\frac{n-2}{1-r^2}} \qquad \text{d.f.} = n - 2$$

The regression line equation:

$$y' = a + bx$$

where

$$a = \frac{(\Sigma y)(\Sigma x^2) - (\Sigma x)(\Sigma xy)}{n(\Sigma x^2) - (\Sigma x)^2}$$

$$b = \frac{n(\Sigma xy) - (\Sigma x)(\Sigma y)}{n(\Sigma x^2) - (\Sigma x)^2}$$

Formula for the standard error of the estimate:

$$s_{\text{est}} = \sqrt{\frac{\Sigma(y - y')^2}{n - 2}}$$

or

$$s_{\text{est}} = \sqrt{\frac{\Sigma y^2 - a\Sigma y - b\Sigma xy}{n - 2}}$$

Formula for the prediction interval for a value y':

$$y' - t_{\alpha/2}s_{\text{est}}\sqrt{1 + \frac{1}{n} + \frac{n(x - \overline{X})^2}{n\Sigma x^2 - (\Sigma x)^2}} < y$$

$$< y' + t_{\alpha/2}s_{\text{est}}\sqrt{1 + \frac{1}{n} + \frac{n(x - \overline{X})^2}{n\Sigma x^2 - (\Sigma x)^2}}$$

$$\text{d.f.} = n - 2$$

Formula for the multiple correlation coefficient:

$$R = \sqrt{\frac{r_{yx_1}^2 + r_{yx_2}^2 - 2r_{yx_1} \cdot r_{yx_2} \cdot r_{x_1x_2}}{1 - r_{x_1x_2}^2}}$$

Formula for the F test for the multiple correlation coefficient:

$$F = \frac{R^2/k}{(1 - R^2)/(n - k - 1)}$$

with d.f.N $= n - k$ and d.f.D $= n - k - 1$.

Formula for the adjusted R^2:

$$R_{\text{adj}}^2 = 1 - \frac{(1 - R^2)(n - 1)}{n - k - 1}$$

≡ Chapter Quiz

Determine whether each statement is true or false. If the statement is false, explain why.

1. A negative relationship between two variables means that for the most part, as the x variable increases, the y variable increases.

2. A correlation coefficient of -1 implies a perfect linear relationship between the variables.

3. Even if the correlation coefficient is high (near $+1$) or low (near -1), it may not be significant.

4. When the correlation coefficient is significant, you can assume x causes y.

5. It is not possible to have a significant correlation by chance alone.

6. In multiple regression, there are several dependent variables and one independent variable.

Select the best answer.

7. The strength of the linear relationship between two quantitative variables is determined by the value of
   a. r c. x
   b. a d. s_{est}

8. To test the significance of r, a(n) _____ test is used.
   a. t c. χ^2
   b. F d. None of the above

9. The test of significance for r has _____ degrees of freedom.
   a. 1   c. $n - 1$
   b. n d. $n - 2$

10. The equation of the regression line used in statistics is
    a. $x = a + by$ c. $y' = a + bx$
    b. $y = bx + a$ d. $x = ay + b$

11. The coefficient of determination is
    a. r c. a
    b. r^2 d. b

Complete the following statements with the best answer.

12. A statistical graph of two quantitative variables is called a(n) _____.

13. The x variable is called the _____ variable.

14. The range of r is from _____ to _____.

15. The sign of r and _____ will always be the same.

16. The regression line is called the _____.

17. If all the points fall on a straight line, the value of r will be _____ or _____.

For Exercises 18 through 21, do a complete regression analysis.
   a. Draw the scatter plot.
   b. Compute the value of the correlation coefficient.
   c. Test the significance of the correlation coefficient at $\alpha = 0.05$.
   d. Determine the regression line equation if r is significant.
   e. Plot the regression line on the scatter plot if appropriate.
   f. Predict y' for a specific value of x if appropriate.

18. **Prescription Drug Prices** A medical researcher wants to determine the relationship between the price per dose of prescription drugs in the United States and the price of the same dose in Australia. The data are shown. Describe the relationship.

U.S. price x	3.31	3.16	2.27	3.13	2.54	1.98	2.22
Australian price y	1.29	1.75	0.82	0.83	1.32	0.84	0.82

19. **Age and Driving Accidents** A study is conducted to determine the relationship between a driver's age and the number of accidents he or she has over a 1-year period. The data are shown here. If there is a significant relationship, predict the number of accidents of a driver who is 64.

Driver's age x	63	65	60	62	66	67	59
No. of accidents y	2	3	1	0	3	1	4

20. **Age and Cavities** A researcher desires to know if the age of a child is related to the number of cavities he or she has. The data are shown here. If there is a significant relationship, predict the number of cavities for a child of 11.

Age of child x	6	8	9	10	12	14
No. of cavities y	2	1	3	4	6	5

21. **Fat and Cholesterol** A study is conducted with a group of dieters to see if the number of grams of fat each consumes per day is related to cholesterol level. The data are shown here. If there is a significant relationship, predict the cholesterol level of a dieter who consumes 8.5 grams of fat per day.

Fat grams x	6.8	5.5	8.2	10	8.6	9.1	8.6	10.4
Cholesterol level y	183	201	193	283	222	250	190	218

22. For Exercise 20, find the standard error of the estimate.

23. For Exercise 21, find the standard error of the estimate.

24. For Exercise 20, find the 90% prediction interval of the number of cavities for a 7-year-old.

25. For Exercise 21, find the 95% prediction interval of the cholesterol level of a person who consumes 10 grams of fat.

26. (Opt.) A study was conducted, and a significant relationship was found among the number of hours a teenager watches television per day x_1, the number of hours the teenager talks on the telephone per day x_2, and the teenager's weight y. The regression equation is $y' = 98.7 + 3.82x_1 + 6.51x_2$. Predict a teenager's weight if she averages 3 hours of TV and 1.5 hours on the phone per day.

27. (Opt.) Find R when $r_{yx_1} = 0.561$ and $r_{yx_2} = 0.714$ and $r_{x_1x_2} = 0.625$.

28. (Opt.) Find R^2_{adj} when $R = 0.774$, $n = 8$, and $k = 2$.

Critical Thinking Challenges

Product Sales When the points in a scatter plot show a curvilinear trend rather than a linear trend, statisticians have methods of fitting curves rather than straight lines to the data, thus obtaining a better fit and a better prediction model. One type of curve that can be used is the logarithmic regression curve. The data shown are the number of items of a new product sold over a period of 15 months at a certain store. Notice that sales rise during the beginning months and then level off later on.

Month x	1	3	6	8	10	12	15
No. of items sold y	10	12	15	19	20	21	21

1. Draw the scatter plot for the data.

2. Find the equation of the regression line.

3. Describe how the line fits the data.

4. Using the log key on your calculator, transform the x values into log x values.

5. Using the log x values instead of the x values, find the equation of a and b for the regression line.

6. Next, plot the curve $y = a + b \log x$ on the graph.

7. Compare the line $y = a + bx$ with the curve $y = a + b \log x$ and decide which one fits the data better.

8. Compute r, using the x and y values; then compute r, using the log x and y values. Which is higher?

9. In your opinion, which (the line or the logarithmic curve) would be a better predictor for the data? Why?

Data Projects

Use a significance level of 0.05 for all tests below.

1. **Business and Finance** Use the stocks in data project 1 of Chapter 2 identified as the Dow Jones Industrials as the sample. For each, note the current price and the amount of the last year's dividends. Are the two variables linearly related? How much variability in amount of dividend is explained by the price?

2. **Sports and Leisure** For each team in major league baseball note the number of wins the team had last year and the number of home runs by its best home run hitter. Is the number of wins linearly related to the number of home runs hit? How much variability in total wins is explained by home runs hit? Write a regression equation to determine how many wins you would expect a team to have, knowing its top home run output.

3. **Technology** Use the data collected in data project 3 of Chapter 2 for this problem. For the data set note the length of the song and the year it was released. Is there a linear relationship between the length of a song and the year it was released? Is the sign on the correlation coefficient positive or negative? What does the sign on the coefficient indicate about the relationship?

4. **Health and Wellness** Use a fast-food restaurant to compile your data. For each menu item note its fat grams and its total calories. Is there a linear relationship between the two variables? How much variance in total calories is explained by fat grams? Write a regression equation to determine how many total calories you would expect in an item, knowing its fat grams.

5. **Politics and Economics** For each state find its average SAT Math score, SAT English score, and average household income. Which has the strongest linear relationship, SAT Math and SAT English, SAT Math and income, or SAT English and income?

6. **Your Class** Use the data collected in data project 6 of Chapter 2 regarding heart rates. Is there a linear relationship between the heart rates before and after exercise? How much of the variability in heart rate after exercise is explained by heart rate before exercise? Write a regression equation to determine what heart rate after exercise you would expect for a person, given the person's heart rate before exercise.

Answers to Applying the Concepts

Section 10–1   Stopping Distances

1. The independent variable is miles per hour (mph).

2. The dependent variable is braking distance (feet).

3. Miles per hour is a continuous quantitative variable.

4. Braking distance is a continuous quantitative variable.

5. A scatter plot of the data is shown.

Scatter plot of braking distance vs. mph

6. There might be a linear relationship between the two variables, but there is a bit of a curve in the plot.

7. Changing the distances between the mph increments will change the appearance of the relationship.

8. There is a positive relationship between the two variables—higher speeds are associated with longer braking distances.

9. The strong relationship between the two variables suggests that braking distance can be accurately predicted from mph. We might still have some concern about the curve in the plot.

10. Answers will vary. Some other variables that might affect braking distance include road conditions, driver response time, and condition of the brakes.

11. The correlation coefficient is $r = 0.966$.

12. The value for $r = 0.966$ is significant at $\alpha = 0.05$. This confirms the strong positive relationship between the variables.

Section 10–2   Stopping Distances Revisited

1. The linear regression equation is
$$y' = -151.900 + 6.451x$$

2. The slope says that for each additional mile per hour a car is traveling, we expect the stopping distance to increase by 6.45 feet, on average. The y intercept is the braking distance we would expect for a car traveling 0 mph—this is meaningless in this context, but is an important part of the model.

3. $y' = -151.900 + 6.451(45) = 138.4$ The braking distance for a car traveling 45 mph is approximately 138 feet.

4. $y' = -151.900 + 6.451(100) = 493.2$ The braking distance for a car traveling 100 mph is approximately 493 feet.

5. It is not appropriate to make predictions of braking distance for speeds outside of the given data values (for example, the 100 mph in the previous problem) because we know nothing about the relationship between the two variables outside of the range of the data.

Section 10–3   Interpreting Simple Linear Regression

1. Both variables are moving in the same direction. In other words, the two variables are positively associated. This is so because the correlation coefficient is positive.

2. The unexplained variation of 3026.49 measures the distances from the prediction line to the actual values.

3. The slope of the regression line is 0.725983.

4. The y intercept is 16.5523.

5. The critical value of 0.378419 can be found in a table.

6. The allowable risk of making a type I error is 0.10, the level of significance.

7. The variation explained by the regression is 0.631319, or about 63.1%.

8. The average scatter of points about the regression line is 12.9668, the standard error of the estimate.

9. The null hypothesis is that there is no correlation, $H_0: \rho = 0$.

10. We compare the test statistic of 0.794556 to the critical value to see if the null hypothesis should be rejected.

11. Since $0.794556 > 0.378419$, we reject the null hypothesis and find that there is enough evidence to conclude that the correlation is not equal to zero.

Section 10–4   More Math Means More Money

1. The dependent variable is yearly income 10 years after high school.

2. The independent variables are number of math and science courses taken and number of hours worked per week during the senior year of high school.

3. Multiple regression assumes that the independent variables are not highly correlated.

4. We expect a person's yearly income 10 years after high school to be $4540 more, on average, for each

additional math or science course taken, all other variables held constant. We expect a person's yearly income 10 years after high school to be $1290 more, on average, for each additional hour worked per week during the senior year of high school, all other variables held constant.

5. $y' = 6000 + 4540(8) + 1290(20) = 68{,}120$. The predicted yearly income 10 years after high school is $68,120.

6. The multiple correlation coefficient of 0.926 means that there is a fairly strong positive relationship between the independent variables (number of math and science courses and hours worked during senior year of high school) and the dependent variable (yearly income 10 years after high school).

7. $R^2 = (0.926)^2 = 0.857$

8. $R_{\text{adj}}^2 = 1 - \dfrac{(1 - R^2)(n - 1)}{n - k - 1}$

   $= 1 - \dfrac{(1 - 0.857)(20 - 1)}{20 - 2 - 1}$

   $= 1 - \dfrac{(0.143)(19)}{17} = 0.840$

9. The equation appears to be a fairly good predictor of income, since 84% of the variation in yearly income 10 years after high school is explained by the regression model.

10. Answers will vary. One possible answer is that yearly income 10 years after high school increases with more math and science classes and more hours of work during the senior year of high school. The number of math and science classes has a higher coefficient, so more math and science does mean more money!

Other Chi-Square Tests

≡ STATISTICS TODAY

Statistics and Heredity

An Austrian monk, Gregor Mendel (1822–1884), studied genetics, and his principles are the foundation for modern genetics. Mendel used his spare time to grow a variety of peas at the monastery. One of his many experiments involved crossbreeding peas that had smooth yellow seeds with peas that had wrinkled green seeds. He noticed that the results occurred with regularity. That is, some of the offspring had smooth yellow seeds, some had smooth green seeds, some had wrinkled yellow seeds, and some had wrinkled green seeds. Furthermore, after several experiments, the percentages of each type seemed to remain approximately the same. Mendel formulated his theory based on the assumption of dominant and recessive traits and tried to predict the results. He then crossbred his peas and examined 556 seeds over the next generation.

Finally, he compared the actual results with the theoretical results to see if his theory was correct. To do this, he used a "simple" chi-square test, which is explained in this chapter. See Statistics Today—Revisited at the end of this chapter.

Source: J. Hodges, Jr., D. Krech, and R. Crutchfield, *Stat Lab, An Empirical Introduction to Statistics* (New York: McGraw-Hill), pp. 228–229. Used with permission.

OUTLINE

Introduction
11–1 Test for Goodness of Fit
11–2 Tests Using Contingency Tables
Summary

OBJECTIVES

After completing this chapter, you should be able to

1 Test a distribution for goodness of fit, using chi-square.

2 Test two variables for independence, using chi-square.

3 Test proportions for homogeneity, using chi-square.

Introduction

The chi-square distribution was used in Chapters 7 and 8 to find a confidence interval for a variance or standard deviation and to test a hypothesis about a single variance or standard deviation.

It can also be used for tests concerning *frequency distributions,* such as "If a sample of buyers is given a choice of automobile colors, will each color be selected with the same frequency?" The chi-square distribution can be used to test the *independence* of two variables, for example, "Are senators' opinions on gun control independent of party affiliations?" That is, do the Republicans feel one way and the Democrats feel differently, or do they have the same opinion?

Finally, the chi-square distribution can be used to test the *homogeneity of proportions.* For example, is the proportion of high school seniors who attend college immediately after graduating the same for the northern, southern, eastern, and western parts of the United States?

This chapter explains the chi-square distribution and its applications. In addition to the applications mentioned here, chi-square has many other uses in statistics.

11–1   Test for Goodness of Fit

OBJECTIVE

Test a distribution for goodness of fit, using chi-square.

In addition to being used to test a single variance, the chi-square statistic can be used to see whether a frequency distribution fits a specific pattern. For example, to meet customer demands, a manufacturer of running shoes may wish to see whether buyers show a preference for a specific style. A traffic engineer may wish to see whether accidents occur more often on some days than on others, so that she can increase police patrols accordingly. An emergency service may want to see whether it receives more calls at certain times of the day than at others, so that it can provide adequate staffing.

Recall the characteristics of the chi-square distribution:

1. The chi-square distribution is a family of curves based on the degrees of freedom.

2. The chi-square distributions are positively skewed.

3. All chi-square values are greater than or equal to zero.

4. The total area under each chi-square distribution is equal to 1.

When you are testing to see whether a frequency distribution fits a specific pattern, you can use the chi-square *goodness-of-fit test.*

> The **chi-square goodness-of-fit test** is used to test the claim that an observed frequency distribution fits some given expected frequency distribution.

For example, suppose as a market analyst you wished to see whether consumers have any preference among five flavors of a new fruit soda. A sample of 100 people provided these data:

Cherry	Strawberry	Orange	Lime	Grape
32	28	16	14	10

Since the frequencies for each flavor were obtained from a sample, these actual frequencies are called the **observed frequencies.** The frequencies obtained by calculation (as if there were no preference) are called the **expected frequencies.**

To calculate the expected frequencies, there are two rules to follow.

1. If all the expected frequencies are equal, the expected frequency E can be calculated by using $E = n/k$, where n is the total number of observations and k is the number of categories.

Historical Note

Karl Pearson (1857–1936) first used the chi-square distribution as a goodness-of-fit test for data. He developed many types of descriptive graphs and gave them unusual names such as stigmograms, topograms, stereograms, and radiograms.

2. If all the expected frequencies are not equal, then the expected frequency E can be calculated by $E = n \cdot p$, where n is the total number of observations and p is the probability for that category.

Looking at the new fruit flavors example, if there were no preference, you would expect each flavor to be selected with equal frequency. In this case, the equal frequency is $100/5 = 20$. That is, *approximately* 20 people would select each flavor. A completed table for the test is shown.

Frequency	Cherry	Strawberry	Orange	Lime	Grape
Observed	32	28	16	14	10
Expected	20	20	20	20	20

The observed frequencies will almost always differ from the expected frequencies due to sampling error; that is, the values differ from sample to sample. But the question is: Are these differences significant (a preference exists), or are they due to chance? The chi-square goodness-of-fit test will enable the researcher to determine the answer.

Before computing the test value, you must state the hypotheses. The null hypothesis should be a statement indicating that there is no difference or no change. For this example, the hypotheses are as follows:

H_0: Consumers show no preference for flavors of the fruit soda.

H_1: Consumers show a preference.

Next, we need a measure of discrepancy between the observed values O and the expected values E, so we use the test statistic for the chi-square goodness-of-fit test.

Formula for the Chi-Square Goodness-of-Fit Test

$$\chi^2 = \sum \frac{(O - E)^2}{E}$$

with degrees of freedom equal to the number of categories minus 1, and where
O = observed frequency
E = expected frequency

Notice that the value of the test statistic is based on the difference between the observed values and the expected values. If the observed values are significantly different from the expected values, then there is enough evidence to reject the null hypothesis.

When there is perfect agreement between the observed and the expected values, $\chi^2 = 0$. Also, χ^2 can never be negative. Finally, the test is right-tailed because "H_0: Good fit" and "H_1: Not a good fit" mean that χ^2 will be small in the first case and large in the second case.

In the goodness-of-fit test, the degrees of freedom are equal to the number of categories minus 1. For this example, there are five categories (cherry, strawberry, orange, lime, and grape); hence, the degrees of freedom are $5 - 1 = 4$. This is so because the number of subjects in each of the first four categories is free to vary. But in order for the sum to be 100—the total number of subjects—the number of subjects in the last category is fixed.

Two assumptions are needed for the goodness-of-fit test. These assumptions are given next.

Assumptions for the Chi-Square Goodness-of-Fit Test

1. The data are obtained from a random sample.
2. The expected frequency for each category must be 5 or more.

In this book, the assumptions will be stated in the exercises; however, when encountering statistics in other situations, you must check to see that these assumptions have been met before proceeding.

For use of the chi-square goodness-of-fit test, statisticians have determined that the expected frequencies should be at least 5, as stated in the assumptions. The reasoning is as follows: The chi-square distribution is continuous, whereas the goodness-of-fit test is discrete. However, the continuous distribution is a good approximation and can be used when the expected value for each class is at least 5. If an expected frequency of a class is less than 5, then that class can be combined with another class so that the expected frequency is 5 or more.

The steps for the chi-square goodness-of-fit test are summarized in this Procedure Table.

Procedure Table

The Chi-Square Goodness-of-Fit Test

Step 1   State the hypotheses and identify the claim.

Step 2   Find the critical value from Table G. The test is always right-tailed.

Step 3   Compute the test value.
Find the sum of the $\dfrac{(O - E)^2}{E}$ values.

Step 4   Make the decision.

Step 5   Summarize the results.

Example 11–1 demonstrates the situation when the expected values of the categories are equal.

EXAMPLE 11–1   Fruit Soda Flavor Preference

Is there enough evidence to reject the claim that there is no preference in the selection of fruit soda flavors, using the data shown previously? Let $\alpha = 0.05$.

SOLUTION

Step 1   State the hypotheses and identify the claim.

H_0: Consumers show no preference for flavors (claim).
H_1: Consumers show a preference.

Step 2   Find the critical value. The degrees of freedom are $5 - 1 = 4$, and $\alpha = 0.05$. Hence, the critical value from Table G in Appendix A is 9.488.

Step 3   Compute the test value. Note the expected values are found by $E = n/k = 100/5 = 20$.

The table looks like this.

Frequency	Cherry	Strawberry	Orange	Lime	Grape
Observed	32	28	16	14	10
Expected	20	20	20	20	20

The test value is computed by subtracting the expected value from the corresponding observed value, squaring the result and dividing by the expected value, and finding the sum of all these values.

$$\chi^2 = \sum \frac{(O - E)^2}{E}$$

$$= \frac{(32 - 20)^2}{20} + \frac{(28 - 20)^2}{20} + \frac{(16 - 20)^2}{20} + \frac{(14 - 20)^2}{20} + \frac{(10 - 20)^2}{20}$$

$$= 18.000$$

Step 4   Make the decision. The decision is to reject the null hypothesis, since 18.000 > 9.488, as shown in Figure 11–1.

FIGURE 11–1
Critical and Test Values
for Example 11–1

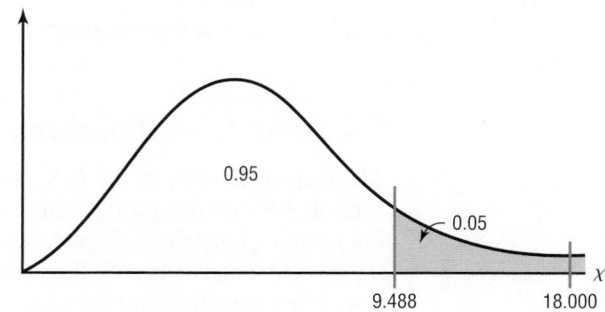

Step 5   Summarize the results. There is enough evidence to reject the claim that consumers show no preference for the flavors.

Also *P*-values can be found for this test. In Example 11–1, the test value was 18.000. If you look across the row with d.f. = 4 of Table G, you will find that 18.000 is beyond 14.860, which corresponds to the 0.005 α value at the top of the table. Hence, *P*-value < 0.005, and the null hypothesis would be rejected.

To get some idea of why this test is called the goodness-of-fit test, examine graphs of the observed values and expected values from Example 11–1. See Figure 11–2. From the graphs, you can see whether the observed values and expected values are close together or far apart. In this case, the observed values and the expected values are far apart, so this is not a good fit. As a result, we reject the null hypothesis.

FIGURE 11–2
Graphs of the Observed and
Expected Values for Soda
Flavors

When the observed values and expected values are close together, the chi-square test value will be small. Then the decision will be to not reject the null hypothesis—hence, this is "a good fit." See Figure 11–3(a). When the observed values and the expected values are far apart, the chi-square test value will be large. Then the null hypothesis will be rejected—hence, there is "not a good fit." See Figure 11–3(b).

FIGURE 11–3

Results of the
Goodness-of-Fit Test

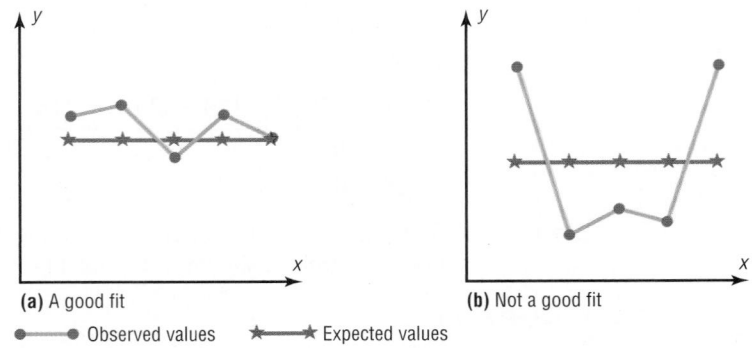

(a) A good fit   (b) Not a good fit

●────● Observed values   ★────★ Expected values

EXAMPLE 11–2   Education Level of Adults

The Census Bureau of the U.S. government found that 13% of adults did not finish high school, 30% graduated from high school only, 29% had some college education but did not obtain a bachelor's degree, and 28% were college graduates. To see if these proportions were consistent with those people who lived in the Lincoln County area, a local researcher selected a random sample of 300 adults and found that 43 did not finish high school, 76 were high school graduates only, 96 had some college education, and 85 were college graduates. At $\alpha = 0.10$, test the claim that the proportions are the same for the adults in Lincoln County as those stated by the Census Bureau.

SOLUTION

Step 1   State the hypotheses and identify the claim.

H_0: The proportion of people in each category is as follows: 13% did not finish high school, 30% were high school graduates only, 29% had some college education but did not graduate, and 28% had a college degree (claim).

H_1: The distribution is not the same as stated in the null hypothesis.

Step 2   Find the critical value. Since $\alpha = 0.10$ and the degrees of freedom are $4 - 1 = 3$, the critical value is 6.251.

Step 3   Compute the test value. First, we must calculate the expected values. Multiply the total number of people surveyed (300) by the percentages of people in each category.

$$0.13 \times 300 = 39$$
$$0.30 \times 300 = 90$$
$$0.29 \times 300 = 87$$
$$0.28 \times 300 = 84$$

The table looks like this:

Frequency	Did not finish high school	H.S. graduate	Some college	College graduate
Observed	43	76	96	85
Expected	39	90	87	84

Next calculate the test value.

$$x^2 = \sum \frac{(O - E)^2}{E} = \frac{(43 - 39)^2}{39} + \frac{(76 - 90)^2}{90} + \frac{(96 - 87)^2}{87} + \frac{(85 - 84)^2}{84}$$
$$= 0.410 + 2.178 + 0.931 + 0.012 = 3.531$$

Step 4   Make the decision. Since $3.531 < 6.251$, the decision is not to reject the null hypothesis. See Figure 11–4.

FIGURE 11–4
Critical and Test Values for Example 11–2

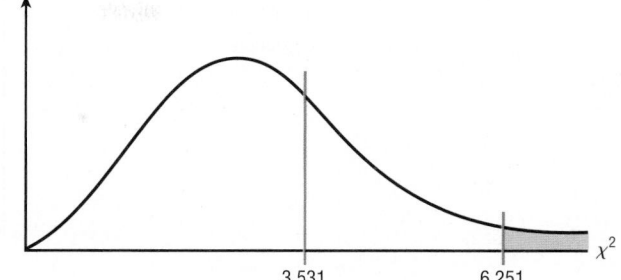

Step 5   Summarize the results. There is not enough evidence to reject the claim. It can be concluded that the percentages are not significantly different from those given in the null hypothesis. That is, the proportions are not significantly different from those stated by the U.S. Census Bureau.

EXAMPLE 11–3   Firearm Deaths

A researcher read that firearm-related deaths for people aged 1 to 18 years were distributed as follows: 74% were accidental, 16% were homicides, and 10% were suicides. In her district, there were 68 accidental deaths, 27 homicides, and 5 suicides during the past year. At $\alpha = 0.10$, test the claim that the percentages are equal.

Source: Centers for Disease Control and Prevention.

SOLUTION

Step 1   State the hypotheses and identify the claim:

H_0: The deaths due to firearms for people aged 1 through 18 years are distributed as follows: 74% accidental, 16% homicides, and 10% suicides (claim).

H_1: The distribution is not the same as stated in the null hypothesis.

Step 2   Find the critical value. Since $\alpha = 0.10$ and the degrees of freedom are $3 - 1 = 2$, the critical value is 4.605.

Step 3   Compute the test value.

First calculate the expected values, using the formula $E = n \cdot p$ as shown.

$$100 \times 0.74 = 74$$
$$100 \times 0.16 = 16$$
$$100 \times 0.10 = 10$$

The table looks like this.

Frequency	Accidental	Homicides	Suicides
Observed	68	27	5
Expected	74	16	10

$$\chi^2 = \sum \frac{(O - E)^2}{E}$$
$$= \frac{(68 - 74)^2}{74} + \frac{(27 - 16)^2}{16} + \frac{(5 - 10)^2}{10}$$
$$= 10.549$$

Step 4   Reject the null hypothesis, since $10.549 > 4.605$, as shown in Figure 11–5.

FIGURE 11–5
Critical and Test Values
for Example 11–3

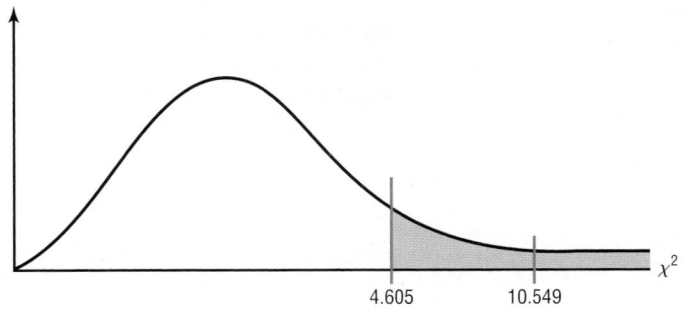

Step 5   Summarize the results. There is enough evidence to reject the claim that the distribution is 74% accidental, 16% homicides, and 10% suicides.

Test of Normality (Optional)

The chi-square goodness-of-fit test can be used to test a variable to see if it is normally distributed. The null hypotheses are

H_0: The variable is normally distributed.

H_1: The variable is not normally distributed.

The procedure is somewhat complicated. It involves finding the expected frequencies for each class of a frequency distribution by using the standard normal distribution. Then the actual frequencies (i.e., observed frequencies) are compared to the expected frequencies, using the chi-square goodness-of-fit test. If the observed frequencies are close in value to the expected frequencies, then the chi-square test value will be small and the null hypothesis cannot be rejected. In this case, it can be concluded that the variable is approximately normally distributed.

On the other hand, if there is a large difference between the observed frequencies and the expected frequencies, then the chi-square test value will be larger and the null hypothesis can be rejected. In this case, it can be concluded that the variable is not normally distributed. Example 11–4 illustrates the procedure for the chi-square test of normality. To find the areas in the examples, you might want to review Section 6–2.

Example 11–4 shows how to do the calculations.

EXAMPLE 11–4   Test of Normality

Use chi-square to determine if the variable shown in the frequency distribution is normally distributed. Use $\alpha = 0.05$.

Boundaries	Frequency
89.5–104.5	24
104.5–119.5	62
119.5–134.5	72
134.5–149.5	26
149.5–164.5	12
164.5–179.5	4
	Total = 200

SOLUTION

H_0: The variable is normally distributed.

H_1: The variable is not normally distributed.

First find the mean and standard deviation of the variable. (*Note*: s is used to approximate σ.)

Boundaries	f	X_m	$f \cdot X_m$	$f \cdot X_m^2$
89.5–104.5	24	97	2,328	225,816
104.5–119.5	62	112	6,944	777,728
119.5–134.5	72	127	9,144	1,161,288
134.5–149.5	26	142	3,692	524,264
149.5–164.5	12	157	1,884	295,788
164.5–179.5	4	172	688	118,336
	200		24,680	3,103,220

$$\overline{X} = \frac{24{,}680}{200} = 123.4$$

$$s = \sqrt{\frac{200(3{,}103{,}220) - 24{,}680^2}{200(199)}} = \sqrt{290} = 17.03$$

Next find the area under the standard normal distribution, using z values and Table E for each class.

The z score for $x = 104.5$ is found as

$$z = \frac{104.5 - 123.4}{17.03} = -1.11$$

The area for $z < -1.11$ is 0.1335.

The z score for 119.5 is found as

$$z = \frac{119.5 - 123.4}{17.03} = -0.23$$

The area for $-1.11 < z < -0.23$ is $0.4090 - 0.1335 = 0.2755$.

The z score for 134.5 is found as

$$z = \frac{134.5 - 123.4}{17.03} = 0.65$$

The area for $-0.23 < z < 0.65$ is $0.7422 - 0.4090 = 0.3332$.

The z score for 149.5 is found as

$$z = \frac{149.5 - 123.4}{17.03} = 1.53$$

The area for $0.65 < z < 1.53$ is $0.9370 - 0.7422 = 0.1948$.

The z score for 164.5 is found as

$$z = \frac{164.5 - 123.4}{17.03} = 2.41$$

The area for $1.53 < z < 2.41$ is $0.9920 - 0.9370 = 0.0550$.

The area for $z > 2.41$ is $1.0000 - 0.9920 = 0.0080$.

Find the expected frequencies for each class by multiplying the area by 200. The expected frequencies are found by

$$0.1335 \cdot 200 = 26.7$$
$$0.2755 \cdot 200 = 55.1$$
$$0.3332 \cdot 200 = 66.64$$
$$0.1948 \cdot 200 = 38.96$$
$$0.0550 \cdot 200 = 11.0$$
$$0.0080 \cdot 200 = 1.6$$

Note: Since the expected frequency for the last category is less than 5, it can be combined with the previous category.

The table looks like this.

0	24	62	72	26	16
E	26.7	55.1	66.64	38.96	12.6

Finally, find the chi-square test value using the formula $\chi^2 = \sum \dfrac{(O - E)^2}{E}$.

$$\chi^2 = \frac{(24 - 26.7)^2}{26.7} + \frac{(62 - 55.1)^2}{55.1} + \frac{(72 - 66.64)^2}{66.64} + \frac{(26 - 38.96)^2}{38.96}$$
$$+ \frac{(16 - 12.6)^2}{12.6}$$
$$= 6.797$$

The critical value in this test has the degrees of freedom equal to the number of categories minus 3 since 1 degree of freedom is lost for each parameter that is estimated. In this case, the mean and standard deviation have been estimated, so 2 additional degrees of freedom are needed.

The C.V. with d.f. $= 5 - 3 = 2$ and $\alpha = 0.05$ is 5.991, so the null hypothesis is rejected. Hence, the distribution can be considered not normally distributed.

Note: At $\alpha = 0.01$, the C.V. $= 9.210$ and the null hypothesis would not be rejected. Hence, we could consider that the variable is normally distributed at $\alpha = 0.01$. So it is important to decide which level of significance you want to use.

Applying the Concepts 11–1

Skittles Color Distribution

M&M/Mars, the makers of Skittles candies, states that the flavor blend is 20% for each flavor. Skittles is a combination of lemon, lime, orange, strawberry, and grape flavored candies. The following data list the results of four randomly selected bags of Skittles and their flavor blends. Use the data to answer the questions.

Bag	Yellow	Green	Orange	Red	Purple
			Flavor		
1	14	7	20	10	7
2	17	20	5	5	13
3	4	4	16	13	21
4	17	12	9	16	3
Total	52	43	50	44	44

1. Are the variables quantitative or qualitative?

2. What type of test can be used to compare the observed values to the expected values?

3. Compute a chi-square test on the total values.

4. What hypotheses should you use?

5. What are the degrees of freedom for the test? What is the critical value?

6. What is your conclusion?

See page 645 for the answers.

≡ Exercises 11–1

1. How does the goodness-of-fit test differ from the chi-square variance test?

2. How are the degrees of freedom computed for the goodness-of-fit test?

3. How are the expected values computed for the goodness-of-fit test?

4. When the expected frequency is less than 5 for a specific class, what should be done so that you can use the goodness-of-fit test?

For Exercises 5 through 18, perform these steps.

   a. State the hypotheses and identify the claim.

   b. Find the critical value.

   c. Compute the test value.

   d. Make the decision.

   e. Summarize the results.

Use the traditional method of hypothesis testing unless otherwise specified. Assume all assumptions are met.

5. **Types of Shopping Bags Used** In a magazine survey, 60% of respondents said that they used reusable shopping bags, 32% asked for plastic, and 8% requested paper. A random sample of 300 shoppers revealed that 28 asked for paper, 120 requested plastic, and the remaining shoppers had reusable bags. At $\alpha = 0.01$, does this differ from the results of the survey?

6. **Combatting Midday Drowsiness** A researcher wishes to see if the five ways (drinking decaffeinated beverages, taking a nap, going for a walk, eating a sugary snack, other) people use to combat midday drowsiness are equally distributed among office workers. A random sample of 60 office workers is selected, and the following data are obtained. At $\alpha = 0.10$, can it be concluded that there is no preference? Why would the results be of interest to an employer?

Method	Beverage	Nap	Walk	Snack	Other
Number	21	16	10	8	5

Source: Based on information from Harris Interactive.

7. **Music Sales** In a recent year, 77.8% of recorded music sales were full-length CDs; 12.8%, digital downloads; 3.8%, singles; and the rest, a mixture of other formats. A random survey of college students and their recent music purchases indicated that out of 200 purchases, 48 were downloads, 135 were full-length CDs, 10 were singles, and the rest fit into the "other" category. At the 0.05 level of significance, is there sufficient evidence to conclude that at least one of the proportions differs from its original value?

Source: *New York Times Almanac.*

8. **On-Time Performance by Airlines** According to the Bureau of Transportation Statistics, on-time performance by the airlines is described as follows:

Action	% of Time
On time	70.8
National Aviation System delay	8.2
Aircraft arriving late	9.0
Other (because of weather and other conditions)	12.0

Records of 200 randomly selected flights for a major airline company showed that 125 planes were on time; 40 were delayed because of weather, 10 because of a National Aviation System delay, and the rest because of arriving late. At $\alpha = 0.05$, do these results differ from the government's statistics?

Source: www.transtats.bts.gov

9. **Genetically Modified Food** An ABC News poll asked adults whether they felt genetically modified food was safe to eat. Thirty-five percent felt it was safe, 52% felt it was not safe, and 13% had no opinion. A random sample of 120 adults was asked the same question at a local county fair. Forty people felt that genetically modified food was safe, 60 felt that it was not safe, and 20 had no opinion. At the 0.01 level of significance, is there sufficient evidence to conclude that the proportions differ from those reported in the poll?

Source: ABCNews.com Poll, www.pollingreport.com

10. Truck Colors In a recent year, the most popular colors for light trucks were white, 30%; black, 17%; red, 14%; silver, 12%; gray, 11%; blue, 8%; and other, 8%. A survey of randomly selected light truck owners in a particular area revealed the following. At $\alpha = 0.05$, do the proportions differ from those stated?

White	Black	Red	Silver	Gray	Blue	Other
45	32	30	30	22	15	6

Source: *World Almanac.*

11. Assessment of Mathematics Students As part of the Mathematics Assessment, eighth-graders were asked about the frequency with which they used calculators while taking tests or quizzes. The results for national public schools were as follows: never, 28%; sometimes, 51%; and always, 21%. A random sample of 140 eighth-grade students in a large urban school district indicated that 30 said never, 78 said sometimes, and 32 said always. At $\alpha = 0.05$, do these proportions differ from the national report?

Source: Nationsreportcard.gov

12. Ages of Head Start Program Students The Head Start Program provides a wide range of services to low-income children up to the age of 5 years and their families. Its goals are to provide services to improve social and learning skills and to improve health and nutrition status so that the participants can begin school on an equal footing with their more advantaged peers. The distribution of ages for participating children is as follows: 4% five-year-olds, 52% four-year-olds, 34% three-year-olds, and 10% under 3 years. When the program was assessed in a particular region, it was found that of the 200 randomly selected participants, 20 were 5 years old, 120 were 4 years old, 40 were 3 years old, and 20 were under 3 years. Is there sufficient evidence at $\alpha = 0.05$ that the proportions differ from the program's? Use the P-value method.

Source: *New York Times Almanac*/www.fedstats.dhhs.gov

13. Firearms Deaths According to the National Safety Council, 10% of the annual deaths from firearms were victims from birth through 19 years of age. Half of the deaths from firearms were victims aged 20 through 44 years, and 40% of victims were aged 45 years and over. A random sample of 100 deaths by firearms in a particular state indicated the following: 13 were victims from birth through 19 years, 62 were aged 20 through 44 years, and the rest were 45 years old and older. At the 0.05 level of significance, are the results different from those cited by the National Safety Council?

Source: *World Almanac.*

14. College Degree Recipients A survey of 800 randomly selected recent degree recipients found that 155 received

associate degrees; 450, bachelor degrees; 20, first professional degrees; 160, master degrees; and 15, doctorates. Is there sufficient evidence to conclude that at least one of the proportions differs from a report which stated that 23.3% were associate degrees; 51.1%, bachelor degrees; 3%, first professional degrees; 20.6%, master degrees; and 2%, doctorates? Use $\alpha = 0.05$.

Source: *New York Times Almanac.*

15. Internet Users A survey was targeted at determining if educational attainment affected Internet use. Randomly selected shoppers at a busy mall were asked if they used the Internet and their highest level of education attained. The results are listed below. Is there sufficient evidence at the 0.05 level of significance that the proportion of Internet users differs for any of the groups?

Graduated college +	Attended college	Did not attend
44	41	40

Source: www.infoplease.com

16. Types of Automobiles Purchased In a recent year U.S. retail automobile sales were categorized as listed below.

Luxury 15.6%   large 6%   midsize 42%   small 36.4%

A random sample of 150 recent purchases indicated the following results: 25 were luxury models, 12 were large cars, 60 were midsize, and 53 were small. At the 0.10 level of significance, is there sufficient evidence to conclude that the proportions of each type of car purchased differed from the report?

Source: *World Almanac.*

17. Paying for Prescriptions A medical researcher wishes to determine if the way people pay for their medical prescriptions is distributed as follows: 60% personal funds, 25% insurance, 15% Medicare. A random sample of 50 people found that 32 paid with their own money, 10 paid using insurance, and 8 paid using Medicare. At $\alpha = 0.05$, is the assumption correct? Use the P-value method. What would be an implication of the results?

Source: U.S. Health Care Financing.

18. Education Level and Health Insurance A researcher wishes to see if the number of randomly selected adults who do not have health insurance is equally distributed among three categories (less than 12 years of education, 12 years of education, more than 12 years of education). A sample of 60 adults who do not have health insurance is selected, and the results are shown. At $\alpha = 0.05$, can it be concluded that the frequencies are not equal? Use the P-value method. If the null hypothesis is rejected, give a possible reason for this.

Category	Less than 12 years	12 years	More than 12 years
Frequency	29	20	11

Source: U.S. Census Bureau.

≡ Extending the Concepts

19. Tossing Coins Three coins are tossed 72 times, and the number of heads is shown. At $\alpha = 0.05$, test the null hypothesis that the coins are balanced and randomly tossed. (*Hint:* Use the binomial distribution.)

No. of heads	0	1	2	3
Frequency	3	10	17	42

20. State Lottery Numbers Select a three-digit state lottery number over a period of 50 days. Count the number of times each digit, 0 through 9, occurs. Test the claim, at $\alpha = 0.05$, that the digits occur at random.

≡ Technology

TI-84 Plus
Step by Step

Step by Step

Goodness-of-Fit Test

Example TI11–1

This pertains to Example 11–1 from the text. At the 5% significance level, test the claim that there is no preference in the selection of fruit soda flavors for the data.

Frequency	Cherry	Strawberry	Orange	Lime	Grape
Observed	32	28	16	14	10
Expected	20	20	20	20	20

To calculate the test statistic:

1. Enter the observed frequencies in L_1 and the expected frequencies in L_2.
2. Press **2nd [QUIT]** to return to the home screen.
3. Press **2nd [LIST]**, move the cursor to MATH, and press **5** for sum(.
4. Type $(L_1 - L_2)^2/L_2)$, then press **ENTER**.

To calculate the *P*-value:

Press **2nd [DISTR]**, then press **8** to get χ^2cdf(.
For this *P*-value, the χ^2cdf(command has the form χ^2cdf(test statistic, ∞, degrees of freedom).
Use E99 for ∞. Type **2nd [EE]** to get the small E.
For this example use χ^2cdf(18, E99,4):

Since *P*-value = 0.001234098 < 0.05 = significance level, reject H_0 and conclude H_1. Therefore, there is enough evidence to reject the claim that consumers show no preference for soda flavors.

Note: On the newer TI-84 calculator, there is a goodness-of-fit test. Put the observed values in L1 and the expected values in L2 and then in TESTS-ALPHA D, enter df, and calculate.

EXCEL
Step by Step

Chi-Square Goodness-of-Fit Test

Excel does not have a procedure to conduct the goodness-of-fit test. However, you may conduct this test using the MegaStat Add-in available in your online resources. If you have not installed this add-in, do so, following the instructions from the Chapter 1 Excel Step by Step.

This example pertains to Example 11–1 from the text.

Example XL11–1

Test the claim that there is no preference for soda flavor. Use a significance level of $\alpha = 0.05$. The table of frequencies is shown below.

Frequency	Cherry	Strawberry	Orange	Lime	Grape
Observed	32	28	16	14	10
Expected	20	20	20	20	20

1. Enter the observed frequencies in row 1 (cells: A1 to E1) of a new worksheet.
2. Enter the expected frequencies in row 2 (cells: A2 to E2).
3. From the toolbar, select Add-Ins, **MegaStat>Chi-Square/Crosstab>Goodness of Fit Test.** *Note:* You may need to open MegaStat from the MegaStat.xls file on your computer's hard drive.
4. In the dialog box, type **A1:E1** for the Observed values and **A2:E2** for the Expected values. Then click [OK].

Goodness-of-Fit Test

Observed	Expected	$O - E$	$(O - E)^2/E$	% of chisq
32	20.000	12.000	7.200	40.00
28	20.000	8.000	3.200	17.78
16	20.000	−4.000	0.800	4.44
14	20.000	−6.000	1.800	10.00
10	20.000	−10.000	5.000	27.78
100	100.000	0.000	18.000	100.00
18.00	chi-square			
4	df			
0.0012	*P*-value			

Since the *P*-value is less than the significance level, the null hypothesis is rejected and thus the claim of no preference is rejected.

Chi-Square Test for Normality

Example XL11–2

This example refers to Example 11–4. At the 5% significance level, determine if the variable is normally distributed.

Start with the table of observed and expected values:

Observed	24	62	72	26	16
Expected	26.7	55.1	66.64	38.96	12.6

1. Enter the Observed values in row 1 of a new worksheet.
2. Enter the Expected values in row 2.

Note: You may include labels for the observed and expected values in cells A1 and A2, respectively.

3. Select the Insert Function Icon from the Toolbar.
4. In the Insert Function dialog box, select the Statistical category and the CHITEST function.
5. Type **B1:F1** for the Actual Range and **B2:F2** for the Expected Range, then click [OK].

The *P*-value of 0.1470 is greater than the significance level of 0.05. So we do not reject the null hypothesis. Thus, the distribution of the variable is approximately normal.

MINITAB

Step by Step

Chi-Square Goodness of Fit

For Example 11–1, is there a preference for flavor of soda?

1. Enter the Observed Frequencies.
   a) Optional: type in the flavors in C1. Name the column Flavors.
   b) Type in the Observed counts in C2. Name the column Obs.
2. Select **Stat>Tables>Chi-Square Goodness of Fit (One Variable)**.
   a) Check the ratio button for Observed Counts then select C2 Obs.
   b) In the dialog box for Categorical names, select C1 Flavors (optional).
   c) Select the option for Equal proportions, then click [OK].

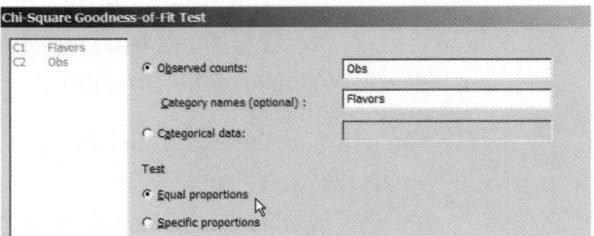

The session window will contain the results as shown:

Chi-Square Goodness-of-Fit Test for Observed Counts in Variable: Obs

Using category names in Flavors

Category	Observed	Test Proportion	Expected	Contribution to Chi-Sq
Cherry	32	0.2	20	7.2
Strawberry	28	0.2	20	3.2
Orange	16	0.2	20	0.8
Lime	14	0.2	20	1.8
Grape	10	0.2	20	5.0

N	DF	Chi-Sq	P-Value
100	4	18	0.001

11–2 Tests Using Contingency Tables

When data can be tabulated in table form in terms of frequencies, several types of hypotheses can be tested by using the chi-square test.

Two such tests are the independence of variables test and the homogeneity of proportions test. The test of independence of variables is used to determine whether two variables are independent of or related to each other when a single sample is selected. The test of homogeneity of proportions is used to determine whether the proportions for a variable are equal when several samples are selected from different populations. Both tests use the chi-square distribution and a contingency table, and the test value is found in the same way. The independence test will be explained first.

OBJECTIVE ②

Test two variables for independence, using chi-square.

Test for Independence

The chi-square **independence test** is used to test whether two variables are independent of each other.

Formula for the Chi-Square Independence Test

$$\chi^2 = \sum \frac{(O - E)^2}{E}$$

with degrees of freedom equal to the number of categories minus 1, and where
O = observed frequency
E = expected frequency

Assumptions for Chi-Square Independence Test

1. The data are obtained from a random sample.
2. The expected value in each cell must be 5 or more. If the expected values are not 5 or more, combine categories.

In this book, the assumptions will be stated in the exercises; however, when encountering statistics in other situations, you must check to see that these assumptions have been met before proceeding.

The null hypotheses for the chi-square independence test are generally, with some variations, stated as follows:

H_0: The variables are independent of each other.

H_1: The variables are dependent upon each other.

The data for the two variables are placed in a **contingency table.** One variable is called the *row variable,* and the other variable is called the *column variable.* The table is called an $R \times C$ *table,* where R is the number of rows and C is the number of columns. (Remember, rows go across or horizontally, and columns go up and down or vertically.) For example, a 2×3 contingency table would look like this.

	Column 1	Column 2	Column 3
Row 1	$C_{1,2}$	$C_{1,2}$	$C_{1,3}$
Row 2	$C_{2,1}$	$C_{2,2}$	$C_{2,3}$

Each value in the table is called a **cell value.** For example, the cell value $C_{2,3}$ means that it is in the second row (2) and third column (3).

The observed values are obtained from the sample data. (That is, they are given in the problem.) The expected values are computed from the observed values, and they are based on the assumption that the two variables are independent.

The formula for computing the expected values for each cell is

$$\text{Expected value} = \frac{(\text{row sum})(\text{column sum})}{\text{grand total}}$$

As with the chi-square goodness-of-fit test, if there is little difference between the observed values and the expected values, then the value of the test statistic will be small and the null hypothesis will not be rejected. Hence, the variables are independent of each other.

However, if there are large differences in the observed values and the expected values, then the test statistic will be large and the null hypothesis will be rejected. In this case, there is enough evidence to say that the variables are dependent on or related to each other. This test is always right-tailed.

The degrees of freedom for the chi-square test of independence are based on the size of the contingency table. The formula for the degrees of freedom is $(R - 1)(C - 1)$, that is, (rows $-$ 1)(columns $-$ 1). For a 2×3 table, the degrees of freedom would be $(2 - 1)(3 - 1) = 1(2) = 2$.

As an example, suppose a new postoperative procedure is administered to a number of patients in a large hospital. The researcher can ask the question, Do the doctors feel differently about this procedure from the nurses, or do they feel basically the same way? Note that the question is not whether they prefer the procedure but whether there is a difference of opinion between the two groups.

To answer this question, a researcher selects a sample of nurses and doctors and tabulates the data in table form, as shown.

Group	Prefer new procedure	Prefer old procedure	No preference
Nurses	100	80	20
Doctors	50	120	30

As the survey indicates, 100 nurses prefer the new procedure, 80 prefer the old procedure, and 20 have no preference; 50 doctors prefer the new procedure, 120 like the old procedure, and 30 have no preference. Since the main question is whether there is a difference in opinion, the null hypothesis is stated as follows:

H_0: The opinion about the procedure is *independent* of the profession.

The alternative hypothesis is stated as follows:

H_1: The opinion about the procedure is *dependent* on the profession.

If the null hypothesis is not rejected, the test means that both professions feel basically the same way about the procedure and that the differences are due to chance. If the null hypothesis is rejected, the test means that one group feels differently about the procedure from the other. Remember that rejection does *not* mean that one group favors the procedure and the other does not. Perhaps both groups favor it or both dislike it, but in different proportions.

Recall that the degrees of freedom for any contingency table are (rows $-$ 1) times (columns $-$ 1); that is, d.f. $= (R - 1)(C - 1)$. In this case, $(2 - 1)(3 - 1) = (1)(2) = 2$. The reason for this formula for d.f. is that all the expected values except one are free to vary in each row and in each column. The critical value for $\alpha = 0.05$ from Table G is 5.991.

To test the null hypothesis by using the chi-square independence test, you must compute the expected frequencies, assuming that the null hypothesis is true. These frequencies are computed by using the observed frequencies given in the table.

Using the previous table, you can compute the expected frequencies for each block (or cell), as shown next.

1. Find the sum of each row and each column, and find the grand total, as shown.

Group	Prefer new procedure	Prefer old procedure	No preference	Total
Nurses	100	80	20	Row 1 sum 200
Doctors	+50	+120	+30	Row 2 sum 200
Total	150	200	50	400
	Column 1 sum	Column 2 sum	Column 3 sum	Grand total

2. For each cell, multiply the corresponding row sum by the column sum and divide by the grand total, to get the expected value:

$$\text{Expected value} = \frac{\text{row sum} \times \text{column sum}}{\text{grand total}}$$

For example, for $C_{1,2}$, the expected value, denoted by $E_{1,2}$, is (refer to the previous tables)

$$E_{1,2} = \frac{(200)(200)}{400} = 100$$

For each cell, the expected values are computed as follows:

$$E_{1,1} = \frac{(200)(150)}{400} = 75 \qquad E_{1,2} = \frac{(200)(200)}{400} = 100 \qquad E_{1,3} = \frac{(200)(50)}{400} = 25$$

$$E_{2,1} = \frac{(200)(150)}{400} = 75 \qquad E_{2,2} = \frac{(200)(200)}{400} = 100 \qquad E_{2,3} = \frac{(200)(50)}{400} = 25$$

The expected values can now be placed in the corresponding cells along with the observed values, as shown.

Group	Prefer new procedure	Prefer old procedure	No preference	Total
Nurses	100 (75)	80 (100)	20 (25)	200
Doctors	50 (75)	120 (100)	30 (25)	200
Total	150	200	50	400

The rationale for the computation of the expected frequencies for a contingency table uses proportions. For $C_{1,1}$ a total of 150 out of 400 people prefer the new procedure. And since there are 200 nurses, you would expect, if the null hypothesis were true, (150/400)(200), or 75, of the nurses to be in favor of the new procedure.

The test value can now be computed by using the formula

$$\chi^2 = \sum \frac{(O-E)^2}{E}$$

$$= \frac{(100-75)^2}{75} + \frac{(80-100)^2}{100} + \frac{(20-25)^2}{25} + \frac{(50-75)^2}{75}$$

$$+ \frac{(120-100)^2}{100} + \frac{(30-25)^2}{25}$$

$$= 26.667$$

FIGURE 11–6
Critical and Test Values for the Postoperative Procedures Example

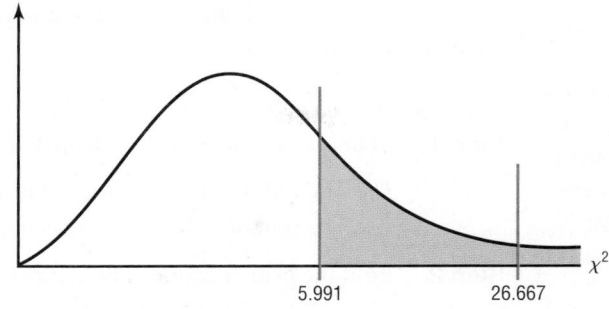

Next make the decision. Since the test value 26.667 is larger than the critical value 5.991, the decision is to reject the null hypothesis. See Figure 11–6.

The conclusion is that there is enough evidence to support the claim that opinion is related to (dependent on) profession, that is, that the doctors and nurses differ in their opinions about the procedure.

The P-values can be found as previously shown. In this case, if we look across row 2 (d.f. = 2), we see that the chi-square value of 10.597 corresponds to the α value of 0.005. Since our test value is 26.667 and is larger than 10.597, the P-value < 0.005, and the null hypothesis can be rejected.

The Procedure Table for performing the chi-square independence test is given next.

Procedure Table

The Chi-Square Independence Test

Step 1 State the hypotheses and identify the claim.

Step 2 Find the critical value for the right tail. Use Table G.

Step 3 Compute the test value. To compute the test value, first find the expected values. For each cell of the contingency table, use the formula

$$E = \frac{(\text{row sum})(\text{column sum})}{\text{grand total}}$$

to get the expected value. To find the test value, use the formula

$$\chi^2 = \sum \frac{(O - E)^2}{E}$$

Step 4 Make the decision.

Step 5 Summarize the results.

Examples 11–5 and 11–6 illustrate the procedure for the chi-square test of independence.

EXAMPLE 11–5   Hospitals and Infections

A researcher wishes to see if there is a relationship between the hospital and the number of patient infections. A random sample of 3 hospitals was selected, and the number of infections for a specific year has been reported. The data are shown next.

Hospital	Surgical site infections	Pneumonia infections	Bloodstream infections	Total
A	41	27	51	119
B	36	3	40	79
C	169	106	109	384
Total	246	136	200	582

Source: Pennsylvania Health Care Cost Containment Council.

At $\alpha = 0.05$, can it be concluded that the number of infections is related to the hospital where they occurred?

SOLUTION

Step 1   State the hypothesis and identify the claim.

H_0: The number of infections is independent of the hospital.

H_1: The number of infections is dependent on the hospital (claim).

Step 2   Find the critical value. The critical value using Table G at $\alpha = 0.05$ with $(3 - 1)(3 - 1) = (2)(2) = 4$ degrees of freedom is 9.488.

Step 3   Compute the test value. First find the expected values.

$$E_{1,1} = \frac{(119)(246)}{582} = 50.30 \qquad E_{1,2} = \frac{(119)(136)}{582} = 27.81 \qquad E_{1,3} = \frac{(119)(200)}{582} = 40.89$$

$$E_{2,1} = \frac{(79)(246)}{582} = 33.39 \qquad E_{2,2} = \frac{(79)(136)}{582} = 18.46 \qquad E_{2,3} = \frac{(79)(200)}{582} = 27.15$$

$$E_{3,1} = \frac{(384)(246)}{582} = 162.31 \qquad E_{3,2} = \frac{(384)(136)}{582} = 89.73 \qquad E_{3,3} = \frac{(384)(200)}{582} = 131.96$$

The completed table is shown.

Hospital	Surgical site infections	Pneumonia infections	Bloodstream infections	Total
A	41 (50.30)	27 (27.81)	51 (40.89)	119
B	36 (33.39)	3 (18.46)	40 (27.15)	79
C	169 (162.31)	106 (89.73)	109 (131.96)	384
Total	246	136	200	582

Then substitute in the formula and evaluate to find the test statistic value.

$$\chi^2 = \sum \frac{(O - E)^2}{E}$$

$$= \frac{(41 - 50.30)^2}{50.30} + \frac{(27 - 27.81)^2}{27.81} + \frac{(51 - 40.89)^2}{40.89}$$

$$+ \frac{(36 - 33.39)^2}{33.39} + \frac{(3 - 18.46)^2}{18.46} + \frac{(40 - 27.15)^2}{27.15}$$

$$+ \frac{(169 - 162.31)^2}{162.31} + \frac{(106 - 89.73)^2}{89.73} + \frac{(109 - 131.96)^2}{131.96}$$

$$= 1.719 + 0.024 + 2.500 + 0.204 + 12.948 + 6.082$$

$$+ 0.276 + 2.950 + 3.995$$

$$= 30.698$$

Step 4   Make the decision. The decision is to reject the null hypothesis since $30.698 > 9.488$. That is, the test value lies in the critical region, as shown in Figure 11–7.

FIGURE 11–7
Critical and Test Values for
Example 11–5

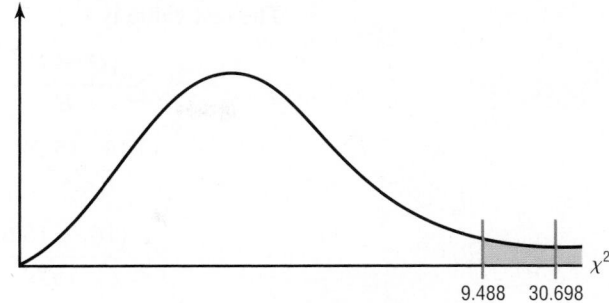

9.488 30.698

Step 5   Summarize the results. There is enough evidence to support the claim that the number of infections is related to the hospital where they occurred.

EXAMPLE 11–6   Sports Preference of Males and Females

A researcher wished to see if there is a difference in the favorite sport of males and the favorite sport of females. She selected a sample of 32 males and 48 females and asked them which of three sports was their favorite. The results are shown.

Gender	Football	Baseball	Hockey	Total
Male	18	10	4	32
Female	20	16	12	48
Total	38	26	16	80

At $\alpha = 0.10$, can the researcher conclude that sports preference is related to gender?

SOLUTION

Step 1   State the hypotheses and identify the claim.

H_0: Sports preference is independent of the gender of the person.
H_1: Sports preference is related to the gender of the person (claim).

Step 2   Find the critical value. The critical value is 4.605, since the degrees of freedom are $(2 - 1)(3 - 1) = 2$.

Step 3   Compute the test value. First compute the expected values.

$$E_{1,1} = \frac{(32)(38)}{80} = 15.2 \qquad E_{1,2} = \frac{(32)(26)}{80} = 10.4 \qquad E_{1,3} = \frac{(32)(16)}{80} = 6.4$$

$$E_{2,1} = \frac{(48)(38)}{80} = 22.8 \qquad E_{2,2} = \frac{(48)(26)}{80} = 15.6 \qquad E_{2,3} = \frac{(48)(16)}{80} = 9.6$$

The completed table is shown.

Gender	Football	Baseball	Hockey	Total
Male	18 (15.2)	10 (10.4)	4 (6.4)	32
Female	20 (22.8)	16 (15.6)	12 (9.6)	48
Total	38	26	16	80

The test value is

$$x^2 = \sum \frac{(O - E)^2}{E}$$

$$= \frac{(18 - 15.2)^2}{15.2} + \frac{(10 - 10.4)^2}{10.4} + \frac{(4 - 6.4)^2}{6.4} + \frac{(20 - 22.8)^2}{22.8}$$

$$+ \frac{(16 - 15.6)^2}{15.6} + \frac{(12 - 9.6)^2}{9.6}$$

$$= 0.516 + 0.015 + 0.900 + 0.344 + 0.010 + 0.600 = 2.385$$

Step 4   Make the decision. The decision is to not reject the null hypothesis, since 2.385 < 4.605. See Figure 11–8.

FIGURE 11–8
Critical and Test Values for Example 11–6

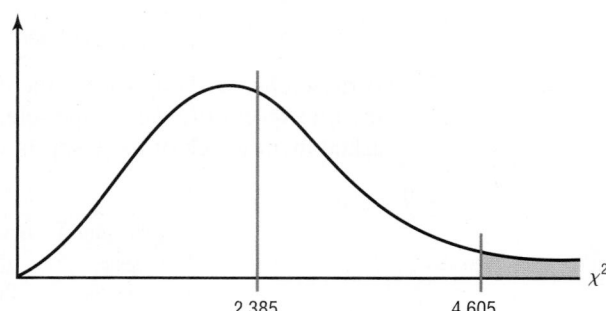

Step 5   Summarize the results. There is not enough evidence to support the claim that sports preference is related to the gender of the person.

In this case, the *P*-value is between 0.10 and 0.90. The TI-84 gives a *P*-value of 0.303. Again, this supports the decision and summary stated previously.

Test for Homogeneity of Proportions

OBJECTIVE ❸

Test proportions for homogeneity, using chi-square.

The second chi-square test that uses a contingency table is called the **homogeneity of proportions test.**

> The *test of* **homogeneity of proportions** is used to test the claim that different populations have the same proportion of subjects who have a certain attitude or characteristic.

Interesting Facts

Water is the most critical nutrient in your body. It is needed for just about everything that happens. Water is lost fast: 2 cups daily are lost just exhaling, 10 cups through normal waste and body cooling, and 1 to 2 quarts per hour running, biking, or working out.

In this situation, samples are selected from several different populations, and the researcher is interested in determining whether the proportions of elements that have a common characteristic are the same for each population. The sample sizes are specified in advance, making either the row totals or column totals in the contingency table known before the samples are selected. For example, a researcher may select a sample of 50 freshmen, 50 sophomores, 50 juniors, and 50 seniors and then find the proportion of students who are smokers in each level. The researcher will then compare the proportions for each group to see if they are equal. The hypotheses in this case would be

H_0: $p_1 = p_2 = p_3 = p_4$

H_1: At least one proportion is different from the others.

If the researcher does not reject the null hypothesis, it can be assumed that the proportions are equal and the differences in them are due to chance. Hence, the proportion of students who smoke is the same for grade levels freshmen through senior. When the null hypothesis is rejected, it can be assumed that the proportions are not all equal.

The assumptions for the test of homogeneity of proportions are the same as the assumptions for the chi-square test of independence. The procedure for this test is the same as the procedure for the chi-square test of independence.

EXAMPLE 11–7 Happiness and Income

A psychologist randomly selected 100 people from each of four income groups and asked them if they were "very happy." For people who made less than $30,000, 24% responded yes. For people who made $30,000 to $74,999, 33% responded yes. For people who made $75,000 to $90,999, 38% responded yes, and for people who made $100,000 or more, 49% responded yes. At $\alpha = 0.05$, test the claim that there is no difference in the proportion of people in each economic group who were very happy.

SOLUTION

It is necessary to make a table showing the number of people in each group who responded yes and the number of people in each group who responded no.

For group 1, 24% of the people responded yes, so 24% of 100 = 0.24(100) = 24 responded yes and 100 − 24 = 76 responded no.

For group 2, 33% of the people responded yes, so 33% of 100 = 0.33(100) = 33 responded yes and 100 − 33 = 67 responded no.

For group 3, 38% of the people responded yes, so 38% of 100 = 0.38(100) = 38 people responded yes and 100 − 38 = 62 people responded no.

For group 4, 49% of the people responded yes, so 49% of 100 = 0.49(100) = 49 responded yes, and 100 − 49 = 51 people responded no.

Tabulate the data in a table, and find the sums of the rows and columns as shown.

Household income	Less than $30,000 (24%)	$30,000– $74,999 (33%)	$75,000– $99,999 (38%)	$100,000 or more (49%)	Total
Yes	24	33	38	49	144
No	76	67	62	51	256
	100	100	100	100	400

Source: Based on information from Princeton Survey Research Associates International.

Step 1 State the hypotheses and identify the claim.

H_0: $p_1 = p_2 = p_3 = p_4$ (claim)

H_1: At least one proportion differs from the others.

Step 2 Find the critical value. The formula for the degrees of freedom is the same as before: $(R - 1)(C - 1) = (2 - 1)(4 - 1) = 1(3) = 3$. The critical value is 7.815.

Step 3 Compute the test value. Since we want to test the claim that the proportions are equal, we use the expected value as $\frac{1}{4} \cdot 400 = 100$. First compute the expected values as shown previously.

$$E_{1,1} = \frac{(144)(100)}{400} = 36 \quad E_{1,2} = \frac{(144)(100)}{400} = 36 \quad E_{1,3} = \frac{(144)(100)}{400} = 36 \quad E_{1,4} = \frac{(144)(100)}{400} = 36$$

$$E_{2,1} = \frac{(256)(100)}{400} = 64 \quad E_{2,2} = \frac{(256)(100)}{400} = 64 \quad E_{2,3} = \frac{(256)(100)}{400} = 64 \quad E_{2,4} = \frac{(256)(100)}{400} = 64$$

The completed table is shown.

Household income	Less than $30,000 (24%)	$30,000–$74,999 (33%)	$75,000–$99,999 (38%)	$100,000 or more (49%)	Total
Yes	24 (36)	33 (36)	38 (36)	49 (36)	144
No	76 (64)	67 (64)	62 (64)	51 (64)	256
	100	100	100	100	400

Next calculate the test value.

$$\chi^2 = \sum \frac{(O - E)^2}{E}$$

$$= \frac{(24 - 36)^2}{36} + \frac{(33 - 36)^2}{36} + \frac{(38 - 36)^2}{36} + \frac{(49 - 36)^2}{36}$$

$$+ \frac{(76 - 64)^2}{64} + \frac{(67 - 64)^2}{64} + \frac{(62 - 64)^2}{64} + \frac{(51 - 64)^2}{64}$$

$$= 4.000 + 0.250 + 0.111 + 4.694 + 2.250 + 0.141 + 0.063 + 2.641$$

$$= 14.150$$

Step 4   Make the decision. Reject the null hypothesis since $14.150 > 7.815$. See Figure 11–9.

FIGURE 11–9
Critical and Test Values for Example 11–7

Step 5   Summarize the results. There is enough evidence to reject the claim that there is no difference in the proportions. Hence, the incomes seem to make a difference in the proportions.

When the degrees of freedom for a contingency table are equal to 1—that is, the table is a 2×2 table—some statisticians suggest using the *Yates correction for continuity*. The formula for the test is then

$$\chi^2 = \sum \frac{(|O - E| - 0.5)^2}{E}$$

Since the chi-square test is already conservative, most statisticians agree that the Yates correction is not necessary. (See Exercise 33 in Extending the Concepts.)

Applying the Concepts 11–2

Satellite Dishes in Restricted Areas

The Senate is expected to vote on a bill to allow the installation of satellite dishes of any size in deed-restricted areas. The House had passed a similar bill. An opinion poll was taken to see whether how a person felt about satellite dish restrictions was related to his or her age. A chi-square test was run, creating the following computer-generated information.

Degrees of freedom d.f. = 6
Test statistic χ^2 = 61.25
Critical value C.V. = 12.6
P-value = 0.00
Significance level = 0.05

	18–29	30–49	50–64	65 and up
For	96 (79.5)	96 (79.5)	90 (79.5)	36 (79.5)
Against	201 (204.75)	189 (204.75)	195 (204.75)	234 (204.75)
Don't know	3 (15.75)	15 (15.75)	15 (15.75)	30 (15.75)

1. Which number from the output is compared to the significance level to check if the null hypothesis should be rejected?

2. Which number from the output gives the probability of a type I error that is calculated from your sample data?

3. Was a right-, left-, or two-tailed test run? Why?

4. Can you tell how many rows and columns there were by looking at the degrees of freedom?

5. Does increasing the sample size change the degrees of freedom?

6. What are your conclusions? Look at the observed and expected frequencies in the table to draw some of your own specific conclusions about response and age.

7. What would your conclusions be if the level of significance were initially set at 0.10?

8. Does chi-square tell you which cell's observed and expected frequencies are significantly different?

See page 645 for the answers.

Exercises 11–2

1. How is the chi-square independence test similar to the goodness-of-fit test? How is it different?

2. How are the degrees of freedom computed for the independence test?

3. Generally, how would the null and alternative hypotheses be stated for the chi-square independence test?

4. What is the name of the table used in the independence test?

5. How are the expected values computed for each cell in the table?

6. How are the null and alternative hypotheses stated for the test of homogeneity of proportions?

For Exercises 7 through 31, perform the following steps.

   a.   State the hypotheses and identify the claim.

   b.   Find the critical value.

   c.   Compute the test value.

   d.   Make the decision.

   e.   Summarize the results.

Use the traditional method of hypothesis testing unless otherwise specified. Assume all assumptions are valid.

7. **Restaurants and Types of Meals Purchased** A random sample of 100 patrons from three different restaurants, each of which serves breakfast, lunch, and dinner, were asked which meal they purchased. The

results are shown in the table below. Check the data for a dependent relationship at $\alpha = 0.01$.

	Restaurant A	Restaurant B	Restaurant C
Breakfast	26	29	43
Lunch	53	27	33
Dinner	21	44	24

8. **Ethnicity and Movie Admissions** Are movie admissions related to ethnicity? A 2007 study indicated the following numbers of admissions (in thousands) for two different years. At the 0.05 level of significance, can it be concluded that movie attendance by year was dependent upon ethnicity?

	Caucasian	Hispanic	African-American	Other
2006	936	240	195	101
2007	909	297	150	115

Source: *MPAA Study 2007.*

9. **Endangered or Threatened Species** Can you conclude a relationship between the class of vertebrate and whether it is endangered or threatened? Use the 0.05 level of significance. Is there a different result for the 0.01 level of significance?

	Mammal	Bird	Reptile	Amphibian	Fish
Endangered	68	76	14	13	76
Threatened	13	15	23	10	61

Source: www.infoplease.com

10. **Women in the Military** This table lists the numbers of officers and enlisted personnel for women in the military. At $\alpha = 0.05$, is there sufficient evidence to conclude that a relationship exists between rank and branch of the Armed Forces?

	Officers	Enlisted
Army	10,791	62,491
Navy	7,816	42,750
Marine Corps	932	9,525
Air Force	11,819	54,344

Source: *New York Times Almanac.*

11. **Violent Crimes** A record of violent crimes for a random sample of cities from the list of U.S. cities with the fewest crimes is shown below. At $\alpha = 0.05$, is there sufficient evidence to indicate a relationship between the city and the type of crime committed?

	Forcible rape	Robbery	Aggravated assault
Cary, NC	14	35	70
Amherst, NY	10	33	76
Simi Valley, CA	14	37	77
Norman, OK	47	36	53

Source: *Time Almanac.*

12. **Population and Age** Is the size of the population by age related to the state that it's in? Use $\alpha = 0.05$. (Population values are in thousands.)

	Under 5	5–17	18–24	25–44	45–64	65+
Pennsylvania	721	2140	1025	3515	2702	1899
Ohio	740	2104	1065	3359	2487	1501

Source: *New York Times Almanac.*

13. **Unemployment Time and Type of Industry** Is the length of unemployment related to the type of industry? A random sample of unemployed workers from three different sectors yielded the following data. At the 0.05 level of significance, are the two categories dependent?

	Less than 5 weeks	5–14 weeks	15–26 weeks
Transportation/ utilities	85	110	80
Information	48	57	45
Financial activities	83	111	114

Source: *World Almanac.*

14. **Congressional Representatives** Four states were randomly selected, and their members in the U.S. House of Representatives (113th Congress) are noted. At $\alpha = 0.10$, can it be concluded that there is a dependent relationship between the state and the political party affiliation of its representatives?

	California	Florida	Illinois	Texas
Democrat	38	10	12	12
Republican	15	17	6	24

Source: *New York Times Almanac.*

15. **Student Majors at Colleges** The table shows the number of students (in thousands) participating in various programs at both two-year and four-year institutions. At $\alpha = 0.05$, can it be concluded that there is a relationship between program of study and type of institution?

	Two-year	Four-year
Agriculture and related sciences	36	52
Criminal justice	210	231
Foreign languages and literature	28	59
Mathematics and statistics	28	63

Source: *Time Almanac.*

16. **Organ Transplantation** Listed is information regarding organ transplantation for three different years. Based on these data, is there sufficient evidence at $\alpha = 0.01$ to conclude that a relationship exists between year and type of transplant?

Year	Heart	Kidney/pancreas	Lung
2003	2056	870	1085
2004	2016	880	1173
2005	2127	903	1408

Source: www.infoplease.com

17. Study Groups and Professors Students at a particular college must choose a statistics professor and a study group. Is there a relationship between the two choices at $\alpha = 0.05$?

	Group 5a	Group 5b	Group 5c
Prof. Q	25	22	15
Prof. E	16	15	24
Prof. D	17	18	22

18. Record CDs Sold Are the sales of CDs (in thousands) by genre related to the year in which the sales occurred? Use the 0.05 level of significance.

Year	Classical	Jazz	Soundtracks
2005	15,875	17,139	22,849
2004	18,686	18,794	27,367

Source: *Time Almanac.*

19. Recreational Reading and Gender A book publisher wishes to determine whether there is a difference in the type of book selected by males and females for recreational reading. A random sample provides the data given here. At $\alpha = 0.05$, test the claim that the type of book selected is independent of the gender of the individual. Use the *P*-value method.

	Type of book		
Gender	Mystery	Romance	Self-help
Male	243	201	191
Female	135	149	202

20. Effectiveness of New Drug To test the effectiveness of a new drug, a researcher gives one group of randomly selected individuals the new drug and another group of randomly selected individuals a placebo. The results of the study are shown here. At $\alpha = 0.10$, can the researcher conclude that the drug results differ from those of the placebo? Use the *P*-value method.

Medication	Effective	Not effective
Drug	32	9
Placebo	12	18

21. Hospitals and Cesarean Delivery Rates The national Cesarean delivery rate for a recent year was 32.2% (number of live births performed by Cesarean section). A random sample of 100 birth records from three large hospitals showed the following results for type of birth. Test for homogeneity of proportions using $\alpha = 0.10$.

	Hospital A	Hospital B	Hospital C
Cesarean	44	28	39
Non-Cesarean	56	72	61

Source: *World Almanac.*

22. Foreign Language Speaking Dorms A local college recently made the news by offering foreign language–speaking dorm rooms to its students. When questioned at another school, 50 randomly selected students from each class responded as shown. At $\alpha = 0.05$, is there sufficient evidence to conclude that the proportions of students favoring foreign language–speaking dorms are not the same for each class?

	Freshmen	Sophomores	Juniors	Seniors
Yes (favor)	10	15	20	22
No	40	35	30	28

23. Youth Physical Fitness According to a recent survey, 64% of Americans between the ages of 6 and 17 years cannot pass a basic fitness test. A physical education instructor wishes to determine if the percentages of such students in different schools in his school district are the same. He administers a basic fitness test to 120 randomly selected students in each of four schools. The results are shown here. At $\alpha = 0.05$, test the claim that the proportions who pass the test are equal.

	Southside	West End	East Hills	Jefferson
Passed	49	38	46	34
Failed	71	82	74	86
Total	120	120	120	120

Source: *The Harper's Index Book.*

24. Participation in Market Research Survey An advertising firm has decided to ask 92 customers at each of three local shopping malls if they are willing to take part in a market research survey. According to previous studies, 38% of Americans refuse to take part in such surveys. The results are shown here. At $\alpha = 0.01$, test the claim that the proportions of those who are willing to participate are equal.

	Mall A	Mall B	Mall C
Will participate	52	45	36
Will not participate	40	47	56
Total	92	92	92

Source: *The Harper's Index Book.*

25. Workforce Distribution A researcher wishes to see if the proportions of workers for each type of job have changed during the last 10 years. A random sample of 100 workers in Pennsylvania is selected, and the results are shown. At $\alpha = 0.05$, test the claim that the proportions have not changed. Can the results be generalized to the population of the United States?

	Services	Manu-facturing	Government	Other
10 years ago	14	13	17	15
Now	11	12	8	10
Total	25	25	25	25

26. Mothers Working Outside the Home According to a recent survey, 59% of Americans aged 8 to 17 years would prefer that their mothers work outside the home, regardless of what they do now. A school district psychologist decided to select three random samples of 60 students each in elementary, middle, and high school to see how the students in her district felt about the issue. At $\alpha = 0.10$, test the claim that the proportions of the students who prefer that their mothers have jobs outside the home are equal.

	Elementary	Middle	High
Prefer mothers work	29	38	51
Prefer mothers not work	31	22	9
Total	60	60	60

Source: Daniel Weiss, *100% American.*

27. **Volunteer Practices of Students** The Bureau of Labor Statistics reported information on volunteers by selected characteristics. They found that 24.4% of the population aged 16 to 24 years volunteers a median number of 36 hours per year. A survey of 75 randomly selected students in each age group revealed the following data on volunteer practices. At $\alpha = 0.05$, can it be concluded that the proportions of volunteers are the same for each group?

		Age			
	18	19	20	21	22
Yes (volunteer)	19	18	23	31	13
No	56	57	52	44	62

Source: *Time Almanac.*

28. **Fathers in the Delivery Room** On average, 79% of American fathers are in the delivery room when their children are born. A physician's assistant surveyed 300 randomly selected first-time fathers to determine if they had been in the delivery room when their children were born. The results are shown here. At $\alpha = 0.05$, is there enough evidence to reject the claim that the proportions of those who were in the delivery room at the time of birth are the same?

	Hos-pital A	Hos-pital B	Hos-pital C	Hos-pital D
Present	66	60	57	56
Not present	9	15	18	19
Total	75	75	75	75

Source: Daniel Weiss, *100% American.*

29. **Injuries on Monkey Bars** A children's playground equipment manufacturer read in a survey that 55% of all U.S. playground injuries occur on the monkey bars. The manufacturer wishes to investigate playground injuries in four different parts of the country to determine if the proportions of accidents on the monkey bars are equal. The results are shown here. At $\alpha = 0.05$, test the claim that the proportions are equal. Use the *P*-value method.

Accidents	North	South	East	West
On monkey bars	15	18	13	16
Not on monkey bars	15	12	17	14
Total	30	30	30	30

Source: Michael D. Shook and Robert L. Shook, *The Book of Odds.*

30. **Thanksgiving Travel** According to the American Automobile Association, 31 million Americans travel over the Thanksgiving holiday. To determine whether to stay open or not, a national restaurant chain surveyed 125 customers at each of four locations to see if they would be traveling over the holiday. The results are shown here. At $\alpha = 0.10$, test the claim that the proportions of Americans who will travel over the Thanksgiving holiday are equal. Use the *P*-value method.

	Loca-tion A	Loca-tion B	Loca-tion C	Loca-tion D
Will travel	37	52	46	49
Will not travel	88	73	79	76
Total	125	125	125	125

Source: Michael D. Shook and Robert L. Shook, *The Book of Odds.*

31. **Grocery Lists** The vice president of a large supermarket chain wished to determine if her customers made a list before going grocery shopping. She surveyed 288 customers in three stores. The results are shown here. At $\alpha = 0.10$, test the claim that the proportions of the customers in the three stores who made a list before going shopping are equal.

	Store A	Store B	Store C
Made list	77	74	68
No list	19	22	28
Total	96	96	96

Source: Daniel Weiss, *100% American.*

Extending the Concepts

32. For a 2 × 2 table, *a*, *b*, *c*, and *d* are the observed values for each cell, as shown.

a	b
c	d

The chi-square test value can be computed as

$$\chi^2 = \frac{n(ad - bc)^2}{(a + b)(a + c)(c + d)(b + d)}$$

It has been suggested that color is related to appetite in humans. For example, if the walls in a restaurant are painted certain colors, it is thought that the customer will eat more food. A study was done at the University of Illinois and the University of Pennsylvania. When people were given six varieties of jellybeans mixed in a bowl or separated by color, they ate about twice as many from the bowl with the mixed jellybeans as from the bowls that were separated by color.

It is thought that when the jellybeans were mixed, people felt that it offered a greater variety of choices, and the variety of choices increased their appetites.

In this case one variable—color—is categorical, and the other variable—amount of jellybeans eaten—is numerical. Could a chi-square goodness-of-fit test be used here? If so, suggest how it could be set up.

where $n = a + b + c + d$. Using this formula, compute the χ^2 test value and then the formula $\Sigma(O - E)^2/E$, and compare the results. Use the following table.

12	15
9	23

33. For the contingency table shown in Exercise 32, compute the chi-square test value by using the Yates correction (page 632) for continuity.

34. When the chi-square test value is significant and there is a relationship between the variables, the

strength of this relationship can be measured by using the *contingency coefficient*. The formula for the contingency coefficient is

$$C = \sqrt{\frac{\chi^2}{\chi^2 + n}}$$

where χ^2 is the test value and n is the sum of frequencies of the cells. The contingency coefficient will always be less than 1. Compute the contingency coefficient for Exercises 8 and 20.

≡ Technology   Step by Step

TI-84 Plus
Step by Step

Chi-Square Test for Independence

1. Press **2nd** [X^{-1}] for **MATRIX** and move the cursor to Edit; then press **ENTER**.
2. Enter the number of rows and columns. Then press **ENTER**.
3. Enter the values in the matrix as they appear in the contingency table.
4. Press **STAT** and move the cursor to TESTS. Press **C (ALPHA PRGM)** for χ^2-Test. Make sure the observed matrix is [A] and the expected matrix is [B].
5. Move the cursor to Calculate and press **ENTER**.

Example TI11–2

Using the data shown from Example 11–6, test the claim of independence at $\alpha = 0.10$.

	Football	Baseball	Hockey
Male	18	10	4
Female	20	16	12

The test value is 2.385290148. The *P*-value is 0.3034176395. The decision is to not reject the null hypothesis, since this value is greater than 0.10. You can find the expected values by pressing **MATRIX,** moving the cursor to [B], and pressing **ENTER** twice.

EXCEL
Step by Step

Tests Using Contingency Tables

Excel does not have a procedure to conduct tests using contingency tables without including the expected values. However, you may conduct such tests using the MegaStat Add-in available in your online resources. If you have not installed this add-in, do so, following the instructions from the Chapter 1 Excel Step by Step.

Example XL11–3

The table below shows the number of years of college a person has completed and the residence of the person.

Using a significance level $\alpha = 0.05$, determine whether the number of years of college a person has completed is related to residence.

1. Enter the location variable labels in column A, beginning at cell A2.
2. Enter the categories for the number of years of college in cells B1, C1, and D1, respectively.
3. Enter the observed values in the appropriate block (cell).
4. From the toolbar, select Add-Ins, **MegaStat>Chi-Square/Crosstab>Contingency Table.** *Note:* You may need to open MegaStat from the MegaStat.xls file on your computer's hard drive.
5. In the dialog box, type **A1:D4** for the Input range.
6. Check chi-square from the Output Options.
7. Click [OK].

Chi-Square Contingency Table Test for Independence

	None	4-year	Advanced	Total
Urban	15	12	8	35
Suburban	8	15	9	32
Rural	6	8	7	21
Total	29	35	24	88

3.01	chi-square
4	df
.5569	*P*-value

The results of the test indicate that at the 5% level of significance, there is not enough evidence to conclude that a person's location is dependent on number of years of college.

MINITAB
Step by Step

Chi-Square Test of Independence from Contingency Table

Example 11–5

Is there a relationship between the type of infection and the hospital?

1. Enter the Observed Frequencies for the type of infection in C1 Surgical Site, C2 Pneumonia, and C3 Bloodstream. Do not include labels or totals.

⊞ Worksheet 1 ***			
↓	**C1**	**C2**	**C3**
	Surgical Site	**Pneumonia**	**Bloodstream**
1	41	27	51
2	36	3	40
3	169	106	109

2. Select **Stat>Tables>Chi-Square Test (Two-way Table in Worksheet)**

    a) Drag the mouse over the three columns of Observed counts.

    b) Click on [Select], then [OK].

The results are displayed in the session window.

Chi-Square Test: Surgical Site, Pneumonia, Bloodstream
Expected counts are printed below observed counts
Chi-Square contributions are printed below expected counts

	Surgical Site	Pneumonia	Bloodstream	Total
1	41	27	51	119
	50.30	27.81	40.89	
	1.719	0.023	2.498	
2	36	3	40	79
	33.39	18.46	27.15	
	0.204	12.948	6.084	
3	169	106	109	384
	162.31	89.73	131.96	
	0.276	2.949	3.994	
Total	246	136	200	582

Chi-Sq = 30.696, DF = 4, P-Value = 0.000

There is a relationship between infection type and hospital.

Construct a Contingency Table and Calculate the Chi-Square Test Statistic

In Chapter 4 we learned how to construct a contingency table by using gender and smoking status in the Data Bank file described in Appendix B. Are smoking status and gender related? Who is more likely to smoke, men or women?

1. Use **File>Open Worksheet** to open the Data Bank file. Remember, do *not* click the file icon.

2. Select **Stat>Tables>Cross Tabulation and Chi-Square.**

3. Double-click Smoking Status for rows and Gender for columns.

4. The Display option for Counts should be checked.

5. Click [Chi-Square].

    a) Check Chi-Square analysis.

    b) Check Expected cell counts.

6. Click [OK] twice.

In the session window the contingency table and the chi-square analysis will be displayed.

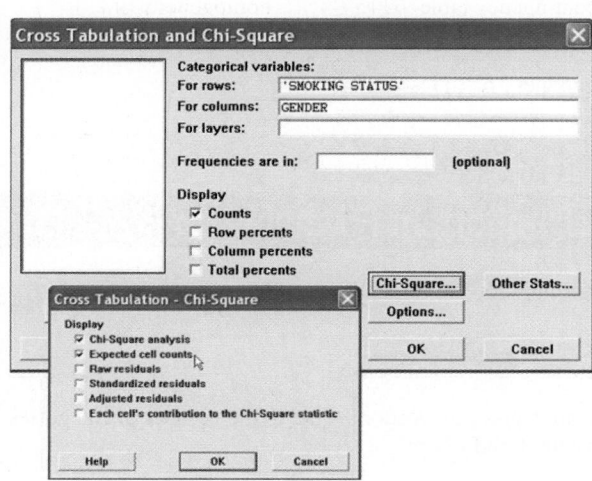

Tabulated statistics: SMOKING STATUS, GENDER

Rows: SMOKING   STATUS   Columns: Gender

	F	M	All
0	25	22	47
	23.50	23.50	47.00
1	18	19	37
	18.50	18.50	37.00
2	7	9	16
	8.00	8.00	16.00
All	50	50	100
	50.00	50.00	100.00

Cell Contents: Count
                                Expected count

Pearson Chi-Square = 0.469, DF = 2, P-Value = 0.791

There is not enough evidence to conclude that smoking is related to gender.

Summary

- Three uses of the chi-square distribution were explained in this chapter. It can be used as a goodness-of-fit test to determine whether the frequencies of a distribution are the same as the hypothesized frequencies. For example, is the number of defective parts produced by a factory the same each day? This test is always a right-tailed test. (11–1)

- The test of independence is used to determine whether two variables are related or are independent. This test uses a contingency table and is always a right-tailed test.

An example of its use is a test to determine if attitudes about trash recycling are dependent on whether residents live in urban or rural areas. (11–2)

- Finally, the homogeneity of proportions test is used to determine if several proportions are all equal when samples are selected from different populations. (11–2)

  The chi-square distribution is also used for other types of statistical hypothesis tests, such as the Kruskal-Wallis test, which is explained in Chapter 13.

Important Terms

contingency table 624

expected frequency 610

goodness-of-fit test 610

homogeneity of
proportions test 630

independence test 624

observed frequency 610

Important Formulas

Formula for the chi-square test for goodness of fit:

$$\chi^2 = \sum \frac{(O - E)^2}{E}$$

with degrees of freedom equal to the number of categories minus 1 and where

O = observed frequency

E = expected frequency

Formula for the chi-square independence and homogeneity of proportions tests:

$$\chi^2 = \sum \frac{(O - E)^2}{E}$$

with degrees of freedom equal to (rows − 1) times (columns − 1). Formula for the expected value for each cell:

$$E = \frac{(\text{row sum})(\text{column sum})}{\text{grand total}}$$

≡ Review Exercises

For Exercises 1 through 10, follow these steps.

 a. State the hypotheses and identify the claim.

 b. Find the critical value(s).

 c. Compute the test value.

 d. Make the decision.

 e. Summarize the results.

Use the traditional method of hypothesis testing unless otherwise specified. Assume all assumptions have been met.

Section 11–1

 1. **Traffic Accident Fatalities** A traffic safety report indicated that for the 21–24 year age group, 31.58% of traffic fatalities were victims who had used a seat belt. Victims who were not wearing a seat belt accounted for 59.83% of the deaths, and the status of the rest was unknown. A study of 120 randomly selected traffic fatalities in a particular region showed that for this age group, 35 of the victims had used a seat belt, 78 had not, and the status of the rest was unknown. At $\alpha = 0.05$, is there sufficient evidence that the proportions differ from those in the report?

 Source: *New York Times Almanac.*

 2. **Displaced Workers** The reasons that workers in the 25–54 year old category were displaced are listed.

Plant closed/moved	44.8%
Insufficient work	25.2%
Position eliminated	30%

 A random sample of 180 displaced workers (in this age category) found that 40 lost their jobs due to their position being eliminated, 53 due to insufficient work, and the rest due to the company being closed or moving. At the 0.01 level of significance, are these proportions different from those from the U.S. Department of Labor?

 Source: *BLS-World Almanac.*

 3. **Gun Sale Denials** A police investigator read that the reasons why gun sales to applicants were denied were distributed as follows: criminal history of felonies, 75%; domestic violence conviction, 11%; and drug abuse, fugitive, etc., 14%. A random sample of applicants in a large study who were refused sales is obtained and is distributed as follows. At $\alpha = 0.10$, can it be concluded that the distribution is as stated? Do you think the results might be different in a rural area?

Reason	Criminal history	Domestic violence	Drug abuse, etc.
Number	120	42	38

 Source: Based on FBI statistics.

 4. **Types of Pitches Thrown** A starting pitcher for a National League contender in Major League Baseball has the following pitch arsenal: 62% fastball, 18% curve, 17% slider, and 3% change-up. In a recent game, he threw the following number of pitches. Is there sufficient evidence at $\alpha = 0.05$ that he deviated from his usual pitch count?

 Fastball 56   curve 30   slider 20   change-up 5

Section 11–2

 5. **Pension Investments** A survey was conducted on how a lump-sum pension would be invested by randomly selected 45-year-olds and randomly selected 65-year-olds. The data are shown here. At $\alpha = 0.05$, is there a relationship between the age of the investor and the way the money would be invested?

	Large company stock funds	Small company stock funds	Inter- national stock funds	CDs or money market funds	Bonds
Age 45	20	10	10	15	45
Age 65	42	24	24	6	24

 Source: *USA TODAY.*

 6. **Tornadoes** According to records from the Storm Prediction Center, the following numbers of tornadoes occurred in the first quarter of each of years 2003–2006. Is there sufficient evidence to conclude that a relationship exists between the month and year in which the tornadoes occurred? Use $\alpha = 0.05$.

	2006	**2005**	**2004**	**2003**
January	48	33	3	0
February	12	10	9	18
March	113	62	50	43

 Source: National Weather Service Storm Prediction Center.

 7. **Employment of High School Females** A guidance counselor wishes to determine if the proportions of female high school students in his school district who have jobs are equal to the national average of 36%. He randomly surveys 80 female students, ages 16 through 18 years, to determine if they work. The results are shown. At $\alpha = 0.01$, test the claim that the proportions of female students who work are equal. Use the *P*-value method.

	16-year-olds	**17-year-olds**	**18-year-olds**
Work	45	31	38
Don't work	35	49	42
Total	80	80	80

 Source: Michael D. Shook and Robert L. Shook, *The Book of Odds.*

 8. **Risk of Injury** The risk of injury is higher for males compared to females (57% versus 43%). A hospital emergency room supervisor wishes to determine if the proportions of injuries to males in his hospital are the

≡ STATISTICS TODAY

Statistics and Heredity— **Revisited**

Using probability, Mendel predicted the following:

	Smooth		Wrinkled	
	Yellow	Green	Yellow	Green
Expected	0.5625	0.1875	0.1875	0.0625

The observed results were these:

	Smooth		Wrinkled	
	Yellow	Green	Yellow	Green
Observed	0.5666	0.1942	0.1816	0.0556

Using chi-square tests on the data, Mendel found that his predictions were accurate in most cases (i.e., a good fit), thus supporting his theory. He reported many highly successful experiments. Mendel's genetic theory is simple but useful in predicting the results of hybridization.

A Fly in the Ointment

Although Mendel's theory is basically correct, an English statistician named R. A. Fisher examined Mendel's data some 50 years later. He found that the observed (actual) results agreed too closely with the expected (theoretical) results and concluded that the data had been falsified in some way. The results were too good to be true. Several explanations have been proposed, ranging from deliberate misinterpretation to an assistant's error, but no one can be sure how this happened.

---

same for each of 4 months. He randomly surveys 100 injuries treated in his ER for each month. The results are shown. At $\alpha = 0.05$, can he reject the claim that the proportions of injuries for males are equal for each of the four months?

	May	**June**	**July**	**August**
Male	51	47	58	63
Female	49	53	42	37
Total	100	100	100	100

Source: Michael D. Shook and Robert L. Shook, *The Book of Odds.*

9. **Health Insurance Coverage** Based on the following data showing the numbers of people (in thousands), who were randomly selected, with and without health insurance, can it be concluded at the 0.01 level of significance that the proportion with or without health insurance is related to the state chosen?

	With	**Without**
Arkansas	552	123
Montana	793	146
North Dakota	553	61
Wyoming	447	70

Source: *New York Times Almanac.*

10. **Cardiovascular Procedures** Is the frequency of cardiovascular procedure related to gender? The following data were obtained for selected procedures for a recent year. At $\alpha = 0.10$, is there sufficient evidence to conclude a dependent relationship between gender and procedure?

	Coronary artery stent	**Coronary artery bypass**	**Pacemaker**
Men	425	320	198
Women	227	123	219

Source: *New York Times Almanac.*

≡ Data Analysis

The Data Bank is located in Appendix B, or on the World Wide Web by following links from www.mhhe.com/math/stat/bluman

1. Select a random sample of 40 individuals from the Data Bank. Use the chi-square goodness-of-fit test to see if the marital status of individuals is equally distributed.

2. Use the chi-square test of independence to test the hypothesis that smoking is independent of gender. Use a random sample of at least 75 people.

3. Using the data from Data Set X in Appendix B, classify the data as 1–3, 4–6, 7–9, etc. Use the chi-square goodness-of-fit test to see if the number of times each ball is drawn is equally distributed.

Chapter Quiz

Determine whether each statement is true or false. If the statement is false, explain why.

1. The chi-square test of independence is always two-tailed.

2. The test values for the chi-square goodness-of-fit test and the independence test are computed by using the same formula.

3. When the null hypothesis is rejected in the goodness-of-fit test, it means there is close agreement between the observed and expected frequencies.

Select the best answer.

4. The values of the chi-square variable cannot be
   - a. Positive
   - b. 0
   - c. Negative
   - d. None of the above

5. The null hypothesis for the chi-square test of independence is that the variables are
   - a. Dependent
   - b. Independent
   - c. Related
   - d. Always 0

6. The degrees of freedom for the goodness-of-fit test are
   - a. 0
   - b. 1
   - c. Sample size − 1
   - d. Number of categories − 1

Complete the following statements with the best answer.

7. The degrees of freedom for a 4 × 3 contingency table are _____.

8. An important assumption for the chi-square test is that the observations must be _____.

9. The chi-square goodness-of-fit test is always _____-tailed.

10. In the chi-square independence test, the expected frequency for each class must always be _____.

For Exercises 11 through 19, follow these steps.
   - a. State the hypotheses and identify the claim.
   - b. Find the critical value.
   - c. Compute the test value.
   - d. Make the decision.
   - e. Summarize the results.

Use the traditional method of hypothesis testing unless otherwise specified.

11. **Job Loss Reasons** A survey of why randomly selected people lost their jobs produced the following results. At $\alpha = 0.05$, test the claim that the number of responses is equally distributed. Do you think the results might be different if the study were done 10 years ago?

Reason	Company closing	Position abolished	Insufficient work
Number	26	18	28

Source: Based on information from U.S. Department of Labor.

12. **Consumption of Takeout Foods** A food service manager read that the place where people consumed takeout food is distributed as follows: home, 53%; car, 19%; work, 14%; other, 14%. A survey of 300 randomly selected individuals showed the following results. At $\alpha = 0.01$, can it be concluded that the distribution is as stated? Where would a fast-food restaurant want to target its advertisements?

Place	Home	Car	Work	Other
Number	142	57	51	50

Source: Beef Industry Council.

13. **Television Viewing** A survey of randomly selected people found that 62% of the respondents stated that they never watched the home shopping channels on cable television, 23% stated that they watched the channels rarely, 11% stated that they watched them occasionally, and 4% stated that they watched them frequently. A group of 200 randomly selected college students was surveyed; 105 stated that they never watched the home shopping channels, 72 stated that they watched them rarely, 13 stated that they watched them occasionally, and 10 stated that they watched them frequently. At $\alpha = 0.05$, can it be concluded that the college students differ in their preference for the home shopping channels?

Source: Based on information obtained from *USA TODAY* Snapshots.

14. **Ways to Get to Work** The 2010 Census indicated the following percentages for means of commuting to work for workers over 15 years of age.

Alone	76.6
Carpooling	9.7
Public	4.9
Walked	2.8
Other	1.7
Worked at home	4.3

A random sample of workers found that 320 drove alone, 100 carpooled, 30 used public transportation, 20 walked, 10 used other forms of transportation, and 20 worked at home. Is there sufficient evidence to conclude that the proportions of workers using each type of transportation differ from those in the Census report? Use $\alpha = 0.05$.

Source: U.S. Census Bureau, *Washington Observer-Reporter.*

15. **Favorite Ice Cream Flavor** A survey of randomly selected women and randomly selected men asked what their favorite ice cream flavor was. The results are shown. At $\alpha = 0.05$, can it be concluded that the favorite flavor is independent of gender?

	Flavor			
	Vanilla	Chocolate	Strawberry	Other
Women	62	36	10	2
Men	49	37	5	9

16. Types of Pizzas Purchased A pizza shop owner wishes to determine if the type of pizza a person selects is related to the age of the individual. The data obtained from a sample are shown. At $\alpha = 0.10$, is the age of the purchaser related to the type of pizza ordered? Use the *P*-value method.

Type of pizza

Age	Plain	Pepperoni	Mushroom	Double cheese
10–19	12	21	39	71
20–29	18	76	52	87
30–39	24	50	40	47
40–49	52	30	12	28

17. Pennant Colors Purchased A survey at a ballpark shows the following selection of pennants sold to randomly selected fans. The data are presented here. At $\alpha = 0.10$, is the color of the pennant purchased independent of the gender of the individual?

	Blue	Yellow	Red
Men	519	659	876
Women	487	702	787

18. Tax Credit Refunds In a survey of randomly selected children ages 8 through 11 years, data were obtained as to what they think their parents should do with the money from a $400 tax credit.

	Keep it for themselves	Give it to their children	Don't know
Girls	162	132	6
Boys	147	147	6

At $\alpha = 0.10$, is there a relationship between the feelings of the children and the gender of the children?

Source: Based on information from *USA TODAY* Snapshot.

19. Employment Satisfaction A survey of 60 randomly selected men and 60 randomly selected women asked if they would be happy spending the rest of their careers with their present employers. The results are shown. At $\alpha = 0.10$, can it be concluded that the proportions are equal? If they are not equal, give a possible reason for the difference.

	Yes	No	Undecided
Men	40	15	5
Women	36	9	15

Source: Based on information from a Maritz Poll.

Critical Thinking Challenges

1. Random Digits Use your calculator or the MINITAB random number generator to generate 100 two-digit random numbers. Make a grouped frequency distribution, using the chi-square goodness-of-fit test to see if the distribution is random. To do this, use an expected frequency of 10 for each class. Can it be concluded that the distribution is random? Explain.

2. Lottery Numbers Simulate the state lottery by using your calculator or MINITAB to generate 100 three-digit random numbers. Group these numbers 000–099, 100–199, etc. Use the chi-square goodness-of-fit test to see if the numbers are random. The expected frequency for each class should be 10. Explain why.

3. Purchase a bag of M&M's candy and count the number of pieces of each color. Using the information as your sample, state a hypothesis for the distribution of colors, and compare your hypothesis to H_0: The distribution of colors of M&M's candy is 13% brown, 13% red, 14% yellow, 16% green, 20% orange, and 24% blue.

Data Projects

Use a significance level of 0.05 for all tests below.

1. Business and Finance Many of the companies that produce multicolored candy will include on their website information about the production percentages for the various colors. Select a favorite multicolored candy. Find out what percentage of each color is produced. Open up a bag of the candy, noting how many of each color are in the bag (be careful to count them before you eat them). Is the bag distributed as expected based on the production percentages? If no production percentages can be found, test to see if the colors are uniformly distributed.

2. Sports and Leisure Use a local (or favorite) basketball, football, baseball, or hockey team as the data set. For the most recently completed season, note the team's home record for wins and losses. Test to see whether home field advantage is independent of sport.

3. Technology Use the data collected in data project 3 of Chapter 2 regarding song genres. Do the data indicate that songs are uniformly distributed among the genres?

4. **Health and Wellness** Research the percentages of each blood type that the Red Cross states are in the population. Now use your class as a sample. For each student note the blood type. Is the distribution of blood types in your class as expected based on the Red Cross percentages?

5. **Politics and Economics** Research the distribution (by percent) of registered Republicans, Democrats, and Independents in your state. Use your class as a sample.

For each student, note the party affiliation. Is the distribution as expected based on the percentages for your state? What might be problematic about using your class as a sample for this exercise?

6. **Your Class** Conduct a classroom poll to determine which of the following sports each student likes best: baseball, football, basketball, hockey, or NASCAR. Also, note the gender of the individual. Is preference for sport independent of gender?

Answers to Applying the Concepts

Section 11–1   Skittles Color Distribution

1. The variables are qualitative, and we have the counts for each category.

2. We can use a chi-square goodness-of-fit test.

3. There are a total of 233 candies, so we would expect 46.6 of each color. Our test statistic is $\chi^2 = 1.442$.

4. H_0: The colors are equally distributed.
   H_1: The colors are not equally distributed.

5. There are $5 - 1 = 4$ degrees of freedom for the test. The critical value depends on the choice of significance level. At the 0.05 significance level, the critical value is 9.488.

6. Since $1.442 < 9.488$, we fail to reject the null hypothesis. There is not enough evidence to conclude that the colors are not equally distributed.

Section 11–2   Satellite Dishes in Restricted Areas

1. We compare the P-value to the significance level of 0.05 to check if the null hypothesis should be rejected.

2. The P-value gives the probability of a type I error.

3. This is a right-tailed test, since chi-square tests of independence are always right-tailed.

4. You cannot tell how many rows and columns there were just by looking at the degrees of freedom.

5. Increasing the sample size does not increase the degrees of freedom, since the degrees of freedom are based on the number of rows and columns.

6. We will reject the null hypothesis. There are a number of cells where the observed and expected frequencies are quite different.

7. If the significance level were initially set at 0.10, we would still reject the null hypothesis.

8. No, the chi-square value does not tell us which cells have observed and expected frequencies that are very different.

Analysis of Variance

⩙ STATISTICS TODAY

Is Seeing Really Believing?

Many adults look on the eyewitness testimony of children with skepticism. They believe that young witnesses' testimony is less accurate than the testimony of adults in court cases. Several statistical studies have been done on this subject.

In a preliminary study, three researchers randomly selected fourteen 8-year-olds, fourteen 12-year-olds, and fourteen adults. The researchers showed each group the same video of a crime being committed. The next day, each witness responded to direct and cross-examination questioning. Then the researchers, using statistical methods explained in this chapter, were able to determine if there were differences in the accuracy of the testimony of the three groups on direct examination and on cross-examination. The statistical methods used here differ from the ones explained in Chapter 9 because there are three groups rather than two. See Statistics Today—Revisited at the end of this chapter.

Source: C. Luus, G. Wells, and J. Turtle, "Child Eyewitnesses: Seeing Is Believing," *Journal of Applied Psychology* 80, no. 2, pp. 317–26.

OUTLINE

Introduction
12–1 One-Way Analysis of Variance
12–2 The Scheffé Test and the Tukey Test
12–3 Two-Way Analysis of Variance
Summary

OBJECTIVES

After completing this chapter, you should be able to

1 Use the one-way ANOVA technique to determine if there is a significant difference among three or more means.

2 Determine which means differ, using the Scheffé or Tukey test if the null hypothesis is rejected in the ANOVA.

3 Use the two-way ANOVA technique to determine if there is a significant difference in the main effects or interaction.

Historical Note

The methods of analysis
of variance were
developed by R. A.
Fisher in the
early 1920s.

Introduction

The F test, used to compare two variances as shown in Chapter 9, can also be used to compare three or more means. This technique is called *analysis of variance,* or *ANOVA.* It is used to test claims involving three or more means. (*Note:* The F test can also be used to test the equality of two means. But since it is equivalent to the t test in this case, the t test is usually used instead of the F test when there are only two means.) For example, suppose a researcher wishes to see whether the means of the time it takes three groups of students to solve a computer problem using HTML, Java, and PHP are different. The researcher will use the ANOVA technique for this test. The z and t tests should not be used when three or more means are compared, for reasons given later in this chapter.

For three groups, the F test can show only whether a difference exists among the three means. It cannot reveal where the difference lies—that is, between $\overline{X}_1$ and $\overline{X}_2$, or $\overline{X}_1$ and $\overline{X}_3$, or $\overline{X}_2$ and $\overline{X}_3$. If the F test indicates that there is a difference among the means, other statistical tests are used to find where the difference exists. The most commonly used tests are the Scheffé test and the Tukey test, which are also explained in this chapter.

The analysis of variance that is used to compare three or more means is called a *one-way analysis of variance* since it contains only one variable. In the previous example, the variable is the type of computer language used. The analysis of variance can be extended to studies involving two variables, such as type of computer language used and mathematical background of the students. These studies involve a *two-way analysis of variance.* Section 12–3 explains the two-way analysis of variance.

12–1 One-Way Analysis of Variance

OBJECTIVE

Use the one-way ANOVA technique to determine if there is a significant difference among three or more means.

When an F test is used to test a hypothesis concerning the means of three or more populations, the technique is called **analysis of variance** (commonly abbreviated as **ANOVA**).

> The **one-way analysis of variance** test is used to test the equality of three or more means using sample variances.

The procedure used in this section is called the **one-way analysis of variance** because there is only one independent variable that distinguishes between the different populations in the study. The independent variable is also called a *factor.*

At first glance, you might think that to compare the means of three or more samples, you can use the t test, comparing two means at a time. But there are several reasons why the t test should not be done.

First, when you are comparing two means at a time, the rest of the means under study are ignored. With the F test, all the means are compared simultaneously. Second, when you are comparing two means at a time and making all pairwise comparisons, the probability of rejecting the null hypothesis when it is true is increased, since the more t tests that are conducted, the greater is the likelihood of getting significant differences by chance alone. Third, the more means there are to compare, the more t tests are needed. For example, for the comparison of 3 means two at a time, 3 t tests are required. For the comparison of 5 means two at a time, 10 tests are required. And for the comparison of 10 means two at a time, 45 tests are required.

As the number of populations to be compared increases, the probability of making a type I error using multiple t tests for a given level of significance α also increases. To address this problem, the technique of analysis of variance is used. This technique involves a comparison of two estimates of the same population variance.

Recall that the characteristics of the F distribution are as follows:

1. The values of F cannot be negative, because variances are always positive or zero.

2. The distribution is positively skewed.

3. The mean value of F is approximately equal to 1.

4. The F distribution is a family of curves based on the degrees of freedom of the variance of the numerator and the degrees of freedom of the variance of the denominator.

Even though you are comparing three or more means in this use of the F test, *variances* are used in the test instead of means.

With the F test, two different estimates of the population variance are made. The first estimate is called the **between-group variance,** and it involves finding the variance of the means. The second estimate, the **within-group variance,** is made by computing the variance using all the data and is not affected by differences in the means. If there is no difference in the means, the between-group variance estimate will be approximately equal to the within-group variance estimate, and the F test value will be approximately equal to one. The null hypothesis will not be rejected. However, when the means differ significantly, the between-group variance will be much larger than the within-group variance; the F test value will be significantly greater than one; and the null hypothesis will be rejected. Since variances are compared, this procedure is called *analysis of variance* (ANOVA).

The formula for the F test is

$$F = \frac{\text{variance between groups}}{\text{variance within groups}}$$

The variance between groups measures the differences in the means that result from the different treatments given to each group. To calculate this value, it is necessary to find the *grand mean* $\overline{X}_{\text{GM}}$, which is the mean of all the values in all of the samples. The formula for the grand mean is

$$\overline{X}_{\text{GM}} = \frac{\Sigma X}{N}$$

This value is used to find the between-group variance s_B^2. This is the variance among the means using the sample sizes as weights.

The formula for the between-group variance, denoted by s_B^2, is

$$s_B^2 = \frac{\Sigma n_i (\overline{X}_i - \overline{X}_{\text{GM}})}{k - 1}$$

where k = number of groups

n_i = sample size

$\overline{X}_i$ = sample mean

This formula can be written out as

$$s_B^2 = \frac{n_1(\overline{X}_1 - \overline{X}_{\text{GM}})^2 + n_2(\overline{X}_2 - \overline{X}_{\text{GM}})^2 + \cdots + n_k(\overline{X}_k - \overline{X}_{\text{GM}})^2}{k - 1}$$

Next find the within group variance, denoted by s_W^2. The formula finds the overall variance by calculating a weighted average of the individual variances. It does not involve using differences of means. The formula for the within-group variance is

$$s_W^2 = \frac{\Sigma(n_i - 1)s_i^2}{\Sigma(n_i - 1)}$$

where n_i = sample size

s_i^2 = variance of sample

This formula can be written out as

$$s_W^2 = \frac{(n_1 - 1)s_1^2 + (n_2 - 1)s_2^2 + \cdots + (n_k - 1)s_k^2}{(n_1 - 1) + (n_2 - 2) + \cdots + (n_k - 1)}$$

Finally, the F test value is computed. The formula can now be written using the symbols s_B^2 and s_W^2.

The formula for the F test for one-way analysis of variance is

$$F = \frac{s_B^2}{s_W^2}$$

where s_B^2 = between-group variance
s_W^2 = within-group variance

As stated previously, a significant test value means that there is a high probability that this difference in means is not due to chance, but it does not indicate where the difference lies.

The degrees of freedom for this F test are d.f.N. $= k - 1$, where k is the number of groups, and d.f.D. $= N - k$, where N is the sum of the sample sizes of the groups $N = n_1 + n_2 + \cdots + n_k$. The sample sizes need not be equal. The F test to compare means is always right-tailed.

The results of the one-way analysis of variance can be summarized by placing them in an **ANOVA summary table.** The numerator of the fraction of the s_B^2 term is called the **sum of squares between groups,** denoted by SS_B. The numerator of the s_W^2 term is called the **sum of squares within groups,** denoted by SS_W. This statistic is also called the *sum of squares for the error.* SS_B is divided by d.f.N. to obtain the between-group variance. SS_W is divided by $N - k$ to obtain the within-group or error variance. These two variances are sometimes called **mean squares,** denoted by MS_B and MS_W. These terms are used to summarize the analysis of variance and are placed in a summary table, as shown in Table 12–1.

TABLE 12–1	Analysis of Variance Summary Table			
Source	**Sum of squares**	**d.f.**	**Mean square**	**F**
Between	SS_B	$k - 1$	MS_B	
Within (error)	SS_W	$N - k$	MS_W	
Total				

In the table,

SS_B = sum of squares between groups

SS_W = sum of squares within groups

k = number of groups

$N = n_1 + n_2 + \cdots + n_k$ = sum of sample sizes for groups

$$MS_B = \frac{SS_B}{k - 1}$$

$$MS_W = \frac{SS_W}{N - k}$$

$$F = \frac{MS_B}{MS_W}$$

To use the F test to compare two or more means, the following assumptions must be met.

Assumptions for the *F* Test for Comparing Three or More Means
1. The populations from which the samples were obtained must be normally or approximately normally distributed.
2. The samples must be independent of one another.
3. The variances of the populations must be equal.
4. The samples must be simple random samples, one from each of the populations.

In this book, the assumptions will be stated in the exercises; however, when encountering statistics in other situations, you must check to see that these assumptions have been met before proceeding.

The steps for computing the *F* test value for the ANOVA are summarized in this Procedure Table.

Procedure Table

Finding the *F* Test Value for the Analysis of Variance

Step 1   Find the mean and variance of each sample.

$$(\overline{X}_1, s_1^2), (\overline{X}_2, s_2^2), \ldots, (\overline{X}_k, s_k^2)$$

Step 2   Find the grand mean.

$$\overline{X}_{GM} = \frac{\Sigma X}{N}$$

Step 3   Find the between-group variance.

$$s_B^2 = \frac{\Sigma n_i(\overline{X}_i - \overline{X}_{GM})^2}{k - 1}$$

Step 4   Find the within-group variance.

$$s_W^2 = \frac{\Sigma(n_i - 1)s_i^2}{\Sigma(n_i - 1)}$$

Step 5   Find the *F* test value.

$$F = \frac{s_B^2}{s_W^2}$$

The degrees of freedom are

$$\text{d.f.N.} = k - 1$$

where *k* is the number of groups, and

$$\text{d.f.D.} = N - k$$

where *N* is the sum of the sample sizes of the groups

$$N = n_1 + n_2 + \cdots + n_k$$

The one-way analysis of variance follows the regular five-step hypothesis-testing procedure.

Step 1   State the hypotheses.

Step 2   Find the critical values.

Step 3   Compute the test value.

Step 4   Make the decision.

Step 5   Summarize the results.

Examples 12–1 and 12–2 illustrate the computational procedure for the ANOVA technique for comparing three or more means, and the steps are summarized in the Procedure Table.

EXAMPLE 12–1   Miles per Gallon

A researcher wishes to see if there is a difference in the fuel economy for city driving for three different types of automobiles: small automobiles, sedans, and luxury automobiles. He randomly samples four small automobiles, five sedans, and three luxury automobiles. The miles per gallon for each is shown. At $\alpha = 0.05$, test the claim that there is no difference among the means. The data are shown.

Small	Sedans	Luxury
36	43	29
44	35	25
34	30	24
35	29	
	40	

Source: U.S. Environmental Protection Agency.

Step 1   State the hypotheses and identify the claim.

H_0: $\mu_1 = \mu_2 = \mu_3$ (claim)
H_1: At least one mean is different from the others

Step 2   Find the critical value.

$$N = 12 \qquad k = 3$$
$$\text{d.f.N.} = k - 1 = 3 - 1 = 2$$
$$\text{d.f.D.} = N - k = 12 - 3 = 9$$

The critical value from Table H in Appendix A with $\alpha = 0.05$ is 4.26.

Step 3   Compute the test value.

a. Find the mean and variance for each sample. (Use the formulas in Chapter 3.)

For the small cars: $\overline{X} = 37.25$ $s^2 = 20.917$
For the sedans: $\overline{X} = 35.4$ $s^2 = 37.3$
For the luxury cars: $\overline{X} = 26$ $s^2 = 7$

b. Find the grand mean.

$$\overline{X}_{\text{GM}} = \frac{\Sigma X}{N} = \frac{36 + 44 + 34 + \cdots + 24}{12} = \frac{404}{12} = 33.667$$

c. Find the between-group variance.

$$s_B^2 = \frac{\Sigma n(\overline{X}_i - \overline{X}_{\text{GM}})^2}{k - 1}$$
$$= \frac{4(37.25 - 33.667)^2 + 5(35.4 - 33.667)^2 + 3(26 - 33.667)^2}{3 - 1}$$
$$= \frac{242.717}{2} = 121.359$$

d. Find the within-group variance.

$$s_W^2 = \frac{\Sigma(n_i - 1)s_i^2}{\Sigma(n_i - 1)} = \frac{(4 - 1)(20.917) + (5 - 1)(37.3) + (3 - 1)7}{(4 - 1) + (5 - 1) + (3 - 1)}$$
$$= \frac{225.951}{9} = 25.106$$

e. Find the *F* test value.

$$F = \frac{s_B^2}{s_W^2} = \frac{121.359}{25.106} = 4.83$$

Step 4 Make the decision. The test value 4.83 > 4.26, so the decision is to reject the null hypothesis. See Figure 12–1.

FIGURE 12–1   Critical Value and Test Value for Example 12–1

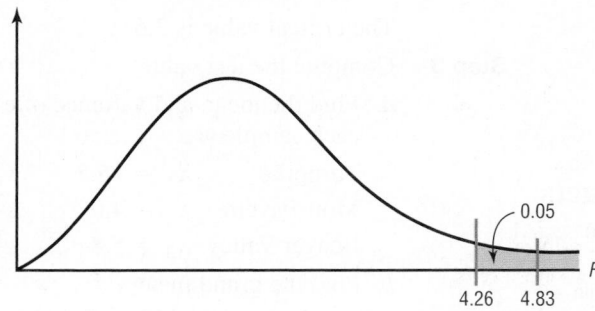

Step 5 Summarize the results. There is enough evidence to conclude that at least one mean is different from the others.

The **ANOVA summary table** is shown in Table 12–2.

TABLE 12–2 Analysis of Variance Summary Table for Example 12–1				
Source	**Sum of squares**	**d.f.**	**Mean square**	**F**
Between	242.717	2	121.359	4.83
Within (error)	225.954	9	25.106	
Total	468.671	11		

The *P*-values for ANOVA are found by using the same procedure shown in Section 9–5. For Example 12–1, the *F* test value is 4.83. In Table H with d.f.N. = 2 and d.f.D. = 9, the *F* test value falls between $\alpha = 0.025$ with an *F* value of 5.71 and $\alpha = 0.05$ with an *F* value of 4.26. Hence, $0.025 < P\text{-value} < 0.05$. In this case, the null hypothesis is rejected at $\alpha = 0.05$ since the *P*-value < 0.05. The TI-84 *P*-value is 0.0375.

EXAMPLE 12–2   Employees at Toll Road Interchanges

A state employee wishes to see if there is a significant difference in the number of employees at the interchanges of three state toll roads. The data are shown. At $\alpha = 0.05$, can it be concluded that there is a significant difference in the average number of employees at each interchange?

Pennsylvania Turnpike	Greensburg Bypass/ Mon-Fayette Expressway	Beaver Valley Expressway
7	10	1
14	1	12
32	1	1
19	0	9
10	11	1
11	1	11

Source: Pennsylvania Turnpike Commission.

SOLUTION

Step 1   State the hypotheses and identify the claim.

H_0: $\mu_1 = \mu_2 = \mu_3$

H_1: At least one mean is different from the others (claim).

Step 2   Find the critical value. Since $k = 3$, $N = 18$, and $\alpha = 0.05$,

d.f.N. $= k - 1 = 3 - 1 = 2$

d.f.D. $= N - k = 18 - 3 = 15$

The critical value is 3.68.

Step 3   Compute the test value.

a. Find the mean and variance of each sample. The mean and variance for each sample are

Turnpike $\bar{X}_1 = 15.5$ $s_1^2 = 81.9$
Mon-Fayette $\bar{X}_2 = 4.0$ $s_2^2 = 25.6$
Beaver Valley $\bar{X}_3 = 5.8$ $s_3^2 = 29.0$

b. Find the grand mean.

$$\bar{X}_{\text{GM}} = \frac{\Sigma X}{N} = \frac{7 + 14 + 32 + \cdots + 11}{18} = \frac{152}{18} = 8.44$$

c. Find the between-group variance.

$$s_B^2 = \frac{\Sigma n_i(\bar{X}_i - \bar{X}_{\text{GM}})^2}{k - 1}$$

$$= \frac{6(15.5 - 8.44)^2 + 6(4 - 8.44)^2 + 6(5.8 - 8.44)^2}{3 - 1}$$

$$= \frac{459.16}{2} = 229.58$$

d. Find the within-group variance.

$$s_W^2 = \frac{\Sigma(n_i - 1)s_i^2}{\Sigma(n_i - 1)}$$

$$= \frac{(6 - 1)(81.9) + (6 - 1)(25.6) + (6 - 1)(29.0)}{(6 - 1) + (6 - 1) + (6 - 1)}$$

$$= \frac{682.50}{15} = 45.50$$

e. Find the F test value.

$$F = \frac{s_B^2}{s_W^2} = \frac{229.58}{45.50} = 5.05$$

Step 4   Make the decision. Since $5.05 > 3.68$, the decision is to reject the null hypothesis. See Figure 12–2.

FIGURE 12–2   Critical Value and Test Value for Example 12–2

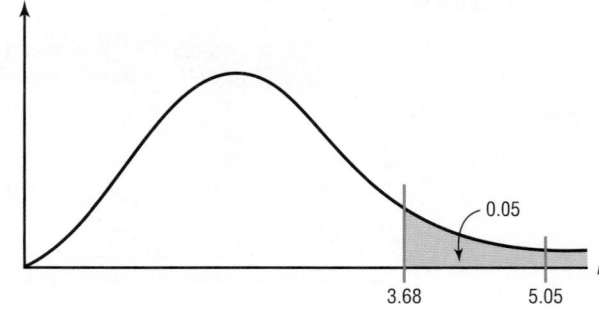

Step 5   Summarize the results. There is enough evidence to support the claim that there is a difference among the means. The ANOVA summary table for this example is shown in Table 12–3.

TABLE 12–3	Analysis of Variance Summary Table for Example 12–2			
Source	**Sum of squares**	**d.f.**	**Mean square**	**F**
Between	459.16	2	229.58	5.05
Within	682.50	15	45.50	
Total	1141.66	17		

The P-values for ANOVA are found by using the procedure shown in Section 9–2. For Example 12–2, find the two α values in the tables for the F distribution (Table H), using d.f.N. = 2 and d.f.D. = 15, where F = 5.05 falls between. In this case, 5.05 falls between 4.77 and 6.36, corresponding, respectively, to α = 0.025 and α = 0.01; hence, $0.01 < P\text{-value} < 0.025$. Since the P-value is between 0.01 and 0.025 and since P-value < 0.05 (the originally chosen value for α), the decision is to reject the null hypothesis. (The P-value obtained from a calculator is 0.021.)

When the null hypothesis is rejected in ANOVA, it only means that at least one mean is different from the others. To locate the difference or differences among the means, it is necessary to use other tests such as the Tukey or the Scheffé test.

≡Applying the Concepts 12–1

Colors That Make You Smarter

The following set of data values was obtained from a study of people's perceptions on whether the color of a person's clothing is related to how intelligent the person looks. The subjects rated the person's intelligence on a scale of 1 to 10. Randomly selected group 1 subjects were shown people with clothing in shades of blue and gray. Randomly selected group 2 subjects were shown people with clothing in shades of brown and yellow. Randomly selected group 3 subjects were shown people with clothing in shades of pink and orange. The results follow.

Group 1	Group 2	Group 3
8	7	4
7	8	9
7	7	6
7	7	7
8	5	9
8	8	8
6	5	5
8	8	8
8	7	7
7	6	5
7	6	4
8	6	5
8	6	4

1. Use ANOVA to test for any significant differences between the means.

2. What is the purpose of this study?

3. Explain why separate t tests are not accepted in this situation.

See page 686 for the answers.

Exercises 12–1

1. What test is used to compare three or more means?
2. State three reasons why multiple *t* tests cannot be used to compare three or more means.
3. What are the assumptions for ANOVA?
4. Define between-group variance and within-group variance.
5. State the hypotheses used in the ANOVA test.
6. When there is no significant difference among three or more means, the value of *F* will be close to what number?

For Exercises 7 through 20, assume that all variables are normally distributed, that the samples are independent, that the population variances are equal, and that the samples are simple random samples, one from each of the populations. Also, for each exercise, perform the following steps.

   a. State the hypotheses and identify the claim.
   b. Find the critical value.
   c. Compute the test value.
   d. Make the decision.
   e. Summarize the results, and explain where the differences in the means are.

Use the traditional method of hypothesis testing unless otherwise specified.

7. **Tire Prices** A large tire company held an end-of-season clearance sale. Listed are sale prices for random samples of different models for three different brands. Is there sufficient evidence at $\alpha = 0.05$ to conclude a difference in mean prices for the three brands?

Brand A	Brand B	Brand C
112	125	113
100	150	119
120	103	136
93	120	151
119	131	162
108	166	141
103	158	150

8. **Sodium Contents of Foods** The amount of sodium (in milligrams) in one serving for a random sample of three different kinds of foods is listed. At the 0.05 level of significance, is there sufficient evidence to conclude that a difference in mean sodium amounts exists among condiments, cereals, and desserts?

Condiments	Cereals	Desserts
270	260	100
130	220	180
230	290	250
180	290	250
80	200	300
70	320	360
200	140	300
		160

Source: *The Doctor's Pocket Calorie, Fat, and Carbohydrate Counter.*

9. **Hybrid Vehicles** A study was done before the recent surge in gasoline prices to compare the cost to drive 25 miles for different types of hybrid vehicles. The cost of a gallon of gas at the time of the study was approximately $2.50. Based on the information given for different models of hybrid cars, trucks, and SUVs, is there sufficient evidence to conclude a difference in the mean cost to drive 25 miles? Use $\alpha = 0.05$. (The information in this exercise will be used in Exercise 3 in Section 12–2.)

Hybrid cars	Hybrid SUVs	Hybrid trucks
2.10	2.10	3.62
2.70	2.42	3.43
1.67	2.25	
1.67	2.10	
1.30	2.25	

Source: www.fueleconomy.com

10. **Healthy Eating** Americans appear to be eating healthier. Between 1970 and 2007 the per capita consumption of broccoli increased 1000% from 0.5 to 5.5 pounds. A nutritionist followed a group of people randomly assigned to one of three groups and noted their monthly broccoli intake (in pounds). At $\alpha = 0.05$, is there a difference in means?

Group A	Group B	Group C
2.0	2.0	3.7
1.5	1.5	2.5
0.75	4.0	4.0
1.0	3.0	5.1
1.3	2.5	3.8
3.0	2.0	2.9

Source: *World Almanac.*

11. **Student Loans** The average undergraduate student loan for a recent year was $8500. A random sample of students from three different schools revealed the following loan amounts for the last school year. Based on the $\alpha = 0.05$ level of significance, is there a difference in means?

College A	College B	College C
9,000	10,000	12,000
10,500	15,000	15,000
12,600	16,000	16,500
10,900	14,500	15,500
15,000	12,000	14,000
11,000		12,800

Source: *World Almanac.*

12. **Weight Gain of Athletes** A researcher wishes to see whether there is any difference in the weight gains of athletes following one of three special diets. Athletes are randomly assigned to three groups and placed on the diet

for 6 weeks. The weight gains (in pounds) are shown here. At $\alpha = 0.05$, can the researcher conclude that there is a difference in the diets?

Diet A	Diet B	Diet C
3	10	8
6	12	3
7	11	2
4	14	5
	8	
	6	

A computer printout for this problem is shown. Use the P-value method and the information in this printout to test the claim. (The information in this exercise will be used in Exercise 4 of Section 12–2.)

Computer Printout for Exercise 12

ANALYSIS OF VARIANCE SOURCE TABLE

Source	df	Sum of Squares	Mean Square	F	P-value
Bet Groups	2	101.095	50.548	7.740	0.00797
W/I Groups	11	71.833	6.530		
Total	13	172.929			

DESCRIPTIVE STATISTICS

Condit	N	Means	St Dev
diet A	4	5.000	1.826
diet B	6	10.167	2.858
diet C	4	4.500	2.646

13. Expenditures per Pupil The per-pupil costs (in thousands of dollars) for cyber charter school tuition for school districts in three areas of southwestern Pennsylvania are shown. At $\alpha = 0.05$, is there a difference in the means? If so, give a possible reason for the difference. (The information in this exercise will be used in Exercise 5 of Section 12–2.)

Area I	Area II	Area III
6.2	7.5	5.8
9.3	8.2	6.4
6.8	8.5	5.6
6.1	8.2	7.1
6.7	7.0	3.0
6.9	9.3	3.5

Source: *Tribune-Review.*

14. Cell Phone Bills The average local cell phone monthly bill is $50.07. A random sample of monthly bills from three different providers is listed below. At $\alpha = 0.05$, is there a difference in mean bill amounts among providers?

Provider X	Provider Y	Provider Z
48.20	105.02	59.27
60.59	85.73	65.25
72.50	61.95	70.27
55.62	75.69	42.19
89.47	82.11	52.34

Source: *World Almanac.*

15. Television Viewing Time The average U.S. television viewing time (2010–2011) for all viewers is 34 hours and 16 minutes per week. Random samples of three different groups indicated their weekly viewing habits (in hours) as listed below. At the 0.05 level of significance, is there evidence of a difference in means between the groups?

Men 21+ years	Women 21+ years	"Teens" 12–20 years
28	32	44
26	31	37
20	47	40
25	40	31
31	34	28
		34

Source: *World Almanac.*

16. Annual Child Care Costs Annual child care costs for infants are considerably higher than for older children. At $\alpha = 0.05$, can you conclude a difference in mean infant day care costs for different regions of the United States? (Annual costs per infant are given in dollars.)

New England	Midwest	Southwest
10,390	9,449	7,644
7,592	6,985	9,691
8,755	6,677	5,996
9,464	5,400	5,386
7,328	8,372	

Source: www.naccrra.org (National Association of Child Care Resources and Referral Agencies: "Breaking the Piggy Bank").

17. Microwave Oven Prices A research organization tested microwave ovens. At $\alpha = 0.10$, is there a significant difference in the average prices of the three types of oven?

	Watts	
1000	**900**	**800**
270	240	180
245	135	155
190	160	200
215	230	120
250	250	140
230	200	180
	200	140
	210	130

A computer printout for this exercise is shown. Use the P-value method and the information in this printout to test the claim. (The information in this exercise will be used in Exercise 6 of Section 12–2.)

Computer Printout for Exercise 17

ANALYSIS OF VARIANCE SOURCE TABLE

Source	df	Sum of Squares	Mean Square	F	P-value
Bet Groups	2	21729.735	10864.867	10.118	0.00102
W/I Groups	19	20402.083	1073.794		
Total	21	42131.818			

DESCRIPTIVE STATISTICS

Condit	N	Means	St Dev
1000	6	233.333	28.23
900	8	203.125	39.36
800	8	155.625	28.21

18. Calories in Fast-Food Sandwiches Three popular fast-food restaurant franchises specializing in burgers were surveyed to find out the number of calories in their frequently ordered sandwiches. At the 0.05 level of significance, can it be concluded that a difference in mean number of calories per burger exists? The information in this exercise will be used for Exercise 7 in Section 12–2.

FF#1	FF#2	FF#3
970	1010	740
880	970	540
840	920	510
710	850	510
	820	

Source: www.fatcalories.com

19. Number of Pupils in a Class A large school district has several middle schools. Three schools were randomly chosen, and four classes were selected from each. The numbers of pupils in each class are shown here. At $\alpha = 0.10$, is there sufficient evidence that the mean number of students per class differs among schools?

MS 1	MS 2	MS 3
21	28	25
25	22	20
19	25	23
17	30	22

20. Average Debt of College Graduates Kiplinger's listed the top 100 public colleges based on many factors. From that list, here is the average debt at graduation for various schools in four selected states. At $\alpha = 0.05$, can it be concluded that the average debt at graduation differs for these four states?

New York	Virginia	California	Pennsylvania
14,734	14,524	13,171	18,105
16,000	15,176	14,431	17,051
14,347	12,665	14,689	16,103
14,392	12,591	13,788	22,400
12,500	18,385	15,297	17,976

Source: www.Kiplinger.com

Technology   Step by Step

TI-84 Plus
Step by Step

One-Way Analysis of Variance (ANOVA)

1. Enter the data into L_1, L_2, L_3, etc.
2. Press **STAT** and move the cursor to TESTS.
3. Press **H (ALPHA∧)** for ANOVA(.
4. Type each list followed by a comma. End with) and press **ENTER**.

Example TI12–1

Test the claim H_0: $\mu_1 = \mu_2 = \mu_3 =$ at $\alpha = 0.05$ for these data from Example 12–1.

Small	Sedans	Luxury
36	43	29
44	35	25
34	30	24
35	29	
	40	

Input   Input

Output   Output

The F test value is 4.833923434. The P-value is 0.0375117442, which is significant at $\alpha = 0.05$. The factor variable has

$$\text{d.f.} = 2$$
$$\text{SS} = 242.716667$$
$$\text{MS} = 121.358333$$

The error has

$$\text{d.f.} = 9$$
$$\text{SS} = 225.95$$
$$\text{MS} = 25.1055556$$

EXCEL
Step by Step

One-Way Analysis of Variance (ANOVA)

Example XL12–1

1. Enter the data below in columns A, B, and C of an Excel worksheet.

10	6	5
12	8	9
9	3	12
15	0	8
13	2	4

2. From the toolbar, select **Data,** then **Data Analysis.**
3. Select **Anova: Single Factor.**
4. Type in **A1:C5** in the **Input Range** box.
5. Check **Grouped By: Columns.**
6. Type **0.05** for the **Alpha level.**
7. Under the **Output options,** check the **Output Range** and type **E2.**
8. Click [OK].

The results of the ANOVA are shown below.

Anova: Single Factor						
SUMMARY						
Groups	*Count*	*Sum*	*Average*	*Variance*		
Column 1	5	59	11.8	5.7		
Column 2	5	19	3.8	10.2		
Column 3	5	38	7.6	10.3		
ANOVA						
Source of Variation	*SS*	*df*	*MS*	*F*	*P-value*	*F crit*
Between Groups	160.1333333	2	80.06666667	9.167938931	0.003831317	3.885293835
Within Groups	104.8	12	8.733333333			
Total	264.9333333	14				

MINITAB
Step by Step

One-Way Analysis of Variance (ANOVA)

Example 12–1

Is there a difference in the average city MPG rating by type of vehicle?

1. Enter the MPG ratings in C1 Small, C2 Sedan, and C3 Luxury.

↓	C1	C2	C3
	Small	Sedan	Luxury
1	36	43	29
2	44	35	25
3	34	30	24
4	35	29	
5		40	

2. Select **Stat>ANOVA>One-way (unstacked)**.

   a. Drag the mouse over the three columns of Observed counts.
   b. Click on [Select].
   c. Click [OK].

The results are displayed in the session window.

One-way ANOVA: Small, Sedan, Luxury

Source	DF	SS	MS	F	P
Factor	2	242.7	121.4	4.83	0.038
Error	9	226.0	25.1		
Total	11	468.7			

$S = 5.011$ R-Sq = 51.79%   R-Sq(adj) = 41.08%

Individual 95% CIs For Mean Based on Pooled StDev

Level	N	Mean	StDev	-----------+-----------+-----------+-----------+-
Small	4	37.250	4.573	(------------*------------)
Sedan	5	35.400	6.107	(------------*------------)
Luxury	3	26.000	2.646	(--------------*--------------)

```
                           -----------+-----------+-----------+-----------+-
                              24.0       30.0        36.0       42.0
```

Pooled StDev = 5.011

12–2   The Scheffé Test and the Tukey Test

When the null hypothesis is rejected using the F test, the researcher may want to know where the difference among the means is. Several procedures have been developed to determine where the significant differences in the means lie after the ANOVA procedure has been performed. Among the most commonly used tests are the *Scheffé test* and the *Tukey test*.

OBJECTIVE ②

Determine which means differ, using the Scheffé or Tukey test if the null hypothesis is rejected in the ANOVA.

Scheffé Test

To conduct the **Scheffé test,** you must compare the means two at a time, using all possible combinations of means. For example, if there are three means, the following comparisons must be done:

$$\overline{X}_1 \text{ versus } \overline{X}_2 \qquad \overline{X}_1 \text{ versus } \overline{X}_3 \qquad \overline{X}_2 \text{ versus } \overline{X}_3$$

Unusual Stat

According to the *British Medical Journal*, the body's circadian rhythms produce drowsiness during the midafternoon, matched only by the 2:00 A.M. to 7:00 A.M. period for sleep-related traffic accidents.

Formula for the Scheffé Test

$$F_S = \frac{(\bar{X}_i - \bar{X}_j)^2}{s_W^2[(1/n_i) + (1/n_j)]}$$

where $\bar{X}_i$ and $\bar{X}_j$ are the means of the samples being compared, n_i and n_j are the respective sample sizes, and s_W^2 is the within-group variance.

To find the critical value F' for the Scheffé test, multiply the critical value for the F test by $k - 1$:

$$F' = (k - 1)(\text{C.V.})$$

There is a significant difference between the two means being compared when the F test value, F_S, is greater than the critical value, F'. Example 12–3 illustrates the use of the Scheffé test.

EXAMPLE 12–3

Use the Scheffé test to test each pair of means in Example 12–1 to see if a significant difference exists between each pair of means. Use $\alpha = 0.05$.

SOLUTION

The F critical value for Example 12–1 is 4.26. Then the critical value for the individual tests with d.f.N. $= 2$ and d.f.D. $= 9$ is

$$F' = (k - 1)(\text{C.V.}) = (3 - 1)(4.26) = 8.52$$

a. For $\bar{X}_1$ versus $\bar{X}_2$,

$$F_S = \frac{(\bar{X}_1 - \bar{X}_2)^2}{s_W^2[(1/n_1) + (1/n_2)]} = \frac{(37.25 - 35.4)^2}{25.106(\frac{1}{4} + \frac{1}{5})} = 0.30$$

Since $0.30 < 8.52$, the decision is that μ_1 is not significantly different from μ_2.

b. For $\bar{X}_1$ versus $\bar{X}_3$,

$$F_S = \frac{(\bar{X}_1 - \bar{X}_3)^2}{s_W^2[(1/n_1) + (1/n_3)]} = \frac{(37.25 - 26)^2}{25.106(\frac{1}{4} + \frac{1}{3})} = 8.64$$

Since $8.64 > 8.52$, the decision is that μ_1 is significantly different from μ_3.

c. For $\bar{X}_2$ versus $\bar{X}_3$,

$$F_S = \frac{(\bar{X}_2 - \bar{X}_3)^2}{s_W^2[(1/n_2) + (1/n_3)]} = \frac{(35.4 - 26)^2}{25.106(\frac{1}{5} + \frac{1}{3})} = 6.60$$

Since $6.60 < 8.64$, the decision is that μ_2 is not significantly different from μ_3. Hence, only the mean of the small cars is not equal to the mean of luxury cars.

On occasion, when the F test value is greater than the critical value, the Scheffé test may not show any significant differences in the pairs of means. This result occurs because the difference may actually lie in the average of two or more means when compared with the other mean. The Scheffé test can be used to make these types of comparisons, but the technique is beyond the scope of this book.

This study involved three groups. The results showed that patients in all three groups felt better after 2 years. State possible null and alternative hypotheses for this study. Was the null hypothesis rejected? Explain how the statistics could have been used to arrive at the conclusion.

HEALTH

TRICKING KNEE PAIN

You sign up for a clinical trial of arthroscopic surgery used to relieve knee pain caused by arthritis. You're sedated and wake up with tiny incisions. Soon your bum knee feels better. Two years later you find out you had "placebo" surgery. In a study at the Houston VA Medical Center, researchers divided 180 patients into three groups: two groups had damaged cartilage removed, while the third got simulated surgery. Yet an equal number of patients in all groups felt better after two years. Some 650,000 people have the surgery annually, but they're wasting their money, says Dr. Nelda P. Wray, who led the study. And the patients who got fake surgery? "They aren't angry at us," she says. "They still report feeling better."

— STEPHEN P. WILLIAMS

Tukey Test

The **Tukey test** can also be used after the analysis of variance has been completed to make pairwise comparisons between means when the groups have the same sample size. The symbol for the test value in the Tukey test is q.

Formula for the Tukey Test

$$q = \frac{\bar{X}_i - \bar{X}_j}{\sqrt{s_W^2/n}}$$

where $\bar{X}_i$ and $\bar{X}_j$ are the means of the samples being compared, n is the size of the samples, and s_W^2 is the within-group variance.

When the absolute value of q is greater than the critical value for the Tukey test, there is a significant difference between the two means being compared.

The critical value for the Tukey test is found using Table N in Appendix A, where k is the number of means in the original problem and v is the degrees of freedom for s_W^2, which is $N - k$. The value of k is found across the top row, and v is found in the left column.

EXAMPLE 12–4

Using the Tukey test, test each pair of means in Example 12–2 to see whether a specific difference exists, at $\alpha = 0.05$.

SOLUTION

a. For $\overline{X}_1$ versus $\overline{X}_2$,

$$q = \frac{\overline{X}_1 - \overline{X}_2}{\sqrt{s_W^2/n}} = \frac{15.5 - 4.0}{\sqrt{45.50/5}} = 3.812$$

b. For $\overline{X}_1$ versus $\overline{X}_3$,

$$q = \frac{\overline{X}_1 - \overline{X}_3}{\sqrt{s_W^2/n}} = \frac{15.5 - 5.8}{\sqrt{45.50/5}} = 3.216$$

c. For $\overline{X}_2$ versus $\overline{X}_3$,

$$q = \frac{\overline{X}_2 - \overline{X}_3}{\sqrt{s_W^2/n}} = \frac{4.0 - 5.8}{\sqrt{45.50/5}} = -0.597$$

To find the critical value for the Tukey test, use Table N in Appendix A. The number of means k is found in the row at the top, and the degrees of freedom for s_W^2 are found in the left column (denoted by v). Since $k = 3$, d.f. $= 18 - 3 = 15$, and $\alpha = 0.05$, the critical value is 3.67. See Figure 12–3. Hence, the only q value that is greater in absolute value than the critical value is the one for the difference between $\overline{X}_1$ and $\overline{X}_2$. The conclusion, then, is that there is a significant difference in means for the turnpike and the Mon-Fayette Expressway.

FIGURE 12–3   Finding the Critical Value in Table N for the Tukey Test (Example 12–4)

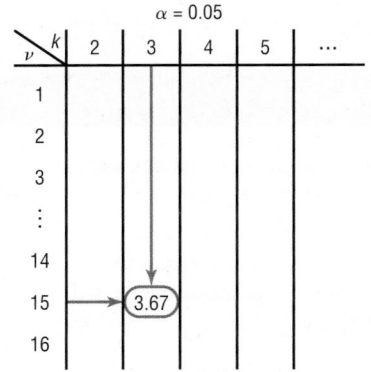

You might wonder why there are two different tests that can be used after the ANOVA. Actually, there are several other tests that can be used in addition to the Scheffé and Tukey tests. It is up to the researcher to select the most appropriate test. The Scheffé test is the most general, and it can be used when the samples are of different sizes. Furthermore, the Scheffé test can be used to make comparisons such as the average of $\overline{X}_1$ and $\overline{X}_2$ compared with $\overline{X}_3$. However, the Tukey test is more powerful than the Scheffé test for making pairwise comparisons for the means. A rule of thumb for pairwise comparisons is to use the Tukey test when the samples are equal in size and the Scheffé test when the samples differ in size. This rule will be followed in this textbook.

≛ Applying the Concepts 12–2

Colors That Make You Smarter

The following set of data values was obtained from a study of people's perceptions on whether the color of a person's clothing is related to how intelligent the person looks. The subjects rated the person's intelligence on a scale of 1 to 10. Randomly selected group 1 subjects were shown people with clothing in shades of blue and gray. Randomly selected group 2 subjects were shown people with clothing in shades of brown and yellow. Randomly selected group 3 subjects were shown people with clothing in shades of pink and orange. The results follow.

Group 1	Group 2	Group 3
8	7	4
7	8	9
7	7	6
7	7	7
8	5	9
8	8	8
6	5	5
8	8	8
8	7	7
7	6	5
7	6	4
8	6	5
8	6	4

1. Use the Tukey test to test all possible pairwise comparisons.

2. Are there any contradictions in the results?

3. Explain why separate *t* tests are not accepted in this situation.

4. When would Tukey's test be preferred over the Scheffé method? Explain.

See page 686 for the answers.

≛ Exercises 12–2

1. What two tests can be used to compare two means when the null hypothesis is rejected using the one-way ANOVA *F* test?

2. Explain the difference between the two tests used to compare two means when the null hypothesis is rejected using the one-way ANOVA *F* test.

For Exercises 3 through 8, the null hypothesis was rejected. Use the Scheffé test when sample sizes are unequal or the Tukey test when sample sizes are equal, to test the differences between the pairs of means. Assume all variables are normally distributed, samples are independent, and the population variances are equal.

3. Exercise 9 in Section 12–1.

4. Exercise 12 in Section 12–1.

5. Exercise 13 in Section 12–1.

6. Exercise 17 in Section 12–1.

7. Exercise 18 in Section 12–1.

8. Exercise 20 in Section 12–1.

For Exercises 9 through 13, do a complete one-way ANOVA. If the null hypothesis is rejected, use either the Scheffé or Tukey test to see if there is a significant difference in the pairs of means. Assume all assumptions are met.

9. Emergency Room Visits Fractures accounted for 2.7% of all U.S. emergency room visits for a total of 454,000 visits for a recent year. A random sample of weekly ER visits is recorded for three hospitals in a large metropolitan area during the summer months. At $\alpha = 0.05$, is there sufficient evidence to conclude a difference in means?

Hospital X	Hospital Y	Hospital Z
28	30	25
27	18	20
40	34	30
45	28	22
29	26	18
25	31	20

Source: *World Almanac.*

10. Weights of Digital Cameras The data consist of the weights in ounces of three different types of digital camera. Use $\alpha = 0.05$ to see if the means are equal.

2–3 Megapixels	4–5 Megapixels	6–8 Megapixels
6	14	19
8	11	27
7	15	21
11	24	23
4	17	24
8	10	33

11. Fiber Content of Foods The number of grams of fiber per serving for a random sample of three different kinds of foods is listed. Is there sufficient evidence at the 0.05 level of significance to conclude that there is a difference in mean fiber content among breakfast cereals, fruits, and vegetables?

Breakfast cereals	Fruits	Vegetables
3	5.5	10
4	2	1.5
6	4.4	3.5
4	1.6	2.7
10	3.8	2.5
5	4.5	6.5
6	2.8	4
8		3
5		

Source: *The Doctor's Pocket Calorie, Fat, and Carbohydrate Counter.*

12. Per-Pupil Expenditures The expenditures (in dollars) per pupil for states in three sections of the country are listed. Using $\alpha = 0.05$, can you conclude that there is a difference in means?

Eastern third	Middle third	Western third
4946	6149	5282
5953	7451	8605
6202	6000	6528
7243	6479	6911
6113		

Source: *New York Times Almanac.*

13. Weekly Unemployment Benefits The average weekly unemployment benefit for the entire United States is $297. Three states are randomly selected, and a sample of weekly unemployment benefits is recorded for each. At $\alpha = 0.05$, is there sufficient evidence to conclude a difference in means? If so, perform the appropriate test to find out where the difference exists.

Florida	Pennsylvania	Maine
200	300	250
187	350	195
192	295	275
235	362	260
260	280	220
175	340	290

Source: *World Almanac.*

12–3 Two-Way Analysis of Variance

OBJECTIVE 3

Use the two-way ANOVA technique to determine if there is a significant difference in the main effects or interaction.

The analysis of variance technique shown previously is called a **one-way ANOVA** since there is only *one independent variable*. The **two-way ANOVA** is an extension of the one-way analysis of variance; it involves *two independent variables*. The independent variables are also called **factors.**

The two-way analysis of variance is quite complicated, and many aspects of the subject should be considered when you are using a research design involving a two-way ANOVA. For the purposes of this textbook, only a brief introduction to the subject will be given.

In doing a study that involves a two-way analysis of variance, the researcher is able to test the effects of two independent variables or factors on one *dependent variable*. In addition, the interaction effect of the two variables can be tested.

FIGURE 12–4
Treatment Groups for
the Plant Food–Soil
Type Experiment

For example, suppose a researcher wishes to test the effects of two different types of plant food and two different types of soil on the growth of certain plants. The two independent variables are the type of plant food and the type of soil, while the dependent variable is the plant growth. Other factors, such as water, temperature, and sunlight, are held constant.

To conduct this experiment, the researcher sets up four groups of plants. See Figure 12–4. Assume that the plant food type is designated by the letters A_1 and A_2 and the soil type by the Roman numerals I and II. The groups for such a two-way ANOVA are sometimes called **treatment groups.** The four groups are

Group 1   Plant food A_1, soil type I

Group 2   Plant food A_1, soil type II

Group 3   Plant food A_2, soil type I

Group 4   Plant food A_2, soil type II

The plants are assigned to the groups at random. This design is called a 2×2 (read "two-by-two") design, since each variable consists of two **levels,** that is, two different treatments.

The two-way ANOVA enables the researcher to test the effects of the plant food and the soil type in a single experiment rather than in separate experiments involving the plant food alone and the soil type alone.

In this case, the effect of the plant food is the change in the response variable that results from changing the level or the type of food. The effect of soil type is the change in the response variable that results from changing the level or type of soil. These two effects of the independent variable are called the **main effects.** Furthermore, the researcher can test an additional hypothesis about the effect of the *interaction* of the two variables—plant food and soil type—on plant growth. For example, is there a difference between the growth of plants using plant food A_1 and soil type II and the growth of plants using plant food A_2 and soil type I? When a difference of this type occurs, the experiment is said to have a significant **interaction effect.** The interaction effect represents the joint effect of the two factors over and above the effects of each factor considered separately. That is, the types of plant food affect the plant growth differently in different soil types. When the interaction effect is statistically significant, the researcher should not consider the effects of the individual factors without considering the interaction effect.

There are many different kinds of two-way ANOVA designs, depending on the number of levels of each variable. Figure 12–5 shows a few of these designs. As stated previously, the plant food–soil type experiment uses a 2×2 ANOVA.

The design in Figure 12–5(a) is called a 3×2 design, since the factor in the rows has three levels and the factor in the columns has two levels. Figure 12–5(b) is a 3×3 design,

FIGURE 12–5

Some Types of
Two-Way ANOVA Designs

(a) 3 × 2 design

(b) 3 × 3 design

(c) 4 × 3 design

since each factor has three levels. Figure 12–5(c) is a 4 × 3 design, since the factor in the rows has four levels and the factor in the columns has three levels.

The two-way ANOVA design has several null hypotheses. There is one for each independent variable and one for the interaction. In the plant food–soil type problem, the hypotheses are as follows:

1. The hypotheses regarding the plant food–soil type interaction effect are stated as follows.

   H_0: There is no interaction effect between type of plant food used and type of soil used on plant growth.

   H_1: There is an interaction effect between food type and soil type on plant growth.

2. The hypotheses regarding plant food are stated as follows.

   H_0: There is no difference in means of heights of plants grown using different foods.

   H_1: There is a difference in means of heights of plants grown using different foods.

3. The hypotheses regarding soil type are stated as follows:

   H_0: There is no difference in means of heights of plants grown in different soil types.

   H_1: There is a difference in means of heights of plants grown in different soil types.

As with the one-way ANOVA, a between-group variance estimate is calculated, and a within-group variance estimate is calculated. An F test is then performed for each of the independent variables and the interaction. The results of the two-way ANOVA are summarized in a two-way table, as shown in Table 12–4 for the plant experiment.

TABLE 12–4 ANOVA Summary Table for Plant Food and Soil Type			
Source	**Sum of squares**	**d.f.**	**Mean square**	**F**
Plant food Soil type Interaction Within (error) Total			

In general, the two-way ANOVA summary table is set up as shown in Table 12–5.

TABLE 12–5 ANOVA Summary Table

Source	Sum of squares	d.f.	Mean square	F
A	SS_A	$a - 1$	MS_A	F_A
B	SS_B	$b - 1$	MS_B	F_B
$A \times B$	$SS_{A \times B}$	$(a - 1)(b - 1)$	$MS_{A \times B}$	$F_{A \times B}$
Within (error)	SS_W	$ab(n - 1)$	MS_W	
Total				

In the table,

$$SS_A = \text{sum of squares for factor } A$$
$$SS_B = \text{sum of squares for factor } B$$
$$SS_{A \times B} = \text{sum of squares for interaction}$$
$$SS_W = \text{sum of squares for within-group term or error term}$$
$$a = \text{number of levels of factor } A$$
$$b = \text{number of levels of factor } B$$
$$n = \text{number of subjects in each group}$$

$$MS_A = \frac{SS_A}{a - 1}$$

$$MS_B = \frac{SS_B}{b - 1}$$

$$MS_{A \times B} = \frac{SS_{A \times B}}{(a - 1)(b - 1)}$$

$$MS_W = \frac{SS_W}{ab(n - 1)}$$

$$F_A = \frac{MS_A}{MS_W} \quad \text{with d.f.N.} = a - 1, \text{d.f.D.} = ab(n - 1)$$

$$F_B = \frac{MS_B}{MS_W} \quad \text{with d.f.N.} = b - 1, \text{d.f.D.} = ab(n - 1)$$

$$F_{A \times B} = \frac{MS_{A \times B}}{MS_W} \quad \text{with d.f.N.} = (a - 1)(b - 1), \text{d.f.D.} = ab(n - 1)$$

The assumptions for the two-way analysis of variance are basically the same as those for the one-way ANOVA, except for sample size.

Assumptions for the Two-Way ANOVA

1. The populations from which the samples were obtained must be normally or approximately normally distributed.
2. The samples must be independent.
3. The variances of the populations from which the samples were selected must be equal.
4. The groups must be equal in sample size.

In this book, the assumptions will be stated in the exercises; however, when encountering statistics in other situations, you must check to see that these assumptions have been met before proceeding.

The two-way analysis of variance follows the regular five-step hypothesis-testing procedure.

Step 1 State the hypotheses.

Step 2 Find the critical values.

Step 3   Compute the test value.

Step 4   Make the decision.

Step 5   Summarize the results.

The computational procedure for the two-way ANOVA is quite lengthy. For this reason, it will be omitted in Example 12–5, and only the two-way ANOVA summary table will be shown. The table used in Example 12–5 is similar to the one generated by most computer programs. You should be able to interpret the table and summarize the results.

EXAMPLE 12–5   Gasoline Consumption

A researcher wishes to see whether the type of gasoline used and the type of automobile driven have any effect on gasoline consumption. Two types of gasoline, regular and high-octane, will be used, and two types of automobiles, two-wheel- and all-wheel-drive, will be used in each group. There will be two automobiles in each group, for a total of eight automobiles used. Using a two-way analysis of variance, determine if there is an interactive effect, an effect due to the type of gasoline used, and an effect due to the type of vehicle driven.

The data (in miles per gallon) are shown here, and the summary table is given in Table 12–6.

	Type of automobile	
Gas	Two-wheel-drive	All-wheel-drive
Regular	26.7	28.6
	25.2	29.3
High-octane	32.3	26.1
	32.8	24.2

TABLE 12–6   ANOVA Summary Table for Example 12–5

Source	SS	d.f.	MS	F
Gasoline A	3.920			
Automobile B	9.680			
Interaction $(A \times B)$	54.080			
Within (error)	3.300			
Total	70.980			

SOLUTION

Step 1   State the hypotheses. The hypotheses for the interaction are

H_0: There is no interaction effect between type of gasoline used and type of automobile a person drives on gasoline consumption.

H_1: There is an interaction effect between type of gasoline used and type of automobile a person drives on gasoline consumption.

The hypotheses for the gasoline types are

H_0: There is no difference between the means of gasoline consumption for two types of gasoline.

H_1: There is a difference between the means of gasoline consumption for two types of gasoline.

The hypotheses for the types of automobile driven are

H_0: There is no difference between the means of gasoline consumption for two-wheel-drive and all-wheel-drive automobiles.

H_1: There is a difference between the means of gasoline consumption for two-wheel-drive and all-wheel-drive automobiles.

Step 2 Find the critical values for each F test. In this case, each independent variable, or factor, has two levels. Hence, a 2×2 ANOVA table is used. Factor A is designated as the gasoline type. It has two levels, regular and high-octane; therefore, $a = 2$. Factor B is designated as the automobile type. It also has two levels; therefore, $b = 2$. The degrees of freedom for each factor are as follows:

$$\text{Factor } A: \qquad \text{d.f.N.} = a - 1 = 2 - 1 = 1$$

$$\text{Factor } B: \qquad \text{d.f.N.} = b - 1 = 2 - 1 = 1$$

$$\text{Interaction } (A \times B): \qquad \text{d.f.N.} = (a - 1)(b - 1)$$

$$= (2 - 1)(2 - 1) = 1 \cdot 1 = 1$$

$$\text{Within (error):} \qquad \text{d.f.D.} = ab(n - 1)$$

$$= 2 \cdot 2(2 - 1) = 4$$

where n is the number of data values in each group. In this case, $n = 2$.

The critical value for the F_A test is found by using $\alpha = 0.05$, d.f.N. $= 1$, and d.f.D. $= 4$. In this case, $F_A = 7.71$. The critical value for the F_B test is found by using $\alpha = 0.05$, d.f.N. $= 1$, and d.f.D. $= 4$; also F_B is 7.71. Finally, the critical value for the $F_{A \times B}$ test is found by using d.f.N. $= 1$ and d.f.D. $= 4$; it is also 7.71.

Note: If there are different levels of the factors, the critical values will not all be the same. For example, if factor A has three levels and factor b has four levels, and if there are two subjects in each group, then the degrees of freedom are as follows:

$$\text{d.f.N.} = a - 1 = 3 - 1 = 2 \qquad \qquad \text{factor } A$$

$$\text{d.f.N.} = b - 1 = 4 - 1 = 3 \qquad \qquad \text{factor } B$$

$$\text{d.f.N.} = (a - 1)(b - 1) = (3 - 1)(4 - 1)$$

$$= 2 \cdot 3 = 6 \qquad \qquad \text{factor } A \times B$$

$$\text{d.f.D.} = ab(n - 1) = 3 \cdot 4(2 - 1) = 12 \qquad \text{within (error) factor}$$

Step 3 Complete the ANOVA summary table to get the test values. The mean squares are computed first.

$$\text{MS}_A = \frac{\text{SS}_A}{a - 1} = \frac{3.920}{2 - 1} = 3.920$$

$$\text{MS}_B = \frac{\text{SS}_B}{b - 1} = \frac{9.680}{2 - 1} = 9.680$$

$$\text{MS}_{A \times B} = \frac{\text{SS}_{A \times B}}{(a - 1)(b - 1)} = \frac{54.080}{(2 - 1)(2 - 1)} = 54.080$$

$$\text{MS}_W = \frac{\text{SS}_W}{ab(n - 1)} = \frac{3.300}{4} = 0.825$$

The F values are computed next.

$$F_A = \frac{\text{MS}_A}{\text{MS}_W} = \frac{3.920}{0.825} = 4.752 \qquad \text{d.f.N.} = a - 1 = 1 \qquad \text{d.f.D.} = ab(n - 1) = 4$$

$$F_B = \frac{\text{MS}_B}{\text{MS}_W} = \frac{9.680}{0.825} = 11.733 \qquad \text{d.f.N.} = b - 1 = 1 \qquad \text{d.f.D.} = ab(n - 1) = 4$$

$$F_{A \times B} = \frac{\text{MS}_{A \times B}}{\text{MS}_W} = \frac{54.080}{0.825} = 65.552 \qquad \text{d.f.N.} = (a - 1)(b - 1) = 1 \qquad \text{d.f.D.} = ab(n - 1) = 4$$

The completed ANOVA table is shown in Table 12–7.

TABLE 12–7	Completed ANOVA Summary Table for Example 12–5			
Source	**SS**	**d.f.**	**MS**	**F**
Gasoline A	3.920	1	3.920	4.752
Automobile B	9.680	1	9.680	11.733
Interaction ($A \times B$)	54.080	1	54.080	65.552
Within (error)	3.300	4	0.825	
Total	70.980	7		

Step 4   Make the decision. Since $F_B = 11.733$ and $F_{A \times B} = 65.552$ are greater than the critical value 7.71, the null hypotheses concerning the type of automobile driven and the interaction effect should be rejected. Since the interaction effect is statistically significant, no decision should be made about the automobile type without further investigation.

Step 5   Summarize the results. Since the null hypothesis for the interaction effect was rejected, it can be concluded that the combination of type of gasoline and type of automobile does affect gasoline consumption.

Interesting Fact

Some birds can fly as high as 5 miles.

In the preceding analysis, the effect of the type of gasoline used and the effect of the type of automobile driven are called the *main effects*. If there is no significant interaction effect, the main effects can be interpreted independently. However, if there is a significant interaction effect, the main effects must be interpreted cautiously, if at all.

To interpret the results of a two-way analysis of variance, researchers suggest drawing a graph, plotting the means of each group, analyzing the graph, and interpreting the results. In Example 12–5, find the means for each group or cell by adding the data values in each cell and dividing by n. The means for each cell are shown in the chart here.

	Type of automobile	
Gas	**Two-wheel-drive**	**All-wheel-drive**
Regular	$\bar{X} = \dfrac{26.7 + 25.2}{2} = 25.95$	$\bar{X} = \dfrac{28.6 + 29.3}{2} = 28.95$
High-octane	$\bar{X} = \dfrac{32.3 + 32.8}{2} = 32.55$	$\bar{X} = \dfrac{26.1 + 24.2}{2} = 25.15$

The graph of the means for each of the variables is shown in Figure 12–6. In this graph, the lines cross each other. When such an intersection occurs and the interaction is significant, the interaction is said to be a **disordinal interaction.** When there is a disordinal interaction, you should not interpret the main effects without considering the interaction effect.

The other type of interaction that can occur is an *ordinal interaction*. Figure 12–7 shows a graph of means in which an ordinal interaction occurs between two variables. The lines do not cross each other, nor are they parallel. If the F test value for the interaction is significant and the lines do not cross each other, then the interaction is said to be an **ordinal interaction** and the main effects can be interpreted independently of each other.

Finally, when there is no significant interaction effect, the lines in the graph will be parallel or approximately parallel. When this situation occurs, the main effects can be interpreted independently of each other because there is no significant interaction. Figure 12–8 shows the graph of two variables when the interaction effect is not significant; the lines are parallel.

FIGURE 12–6

Graph of the Means
of the Variables in
Example 12–5

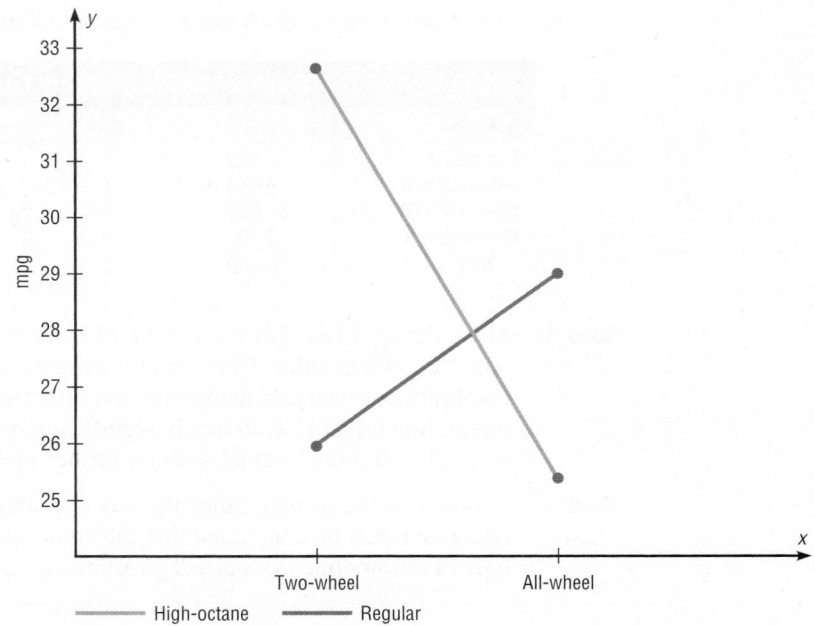

FIGURE 12–7

Graph of Two Variables
Indicating an Ordinal
Interaction

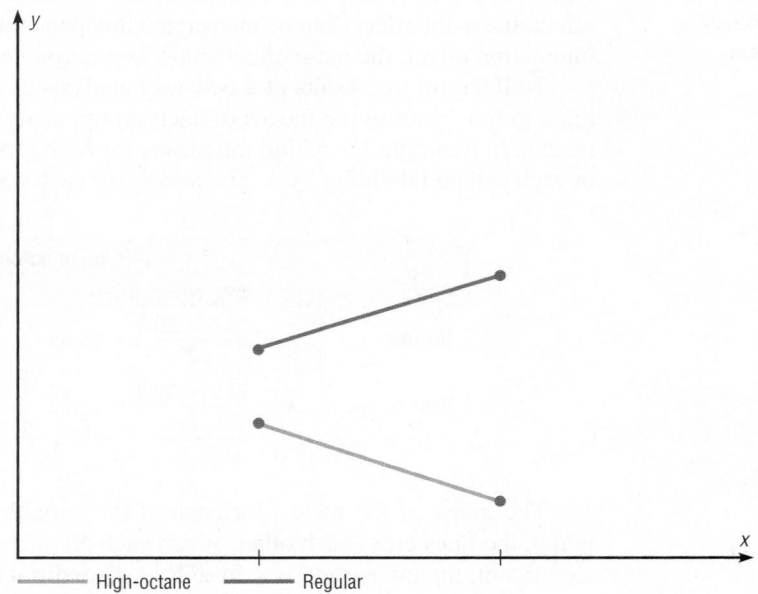

Example 12–5 was an example of a 2×2 two-way analysis of variance, since each independent variable had two levels. For other types of variance problems, such as a 3×2 or a 4×3 ANOVA, interpretation of the results can be quite complicated. Procedures using tests such as the Tukey and Scheffé tests for analyzing the cell means exist and are similar to the tests shown for the one-way ANOVA, but they are beyond the scope of this textbook. Many other designs for analysis of variance are available to researchers, such as three-factor designs and repeated-measure designs; they are also beyond the scope of this book.

FIGURE 12–8
Graph of Two Variables
Indicating No Interaction

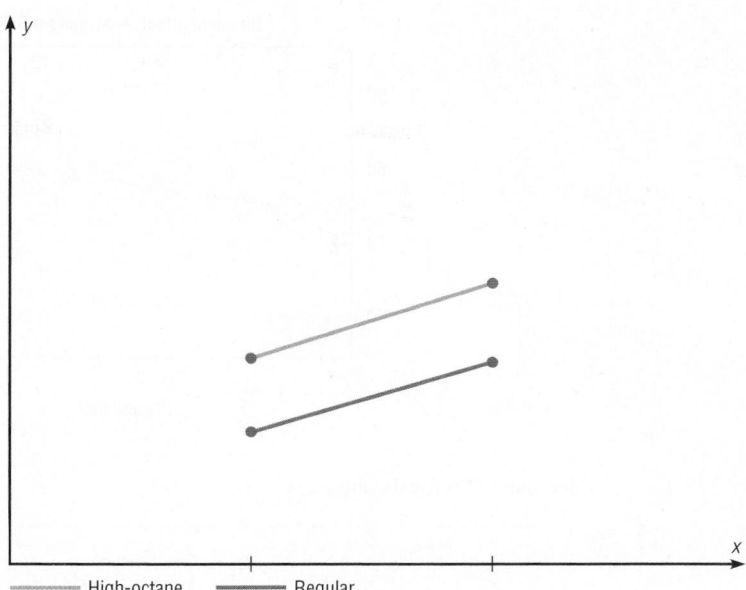

High-octane   Regular

In summary, the two-way ANOVA is an extension of the one-way ANOVA. The former can be used to test the effects of two independent variables and a possible interaction effect on a dependent variable.

Applying the Concepts 12–3

Automobile Sales Techniques

The following outputs are from the result of an analysis of how car sales are affected by the experience of the salesperson and the type of sales technique used. Experience was broken up into four levels, and two different sales techniques were used. Analyze the results and draw conclusions about level of experience with respect to the two different sales techniques and how they affect car sales.

Two-Way Analysis of Variance

Analysis of Variance for Sales

Source	DF	SS	MS
Experience	3	3414.0	1138.0
Presentation	1	6.0	6.0
Interaction	3	414.0	138.0
Error	16	838.0	52.4
Total	23	4672.0	

Individual 95% CI

Experience	Mean
1	62.0
2	63.0
3	78.0
4	91.0

```
          ------------+-----------+-----------+-----------+-----------
1  62.0   (----------*----------)
2  63.0    (----------*----------)
3  78.0                        (-----------*----------)
4  91.0                                    (-----------*----------)
          -----------+-----------+-----------+-----------+-----------
                   60.0        70.0        80.0        90.0
```

Individual 95% CI

Presentation	Mean
1	74.0
2	73.0

```
          -----------+-----------+-----------+-----------+-----------
1  74.0      (--------------------------*--------------------------)
2  73.0   (--------------------------*--------------------------)
          -----------+-----------+-----------+-----------+-----------
```

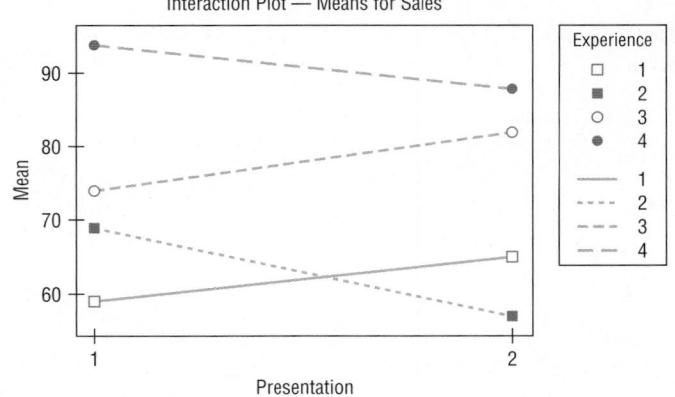

See page 686 for the answers.

Exercises 12–3

1. How does the two-way ANOVA differ from the one-way ANOVA?

2. Explain what is meant by *main effects* and *interaction effect*.

3. How are the values for the mean squares computed?

4. How are the *F* test values computed?

5. In a two-way ANOVA, variable *A* has three levels and variable *B* has two levels. There are five data values in each cell. Find each degrees-of-freedom value.

    a. d.f.N. for factor *A*

    b. d.f.N. for factor *B*

    c. d.f.N. for factor *A* × *B*

    d. d.f.D. for the within (error) factor

6. In a two-way ANOVA, variable *A* has six levels and variable *B* has five levels. There are seven data values in each cell. Find each degrees-of-freedom value.

    a. d.f.N. for factor *A*

    b. d.f.N. for factor *B*

    c. d.f.N. for factor *A* × *B*

    d. d.f.D. for the within (error) factor

7. What are the two types of interactions that can occur in the two-way ANOVA?

8. When can the main effects for the two-way ANOVA be interpreted independently?

For Exercises 9 through 15, perform these steps. Assume that all variables are normally or approximately normally distributed, that the samples are independent, and that the population variances are equal.

    a. State the hypotheses.

    b. Find the critical value for each *F* test.

    c. Complete the summary table and find the test value.

    d. Make the decision.

    e. Summarize the results. (Draw a graph of the cell means if necessary.)

9. Soap Bubble Experiments Hands-on soap bubble experiments are a great way to teach mathematics. In an effort to find the best possible bubble solution, two different soap concentrations were used along with two different amounts of glycerin additive. Students were then given a flat glass plate and a straw and were asked to blow their best bubble. The diameters of the resulting bubbles (in millimeters) are listed below. Can an interaction be concluded between the soap solution and the glycerin? Is there a difference in mean length of bubble diameter with respect to the concentration of soap to water? With respect to amount of glycerin additive? Use $\alpha = 0.05$.

	+1 Unit glycerin	+2 Units glycerin
Soap:water 13:25	115, 113, 105, 110	98, 100, 90, 95
Soap:water 1:2	90, 102, 100, 98	99, 100, 102, 95

10. Increasing Plant Growth A gardening company is testing new ways to improve plant growth. Twelve plants are randomly selected and exposed to a combination of two factors, a "Grow-light" in two different strengths and a plant food supplement with different mineral supplements. After a number of days, the plants are measured for growth, and the results (in inches) are put into the appropriate boxes.

	Grow-light 1	Grow-light 2
Plant food A	9.2, 9.4, 8.9	8.5, 9.2, 8.9
Plant food B	7.1, 7.2, 8.5	5.5, 5.8, 7.6

Can an interaction between the two factors be concluded? Is there a difference in mean growth with respect to light? With respect to plant food? Use $\alpha = 0.05$.

11. **Environmentally Friendly Air Freshener** As a new type of environmentally friendly, natural air freshener is being developed, it is tested to see whether the

effects of temperature and humidity affect the length of time that the scent is effective. The numbers of days that the air freshener had a significant level of scent are listed below for two temperature and humidity levels. Can an interaction between the two factors be concluded? Is there a difference in mean length of effectiveness with respect to humidity? With respect to temperature? Use $\alpha = 0.05$.

	Temperature 1	Temperature 2
Humidity 1	35, 25, 26	35, 31, 37
Humidity 2	28, 22, 21	23, 19, 18

12. **Home-Building Times** A contractor wishes to see whether there is a difference in the time (in days) it takes two subcontractors to build three different types of homes. At $\alpha = 0.05$, analyze the data shown here, using a two-way ANOVA. See below for raw data.

Data for Exercise 12

	Home type		
Subcontractor	**I**	**II**	**III**
A	25, 28, 26, 30, 31	30, 32, 35, 29, 31	43, 40, 42, 49, 48
B	15, 18, 22, 21, 17	21, 27, 18, 15, 19	23, 25, 24, 17, 13

ANOVA Summary Table for Exercise 12

Source	SS	d.f.	MS	F
Subcontractor	1672.553			
Home type	444.867			
Interaction	313.267			
Within	328.800			
Total	2759.487			

13. **Durability of Paint** A pigment laboratory is testing both dry additives and solution-based additives to see their effect on the durability rating (a number from 1 to 10) of a finished paint product. The paint to be tested is divided into four equal quantities, and a different combination of the two additives is added to one-fourth of each quantity. After a prescribed number of hours, the durability rating is obtained for each of the 16 samples, and the results are recorded below in the appropriate space.

	Dry additive 1	Dry additive 2
Solution additive A	9, 8, 5, 6	4, 5, 8, 9
Solution additive B	7, 7, 6, 8	10, 8, 6, 7

Can an interaction be concluded between the dry and solution additives? Is there a difference in mean durability rating with respect to dry additive used? With respect to solution additive? Use $\alpha = 0.05$.

14. **Types of Outdoor Paint** Two types of outdoor paint, enamel and latex, were tested to see how long (in months) each lasted before it began to crack, flake, and peel. They were tested in four geographic locations in the United States to study the effects of climate on the paint. At $\alpha = 0.01$, analyze the data shown, using a two-way ANOVA shown below. Each group contained five test panels. See below for raw data.

Data for Exercise 14

	Geographic location			
Type of paint	**North**	**East**	**South**	**West**
Enamel	60, 53, 58, 62, 57	54, 63, 62, 71, 76	80, 82, 62, 88, 71	62, 76, 55, 48, 61
Latex	36, 41, 54, 65, 53	62, 61, 77, 53, 64	68, 72, 71, 82, 86	63, 65, 72, 71, 63

ANOVA Summary Table for Exercise 14

Source	SS	d.f.	MS	F
Paint type	12.1			
Location	2501.0			
Interaction	268.1			
Within	2326.8			
Total	5108.0			

15. **Age and Sales** A company sells three items: swimming pools, spas, and saunas. The owner decides to see whether the age of the sales representative and the type of item affect monthly sales. At $\alpha = 0.05$, analyze the data

shown, using a two-way ANOVA. Sales are given in hundreds of dollars for a randomly selected month, and five salespeople were selected for each group.

ANOVA Summary Table for Exercise 15

Source	SS	d.f.	MS	F
Age	168.033			
Product	1,762.067			
Interaction	7,955.267			
Within	2,574.000			
Total	12,459.367			

Data for Exercise 15

Age of salesperson	Product		
	Pool	Spa	Sauna
Over 30	56, 23, 52, 28, 35	43, 25, 16, 27, 32	47, 43, 52, 61, 74
30 or under	16, 14, 18, 27, 31	58, 62, 68, 72, 83	15, 14, 22, 16, 27

▤ Technology   Step by Step

TI-84 Plus
Step by Step

The TI-84 Plus does not have a built-in function for two-way analysis of variance. However, the downloadable program named TWOWAY is available on the Online Learning Center. Follow the instructions for downloading the program.

Performing a Two-Way Analysis of Variance

1. Enter the data values of the dependent variable into L_1 and the coded values for the levels of the factors into L_2 and L_3.

2. Press **PRGM,** move the cursor to the program named TWOWAY, and press **ENTER** twice.

3. Type L_1 for the list that contains the dependent variable and press **ENTER.**

4. Type L_2 for the list that contains the coded values for the first factor and press **ENTER.**

5. Type L_3 for the list that contains the coded values for the second factor and press **ENTER.**

6. The program will show the statistics for the first factor.

7. Press **ENTER** to see the statistics for the second factor.

8. Press **ENTER** to see the statistics for the interaction.

9. Press **ENTER** to see the statistics for the error.

10. Press **ENTER** to clear the screen.

Example TI12–2

Perform a two-way analysis of variance for the gasoline data (Example 12–5 in the text). The gas mileages are the data values for the dependent variable. Factor A is the type of gasoline (1 for regular, 2 for high-octane). Factor B is the type of automobile (1 for two-wheel-drive, 2 for all-wheel-drive).

Gas mileages (L_1)	Type of gasoline (L_2)	Type of automobile (L_3)
26.7	1	1
25.2	1	1
32.3	2	1
32.8	2	1
28.6	1	2
29.3	1	2
26.1	2	2
24.2	2	2

EXCEL
Step by Step

Two-Way Analysis of Variance (ANOVA)

This example pertains to Example 12–5 from the text.

Example XL12–3

A researcher wishes to see if type of gasoline used and type of automobile driven have any effect on gasoline consumption. Use $\alpha = 0.05$.

1. Enter the data exactly as shown in the figure below in an Excel worksheet.

	A	B	C
1		2- wheel Drive	All-wheel drive
2	Regular	26.7	28.6
3		25.2	29.3
4	Hi-octane	32.3	26.1
5		32.8	24.2

2. From the toolbar, select **Data**, then **Data Analysis**.
3. Select **Anova: Two-Factor With Replication** under **Analysis tools**, then [OK].
4. In the **Anova: Single Factor** dialog box, type **A1:C5** for the **Input Range.**
5. Type **2** for the Rows per sample.
6. Type **0.05** for the **Alpha level.**
7. Under **Output options,** check **Output Range** and type **E2.**
8. Click [OK].

The two-way ANOVA table is shown below.

ANOVA						
Source of Variation	SS	df	MS	F	P-value	F crit
Sample	3.92	1	3.92	4.751515152	0.094766001	7.708647421
Columns	9.68	1	9.68	11.73333333	0.026647909	7.708647421
Interaction	54.08	1	54.08	65.55151515	0.00126491	7.708647421
Within	3.3	4	0.825			
Total	70.98	7				

MINITAB
Step by Step

Two-Way Analysis of Variance

For Example 12–5, how do gasoline type and vehicle type affect gasoline mileage?

1. Enter the data into three columns of a worksheet. The data for this analysis have to be "stacked" as shown.

   a) All the gas mileage data are entered in a single column named MPG.

   b) The second column contains codes identifying the gasoline type, a 1 for regular or a 2 for high-octane.

   c) The third column will contain codes identifying the type of automobile, 1 for two-wheel-drive or 2 for all-wheel-drive.

↓	C1	C2	C3
	MPG	GasCode	TypeCode
1	26.7	1	1
2	25.2	1	1
3	32.3	2	1
4	32.8	2	1
5	28.6	1	2
6	29.3	1	2
7	26.1	2	2
8	24.2	2	2

2. Select **Stat>ANOVA>Two-Way.**

   a) Double-click MPG in the list box.

   b) Double-click GasCode as Row factor.

   c) Double-click TypeCode as Column factor.

   d) Check the boxes for Display means, then click [OK].

The session window will contain the results.

Two-Way ANOVA: MPG versus GasCode, TypeCode

Source	DF	SS	MS	F	P
GasCode	1	3.92	3.920	4.75	0.095
TypeCode	1	9.68	9.680	11.73	0.027
Interaction	1	54.08	54.080	65.55	0.001
Error	4	3.30	0.825		
Total	7	70.98			

```
                       Individual 95% CIs For Mean Based on
                       Pooled StDev
GasCode    Mean    --------+--------+--------+--------+-
1          27.45   (-------------*-------------)
2          28.85                (-------------*-------------)
                   --------+--------+--------+--------+-
                       27.0    28.0     29.0     30.0
                       Individual 95% CIs For Mean Based on
                       Pooled StDev
TypeCode   Mean    -----+---------+---------+---------+----
1          29.25                   (-----------*----------)
2          27.05   (----------*------------)
                   -----+---------+---------+---------+----
                       26.4      27.6      28.8     30.0
```

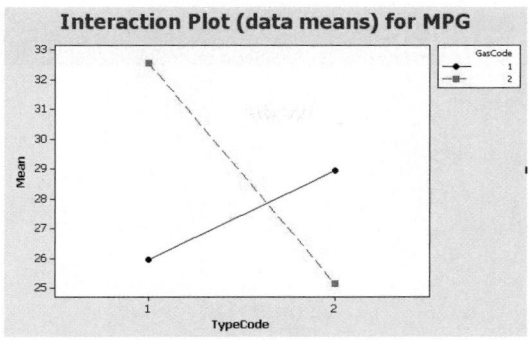

Interaction Plot (data means) for MPG

Plot Interactions

3. Select **Stat>ANOVA>Interactions Plot.**

   a) Double-click MPG for the response variable and GasCodes and TypeCodes for the factors.

   b) Click [OK].

Intersecting lines indicate a significant interaction of the two independent variables.

Summary

- The *F* test, as shown in Chapter 9, can be used to compare two sample variances to determine whether they are equal. It can also be used to compare three or more means. When three or more means are compared, the technique is called analysis of variance (ANOVA). The ANOVA technique uses two estimates of the population variance. The between-group variance is the variance of the sample means; the within-group variance is the overall variance of all the values. When there is no significant difference among the means, the two estimates will be approximately equal and the *F* test value will be close to 1. If there is a significant difference among the means, the between-group variance estimate will be larger than the within-group variance estimate and a significant test value will result. (12–1)

- If there is a significant difference among means, the researcher may wish to see where this difference lies.

Several statistical tests can be used to compare the sample means after the ANOVA technique has been done. The most common are the Scheffé test and the Tukey test. When the sample sizes are the same, the Tukey test can be used. The Scheffé test is more general and can be used when the sample sizes are equal or not equal. (12–2)

- When there is one independent variable, the analysis of variance is called a one-way ANOVA. When there are two independent variables, the analysis of variance is called a two-way ANOVA. The two-way ANOVA enables the researcher to test the effects of two independent variables and a possible interaction effect on one dependent variable. If an interaction effect is found to be statistically significant, the researcher must investigate further to find out if the main effects can be examined. (12–3)

Important Terms

analysis of variance (ANOVA) 648

ANOVA summary table 650

between-group variance 649

disordinal interaction 671

factors 665

interaction effect 666

level 666

main effects 666

mean square 650

one-way ANOVA 648

ordinal interaction 671

Scheffé test 660

sum of squares between groups 650

sum of squares within groups 650

treatment groups 666

Tukey test 662

two-way ANOVA 665

within-group variance 649

Important Formulas

Formulas for the ANOVA test:

$$\bar{X}_{GM} = \frac{\Sigma X}{N}$$

$$F = \frac{s_B^2}{s_W^2}$$

where

$$s_B^2 = \frac{\Sigma n_i(\bar{X}_i - \bar{X}_{GM})^2}{k - 1} \qquad s_W^2 = \frac{\Sigma(n_i - 1)s_i^2}{\Sigma(n_i - 1)}$$

d.f.N. = $k - 1$ $N = n_1 + n_2 + \cdots + n_k$

d.f.D. = $N - k$ k = **number of groups**

Formulas for the Scheffé test:

$$F_s = \frac{(\bar{X}_i - \bar{X}_j)^2}{s_W^2[(1/n_i) + (1/n_i)]} \quad \text{and} \quad F' = (k - 1)(\text{C.V.})$$

Formula for the Tukey test:

$$q = \frac{\bar{X}_i - \bar{X}_j}{\sqrt{s_W^2/n}}$$

d.f.N. = k   and   **d.f.D. = degrees of freedom for s_W^2**

Formulas for the two-way ANOVA:

$$MS_A = \frac{SS_A}{a - 1} \qquad\qquad F_A = \frac{MS_A}{MS_W} \qquad \textbf{d.f.N.} = a - 1$$
$$\textbf{d.f.D.} = ab(n - 1)$$

$$MS_B = \frac{SS_B}{b - 1} \qquad\qquad F_B = \frac{MS_B}{MS_W} \qquad \textbf{d.f.N.} = b - 1$$
$$\textbf{d.f.D.} = ab(n - 1)$$

$$MS_{A \times B} = \frac{SS_{A \times B}}{(a - 1)(b - 1)} \qquad F_{A \times B} = \frac{MS_{A \times B}}{MS_W} \qquad \textbf{d.f.N.} = (a - 1)(b - 1)$$
$$\textbf{d.f.D.} = ab(n - 1)$$

$$MS_W = \frac{SS_W}{ab(n - 1)}$$

Review Exercises

If the null hypothesis is rejected in Exercises 1 through 8, use the Scheffé test when the sample sizes are unequal to test the differences between the means, and use the Tukey test when the sample sizes are equal. For these exercises, perform these steps. Assume the assumptions have been met.

    a. State the hypotheses and identify the claim.

    b. Find the critical value(s).

    c. Compute the test value.

    d. Make the decision.

    e. Summarize the results.

Sections 12–1 and 12–2

Use the traditional method of hypothesis testing unless otherwise specified.

  1. Lengths of Various Types of Bridges The data represent the lengths in feet of three types of bridges in the United States. At $\alpha = 0.01$, test the claim that there is no significant difference in the means of the lengths of the types of bridges.

Simple truss	Segmented concrete	Continuous plate
745	820	630
716	750	573
700	790	525
650	674	510
647	660	480
625	640	460
608	636	451
598	620	450
550	520	450
545	450	425
534	392	420
528	370	360

Source: *World Almanac and Book of Facts.*

  2. Number of State Parks The numbers of state parks found in selected states in three different regions of the country are listed. At $\alpha = 0.05$, can it be concluded that the average number of state parks differs by region?

South	West	New England
51	28	94
64	44	72
35	24	14
24	31	52
47	40	

Source: *Time Almanac.*

3. **Carbohydrates in Cereals** The number of carbohydrates per serving in randomly selected cereals from three manufacturers is shown. At the 0.05 level of significance, is there sufficient evidence to conclude a difference in the average number of carbohydrates?

Manufacturer 1	Manufacturer 2	Manufacturer 3
25	23	24
26	44	39
24	24	28
26	24	25
26	36	23
41	27	32
26	25	
43		

Source: *The Doctor's Pocket Calorie, Fat, and Carbohydrate Counter.*

4. **Grams of Fat per Serving of Pizza** The number of grams of fat per serving for three different kinds of pizza from several manufacturers is listed. At the 0.01 level of significance, is there sufficient evidence that a difference exists in mean fat content?

Cheese	Pepperoni	Supreme/Deluxe
18	20	16
11	17	27
19	15	17
20	18	17
16	23	12
21	23	27
16	21	20

Source: *The Doctor's Pocket Calorie, Fat, and Carbohydrate Counter.*

5. **Iron Content of Foods and Drinks** The iron content in three different types of food is shown. At the 0.10 level of significance, is there sufficient evidence to conclude that a difference in mean iron content exists for meats and fish, breakfast cereals, and nutritional high-protein drinks?

Meats and fish	Breakfast cereals	Nutritional drinks
3.4	8	3.6
2.5	2	3.6
5.5	1.5	4.5
5.3	3.8	5.5
2.5	3.8	2.7
1.3	6.8	3.6
2.7	1.5	6.3
	4.5	

Source: *The Doctor's Pocket Calorie, Fat, and Carbohydrate Counter.*

6. **Temperatures in January** The average January high temperatures (in degrees Fahrenheit) for selected tourist cities on different continents are listed. Is there sufficient evidence to conclude a difference in mean temperatures for the three areas? Use the 0.05 level of significance.

Europe	Central and South America	Asia
41	87	89
38	75	35
36	66	83
56	84	67
50	75	48

Source: *Time Almanac.*

7. **School Incidents Involving Police Calls** A researcher wishes to see if there is a difference in the average number of times local police were called in school incidents. Random samples of school districts were selected, and the numbers of incidents for a specific year were reported. At $\alpha = 0.05$, is there a difference in the means? If so, suggest a reason for the difference.

County A	County B	County C	County D
13	16	15	11
11	33	12	31
2	12	19	3
	2	2	
	2		

Source: U.S. Department of Education.

8. **Carbohydrates in Juices** Listed are the numbers of grams of carbohydrates in a random sample of eight-ounce servings of various types of juices. At the 0.01 level of significance, is there evidence of a difference in means?

Apple mix	Orange mix	Veggie mix
23	29	10
31	30	19
26	29	12
32	31	23
30	37	11

Section 12–3

9. **Review Preparation for Statistics** A statistics instructor wanted to see if student participation in review preparation methods led to higher examination scores. Five students were randomly selected and placed in each test group for a three-week unit on statistical inference. Everyone took the same examination at the end of the unit, and the resulting scores are shown. Is there sufficient evidence at $\alpha = 0.05$ to conclude an interaction between the two factors? Is there sufficient

evidence to conclude a difference in mean scores based on formula delivery system? Is there sufficient evidence

to conclude a difference in mean scores based on the review organization technique?

	Formulas provided	**Student-made formula cards**
Student-led review	89, 76, 80, 90, 75	94, 86, 80, 79, 82
Instructor-led review	75, 80, 68, 65, 79	88, 78, 85, 65, 72

10. Effects of Different Types of Diets A medical researcher wishes to test the effects of two different diets and two different exercise programs on the glucose level in a person's blood. The glucose level is measured in milligrams per deciliter (mg/dl). Three subjects are randomly assigned to each group. Analyze the data shown here, using a two-way ANOVA with $\alpha = 0.05$.

Exercise program	Diet	
	A	**B**
I	62, 64, 66	58, 62, 53
II	65, 68, 72	83, 85, 91

ANOVA Summary Table for Exercise 10

Source	SS	d.f.	MS	F
Exercise	816.750			
Diet	102.083			
Interaction	444.083			
Within	108.000			
Total	1470.916			

▰ STATISTICS TODAY

Is Seeing Really Believing? —Revisited

To see if there were differences in the testimonies of the witnesses in the three age groups, the witnesses responded to 17 questions, 10 on direct examination and 7 on cross-examination. These were then scored for accuracy. An analysis of variance test with age as the independent variable was used to compare the total number of questions answered correctly by the groups. The results showed no significant differences among the age groups for the direct examination questions. However, there was a significant difference among the groups on the cross-examination questions. Further analysis showed the 8-year-olds were significantly less accurate under cross-examination compared to the other two groups. The 12-year-old and adult eyewitnesses did not differ in the accuracy of their cross-examination responses.

▰ Data Analysis

The Data Bank is found in Appendix B, or on the World Wide Web by following links from www.mhhe.com/math/stat/bluman

1. From the Data Bank, select a random sample of subjects, and test the hypothesis that the mean cholesterol levels of the nonsmokers, less-than-one-pack-a-day smokers, and one-pack-plus smokers are equal. Use an ANOVA test. If the null hypothesis is rejected, conduct the Scheffé test to find where the difference is. Summarize the results.

2. Repeat Exercise 1 for the mean IQs of the various educational levels of the subjects.

3. Using the Data Bank, randomly select 12 subjects and randomly assign them to one of the four groups in the following classifications.

	Smoker	**Nonsmoker**
Male		
Female		

Use one of these variables—weight, cholesterol, or systolic pressure—as the dependent variable, and perform a two-way ANOVA on the data. Use a computer program to generate the ANOVA table.

Chapter Quiz

Determine whether each statement is true or false. If the statement is false, explain why.

1. In analysis of variance, the null hypothesis should be rejected only when there is a significant difference among all pairs of means.

2. The F test does not use the concept of degrees of freedom.

3. When the F test value is close to 1, the null hypothesis should be rejected.

4. The Tukey test is generally more powerful than the Scheffé test for pairwise comparisons.

Select the best answer.

5. Analysis of variance uses the _____ test.

   a. z   *c.* χ^2
   b. t   *d. F*

6. The null hypothesis in ANOVA is that all the means are _____.

   a. Equal   *c.* Variable
   b. Unequal   *d.* None of the above

7. When you conduct an F test, _____ estimates of the population variance are compared.

   a. Two   *c.* Any number of
   b. Three   *d.* No

8. If the null hypothesis is rejected in ANOVA, you can use the _____ test to see where the difference in the means is found.

   a. z or *t*   *c.* Scheffé or Tukey
   b. F or χ^2 *d.* Any of the above

Complete the following statements with the best answer.

9. When three or more means are compared, you use the _____ technique.

10. If the null hypothesis is rejected in ANOVA, the _____ test should be used when sample sizes are equal.

For Exercises 11 through 17, use the traditional method of hypothesis testing unless otherwise specified. Assume the assumptions have been met.

11. **Gasoline Prices** Random samples of summer gasoline prices per gallon are listed for three different states. Is there sufficient evidence of a difference in mean prices? Use $\alpha = 0.01$.

State 1	State 2	State 3
3.20	3.68	3.70
3.25	3.50	3.65
3.18	3.70	3.75
3.15	3.65	3.72

12. **Voters in Presidential Elections** In a recent Presidential election, a random sample of the percentage of voters who voted is shown. At $\alpha = 0.05$, is there a difference in the mean percentage of voters who voted?

Northeast	Southeast	Northwest	Southwest
65.3	54.8	60.5	42.3
59.9	61.8	61.0	61.2
66.9	49.6	74.0	54.7
64.2	58.6	61.4	56.7

Source: Committee for the Study of the American Electorate.

13. **Ages of Late-Night TV Talk Show Viewers** A media researcher wanted to see if there was a difference in the ages of viewers of three late-night television talk shows. Three random samples of viewers were selected, and the ages of the viewers are shown. At $\alpha = 0.01$, is there a difference in the means of the ages of the viewers? Why is the average age of a viewer important to a television show writer?

David Letterman	Jay Leno	Conan O'Brien
53	48	40
46	51	36
48	57	35
42	46	42
35	38	39

Source: Based on information from Nielsen Media Research.

14. **Prices of Body Soap** A consumer group desired to compare the mean price for 12-ounce bottles of liquid body soap from two nationwide brands and one store brand. Four different bottles of each were randomly selected at a large discount drug store, and the prices are noted. At the 0.05 level of significance, is there sufficient evidence to conclude a difference in mean prices? If so, perform the appropriate test to find out where.

Brand X	Brand Y	Store brand
5.99	8.99	4.99
6.99	7.99	3.99
8.59	6.29	5.29
6.49	7.29	4.49

15. **Air Pollution** A lot of different factors contribute to air pollution. One particular factor, particulate matter, was measured for prominent cities of three continents. Particulate matter includes smoke, soot, dust, and liquid droplets from combustion such that the particle is less than 10 microns in diameter and thus capable of reaching deep into the respiratory system. The measurements are listed here. At the 0.05 level of significance, is there sufficient evidence to conclude a

difference in means? If so, perform the appropriate test to find out where the differences in means are.

Asia	Europe	Africa
79	34	33
104	35	16
40	30	43
73	43	

Source: *World Almanac.*

16. **Alumni Gift Solicitation** Several students volunteered for an alumni phone-a-thon to solicit alumni gifts. The number of calls made by randomly selected students from each class is listed. At $\alpha = 0.05$, is there sufficient evidence to conclude a difference in means?

Freshmen	Sophomores	Juniors	Seniors
25	17	20	20
29	25	24	25
32	20	25	26
15	26	30	32
18	30	15	19
26	28	18	20
35			

17. **Diets and Exercise Programs** A researcher conducted a study of two different diets and two different exercise programs. Three randomly selected subjects were assigned to each group for one month. The values indicate the amount of weight each lost.

Exercise program	Diet	
	A	**B**
I	5, 6, 4	8, 10, 15
II	3, 4, 8	12, 16, 11

Answer the following questions for the information in the printout shown.

a. What procedure is being used?
b. What are the names of the two variables?
c. How many levels does each variable contain?
d. What are the hypotheses for the study?
e. What are the *F* values for the hypotheses? State which are significant, using the *P*-values.
f. Based on the answers to part *e,* which hypotheses can be rejected?

Computer Printout for Problem 17
_____

Datafile: NONAME.SST   Procedure: Two-way ANOVA

TABLE OF MEANS:

	DIET		
	A	B	Row Mean
EX PROG I	5.000	11.000	8.000
II	5.000	13.000	9.000
Col Mean	5.000	12.000	
Tot Mean	8.500		

SOURCE TABLE:

Source	df	Sums of Squares	Mean Square	F Ratio	p-value
DIET	1	147.000	147.000	21.000	0.00180
EX PROG	1	3.000	3.000	0.429	0.53106
DIET X EX P	1	3.000	3.000	0.429	0.53106
Within	8	56.000	7.000		
Total	11	209.000			

Critical Thinking Challenges

Adult Children of Alcoholics

Shown here are the abstract and two tables from a research study entitled "Adult Children of Alcoholics: Are They at Greater Risk for Negative Health Behaviors?" by Arlene E. Hall. Based on the abstract and the tables, answer these questions.

1. What was the purpose of the study?

2. How many groups were used in the study?

3. By what means were the data collected?

4. What was the sample size?

5. What type of sampling method was used?

6. How might the population be defined?

7. What may have been the hypothesis for the ANOVA part of the study?

8. Why was the one-way ANOVA procedure used, as opposed to another test, such as the *t* test?

9. What part of the ANOVA table did the conclusion "ACOAs had significantly lower wellness scores (WS) than non-ACOAs" come from?

10. What level of significance was used?

11. In the following excerpts from the article, the researcher states that

> ... using the Tukey-HSD procedure revealed a significant difference between ACOAs and non-ACOAs, p = 0.05, but no significant difference was found between ACOAs and Unsures or between non-ACOAs and Unsures.

Using Tables 12–8 and 12–9 and the means, explain why the Tukey test would have enabled the researcher to draw this conclusion.

> **Abstract** *The purpose of the study was to examine and compare the health behaviors of adult children of alcoholics (ACOAs) and their non-ACOA peers within a university population. Subjects were 980 undergraduate students from a major university in the East. Three groups (ACOA, non-ACOA, and Unsure) were identified from subjects' responses to three direct questions regarding parental drinking behaviors. A questionnaire was used to collect data for the study. Included were questions related to demographics, parental drinking behaviors, and the College Wellness Check (WS), a health risk appraisal designed especially for college students (Dewey & Cabral, 1986). Analysis of variance procedures revealed that ACOAs had significantly lower wellness scores (WS) than non-ACOAs. Chi-square analyses of the individual variables revealed that ACOAs and non-ACOAs were significantly different on 15 of the*

> *50 variables of the WS. A discriminant analysis procedure revealed the similarities between Unsure subjects and ACOA subjects. The results provide valuable information regarding ACOAs in a nonclinical setting and contribute to our understanding of the influences related to their health risk behaviors.*

TABLE 12–8   Means and Standard Deviations for the Wellness Scores (WS) Group by (N = 945)

Group	N	$\bar{X}$	S.D.
ACOAs	143	69.0	13.6
Non-ACOAs	746	73.2	14.5
Unsure	56	70.1	14.0
Total	945	212.3	42.1

TABLE 12–9   ANOVA of Group Means for the Wellness Scores (WS)

Source	d.f.	SS	MS	F
Between groups	2	2,403.5	1,201.7	5.9*
Within groups	942	193,237.4	205.1	
Total	944	195,640.9		

*$p < 0.01$

Source: Arlene E. Hall, "Adult Children of Alcoholics: Are They at Greater Risk for Negative Health Behaviors?" *Journal of Health Education* 12, no. 4, pp. 232–238.

Data Projects

Use a significance level of 0.05 for all tests.

1. **Business and Finance** Select 10 stocks at random from the Dow Jones Industrials, the NASDAQ, and the S&P 500. For each, note the gain or loss in the last quarter. Use analysis of variance to test the claim that stocks from all three groups have had equal performance.

2. **Sports and Leisure** Use total earnings data for movies that were released in the previous year. Sort them by rating (G, PG, PG13, and R). Is the mean revenue for movies the same regardless of rating?

3. **Technology** Use the data collected in data project 3 of Chapter 2 regarding song lengths. Consider only three genres. For example, use rock, alternative, and hip hop/rap. Conduct an analysis of variance to determine if the mean song lengths for the genres are the same.

4. **Health and Wellness** Select 10 cereals from each of the following categories: cereal targeted at children, cereal targeted at dieters, and cereal that fits neither of the previous categories. For each cereal note its calories per cup (this may require some computation since serving sizes vary for cereals). Use analysis of variance to test the claim that the calorie content of these different types of cereals is the same.

5. **Politics and Economics** Conduct an anonymous survey and ask the participants to identify which of the following categories describes them best: registered Republican, Democrat, or Independent, or not registered to vote. Also ask them to give their age to obtain your data. Use an analysis of variance to determine whether there is a difference in mean age between the different political designations.

6. **Your Class** Split the class into four groups, those whose favorite type of music is rock, whose favorite is country, whose favorite is rap or hip hop, and those whose favorite is another type of music. Make a list of the ages of students for each of the four groups. Use analysis of variance to test the claim that the means for all four groups are equal.

Answers to Applying the Concepts

Section 12–1   Colors That Make You Smarter

1. The ANOVA produces a test statistic of $F = 3.06$, with a P-value of 0.059. We would fail to reject the null hypothesis and find that there is not enough evidence to conclude at $\alpha = 0.05$ that the color of a person's clothing is related to people's perceptions of how intelligent the person looks.

2. The purpose of the study was to determine if the color of a person's clothing is related to people's perceptions of how intelligent the person looks.

3. We would have to perform three separate t tests, which would inflate the error rate.

Section 12–2   Colors That Make You Smarter

1. Tukey's pairwise comparisons show no significant difference in the three pairwise comparisons of the means.

2. This agrees with the nonsignificant results of the general ANOVA test conducted in Applying the Concepts 12–1.

3. The t tests should not be used since they would inflate the error rate.

4. We prefer the Tukey test over the Scheffé test when the samples are all the same size.

Section 12–3   Automobile Sales Techniques

There is no significant difference between levels 1 and 2 of experience. Level 3 and level 4 salespersons did significantly better than those at levels 1 and 2, with level 4 showing the best results, on average. If type of presentation is taken into consideration, the interaction plot shows a significant difference. The best combination seems to be level 4 experience with presentation style 1.

Hypothesis-Testing Summary 2*

7. Test of the significance of the correlation coefficient.

   Example: $H_0: \rho = 0$

   Use a t test:

   $$t = r\sqrt{\frac{n-2}{1-r^2}} \qquad \text{with d.f.} = n-2$$

8. Formula for the F test for the multiple correlation coefficient.

   Example: $H_0: \rho = 0$

   $$F = \frac{R^2/k}{(1-R^2)/(n-k-1)}$$

   $$\text{d.f.N.} = n-k \qquad \text{d.f.D.} = n-k-1$$

9. Comparison of a sample distribution with a specific population.

   Example: H_0: There is no difference between the two distributions.

   Use the chi-square goodness-of-fit test:

   $$\chi^2 = \sum \frac{(O-E)^2}{E}$$

   $$\text{d.f.} = \text{no. of categories} - 1$$

10. Comparison of the independence of two variables.

    Example: H_0: Variable A is independent of variable B.

Use the chi-square independence test:

$$\chi^2 = \sum \frac{(O-E)^2}{E}$$

$$\text{d.f.} = (R-1)(C-1)$$

11. Test for homogeneity of proportions.

    Example: $H_0: p_1 = p_2 = p_3$

    Use the chi-square test:

    $$\chi^2 = \sum \frac{(O-E)^2}{E}$$

    $$\text{d.f.} = (R-1)(C-1)$$

12. Comparison of three or more sample means.

    Example: $H_0: \mu_1 = \mu_2 = \mu_3$

    Use the analysis of variance test:

    $$F = \frac{s_B^2}{s_W^2}$$

    where

    $$s_B^2 = \frac{\sum n_i (\bar{X}_i - \bar{X}_{\text{GM}})^2}{k-1}$$

    $$s_W^2 = \frac{\sum (n_i - 1)s_i^2}{\sum (n_i - 1)}$$

    $\text{d.f.N.} = k-1 \qquad N = n_1 + n_2 + \cdots + n_k$

    $\text{d.f.D.} = N-k \qquad k = \text{number of groups}$

*This summary is a continuation of Hypothesis-Testing Summary 1, at the end of Chapter 9.

13. Test when the F value for the ANOVA is significant. Use the Scheffé test to find what pairs of means are significantly different.

$$F_s = \frac{(\bar{X}_i - \bar{X}_j)^2}{s_W^2[(1/n_i) + (1/n_j)]}$$

$$F' = (k - 1)(\text{C.V.})$$

Use the Tukey test to find which pairs of means are significantly different.

$$q = \frac{\bar{X}_i - \bar{X}_j}{\sqrt{s_W^2/n}} \qquad \begin{array}{l} \text{d.f.N.} = k \\ \text{d.f.D.} = \text{degrees of freedom for } s_W^2 \end{array}$$

14. Test for the two-way ANOVA.

Example:

H_0: There is no significant difference between the variables.

H_0: There is no interaction effect between the variables.

$$MS_A = \frac{SS_A}{a - 1}$$

$$MS_B = \frac{SS_B}{b - 1}$$

$$MS_{A \times B} = \frac{SS_{A \times B}}{(a - 1)(b - 1)}$$

$$MS_W = \frac{SS_W}{ab(n - 1)}$$

$$F_A = \frac{MS_A}{MS_W} \qquad \begin{array}{l} \text{d.f.N.} = a - 1 \\ \text{d.f.D.} = ab(n - 1) \end{array}$$

$$F_B = \frac{MS_B}{MS_W} \qquad \begin{array}{l} \text{d.f.N.} = (b - 1) \\ \text{d.f.D.} = ab(n - 1) \end{array}$$

$$F_{A \times B} = \frac{MS_{A \times B}}{MS_W} \qquad \begin{array}{l} \text{d.f.N.} = (a - 1)(b - 1) \\ \text{d.f.D.} = ab(n - 1) \end{array}$$

13

Nonparametric Statistics

STATISTICS TODAY

Too Much or Too Little?

Suppose a manufacturer of ketchup wishes to check the bottling machines to see if they are functioning properly. That is, are they dispensing the right amount of ketchup per bottle? A 40-ounce bottle is currently used. Because of the natural variation in the manufacturing process, the amount of ketchup in a bottle will not always be exactly 40 ounces. Some bottles will contain less than 40 ounces, and others will contain more than 40 ounces. To see if the variation is due to chance or to a malfunction in the manufacturing process, a runs test can be used. The runs test is a nonparametric statistical technique. See Statistics Today—Revisited at the end of this chapter. This chapter explains such techniques, which can be used to help the manufacturer determine the answer to the question.

OUTLINE

Introduction

13–1 Advantages and Disadvantages of Nonparametric Methods

13–2 The Sign Test

13–3 The Wilcoxon Rank Sum Test

13–4 The Wilcoxon Signed-Rank Test

13–5 The Kruskal-Wallis Test

13–6 The Spearman Rank Correlation Coefficient and the Runs Test

Summary

OBJECTIVES

After completing this chapter, you should be able to

1 State the advantages and disadvantages of nonparametric methods.

2 Test hypotheses, using the sign test.

3 Test hypotheses, using the Wilcoxon rank sum test.

4 Test hypotheses, using the signed-rank test.

5 Test hypotheses, using the Kruskal-Wallis test.

6 Compute the Spearman rank correlation coefficient.

7 Test hypotheses, using the runs test.

Introduction

Statistical tests, such as the z, t, and F tests, are called parametric tests. **Parametric tests** are statistical tests for population parameters such as means, variances, and proportions that involve assumptions about the populations from which the samples were selected. One assumption is that these populations are normally distributed. But what if the population in a particular hypothesis-testing situation is *not* normally distributed? Statisticians have developed a branch of statistics known as **nonparametric statistics** or **distribution-free statistics** to use when the population from which the samples are selected is not normally distributed or is distributed in any other particular way. Nonparametric statistics can also be used to test hypotheses that do not involve specific population parameters, such as μ, σ, or p.

> **Nonparametric statistical tests** are used to test hypotheses about population parameters when the assumption about normality cannot be met.

For example, a sportswriter may wish to know whether there is a relationship between the rankings of two judges on the diving abilities of 10 Olympic swimmers. In another situation, a sociologist may wish to determine whether men and women enroll at random for a specific drug rehabilitation program. The statistical tests used in these situations are nonparametric or distribution-free tests. The term *nonparametric* is used for both situations.

The nonparametric tests explained in this chapter are the sign test, the Wilcoxon rank sum test, the Wilcoxon signed-rank test, the Kruskal-Wallis test, and the runs test. In addition, the Spearman rank correlation coefficient, a statistic for determining the relationship between ranks, is explained.

13–1   Advantages and Disadvantages of Nonparametric Methods

OBJECTIVE

State the advantages and disadvantages of nonparametric methods.

As stated previously, nonparametric tests and statistics can be used in place of their parametric counterparts (z, t, and F) when the assumption of normality cannot be met. However, you should not assume that these statistics are a better alternative than the parametric statistics. There are both advantages and disadvantages in the use of nonparametric methods.

Advantages

There are six advantages that nonparametric methods have over parametric methods:

1. They can be used to test population parameters when the variable is not normally distributed.
2. They can be used when the data are nominal or ordinal.
3. They can be used to test hypotheses that do not involve population parameters.
4. In some cases, the computations are easier than those for the parametric counterparts.
5. They are easy to understand.
6. There are fewer assumptions that have to be met, and the assumptions are easier to verify.

Disadvantages

There are three disadvantages of nonparametric methods:

1. They are *less sensitive* than their parametric counterparts when the assumptions of the parametric methods are met. Therefore, larger differences are needed before the null hypothesis can be rejected.

| Interesting Fact

Older men have the biggest ears. James Heathcote, M.D., says, "On average, our ears seem to grow 0.22 millimeter a year. This is roughly a centimeter during the course of 50 years."

2. They tend to use *less information* than the parametric tests. For example, the sign test requires the researcher to determine only whether the data values are above or below the median, not how much above or below the median each value is.

3. They are *less efficient* than their parametric counterparts when the assumptions of the parametric methods are met. That is, larger sample sizes are needed to overcome the loss of information. For example, the nonparametric sign test is about 60% as efficient as its parametric counterpart, the z test. Thus, a sample size of 100 is needed for use of the sign test, compared with a sample size of 60 for use of the z test to obtain the same results.

Since there are both advantages and disadvantages to the nonparametric methods, the researcher should use caution in selecting these methods. If the parametric assumptions can be met, the parametric methods are preferred. However, when parametric assumptions cannot be met, the nonparametric methods are a valuable tool for analyzing the data.

The basic assumption for nonparametric statistics are as follows:

Assumptions for Nonparametric Statistics

1. The sample or samples are randomly selected.
2. If two or more samples are used, they must be independent of each other unless otherwise stated.

In this book, the assumptions will be stated in the exercises; however, when encountering statistics in other situations, you must check to see that these assumptions have been met before proceeding.

Ranking

Many nonparametric tests involve the **ranking** of data, that is, the positioning of a data value in a data array according to some rating scale. Ranking is an ordinal variable. For example, suppose a judge decides to rate five speakers on an ascending scale of 1 to 10, with 1 being the best and 10 being the worst, for categories such as voice, gestures, logical presentation, and platform personality. The ratings are shown in the chart.

Speaker	A	B	C	D	E
Rating	8	6	10	3	1

The rankings are shown next.

Speaker	E	D	B	A	C
Rating	1	3	6	8	10
Ranking	1	2	3	4	5

Since speaker E received the lowest score, 1 point, he or she is ranked first. Speaker D received the next-lower score, 3 points; he or she is ranked second; and so on.

What happens if two or more speakers receive the same number of points? Suppose the judge awards points as follows:

Speaker	A	B	C	D	E
Rating	8	6	10	6	3

The speakers are then ranked as follows:

Speaker	E	D	B	A	C
Rating	3	6	6	8	10
Ranking	1	Tie for 2nd and 3rd		4	5

When there is a tie for two or more places, the average of the ranks must be used. In this case, each would be ranked as

$$\frac{2 + 3}{2} = \frac{5}{2} = 2.5$$

Hence, the rankings are as follows:

Speaker	E	D	B	A	C
Rating	3	6	6	8	10
Ranking	1	2.5	2.5	4	5

Many times, the data are already ranked, so no additional computations must be done. For example, if the judge does not have to award points but can simply select the speakers who are best, second-best, third-best, and so on, then these ranks can be used directly.

Also *P*-values can be found for nonparametric statistical tests, and the *P*-value method can be used to test hypotheses that use nonparametric tests. For this chapter, the *P*-value method will be limited to some of the nonparametric tests that use the standard normal distribution or the chi-square distribution.

≣ Applying the Concepts 13–1

Ranking Data

The following table lists the percentages of patients who experienced side effects from a drug used to lower a person's cholesterol level.

Side effect	Percent
Chest pain	4.0
Rash	4.0
Nausea	7.0
Heartburn	5.4
Fatigue	3.8
Headache	7.3
Dizziness	10.0
Chills	7.0
Cough	2.6

Rank each value in the table.

See page 740 for the answer.

≣ Exercises 13–1

1. What is meant by *nonparametric statistics?*

2. When should nonparametric statistics be used?

3. List the advantages of nonparametric statistics.

4. List the disadvantages of nonparametric statistics.

5. Why does the term *distribution-free* describe nonparametric procedures?

6. Explain what is meant by the efficiency of a nonparametric test.

For Exercises 7 through 12, rank each set of data.

7. 22, 66, 32, 43, 65, 43, 71, 34

8. 83, 460, 582, 177, 241

9. 19.4, 21.8, 3.2, 23.1, 5.9, 10.3, 11.1

10. 10.9, 20.2, 43.9, 9.5, 17.6, 5.6, 32.6, 0.85, 17.6

11. 28, 50, 52, 11, 71, 36, 47, 88, 41, 50, 71, 50

12. 90.6, 47.0, 82.2, 9.27, 327.0, 52.9, 18.0, 145.0, 34.5, 9.54

13–2 The Sign Test

OBJECTIVE ②

Test hypotheses, using the sign test.

Single-Sample Sign Test

The simplest nonparametric test, the **sign test** for single samples, is used to test the value of a median for a specific sample.

> The **sign test** for a single sample is a nonparametric test used to test the value of a population median.

When using the sign test, the researcher hypothesizes the specific value for the median of a population; then he or she selects a random sample of data and compares each value with the conjectured median. If the data value is above the conjectured median, it is assigned a plus sign. If the data value is below the conjectured median, it is assigned a minus sign. And if it is exactly the same as the conjectured median, it is assigned a 0. Then the numbers of plus and minus signs are compared to determine if they are significantly different. If the null hypothesis is true, the number of plus signs should be approximately equal to the number of minus signs. If the null hypothesis is not true, there will be a disproportionate number of plus or minus signs.

There are two cases for using the sign test. The first case is when the sample size n is less than or equal to 25. The other case is when the sample size n is greater than 25.

Test Value for the Sign Test

If $n \leq 25$, the test value is the smaller number of plus or minus signs. When $n > 25$, the test value is

$$z = \frac{(X + 0.5) - 0.5n}{\dfrac{\sqrt{n}}{2}}$$

where X is the smaller number of plus signs and n is the total number of plus or minus signs.

For example, when $n \leq 25$, if there are 8 positive signs and 3 negative signs, the test value is 3. When the sample size is 25 or less, Table J in Appendix A is used to determine the critical value. For a specific α, if the test value is less than or equal to the critical value obtained from the table, the null hypothesis should be rejected. The values in Table J are obtained from the binomial distribution when $p = 0.5$. The derivation is omitted here. When $n > 25$, the normal approximation with Table E can be used for the critical values. In this case, $\mu = np$ or $0.5n$ since $p = 0.5$ and $\sigma = \sqrt{npq}$ or $\sqrt{n}/2$ since p and $q = 0.5$ and $\sqrt{npq} = \sqrt{n(0.5)(0.5)}$ or $0.5\sqrt{n}$ which is the same as $\sqrt{n}/2$.

The Procedure Table for the sign test is given next.

Procedure Table

Performing the Sign Test

Step 1   State the hypotheses and identify the claim.

Step 2   Find the critical value. Use Table J in Appendix A when $n \leq 25$ and Table E when $n > 25$.

Step 3   Compute the test value.

Step 4   Make the decision.

Step 5   Summarize the result.

EXAMPLE 13–1   Patients at a Medical Center

The manager of Green Valley Medical Center claims that the median number of patients seen by doctors who work at the center is 80 per day. To test this claim, 20 days are randomly selected and the number of patients seen is recorded and shown. At $\alpha = 0.05$, test the claim.

82	85	93	81	80
86	95	89	74	62
72	84	88	81	83
105	80	86	81	87

SOLUTION

Step 1   State the hypotheses and identify the claim.

H_0: Median = 80 (claim).
H_1: Median ≠ 80.

Step 2   Find the critical value.
Subtract the hypothesized median, 80, from each data value. If the data value falls above the hypothesized median, assign the value a + sign. If the data value falls below the hypothesized median, assign the data value a − sign. If the data value is equal to the median, assign it a 0.

$82 - 80 = +2$, so 82 is assigned a + sign.
$86 - 80 = +6$, so 86 is assigned a + sign.
$72 - 80 = -8$, so 72 is assigned a − sign.
etc.

The completed table is shown.

+	+	+	+	0
+	+	+	−	−
−	+	+	+	+
+	0	+	+	+

Since $n \leq 25$, refer to Table J in Appendix A. In this case, $n = 20 - 2 = 18$ (There are two zeroes) and $\alpha = 0.05$. The critical value for a two-tailed test is 4. See Figure 13–1.

FIGURE 13–1

Finding the Critical
Value in Table J for
Example 13–1

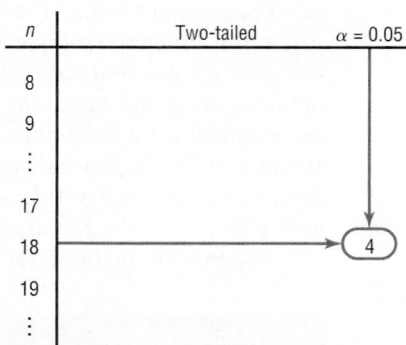

Step 3   Compute the test value. Count the number of + and − signs in step 2, and use the smaller value as the test value. In this case, there are 15 plus signs and 3 minus signs, so the test value is 3.

Step 4   Make the decision. Compare the test value 3 with the critical value 4. If the test value is less than or equal to the critical value, the null hypothesis is rejected. In this case, the null hypothesis is rejected since 3 < 4.

Step 5   Summarize the results. There is enough evidence to reject the null hypothesis that the median of the number of patients seen per day is 80.

EXAMPLE 13–2   Age of Foreign-Born Residents

Based on information from the U.S. Census Bureau, the median age of foreign-born U.S. residents is 36.4 years. A researcher selects a sample of 50 foreign-born U.S. residents in his area and finds that 21 are older than 36.4 years. At $\alpha = 0.05$, test the claim that the median age of the residents is at least 36.4 years.

SOLUTION

Step 1   State the hypotheses and identify the claim.

$$H_0: \text{MD} = 36.4 \text{ (claim)} \qquad \text{and} \qquad H_1: \text{MD} < 36.4$$

Step 2   Find the critical value. Since $\alpha = 0.05$ and $n = 50$, and since this is a left-tailed test, the critical value is -1.65, obtained from Table E.

Step 3   Compute the test value.

$$z = \frac{(X + 0.5) - 0.5n}{\sqrt{n}/2} = \frac{(21 + 0.5) - 0.5(50)}{\sqrt{50}/2} = \frac{-3.5}{3.5355} = -0.99$$

Step 4   Make the decision. Since the test value of -0.99 is greater than -1.65, the decision is to not reject the null hypothesis.

Step 5   Summarize the results. There is not enough evidence to reject the claim that the median age of the residents is at least 36.4 years.

In Example 13–2, the sample size was 50, and 21 residents are older than 36.4 years. So $50 - 21$, or 29, residents are not older than 36.4. The value of X corresponds to the smaller of the two numbers 21 and 29. In this case, $X = 21$ is used in the formula; since 21 is the smaller of the two numbers, the value of X is 21.

Suppose a researcher hypothesized that the median age of houses in a certain municipality was 40 years. In a random sample of 100 houses, 68 were older than 40 years. Then the value used for X in the formula would be $100 - 68$, or 32, since it is the smaller of the two numbers 68 and 32. When 40 is subtracted from the age of a house older than 40 years, the answer is positive. When 40 is subtracted from the age of a house that is less than 40 years old, the result is negative. There would be 68 positive signs and 32 negative signs (assuming that no house was exactly 40 years old). Hence, 32 would be used for X, since it is the smaller of the two values.

Because the sign test uses the smaller number of plus or minus signs, the test is either a two-tailed test or a left-tailed test. When the test is two-tailed, the critical value is found on the left side of the standard normal distribution. When the sign test is a right-tailed test, the formula is

$$z = \frac{(X - 0.5) - 0.5n}{\sqrt{n}/2}$$

and the larger number of plus or minus signs is used for X. In this case, the hypotheses would be

$$H_0: \text{median} = k$$
$$H_1: \text{median} > k$$

The right side of the z distribution would be used for the critical value.

Paired-Sample Sign Test

The sign test can also be used to test sample means in a comparison of two dependent samples, such as a before-and-after test. Recall that when dependent samples are taken from normally distributed populations, the t test is used (Section 9–4). When the condition of normality cannot be met, the nonparametric sign test can be used.

> The **paired-sample sign test** is a nonparametric test that is used to test the difference between two population medians when the samples are dependent.

In a before-and-after test, the variable X_B represents the values before a treatment is given to the subjects while the variable X_A represents the value of the variables after the treatment is given. This test can be left-tailed, right-tailed, or two-tailed. Here the variables X_B and X_A are subtracted $(X_B - X_A)$ from each other, and a plus or minus sign is given to each answer. Zeros are ignored. If the number of plus signs is approximately equal to the number of minus signs, then the null hypothesis is not rejected. If the difference in the number of $+$ and $-$ signs is significant, then the null hypothesis is rejected.

Two Assumptions for the Paired-Sign Test

1. The sample is random.
2. The variables are dependent or paired.

In this book, the assumptions will be stated in the exercises; however, when encountering statistics in other situations, you must check to see that these assumptions have been met before proceeding.

The procedure for the paired-sample sign test is the same as the procedure for the single-sample sign test shown previously.

EXAMPLE 13–3   Ear Infections in Swimmers

A medical researcher believed the number of ear infections in swimmers can be reduced if the swimmers use earplugs. A sample of 10 people was selected, and the number of infections for a four-month period was recorded. During the first two months, the swimmers did not use the earplugs; during the second two months, they did. At the beginning of the second two-month period, each swimmer was examined to make sure that no infection was present. The data are shown here. At $\alpha = 0.05$, can the researcher conclude that using earplugs reduced the number of ear infections?

	Number of ear infections	
Swimmer	**Before, X_B**	**After, X_A**
A	3	2
B	0	1
C	5	4
D	4	0
E	2	1
F	4	3
G	3	1
H	5	3
I	2	2
J	1	3

SOLUTION

Step 1   State the hypotheses and identify the claim.

        H_0: The number of ear infections will not be reduced.

        H_1: The number of ear infections will be reduced (claim).

Step 2   Find the critical value. Subtract the after values X_A from the before values X_B, and indicate the difference by a positive or negative sign or 0, according to the value, as shown in the table.

Swimmer	Before, X_B	After, X_A	Sign of difference
A	3	2	+
B	0	1	−
C	5	4	+
D	4	0	+
E	2	1	+
F	4	3	+
G	3	1	+
H	5	3	+
I	2	2	0
J	1	3	−

        From Table J, with $n = 9$ (the total number of positive and negative signs; the 0 is not counted) and $\alpha = 0.05$ (one-tailed), at most 1 negative sign is needed to reject the null hypothesis because 1 is the smallest entry in the $\alpha = 0.05$ column of Table J.

Step 3   Compute the test value. Since $n \leq 25$, we will count the number of positive and negative signs found in step 2 and use the smaller value as the test value. There are 7 positive signs and 2 negative signs, so the test value is 2.

Step 4   Make the decision. Compare the test value 2 with the critical value 1. If the test value is less than or equal to the critical value, the null hypothesis is rejected. In this case, $2 > 1$, so the decision is not to reject the null hypothesis.

Step 5   Summarize the results. There is not enough evidence to support the claim that the use of earplugs reduced the number of ear infections.

     When conducting a one-tailed sign test, the researcher must scrutinize the data to determine whether they support the null hypothesis. If the data support the null hypothesis, there is no need to conduct the test. In Example 13–3, the null hypothesis states that the number of ear infections will not be reduced. The data would support the null hypothesis if there were more negative signs than positive signs. The reason is that the before values X_B in most cases would be smaller than the after values X_A, and the $X_B - X_A$ values would be negative more often than positive. This would indicate that there is not enough evidence to reject the null hypothesis. The researcher would stop here, since there is no need to continue the procedure.

     On the other hand, if the number of ear infections were reduced, the X_B values, for the most part, would be larger than the X_A values, and the $X_B - X_A$ values would most often be positive, as in Example 13–3. Hence, the researcher would continue the procedure. A word of caution is in order, and a little reasoning is required.

     When the sample size is 26 or more, the normal approximation can be used in the same manner as in Example 13–2.

≡ Applying the Concepts 13–2

Clean Air

An environmentalist suggests that the median of the number of days per month that a large city failed to meet the EPA acceptable standards for clean air is 11 days per month. A random sample of 20 months shows the number of days per month that the air quality was below the EPA's standards.

15	14	1	9	0	3	3	1	10	8
6	16	21	22	3	19	16	5	23	13

1. What is the claim?
2. What test would you use to test the claim? Why?
3. State the hypotheses.
4. Select a value for α and find the corresponding critical value.
5. What is the test value?
6. What is your decision?
7. Summarize the results.
8. Could a parametric test be used?

See page 740 for the answers.

≡ Exercises 13–2

1. Why is the sign test the simplest nonparametric test to use?

2. What population parameter can be tested with the sign test?

3. In the sign test, what is used as the test value when $n < 26$?

4. When $n \geq 26$, what is used in place of Table J for the sign test?

For Exercises 5 through 20, perform these steps.

 a. State the hypotheses and identify the claim.
 b. Find the critical value(s).
 c. Compute the test value.
 d. Make the decision.
 e. Summarize the results.

Use the traditional method of hypothesis testing unless otherwise specified.

5. Ages at First Marriage for Women The median age at first marriage in 2010 for women was 26.1 years—the highest it has ever been. A random sample of women's ages (in years) from recently applied for marriage licenses resulted in the following set of ages. At $\alpha = 0.05$, is there sufficient evidence that the median is not 26.1 years?

34.6	31.2	28.9	28.4	24.3
29.8	25.9	21.4	25.1	26.2
28.3	30.6	35.6	34.2	34.1

Source: *World Almanac 2012.*

6. Game Attendance An athletic director suggests the median number for the paid attendance at 20 local football games is 3000. The data for a random sample are shown. At $\alpha = 0.05$, is there enough evidence to reject the claim? If you were printing the programs for the games, would you use this figure as a guide?

6210	3150	2700	3012	4875
3540	6127	2581	2642	2573
2792	2800	2500	3700	6030
5437	2758	3490	2851	2720

Source: *Pittsburgh Post Gazette.*

7. Annual Incomes for Men The U.S. median annual income for men in 2010 (in constant dollars) was $32,137. A random sample of recent male college graduates indicated the following incomes. At the 0.05 level of significance, test the claim that the median is more than $32,137.

35,000	37,682	39,800	32,500	30,000
41,050	36,198	31,500	29,650	35,800
34,500	38,850	39,750		

Source: *World Almanac 2012.*

8. Weekly Earnings of Women According to the Women's Bureau of the U.S. Department of Labor, the occupation with the highest median weekly earnings among women is pharmacist with median weekly earnings of $1603. Based on the weekly earnings listed from a random sample of female pharmacists, can it be concluded that the median is less than $1603? Use $\alpha = 0.05$.

1550	1355	1777
1430	1570	1701
2465	1655	1484
1429	1829	1812
1217	1501	1449

9. **Natural Gas Costs** For a specific year, the median price of natural gas was $10.86 per 1000 cubic feet. A researcher wishes to see if there is enough evidence to reject the claim. Out of 42 randomly selected households, 18 paid less than $10.86 per 1000 cubic feet for natural gas. Test the claim at $\alpha = 0.05$. How could a prospective home buyer use this information?

Source: Based on information from the Energy Information Administration.

10. **Family Income** The median U.S. family income is believed to be $63,211. In a survey of randomly selected families in a particular neighborhood, it was found that out of 40 families surveyed, 10 had incomes below $63,211. At the 0.05 level of significance, is there sufficient evidence to conclude that the median income is not $63,211?

11. **Number of Faculty for Proprietary Schools** An educational researcher believes that the median number of faculty for proprietary (for-profit) colleges and universities is 150. The data provided list the number of faculty at a randomly selected number of proprietary colleges and universities. At the 0.05 level of significance, is there sufficient evidence to reject his claim?

372	111	165	95	191	83	136	149	37	119
142	136	137	171	122	133	133	342	126	64
61	100	225	127	92	140	140	75	108	96
138	318	179	243	109					

Source: *World Almanac.*

12. **Deaths due to Severe Weather** A meteorologist suggests that the median number of deaths per year from tornadoes in the United States is 60. The number of deaths for a randomly selected sample of 11 years is shown. At $\alpha = 0.05$, is there enough evidence to reject the claim? If you took proper safety precautions during a tornado, would you feel relatively safe?

| 53 | 39 | 39 | 67 | 69 | 40 |
| 25 | 33 | 30 | 130 | 94 | |

Source: NOAA.

13. **Students' Opinions on Lengthening the School Year** One hundred randomly selected students are asked if they favor increasing the school year by 20 days. The responses are 62 no, 36 yes, and 2 undecided. At $\alpha = 0.10$, test the hypothesis that 50% of the students are against extending the school year. Use the *P*-value method.

14. **Television Viewers** A researcher read that the median age for viewers of the Carson Daly show is 39 years. To test the claim, 75 randomly selected viewers were surveyed, and 27 were under the age of 39. At $\alpha = 0.01$, test the claim. Give one reason why an advertiser might like to know the results of this study. Use the *P*-value method.

Source: Nielsen Media Research.

15. **Diet Medication and Weight** A study was conducted to see whether a certain diet medication had an effect on the weights (in pounds) of eight randomly selected women. Their weights were taken before and six weeks after daily administration of the medication. The data are shown here. At $\alpha = 0.05$, can you conclude that the medication had an effect (increase or decrease) on the weights of the women?

Subject	A	B	C	D	E	F	G	H
Weight before	187	163	201	158	139	143	198	154
Weight after	178	162	188	156	133	150	175	150

16. **Exam Scores** A statistics professor wants to investigate the relationship between a student's midterm examination score and the score on the final. Eight students were randomly selected, and their scores on the two examinations are noted. At the 0.10 level of significance, is there sufficient evidence to conclude that there is a difference in scores?

Student	1	2	3	4	5	6	7	8
Midterm	75	92	68	85	65	80	75	80
Final	82	90	79	95	70	83	72	79

17. **Teaspoon Size** How big is a teaspoon? Many cookie recipes call for a teaspoon of dough to be dropped for each cookie. Eight randomly selected volunteer bakers baked a standard chocolate chip cookie recipe, making the cookies their usual "teaspoon" size. The number of cookies was recorded for each baker. Each volunteer was then given a new device that automatically dispenses a teaspoon of dough and then was asked to bake another batch of cookies, counting the results. At $\alpha = 0.10$, is there a difference in the number of cookies per baker?

Baker	1	2	3	4	5	6	7	8
First batch	36	35	40	38	36	39	36	39
Second batch	38	39	39	40	39	42	35	36

18. **Effects of a Pill on Appetite** A researcher wishes to test the effects of a pill on a person's appetite. Twelve randomly selected subjects are allowed to eat a meal of their choice, and their caloric intake is measured. The next day, the same subjects take the pill and eat a meal of their choice. The caloric intake of the second meal is measured. The data are shown here. At $\alpha = 0.02$, can the

researcher conclude that the pill had an effect on a person's appetite?

Subject	1	2	3	4	5	6	7
Meal 1	856	732	900	1321	843	642	738
Meal 2	843	721	872	1341	805	531	740

Subject	8	9	10	11	12
Meal 1	1005	888	756	911	998
Meal 2	900	805	695	878	914

19. Television Viewers A researcher wishes to determine if the number of viewers for 10 randomly selected returning television shows has not changed since last year. The data are given in millions of viewers. At $\alpha = 0.01$, test the claim that the number of viewers has not changed. Depending on your answer, would a television executive plan to air these programs for another year?

Show	1	2	3	4	5	6
Last year	28.9	26.4	20.8	25.0	21.0	19.2
This year	26.6	20.5	20.2	19.1	18.9	17.8

Show	7	8	9	10
Last year	13.7	18.8	16.8	15.3
This year	16.8	16.7	16.0	15.8

Source: Based on information from Nielsen Media Research.

20. Routine Maintenance and Defective Parts A manufacturer believes that if routine maintenance (cleaning and oiling of machines) is increased to once a day rather than once a week, the number of defective parts produced by the machines will decrease. Nine machines are randomly selected, and the number of defective parts produced over a 24-hour operating period is counted. Maintenance is then increased to once a day for a week, and the number of defective parts each machine produces is again counted over a 24-hour operating period. The data are shown. At $\alpha = 0.01$, can the manufacturer conclude that increased maintenance reduces the number of defective parts manufactured by the machines?

Machine	1	2	3	4	5	6	7	8	9
Before	6	18	5	4	16	13	20	9	3
After	5	16	7	4	18	12	14	7	1

Extending the Concepts

Confidence Interval for the Median

The confidence interval for the median of a set of values less than or equal to 25 in number can be found by ordering the data from smallest to largest, finding the median, and using Table J. For example, to find the 95% confidence interval of the true median for 17, 19, 3, 8, 10, 15, 1, 23, 2, 12, order the data:

1, 2, 3, 8, 10, 12, 15, 17, 19, 23

From Table J, select $n = 10$ and $\alpha = 0.05$, and find the critical value. Use the two-tailed row. In this case, the critical value is 1. Add 1 to this value to get 2. In the ordered list, count from the left two numbers and from the right two numbers, and use these numbers to get the confidence interval, as shown:

1, 2, 3, 8, 10, 12, 15, 17, 19, 23

$2 \le MD \le 19$

Always add 1 to the number obtained from the table before counting. For example, if the critical value is 3, then count 4 values from the left and right.

For Exercises 21 through 25, find the confidence interval of the median, indicated in parentheses, for each set of data.

21. 3, 12, 15, 18, 16, 15, 22, 30, 25, 4, 6, 9 (95%)

22. 101, 115, 143, 106, 100, 142, 157, 163, 155, 141, 145, 153, 152, 147, 143, 115, 164, 160, 147, 150 (90%)

23. 8.2, 7.1, 6.3, 5.2, 4.8, 9.3, 7.2, 9.3, 4.5, 9.6, 7.8, 5.6, 4.7, 4.2, 9.5, 5.1 (98%)

24. 1, 8, 2, 6, 10, 15, 24, 33, 56, 41, 58, 54, 5, 3, 42, 31, 15, 65, 21 (99%)

25. 12, 15, 18, 14, 17, 19, 25, 32, 16, 47, 14, 23, 27, 42, 33, 35, 39, 41, 21, 19 (95%)

Technology Step by Step

EXCEL
Step by Step

The Sign Test

Excel does not have a procedure to conduct the sign test. However, you may conduct this test by using the MegaStat Add-in available online. If you have not installed this add-in, do so, following the instructions from the Chapter 1 Excel Step by Step.

1. Enter the data from Example 13–1 into column A of a new worksheet.
2. From the toolbar, select Add-Ins, **MegaStat>Nonparametric Tests>Sign Test**. *Note:* You may need to open MegaStat from the MegaStat.xls file on your computer's hard drive.

3. Type **A1:A20** for the Input range.

4. Type **40** for the Hypothesized value, and select the "not equal" Alternative.

5. Click [OK].

The *P*-value is 0.0075. Reject the null hypothesis.

MINITAB
Step by Step

The Sign Test

Example 13–1

Is the median number of patients seen by doctors 80 per day?

1. Enter the data into C1 of a MINITAB worksheet. Name the column MedCtrPatients.

2. Select **Stat>Nonparametrics>1-Sample Sign.**

   a) Double click C1 MedCtrPatients for the variable.
   b) Click on the ratio button for Test Median, then type 80 in the dialog box.
   c) Click [OK].

Sign Test for Median: MedCtrPatients

Sign test of median = 80.00 versus not = 80.00

	N	Below	Equal	Above	P	Median
MedCtrPatients	20	3	2	15	0.0075	83.50

The results are displayed in the session window. The sample median is 83.5. Since the *P*-value of 0.0075 is less than alpha, the null hypothesis is rejected.

The Paired-Sample Sign Test

1. Enter the data for Example 13–3 into a worksheet; only the Before and After columns are necessary. Calculate a column with the differences to begin the process.

2. Select **Calc>Calculator.**

3. Type **D** in the box for Store result in variable.

4. Move to the Expression box, then click on Before, the subtraction sign, and After. The completed entry is shown.

5. Click [OK].

MINITAB will calculate the differences and store them in the first available column with the name "D." Use the instructions for the Sign Test on the differences *D* with a hypothesized value of zero.

Sign Test for Median: D

Sign test of median = 0.00000 versus not = 0.00000

	N	Below	Equal	Above	P	Median
D	10	2	1	7	0.1797	1.000

The *P*-value is 0.1797. Do not reject the null hypothesis.

13–3 The Wilcoxon Rank Sum Test

OBJECTIVE 3

Test hypotheses, using the Wilcoxon rank sum test.

Interesting Fact

One in four married women now earns more than her husband.

The sign test does not consider the magnitude of the data. For example, whether a value is 1 point or 100 points below the median, it will receive a negative sign. And when you compare values in the pretest/posttest situation, the magnitude of the differences is not considered. The Wilcoxon tests consider differences in magnitudes by using ranks.

The two tests considered in this section and in Section 13–4 are the **Wilcoxon rank sum test,** which is used for independent samples, and the **Wilcoxon signed-rank test,** which is used for dependent samples. Both tests are used to compare distributions. The parametric equivalents are the z and t tests for independent samples (Sections 9–1 and 9–2) and the t test for dependent samples (Section 9–3). For the parametric tests, as stated previously, the samples must be selected from approximately normally distributed populations, but the assumptions for the Wilcoxon tests are different.

First let's look at the Wilcoxon rank sum test, sometimes called the Mann-Whitney test.

> The **Wilcoxon rank sum test** is a nonparametric test that uses ranks to determine if two independent samples were selected from populations that have the same distributions.

In the Wilcoxon rank sum test, the values of the data for both samples are combined and then ranked. If the null hypothesis is true—meaning that there is no difference in the population distributions—then the values in each sample should be ranked approximately the same. Therefore, when the ranks are summed for each sample, the sums should be approximately equal, and the null hypothesis will not be rejected. If there is a large difference in the sums of the ranks, then the distributions are not identical and the null hypothesis will be rejected.

There are two assumptions for this test.

Assumptions for the Wilcoxon Rank Sum Test

1. The samples are random and independent of one another.
2. The size of each sample must be greater than or equal to 10.

In this book, the assumptions will be stated in the exercises; however, when encountering statistics in other situations, you must check to see that these assumptions have been met before proceeding.

For the Wilcoxon rank sum test for independent samples, both sample sizes must be greater than or equal to 10. The formulas needed for the test are given next.

Formula for the Wilcoxon Rank Sum Test When Samples Are Independent

$$z = \frac{R - \mu_R}{\sigma_R}$$

where

$$\mu_R = \frac{n_1(n_1 + n_2 + 1)}{2}$$

$$\sigma_R = \sqrt{\frac{n_1 n_2(n_1 + n_2 + 1)}{12}}$$

R = sum of ranks for smaller sample size (n_1)
n_1 = smaller of sample sizes
n_2 = larger of sample sizes
$n_1 \geq 10$ and $n_2 \geq 10$

Note that if both samples are the same size, either size can be used as n_1.

Table E is used for the critical values.

The steps for the Wilcoxon rank sum test are given in the Procedure Table.

Procedure Table

Wilcoxon Rank Sum Test

Step 1 State the hypotheses and identify the claim.

Step 2 Find the critical value(s). Use Table E.

Step 3 Compute the test value.
    a. Combine the data from the two samples, arrange the combined data in order, and rank each value.
    b. Sum the ranks of the group with the smaller sample size. (*Note:* If both groups have the same sample size, either one can be used.)
    c. Use these formulas to find the test value.

$$\mu_R = \frac{n_1(n_1 + n_2 + 1)}{2}$$

$$\sigma_R = \sqrt{\frac{n_1 n_2(n_1 + n_2 + 1)}{12}}$$

$$z = \frac{R - \mu_R}{\sigma_R}$$

    where R is the sum of the ranks of the data in the smaller sample and n_1 and n_2 are each greater than or equal to 10.

Step 4 Make the decision.

Step 5 Summarize the results.

Example 13–4 illustrates the Wilcoxon rank sum test for independent samples.

EXAMPLE 13–4   Times to Complete an Obstacle Course

Two independent random samples of army and marine recruits are selected, and the time in minutes it takes each recruit to complete an obstacle course is recorded, as shown in the table. At $\alpha = 0.05$, is there a difference in the times it takes the recruits to complete the course?

Army	15	18	16	17	13	22	24	17	19	21	26	28
Marines	14	9	16	19	10	12	11	8	15	18	25	

SOLUTION

Step 1 State the hypotheses and identify the claim.

    H_0: There is no difference in the times it takes the recruits to complete the obstacle course.

    H_1: There is a difference in the times it takes the recruits to complete the obstacle course (claim).

Step 2 Find the critical value. Since $\alpha = 0.05$ and this test is a two-tailed test, use the critical values of $+1.96$ and -1.96 from Table E.

Step 3 Compute the test value.

    a. Combine the data from the two samples, arrange the combined data in ascending order, and rank each value. Be sure to indicate the group.

Time	8	9	10	11	12	13	14	15	15	16	16	17
Group	M	M	M	M	M	A	M	A	M	A	M	A
Rank	1	2	3	4	5	6	7	8.5	8.5	10.5	10.5	12.5

Time	17	18	18	19	19	21	22	24	25	26	28
Group	A	M	A	A	M	A	A	A	M	A	A
Rank	12.5	14.5	14.5	16.5	16.5	18	19	20	21	22	23

b. Sum the ranks of the group with the smaller sample size. (*Note:* If both groups have the same sample size, either one can be used.) In this case, the sample size for the marines is smaller.

$$R = 1 + 2 + 3 + 4 + 5 + 7 + 8.5 + 10.5 + 14.5 + 16.5 + 21$$
$$= 93$$

c. Substitute in the formulas to find the test value.

$$\mu_R = \frac{n_1(n_1 + n_2 + 1)}{2} = \frac{(11)(11 + 12 + 1)}{2} = 132$$

$$\sigma_R = \sqrt{\frac{n_1 n_2(n_1 + n_2 + 1)}{12}} = \sqrt{\frac{(11)(12)(11 + 12 + 1)}{12}}$$

$$= \sqrt{264} = 16.2$$

$$z = \frac{R - \mu_R}{\sigma_R} = \frac{93 - 132}{16.2} = -2.41$$

Step 4 Make the decision. The decision is to reject the null hypothesis, since $-2.41 < -1.96$.

Step 5 Summarize the results. There is enough evidence to support the claim that there is a difference in the times it takes the recruits to complete the course.

The *P*-values can be used for Example 13–4. The *P*-value for $z = -2.41$ is 0.0080, and since this is a two-tailed test, $2(0.0080) = 0.016$. Hence, the null hypothesis is rejected at $\alpha = 0.05$.

⬗ Applying the Concepts 13–3

School Lunch

A nutritionist decided to see if there was a difference in the number of calories served for lunch in elementary and secondary schools. She selected a random sample of eight elementary schools and another random sample of eight secondary schools in Pennsylvania. The data are shown.

Elementary	Secondary
648	694
589	730
625	750
595	810
789	860
727	702
702	657
564	761

1. Are the samples independent or dependent?

2. What are the hypotheses?

3. What nonparametric test would you use to test the claim?

4. What critical value would you use?

5. What is the test value?

6. What is your decision?

7. What is the corresponding parametric test?

8. What assumption would you need to meet to use the parametric test?

9. If this assumption were not met, would the parametric test yield the same results?

See page 740 for the answers.

Exercises 13–3

1. What are the minimum sample sizes for the Wilcoxon rank sum test?

2. What is the parametric equivalent test for the Wilcoxon rank sum test?

For Exercises 3 through 12, use the Wilcoxon rank sum test. Assume that the samples are independent. Also perform each of these steps.

   a. State the hypotheses and identify the claim.
   b. Find the critical value(s).
   c. Compute the test value.
   d. Make the decision.
   e. Summarize the results.

Use the traditional method of hypothesis testing unless otherwise specified.

3. **Speed Skating Times** The 2010 women's 1000-meter speed skating winning time was 1:16.56, posted by Christine Nesbitt of Canada. In preparation for the 2014 Winter Olympics in Sochi, several randomly selected students from two different universities posted the following times (rounded to the nearest second). Test the claim that there is no difference in times between universities at $\alpha = 0.05$.

UA	2:05	2:15	1:58	1:42	2:01	1:40	1:39	2:20	1:51	2:03
UB	2:10	2:06	1:35	1:48	1:38	2:00	2:15	2:14	2:27	1:48

4. **Lengths of Prison Sentences** A random sample of men and women in prison was asked to give the length of sentence each received for a certain type of crime. At $\alpha = 0.05$, test the claim that there is no difference in the sentence received by each gender. The data (in months) are shown here.

Males	8	12	6	14	22	27	32	24	26
Females	7	5	2	3	21	26	30	9	4

Males	19	15	13
Females	17	23	12	11	16

5. **Technology Proficiency Test** The following are scores from a technology proficiency test required of all new incoming students at a particular college. Use the Wilcoxon rank sum test to see if there is a difference in scores between randomly selected freshmen and randomly selected transfer students at the 0.05 level of significance.

Freshmen	40	32	40	32	47	39	38	39	29	35	30
Transfers	38	43	35	45	37	36	36	33	46	44	41

6. **Lifetimes of Handheld Video Games** To test the claim that there is no difference in the lifetimes of two brands of handheld video games, a researcher selects a random sample of 11 video games of each brand. The lifetimes (in months) of each brand are shown. At $\alpha = 0.01$, can the researcher conclude that there is a difference in the distributions of lifetimes for the two brands?

Brand A	42	34	39	42	22	47	51	34	41	39	28
Brand B	29	39	38	43	45	49	53	38	44	43	32

7. **Stopping Distances of Automobiles** A researcher wishes to see if the stopping distance for midsize automobiles is different from the stopping distance for compact automobiles at a speed of 70 miles per hour. The data are shown for two random samples. At $\alpha = 0.10$, test the claim that the stopping distances are the same. If one of your safety concerns is stopping distance, will it make a difference which type of automobile you purchase?

Automobile	1	2	3	4	5	6	7	8	9	10
Midsize	188	190	195	192	186	194	188	187	214	203
Compact	200	211	206	297	198	204	218	212	196	193

Source: Based on information from the National Highway Traffic Safety Administration.

8. **Winning Baseball Games** For the years 1970–1993 the National League (NL) and the American League (AL) (major league baseball) were each divided into two divisions: East and West. Below are random samples of the number of games won by each league's Eastern

Division. At $\alpha = 0.05$, is there sufficient evidence to conclude a difference in the number of wins?

NL	89	96	88	101	90	91	92	96	108	100	95
AL	108	86	91	97	100	102	95	104	95	89	88	101

Source: *World Almanac.*

9. **Hunting Accidents** A game commissioner wishes to see if the number of hunting accidents in counties in western Pennsylvania is different from the number of hunting accidents in counties in eastern Pennsylvania. Random samples of counties from the two regions are selected, and the numbers of hunting accidents are shown. At $\alpha = 0.05$, is there a difference in the number of accidents in the two areas? If so, give a possible reason for the difference.

Western Pa.	10	21	11	11	9	17	13	8	15	17
Eastern Pa.	14	3	7	13	11	2	8	5	5	6

Source: Pennsylvania Game Commission.

10. **Medical School Enrollments** Random samples of enrollments from medical schools that specialize in research and in primary care are listed. At $\alpha = 0.05$, can it be concluded that there is a difference?

Research	474 577 605 663 813 443 565 696 692 217
Primary care	783 546 442 662 605 474 587 555 427 320 293

Source: *U.S. News & World Report Best Graduate Schools.*

11. **Speed of Pain Relievers** Volunteers were randomly assigned to one of two groups to test the speed with which a pain reliever brought relief. One group took the standard dose of extra-strength acetaminophen (group A) while the other group (group N) took a newly approved pain-relieving drug. The number of minutes until symptoms abated is listed for each member of each group. At $\alpha = 0.05$, can it be concluded that there is a difference in time until pain is relieved?

Group A	15	20	12	20	17	14	15	17	18	11
Group N	7	14	13	11	10	16	12	9	10	9

12. **Student Participation in a Blood Drive** Students in Greek organizations at schools throughout the country sent volunteers to a yearly blood drive. The numbers from each randomly selected participating school are listed. Test the claim that there is no difference in the number of students participating from fraternities and sororities at $\alpha = 0.10$.

Fraternities	4, 5, 10, 7, 7, 15, 12, 11, 13, 15, 12, 12
Sororities	3, 5, 6, 7, 4, 7, 10, 9, 9, 14

Technology   Step by Step

EXCEL
Step by Step

The Wilcoxon Mann-Whitney Test

Excel does not have a procedure to conduct the Mann-Whitney rank sum test. However, you may conduct this test by using the MegaStat Add-in available online. If you have not installed this add-in, do so, following the instructions from the Chapter 1 Excel Step by Step.

1. Enter the data from Example 13–4 into columns A and B of a new worksheet.

2. From the toolbar, select Add-Ins, **MegaStat>Nonparametric Tests>Wilcoxon-Mann/ Whitney Test**. *Note:* You may need to open MegaStat from the MegaStat.xls file on your computer's hard drive.

3. Type **A1:A12** in the box for Group 1.

4. Type **B1:B11** in the box for Group 2.

5. Check the option labeled **Correct for ties**, and select the "not equal" Alternative.

6. Click [OK].

Wilcoxon Mann-Whitney Test

n	Sum of ranks	
12	183	Group 1
11	93	Group 2
23	276	Total

144.00 Expected value
16.23 Standard deviation
2.37 z, corrected for ties
0.0177 *P*-value (two-tailed)

The *P*-value is 0.0177. Reject the null hypothesis.

MINITAB
Step by Step

Wilcoxon Rank Sum Test (Mann-Whitney)

1. Enter the data for Example 13–4 into two columns of a worksheet.

2. Name the columns **Army** and **Marines.**

3. Select **Stat>Nonparametric>Mann-Whitney.**

4. Double-click Army for the First Sample.

5. Double-click Marines for the Second Sample.

6. Click [OK].

Mann-Whitney Test and CI: Army, Marines

	N	Median
Army	12	18.500
Marines	11	14.000

Point estimate for ETA1−ETA2 is 6.000
95.5 Percent CI for ETA1−ETA2 is (1.003, 9.998)
W = 183.0
Test of ETA1 = ETA2 vs ETA1 not = ETA2 is significant at 0.0178
The test is significant at 0.0177 (adjusted for ties)

The P-value for the test is 0.0177. Reject the null hypothesis. There is a significant difference in the times it takes the recruits to complete the course.

13–4   The Wilcoxon Signed-Rank Test

OBJECTIVE 4

Test hypotheses, using the signed-rank test.

When the samples are dependent, as they would be in a before-and-after test using the same subjects, the Wilcoxon signed-rank test can be used in place of the t test for dependent samples. Again, this test does not require the condition of normality.

> The **Wilcoxon signed-rank test** is a nonparametric test used to test whether two dependent samples have been selected from two populations having the same distributions.

However, the following assumptions for the Wilcoxon signed-rank test must be met before it can be used.

Assumptions for the Wilcoxon Signed-Rank Test

1. The paired data have been obtained from a random sample.
2. The population of differences has a distribution that is approximately symmetric.

In this book, the assumptions will be stated in the exercises; however, when encountering statistics in other situations, you must check to see that these assumptions have been met before proceeding.

Table K in Appendix A is used for the critical values when $n \leq 30$. Use the column for the critical value along with the row for the value of n. See Example 13–5.

To find the test value for the Wilcoxon signed-rank test, denoted by w_s, when $n \leq 30$, rank the absolute values of the differences of each pair of data values. Assign either a $+$ or a $-$ sign to each rank according to the original value of the difference. Then sum the positive ranks and the negative ranks separately. Finally, when $n \leq 30$, select the smaller of the absolute value of the sums as the test value w_s.

When $n > 30$, the normal distribution can be used to approximate the Wilcoxon distribution. The same critical values from Table E used for the z test for specific α values are used. The formula is

$$z = \frac{w_s - \dfrac{n(n+1)}{4}}{\sqrt{\dfrac{n(n+1)(2n+1)}{24}}}$$

where

n = number of pairs where difference is not 0
w_s = smaller sum in absolute value of signed ranks

The steps for the Wilcoxon signed-rank test are given in the Procedure Table.

Procedure Table

Wilcoxon Signed-Rank Test

Step 1 State the hypotheses and identify the claim.

Step 2 Find the critical value from Table K when $n \le 30$ and from Table E when $n > 30$.

Step 3 Compute the test value.

When $n \le 30$:

a. Make a table, as shown.

Before, X_B	After, X_A	Difference $D = X_B - X_A$	Absolute value $\lvert D \rvert$	Rank	Signed rank

b. Find the differences (before − after), denoted by $X_B - X_A$, and place the values in the Difference column.

c. Find the absolute value of each difference, and place the results in the Absolute value column.

d. Rank each absolute value from lowest to highest, and place the rankings in the Rank column.

e. Give each rank a positive or negative sign, according to the sign in the Difference column.

f. Find the sum of the positive ranks and the sum of the negative ranks separately.

g. Select the smaller of the absolute values of the sums, and use this absolute value as the test value w_s.

When $n > 30$, use Table E and the test value

$$z = \frac{w_s - \dfrac{n(n+1)}{4}}{\sqrt{\dfrac{n(n+1)(2n+1)}{24}}}$$

where

n = number of pairs where difference is not 0
w_s = smaller sum in absolute value of signed ranks

Step 4 Make the decision. Reject the null hypothesis if the test value is less than or equal to the critical value.

Step 5 Summarize the results.

The procedure for this test is shown in Example 13–5.

EXAMPLE 13–5   Shoplifting Incidents

In a large department store, the owner wishes to see whether the number of shoplifting incidents per day will change if the number of uniformed security officers is doubled. A random sample of 7 days before security is increased and 7 days after the increase shows the number of shoplifting incidents.

Day	Number of shoplifting incidents	
	Before	**After**
Monday	7	5
Tuesday	2	3
Wednesday	3	4
Thursday	6	3
Friday	5	1
Saturday	8	6
Sunday	12	4

Is there enough evidence to support the claim, at $\alpha = 0.05$, that there is a difference in the number of shoplifting incidents before and after the increase in security?

SOLUTION

Step 1   State the hypotheses and identify the claim.

H_0: There is no difference in the number of shoplifting incidents before and after the increase in security.

H_1: There is a difference in the number of shoplifting incidents before and after the increase in security (claim).

Step 2   Find the critical value from Table K because $n \leq 30$. Since $n = 7$ and $\alpha = 0.05$ for this two-tailed test, the critical value is 2. See Figure 13–2.

FIGURE 13–2

Finding the Critical Value in Table K for Example 13–5

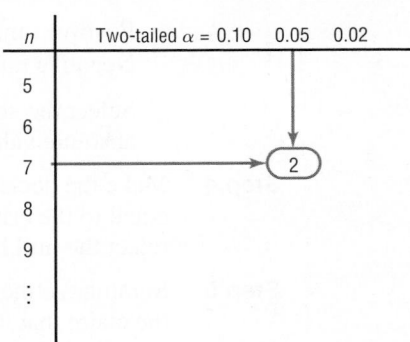

Step 3   Find the test value.

a. Make a table as shown.

Day	Before, X_B	After, X_A	Difference $D = X_B - X_A$	Absolute value $\lvert D \rvert$	Rank	Signed rank
Mon.	7	5				
Tues.	2	3				
Wed.	3	4				
Thurs.	6	3				
Fri.	5	1				
Sat.	8	6				
Sun.	12	4				

b. Find the differences (before minus after), and place the values in the Difference column.

$$7 - 5 = 2 \qquad 6 - 3 = 3 \qquad 8 - 6 = 2$$
$$2 - 3 = -1 \qquad 5 - 1 = 4 \qquad 12 - 4 = 8$$
$$3 - 4 = -1$$

c. Find the absolute value of each difference, and place the results in the Absolute value column. (*Note:* The absolute value of any number except 0 is the positive value of the number. Any differences of 0 should be ignored.)

$$|2| = 2 \qquad |3| = 3 \qquad |2| = 2$$
$$|-1| = 1 \qquad |4| = 4 \qquad |8| = 8$$
$$|-1| = 1$$

d. Rank each absolute value from lowest to highest, and place the rankings in the Rank column. In the case of a tie, assign the values that rank plus 0.5.

Value	2	1	1	3	4	2	8
Rank	3.5	1.5	1.5	5	6	3.5	7

e. Give each rank a plus or minus sign, according to the sign in the Difference column. The completed table is shown here.

Day	Before, X_B	After, X_A	Difference $D = X_B - X_A$	Absolute value $|D|$	Rank	Signed rank
Mon.	7	5	2	2	3.5	+3.5
Tues.	2	3	−1	1	1.5	−1.5
Wed.	3	4	−1	1	1.5	−1.5
Thurs.	6	3	3	3	5	+5
Fri.	5	1	4	4	6	+6
Sat.	8	6	2	2	3.5	+3.5
Sun.	12	4	8	8	7	+7

f. Find the sum of the positive ranks and the sum of the negative ranks separately.

Positive rank sum $(+3.5) + (+5) + (+6) + (+3.5) + (+7) = +25$
Negative rank sum $(-1.5) + (-1.5)$ $= -3$

g. Select the smaller of the absolute values of the sums ($|-3|$), and use this absolute value as the test value w_s. In this case, $w_s = |-3| = 3$.

Step 4 Make the decision. Reject the null hypothesis if the test value is less than or equal to the critical value. In this case, $3 > 2$; hence, the decision is to not reject the null hypothesis.

Step 5 Summarize the results. There is not enough evidence at $\alpha = 0.05$ to support the claim that there is a difference in the number of shoplifting incidents before and after the increase in security. Hence, the security increase probably made no difference in the number of shoplifting incidents.

The rationale behind the signed-rank test can be explained by a diet example. If the diet is working, then the majority of the postweights will be smaller than the preweights. When the postweights are subtracted from the preweights, the majority of the signs will be positive, and the absolute value of the sum of the negative ranks will be small. This sum will probably be smaller than the critical value obtained from Table K, and the null hypothesis will be rejected. On the other hand, if the diet does not work, some people will gain weight, other people will lose weight, and still other people will remain about the same weight. In this case, the sum of the positive ranks and the absolute value of the sum of the negative ranks will be approximately equal and will be about one-half of the sum of the absolute value of all the ranks. In this case, the smaller of the absolute values of the two sums will still be larger than the critical value obtained from Table K, and the null hypothesis will not be rejected.

≡ Applying the Concepts 13–4

Pain Medication

A researcher decides to see how effective a pain medication is. Eight randomly selected subjects were asked to determine the severity of their pain by using a scale of 1 to 10, with 1 being very minor and 10 being very severe. Then each was given the medication, and after 1 hour, they were asked to rate the severity of their pain, using the same scale.

Subject	1	2	3	4	5	6	7	8
Before	8	6	2	3	4	6	2	7
After	6	5	3	1	2	6	1	6

1. What is the purpose of the study?
2. Are the samples independent or dependent?
3. What are the hypotheses?
4. What nonparametric test could be used to test the claim?
5. What significance level would you use?
6. What is your decision?
7. What parametric test could you use?
8. Would the results be the same?

See page 740 for the answers.

≡ Exercises 13–4

1. What is the parametric equivalent test for the Wilcoxon signed-rank test?

2. What is the difference between the Wilcoxon rank sum test and the Wilcoxon signed-rank test?

For Exercises 3 and 4, find the sum of the signed ranks. Assume that the samples are dependent. State which sum is used as the test value.

3.
Pretest	108	97	115	162	156	105	153
Posttest	110	97	103	168	143	112	141

4.
Pretest	65	103	79	92	72	91	76	95
Posttest	72	105	64	95	78	92	76	93

For Exercises 5 through 8, use Table K to determine whether the null hypothesis should be rejected.

5. $w_s = 18$, $n = 15$, $\alpha = 0.02$, two-tailed test

6. $w_s = 53$, $n = 20$, $\alpha = 0.05$, two-tailed test

7. $w_s = 102$, $n = 28$, $\alpha = 0.01$, one-tailed test

8. $w_s = 33$, $n = 18$, $\alpha = 0.01$, two-tailed test

For Exercises 9–14, use the Wilcoxon signed-rank test to test each hypothesis.

9. **Drug Prices** Eight drugs were randomly selected, and the prices for the human doses and the animal doses for the same amounts were compared. At $\alpha = 0.05$, can it be concluded that the prices for the animal doses are significantly less than the prices for the human doses? If the null hypothesis is rejected, give one reason why animal doses might cost less than human doses.

Human dose	0.67	0.64	1.20	0.51	0.87	0.74	0.50	1.22
Animal dose	0.13	0.18	0.42	0.25	0.57	0.57	0.49	1.28

Source: House Committee on Government Reform.

10. **Property Assessments** Test the hypothesis that the randomly selected assessed values have changed between 2006 and 2010. Use $\alpha = 0.05$. Do you think land values in a large city would be normally distributed?

Ward	A	B	C	D	E	F	G	H	I	J	K
2006	184	414	22	99	116	49	24	50	282	25	141
2010	161	382	22	190	120	52	28	50	297	40	148

11. **Weight Loss Through Diet** Eight randomly selected subjects were weighed before and after a new three-week "healthy" diet. At the 0.05 level of significance, can it be concluded that a difference in weight resulted? (Weights are in pounds.)

Subject	A	B	C	D	E	F	G	H
Before	150	195	188	197	204	175	160	180
After	152	190	185	191	200	170	162	179

12. Legal Costs for School Districts A random sample of legal costs (in thousands of dollars) for school districts for two recent consecutive years is shown. At $\alpha = 0.05$, is there a difference in the costs?

Year 1	108	36	65	108	87	94	10	40
Year 2	138	28	67	181	97	126	18	67

Source: *Pittsburgh Tribune-Review.*

13. Drug Prices A researcher wishes to compare the prices for randomly selected prescription drugs in the United States with those in Canada. The same drugs and dosages were compared in each country. At $\alpha = 0.05$, can it be concluded that the drugs in Canada are cheaper?

Drug	1	2	3	4	5	6
United States	3.31	2.27	2.54	3.13	23.40	3.16
Canada	1.47	1.07	1.34	1.34	21.44	1.47

Drug	7	8	9	10
United States	1.98	5.27	1.96	1.11
Canada	1.07	3.39	2.22	1.13

Source: IMS Health and other sources.

14. Bowling Scores Eight randomly selected volunteers at a bowling alley were asked to bowl three games and pick their best score. They were then given a bowling ball made of a new composite material and were allowed to practice with the ball as much as they wanted. The next day they each bowled three games with the new ball and picked their best score. At the 0.05 level of significance, did scores improve?

Bowler	A	B	C	D	E	F	G	H
Day 1	141	176	178	174	135	190	182	141
Day 2	158	144	135	153	195	151	151	183

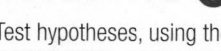 **Technology**   **Step by Step**

MINITAB

Step by Step

Wilcoxon Signed-Rank Test

Test the median value for the differences of two dependent samples. Use Example 13–5.

1. Enter the data into two columns of a worksheet. Name the columns **Before** and **After.**

2. Calculate the differences, using **Calc>Calculator.**

3. Type **D** in the box for Store result in variable.

4. In the expression box, type **Before − After.**

5. Click [OK].

6. Select **Stat>Nonparametric> 1-Sample Wilcoxon.**

7. Select D for the Variable.

8. Click on Test median. The value should be 0.

9. Click [OK].

Wilcoxon Signed-Rank Test: D

Test of median = 0.000000 versus median not = 0.000000

	N	N for Test	Wilcoxon Statistic	P	Estimated Median
D	7	7	25.0	0.076	2.250

The *P*-value of the test is 0.076. Do not reject the null hypothesis.

13–5 The Kruskal-Wallis Test

OBJECTIVE 5

Test hypotheses, using the Kruskal-Wallis test.

The analysis of variance uses the *F* test to compare the means of three or more populations. The assumptions for the ANOVA test are that the populations are normally distributed and that the population variances are equal. When these assumptions cannot be met, the nonparametric **Kruskal-Wallis test,** sometimes called the *H test,* can be used to compare three or more means.

The **Kruskal-Wallis test** is a nonparametric test that is used to determine whether three or more samples came from populations with the same distributions.

The following assumptions must be met to use the Kruskal-Wallis test.

Assumptions for the Kruskal-Wallis Test

1. There are at least three random samples.
2. The size of each sample must be at least 5.

In this book, the assumptions will be stated in the exercises; however, when encountering statistics in other situations, you must check to see that these assumptions have been met before proceeding.

In this test, each sample size must be 5 or more. In these situations, the distribution can be approximated by the chi-square distribution with $k - 1$ degrees of freedom, where $k =$ number of groups. This test also uses ranks. The formula for the test is given next.

In the Kruskal-Wallis test, you consider all the data values as a group and then rank them. Next, the ranks are separated and the H formula is computed. This formula approximates the variance of the ranks. If the samples are from different populations, the sums of the ranks will be different and the H value will be large; hence, the null hypothesis will be rejected if the H value is large enough. If the samples are from the same population, the sums of the ranks will be approximately the same and the H value will be small; therefore, the null hypothesis will not be rejected. This test is always a right-tailed test. The chi-square table, Table G, with d.f. $= k - 1$, should be used for critical values.

Since the test is right-tailed, the null hypothesis will be rejected if the test value is greater than or equal to the critical value.

Formula for the Kruskal-Wallis Test

$$H = \frac{12}{N(N + 1)}\left(\frac{R_1^2}{n_1} + \frac{R_2^2}{n_2} + \cdots + \frac{R_k^2}{n_k}\right) - 3(N + 1)$$

where
  $R_1 =$ sum of ranks of sample 1
  $n_1 =$ size of sample 1
  $R_2 =$ sum of ranks of sample 2
  $n_2 =$ size of sample 2
    .
    .
    .
  $R_k =$ sum of ranks of sample k
  $n_k =$ size of sample k
  $N = n_1 + n_2 + \cdots + n_k$
  $k =$ number of samples

Procedure Table

Kruskal-Wallis Test

Step 1   State the hypotheses and identify the claim.

Step 2   Find the critical value. Use the chi-square table, Table G, with d.f. $= k - 1$ ($k =$ number of groups).

Step 3   Compute the test value.

   a. Arrange the data from lowest to highest and rank each value.

b. Find the sum of the ranks of each group.

c. Substitute in the formula.

$$H = \frac{12}{N(N+1)}\left(\frac{R_1^2}{n_1} + \frac{R_2^2}{n_2} + \cdots + \frac{R_k^2}{n_k}\right) - 3(N+1)$$

where

$N = n_1 + n_2 + \cdots + n_k$
R_k = sum of ranks for kth group
k = number of groups

Step 4   Make the decision.

Step 5   Summarize the results.

Example 13–6 illustrates the procedure for conducting the Kruskal-Wallis test.

EXAMPLE 13–6   Hospital Infections

A researcher wishes to see if the total number of infections that occurred in three groups of randomly selected hospitals is the same. The data are shown in the table. At $\alpha = 0.05$, is there enough evidence to reject the claim that the number of infections in the three groups of hospitals is the same?

Group A	Group B	Group C
557	476	105
315	232	110
920	80	167
178	116	155

Source: Pennsylvania Health Care Cost Containment Council.

SOLUTION

Step 1   State the hypotheses and identify the claim.

H_0: There is no difference in the number of infections in the three groups of hospitals (claim).

H_1: There is a difference in the number of infections in the three groups of hospitals.

Step 2   Find the critical value. Use the chi-square table (Table G) with d.f. $= k - 1$, where k = the number of groups. With $\alpha = 0.05$ and d.f. $= 3 - 1 = 2$, the critical value is 5.991.

Step 3   Compute the test value.

a. Arrange all the data from the lowest value to the highest value and rank each value.

Amount	Group	Rank
80	B	1
105	C	2
110	C	3
116	B	4
155	C	5
167	C	6
178	A	7
232	B	8
315	A	9
476	B	10
557	A	11
920	A	12

b. Find the sum of the ranks for each group.

$$
\begin{array}{lc}
\text{Group A} & 7 + 9 + 11 + 12 = 39 \\
\text{Group B} & 1 + 4 + 8 + 10 = 23 \\
\text{Group C} & 2 + 3 + 5 + 6 = 16
\end{array}
$$

c. Substitute in the formula.

$$
H = \frac{12}{N(N+1)}\left(\frac{R_1^2}{n_1} + \frac{R_2^2}{n_2} + \frac{R_3^2}{n_3}\right) - 3(N+1)
$$

where

$$
N = 12 \qquad R_1 = 39 \qquad R_2 = 23 \qquad R_3 = 16
$$
$$
n_1 = n_2 = n_3 = 4
$$

Therefore,

$$
H = \frac{12}{12(12+1)}\left(\frac{39^2}{4} + \frac{23^2}{4} + \frac{16^2}{4}\right) - 3(12+1)
$$
$$
= 5.346
$$

Step 4 Make the decision. Since the test value of 5.346 is less than the critical value of 5.991, the decision is to not reject the null hypothesis.

Step 5 Summarize the results. There is not enough evidence to reject the claim that there is no difference in the number of infections in the groups of hospitals. Hence, the differences are not significant at $\alpha = 0.05$.

Applying the Concepts 13–5

Heights of Waterfalls

You are doing research for an article on the waterfalls on our planet. You want to make a statement about the heights of waterfalls on three continents. Three random samples of waterfall heights (in feet) are shown.

North America	Africa	Asia
600	406	330
1200	508	830
182	630	614
620	726	1100
1170	480	885
442	2014	330

1. What questions are you trying to answer?

2. What nonparametric test would you use to find the answer?

3. What are the hypotheses?

4. Select a significance level and run the test. What is the H value?

5. What is your conclusion?

6. What is the corresponding parametric test?

7. What assumptions would need to be made to conduct the corresponding parametric test?

See page 740 for the answers.

☰ Exercises 13–5

For Exercises 1 through 12, use the Kruskal-Wallis test and perform these steps.

   a. State the hypotheses and identify the claim.
   b. Find the critical value.
   c. Compute the test value.
   d. Make the decision.
   e. Summarize the results.

Use the traditional method of hypothesis testing unless otherwise specified.

1. Calories in Cereals Random samples of four different cereals show the following numbers of calories for the suggested serving size of each brand. At $\alpha = 0.05$, is there a difference in the number of calories for the different brands?

Brand A	Brand B	Brand C	Brand D
112	110	109	106
120	118	116	122
135	123	125	130
125	128	130	117
108	102	128	116
121	101	132	114

2. Mathematics Literacy Scores Through the Organization for Economic Cooperation and Development (OECD), 15-year-olds are tested in member countries in mathematics, reading, and science literacy. Listed are randomly selected total mathematics literacy scores (i.e., both genders) for selected countries in different parts of the world. Test, using the Kruskal-Wallis test, to see if there is a difference in means at $\alpha = 0.05$.

Western Hemisphere	Europe	Eastern Asia
527	520	523
406	510	547
474	513	547
381	548	391
411	496	549

Source: www.nces.ed.gov

3. Local Crimes The numbers of local crimes reported during a week for randomly selected weeks in the newspaper's police report for three towns are listed having been selected randomly from several day's editions. At $\alpha = 0.01$, is there a difference in the number of crimes committed in each town?

Town A	Town B	Town C
20	18	5
15	9	8
14	11	13
7	2	17
12	1	4
10		16

4. Sodium Content of Microwave Dinners Three brands of microwave dinners were advertised as low in sodium.

Random samples of the three different brands show the following milligrams of sodium. At $\alpha = 0.05$, is there a difference in the amount of sodium among the brands?

Brand A	Brand B	Brand C
810	917	893
702	912	790
853	952	603
703	958	744
892	893	623
732		743
713		609
613		

5. Unemployment Benefits In Chapter 12, we did an exercise while assuming that the populations were normally distributed and that the population variances were equal. Assume that this is not the case. Using the Kruskal-Wallis test, is the outcome affected? Do you think unemployment benefits are normally distributed? Test for a difference in means at $\alpha = 0.05$.

Florida	Pennsylvania	Maine
200	300	250
187	350	195
192	295	275
235	362	260
260	280	220
175	340	290

6. Job Offers for Chemical Engineers A recent study recorded the number of job offers received by randomly selected, newly graduated chemical engineers at three colleges. The data are shown here. At $\alpha = 0.05$, is there a difference in the average number of job offers received by the graduates at the three colleges?

College A	College B	College C
6	2	10
8	1	12
7	0	9
5	3	13
6	6	4

7. Expenditures for Pupils The expenditures in dollars per pupil for randomly selected states in three sections of the country are listed below. At $\alpha = 0.05$, can it be concluded that there is a difference in spending between regions?

Eastern third	Middle third	Western third
6701	9854	7584
6708	8414	5474
9186	7279	6622
6786	7311	9673
9261	6947	7353

Source: *New York Times Almanac.*

8. Printer Costs An electronics store manager wishes to compare the costs (in dollars) of three types of computer printers. The randomly selected data are shown. At $\alpha = 0.05$, can it be concluded that there is a difference in the prices? Based on your answer, do you think that a certain type of printer generally costs more than the other types?

Inkjet printers	Multifunction printers	Laser printers
149	98	192
199	119	159
249	149	198
239	249	198
99	99	229
79	199	

9. Number of Crimes per Week In a large city, the number of crimes per week in five precincts is recorded for five randomly selected weeks. The data are shown here. At $\alpha = 0.01$, is there a difference in the number of crimes?

Precinct 1	Precinct 2	Precinct 3	Precinct 4	Precinct 5
105	87	74	56	103
108	86	83	43	98
99	91	78	52	94
97	93	74	58	89
92	82	60	62	88

10. Amounts of Caffeine in Beverages The amounts of caffeine in randomly selected regular (small) servings of assorted beverages are listed. If someone wants to limit caffeine intake, does it really matter which beverage she or he chooses? Is there a difference in caffeine content at $\alpha = 0.05$?

Teas	Coffees	Colas
70	120	35
40	80	48
30	160	55
25	90	43
40	140	42

Source: *Doctor's Pocket Calorie, Fat & Carbohydrate Counter.*

11. Maximum Speeds of Animals A human is said to be able to reach a maximum speed of 27.89 miles per hour. The maximum speeds of various randomly selected types of other animals are listed below. Based on these particular groupings, is there evidence of a difference in speeds? Use the 0.05 level of significance.

Predatory mammals	Deerlike animals	Domestic animals
70	50	47.5
50	35	39.35
43	32	35
42	30	30
40	61	11

12. Prices of Vitamin/Mineral Supplements The prices for 30-count packages of randomly selected store-brand vitamin/mineral supplements are listed from three different sources. At the 0.01 level of significance, can a difference in prices be concluded?

Grocery store	Drugstore	Discount store
6.79	7.69	7.49
6.09	8.19	6.89
5.49	6.19	7.69
7.99	5.15	7.29
6.10	6.14	4.95

≡ Technology   Step by Step

EXCEL

Step by Step

The Kruskal-Wallis Test

Excel does not have a procedure to conduct the Kruskal-Wallis test. However, you may conduct this test by using the MegaStat Add-in available online. If you have not installed this add-in, do so, following the instructions from the Chapter 1 Excel Step by Step.

Example: Milliequivalents of Potassium in Breakfast Drinks

A researcher tests three different brands of breakfast drinks to see how many milliequivalents of potassium per quart each contains. These data are obtained.

Brand A	Brand B	Brand C
4.7	5.3	6.3
3.2	6.4	8.2
5.1	7.3	6.2
5.2	6.8	7.1
5.0	7.2	6.6

At $\alpha = 0.05$, is there enough evidence to reject the hypothesis that all brands contain the same amount of potassium?

1. Enter the data from the example into columns A, B, and C of a new worksheet.
2. From the toolbar, select Add-Ins, **MegaStat>Nonparametric Tests>Kruskal-Wallis Test.** *Note:* You may need to open MegaStat from the MegaStat.xls file on your computer's hard drive.
3. Type **A1:C5** in the box for Input range.
4. Check the option labeled Correct for ties, and select the "not equal" Alternative.
5. Click [OK].

Kruskal-Wallis Test

Median	n	Avg. rank	
5.00	5	3.00	Group 1
6.80	5	10.60	Group 2
6.60	5	10.40	Group 3
6.30	15		Total

9.380	H
2	d.f.
0.0092	P-value

Multiple comparison values for avg. ranks
6.77(0.05)   8.30(0.01)

The P-value is 0.0092. Reject the null hypothesis.

MINITAB
Step by Step

Kruskal-Wallis Test

Hospital Infections

Is the number of infections that occurred in three groups of hospitals the same?

1. Enter all of the infection data into C1 of a MINITAB worksheet. Name the column Infections.
2. Enter the group identifiers A, B, or C into C2. Name the column **Group.** The data must be entered in this stacked format.
3. Select **Stat>Nonparametrics>Kruskal-Wallis.**
   a) Double-click C1 **Infections** for the response variable.
   b) Double-click C2 **Group** for the factor variable.
   c) Click [OK].

↓	C1	C2-T
	Infections	Group
1	557	A
2	315	A
3	920	A
4	476	B
5	232	B
6	80	B
7	116	B
8	105	C
9	110	C
10	167	C
11	155	C
12		

Kruskal-Wallis Test: Infections versus Group
Kruskal-Wallis Test on Infections

Group	N	Median	Ave Rank	Z
A	3	557.0	9.7	2.25
B	4	174.0	5.3	−0.57
C	4	132.5	4.0	−1.51
Overall	11		6.0	

$H = 5.33$ $DF = 2$ $P = 0.070$

The null hypothesis is not rejected since the P-value is greater than alpha.

13–6 The Spearman Rank Correlation Coefficient and the Runs Test

Historical Note

Charles Spearman, who was a student of Karl Pearson, developed the Spearman rank correlation in the early 1900s. Other nonparametric statistical methods were also devised around this time.

The techniques of regression and correlation were explained in Chapter 10. To determine whether two variables are linearly related, you use the Pearson product moment correlation coefficient. Its values range from $+1$ to -1. One assumption for testing the hypothesis that $\rho = 0$ for the Pearson coefficient is that the populations from which the samples are obtained are normally distributed. If this requirement cannot be met, the nonparametric equivalent, called the **Spearman rank correlation coefficient** (denoted by r_s), can be used when the data are ranked.

> The Spearman rank correlation coefficient is a nonparametric statistic that uses ranks to determine if there is a relationship between two variables.

Rank Correlation Coefficient

The computations for the rank correlation coefficient are simpler than those for the Pearson coefficient and involve ranking each set of data. The difference in ranks is found, and r_s is computed by using these differences. If both sets of data have the same ranks, r_s will be $+1$. If the sets of data are ranked in exactly the opposite way, r_s will be -1. If there is no relationship between the rankings, r_s will be near 0.

The assumptions for the Spearman rank correlation coefficients are given next.

> **Assumptions for Spearman's Rank Correlation Coefficient**
>
> 1. The sample is a random sample.
> 2. The data consist of two measurements or observations taken on the same individual.

In this book, the assumptions will be stated in the exercises; however, when encountering statistics in other situations, you must check to see that these assumptions have been met before proceeding.

OBJECTIVE

Compute the Spearman rank correlation coefficient.

> **Formula for Computing the Spearman Rank Correlation Coefficient**
>
> $$r_s = 1 - \frac{6\Sigma d^2}{n(n^2 - 1)}$$
>
> where
>
> d = difference in ranks
> n = number of data pairs

This formula is algebraically equivalent to the formula for r given in Chapter 10, except that ranks are used instead of raw data.

The computational procedure is shown in Example 13–7. For a test of the significance of r_s, Table L is used for values of n up to 30. For larger values, the normal distribution can be used.

This test can be left-tailed, right-tailed, or two-tailed. However, in this book, all tests will be two-tailed. The hypotheses are

$$H_0: \rho = 0$$

$$H_1: \rho \neq 0$$

where ρ is the population correlation coefficient.

Procedure Table

Finding and Testing the Value of Spearman's Rank Correlation Coefficient

Step 1   State the hypotheses.

Step 2   Find the critical value.

Step 3   Find the test value.

      a. Rank the values in each data set.

      b. Subtract the rankings for each pair of data values $(X_1 - X_2)$.

      c. Square the differences.

      d. Find the sum of the squares.

      e. Substitute in the formula.

$$r_s = 1 - \frac{6\Sigma d^2}{n(n^2 - 1)}$$

    where

        d = difference in ranks

        n = number of pairs of data

Step 4   Make the decision.

Step 5   Summarize the results.

EXAMPLE 13–7   Bank Branches and Deposits

A researcher wishes to see if there is a relationship between the number of branches a bank has and the total number of deposits (in billions of dollars) the bank receives. A sample of eight regional banks is selected, and the number of branches and the amount of deposits are shown in the table. At $\alpha = 0.05$, is there a significant linear correlation between the number of branches and the amount of the deposits?

Bank	Number of branches	Deposits (in billions)
A	209	$23
B	353	31
C	19	7
D	201	12
E	344	26
F	132	5
G	401	24
H	126	4

Source: SNL Financial.

SOLUTION

Step 1   State the hypotheses.

      $H_0: \rho = 0$ and $H_1: \rho \neq 0$

Step 2   Find the critical value. Use Table L to find the value for $n = 8$ and $\alpha = 0.05$. It is ± 0.738. See Figure 13–3.

FIGURE 13–3

Finding the Critical Value in
Table L for Example 13–7

Step 3   Find the test value.

    a. Rank each data set as shown in the table.

Bank	Branches	Rank	Deposits	Rank
A	209	5	23	5
B	353	7	31	8
C	19	1	7	3
D	201	4	12	4
E	344	6	26	7
F	132	3	5	2
G	401	8	24	6
H	126	2	4	1

    Let X_1 be the rank of the branches and X_2 be the rank of the deposits.

    b. Subtract the ranking $(X_1 - X_2)$.

$$5 - 5 = 0 \qquad 7 - 8 = -1 \qquad 1 - 3 = -2 \qquad \text{etc.}$$

    c. Square the differences.

$$0^2 = 0 \qquad (-1)^2 = 1 \qquad (-2)^2 = 4 \qquad \text{etc.}$$

    d. Find the sum of the squares.

$$0 + 1 + 4 + 0 + 1 + 1 + 4 + 1 = 12$$

The results can be summarized in a table as shown.

X_1	X_2	$d = X_1 - X_2$	d^2
5	5	0	0
7	8	−1	1
1	3	−2	4
4	4	0	0
6	7	−1	1
3	2	1	1
8	6	2	4
2	1	1	1
			$\Sigma d^2 = 12$

    e. Substitute in the formula for r_s.

$$r_s = 1 - \frac{6\Sigma d^2}{n(n^2 - 1)} \qquad \text{where } n = \text{number of pairs}$$

$$r_s = 1 - \frac{6 \cdot 12}{8(8^2 - 1)} = 1 - \frac{72}{504} = 0.857$$

Unusual Stat

You are almost twice as
likely to be killed while
walking with your back
to traffic as you are
when facing traffic,
according to the National
Safety Council.

Step 4   Make the decision. Reject the null hypothesis since $r_s = 0.857$, which is greater than the critical value of 0.738.

Step 5   Summarize the results. There is enough evidence to say that there is a linear relationship between the number of branches a bank has and the deposits of the bank.

OBJECTIVE **7**

Test hypotheses, using the runs test.

The Runs Test

When samples are selected, you assume that they are selected at random. How do you know if the data obtained from a sample are truly random?

One way to answer this question is to use the *runs test*. Before you can use the runs test, you must be able to determine the number of runs in a sequence of events.

> A **run** is a succession of identical letters preceded or followed by a different letter or no letter at all, such as the beginning or end of the succession.

Consider the following situations for a researcher interviewing 20 people for a survey. Let their gender be denoted by M for male and F for female. Suppose the participants were chosen as follows:

Situation 1   M M M M M M M M M M F F F F F F F F F F

It does not look as if the people in this sample were selected at random, since 10 males were selected first, followed by 10 females.

Consider a different selection:

Situation 2   F M F M F M F M F M F M F M F M F M F M

In this case, it seems as if the researcher selected a female, then a male, etc. This selection is probably not random either.

Finally, consider the following selection:

Situation 3   F F F M M F M F M M F F M M F F M M M F

This selection of data looks as if it may be random, since there is a mix of males and females and no apparent pattern to their selection.

Let's examine each of the three situations to determine the number of runs. The first situation presented has two runs:

Run 1   M M M M M M M M M M
Run 2   F F F F F F F F F F

The second situation has 20 runs. (Each letter constitutes one run.)

The third situation has 11 runs.

Run 1	F F F	Run 5	F	Run 9	F F
Run 2	M M	Run 6	M M	Run 10	M M M
Run 3	F	Run 7	F F	Run 11	F
Run 4	M	Run 8	M M		

The number of runs is used to determine the value of the test statistic. Here, n_1 represents the number of items in category 1 and n_2 represents the number of items in category 2.

In the preceding situation, there were 10 males and 10 females; hence, $n_1 = 10$ and $n_2 = 10$. Also, G is used to denote the number of runs. In situation 1, $G = 2$; in situation 2, $G = 20$; and in situation 3, $G = 11$.

EXAMPLE 13–8

Determine the number of runs and the values of n_1 and n_2 in each sequence.

    a. M M F F F M F F

    b. H T H H H

    c. A B A A A B B A B B B

SOLUTION

    a. There are four runs, as shown.

        M M   F F F   M   F F

         1   2   3   4

    There are 3 M's and 5 F's, so $n_1 = 3$ and $n_2 = 5$.

    b. There are three runs, as shown.

        H   T   H H H

        1   2   3

    There are 4 heads and 1 tail, so $n_1 = 4$ and $n_2 = 1$.

    c. There are six runs, as shown.

        A   B   A A A   B B   A   B B B

        1   2   3   4   5   6

    There are 5 A's and 6 B's, so $n_1 = 5$ and $n_2 = 6$.

Rather than try to guess whether the numbers of runs occur at random, statisticians have devised a nonparametric test to determine this. As previously mentioned, it is called the runs test.

> The **runs test for randomness** is a nonparametric test that is used to determine if a sequence of data values occurs at random.

The test for randomness considers the number of runs rather than the frequency of the letters. For example, for data to be selected at random, there should not be too few or too many runs, as in situations 1 and 2. The runs test does not consider the questions of how many males or females were selected or how many of each are in a specific run.

When the data are numerical, you can use the median of the data to determine the number of runs. First find the median for the data, and then subtract the median from each value. If the data value is above the median, assign it the letter A. If the data value falls below the median, assign it the letter B. Ignore any data values that are equal to the median.

The runs test can be used provided that the following assumptions are met.

Assumptions for the Runs Test for Randomness

  1. The data from the sample are arranged in the order in which they were selected.
  2. Each letter, number, or event can be classified into one or two mutually exclusive categories.

In this book, the assumptions will be stated in the exercises; however, when encountering statistics in other situations, you must check to see that these assumptions have been met before proceeding.

Formulas for the Test Statistic Value for the Runs Test

When $n_1 \leq 20$ and $n_2 \leq 20$, use the number of runs denoted by G, as the test statistic value. When $n_1 > 20$ or $n_2 > 20$—or when $n_1 > 20$ *and* $n_2 > 20$—use

$$z = \frac{G - \mu_G}{\sigma_G}$$

where

$$\mu_G = \frac{2n_1 n_2}{n_1 + n_2} + 1$$

$$\sigma_G = \sqrt{\frac{2n_1 n_2 (2n_1 n_2 - n_1 - n_2)}{(n_1 + n_2)^2 (n_1 + n_2 - 1)}}$$

Procedure Table

The Runs Test

Step 1   State the hypotheses and identify the claim.

Step 2   Find the critical values.

     a. Use Table M when $n_1 \leq 20$ and $n_2 \leq 20$.

     b. Use Table E when $n_1 > 20$ or $n_2 > 20$ or when $n_1 > 20$ *and* $n_2 > 20$.

Step 3   Find the test value.

     a. Use the number of runs if $n_1 \leq 20$ and $n_2 \leq 20$.

     b. Use the formula when $n_1 > 20$ or $n_2 > 20$ or when $n_1 > 20$ *and* $n_2 > 20$.

$$z = \frac{G - \mu_G}{\sigma_G}$$

Step 4   Make the decision.

Step 5   Summarize the results.

To determine whether the number of runs is within the random range, use Table M in Appendix A when $n_1 \leq 20$ and $n_2 \leq 20$. The values are for a two-tailed test with $\alpha = 0.05$. For a sample of 12 males and 8 females, the table values shown in Figure 13–4 mean that any number of runs from 7 to 15 would be considered random. If the number of runs is 6 or less or is 16 or more, then the sample is probably not random and the null hypothesis should be rejected.

FIGURE 13–4
Finding the Critical Value in Table M

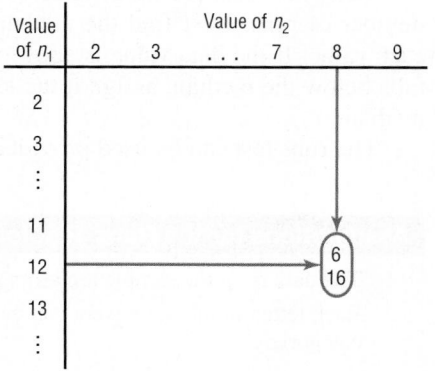

Example 13–9 shows the procedure for conducting the runs test by using letters as data. Example 13–10 shows how the runs test can be used for numerical data. Example 13–11 shows how to use the runs test when $n_1 > 20$ and $n_2 > 20$.

EXAMPLE 13–9 Gender of Train Passengers

On a commuter train, the conductor wishes to see whether the passengers enter the train at random. He observes the first 25 people, with the following sequence of males (M) and females (F).

$$F\,F\,F\,M\,M\,F\,F\,F\,F\,M\,F\,M\,M\,M\,F\,F\,F\,F\,M\,M\,F\,F\,F\,M\,M$$

Test for randomness at $\alpha = 0.05$.

SOLUTION

Step 1 State the hypotheses and identify the claim.

H_0: The passengers board the train at random, according to gender (claim).

H_1: The passengers do not board the train at random, according to gender.

Step 2 Determine the critical value. There are 10 M's and 15 F's, so $n_1 = 10$ and $n_2 = 15$. Using Table M and $\alpha = 0.05$, the critical value is $\begin{smallmatrix}7\\18\end{smallmatrix}$ which means do not reject H_0 if the number of runs is between 7 and 18.

Step 3 Find the test value. Determine the number of runs. Arrange the letters according to runs of males and females, as shown.

Run	Gender
1	F F F
2	M M
3	F F F F
4	M
5	F
6	M M M
7	F F F F
8	M M
9	F F F
10	M M

There are 10 runs.

Step 4 Make the decision. Compare these critical values with the number of runs. Since the number of runs is 10 and 10 is between 7 and 18, do not reject the null hypothesis.

Step 5 Summarize the results. There is not enough evidence to reject the hypothesis that the passengers board the train at random according to gender.

EXAMPLE 13–10 Ages of Drug Program Participants

Twenty people enrolled in a drug abuse program. Test the claim that the ages of the people, according to the order in which they enroll, occur at random, at $\alpha = 0.05$. The data are 18, 36, 19, 22, 25, 44, 23, 27, 27, 35, 19, 43, 37, 32, 28, 43, 46, 19, 20, 22.

SOLUTION

Step 1 State the hypotheses and identify the claim.

H_0: The ages of the people, according to the order in which they enroll in a drug program, occur at random (claim).

H_1: The ages of the people, according to the order in which they enroll in a drug program, do not occur at random.

Step 2 Find the critical value.

Find the median of the data. Arrange the data in ascending order.

18 19 19 19 20 22 22 23 25 27 27

28 32 35 36 37 43 43 44 46

The median is 27.

Replace each number in the original sequence as written in the example with an A if it is above the median and with a B if it is below the median. Eliminate any numbers that are equal to the median.

Recall the original sequence is 18, 36, 19, 22, . . . , 22. Then

18 is below the median, so it is B;

36 is above the median, so it is A;

19 is below the median, so it is B;

etc.

The sequence of letters, then, is

B A B B B A B A B A A A A A A B B B

There are 9 A's and 9 B's. Table M shows that with $n_1 = 9$, $n_2 = 9$, and $\alpha = 0.05$, the number of runs should be between 5 and 15.

Step 3 Find the test value. Determine the number of runs from the sequence of letters.

Run	Letters
1	B
2	A
3	B B B
4	A
5	B
6	A
7	B
8	A A A A A A
9	B B B

The number of runs $G = 9$.

Step 4 Make the decision. Since there are 9 runs and 9 falls between the critical values 5 and 15, the null hypothesis is not rejected.

Step 5 Summarize the results. There is not enough evidence to reject the hypothesis that the ages of the people who enroll occur at random.

EXAMPLE 13–11 Baseball All-Star Winners

The data show the winners of the baseball all-star games (N = National League, A = American League) from 1962 to 2012. At $\alpha = 0.05$, can it be concluded that the sequence of winners is random?

A N N N N N N N N A

N N N N N N N N N N

N A N N A N A A A A

A A N N N A A A A A

A A A A A A A N N N

(Note: The tie in 2002 has been omitted.)

SOLUTION

Step 1   State the hypotheses and identify the claim.

H_0: The winners occur at random (claim).

H_1: The winners do not occur at random.

Step 2   Determine the actual values.

Since $n_1 > 20$ and $n_2 > 20$, Table E is used. At $\alpha = 0.05$, the critical values are ± 1.96.

Step 3   Find the test value.

$$n_1 \text{ (National)} = 28 \qquad n_2 \text{ (American)} = 22$$

The number of runs is

1. A
2. NNNNNNNN
3. A
4. NNNNNNNNNNN
5. A
6. NN
7. A
8. N
9. AAAAAA
10. NNN
11. AAAAAAAAAAA
12. NNN

There are $G = 12$ runs.

$$\mu_G = \frac{2n_1 n_2}{n_1 + n_2} + 1$$

$$= \frac{2(28)(22)}{28 + 22} + 1 = 25.64$$

$$\sigma_G = \sqrt{\frac{2n_1 n_2 (2n_1 n_2 - n_1 - n_2)}{(n_1 + n_2)^2 (n_1 + n_2 - 1)}}$$

$$= \sqrt{\frac{2(28)(22)[2(28)(22) - 28 - 22]}{(28 + 22)^2 (28 + 22 - 1)}} = 3.448$$

$$z = \frac{G - \mu_G}{\sigma_G}$$

$$= \frac{12 - 25.64}{3.448}$$

$$= -3.96$$

Step 4   Make the decision. Since $-3.96 < -1.96$, the decision is to reject the null hypothesis.

Step 5   Summarize the results. There is enough evidence to reject the claim that the sequence of winners occurs at random.

Applying the Concepts 13–6

Tall Trees

As a biologist, you wish to see if there is a relationship between the heights of tall trees and their diameters. You find the following data for the diameter (in inches) of the tree at 4.5 feet from the ground and the corresponding heights (in feet).

Diameter (in.)	Height (ft)
1024	261
950	321
451	219
505	281
761	159
644	83
707	191
586	141
442	232
546	108

Source: *The World Almanac and Book of Facts.*

1. What question are you trying to answer?

2. What type of nonparametric analysis could be used to answer the question?

3. What would be the corresponding parametric test that could be used?

4. Which test do you think would be better?

5. Perform both tests and write a short statement comparing the results.

See page 740 for the answer.

Exercises 13–6

For Exercises 1 through 4, find the critical value from Table L for the rank correlation coefficient, given sample size n and α. Assume that the test is two-tailed.

1. $n = 14$, $\alpha = 0.01$

2. $n = 28$, $\alpha = 0.02$

3. $n = 10$, $\alpha = 0.05$

4. $n = 9$, $\alpha = 0.01$

For Exercises 5 through 14, perform these steps.

   a. Find the Spearman rank correlation coefficient.

   b. State the hypotheses.

   c. Find the critical value. Use $\alpha = 0.05$.

   d. Make the decision.

   e. Summarize the results.

Use the traditional method of hypothesis testing unless otherwise specified.

5. **Mathematics Achievement Test Scores** The National Assessment of Educational Progress (U.S. Department of Education) tests mathematics, reading, and science achievement in grades 4 and 8. A random sample of states is selected, and their mathematics achievement scores are noted for fourth- and eighth-graders. At $\alpha = 0.05$, can a linear relationship be concluded between the data?

Grade 4	89	84	80	89	88	77	80
Grade 8	81	75	66	76	80	59	74

Source: *World Almanac.*

6. **Subway and Commuter Rail Passengers** Six cities are randomly selected, and the number of daily passenger trips (in thousands) for subways and commuter rail service is obtained. At $\alpha = 0.05$, is there a relationship between the variables? Suggest one reason why the transportation authority might use the results of this study.

City	1	2	3	4	5	6
Subway	845	494	425	313	108	41
Rail	39	291	142	103	33	39

Source: American Public Transportation Association.

7. Motion Picture Releases and Gross Revenue In Chapter 10 it was demonstrated that there was a significant linear relationship between the numbers of releases that a motion picture studio put out and its gross receipts for the year. Is there a relationship between the two at the 0.05 level of significance?

No. of releases	361	270	306	22	35	10	8	12	21
Receipts	2844	1967	1371	1064	667	241	188	154	125

Source: www.showbizdata.com

8. Hospitals and Nursing Homes Find the Spearman rank correlation coefficient for the following data, which represent the number of hospitals and nursing homes in each of seven randomly selected states. At the 0.05 level of significance, is there enough evidence to conclude that there is a correlation between the two?

Hospitals	107	61	202	133	145	117	108
Nursing homes	230	134	704	376	431	538	373

Source: World Almanac.

9. Calories and Cholesterol in Fast-Food Sandwiches Use the Spearman rank correlation coefficient to see if there is a linear relationship between these two sets of data, representing the number of calories and the amount of cholesterol in randomly selected fast-food sandwiches.

Calories	580	580	270	470	420	415	330	430
Cholesterol (mg)	205	225	285	270	185	215	185	220

Source: www.fatcalories.com

10. Book Publishing The data below show the number of books published in six different randomly selected subject areas for the years 2000 and 2012. Use $\alpha = 0.05$ to see if there is a relationship between the two data sets. Do you think the same relationship will hold true 20 years from now? (In case you're curious, the subjects represented are agriculture, home economics, literature, music, science, and sports and recreation.)

2000	461	879	1686	357	3109	971
2012	1065	3639	4671	2764	8509	4806

11. Class Size and Average Grade In a previous exercise (in Chapter 10) data were provided to see if there was a relationship between class size and average grade. Assume now that the population is not normally distributed, and perform the same task using the Spearman rank correlation coefficient. Compare the results. Use $\alpha = 0.05$.

Class size	15	10	8	20	18	6
Avg. grade	85	90	82	80	84	92

12. Motor Vehicle Thefts and Burglaries Is there a relationship between the number of motor vehicle (MV) thefts and the number of burglaries (per 100,000 population) for different randomly selected metropolitan areas? Use $\alpha = 0.05$.

MV theft	220.5	499.4	285.6	159.2	104.3	444
Burglary	913.6	909.2	803.6	520.9	477.8	993.7

Source: New York Times Almanac.

13. Cyber School Enrollments Shown are the numbers of students enrolled in cyber school for five randomly selected school districts and the per-pupil costs for the cyber school education. At $\alpha = 0.10$, is there a relationship between the two variables? How might this information be useful to school administrators?

Number of students	10	6	17	8	11
Per-pupil cost	7200	9393	7385	4500	8203

Source: Pittsburgh Tribune-Review.

14. Drug Prices Shown are the price for a human dose of several randomly selected prescription drugs and the price for an equivalent dose for animals. At $\alpha = 0.10$, is there a relationship between the variables?

Humans	0.67	0.64	1.20	0.51	0.87	0.74	0.50	1.22
Animals	0.13	0.18	0.42	0.25	0.57	0.57	0.49	1.28

Source: House Committee on Government Reform.

15. Cavities in Fourth-Grade Students A school dentist wanted to test the claim, at $\alpha = 0.05$, that the number of cavities in fourth-grade students is random. Forty students were checked, and the number of cavities each had is shown here. Test for randomness of the values above or below the median.

0	4	6	0	6	2	5	3	1	5	1
2	2	1	3	7	3	6	0	2	6	0
2	3	1	5	2	1	3	0	2	3	7
3	1	5	1	1	2	2				

16. Daily Lottery Numbers Listed below are the daily numbers (daytime drawing) for the Pennsylvania State Lottery for February 2007. Using O for odd and E for even, test for randomness at $\alpha = 0.05$.

270	054	373	204	908	121	121
804	116	467	357	926	626	247
783	554	406	272	508	764	890
441	964	606	568	039	370	583

Source: www.palottery.com

17. Amusement Park Admission Price A popular amusement park charges a daily admission price that includes all rides. At the end of summer they sponsor a series of nightly parades featuring high school bands from the tristate area. A spectator admission, substantially less than the standard one, is available for people who just want to eat and watch the parade, but not ride. Denoting full admission by F and spectator admission by S, the following 40 admissions were sold on a given day. At $\alpha = 0.05$, test for randomness.

S S F S F S F F S F S S F F F S F F S S

S F F F F S F F F S F S S F S S F F S S

18. Random Numbers Random? A calculator generated these integers randomly. Apply the runs test to see if you can reject the hypothesis that the numbers are truly random. Use $\alpha = 0.05$.

```
1   1   1   1   1   1   2   1   1   1   1
2   2   1   2   1   2   2   1   2   1   1
2   1   1
```

19. Concert Seating As students, faculty, friends, and family arrived for the Spring Wind Ensemble Concert at Shafer Auditorium, they were asked whether they were going to sit in the balcony (B) or on the ground floor (G). Use the responses listed below and test for randomness at $\alpha = 0.05$.

```
B B G G B B G B B B B B G B B
G G B B B B G G G G B G B B B G G
```

20. Gender of Shoppers Twenty shoppers are in a checkout line at a grocery store. At $\alpha = 0.05$, test for randomness of their gender: male (M) or female (F). The data are shown here.

F M M F F M F M M F

F M M M F F F F F M

21. Employee Absences A supervisor records the number of employees absent over a 30-day period. Test for randomness, at $\alpha = 0.05$.

```
27    6   19   24   18   12   15   17   18   20
 0    9    4   12    3    2    7    7    0    5
32   16   38   31   27   15    5    9    4   10
```

22. Skiing Conditions A ski lodge manager observes the weather for the month of February. If his customers are able to ski, he records S; if weather conditions do not permit skiing, he records N. Test for randomness, at $\alpha = 0.05$.

```
S S S S S N N N N N N N
N S S S N N S S S S S S S
```

23. On-Demand Movie Rentals Listed are the numbers of on-demand movies rented per month for 20 customers of a particular cable service. Test the data for randomness at the 0.05 level of significance. What would have to occur to effect the opposite result? Discuss how the data would have to change.

```
0    2   14   20   13    6    1   20    4    8
2    5   17    7   12   12    1    0    0   14
```

24. Tossing a Coin Toss a coin 30 times and record the outcomes (H or T). Test the results for randomness at $\alpha = 0.05$. Repeat the experiment a few times and compare your results.

25. Gender of Patients at a Medical Center The gender of the patients at a medical center is recorded. Test the claim at $\alpha = 0.05$ that they are admitted at random.

```
F   F   M   M   M   M   M   F   F   F
M   M   M   M   M   M   F   M   M   F
F   F   F   M   M   M   F   M   F   M
M   M   M   M   M   F   M   M   F   M
F   F   M   F   F   F   F   F   F   M
```

26. Speeding Tickets A police chief records the gender of the drivers who receive speeding tickets. Test the claim at $\alpha = 0.05$ that the gender of the ticketed drivers is random.

```
M   M   M   F   F   M   F   M   F   M
M   F   M   M   M   F   M   M   F   F
F   M   M   F   M   M   F   M   M   M
M   M   F   M   F   F   F   M   M   M
F   F   M   F   F   F   M   M   M   M
```

27. Accidents or Illnesses The people who went to the emergency room at a local hospital were treated for an accident (A) or illness (I). Test the claim $\alpha = 0.10$ that the reason given occurred at random.

```
I   A   I   A   A   A   A   A   A   I
A   I   I   A   A   I   I   A   A   A
A   I   A   I   A   A   A   I   I   A
A   I   I   A   A   I   A   I   A   I
A   I   A   A   I   I   A   A   A   I
I   A   I   A   A   I   I   A   A   A
```

28. Glasses or Contact Lenses The people who were tested for drivers' licenses who wear glasses (G) or contact lenses (C) are recorded in the order they are tested. Is the sequence random at $\alpha = 0.05$?

```
G   C   C   C   G   C   C   G   G   C
C   C   G   G   C   G   C   C   G   G
C   C   C   G   G   C   C   G   C   G
C   C   C   C   G   C   G   G   G   G
C   C   C   C   C   C   C   C   C   G
```

≡ Extending the Concepts

When $n \geq 30$, the formula $r = \dfrac{\pm z}{\sqrt{n-1}}$ can be used to find the critical values for the rank correlation coefficient. For example, if $n = 40$ and $\alpha = 0.05$ for a two-tailed test,

$$r = \frac{\pm 1.96}{\sqrt{40-1}} = \pm 0.314$$

Hence, any r_s greater than or equal to $+0.314$ or less than or equal to -0.314 is significant.

For Exercises 29 through 33, find the critical r value for each (assume that the test is two-tailed).

29. $n = 50$, $\alpha = 0.05$

30. $n = 30$, $\alpha = 0.01$

31. $n = 35$, $\alpha = 0.02$

32. $n = 60$, $\alpha = 0.10$

33. $n = 40$, $\alpha = 0.01$

≝ Technology — Step by Step

EXCEL
Step by Step

Spearman Rank Correlation Coefficient

Example: Textbook Ratings

Two students were asked to rate eight different textbooks for a specific course on an ascending scale from 0 to 20 points. Points were assigned for each of several categories, such as reading level, use of illustrations, and use of color. At $\alpha = 0.05$, test the hypothesis that there is a significant linear correlation between the two students' ratings. The data are shown in the following table.

Textbook	Student 1's rating	Student 2's rating
A	4	4
B	10	6
C	18	20
D	20	14
E	12	16
F	2	8
G	5	11
H	9	7

Excel does not have a procedure to compute the Spearman rank correlation coefficient. However, you may compute this statistic by using the MegaStat Add-in available online. If you have not installed this add-in, do so, following the instructions from the Chapter 1 Excel Step by Step.

1. Enter the rating scores from the example into columns A and B of a new worksheet.

2. From the toolbar, select Add-Ins, **MegaStat>Nonparametric Tests>Spearman Coefficient of Rank Correlation.** *Note:* You may need to open MegaStat from the MegaStat.xls file on your computer's hard drive.

3. Type **A1:B8** in the box for Input range.

4. Check the Correct for ties option.

5. Click [OK].

Spearman Coefficient of Rank Correlation

	#1	#2
#1	1.000	
#2	.643	1.000

8 sample size

±0.707 critical value .05 (two-tail)
±0.834 critical value .01 (two-tail)

Since the correlation coefficient 0.643 is less than the critical value, there is not enough evidence to reject the null hypothesis of a nonzero correlation between the variables.

MINITAB
Step by Step

Spearman Rank Correlation

Example 13–7 Bank Branches and Deposits

Is there a correlation between the number of branches and the number of deposits? Use the calculator to determine the ranks; then use Pearson's correlation to calculate r_s.

1. Enter the data into C1 and C2 of a new MINITAB worksheet.

2. Name the columns Branches and Deposits.

3. Calculate the ranks and store them.

   a) Select **Data>Rank.**

   b) Choose Branches for **Rank data in:** and then name the column RankBranches.

   c) Click the edit last dialog box icon, then choose Deposits for **Rank data in.** Name this column RankDeposits.

The worksheet is shown. The Pearson correlation on these ranks will produce Spearman's rank correlation.

4. Stat>Basic Statistics>Correlation.

   a) Select the two columns of Ranks, C3 and C4.

   b) Deselect the *P*-value as this will not be correct for Spearman's test.

   c) Click [OK].

The results are displayed in the session window. Compare the correlation coefficient to the critical value.

Correlations: RankBranches, RankDeposits

Pearson correlation of RankBranches and RankDeposits = 0.857

Reject the null hypothesis since this is greater than the critical value.

Runs Test for Randomness

1. Sequence is important! Enter the data down C1 in the same order they were collected. Do not sort them! Use the data from Example 13–10.

2. Calculate the median and store it as a constant.

   a) Select **Calc>Column Statistics.**

   b) Check the option for Median.

   c) Use C1 Age for the Input Variable.

   d) Type the name of the constant MedianAge in the Store result in text box.

   e) Click [OK].

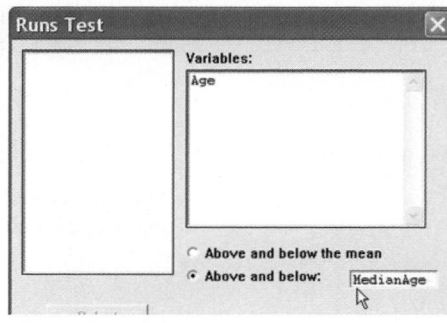

3. Select **Stat>Nonparametric>Runs Test.**

4. Select C1 Age as the variable.

5. Click the button for Above and below, then select MedianAge in the text box.

6. Click [OK]. The results will be displayed in the session window.

Runs Test: Age

Runs test for Age
Runs above and below K = 27

The observed number of runs = 9
The expected number of runs = 10.9
9 observations above K, 11 below
* N is small, so the following approximation may be invalid.
P-value = 0.378

The *P*-value is 0.378. Do not reject the null hypothesis.

Summary

- In many research situations, the assumptions (particularly the assumption of normality) for the use of parametric statistics cannot be met. Also, some statistical studies do not involve parameters such as means, variances, and proportions. For both situations, statisticians have developed nonparametric statistical methods, also called *distribution-free methods*. (13–1)

- There are several advantages to the use of nonparametric methods. The most important one is that no knowledge of the population distributions is required.

Other advantages include ease of computation and understanding. The major disadvantage is that they are less efficient than their parametric counterparts when the assumptions for the parametric methods are met. In other words, larger sample sizes are needed to get results as accurate as those given by their parametric counterparts. (13–1)

- This list gives the nonparametric statistical tests presented in this chapter, along with their parametric counterparts.

Nonparametric test	Parametric test	Condition
Single-sample sign test (13–2)	z or t test	One sample
Paired-sample sign test (13–2)	z or t test	Two dependent samples
Wilcoxon rank sum test (13–3)	z or t test	Two independent samples
Wilcoxon signed-rank test (13–4)	t test	Two dependent samples
Kruskal-Wallis test (13–5)	ANOVA	Three or more independent samples
Spearman rank correlation coefficient (13–6)	Pearson's correlation coefficient	Relationships between variables
Runs test (13–6)	None	Randomness

- When the assumptions of the parametric tests can be met, the parametric tests should be used instead of their nonparametric counterparts.

Important Terms

distribution-free statistics 690

Kruskal-Wallis test 712

nonparametric statistics 690

paired-sample sign test 696

parametric tests 690

ranking 691

run 722

runs test 723

sign test 693

Spearman rank correlation coefficient 719

Wilcoxon rank sum test 702

Wilcoxon signed-rank test 707

Important Formulas

Formula for the *z* test value in the sign test:

$$z = \frac{(X + 0.5) - 0.5n}{\sqrt{n}/2}$$

where

n = sample size (greater than or equal to 26)

X = smaller number of positive or negative signs

Formula for the Wilcoxon rank sum test:

$$z = \frac{R - \mu_R}{\sigma_R}$$

where

$$\mu_R = \frac{n_1(n_1 + n_2 + 1)}{2}$$

$$\sigma_R = \sqrt{\frac{n_1 n_2(n_1 + n_2 + 1)}{12}}$$

    R = sum of ranks for smaller sample size (n_1)
    n_1 = smaller of sample sizes
    n_2 = larger of sample sizes
    $n_1 \geq 10$ and $n_2 \geq 10$

Formula for the Wilcoxon signed-rank test:

$$z = \frac{w_s - \frac{n(n+1)}{4}}{\sqrt{\frac{n(n+1)(2n+1)}{24}}}$$

where

    n = number of pairs where difference is not 0 and
        $n \geq 30$
    w_s = smaller sum in absolute value of signed ranks

Formula for the Kruskal-Wallis test:

$$H = \frac{12}{N(N+1)}\left(\frac{R_1^2}{n_1} + \frac{R_2^2}{n_2} + \cdots + \frac{R_k^2}{n_k}\right) - 3(N+1)$$

where

    R_1 = sum of ranks of sample 1
    n_1 = size of sample 1

    R_2 = sum of ranks of sample 2
    n_2 = size of sample 2
    $\vdots$

    R_k = sum of ranks of sample k
    n_k = size of sample k
    $N = n_1 + n_2 + \cdots + n_k$
    k = number of samples

Formula for the Spearman rank correlation coefficient:

$$r_s = 1 - \frac{6\Sigma d^2}{n(n^2 - 1)}$$

where

    d = difference in ranks
    n = number of data pairs

Formulas for the test statistic value for the runs test:

    When $n_1 \leq 20$ and $n_2 \leq 20$, use the number of runs, denoted by G, as the test statistic value.

    When $n_1 > 20$ or $n_2 > 20$ or when $n_1 > 20$ *and* $n_2 > 20$, use

$$z = \frac{G - \mu_G}{\sigma_G}$$

where

$$\mu_G = \frac{2n_1 n_2}{n_1 + n_2} + 1$$

$$\sigma_G = \sqrt{\frac{2n_1 n_2(2n_1 n_2 - n_1 - n_2)}{(n_1 + n_2)^2(n_1 + n_2 - 1)}}$$

≣ Review Exercises

For Exercises 1 through 13, follow this procedure:
    a. State the hypotheses and identify the claim.
    b. Find the critical value(s).
    c. Compute the test value.
    d. Make the decision.
    e. Summarize the results.

Use the traditional method of hypothesis testing unless otherwise specified.

Section 13–2

1. **Price of Pizza** A marketing student hypothesized that the median price for a 12-inch pepperoni pizza is $9.00. A random selection of 30 restaurants within a 30-mile radius indicated the following prices for a 12-inch pepperoni pizza. Test the claim that the median price is not over 9.00 at $\alpha = 0.05$.

10.00 6.99 12.00 10.99 11.99 9.50   9.85 10.00 12.00 12.00
8.75 12.00 11.99 6.99 9.99 10.50 10.00 9.50 9.99 8.99
12.00 9.95 8.99 9.50 7.99 8.99 10.95 7.99 8.75 10.00

2. **Lifetime of Truck Tires** A tire manufacturer claims that the median lifetime of a certain brand of truck tires is 40,000 miles. A random sample of 30 tires shows that 12 lasted longer than 40,000 miles. Is there enough evidence to reject the claim at $\alpha = 0.05$? Use the sign test.

3. **Grocery Store Repricing** A grocery store chain has decided to help customers save money by instituting "temporary repricing" to help cut costs. Nine randomly selected products from the sale flyer are featured below with their regular price and their "temporary" new price. Using the paired-sample sign test and $\alpha = 0.05$, is there evidence of a difference in price? Comment on your results.

Old	2.59	0.69	1.29	3.10	1.89	2.05	1.58	2.75	1.99
New	2.09	0.70	1.18	2.95	1.59	1.75	1.32	2.19	1.99

Section 13–3

4. Record High Temperatures Shown here are the record high temperatures for Dawson Creek in British Columbia, Canada, and for Whitehorse in Yukon, Canada, for a randomly selected 12-month period. Using the Wilcoxon rank sum test at $\alpha = 0.05$, do you find a difference in the record high temperatures? Use the *P*-value method.

Dawson Creek	52	60	57	71	86	89	94	93	88	80	66	52
White-horse	47	50	51	69	86	89	91	86	80	66	51	47

Source: *The USA TODAY Weather Almanac.*

5. Hours Worked by Student Employees Student employees are a major part of most college campus employment venues. Two major randomly selected departments that participate in student hiring are listed with the number of hours worked by students for a month. At the 0.10 level of significance, is there sufficient evidence to conclude a difference? Is the conclusion the same for the 0.05 level of significance?

Athletics	20	24	17	12	18	22	25	30	15	19
Library	35	28	24	20	25	18	22	26	31	21	19

Section 13–4

6. Fuel Efficiency of Automobiles Twelve randomly selected automobiles were tested to see how many miles per gallon each one obtained. Under similar driving conditions, they were tested again, using a special additive. The data are shown. At $\alpha = 0.05$, did the additive improve gas mileage? Use the Wilcoxon signed-rank test.

Before		After	
13.6	18.3	22.6	23.7
18.2	19.5	21.9	20.8
16.1	18.2	25.3	25.3
15.3	16.7	28.6	27.2
19.2	21.3	15.2	17.2
18.8	17.2	16.3	18.5

7. Lunch Costs Randomly selected full-time employees in a large city were asked how much they spent on a typical weekday lunch and how much they spent on the weekend. The amounts are listed. At $\alpha = 0.05$, is there sufficient evidence to conclude a difference in the amounts spent?

Weekday	7.00	5.50	4.50	10.00	6.75	5.00	6.00
Weekend	6.00	10.00	7.00	12.00	8.50	7.00	8.00

Section 13–5

8. Breaking Strengths of Ropes Random samples of three types of ropes are tested for breaking strength. The data (in pounds) are shown. At $\alpha = 0.05$, is there a difference in the breaking strength of the ropes? Use the Kruskal-Wallis test.

Cotton	Nylon	Hemp
230	356	506
432	303	527
505	361	581
487	405	497
451	432	459
380	378	507
462	361	562
531	399	571
366	372	499
372	363	475
453	306	505
488	304	561
462	318	532
467	322	501

9. Beach Temperatures for July The National Oceanographic Data Center provides useful data for vacation planning. Below are listed beach temperatures in the month of July for various randomly selected U.S. coastal areas. Using the 0.05 level of significance, can it be concluded that there is a difference in temperatures? Omit the Southern Pacific temperatures and repeat the procedure. Is the conclusion the same?

Southern Pacific	Western Gulf	Eastern Gulf	Southern Atlantic
67	86	87	76
68	86	87	81
66	84	86	82
69	85	86	84
63	79	85	80
62	85	84	86
		85	87

Source: www.nodc.noaa.gov

Section 13–6

10. Homework Exercises and Exam Scores A statistics instructor wishes to see whether there is a relationship between the number of homework exercises a student completes and her or his exam score. The randomly selected data are shown. Using the Spearman rank correlation coefficient, test the hypothesis that there is no relationship at $\alpha = 0.05$.

Homework problems	63	55	58	87	89	52	46	75	105
Exam score	85	71	75	98	93	63	72	89	100

11. Manuscript Pages and References A professor examined a random selection of mathematics research papers to see if there was a relationship between the number of pages in the paper and the number of resources cited in the bibliography. Using the Spearman rank coefficient of correlation, test for a relationship at $\alpha = 0.05$.

Pages	15	25	23	30	18	28	35
Sources	10	18	18	15	13	23	20

12. **Paper or Plastic Bags** At a grocery store the clerk asks customers whether they want paper, denoted by R, or plastic, denoted by C. A sample of 30 customers' requests is shown below. Test for randomness at $\alpha = 0.05$.

R	C	C	C	R	C	C	R	R	C
C	C	C	R	C	R	C	R	R	C
C	C	R	C	R	C	R	R	C	C

13. **Exam Scores** An instructor wishes to see whether grades of students who finish an exam occur at random. Shown here are the grades of 30 students in the order that they finished an exam. (Read from left to right across each row, and then proceed to the next row.) Test for randomness, at $\alpha = 0.05$.

87	93	82	77	64	98
100	93	88	65	72	73
56	63	85	92	95	91
88	63	72	79	55	53
65	68	54	71	73	72

14. **Fiction or Nonfiction Books** A bookstore owner records the 48 books purchased by customers. He classifies them as either fiction (F) or nonfiction (N). At $\alpha = 0.10$, does the typical book purchased occur at random?

F	F	F	F	F	F	N	N
F	N	N	N	N	F	F	F
F	F	F	F	N	N	N	F
N	N	N	N	N	F	F	F
N	N	N	F	F	F	F	F
F	F	F	F	N	N	F	F

≡ STATISTICS TODAY

Too Much or Too Little? —Revisited

In this case, the manufacturer would select a sequence of bottles and see how many bottles contained more than 40 ounces, denoted by plus, and how many bottles contained less than 40 ounces, denoted by minus. The sequence could then be analyzed according to the number of runs, as explained in Section 13–6. If the sequence were not random, then the machine would need to be checked to see if it was malfunctioning. Another method that can be used to see if machines are functioning properly is *statistical quality control.* This method is beyond the scope of this book.

≡ Data Analysis

The Data Bank is found in Appendix B, or on the World Wide Web by following links from www.mhhe.com/math/stat/bluman

1. From the Data Bank, choose a sample and use the sign test to test one of the following hypotheses.

   a. For serum cholesterol, test H_0: median = 220 milligram percent (mg%).

   b. For systolic pressure, test H_0: median = 120 millimeters of mercury (mm Hg).

   c. For IQ, test H_0: median = 100.

   d. For sodium level, test H_0: median = 140 mEq/l.

2. From the Data Bank, select a sample of subjects. Use the Kruskal-Wallis test to see if the sodium levels of smokers and nonsmokers are equal.

3. From the Data Bank select a sample of 50 subjects. Use the Wilcoxon rank sum test to see if the means of the sodium levels of the males differ from those of the females.

≡ Chapter Quiz

Determine whether each statement is true or false. If the statement is false, explain why.

1. Nonparametric statistics cannot be used to test the difference between two means.

2. Nonparametric statistics are more sensitive than their parametric counterparts.

3. Nonparametric statistics can be used to test hypotheses about parameters other than means, proportions, and standard deviations.

4. Parametric tests are preferred over their nonparametric counterparts, if the assumptions can be met.

Select the best answer.

5. The _____ test is used to test means when samples are dependent and the normality assumption cannot be met.
   a. Wilcoxon signed-rank   c. Sign
   b. Wilcoxon rank sum   d. Kruskal-Wallis

6. The Kruskal-Wallis test uses the _____ distribution.

   a. z   *c.* Chi-square

   b. t   *d.* F

7. The nonparametric counterpart of ANOVA is the

   _____.

   a. Wilcoxon signed-rank test

   b. Sign test

   c. Runs test

   d. None of the above

8. To see if two rankings are related, you can use the

   _____.

   a. Runs test

   b. Spearman correlation coefficient

   c. Sign test

   d. Kruskal-Wallis test

Complete the following statements with the best answer.

9. When the assumption of normality cannot be met, you can use _____ tests.

10. When data are _____ or _____ in nature, non-parametric methods are used.

11. To test to see whether a median was equal to a specific value, you would use the _____ test.

12. Nonparametric tests are less _____ than their para-metric counterparts.

For the following exercises, use the traditional method of hypothesis testing unless otherwise specified.

13. **Home Prices** The median price for an existing home in 2009 was $177,500. A random sample of homes for sale listed by a local realtor indicated homes available for the following prices. Test the claim that the median is not $177,500. Use $\alpha = 0.05$.

184,500   174,900   155,000   210,000   235,500   399,900
355,900   182,500   229,900   199,900   169,900   219,900

Source: *World Almanac.*

14. **Lifetimes of Batteries** A battery manufacturer claims that the median lifetime of a certain brand of heavy-duty battery is 1200 hours. A sample of 25 batteries shows that 15 lasted longer than 1200 hours. Test the claim at $\alpha = 0.05$. Use the sign test.

15. **Weights of Turkeys** A special diet is fed to adult turkeys to see if they will gain weight. The before-and-after weights (in pounds) are given here. Use the paired-sample sign test at $\alpha = 0.05$ to see if there is weight gain.

Before	28	24	29	30	32	33	25	26	28
After	30	29	31	32	32	35	29	25	31

16. **Charity Donations** Two teams of 10 members each solicited donations for their participation in a charity walk for blood cancer research. The teams received the following amounts. At $\alpha = 0.05$, can it be concluded that there is a difference in amounts?

Team A	100	50	65	50	60	75	100	150	108	120
Team B	135	90	80	140	155	60	200	58	70	72

17. **Textbook Costs** Samples of students majoring in law and nursing are randomly selected, and the amount each spent on textbooks for the spring semester is recorded here, in dollars. Using the Wilcoxon rank sum test at $\alpha = 0.10$, is there a difference in the amount spent by each group?

Law	167	158	162	106	98	206	112	121
Nursing	98	198	209	168	157	126	104	122

Law	133	145	151	199
Nursing	111	138	116	201

18. **Student Grade Point Averages** The grade point average of a group of students was recorded for one month. During the next nine-week grading period, the students attended a workshop on study skills. Their GPAs were recorded at the end of the grading period, and the data are shown. Using the Wilcoxon signed-rank test at $\alpha = 0.05$, can it be concluded that the GPA increased?

Before	3.0	2.9	2.7	2.5	2.1	2.6	1.9	2.0
After	3.2	3.4	2.9	2.5	3.0	3.1	2.4	2.8

19. **Sodium Content of Fast-Food Sandwiches** Sometimes calories and cholesterol are not the only considerations in healthy eating. The sodium contents (in mg) are shown for randomly selected sandwiches from three popular fast-food restaurants. Use $\alpha = 0.05$. Is there a difference in the sodium content?

No. 1	No. 2	No. 3
2940	2010	1130
3720	1850	1190
3180	1980	1220
2260	1640	1640
2780	1440	1240

Source: www.fatcalories.com

20. **Medication and Reaction Times** Three different groups of monkeys were fed three different medications for one month to see if the medication has any effect on reaction time. Each monkey was then taught to repeat a series of steps to receive a reward. The number of trials it took each to receive the reward is shown. At $\alpha = 0.05$, does the medication have an effect on reaction time? Use the Kruskal-Wallis test. Use the *P*-value method.

Med. 1	8	7	11	14	8	6	5
Med. 2	3	4	6	7	9	3	4
Med. 3	8	14	13	7	5	9	12

21. Drug Prices Is there a relationship between the prescription drug prices in Canada and Great Britain? Use $\alpha = 0.10$.

Canada	1.47	1.07	1.34	1.34	1.47	1.07	3.39	1.11	1.13
Great Britain	1.67	1.08	1.67	0.82	1.73	0.95	2.86	0.41	1.70

Source: *USA TODAY.*

22. Funding and Enrollment for Head Start Students Is there a relationship between the amount of money (in millions of dollars) spent on the Head Start Program by the states and the number of students enrolled (in thousands)? Use $\alpha = 0.10$.

Funding	100	50	22	88	49	219
Enrollment	16	7	3	14	8	31

Source: Gannet News Service.

23. Birth Registry At the state registry of vital statistics, the birth certificates issued for females (F) and males (M) were tallied. At $\alpha = 0.05$, test for randomness. The data are shown.

M M F F F F F F F F M M M M F F
M F M F M M M F F F

24. Output of Motors The output in revolutions per minute (rpm) of 10 motors was obtained. The motors were tested again under similar conditions after they had been reconditioned. The data are shown. At $\alpha = 0.05$, did the reconditioning improve the motors' performance? Use the Wilcoxon signed-rank test.

Before	413	701	397	602	405	512	450	487	388	351
After	433	712	406	650	450	550	450	500	402	415

25. State Lottery Numbers A statistician wishes to determine if a state's lottery numbers are selected at random. The winning numbers selected for the month of February are shown. Test for randomness at $\alpha = 0.05$.

321	909	715	700	487	808	509	606	943	761
200	123	367	012	444	576	409	128	567	908
103	407	890	193	672	867	003	578		

26. Type of Movies The Old-Time movie channel shows movies 24 hours a day. The movies are either black and white (B) or color (C). A movie buff records 48 movies shown in a row. Test the claim at $\alpha = 0.05$ that the movies are shown in random order.

B B B B B C C C
C C C C C B B B
B B B B B B C C
C C C C C C C C
C C B B B B B B
B B B B B C C C

◢ Critical Thinking Challenges

1. **Tolls for Bridge** Two commuters ride to work together in one car. To decide who pays the toll for a bridge on the way to work, they flip a coin and the loser pays. Explain why over a period of one year, one person might have to pay the toll 5 days in a row. There is no toll on the return trip. (*Hint:* You may want to use random numbers.)

2. **Olympic Medals** Shown in the table are the type and number of medals each country won in the 2012 Summer Olympic Games. You are to rank the countries from highest to lowest. Gold medals are highest, followed by silver, followed by bronze. There are many different ways to rank objects and events. Here are several suggestions.

   a. Rank the countries according to the total medals won.
   b. List some advantages and disadvantages of this method.
   c. Rank each country separately for the number of gold medals won, then for the number of silver medals won, and finally for the number of bronze medals won. Next rank the countries according to the sum of the *ranks* for the categories.
   d. Are the rankings of the countries the same as those in step *a*? Explain any differences.
   e. List some advantages and disadvantages of this method of ranking.
   f. A third way to rank the countries is to assign a weight to each medal. In this case, assign 3 points for each gold medal, 2 points for each silver medal, and 1 point for each bronze medal the country won. Multiply the number of medals by the weights for each medal, and find the sum. For example, since Argentina won 1 gold medal, 1 silver medal, and 2 bronze medals, its rank sum is $(1 \times 3) + (1 \times 2) + (2 \times 1) = 7$. Rank the countries according to this method.

   g. Compare the ranks using this method with those using the other two methods. Are the rankings the same or different? Explain.
   h. List some advantages and disadvantages of this method.
   i. Select two of the rankings, and run the Spearman rank correlation test to see if they differ significantly.

Summer Olympic Games 2012 Final Medal Standings

Country	Gold	Silver	Bronze
Argentina	1	1	2
Canada	1	5	12
Germany	11	19	14
Italy	8	9	11
Norway	2	1	1
Russia	24	26	32
Switzerland	2	2	0
United States	46	29	29

Source: http://www.london2012.com/medals-count/

📑 Data Projects

Use a significance level of 0.05 for all tests below.

1. **Business and Finance** Monitor the price of a stock over a five-week period. Note the amount of gain or loss per day. Test the claim that the median is 0. Perform a runs test to see if the distribution of gains and losses is random.

2. **Sports and Leisure** Watch a basketball game, baseball game, or football game. For baseball, monitor an inning's pitches for balls and strikes (all fouls and balls in play also count as strikes). For football, monitor a series of plays for runs versus passing plays. For basketball, monitor one team's shots for misses versus made shots. For the collected data, conduct a runs test to see if the distribution is random.

3. **Technology** Use the data collected in data project 3 of Chapter 2 regarding song lengths. Consider only three genres. For example, use rock, alternative, and hip

hop/rap. Conduct a Kruskal-Wallis test to determine if the mean song lengths for the genres are the same.

4. **Health and Wellness** Have everyone in class take her or his pulse during the first minute of class. Have everyone take his or her pulse again 30 minutes into class. Conduct a paired-sample sign test to determine if there is a difference in pulse rates.

5. **Politics and Economics** Find the ranking for each state for its mean SAT Mathematics scores, its mean SAT English score, and its mean for income. Conduct a rank correlation analysis using Math and English, Math and income, and English and income. Which pair has the strongest relationship?

6. **Your Class** Have everyone in class take his or her temperature on a healthy day. Test the claim that the median body temperature is 98.6°F.

📑 Hypothesis-Testing Summary 3*

15. Test to see whether the median of a sample is a specific value when $n \geq 26$.

 Example: H_0: median = 100

 Use the sign test:
 $$z = \frac{(X + 0.5) - 0.5n}{\sqrt{n}/2}$$

16. Test to see whether two independent samples are obtained from populations that have identical distributions.

 Example: H_0: There is no difference in the ages of the subjects.

 Use the Wilcoxon rank sum test:
 $$z = \frac{R - \mu_R}{\sigma_R}$$

 where
 $$\mu_R = \frac{n_1(n_1 + n_2 + 1)}{2}$$

 $$\sigma_R = \sqrt{\frac{n_1 n_2(n_1 + n_2 + 1)}{12}}$$

17. Test to see whether two dependent samples have identical distributions.

 Example: H_0: There is no difference in the effects of a tranquilizer on the number of hours a person sleeps at night.

 Use the Wilcoxon signed-rank test:
 $$z = \frac{w_s - \dfrac{n(n + 1)}{4}}{\sqrt{\dfrac{n(n + 1)(2n + 1)}{24}}}$$

 when $n \geq 30$.

18. Test to see whether three or more samples come from identical populations.

 Example: H_0: There is no difference in the weights of the three groups.

 Use the Kruskal-Wallis test:
 $$H = \frac{12}{N(N + 1)}\left(\frac{R_1^2}{n_1} + \frac{R_2^2}{n_2} + \cdots + \frac{R_k^2}{n_k}\right) - 3(N + 1)$$

19. Rank correlation coefficient.
 $$r_s = 1 - \frac{6\Sigma d^2}{n(n^2 - 1)}$$

20. Test for randomness: Use the runs test.

Formulas for the Test Statistic Value for the Runs Test

When $n_1 \leq 20$ and $n_2 \leq 20$, use the number of runs, denoted by G, as the test statistic value. When $n_1 > 20$ or $n_2 > 20$ or when $n_1 > 20$ *and* $n_2 > 20$, use
$$z = \frac{G - \mu_G}{\sigma_G}$$

where
$$\mu_G = \frac{2n_1 n_2}{n_1 + n_2} + 1$$

$$\sigma_G = \sqrt{\frac{2n_1 n_2(2n_1 n_2 - n_1 - n_2)}{(n_1 + n_2)^2(n_1 + n_2 - 1)}}$$

*This summary is a continuation of Hypothesis-Testing Summary 2 at the end of Chapter 12.

≡ Answers to Applying the Concepts

Section 13–1   Ranking Data

Percent	2.6	3.8	4.0	4.0	5.4	7.0	7.0	7.3	10.0
Rank	1	2	3.5	3.5	5	6.5	6.5	8	9

Section 13–2   Clean Air

1. The claim is that the median number of days that a large city failed to meet EPA standards is 11 days per month.

2. We will use the sign test, since we do not know anything about the distribution of the variable and we are testing the median.

3. H_0: median = 11 and H_1: median > 11.

4. If $\alpha = 0.05$, then the critical value is 5.

5. The test value is 9.

6. Since 9 > 5, do not reject the null hypothesis.

7. There is not enough evidence to conclude that the median is not 11 days per month.

8. We cannot use a parametric test in this situation.

Section 13–3   School Lunch

1. The samples are independent since two different random samples were selected.

2. H_0: There is no difference in the number of calories served for lunch in elementary and secondary schools.

   H_1: There is a difference in the number of calories served for lunch in elementary and secondary schools.

3. We will use the Wilcoxon rank sum test.

4. The critical value is ± 1.96 if we use $\alpha = 0.05$.

5. The test statistic is $z = -2.15$.

6. Since $-2.15 < -1.96$, we reject the null hypothesis and conclude that there is a difference in the number of calories served for lunch in elementary and secondary schools.

7. The corresponding parametric test is the two-sample t test.

8. We would need to know that the samples were normally distributed to use the parametric test.

9. Since t tests are robust against variations from normality, the parametric test would yield the same results.

Section 13–4   Pain Medication

1. The purpose of the study is to see how effective a pain medication is.

2. These are dependent samples, since we have before-and-after readings on the same subjects.

3. H_0: The severity of pain after is the same as the severity of pain before the medication was administered.

   H_1: The severity of pain after is less than the severity of pain before the medication was administered.

4. We will use the Wilcoxon signed-rank test.

5. We will choose to use a significance level of 0.05.

6. The test statistic is $w_s = 2.5$. The critical value is 4. Since $2.5 < 4$, we reject the null hypothesis. There is enough evidence to conclude that the severity of pain after is less than the severity of pain before the medication was administered.

7. The parametric test that could be used is the t test for small dependent samples.

8. The results for the parametric test would be the same.

Section 13–5   Heights of Waterfalls

1. We are investigating the heights of waterfalls on three continents.

2. We will use the Kruskal-Wallis test.

3. H_0: There is no difference in the heights of waterfalls on the three continents.

   H_1: There is a difference in the heights of waterfalls on the three continents.

4. We will use the 0.05 significance level. The critical value is 5.991. Our test statistic is $H = 0.01$.

5. Since $0.01 < 5.991$, we fail to reject the null hypothesis. There is not enough evidence to conclude that there is a difference in the heights of waterfalls on the three continents.

6. The corresponding parametric test is analysis of variance (ANOVA).

7. To perform an ANOVA, the population must be normally distributed, the samples must be independent of each other, and the variances of the samples must be equal.

Section 13–6   Tall Trees

1. The biologist is trying to see if there is a relationship between the heights and diameters of tall trees.

2. We will use a Spearman rank correlation analysis.

3. The corresponding parametric test is the Pearson product moment correlation analysis.

4. Answers will vary.

5. The Pearson correlation coefficient is $r = 0.329$. The associated P-value is 0.353. We would fail to reject the null hypothesis that the correlation is zero. The Spearman's rank correlation coefficient is $r_s = 0.115$. We would reject the null hypothesis, at the 0.05 significance level, if $r_s > 0.648$. Since $0.115 < 0.648$, we fail to reject the null hypothesis that the correlation is zero. Both the parametric and nonparametric tests find that the correlation is not statistically significantly different from zero—it appears that no linear relationship exists between the heights and diameters of tall trees.

Sampling and Simulation

Let's Make A Deal

On a game show, the host gives a contestant a choice of three doors. A valuable prize is behind one door and nothing is behind the other two doors. While a contestant selects one door, the host opens one of the other doors that the contestant didn't select and that has no prize behind it. (The host knows in advance which door has the prize.) Then the host asks the contestant if he or she wants to change doors or keep the one that the contestant originally selected. Now the question is, Should the contestant switch doors, or does it really matter? This chapter will show you how you can solve this problem by simulation. For the answer, see Statistics Today—Revisited at the end of the chapter.

OUTLINE

Introduction

14–1 Common Sampling Techniques

14–2 Surveys and Questionnaire Design

14–3 Simulation Techniques and the Monte Carlo Method

Summary

OBJECTIVES

After completing this chapter, you should be able to

1 Demonstrate a knowledge of the four basic sampling methods.

2 Recognize faulty questions on a survey and other factors that can bias responses.

3 Solve problems, using simulation techniques.

Introduction

Most people have heard of Gallup and Nielsen. These and other pollsters gather information about the habits and opinions of the U.S. people. Such survey firms, and the U.S. Census Bureau, gather information by selecting samples from well-defined populations. Recall from Chapter 1 that the subjects in the sample should be a subgroup of the subjects in the population. Sampling methods often use what are called *random numbers* to select samples.

Since many statistical studies use surveys and questionnaires, some information about these is presented in Section 14–2.

Random numbers are also used in *simulation techniques*. Instead of studying a real-life situation, which may be costly or dangerous, researchers create a similar situation in a laboratory or with a computer. Then, by studying the simulated situation, researchers can gain the necessary information about the real-life situation in a less expensive or safer manner. This chapter will explain some common methods used to obtain samples as well as the techniques used in simulations.

14–1   Common Sampling Techniques

OBJECTIVE

Demonstrate a knowledge of the four basic sampling methods.

In Chapter 1, a *population* was defined as all subjects (human or otherwise) under study. Since some populations can be very large, researchers cannot use every single subject, so a sample must be selected. A *sample* is a subgroup of the population. In other words, the number of individuals in the sample is less than the number of individuals in the population. Any subgroup of the population, technically speaking, can be called a sample. However, for researchers to make valid inferences about population characteristics, the sample must be random.

> For a sample to be a **random sample,** every member of the population must have an equal chance of being selected.

When a sample is chosen at random from a population, it is said to be an **unbiased sample.** That is, the sample, for the most part, is representative of the population. Conversely, if a sample is selected incorrectly, it may be a biased sample. Samples are said to be **biased samples** when some type of systematic error has been made in the selection of the subjects.

A sample is used to get information about a population for several reasons:

1. *It saves the researcher time and money.*

2. *It enables the researcher to get information that he or she might not be able to obtain otherwise.* For example, if a person's blood is to be analyzed for cholesterol, a researcher cannot analyze every single drop of blood without killing the person. Or if the breaking strength of cables is to be determined, a researcher cannot test to destruction every cable manufactured, since the company would not have any cables left to sell.

3. *It enables the researcher to get more detailed information about a particular subject.* If only a few people are surveyed, the researcher can conduct in-depth interviews by spending more time with each person, thus getting more information about the subject. This is not to say that the smaller the sample, the better; in fact, the opposite is true. In general, larger samples—if correct sampling techniques are used—give more reliable information about the population.

It would be ideal if the sample were a perfect miniature of the population in all characteristics. This ideal, however, is impossible to achieve, because there are so many human traits (height, weight, IQ, etc.). The best that can be done is to select a sample that will be representative with respect to *some* characteristics, preferably those pertaining to the study. For example, if one-half of the population subjects are female, then approximately one-half of the sample subjects should be female. Likewise, other characteristics, such as age, socioeconomic status, and IQ, should be represented proportionately. To obtain unbiased samples, statisticians have developed several basic sampling methods. The most common methods are *random, systematic, stratified,* and *cluster sampling.* Each method will be explained in detail in this section.

In addition to the basic methods, there are other methods used to obtain samples. Some of these methods are also explained in this section.

Random Sampling

A random sample is obtained by using methods such as random numbers, which can be generated from calculators, computers, or tables. In *random sampling,* the basic requirement is that, for a sample of size *n,* all possible samples of this size have an equal chance of being selected from the population. But before the correct method of obtaining a random sample is explained, several incorrect methods commonly used by various researchers and agencies to gain information are discussed.

One incorrect method commonly used is to ask "the person on the street." News reporters use this technique quite often. Selecting people haphazardly on the street does not meet the requirement for simple random sampling, since not all possible samples of a specific size have an equal chance of being selected. Many people will be at home or at work when the interview is being conducted and therefore do not have a chance of being selected.

Another incorrect technique is to ask a question by either radio or television and have the listeners or viewers call the station to give their responses or opinions. Again, this sample is not random, since only those who feel strongly for or against the issue may respond and people may not have heard or seen the program. A third erroneous method is to ask people to respond by mail. Again, only those who are concerned and who have the time are likely to respond.

These methods do not meet the requirement of random sampling, since not all possible samples of a specific size have an equal chance of being selected. To meet this requirement, researchers can use one of two methods. The first method is to number each element of the population and then place the numbers on cards. Place the cards in a hat or fishbowl, mix them, and then select the sample by drawing the cards. When using this procedure, researchers must ensure that the numbers are well mixed. On occasion, when this procedure is used, the numbers are not mixed well, and the numbers chosen for the sample are those that were placed in the bowl last.

The second and preferred way of selecting a random sample is to use random numbers. Figure 14–1 shows a table of two-digit random numbers generated by a computer. A more detailed table of random numbers is found in Table D of Appendix A.

The theory behind random numbers is that each digit, 0 through 9, has an equal probability of occurring. That is, in every sequence of 10 digits, each digit has a probability of $\frac{1}{10}$ of occurring. This does not mean that in every sequence of 10 digits, you will find each digit. Rather, it means that on the average, each digit will occur once. For example, the digit 2 may occur 3 times in a sequence of 10 digits, but in later sequences, it may not occur at all, thus averaging to a probability of $\frac{1}{10}$.

To obtain a sample by using random numbers, number the elements of the population sequentially and then select each person by using random numbers. This process is shown in Example 14–1.

Random samples can be selected with or without replacement. If the same member of the population cannot be used more than once in the study, then the sample is selected without replacement. That is, once a random number is selected, it cannot be used later.

Note: In the explanations and examples of the sampling procedures, a small population will be used, and small samples will be selected from this population. Small populations

FIGURE 14–1

Table of Random Numbers

79	41	71	93	60	35	04	67	96	04	79	10	86
26	52	53	13	43	50	92	09	87	21	83	75	17
18	13	41	30	56	20	37	74	49	56	45	46	83
19	82	02	69	34	27	77	34	24	93	16	77	00
14	57	44	30	93	76	32	13	55	29	49	30	77
29	12	18	50	06	33	15	79	50	28	50	45	45
01	27	92	67	93	31	97	55	29	21	64	27	29
55	75	65	68	65	73	07	95	66	43	43	92	16
84	95	95	96	62	30	91	64	74	83	47	89	71
62	62	21	37	82	62	19	44	08	64	34	50	11
66	57	28	69	13	99	74	31	58	19	47	66	89
48	13	69	97	29	01	75	58	05	40	40	18	29
94	31	73	19	75	76	33	18	05	53	04	51	41
00	06	53	98	01	55	08	38	49	42	10	44	38
46	16	44	27	80	15	28	01	64	27	89	03	27
77	49	85	95	62	93	25	39	63	74	54	82	85
81	96	43	27	39	53	85	61	12	90	67	96	02
40	46	15	73	23	75	96	68	13	99	49	64	11

are used for illustrative purposes only, because the entire population could be included with little difficulty. In real life, however, researchers must usually sample from very large populations, using the procedures shown in this chapter.

EXAMPLE 14–1   State Governors on Capital Punishment

Suppose a researcher wants to produce a television show featuring in-depth interviews with state governors on the subject of capital punishment. Because of time constraints, the 60-minute program will have room for only 10 governors. The researcher wishes to select the governors at random. Select a random sample of 10 states from 50.

Note: This answer is not unique.

SOLUTION

Step 1   Number each state from 1 to 50, as shown. In this case, they are numbered alphabetically.

01. Alabama	14. Indiana	27. Nebraska	40. South Carolina
02. Alaska	15. Iowa	28. Nevada	41. South Dakota
03. Arizona	16. Kansas	29. New Hampshire	42. Tennessee
04. Arkansas	17. Kentucky	30. New Jersey	43. Texas
05. California	18. Louisiana	31. New Mexico	44. Utah
06. Colorado	19. Maine	32. New York	45. Vermont
07. Connecticut	20. Maryland	33. North Carolina	46. Virginia
08. Delaware	21. Massachusetts	34. North Dakota	47. Washington
09. Florida	22. Michigan	35. Ohio	48. West Virginia
10. Georgia	23. Minnesota	36. Oklahoma	49. Wisconsin
11. Hawaii	24. Mississippi	37. Oregon	50. Wyoming
12. Idaho	25. Missouri	38. Pennsylvania	
13. Illinois	26. Montana	39. Rhode Island	

Step 2   Using the random numbers shown in Figure 14–1, find a starting point. To find a starting point, you generally close your eyes and place your finger anywhere on the table. In this case, the first number selected was 27 in the fourth column. Going down the column and continuing on to the next column, select the first 10 numbers. They are 27, 95, 27, 73, 60, 43, 56, 34, 93, and 06. See Figure 14–2. (Note that 06 represents 6.)

FIGURE 14–2
Selecting a Starting Point and 10 Numbers from the Random Number Table

79	41	71	93	60 ✔	35	04	67	96	04	79	10	86
26	52	53	13	43 ✔	50	92	09	87	21	83	75	17
18	13	41	30	56 ✔	20	37	74	49	56	45	46	83
19	82	02	69	34 ✔	27	77	34	24	93	16	77	00
14	57	44	30	93 ✔	76	32	13	55	29	49	30	77
29	12	18	50	06 ✔	33	15	79	50	28	50	45	45
01	27	92	67	93	31	97	55	29	21	64	27	29
55	75	65	68	65	73	07	95	66	43	43	92	16
84	95	95	96	62	30	91	64	74	83	47	89	71
62	62	21	37	82	62	19	44	08	64	34	50	11
66	57	28	69	13	99	74	31	58	19	47	66	89
48	13	69	97	29	01	75	58	05	40	40	18	29
94	31	73	19	75	76	33	18	05	53	04	51	41
00	06	53	*Start here	01	55	08	38	49	42	10	44	38
46	16	44	㉗✔	80	15	28	01	64	27	89	03	27
77	49	85	95 ✔	62	93	25	39	63	74	54	82	85
81	96	43	27 ✔	39	53	85	61	12	90	67	96	02
40	46	15	73 ✔	23	75	96	68	13	99	49	64	11

Now, refer to the list of states and identify the state corresponding to each number. The sample consists of the following states:

27	Nebraska	43	Texas
95		56	
27	Nebraska	34	North Dakota
73		93	
60		06	Colorado

Step 3 Since the numbers 95, 73, 60, 56, and 93 are too large because there are only 50 states, they are disregarded. And since 27 appears twice, it is also disregarded the second time. Now, you must select six more random numbers between 1 and 50 and omit duplicates, since this sample will be selected without replacement. Make this selection by continuing down the column and moving over to the next column until a total of 10 numbers is selected. The final 10 numbers are 27, 43, 34, 06, 13, 29, 01, 39, 23, and 35. See Figure 14–3.

FIGURE 14–3
The Final 10 Numbers Selected

79	41	71	93	60	�35	04	67	96	04	79	10	86
26	52	53	13	㊸	50	92	09	87	21	83	75	17
18	13	41	30	56	20	37	74	49	56	45	46	83
19	82	02	69	㉞	27	77	34	24	93	16	77	00
14	57	44	30	93	76	32	13	55	29	49	30	77
29	12	18	50	⑥	33	15	79	50	28	50	45	45
01	27	92	67	93	31	97	55	29	21	64	27	29
55	75	65	68	65	73	07	95	66	43	43	92	16
84	95	95	96	62	30	91	64	74	83	47	89	71
62	62	21	37	82	62	19	44	08	64	34	50	11
66	57	28	69	⑬	99	74	31	58	19	47	66	89
48	13	69	97	㉙	01	75	58	05	40	40	18	29
94	31	73	19	75	76	33	18	05	53	04	51	41
00	06	53	98	⓪①	55	08	38	49	42	10	44	38
46	16	44	㉗	80	15	28	01	64	27	89	03	27
77	49	85	95	62	93	25	39	63	74	54	82	85
81	96	43	27	㊴	53	85	61	12	90	67	96	02
40	46	15	73	㉓	75	96	68	13	99	49	64	11

These numbers correspond to the following states:

27	Nebraska	29	New Hampshire
43	Texas	01	Alabama
34	North Dakota	39	Rhode Island
06	Colorado	23	Minnesota
13	Illinois	35	Ohio

Thus, the governors of these 10 states will constitute the sample.

Random sampling has one limitation. If the population is extremely large, it is time-consuming to number and select the sample elements. Also, notice that the random numbers in the table are two-digit numbers. If three digits are needed, then the first digit from the next column can be used, as shown in Figure 14–4. For example, if you wanted to obtain a sample of 5 randomly selected three-digit numbers from Figure 14–4, you would first select a starting point. We will use 40 in the first column as a starting point. Table D in Appendix A gives five-digit random numbers.

FIGURE 14–4
Method for Selecting
Three-Digit Numbers

79	41	71	93	60	35	04	67	96	04	79	10	86
26	52	53	13	43	50	92	09	87	21	83	75	17
18	13	41	30	56	20	37	74	49	56	45	46	83
19	82	02	69	34	27	77	34	24	93	16	77	00
14	57	44	30	93	76	32	13	55	29	49	30	77
29	12	18	50	06	33	15	79	50	28	50	45	45
01	27	92	67	93	31	97	55	29	21	64	27	29
55	75	65	68	65	73	07	95	66	43	43	92	16
84	95	95	96	62	30	91	64	74	83	47	89	71
62	62	21	37	82	62	19	44	08	64	34	50	11
66	57	28	69	13	99	74	31	58	19	47	66	89
48	13	69	97	29	01	75	58	05	40	40	18	29
94	31	73	19	75	76	33	18	05	53	04	51	41
00	06	53	98	01	55	08	38	49	42	10	44	38
46	16	44	27	80	15	28	01	64	27	89	03	27
77	49	85	95	62	93	25	39	63	74	54	82	85
81	96	43	27	39	53	85	61	12	90	67	96	02
40	46	15	73	23	75	96	68	13	99	49	64	11

Use one column and part of the next column for three digits, that is, 404.

Systematic Sampling

A **systematic sample** is a sample obtained by numbering each element in the population selecting some random starting point, and then selecting every *k*th element (third or fifth or tenth, etc.) from the population to be included in the sample.

The procedure of systematic sampling is illustrated in Example 14–2.

EXAMPLE 14–2   Television Show Interviews

Using the population of 50 states in Example 14–1, select a systematic sample of 10 states.

SOLUTION

Step 1   Number the population units as shown in Example 14–1.

The National Weather Service collects various types of data about the weather. For example, each year in the United States about 400 million lightning strikes occur. On average, 400 people are struck by lightning, and 85% of those struck are men. About 100 of these people die. The cause of most of these deaths is not burns, even though temperatures as high as 54,000°F are reached, but heart attacks. The lightning strike short-circuits the body's autonomic nervous system, causing the heart to stop beating. In some instances, the heart will restart on its own. In other cases, the heart victim will need emergency resuscitation.

The most dangerous places to be during a thunderstorm are open fields, golf courses, under trees, and near water, such as a lake or swimming pool. It's best to be inside a building during a thunderstorm although there's no guarantee that the building won't be struck by lightning. Are these statistics descriptive or inferential? Why do you think more men are struck by lightning than women? Should you be afraid of lightning?

Step 2   Since there are 50 states and 10 are to be selected, the rule is to select every fifth state. This rule was determined by dividing 50 by 10, which yields 5.

Step 3   Using the table of random numbers, select the first digit (from 1 to 5) at random. In this case, 4 was selected.

Step 4   Select every fifth number on the list, starting with 4. The numbers include the following:

1 2 3 ④ 5 6 7 8 ⑨ 10 11 12 13 ⑭ · · ·

The selected states are as follows:

4	Arkansas	29	New Hampshire
9	Florida	34	North Dakota
14	Indiana	39	Rhode Island
19	Maine	44	Utah
24	Mississippi	49	Wisconsin

The advantage of systematic sampling is the ease of selecting the sample elements. Also, in many cases, a numbered list of the population units may already exist. For example, the manager of a factory may have a list of employees who work for the company, or there may be an in-house telephone directory.

When doing systematic sampling, you must be careful how the items are arranged on the list. For example, if each unit were arranged, say, as

1. Husband

2. Wife

3. Husband

4. Wife

then the selection of the starting number could produce a sample of all males or all females, depending on whether the starting number is even or odd and whether the number to be added is even or odd. As another example, if the list were arranged in order of heights of individuals, you would get a different average from two samples if the first were selected by using a small starting number and the second by using a large starting number.

Stratified Sampling

A **stratified sample** is a sample obtained by dividing the population into subgroups, called *strata,* according to various homogeneous (similar) characteristics and then randomly selecting members from each stratum for the sample.

For example, a population may consist of males and females who are smokers or nonsmokers. The researcher will want to include in the sample people from each group—that is, males who smoke, males who do not smoke, females who smoke, and females who do not smoke. To accomplish this selection, the researcher divides the population into four subgroups and then selects a random sample from each subgroup. This method ensures that the sample is representative on the basis of the characteristics of gender and smoking. Of course, it may not be representative on the basis of other characteristics.

EXAMPLE 14–3   Selecting Students

Using the population of 20 students shown in Figure 14–5, select a sample of eight students on the basis of gender (male/female) and grade level (freshman/sophomore) by stratification.

FIGURE 14–5
Population of Students for
Example 14–3

1. Ald, Peter	M	Fr		11. Martin, Janice	F	Fr
2. Brown, Danny	M	So		12. Meloski, Gary	M	Fr
3. Bear, Theresa	F	Fr		13. Oeler, George	M	So
4. Carson, Susan	F	Fr		14. Peters, Michele	F	So
5. Collins, Carolyn	F	Fr		15. Peterson, John	M	Fr
6. Davis, William	M	Fr		16. Smith, Nancy	F	Fr
7. Hogan, Michael	M	Fr		17. Thomas, Jeff	M	So
8. Jones, Lois	F	So		18. Toms, Debbie	F	So
9. Lutz, Harry	M	So		19. Unger, Roberta	F	So
10. Lyons, Larry	M	So		20. Zibert, Mary	F	So

SOLUTION

Step 1   Divide the population into two subgroups, consisting of males and females, as shown in Figure 14–6.

FIGURE 14–6
Population Divided into
Subgroups by Gender

Males				**Females**		
1. Ald, Peter	M	Fr		1. Bear, Theresa	F	Fr
2. Brown, Danny	M	So		2. Carson, Susan	F	Fr
3. Davis, William	M	Fr		3. Collins, Carolyn	F	Fr
4. Hogan, Michael	M	Fr		4. Jones, Lois	F	So
5. Lutz, Harry	M	So		5. Martin, Janice	F	Fr
6. Lyons, Larry	M	So		6. Peters, Michele	F	So
7. Meloski, Gary	M	Fr		7. Smith, Nancy	F	Fr
8. Oeler, George	M	So		8. Toms, Debbie	F	So
9. Peterson, John	M	Fr		9. Unger, Roberta	F	So
10. Thomas, Jeff	M	So		10. Zibert, Mary	F	So

Step 2   Divide each subgroup further into two groups of freshmen and sophomores, as shown in Figure 14–7.

FIGURE 14–7
Each Subgroup Divided into
Subgroups by Grade Level

Group 1				Group 2		
1. Ald, Peter	M	Fr		1. Bear, Theresa	F	Fr
2. Davis, William	M	Fr		2. Carson, Susan	F	Fr
3. Hogan, Michael	M	Fr		3. Collins, Carolyn	F	Fr
4. Meloski, Gary	M	Fr		4. Martin, Janice	F	Fr
5. Peterson, John	M	Fr		5. Smith, Nancy	F	Fr

Group 3				Group 4		
1. Brown, Danny	M	So		1. Jones, Lois	F	So
2. Lutz, Harry	M	So		2. Peters, Michele	F	So
3. Lyons, Larry	M	So		3. Toms, Debbie	F	So
4. Oeler, George	M	So		4. Unger, Roberta	F	So
5. Thomas, Jeff	M	So		5. Zibert, Mary	F	So

Step 3   Determine how many students need to be selected from each subgroup to have a proportional representation of each subgroup in the sample. There are four groups, and since a total of eight students is needed for the sample, two students must be selected from each subgroup.

Step 4   Select two students from each group by using random numbers. In this case, the random numbers are as follows:

Group 1   Students 5 and 4   Group 2   Students 5 and 2

Group 3   Students 1 and 3   Group 4   Students 3 and 4

The stratified sample then consists of the following people:

Peterson, John	M	Fr	Smith, Nancy	F	Fr
Meloski, Gary	M	Fr	Carson, Susan	F	Fr
Brown, Danny	M	So	Toms, Debbie	F	So
Lyons, Larry	M	So	Unger, Roberta	F	So

The major advantage of stratification is that it ensures representation of all population subgroups that are important to the study. There are two major drawbacks to stratification, however. First, if there are many variables of interest, dividing a large population into representative subgroups requires a great deal of effort. Second, if the variables are somewhat complex or ambiguous (such as beliefs, attitudes, or prejudices), it is difficult to separate individuals into the subgroups according to these variables.

Cluster Sampling

A **cluster sample** is a sample obtained by selecting a preexisting or natural group, called a *cluster,* and using the members in the cluster for the sample.

For example, many studies in education use already existing classes, such as the seventh grade in Wilson Junior High School. The voters of a certain electoral district might be surveyed to determine their preferences for a mayoral candidate in the upcoming election. Or the residents of an entire city block might be polled to ascertain the percentage of households that have two or more incomes. In cluster sampling, researchers may use all

In this study, the researchers found that subjects did better on fill-in-the-blank questions than on multiple-choice questions. Do you agree with the professor's statement, "Trusting your first impulse is your best strategy"? Explain your answer.

TESTS

Is That Your Final Answer?

Beating game shows takes more than smarts: Contestants must also overcome self-doubt and peer pressure. Two new studies suggest today's hottest game shows are particularly challenging because the very mechanisms employed to help contestants actually lead them astray.

Multiple-choice questions are one such offender, as alternative answers seem to make test-takers ignore gut instincts. To learn why, researchers at Southern Methodist University (SMU) gave two identical tests: one using multiple-choice questions and the other fill-in-the-blank. The results, recently published in the *Journal of Educational Psychology*, show that test-takers were incorrect more often when given false alternatives, and that the longer they considered those alternatives, the more credible the answers looked.

"If you sit and stew, you forget that you know the right answer," says Alan Brown, Ph.D., a psychology professor at SMU. "Trusting your first impulse is your best strategy."

Audiences can also be trouble, says Jennifer Butler, Ph.D., a Wittenberg University psychology professor. Her recent study in the *Journal of Personality and Social Psychology* found that contestants who see audience participation as peer pressure slow down to avoid making embarrassing mistakes. But this strategy backfires, as more contemplation produces more wrong answers. Worse, Butler says, if perceived peer pressure grows unbearable, contestants may opt out of answering at all, "thinking that it's better to stop than to have your once supportive audience come to believe you're an idiot."

— *Sarah Smith*

Source: Reprinted with permission from *Psychology Today Magazine,* (Copyright © 2000 Sussex Publishers, LLC.).

---

units of a cluster if that is feasible, or they may select only part of a cluster to use as a sample. This selection is done by random methods.

There are three advantages to using a cluster sample instead of other types of samples: (1) A cluster sample can reduce costs, (2) it can simplify fieldwork, and (3) it is convenient. For example, in a dental study involving X-raying fourth-grade students' teeth to see how many cavities each child had, it would be a simple matter to select a single classroom and bring the X-ray equipment to the school to conduct the study. If other sampling methods were used, researchers might have to transport the machine to several different schools or transport the pupils to the dental office.

The major disadvantage of cluster sampling is that the elements in a cluster may not have the same variations in characteristics as elements selected individually from a population. The reason is that groups of people may be more homogeneous (alike) in specific clusters such as neighborhoods or clubs. For example, the people who live in a certain neighborhood tend to have similar incomes, drive similar cars, live in similar houses, and, for the most part, have similar habits.

Other Types of Sampling Techniques

In addition to the four basic sampling methods, other methods are sometimes used. In **sequence sampling,** which is used in quality control, successive units taken from production lines are sampled to ensure that the products meet certain standards set by the manufacturing company.

In **double sampling,** a very large population is given a questionnaire to determine those who meet the qualifications for a study. After the questionnaires are reviewed, a second, smaller population is defined. Then a sample is selected from this group.

❙ Interesting Fact

Folks in extra-large aerobics classes—those with 70 to 90 participants—show up more often and are more fond of their classmates than exercisers in sessions of 18 to 26 people, report researchers at the University of Arizona.

In **multistage sampling,** the researcher uses a combination of sampling methods. For example, suppose a research organization wants to conduct a nationwide survey for a new product being manufactured. A sample can be obtained by using the following combination of methods. First the researchers divide the 50 states into four or five regions (or clusters). Then several states from each region are selected at random. Next the states are divided into various areas by using large cities and small towns. Samples of these areas are then selected. Next, each city and each town are divided into districts or wards. Finally, streets in these wards are selected at random, and the families living on these streets are given samples of the product to test and are asked to report the results. This hypothetical example illustrates a typical multistage sampling method.

In **convenience sampling,** the researcher selects subjects from the population who are available to use. These samples are usually not representative of the population, and their use can lead to biased conclusions.

The steps for conducting a sample survey are given in the Procedure Table.

Procedure Table

Conducting a Sample Survey

Step 1   Decide what information is needed.

Step 2   Determine how the data will be collected (phone interview, mail survey, etc.).

Step 3   Select the information-gathering instrument or design the questionnaire if one is not available.

Step 4   Set up a sampling list, if possible.

Step 5   Select the best method for obtaining the sample (random, systematic, stratified, cluster, or other).

Step 6   Conduct the survey and collect the data.

Step 7   Tabulate the data.

Step 8   Conduct the statistical analysis.

Step 9   Report the results.

A question often asked about sampling is, "How large of a sample do I need?" The answer to this question is based on several things. Two important considerations are time and money. The more time and money a researcher has, the larger the sample can be. When random samples are used, larger samples can result in more reliable conclusions. Also as shown in Chapter 7, actual sample size numbers can be obtained if the researcher knows the confidence interval and the degree of accuracy or the margin of error desired.

Applying the Concepts 14–1

The White or Wheat Bread Debate

Read the following study and answer the questions.

A baking company selected 36 women weighing different amounts and randomly assigned them to four different groups. The four groups were white bread only, brown bread only, low-fat white bread only, and low-fat brown bread only. Each group could eat only the type of bread assigned to the group. The study lasted for eight weeks. No other changes in any of the women's diets were allowed. A trained evaluator was used to check for any differences in the women's diets. The results showed that there were no differences in weight gain between the groups over the eight-week period.

1. Did the researchers use a population or a sample for their study?

2. Based on who conducted this study, would you consider the study to be biased?

3. Which sampling method do you think was used to obtain the original 36 women for the study (random, systematic, stratified, or clustered)?

4. Which sampling method would you use? Why?

5. How would you collect a random sample for this study?

6. Does random assignment help representativeness the same as random selection does? Explain.

See page 771 for the answers.

Exercises 14–1

1. Name the four basic sampling techniques.

2. Why are samples used in statistics?

3. What is the basic requirement for a sample?

4. Why should random numbers be used when you are selecting a random sample?

5. List three incorrect methods that are often used to obtain a sample.

6. What is the principle behind random numbers?

7. List the advantages and disadvantages of random sampling.

8. List the advantages and disadvantages of systematic sampling.

9. List the advantages and disadvantages of stratified sampling.

10. List the advantages and disadvantages of cluster sampling.

Use the Overview of U.S. Public Schools data to answer Exercises 11 through 14.

Overview of U.S. Public Schools

State	Pupils per Teacher	Teacher's Avg. Pay
AL	16.0	$47,571
AK	14.9	59,672
AZ	18.9	46,952
AR	12.7	14,700
CA	21.4	68,203
CO	17.0	49,202
CT	13.2	64,350
DE	14.4	57,080
FL	15.9	46,708
GA	14.4	53,112
HI	15.2	55,063
ID	18.2	46,283
IL	14.9	62,077
IN	16.7	49,986
IA	13.8	49,626
KS	13.7	46,657
KY	15.8	49,543
LA	14.0	48,903
ME	11.1	46,106

State	Pupils per Teacher	Teacher's Avg. Pay
MD	14.3	63,971
MA	13.6	69,273
MI	17.1	57,958
MN	15.4	52,431
MS	31.9	45,644
MO	13.3	45,317
MT	13.4	45,759
NE	13.4	46,227
NV	18.5	51,524
NH	12.7	51,443
NJ	12.0	65,130
NM	14.9	46,258
NY	11.8	71,633
NC	14.8	46,850
ND	12.1	42,964
OH	17.1	55,958
OK	15.5	47,691
OR	18.7	55,224
PA	14.0	59,156
RI	13.0	59,686
SC	14.8	47,508
SD	13.4	38,837
TN	14.7	46,290
TX	14.5	48,261
UT	22.4	45,885
VT	9.8	49,084
VA	11.7	50,015
WA	19.3	53,003
WV	14.3	45,959
WI	14.8	51,264
WY	12.3	55,861
U.S.	15.3	55,202

11. **Teacher Data** Using the table of random numbers, select 10 states and find the mean of the average teacher's pay and the mean of the pupils per teacher. How do your results compare with the U.S. figures?

12. **Teacher Data** Select a systematic sample of 10 states, and find the mean of the average teacher's pay and the mean of the pupils per teacher. How do your results compare with the U.S. figures?

13. **Teacher Data** Select a cluster sample of 10 states, and find the mean of the average teacher's pay and the mean of the pupils per teacher. How do your results compare with the U.S. figures?

14. **Teacher Data** Are there any characteristics of these data that might create problems in sampling?

Use the following data for Exercises 15 and 16.

Record Highest Temperatures by State (°F)

Alabama 105	Montana 105
Alaska 85	Nebraska 114
Arizona 122	Nevada 106
Arkansas 111	New Hampshire 102
California 110	New Jersey 106
Colorado 105	New Mexico 107
Connecticut 102	New York 100
Delaware 103	North Carolina 105
Florida 105	North Dakota 112
Georgia 105	Ohio 104
Hawaii 95	Oklahoma 110
Idaho 111	Oregon 107
Illinois 104	Pennsylvania 104
Indiana 104	Rhode Island 104
Iowa 108	South Carolina 105
Kansas 110	South Dakota 112
Kentucky 106	Tennessee 108
Louisiana 102	Texas 113
Maine 103	Utah 107
Maryland 105	Vermont 101
Massachusetts 102	Virginia 105
Michigan 104	Washington 108
Minnesota 105	West Virginia 104
Mississippi 107	Wisconsin 103
Missouri 109	Wyoming 101

15. **Record High Temperatures** Which method of sampling might be good for this set of data? Choose one to select 10 states and calculate the sample mean. Compare with the population mean.

16. **Record High Temperatures** Choose a different method to select 10 states and compute the sample mean high temperature. Compare with your answer in Exercise 15 and with the population mean. Do you see any features of this data set that might affect the results of obtaining a sample mean?

Use the following data for Exercises 17 through 19.

States and Number of Electoral Votes for Each

1. Alabama	9	11. Hawaii	4	21. Massachusetts	11
2. Alaska	3	12. Idaho	4	22. Michigan	16
3. Arizona	11	13. Illinois	20	23. Minnesota	10
4. Arkansas	6	14. Indiana	11	24. Mississippi	6
5. California	55	15. Iowa	6	25. Missouri	10
6. Colorado	9	16. Kansas	6	26. Montana	3
7. Connecticut	7	17. Kentucky	8	27. Nebraska	5
8. Delaware	3	18. Louisiana	8	28. Nevada	6
9. Florida	29	19. Maine	4	29. New Hampshire	4
10. Georgia	16	20. Maryland	10	30. New Jersey	14
				31. New Mexico	5
				32. New York	29
				33. North Carolina	15
				34. North Dakota	3
				35. Ohio	18
				36. Oklahoma	7
				37. Oregon	7
				38. Pennsylvania	20
				39. Rhode Island	4
				40. South Carolina	9
				41. South Dakota	3
				42. Tennessee	11
				43. Texas	38
				44. Utah	6
				45. Vermont	3
				46. Virginia	13
				47. Washington	12
				48. West Virginia	5
				49. Wisconsin	10
				50. Wyoming	3

17. **Electoral Votes** Select a systematic sample of 10 states, and compute the mean number of electoral votes for the sample. Compare this mean with the population mean.

18. **Electoral Votes** Divide the 50 states into five subgroups by geographic location, using a map of the United States. Each subgroup should include 10 states. The subgroups should be northeast, southeast, central, northwest, and southwest. Select two states from each subgroup, and find the mean number of electoral votes for the sample. Compare these means with the population mean.

19. **Electoral Votes** Select a cluster of 10 states, and compute the mean number of electoral votes for the sample. Compare this mean with the population mean.

"Now think carefully. The answer you give will represent the opinion of millions of Americans."

Source: *The Saturday Evening Post*, BFL&MS, Inc.

20. Many research studies described in newspapers and magazines do not report the sample size or the sampling method used. Try to find a research article that gives this information; state the sampling method that was used and the sample size.

▄▆ Technology

Step by Step

TI-84 Plus

Step by Step

Generate Random Numbers

To generate random numbers from 0 to 1 by using the TI-84 Plus:

1. Press **MATH** and move the cursor to PRB and press **1** for rand, then press **ENTER.** The calculator will generate a random decimal from 0 to 1.

2. To generate additional random numbers press **ENTER.**

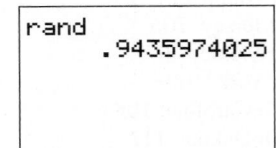

```
rand
        .9435974025
```

To generate a list of random integers between two specific values:

1. Press **MATH** and move the cursor to PRB.

2. Press **5** for randInt(.

3. Enter the lowest value followed by a comma, then the largest value followed by a comma, then the number of random numbers desired followed by). Press **ENTER.**

Example: Generate five three-digit random numbers.

Enter **0, 999, 5**) at the randInt(as shown.

```
randInt(0,999,5
{908 146 514 40▶
```

The calculator will generate five three-digit random numbers. Use the arrow keys to view the entire list.

EXCEL

Step by Step

Generate Random Numbers

The Data Analysis Add-In in Excel has a feature to generate random numbers from a specified probability distribution. For this example, a list of 50 random real numbers will be generated from a uniform distribution. The real numbers will then be rounded to integers between 1 and 50.

1. Open a new worksheet and select the Data tab, then **Data Analysis>Random Number Generation** from Analysis Tools. Click [OK].

2. In the dialog box, type **1** for the Number of Variables. Leave the Number of Random Numbers box empty.

3. For Distribution, select Uniform.

4. In the Parameters box, type **1** for the lower bound and **51** for the upper bound.

5. You may type in an integer value between **1** and **51** for the Random Seed. For this example, type **3** for the Random Seed.

6. Select Output Range and type in **A1:A50.**

7. Click [OK].

The first 10 output numbers are shown.

	A
1	1.073244
2	11.98056
3	15.18195
4	14.87219
5	11.72878
6	36.97674
7	28.01193
8	36.86383
9	42.53111
10	19.56746

To convert the random numbers to a list of integers:

8. Select cell B1 and select the Formulas tab, and then the Insert Function icon.

9. Select the Math & Trig Function category and scroll to the Function name INT to convert the data in column A to integer values.

Note: The INT function rounds the argument (input) down to the nearest integer.

10. Type **A1** for the Number in the INT dialog box. Click [OK].

11. While cell B1 is selected in the worksheet, move the pointer to the lower right-hand corner of the cell until a thick plus sign appears. Right-click on the mouse and drag the plus down to cell **B50;** then release the mouse key.

12. The numbers from column A should have been rounded to integers in column B.

Here is a sample of the data produced from the preceding procedure.

1.073244	1
11.98056	11
15.18195	15
14.87219	14
11.72878	11
36.97674	36
28.01193	28
36.86383	36
42.53111	42
19.56746	19

MINITAB
Step by Step

Select a Random Sample with Replacement

A simple random sample selected with replacement allows some values to be used more than once, duplicates. In the first example, a random sample of integers will be selected with replacement.

1. Select **Calc>Random Data>Integer.**
2. Type **10** for rows of data.
3. Type the name of a column, Random1, in the box for Store in column(s).
4. Type **1** for Minimum and **50** for Maximum, then click [OK].

A sample of 10 integers between 1 and 50 will be displayed in the first column of the worksheet. Every list will be different.

Select a Random Sample Without Replacement

To sample without replacement, make a list of integers and sample from the columns.

1. Select **Calc>Make Patterned Data>Simple Set of Numbers.**
2. Type **Integers** in the text box for Store patterned data in.
3. Type **1** for Minimum and **50** for Maximum. Leave 1 for steps and click [OK]. A list of the integers from 1 to 50 will be created in the worksheet.
4. Select **Calc>Random Data>Sample from columns.**
5. Sample **10** for the number of rows and Integers for the name of the column.
6. Type Random2 as the name of the new column. Be sure to leave the option for Sample with replacement unchecked.
7. Click [OK]. The new sample will be in the worksheet. There will be no duplicates.

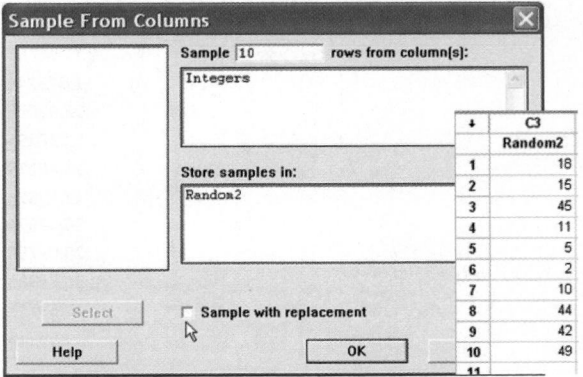

Select a Random Sample from a Normal Distribution

No data are required in the worksheet.

1. Select **Calc>Random Data>Normal . . .**
2. Type **50** for the number of rows.
3. Press TAB or click in the box for Store in column(s). Type in RandomNormal.
4. Type in **500** for the Mean and **75** for the Standard deviation.
5. Click [OK]. The random numbers are in a column of the worksheet. The distribution is sampled "with replacement." However, duplicates are not likely since this distribution is continuous. They are displayed to 3 decimal places, but many more places are stored. Click in any cell such as row 5 of C4 RandomNormal, and you will see more decimal places.
6. To display the list, select **Data>Display data,** then select C1 RandomNormal and click [OK]. They are displayed in the same order they were selected, but going across not down.

14–2 Surveys and Questionnaire Design

OBJECTIVE ❷

Recognize faulty questions on a survey and other factors that can bias responses.

Many statistical studies obtain information from *surveys*. A survey is conducted when a sample of individuals is asked to respond to questions about a particular subject. There are two types of surveys: interviewer-administered and self-administered. Interviewer-administered surveys require a person to ask the questions. The interview can be conducted face to face in an office, on a street, or in the mall, or via telephone.

Self-administered surveys can be done by mail or in a group setting such as a classroom.

When analyzing the results of surveys, you should be very careful about the interpretations. The way a question is phrased can influence the way people respond. For example, when a group of people were asked if they favored a waiting period and background check before guns could be sold, 91% of the respondents were in favor of it and 7% were against it. However, when asked if there should be a national gun registration program costing about 20% of all dollars spent on crime control, only 33% of the respondents were in favor of it and 61% were against it.

As you can see, by phrasing questions in different ways, different responses can be obtained, since the purpose of a national gun registry would include a waiting period and a background check.

When you are writing questions for a questionnaire, it is important to avoid these common mistakes.

1. *Asking biased questions.* By asking questions in a certain way, the researcher can lead the respondents to answer in the way he or she wants them to. For example, asking a question such as "Are you going to vote for candidate Jones even though the latest survey indicates that he will lose the election?" instead of "Are you going to vote for candidate Jones?" may dissuade some people from answering in the affirmative.

2. *Using confusing words.* In this case, the participant misinterprets the meaning of the words and answers the questions in a biased way. For example, the question "Do you think people would live longer if they were on a diet?" could be misinterpreted since there are many different types of diets—weight loss diets, low-salt diets, medically prescribed diets, etc.

3. *Asking double-barreled questions.* Sometimes questions contain compound sentences that require the participant to respond to two questions at the same time. For

example, the question "Are you in favor of a special tax to provide national health care for the citizens of the United States?" asks two questions: "Are you in favor of a national health care program?" and "Do you favor a tax to support it?"

4. *Using double negatives in questions.* Questions with double negatives can be confusing to the respondents. For example, the question "Do you feel that it is not appropriate to have areas where people cannot smoke?" is very confusing since *not* is used twice in the sentence.

5. *Ordering questions improperly.* By arranging the questions in a certain order, the researcher can lead the participant to respond in a way that he or she may otherwise not have done. For example, a question might ask the respondent, "At what age should an elderly person not be permitted to drive?" A later question might ask the respondent to list some problems of elderly people. The respondent may indicate that transportation is a problem based on reading the previous question.

Other factors can also bias a survey. For example, the participant may not know anything about the subject of the question but will answer the question anyway to avoid being considered uninformed. For example, many people might respond yes or no to the following question: "Would you be in favor of giving pensions to the widows of unknown soldiers?" In this case, the question makes no sense since if the soldiers were unknown, their widows would also be unknown.

Many people will make responses on the basis of what they think the person asking the questions wants to hear. For example, if a question states, "How often do you lie?" people may *understate* the incidences of their lying.

Participants will, in some cases, respond differently to questions depending on whether their identity is known. This is especially true if the questions concern sensitive issues such as income, sexuality, and abortion. Researchers try to ensure confidentiality (i.e., keeping the respondent's identity secret) rather than anonymity (soliciting unsigned responses); however, many people will be suspicious in either case.

Still other factors that could bias a survey include the time and place of the survey and whether the questions are open-ended or closed-ended. The time and place where a survey is conducted can influence the results. For example, if a survey on airline safety is conducted immediately after a major airline crash, the results may differ from those obtained in a year in which no major airline disasters occurred.

Finally, the type of questions asked influences the responses. In this case, the concern is whether the question is open-ended or closed-ended.

An *open-ended question* would be one such as "List three activities that you plan to spend more time on when you retire." A *closed-ended question* would be one such as "Which one of these activities do you plan to spend more time on after you retire: traveling; eating out; fishing and hunting; exercising; visiting relatives?"

One problem with a closed-ended question is that the respondent is forced to choose the answers that the researcher gives and cannot supply his or her own. But there is also a problem with open-ended questions in that the results may be so varied that attempting to summarize them might be difficult, if not impossible. Hence, you should be aware of what types of questions are being asked before you draw any conclusions from the survey.

There are several other things to consider when you are conducting a study that uses questionnaires. For example, a pilot study should be done to test the design and usage of the questionnaire (i.e., the *validity* of the questionnaire). The pilot study helps the researcher to pretest the questionnaire to determine if it meets the objectives of the study. It also helps the researcher to rewrite any questions that may be misleading, ambiguous, etc.

If the questions are being asked by an interviewer, some training should be given to that person. If the survey is being done by mail, a cover letter and clear directions should accompany the questionnaire.

Questionnaires help researchers to gather needed statistical information for their studies; however, much care must be given to proper questionnaire design and usage; otherwise, the results will be unreliable.

Unusual Stat

Of people who are struck by lightning, 85% are men.

Applying the Concepts 14–2

Smoking Bans and Profits

Assume you are a restaurant owner and are concerned about the recent bans on smoking in public places. Will your business lose money if you do not allow smoking in your restaurant? You decide to research this question and find two related articles in regional newspapers. The first article states that randomly selected restaurants in Derry, Pennsylvania, that have completely banned smoking have lost 25% of their business. In that study, a survey was used and the owners were asked how much business they thought they lost. The survey was conducted by an anonymous group. It was reported in the second article that there had been a modest increase in business among restaurants that banned smoking in that same area. Sales receipts were collected and analyzed against last year's profits. The second survey was conducted by the Restaurants Business Association.

1. How has the public smoking ban affected restaurant business in Derry, Pennsylvania?
2. Why do you think the surveys reported conflicting results?
3. Should surveys based on anecdotal responses be allowed to be published?
4. Can the results of a sample be representative of a population and still offer misleading information?
5. How critical is measurement error in survey sampling?

See page 771 for the answers.

Exercises 14–2

Exercises 1 through 9 include questions that contain a flaw. Identify the flaw and rewrite the question, following the guidelines presented in this section.

1. Which type of artificial sweetener do you think is the least unhealthy?

2. Do you like the mayor?

3. Do you approve of the mayor's political agenda?

4. Do you approve of the mayor's position on the new soft drink tax?

5. How long have you studied for this examination?

6. Which artificial sweetener do you prefer?

7. If a plane were to crash on the border of New York and New Jersey, where should the survivors be buried?

8. Are you in favor of imposing a tax on tobacco to pay for health care related to diseases caused by smoking?

9. The following "Poll Question of the Day" appeared in a local newspaper. "With the passing of Neil Armstrong (first man to walk on the moon), many remember the historical first walk on the moon. Do you remember watching the television coverage?" Answers included "Yes," "No," and "Vaguely."

10. Find a study that uses a questionnaire. Select any questions that you feel are improperly written.

11. Many television and radio stations have a phone vote poll. If there is one in your area, select a specific day and write a brief paragraph stating the question of the day and state if it could be misleading in any way.

14–3 Simulation Techniques and the Monte Carlo Method

Many real-life problems can be solved by employing simulation techniques.

A **simulation technique** uses a probability experiment to mimic a real-life situation.

Instead of studying the actual situation, which might be too costly, too dangerous, or too time-consuming, scientists and researchers create a similar situation but one that is less expensive, less dangerous, or less time-consuming. For example, NASA uses space shuttle flight simulators so that its astronauts can practice flying the shuttle. Most video games use the computer to simulate real-life sports such as boxing, wrestling, baseball, and hockey.

Simulation techniques go back to ancient times when the game of chess was invented to simulate warfare. Modern techniques date to the mid-1940s when two physicists, John Von Neumann and Stanislaw Ulam, developed simulation techniques to study the behavior of neutrons in the design of atomic reactors.

Mathematical simulation techniques use probability and random numbers to create conditions similar to those of real-life problems. Computers have played an important role in simulation techniques, since they can generate random numbers, perform experiments, tally the outcomes, and compute the probabilities much faster than human beings. The basic simulation technique is called the *Monte Carlo method*. This topic is discussed next.

The Monte Carlo Method

OBJECTIVE 3

Solve problems, using simulation techniques.

The **Monte Carlo method** is a simulation technique using random numbers. Monte Carlo simulation techniques are used in business and industry to solve problems that are extremely difficult or involve a large number of variables. The steps for simulating real-life experiments in the Monte Carlo method are as follows:

Procedure Table
Simulating Experiments Using the Monte Carlo Method
Step 1 List all possible outcomes of the experiment.
Step 2 Determine the probability of each outcome.
Step 3 Set up a correspondence between the outcomes of the experiment and the random numbers.
Step 4 Select random numbers from a table and conduct the experiment.
Step 5 Compute any statistics and state the conclusions.

Before examples of the complete simulation technique are given, an illustration is needed for step 3 (set up a correspondence between the outcomes of the experiment and the random numbers). Tossing a coin, for instance, can be simulated by using random numbers as follows: Since there are only two outcomes, heads and tails, and since each outcome has a probability of $\frac{1}{2}$, the odd digits (1, 3, 5, 7, and 9) can be used to represent a head, and the even digits (0, 2, 4, 6, and 8) can represent a tail.

Suppose a random number 8631 is selected. This number represents four tosses of a single coin and the results T, T, H, H. Or this number could represent one toss of four coins with the same results.

An experiment of rolling a single die can also be simulated by using random numbers. In this case, the digits 1, 2, 3, 4, 5, and 6 can represent the number of spots that appear on the face of the die. The digits 7, 8, 9, and 0 are ignored, since they cannot be rolled.

FIGURE 14–8

Spinner with Four Numbers

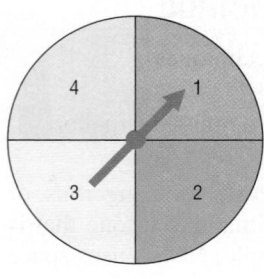

When two dice are rolled, two random digits are needed. For example, the number 26 represents a 2 on the first die and a 6 on the second die. The random number 37 represents a 3 on the first die, but the 7 cannot be used, so another digit must be selected. As another example, a three-digit daily lotto number can be simulated by using three-digit random numbers. Finally, a spinner with four numbers, as shown in Figure 14–8, can be simulated by letting the random numbers 1 and 2 represent 1 on the spinner, 3 and 4 represent 2 on the spinner, 5 and 6 represent 3 on the spinner, and 7 and 8 represent 4 on the spinner, since each number has a probability of $\frac{1}{4}$ of being selected. The random numbers 9 and 0 are ignored in this situation.

Many real-life games, such as bowling and baseball, can be simulated by using random numbers, as shown in Figure 14–9.

FIGURE 14–9

Example of Simulation of a Game

Source: Albert Shuylte, "Simulated Bowling Game," Student Math Notes, March 1986. Published by the National Council of Teachers of Mathematics. Reprinted with permission.

Simulated Bowling Game

Let's use the random digit table to simulate a bowling game. Our game is much simpler than commercial simulation games.

First Ball		Second Ball			
		2-Pin Split		No split	
Digit	Results	Digit	Results	Digit	Results
1–3	Strike	1	Spare	1–3	Spare
4–5	2-pin split	2–8	Leave one pin	4–6	Leave 1 pin
6–7	9 pins down	9–0	Miss both pins	7–8	*Leave 2 pins
8	8 pins down			9	+Leave 3 pins
9	7 pins down			0	Leave all pins
0	6 pins down				

*If there are fewer than 2 pins, result is a spare.
+If there are fewer than 3 pins, those pins are left.

Here's how to score bowling:
1. There are 10 frames to a **game** or **line**.
2. You roll two balls for each frame, unless you knock all the pins down with the first ball (a **strike**).
3. Your score for a frame is the sum of the pins knocked down by the two balls, if you don't knock down all 10.
4. If you knock all 10 pins down with two balls (a **spare**, shown as ▱), your score is 10 pins plus the number knocked down with the next ball.
5. If you knock all 10 pins down with the first ball (a **strike**, shown as ▨), your score is 10 pins plus the number knocked down by the next **two** balls.
6. A **split** (shown as ○) is when there is a big space between the remaining pins. Place in the circle the number of pins remaining after the second ball.
7. A **miss** is shown as —.

Here is how one person simulated a bowling game using the random digits 7 2 7 4 8 2 2 3 6 1 6 0 4 6 1 5 5, chosen in that order from the table.

Frame

	1	2	3	4	5	6	7	8	9	10	
Digit(s)	7/2	7/4	8/2	2	3	6/1	6/0	4/6	1	5/5	
Bowling result	9▱ 19	9— 28	8— 48	▨ 77	▨ 97	9▱ 116	9— 125	8① 134	▨ 153	8① 162	162

Now you try several.

Frame

	1	2	3	4	5	6	7	8	9	10	
Digit(s)											
Bowling result											

	1	2	3	4	5	6	7	8	9	10	
Digit(s)											
Bowling result											

If you wish to, you can change the probabilities in the simulation to better reflect *your* actual bowling ability.

EXAMPLE 14–4 Snoring

According to the CDC, the chance that a person snores while sleeping is 20%. Use random numbers to simulate a sample of 20 people and identify those who snore.

SOLUTION

Now 20% is $\frac{20}{100} = \frac{1}{5}$, so one out of every five people snores while sleeping. Using random digits, select 20 single numbers and assign 1 and 2 as people who snore and 3 through 9 and 0 as people who do not snore. (*Note:* You can use any two digits for those who snore.) Then the 1s and 2s represent people who snore; 0 and 3 through 9 represent those who do not snore.

EXAMPLE 14–5 Outcomes of a Tennis Game

Using random numbers, simulate the outcomes of a tennis game between Bill and Mike, with the additional condition that Bill is twice as good as Mike.

SOLUTION

Since Bill is twice as good as Mike, he will win approximately two games for every one Mike wins; hence, the probability that Bill wins will be $\frac{2}{3}$, and the probability that Mike wins will be $\frac{1}{3}$. The random digits 1 through 6 can be used to represent a game Bill wins; the random digits 7, 8, and 9 can be used to represent Mike's wins. The digit 0 is disregarded. Suppose they play five games, and the random number 86314 is selected. This number means that Bill won games 2, 3, 4, and 5 and Mike won the first game. The sequence is

8	6	3	1	4
M	B	B	B	B

More complex problems can be solved by using random numbers, as shown in Examples 14–6 to 14–8.

EXAMPLE 14–6   Rolling a Die

A die is rolled until a 6 appears. Using simulation, find the average number of rolls needed to obtain a 6. Try the experiment 20 times.

SOLUTION

Step 1   List all possible outcomes. They are 1, 2, 3, 4, 5, 6.

Step 2   Determine the probabilities. Each outcome has a probability of $\frac{1}{6}$.

Step 3   Set up a correspondence between the random numbers and the outcome. Use random numbers 1 through 6. Omit the numbers 7, 8, 9, and 0.

Step 4   Select a block of random numbers, and count each digit 1 through 6 until the first 6 is obtained. For example, the block 857236 means that it takes 4 rolls to get a 6.

8   5   7   2   3   6
     ↑   ↑   ↑   ↑
     5   2   3   6

Trial	Random number	Number of rolls
1	857236	4
2	21048015110 1536	11
3	2336	4
4	241304836	7
5	4216	4
6	375203987581 83716	9
7	7792106	3
8	9956	2
9	96	1
10	89579143426	7
11	8547536	5
12	289186	3
13	6	1
14	094299396	4
15	1036	3
16	0711997336	5
17	510851276	6
18	0236	3
19	01011540923336	10
20	5216	4
	Total	96

Step 5   Compute the results and draw a conclusion. In this case, you must find the average.

$$\overline{X} = \frac{\Sigma X}{n} = \frac{96}{20} = 4.8$$

Hence, the average is about 5 rolls.

   Note: The theoretical average obtained from the expected value formula is 6. If this experiment is done many times, say 1000 times, the results should be closer to the theoretical results.

EXAMPLE 14–7   Selecting a Key

A person selects a key at random from four keys to open a lock. Only one key opens the lock. If the first key does not open the lock, she tries other keys until one opens the lock. Find the average of the number of keys a person will have to try to open the lock. Try the experiment 25 times.

SOLUTION

Step 1   List all possible outcomes of the experiment. They are key 1, key 2, key 3, and key 4.

Step 2   Determine the probability of each outcome. Since a key is selected at random and there are four keys, the probability of selecting each key is $\frac{1}{4}$.

Step 3   Set up a correspondence between the random numbers and the outcomes. Assume that each key is numbered from 1 through 4 and that key 2 opens the lock. Naturally, the person doesn't know this, so she selects the keys at random. For the simulation, select a sequence of random digits, using only 1 through 4, until the digit 2 is reached. The trials are shown here.

Step 4   Select random numbers from the table and repeat the experiment 24 times.

Trial	Random digit (key)	Number	Trial	Random digit (key)	Number
1	2	1	14	2	1
2	2	1	15	4 2	2
3	1 2	2	16	1 3 2	3
4	1 4 3 2	4	17	1 2	2
5	3 2	2	18	2	1
6	3 1 4 2	4	19	3 4 2	3
7	4 2	2	20	2	1
8	4 3 2	3	21	2	1
9	4 2	2	22	2	1
10	2	1	23	4 2	2
11	4 2	2	24	4 3 1 2	4
12	3 1 2	3	25	3 1 2	3
13	3 1 2	3		Total	54

Step 5   Compute any statistics and state the conclusions.

Find the average:

$$\overline{X} = \frac{\Sigma X}{n} = \frac{1 + 1 + \cdots + 3}{25} = \frac{54}{25} = 2.16$$

   The theoretical average is 2.5. Again, only 25 repetitions were used; more repetitions should give a result closer to the theoretical average.

EXAMPLE 14–8   Selecting a Monetary Bill

A box contains five $1 bills, three $5 bills, and two $10 bills. A person selects a bill at random. What is the expected value of the bill? Perform the experiment 25 times.

SOLUTION

Step 1   List all possible outcomes. They are $1, $5, and $10.

Step 2   Assign the probabilities to each outcome:

$$P(\$1) = \tfrac{5}{10} \qquad P(\$5) = \tfrac{3}{10} \qquad P(\$10) = \tfrac{2}{10}$$

Step 3   Set up a correspondence between the random numbers and the outcomes. Use random numbers 1 through 5 to represent a $1 bill being selected, 6 through 8 to represent a $5 bill being selected, and 9 and 0 to represent a $10 bill being selected.

Step 4   Select 25 random numbers and tally the results.

Number	Results ($)
4 5 8 2 9	1, 1, 5, 1, 10
2 5 6 4 6	1, 1, 5, 1, 5
9 1 8 0 3	10, 1, 5, 10, 1
8 4 0 6 0	5, 1, 10, 5, 10
9 6 9 4 3	10, 5, 10, 1, 1

Step 5   Compute the average:

$$\overline{X} = \frac{\Sigma X}{n} = \frac{\$1 + \$1 + \$5 + \cdots + \$1}{25} = \frac{\$116}{25} = \$4.64$$

Hence, the average (expected value) is $4.64.

Recall that using the expected value formula $E(X) = \Sigma[X \cdot P(X)]$ gives a theoretical average of

$$E(X) = \Sigma[X \cdot P(X)] = (0.5)(\$1) + (0.3)(\$5) + (0.2)(\$10) = \$4.00$$

Remember that simulation techniques do not give exact results. The more times the experiment is performed, however, the closer the actual results should be to the theoretical results. (Recall the law of large numbers.)

Applying the Concepts 14–3

Simulations

Answer the following questions:

1. What is the definition of a simulation technique?
2. Have simulation techniques been used for very many years?
3. Is it cost-effective to do simulation testing on some things such as airplanes or automobiles?
4. Why might simulation testing be better than real-life testing? Give examples.

5. When did physicists develop computer simulation techniques to study neutrons?

6. When could simulations be misleading or harmful? Give examples.

7. Could simulations have prevented previous disasters such as the Hindenburg or the 1986 Space Shuttle disaster?

8. What discipline is simulation theory based on?

See page 771 for the answers.

≡ Exercises 14–3

1. Define simulation techniques.

2. Give three examples of simulation techniques.

3. Who is responsible for the development of modern simulation techniques?

4. What role does the computer play in simulation?

5. What are the steps in the simulation of an experiment?

6. What purpose do random numbers play in simulation?

7. What happens when the number of repetitions is increased?

8. Besides random numbers, what other items can be used to perform simulation experiments?

For Exercises 9 through 14, explain how each experiment can be simulated by using random numbers.

9. **Stay-at-Home Parents** Fewer than one-half of all mothers are stay-at-home parents. Recent statistics indicate that 68.1% of all mothers with children under age 18 are in the labor force. Explain how to create a simulation to represent this situation.
   Source: *New York Times Almanac.*

10. **Playing Basketball** Two basketball players have a free-throw contest—one is a 70% shooter and the other is a 75% shooter. They each shoot 20 shots in groups of 5 shots each. Use a calculator to simulate the contest and find out who wins. (Repeat a number of times and compare your answers.)

11. **Television Set Ownership** Thirty-five percent of U.S. households with at least one television set have premium cable service. Explain how to simulate this with random numbers. Use your method to select a random sample of 100 households, and test the hypothesis that p does not equal 35%.

12. **Matching Pennies** Two players match pennies.

13. **Odd Man Out** Three players play odd man out. (Three coins are tossed; if all three match, the game is repeated

and no one wins. If two players match, the third person wins all three coins.)

14. **Foreign-Born Residents** Almost 16% of Texas residents are foreign-born. Explain how to select a sample of 40 based on this scenario.
    Source: factfinder.census.gov

For Exercises 15 through 23, use random numbers to simulate the experiments. The number in parentheses is the number of times the experiment should be repeated.

15. **Rolling a Die** A die is rolled until all faces appear at least once. Find the average number of tosses. (30)

16. **Prizes in Caramel Corn Boxes** A caramel corn company gives four different prizes, one in each box. They are placed in the boxes at random. Find the average number of boxes a person needs to buy to get all four prizes. (40)

17. **Keys to a Door** The probability that a door is locked is 0.6, and there are five keys, one of which will unlock the door. The experiment consists of choosing one key at random and seeing if you can unlock the door. Repeat the experiment 50 times and calculate the empirical probability of unlocking the door. Compare your result to the theoretical probability for this experiment.

18. **Lottery Winner** To win a certain lotto, a person must spell the word *big*. Sixty percent of the tickets contain the letter b, 30% contain the letter i, and 10% contain the letter g. Find the average number of tickets a person must buy to win the prize. (30)

19. **Clay Pigeon Shooting** Two shooters shoot clay pigeons. Gail has an 80% accuracy rate and Paul has a 60% accuracy rate. Paul shoots first. The first person who hits the target wins. Find the probability that each wins. (30).

20. In Exercise 19, find the average number of shots fired. (30)

21. **Basketball Foul Shots** A basketball player has a 60% success rate for shooting foul shots. If she gets two shots, find the probability that she will make one or both shots. (50).

22. Boxing Boxer A is favored to win over boxer B with odds 4:3. Simulate nine rounds between the two and declare a winner. (9)

23. Beanbag Game A children's beanbag game is set up as follows: Two children toss beanbags at the board as shown. They hit the board with a probability of $\frac{1}{2}$ and score a 0 for a miss. When they hit the board, they receive the number of points indicated, with all squares equally likely. If a beanbag falls on a line, they receive the lower score.

Simulate a game between two players for six turns each. (6)

2	3	2
3	5	3
2	3	2

24. Which would be easier to simulate with random numbers, baseball or soccer? Explain.

25. Explain how cards can be used to generate random numbers.

26. Explain how a pair of dice can be used to generate random numbers.

Summary

- To obtain information and make inferences about a large population, researchers select a sample. A sample is a subgroup of the population. Using a sample rather than a population, researchers can save time and money, get more detailed information, and get information that otherwise would be impossible to obtain. (14–1)

- The four most common methods researchers use to obtain samples are random, systematic, stratified, and cluster sampling methods. In random sampling, some type of random method (usually random numbers) is used to obtain the sample. In systematic sampling, the researcher selects every kth person or item after selecting the first one at random. In stratified sampling, the population is divided into subgroups according to various characteristics, and elements are then selected at random from the subgroups. In cluster sampling, the researcher selects an intact group to use as a sample. When the population is large, multistage sampling (a combination of methods) is used to obtain a subgroup of the population. (14–1)

- Researchers must use caution when conducting surveys and designing questionnaires; otherwise, conclusions obtained from these will be inaccurate. Guidelines were presented in Section 14–2. (14–2)

- Most sampling methods use random numbers, which can also be used to simulate many real-life problems or situations. The basic method of simulation is known as the Monte Carlo method. The purpose of simulation is to duplicate situations that are too dangerous, too costly, or too time-consuming to study in real life. Most simulation techniques can be done on the computer or calculator, since they can rapidly generate random numbers, count the outcomes, and perform the necessary computations. (14–3)

  Sampling and simulation are two techniques that enable researchers to gain information that might otherwise be unobtainable.

Important Terms

biased sample 742	double sampling 750	random sample 742	stratified sample 748
cluster sample 749	Monte Carlo method 760	sequence sampling 750	systematic sample 746
convenience sample 751	multistage sampling 751	simulation technique 759	unbiased sample 742

Review Exercises

Section 14–1

Wind Speed of Hurricanes

The 2005 Atlantic hurricane season was notable for many reasons, among them the most named storms and the most hurricanes. Use the data shown to answer questions 1 through 4.

2005 Hurricane Season

Name	Max. Wind	Classification
Arlene	70	Storm
Bret	40	S
Cindy	75	Hurricane
Dennis	150	H
Emily	160	H
Franklin	70	S
Gert	45	S
Harvey	65	S
Irene	105	H
Jose	50	S
Katrina	175	H
Lee	40	S
Maria	115	H
Nate	90	H
Ophelia	85	H
Philippe	80	H
Rita	175	H
Stan	80	H
Unnamed	50	S
Tammy	50	S
Vince	75	H
Wilma	175	H
Alpha	50	S
Beta	115	H
Gamma	55	S
Delta	70	S
Epsilon	85	H
Zeta	65	S

1. **Hurricanes** Select a random sample of eight storms by using random numbers, and find the average maximum wind speed. Compare with the population mean.

2. **Hurricanes** Select a systematic sample of eight storms and calculate the average maximum wind speed. Compare with the population mean.

3. **Hurricanes** Select a cluster of 10 storms. Compute the sample means wind speeds. Compare these sample means with the population means.

4. **Hurricanes** Divide the 28 storms into 4 subgroups. Then select a sample of three storms from each group.

Compute the means for wind speeds. Compare these means to the population mean.

Use the data shown for Exercises 5 through 8.

Unemployment Insurance Data by State, 2010

State	Unemployment rate (%)	Average weekly benefit
AL	9.5	$206
AK	8.0	239
AZ	10.0	214
AR	7.9	278
CA	12.4	301
CO	8.9	347
CT	9.1	327
DE	8.5	247
FL	11.5	231
GA	10.2	273
HI	6.6	416
ID	9.3	255
IL	10.3	317
IN	10.2	295
IA	6.1	321
KS	7.0	326
KY	10.5	289
LA	7.5	209
ME	7.9	274
MD	7.5	316
MA	8.5	392
MI	12.5	297
MN	7.3	356
MS	10.4	190
MO	9.6	244
MT	7.2	272
NE	4.7	252
NV	14.9	318
NH	6.1	272
NJ	9.5	397
NM	8.4	316
NY	8.6	307
NC	10.6	298
ND	3.9	310
OH	10.1	297
OK	7.1	276
OR	10.8	290
PA	8.7	338
RI	11.6	380
SC	11.2	236
SD	4.8	251
TN	9.7	223
TX	8.2	316
UT	7.7	316
VT	6.2	297

State	Unemployment rate (%)	Average weekly benefit
VA	6.9	288
WA	9.6	384
WV	9.1	255
WI	8.3	275
WY	7.0	337
U.S.	9.6	299

5. Select a random sample of 10 states, and find the mean of the unemployment rates and the mean of average weekly benefits. How do your results compare with the U.S. figures?

6. Select a systematic sample of 10 states, and find the mean of the unemployment rates and the mean of the average weekly benefits. How do your results compare with the U.S. figures?

7. Find the mean of the unemployment rates and the mean of the average weekly benefits. How do your results compare with the U.S. figures?

8. Select a cluster sample of 10 states, and find the mean of the unemployment rates and the mean of the average weekly benefits. How do your results compare with the U.S. figures?

Section 14–2

For Exercises 9 through 12, explain what is wrong with each question. Rewrite each one, following the guidelines in this chapter.

9. How often do you run red lights?

10. Do you think students who are not failing should not be tutored?

11. Do you think all automobiles should have heavy-duty bumpers, even though it will raise the price of the cars by $500?

12. When answering questions in a survey, do you prefer open-ended questions or closed-ended questions?

Section 14–3

For Exercises 13 through 16, explain how to simulate each experiment by using random numbers.

13. A baseball player strikes out 40% of the time.

14. An airline overbooks 15% of the time.

15. Player 1 rolls two dice. Player 2 rolls one die. If the number on the single die matches one number of the player who rolled the two dice, player 2 wins. Otherwise, player 1 wins.

16. **Rock, Paper, Scissors** Two players play rock, paper, scissors. The rules are as follows: Since paper covers rock, paper wins. Since rock breaks scissors, rock wins. Since scissors cut paper, scissors win. Each person selects rock, paper, or scissors by random numbers and then compares results.

For Exercises 17 through 21, use random numbers to simulate the experiments. The number in parentheses is the number of times the experiment should be repeated.

17. **Football** A football is placed on the 10-yard line, and a team has four downs to score a touchdown. The team can move the ball only 0 to 5 yards per play. Find the average number of times the team will score a touchdown. (30)

18. In Exercise 17, find the average number of plays it will take to score a touchdown. Ignore the four-downs rule and keep playing until a touchdown is scored. (30)

19. **Rolling a Die** Four dice are rolled 50 times. Find the average of the sum of the number of spots that will appear. (50)

20. **Field Goals** A field goal kicker is successful in 60% of his kicks inside the 35-yard line. Find the probability of kicking three field goals in a row. (50)

21. **Making a Sale** A sales representative finds that there is a 30% probability of making a sale by visiting the potential customer personally. For every 20 calls, find the probability of making three sales in a row. (50)

≡ Data Analysis

The Data Bank is found in Appendix B.

1. From the Data Bank, choose a variable. Select a random sample of 20 individuals, and find the mean of the data.

2. Select a systematic sample of 20 individuals, and using the same variable as in Exercise 1, find the mean.

3. Select a cluster sample of 20 individuals, and using the same variable as in Exercise 1, find the mean.

4. Stratify the data according to marital status and gender, and sample 20 individuals. Compute the mean of the sample variable selected in Exercise 1 (use four groups of five individuals).

5. Compare all four means and decide which one is most appropriate. (*Hint:* Find the population mean.)

▟ STATISTICS TODAY

Let's Make A Deal
—Revisited

It appears that it does not matter whether the contestant switches doors because he is given a choice of two doors, and the chance of winning the prize is 1 out of 2, or $\frac{1}{2}$. This reasoning, however, is incorrect. Consider the three possibilities for the prize. It could be behind door A, B, or C. Suppose that the contestant selected door A. Now the three situations look like this:

	Door		
Case	A	B	C
1	Prize	Empty	Empty
2	Empty	Prize	Empty
3	Empty	Empty	Prize

In case 1, the contestant selected door A, and if the contestant switched after being shown that there was no prize behind either door B or door C, he'd lose. In case 2, the contestant selected door A, and the host will open door C, so if the contestant switched, he or she would win the prize. In case 3, the contestant selected door A, and the host will open door B, so if the contestant switched, he would win the prize. Hence, by switching, the probability of winning is $\frac{2}{3}$ and the probability of losing is $\frac{1}{3}$. The same reasoning can be used no matter which door is selected.

You can simulate this problem by using three cards, say, an ace (the prize), and two other cards. Have a person arrange the cards in a row and let you select a card. After the person turns over one of the cards (a non-ace), switch. Keep track of the number of times you win and compute the probability of winning.

This problem was supposedly used on the television show *Let's Make A Deal*, and the host of the show at that time was Monty Hall. Hence the problem is known as the **Monty Hall Problem** or the **Monty Hall Paradox.** However, in an online interview, Monty Hall stated the he never used the door changing method but only offered the contestant money to give up the original door selected.

▟ Chapter Quiz

Determine whether each statement is true or false. If the statement is false, explain why.

1. When researchers are sampling from large populations, such as adult citizens living in the United States, they may use a combination of sampling techniques to ensure representativeness.

2. Simulation techniques using random numbers are a substitute for performing the actual statistical experiment.

3. When researchers perform simulation experiments, they do not need to use random numbers since they can make up random numbers.

4. Random samples are said to be unbiased.

Select the best answer.

5. When all subjects under study are used, the group is called a _____.
   a. Population
   b. Large group
   c. Sample
   d. Study group

6. When a population is divided into subgroups with similar characteristics and then a sample is obtained, this method is called _____ sampling.
   a. Random
   b. Systematic
   c. Stratified
   d. Cluster

7. Interviewing selected people at a local supermarket can be considered an example of _____ sampling.
   a. Random
   b. Systematic
   c. Convenience
   d. Stratified

Complete the following statements with the best answer.

8. In general, when you conduct sampling, the _____ the sample, the more representative it will be.

9. When samples are not representative, they are said to be _____.

10. When all residents of a street are interviewed for a survey, the sampling method used is _____.

Use the table in the Review Exercises (page 767) for Exercises 11 through 14.

11. Select a random sample of 12 people, and find the mean of the blood pressures of the individuals. Compare this with the population mean.

12. Select a systematic sample of 12 people, and compute the mean of their blood pressures. Compare this with the population mean.

13. Divide the individuals into subgroups of six males and six females. Find the means of their blood pressures. Compare these means with the population mean.

14. Select a cluster sample of 12 people, and find the mean of their blood pressures. Compare this with the population mean.

For Exercises 15 through 19, explain how each could be simulated by using random numbers.

15. A chess player wins 45% of his games.

16. A travel agency has a 5% cancellation rate.

17. Two players select a card from a deck with no face cards. The player who gets the higher card wins.

18. One player rolls two dice. The other player selects a card from a deck. Face cards count as 11 for a jack, 12 for a queen, and 13 for a king. The player with the higher total points wins.

19. Two players toss two coins. If they match, player 1 wins; otherwise, player 2 wins.

For Exercises 20 through 24, use random numbers to simulate the experiments. The number in parentheses is the number of times the experiment should be done.

20. **Phone Sales** A telephone solicitor finds that there is a 15% probability of selling her product over the phone. For every 20 calls, find the probability of making two sales in a row. (100)

21. **Field Goals** A field goal kicker is successful in 65% of his kicks inside the 40-yard line. Find the probability of his kicking four field goals in a row. (40)

22. **Tossing Coins** Two coins are tossed. Find the average number of times two tails will appear. (40)

23. **Selecting Cards** A single card is drawn from a deck. Find the average number of times it takes to draw an ace. (30)

24. **Bowling** A bowler finds that there is a 30% probability that he will make a strike. For every 15 frames he bowls, find the probability of making two strikes. (30)

Critical Thinking Challenges

1. Explain why two different opinion polls might yield different results on a survey. Also, give an example of an opinion poll and explain how the data may have been collected.

2. Use a computer to generate random numbers to simulate the following real-life problem.

In a certain geographic region, 40% of the people have type O blood. On a certain day, the blood center needs 4 pints of type O blood. On average, how many donors are needed to obtain 4 pints of type O blood?

Data Projects

1. **Business and Finance** A car salesperson has six automobiles on the car lot. Roll a die, using the numbers 1 through 6 to represent each car. If only one car can be sold on each day, how long will it take him to sell all the automobiles? In other words, see how many tosses of the die it will take to get the numbers 1 through 6.

2. **Sports and Leisure** Using the rules given in Figure 14–4 on page 761, play the simulated bowling game. Each game consists of 10 frames.

3. **Technology** In a carton of 12 iPods, three are defective. If four are sold on Saturday, find the probability that at least one will be defective. Use random numbers to simulate this exercise 50 times.

4. **Health and Wellness** Of people who go on a special diet, 25% will lose at least 10 pounds in 10 weeks. A drug manufacturer says that if people take its special herbal pill, that will increase the number of people who lose at least 10 pounds in 10 weeks. The company conducts an experiment, giving its pills to 20 people. Seven people lost at least 10 pounds in 10 weeks. The drug manufacturer claims that the study "proves" the success of the herbal pills. Using random numbers, simulate the experiment 30 times, assuming the pills are ineffective. What can you conclude about the result that 7 out of 20 people lost at least 10 pounds?

5. **Politics and Economics** In Exercises 2–3, Exercise 2 shows the numbers of signers of the Declaration of Independence from each state. A student decides to write a paper on two of the signers, who are selected at random. What is the probability that both signers will be from the same state? Use random numbers to simulate the experiment, and perform the experiment 50 times.

6. **Your Class** Simulate the classical birthday problem given in the Critical Thinking Challenge 3 in Chapter 4. Select a sample size of 25 and generate random numbers between 1 and 365. Are there any two random numbers that are the same? Select a sample of 50. Are there any two random numbers that are the same? Repeat the experiments 10 times and explain your answers.

Answers to Applying the Concepts

Section 14–1   The White or Wheat Bread Debate

1. The researchers used a sample for their study.

2. Answers will vary. One possible answer is that we might have doubts about the validity of the study, since the baking company that conducted the experiment has an interest in the outcome of the experiment.

3. The sample was probably a convenience sample.

4. Answers will vary. One possible answer would be to use a simple random sample.

5. Answers will vary. One possible answer is that a list of women's names could be obtained from the city in which the women live. Then a simple random sample could be selected from this list.

6. The random assignment helps to spread variation among the groups. The random selection helps to generalize from the sample back to the population. These are two different issues.

Section 14–2   Smoking Bans and Profits

1. It is uncertain how public smoking bans affected restaurant business in Derry, Pennsylvania, since the survey results were conflicting.

2. Since the data were collected in different ways, the survey results were bound to have different answers. Perceptions of the owners will definitely be different from an analysis of actual sales receipts, particularly if the owners assumed that the public smoking bans would hurt business.

3. Answers will vary. One possible answer is that it would be difficult to not allow surveys based on anecdotal responses to be published. At the same time, it would be good for those publishing such survey results to comment on the limitations of these surveys.

4. We can get results from a representative sample that offer misleading information about the population.

5. Answers will vary. One possible answer is that measurement error is important in survey sampling in order to give ranges for the population parameters that are being investigated.

Section 14–3   Simulations

1. A simulation uses a probability experiment to mimic a real-life situation.

2. Simulation techniques date back to ancient times.

3. It is definitely cost-effective to run simulations for expensive items such as airplanes and automobiles.

4. Simulation testing is safer, faster, and less expensive than many real-life testing situations.

5. Computer simulation techniques were developed in the mid-1940s.

6. Answers will vary. One possible answer is that some simulations are far less harmful than conducting an actual study on the real-life situation of interest.

7. Answers will vary. Simulations could have possibly prevented disasters such as the Hindenburg or the 1986 Space Shuttle disaster. For example, data analysis after the Space Shuttle disaster showed that there was a decent chance that something would go wrong on that flight.

8. Simulation theory is based in probability theory.

APPENDIX A

Tables

Table A   Factorials
Table B   The Binomial Distribution
Table C   The Poisson Distribution
Table D   Random Numbers
Table E   The Standard Normal Distribution
Table F   The *t* Distribution
Table G   The Chi-Square Distribution
Table H   The *F* Distribution
Table I   Critical Values for the PPMC
Table J   Critical Values for the Sign Test
Table K   Critical Values for the Wilcoxon Signed-Rank Test
Table L   Critical Values for the Rank Correlation Coefficient
Table M   Critical Values for the Number of Runs
Table N   Critical Values for the Tukey Test

TABLE A   Factorials

n	*n*!
0	1
1	1
2	2
3	6
4	24
5	120
6	720
7	5,040
8	40,320
9	362,880
10	3,628,800
11	39,916,800
12	479,001,600
13	6,227,020,800
14	87,178,291,200
15	1,307,674,368,000
16	20,922,789,888,000
17	355,687,428,096,000
18	6,402,373,705,728,000
19	121,645,100,408,832,000
20	2,432,902,008,176,640,000

TABLE B   The Binomial Distribution

n	x	0.05	0.1	0.2	0.3	0.4	0.5	0.6	0.7	0.8	0.9	0.95
2	0	0.902	0.810	0.640	0.490	0.360	0.250	0.160	0.090	0.040	0.010	0.002
	1	0.095	0.180	0.320	0.420	0.480	0.500	0.480	0.420	0.320	0.180	0.095
	2	0.002	0.010	0.040	0.090	0.160	0.250	0.360	0.490	0.640	0.810	0.902
3	0	0.857	0.729	0.512	0.343	0.216	0.125	0.064	0.027	0.008	0.001	
	1	0.135	0.243	0.384	0.441	0.432	0.375	0.288	0.189	0.096	0.027	0.007
	2	0.007	0.027	0.096	0.189	0.288	0.375	0.432	0.441	0.384	0.243	0.135
	3		0.001	0.008	0.027	0.064	0.125	0.216	0.343	0.512	0.729	0.857
4	0	0.815	0.656	0.410	0.240	0.130	0.062	0.026	0.008	0.002		
	1	0.171	0.292	0.410	0.412	0.346	0.250	0.154	0.076	0.026	0.004	
	2	0.014	0.049	0.154	0.265	0.346	0.375	0.346	0.265	0.154	0.049	0.014
	3		0.004	0.026	0.076	0.154	0.250	0.346	0.412	0.410	0.292	0.171
	4			0.002	0.008	0.026	0.062	0.130	0.240	0.410	0.656	0.815
5	0	0.774	0.590	0.328	0.168	0.078	0.031	0.010	0.002			
	1	0.204	0.328	0.410	0.360	0.259	0.156	0.077	0.028	0.006		
	2	0.021	0.073	0.205	0.309	0.346	0.312	0.230	0.132	0.051	0.008	0.001
	3	0.001	0.008	0.051	0.132	0.230	0.312	0.346	0.309	0.205	0.073	0.021
	4			0.006	0.028	0.077	0.156	0.259	0.360	0.410	0.328	0.204
	5				0.002	0.010	0.031	0.078	0.168	0.328	0.590	0.774
6	0	0.735	0.531	0.262	0.118	0.047	0.016	0.004	0.001			
	1	0.232	0.354	0.393	0.303	0.187	0.094	0.037	0.010	0.002		
	2	0.031	0.098	0.246	0.324	0.311	0.234	0.138	0.060	0.015	0.001	
	3	0.002	0.015	0.082	0.185	0.276	0.312	0.276	0.185	0.082	0.015	0.002
	4		0.001	0.015	0.060	0.138	0.234	0.311	0.324	0.246	0.098	0.031
	5			0.002	0.010	0.037	0.094	0.187	0.303	0.393	0.354	0.232
	6				0.001	0.004	0.016	0.047	0.118	0.262	0.531	0.735
7	0	0.698	0.478	0.210	0.082	0.028	0.008	0.002				
	1	0.257	0.372	0.367	0.247	0.131	0.055	0.017	0.004			
	2	0.041	0.124	0.275	0.318	0.261	0.164	0.077	0.025	0.004		
	3	0.004	0.023	0.115	0.227	0.290	0.273	0.194	0.097	0.029	0.003	
	4		0.003	0.029	0.097	0.194	0.273	0.290	0.227	0.115	0.023	0.004
	5			0.004	0.025	0.077	0.164	0.261	0.318	0.275	0.124	0.041
	6				0.004	0.017	0.055	0.131	0.247	0.367	0.372	0.257
	7					0.002	0.008	0.028	0.082	0.210	0.478	0.698
8	0	0.663	0.430	0.168	0.058	0.017	0.004	0.001				
	1	0.279	0.383	0.336	0.198	0.090	0.031	0.008	0.001			
	2	0.051	0.149	0.294	0.296	0.209	0.109	0.041	0.010	0.001		
	3	0.005	0.033	0.147	0.254	0.279	0.219	0.124	0.047	0.009		
	4		0.005	0.046	0.136	0.232	0.273	0.232	0.136	0.046	0.005	
	5			0.009	0.047	0.124	0.219	0.279	0.254	0.147	0.033	0.005
	6			0.001	0.010	0.041	0.109	0.209	0.296	0.294	0.149	0.051
	7				0.001	0.008	0.031	0.090	0.198	0.336	0.383	0.279
	8					0.001	0.004	0.017	0.058	0.168	0.430	0.663

TABLE B *(continued)*

n	x	p 0.05	0.1	0.2	0.3	0.4	0.5	0.6	0.7	0.8	0.9	0.95
9	0	0.630	0.387	0.134	0.040	0.010	0.002					
	1	0.299	0.387	0.302	0.156	0.060	0.018	0.004				
	2	0.063	0.172	0.302	0.267	0.161	0.070	0.021	0.004			
	3	0.008	0.045	0.176	0.267	0.251	0.164	0.074	0.021	0.003		
	4	0.001	0.007	0.066	0.172	0.251	0.246	0.167	0.074	0.017	0.001	
	5		0.001	0.017	0.074	0.167	0.246	0.251	0.172	0.066	0.007	0.001
	6			0.003	0.021	0.074	0.164	0.251	0.267	0.176	0.045	0.008
	7				0.004	0.021	0.070	0.161	0.267	0.302	0.172	0.063
	8					0.004	0.018	0.060	0.156	0.302	0.387	0.299
	9						0.002	0.010	0.040	0.134	0.387	0.630
10	0	0.599	0.349	0.107	0.028	0.006	0.001					
	1	0.315	0.387	0.268	0.121	0.040	0.010	0.002				
	2	0.075	0.194	0.302	0.233	0.121	0.044	0.011	0.001			
	3	0.010	0.057	0.201	0.267	0.215	0.117	0.042	0.009	0.001		
	4	0.001	0.011	0.088	0.200	0.251	0.205	0.111	0.037	0.006		
	5		0.001	0.026	0.103	0.201	0.246	0.201	0.103	0.026	0.001	
	6			0.006	0.037	0.111	0.205	0.251	0.200	0.088	0.011	0.001
	7			0.001	0.009	0.042	0.117	0.215	0.267	0.201	0.057	0.010
	8				0.001	0.011	0.044	0.121	0.233	0.302	0.194	0.075
	9					0.002	0.010	0.040	0.121	0.268	0.387	0.315
	10						0.001	0.006	0.028	0.107	0.349	0.599
11	0	0.569	0.314	0.086	0.020	0.004						
	1	0.329	0.384	0.236	0.093	0.027	0.005	0.001				
	2	0.087	0.213	0.295	0.200	0.089	0.027	0.005	0.001			
	3	0.014	0.071	0.221	0.257	0.177	0.081	0.023	0.004			
	4	0.001	0.016	0.111	0.220	0.236	0.161	0.070	0.017	0.002		
	5		0.002	0.039	0.132	0.221	0.226	0.147	0.057	0.010		
	6			0.010	0.057	0.147	0.226	0.221	0.132	0.039	0.002	
	7			0.002	0.017	0.070	0.161	0.236	0.220	0.111	0.016	0.001
	8				0.004	0.023	0.081	0.177	0.257	0.221	0.071	0.014
	9				0.001	0.005	0.027	0.089	0.200	0.295	0.213	0.087
	10					0.001	0.005	0.027	0.093	0.236	0.384	0.329
	11							0.004	0.020	0.086	0.314	0.569
12	0	0.540	0.282	0.069	0.014	0.002						
	1	0.341	0.377	0.206	0.071	0.017	0.003					
	2	0.099	0.230	0.283	0.168	0.064	0.016	0.002				
	3	0.017	0.085	0.236	0.240	0.142	0.054	0.012	0.001			
	4	0.002	0.021	0.133	0.231	0.213	0.121	0.042	0.008	0.001		
	5		0.004	0.053	0.158	0.227	0.193	0.101	0.029	0.003		
	6			0.016	0.079	0.177	0.226	0.177	0.079	0.016		
	7			0.003	0.029	0.101	0.193	0.227	0.158	0.053	0.004	
	8			0.001	0.008	0.042	0.121	0.213	0.231	0.133	0.021	0.002
	9				0.001	0.012	0.054	0.142	0.240	0.236	0.085	0.017
	10					0.002	0.016	0.064	0.168	0.283	0.230	0.099
	11						0.003	0.017	0.071	0.206	0.377	0.341
	12							0.002	0.014	0.069	0.282	0.540

TABLE B *(continued)*

							p					
n	**x**	**0.05**	**0.1**	**0.2**	**0.3**	**0.4**	**0.5**	**0.6**	**0.7**	**0.8**	**0.9**	**0.95**
13	0	0.513	0.254	0.055	0.010	0.001						
	1	0.351	0.367	0.179	0.054	0.011	0.002					
	2	0.111	0.245	0.268	0.139	0.045	0.010	0.001				
	3	0.021	0.100	0.246	0.218	0.111	0.035	0.006	0.001			
	4	0.003	0.028	0.154	0.234	0.184	0.087	0.024	0.003			
	5		0.006	0.069	0.180	0.221	0.157	0.066	0.014	0.001		
	6		0.001	0.023	0.103	0.197	0.209	0.131	0.044	0.006		
	7			0.006	0.044	0.131	0.209	0.197	0.103	0.023	0.001	
	8			0.001	0.014	0.066	0.157	0.221	0.180	0.069	0.006	
	9				0.003	0.024	0.087	0.184	0.234	0.154	0.028	0.003
	10				0.001	0.006	0.035	0.111	0.218	0.246	0.100	0.021
	11					0.001	0.010	0.045	0.139	0.268	0.245	0.111
	12						0.002	0.011	0.054	0.179	0.367	0.351
	13							0.001	0.010	0.055	0.254	0.513
14	0	0.488	0.229	0.044	0.007	0.001						
	1	0.359	0.356	0.154	0.041	0.007	0.001					
	2	0.123	0.257	0.250	0.113	0.032	0.006	0.001				
	3	0.026	0.114	0.250	0.194	0.085	0.022	0.003				
	4	0.004	0.035	0.172	0.229	0.155	0.061	0.014	0.001			
	5		0.008	0.086	0.196	0.207	0.122	0.041	0.007			
	6		0.001	0.032	0.126	0.207	0.183	0.092	0.023	0.002		
	7			0.009	0.062	0.157	0.209	0.157	0.062	0.009		
	8			0.002	0.023	0.092	0.183	0.207	0.126	0.032	0.001	
	9				0.007	0.041	0.122	0.207	0.196	0.086	0.008	
	10				0.001	0.014	0.061	0.155	0.229	0.172	0.035	0.004
	11					0.003	0.022	0.085	0.194	0.250	0.114	0.026
	12					0.001	0.006	0.032	0.113	0.250	0.257	0.123
	13						0.001	0.007	0.041	0.154	0.356	0.359
	14							0.001	0.007	0.044	0.229	0.488
15	0	0.463	0.206	0.035	0.005							
	1	0.366	0.343	0.132	0.031	0.005						
	2	0.135	0.267	0.231	0.092	0.022	0.003					
	3	0.031	0.129	0.250	0.170	0.063	0.014	0.002				
	4	0.005	0.043	0.188	0.219	0.127	0.042	0.007	0.001			
	5	0.001	0.010	0.103	0.206	0.186	0.092	0.024	0.003			
	6		0.002	0.043	0.147	0.207	0.153	0.061	0.012	0.001		
	7			0.014	0.081	0.177	0.196	0.118	0.035	0.003		
	8			0.003	0.035	0.118	0.196	0.177	0.081	0.014		
	9			0.001	0.012	0.061	0.153	0.207	0.147	0.043	0.002	
	10				0.003	0.024	0.092	0.186	0.206	0.103	0.010	0.001
	11				0.001	0.007	0.042	0.127	0.219	0.188	0.043	0.005
	12					0.002	0.014	0.063	0.170	0.250	0.129	0.031
	13						0.003	0.022	0.092	0.231	0.267	0.135
	14							0.005	0.031	0.132	0.343	0.366
	15								0.005	0.035	0.206	0.463

TABLE B *(continued)*

n	x	p 0.05	0.1	0.2	0.3	0.4	0.5	0.6	0.7	0.8	0.9	0.95
16	0	0.440	0.185	0.028	0.003							
	1	0.371	0.329	0.113	0.023	0.003						
	2	0.146	0.275	0.211	0.073	0.015	0.002					
	3	0.036	0.142	0.246	0.146	0.047	0.009	0.001				
	4	0.006	0.051	0.200	0.204	0.101	0.028	0.004				
	5	0.001	0.014	0.120	0.210	0.162	0.067	0.014	0.001			
	6		0.003	0.055	0.165	0.198	0.122	0.039	0.006			
	7			0.020	0.101	0.189	0.175	0.084	0.019	0.001		
	8			0.006	0.049	0.142	0.196	0.142	0.049	0.006		
	9			0.001	0.019	0.084	0.175	0.189	0.101	0.020		
	10				0.006	0.039	0.122	0.198	0.165	0.055	0.003	
	11				0.001	0.014	0.067	0.162	0.210	0.120	0.014	0.001
	12					0.004	0.028	0.101	0.204	0.200	0.051	0.006
	13					0.001	0.009	0.047	0.146	0.246	0.142	0.036
	14						0.002	0.015	0.073	0.211	0.275	0.146
	15							0.003	0.023	0.113	0.329	0.371
	16								0.003	0.028	0.185	0.440
17	0	0.418	0.167	0.023	0.002							
	1	0.374	0.315	0.096	0.017	0.002						
	2	0.158	0.280	0.191	0.058	0.010	0.001					
	3	0.041	0.156	0.239	0.125	0.034	0.005					
	4	0.008	0.060	0.209	0.187	0.080	0.018	0.002				
	5	0.001	0.017	0.136	0.208	0.138	0.047	0.008	0.001			
	6		0.004	0.068	0.178	0.184	0.094	0.024	0.003			
	7		0.001	0.027	0.120	0.193	0.148	0.057	0.009			
	8			0.008	0.064	0.161	0.185	0.107	0.028	0.002		
	9			0.002	0.028	0.107	0.185	0.161	0.064	0.008		
	10				0.009	0.057	0.148	0.193	0.120	0.027	0.001	
	11				0.003	0.024	0.094	0.184	0.178	0.068	0.004	
	12				0.001	0.008	0.047	0.138	0.208	0.136	0.017	0.001
	13					0.002	0.018	0.080	0.187	0.209	0.060	0.008
	14						0.005	0.034	0.125	0.239	0.156	0.041
	15						0.001	0.010	0.058	0.191	0.280	0.158
	16							0.002	0.017	0.096	0.315	0.374
	17								0.002	0.023	0.167	0.418

TABLE B *(continued)*

							p					
n	x	0.05	0.1	0.2	0.3	0.4	0.5	0.6	0.7	0.8	0.9	0.95
18	0	0.397	0.150	0.018	0.002							
	1	0.376	0.300	0.081	0.013	0.001						
	2	0.168	0.284	0.172	0.046	0.007	0.001					
	3	0.047	0.168	0.230	0.105	0.025	0.003					
	4	0.009	0.070	0.215	0.168	0.061	0.012	0.001				
	5	0.001	0.022	0.151	0.202	0.115	0.033	0.004				
	6		0.005	0.082	0.187	0.166	0.071	0.015	0.001			
	7		0.001	0.035	0.138	0.189	0.121	0.037	0.005			
	8			0.012	0.081	0.173	0.167	0.077	0.015	0.001		
	9			0.003	0.039	0.128	0.185	0.128	0.039	0.003		
	10			0.001	0.015	0.077	0.167	0.173	0.081	0.012		
	11				0.005	0.037	0.121	0.189	0.138	0.035	0.001	
	12				0.001	0.015	0.071	0.166	0.187	0.082	0.005	
	13					0.004	0.033	0.115	0.202	0.151	0.022	0.001
	14					0.001	0.012	0.061	0.168	0.215	0.070	0.009
	15						0.003	0.025	0.105	0.230	0.168	0.047
	16						0.001	0.007	0.046	0.172	0.284	0.168
	17							0.001	0.013	0.081	0.300	0.376
	18								0.002	0.018	0.150	0.397
19	0	0.377	0.135	0.014	0.001							
	1	0.377	0.285	0.068	0.009	0.001						
	2	0.179	0.285	0.154	0.036	0.005						
	3	0.053	0.180	0.218	0.087	0.017	0.002					
	4	0.011	0.080	0.218	0.149	0.047	0.007	0.001				
	5	0.002	0.027	0.164	0.192	0.093	0.022	0.002				
	6		0.007	0.095	0.192	0.145	0.052	0.008	0.001			
	7		0.001	0.044	0.153	0.180	0.096	0.024	0.002			
	8			0.017	0.098	0.180	0.144	0.053	0.008			
	9			0.005	0.051	0.146	0.176	0.098	0.022	0.001		
	10			0.001	0.022	0.098	0.176	0.146	0.051	0.005		
	11				0.008	0.053	0.144	0.180	0.098	0.071		
	12				0.002	0.024	0.096	0.180	0.153	0.044	0.001	
	13				0.001	0.008	0.052	0.145	0.192	0.095	0.007	
	14					0.002	0.022	0.093	0.192	0.164	0.027	0.002
	15					0.001	0.007	0.047	0.149	0.218	0.080	0.011
	16						0.002	0.017	0.087	0.218	0.180	0.053
	17							0.005	0.036	0.154	0.285	0.179
	18							0.001	0.009	0.068	0.285	0.377
	19								0.001	0.014	0.135	0.377

TABLE B	(concluded)											
							p					
n	*x*	0.05	0.1	0.2	0.3	0.4	0.5	0.6	0.7	0.8	0.9	0.95
20	0	0.358	0.122	0.012	0.001							
	1	0.377	0.270	0.058	0.007							
	2	0.189	0.285	0.137	0.028	0.003						
	3	0.060	0.190	0.205	0.072	0.012	0.001					
	4	0.013	0.090	0.218	0.130	0.035	0.005					
	5	0.002	0.032	0.175	0.179	0.075	0.015	0.001				
	6		0.009	0.109	0.192	0.124	0.037	0.005				
	7		0.002	0.055	0.164	0.166	0.074	0.015	0.001			
	8			0.022	0.114	0.180	0.120	0.035	0.004			
	9			0.007	0.065	0.160	0.160	0.071	0.012			
	10			0.002	0.031	0.117	0.176	0.117	0.031	0.002		
	11				0.012	0.071	0.160	0.160	0.065	0.007		
	12				0.004	0.035	0.120	0.180	0.114	0.022		
	13				0.001	0.015	0.074	0.166	0.164	0.055	0.002	
	14					0.005	0.037	0.124	0.192	0.109	0.009	
	15					0.001	0.015	0.075	0.179	0.175	0.032	0.002
	16						0.005	0.035	0.130	0.218	0.090	0.013
	17						0.001	0.012	0.072	0.205	0.190	0.060
	18							0.003	0.028	0.137	0.285	0.189
	19								0.007	0.058	0.270	0.377
	20								0.001	0.012	0.122	0.358

Note: All values of 0.0005 or less are omitted.

Source: J. Freund and G. Simon, *Modern Elementary Statistics,* Table "The Binomial Distribution," © 1992 Prentice-Hall, Inc. Reproduced by permission of Pearson Education, Inc.

TABLE C	The Poisson Distribution

					λ					
x	0.1	0.2	0.3	0.4	0.5	0.6	0.7	0.8	0.9	1.0
0	.9048	.8187	.7408	.6703	.6065	.5488	.4966	.4493	.4066	.3679
1	.0905	.1637	.2222	.2681	.3033	.3293	.3476	.3595	.3659	.3679
2	.0045	.0164	.0333	.0536	.0758	.0988	.1217	.1438	.1647	.1839
3	.0002	.0011	.0033	.0072	.0126	.0198	.0284	.0383	.0494	.0613
4	.0000	.0001	.0003	.0007	.0016	.0030	.0050	.0077	.0111	.0153
5	.0000	.0000	.0000	.0001	.0002	.0004	.0007	.0012	.0020	.0031
6	.0000	.0000	.0000	.0000	.0000	.0000	.0001	.0002	.0003	.0005
7	.0000	.0000	.0000	.0000	.0000	.0000	.0000	.0000	.0000	.0001

					λ					
x	1.1	1.2	1.3	1.4	1.5	1.6	1.7	1.8	1.9	2.0
0	.3329	.3012	.2725	.2466	.2231	.2019	.1827	.1653	.1496	.1353
1	.3662	.3614	.3543	.3452	.3347	.3230	.3106	.2975	.2842	.2707
2	.2014	.2169	.2303	.2417	.2510	.2584	.2640	.2678	.2700	.2707
3	.0738	.0867	.0998	.1128	.1255	.1378	.1496	.1607	.1710	.1804
4	.0203	.0260	.0324	.0395	.0471	.0551	.0636	.0723	.0812	.0902
5	.0045	.0062	.0084	.0111	.0141	.0176	.0216	.0260	.0309	.0361
6	.0008	.0012	.0018	.0026	.0035	.0047	.0061	.0078	.0098	.0120
7	.0001	.0002	.0003	.0005	.0008	.0011	.0015	.0020	.0027	.0034
8	.0000	.0000	.0001	.0001	.0001	.0002	.0003	.0005	.0006	.0009
9	.0000	.0000	.0000	.0000	.0000	.0000	.0001	.0001	.0001	.0002

					λ					
x	2.1	2.2	2.3	2.4	2.5	2.6	2.7	2.8	2.9	3.0
0	.1225	.1108	.1003	.0907	.0821	.0743	.0672	.0608	.0550	.0498
1	.2572	.2438	.2306	.2177	.2052	.1931	.1815	.1703	.1596	.1494
2	.2700	.2681	.2652	.2613	.2565	.2510	.2450	.2384	.2314	.2240
3	.1890	.1966	.2033	.2090	.2138	.2176	.2205	.2225	.2237	.2240
4	.0992	.1082	.1169	.1254	.1336	.1414	.1488	.1557	.1622	.1680
5	.0417	.0476	.0538	.0602	.0668	.0735	.0804	.0872	.0940	.1008
6	.0146	.0174	.0206	.0241	.0278	.0319	.0362	.0407	.0455	.0504
7	.0044	.0055	.0068	.0083	.0099	.0118	.0139	.0163	.0188	.0216
8	.0011	.0015	.0019	.0025	.0031	.0038	.0047	.0057	.0068	.0081
9	.0003	.0004	.0005	.0007	.0009	.0011	.0014	.0018	.0022	.0027
10	.0001	.0001	.0001	.0002	.0002	.0003	.0004	.0005	.0006	.0008
11	.0000	.0000	.0000	.0000	.0000	.0001	.0001	.0001	.0002	.0002
12	.0000	.0000	.0000	.0000	.0000	.0000	.0000	.0000	.0000	.0001

					λ					
x	3.1	3.2	3.3	3.4	3.5	3.6	3.7	3.8	3.9	4.0
0	.0450	.0408	.0369	.0334	.0302	.0273	.0247	.0224	.0202	.0183
1	.1397	.1304	.1217	.1135	.1057	.0984	.0915	.0850	.0789	.0733
2	.2165	.2087	.2008	.1929	.1850	.1771	.1692	.1615	.1539	.1465
3	.2237	.2226	.2209	.2186	.2158	.2125	.2087	.2046	.2001	.1954
4	.1734	.1781	.1823	.1858	.1888	.1912	.1931	.1944	.1951	.1954

TABLE C   (continued)

	λ									
x	3.1	3.2	3.3	3.4	3.5	3.6	3.7	3.8	3.9	4.0
5	.1075	.1140	.1203	.1264	.1322	.1377	.1429	.1477	.1522	.1563
6	.0555	.0608	.0662	.0716	.0771	.0826	.0881	.0936	.0989	.1042
7	.0246	.0278	.0312	.0348	.0385	.0425	.0466	.0508	.0551	.0595
8	.0095	.0111	.0129	.0148	.0169	.0191	.0215	.0241	.0269	.0298
9	.0033	.0040	.0047	.0056	.0066	.0076	.0089	.0102	.0116	.0132
10	.0010	.0013	.0016	.0019	.0023	.0028	.0033	.0039	.0045	.0053
11	.0003	.0004	.0005	.0006	.0007	.0009	.0011	.0013	.0016	.0019
12	.0001	.0001	.0001	.0002	.0002	.0003	.0003	.0004	.0005	.0006
13	.0000	.0000	.0000	.0000	.0001	.0001	.0001	.0001	.0002	.0002
14	.0000	.0000	.0000	.0000	.0000	.0000	.0000	.0000	.0000	.0001

	λ									
x	4.1	4.2	4.3	4.4	4.5	4.6	4.7	4.8	4.9	5.0
0	.0166	.0150	.0136	.0123	.0111	.0101	.0091	.0082	.0074	.0067
1	.0679	.0630	.0583	.0540	.0500	.0462	.0427	.0395	.0365	.0337
2	.1393	.1323	.1254	.1188	.1125	.1063	.1005	.0948	.0894	.0842
3	.1904	.1852	.1798	.1743	.1687	.1631	.1574	.1517	.1460	.1404
4	.1951	.1944	.1933	.1917	.1898	.1875	.1849	.1820	.1789	.1755
5	.1600	.1633	.1662	.1687	.1708	.1725	.1738	.1747	.1753	.1755
6	.1093	.1143	.1191	.1237	.1281	.1323	.1362	.1398	.1432	.1462
7	.0640	.0686	.0732	.0778	.0824	.0869	.0914	.0959	.1002	.1044
8	.0328	.0360	.0393	.0428	.0463	.0500	.0537	.0575	.0614	.0653
9	.0150	.0168	.0188	.0209	.0232	.0255	.0280	.0307	.0334	.0363
10	.0061	.0071	.0081	.0092	.0104	.0118	.0132	.0147	.0164	.0181
11	.0023	.0027	.0032	.0037	.0043	.0049	.0056	.0064	.0073	.0082
12	.0008	.0009	.0011	.0014	.0016	.0019	.0022	.0026	.0030	.0034
13	.0002	.0003	.0004	.0005	.0006	.0007	.0008	.0009	.0011	.0013
14	.0001	.0001	.0001	.0001	.0002	.0002	.0003	.0003	.0004	.0005
15	.0000	.0000	.0000	.0000	.0001	.0001	.0001	.0001	.0001	.0002

	λ									
x	5.1	5.2	5.3	5.4	5.5	5.6	5.7	5.8	5.9	6.0
0	.0061	.0055	.0050	.0045	.0041	.0037	.0033	.0030	.0027	.0025
1	.0311	.0287	.0265	.0244	.0225	.0207	.0191	.0176	.0162	.0149
2	.0793	.0746	.0701	.0659	.0618	.0580	.0544	.0509	.0477	.0446
3	.1348	.1293	.1239	.1185	.1133	.1082	.1033	.0985	.0938	.0892
4	.1719	.1681	.1641	.1600	.1558	.1515	.1472	.1428	.1383	.1339

TABLE C   *(continued)*

	λ									
x	5.1	5.2	5.3	5.4	5.5	5.6	5.7	5.8	5.9	6.0
5	.1753	.1748	.1740	.1728	.1714	.1697	.1678	.1656	.1632	.1606
6	.1490	.1515	.1537	.1555	.1571	.1584	.1594	.1601	.1605	.1606
7	.1086	.1125	.1163	.1200	.1234	.1267	.1298	.1326	.1353	.1377
8	.0692	.0731	.0771	.0810	.0849	.0887	.0925	.0962	.0998	.1033
9	.0392	.0423	.0454	.0486	.0519	.0552	.0586	.0620	.0654	.0688
10	.0200	.0220	.0241	.0262	.0285	.0309	.0334	.0359	.0386	.0413
11	.0093	.0104	.0116	.0129	.0143	.0157	.0173	.0190	.0207	.0225
12	.0039	.0045	.0051	.0058	.0065	.0073	.0082	.0092	.0102	.0113
13	.0015	.0018	.0021	.0024	.0028	.0032	.0036	.0041	.0046	.0052
14	.0006	.0007	.0008	.0009	.0011	.0013	.0015	.0017	.0019	.0022
15	.0002	.0002	.0003	.0003	.0004	.0005	.0006	.0007	.0008	.0009
16	.0001	.0001	.0001	.0001	.0001	.0002	.0002	.0002	.0003	.0003
17	.0000	.0000	.0000	.0000	.0000	.0000	.0001	.0001	.0001	.0001

	λ									
x	6.1	6.2	6.3	6.4	6.5	6.6	6.7	6.8	6.9	7.0
0	.0022	.0020	.0018	.0017	.0015	.0014	.0012	.0011	.0010	.0009
1	.0137	.0126	.0116	.0106	.0098	.0090	.0082	.0076	.0070	.0064
2	.0417	.0390	.0364	.0340	.0318	.0296	.0276	.0258	.0240	.0223
3	.0848	.0806	.0765	.0726	.0688	.0652	.0617	.0584	.0552	.0521
4	.1294	.1249	.1205	.1162	.1118	.1076	.1034	.0992	.0952	.0912
5	.1579	.1549	.1519	.1487	.1454	.1420	.1385	.1349	.1314	.1277
6	.1605	.1601	.1595	.1586	.1575	.1562	.1546	.1529	.1511	.1490
7	.1399	.1418	.1435	.1450	.1462	.1472	.1480	.1486	.1489	.1490
8	.1066	.1099	.1130	.1160	.1188	.1215	.1240	.1263	.1284	.1304
9	.0723	.0757	.0791	.0825	.0858	.0891	.0923	.0954	.0985	.1014
10	.0441	.0469	.0498	.0528	.0558	.0588	.0618	.0649	.0679	.0710
11	.0245	.0265	.0285	.0307	.0330	.0353	.0377	.0401	.0426	.0452
12	.0124	.0137	.0150	.0164	.0179	.0194	.0210	.0227	.0245	.0264
13	.0058	.0065	.0073	.0081	.0089	.0098	.0108	.0119	.0130	.0142
14	.0025	.0029	.0033	.0037	.0041	.0046	.0052	.0058	.0064	.0071
15	.0010	.0012	.0014	.0016	.0018	.0020	.0023	.0026	.0029	.0033
16	.0004	.0005	.0005	.0006	.0007	.0008	.0010	.0011	.0013	.0014
17	.0001	.0002	.0002	.0002	.0003	.0003	.0004	.0004	.0005	.0006
18	.0000	.0001	.0001	.0001	.0001	.0001	.0001	.0002	.0002	.0002
19	.0000	.0000	.0000	.0000	.0000	.0000	.0000	.0001	.0001	.0001

TABLE C (continued)

x	λ									
	7.1	**7.2**	**7.3**	**7.4**	**7.5**	**7.6**	**7.7**	**7.8**	**7.9**	**8.0**
0	.0008	.0007	.0007	.0006	.0006	.0005	.0005	.0004	.0004	.0003
1	.0059	.0054	.0049	.0045	.0041	.0038	.0035	.0032	.0029	.0027
2	.0208	.0194	.0180	.0167	.0156	.0145	.0134	.0125	.0116	.0107
3	.0492	.0464	.0438	.0413	.0389	.0366	.0345	.0324	.0305	.0286
4	.0874	.0836	.0799	.0764	.0729	.0696	.0663	.0632	.0602	.0573
5	.1241	.1204	.1167	.1130	.1094	.1057	.1021	.0986	.0951	.0916
6	.1468	.1445	.1420	.1394	.1367	.1339	.1311	.1282	.1252	.1221
7	.1489	.1486	.1481	.1474	.1465	.1454	.1442	.1428	.1413	.1396
8	.1321	.1337	.1351	.1363	.1373	.1382	.1388	.1392	.1395	.1396
9	.1042	.1070	.1096	.1121	.1144	.1167	.1187	.1207	.1224	.1241
10	.0740	.0770	.0800	.0829	.0858	.0887	.0914	.0941	.0967	.0993
11	.0478	.0504	.0531	.0558	.0585	.0613	.0640	.0667	.0695	.0722
12	.0283	.0303	.0323	.0344	.0366	.0388	.0411	.0434	.0457	.0481
13	.0154	.0168	.0181	.0196	.0211	.0227	.0243	.0260	.0278	.0296
14	.0078	.0086	.0095	.0104	.0113	.0123	.0134	.0145	.0157	.0169
15	.0037	.0041	.0046	.0051	.0057	.0062	.0069	.0075	.0083	.0090
16	.0016	.0019	.0021	.0024	.0026	.0030	.0033	.0037	.0041	.0045
17	.0007	.0008	.0009	.0010	.0012	.0013	.0015	.0017	.0019	.0021
18	.0003	.0003	.0004	.0004	.0005	.0006	.0006	.0007	.0008	.0009
19	.0001	.0001	.0001	.0002	.0002	.0002	.0003	.0003	.0003	.0004
20	.0000	.0000	.0001	.0001	.0001	.0001	.0001	.0001	.0001	.0002
21	.0000	.0000	.0000	.0000	.0000	.0000	.0000	.0000	.0001	.0001

x	λ									
	8.1	**8.2**	**8.3**	**8.4**	**8.5**	**8.6**	**8.7**	**8.8**	**8.9**	**9.0**
0	.0003	.0003	.0002	.0002	.0002	.0002	.0002	.0002	.0001	.0001
1	.0025	.0023	.0021	.0019	.0017	.0016	.0014	.0013	.0012	.0011
2	.0100	.0092	.0086	.0079	.0074	.0068	.0063	.0058	.0054	.0050
3	.0269	.0252	.0237	.0222	.0208	.0195	.0183	.0171	.0160	.0150
4	.0544	.0517	.0491	.0466	.0443	.0420	.0398	.0377	.0357	.0337
5	.0882	.0849	.0816	.0784	.0752	.0722	.0692	.0663	.0635	.0607
6	.1191	.1160	.1128	.1097	.1066	.1034	.1003	.0972	.0941	.0911
7	.1378	.1358	.1338	.1317	.1294	.1271	.1247	.1222	.1197	.1171
8	.1395	.1392	.1388	.1382	.1375	.1366	.1356	.1344	.1332	.1318
9	.1256	.1269	.1280	.1290	.1299	.1306	.1311	.1315	.1317	.1318

TABLE C	(continued)								
					λ				
x	**8.1**	**8.2**	**8.3**	**8.4**	**8.5**	**8.6**	**8.7**	**8.8**	**8.9**	**9.0**
10	.1017	.1040	.1063	.1084	.1104	.1123	.1140	.1157	.1172	.1186
11	.0749	.0776	.0802	.0828	.0853	.0878	.0902	.0925	.0948	.0970
12	.0505	.0530	.0555	.0579	.0604	.0629	.0654	.0679	.0703	.0728
13	.0315	.0334	.0354	.0374	.0395	.0416	.0438	.0459	.0481	.0504
14	.0182	.0196	.0210	.0225	.0240	.0256	.0272	.0289	.0306	.0324
15	.0098	.0107	.0116	.0126	.0136	.0147	.0158	.0169	.0182	.0194
16	.0050	.0055	.0060	.0066	.0072	.0079	.0086	.0093	.0101	.0109
17	.0024	.0026	.0029	.0033	.0036	.0040	.0044	.0048	.0053	.0058
18	.0011	.0012	.0014	.0015	.0017	.0019	.0021	.0024	.0026	.0029
19	.0005	.0005	.0006	.0007	.0008	.0009	.0010	.0011	.0012	.0014
20	.0002	.0002	.0002	.0003	.0003	.0004	.0004	.0005	.0005	.0006
21	.0001	.0001	.0001	.0001	.0001	.0002	.0002	.0002	.0002	.0003
22	.0000	.0000	.0000	.0000	.0001	.0001	.0001	.0001	.0001	.0001

					λ				
x	**9.1**	**9.2**	**9.3**	**9.4**	**9.5**	**9.6**	**9.7**	**9.8**	**9.9**	**10.0**
0	.0001	.0001	.0001	.0001	.0001	.0001	.0001	.0001	.0001	.0000
1	.0010	.0009	.0009	.0008	.0007	.0007	.0006	.0005	.0005	.0005
2	.0046	.0043	.0040	.0037	.0034	.0031	.0029	.0027	.0025	.0023
3	.0140	.0131	.0123	.0115	.0107	.0100	.0093	.0087	.0081	.0076
4	.0319	.0302	.0285	.0269	.0254	.0240	.0226	.0213	.0201	.0189
5	.0581	.0555	.0530	.0506	.0483	.0460	.0439	.0418	.0398	.0378
6	.0881	.0851	.0822	.0793	.0764	.0736	.0709	.0682	.0656	.0631
7	.1145	.1118	.1091	.1064	.1037	.1010	.0982	.0955	.0928	.0901
8	.1302	.1286	.1269	.1251	.1232	.1212	.1191	.1170	.1148	.1126
9	.1317	.1315	.1311	.1306	.1300	.1293	.1284	.1274	.1263	.1251
10	.1198	.1210	.1219	.1228	.1235	.1241	.1245	.1249	.1250	.1251
11	.0991	.1012	.1031	.1049	.1067	.1083	.1098	.1112	.1125	.1137
12	.0752	.0776	.0799	.0822	.0844	.0866	.0888	.0908	.0928	.0948
13	.0526	.0549	.0572	.0594	.0617	.0640	.0662	.0685	.0707	.0729
14	.0342	.0361	.0380	.0399	.0419	.0439	.0459	.0479	.0500	.0521
15	.0208	.0221	.0235	.0250	.0265	.0281	.0297	.0313	.0330	.0347
16	.0118	.0127	.0137	.0147	.0157	.0168	.0180	.0192	.0204	.0217
17	.0063	.0069	.0075	.0081	.0088	.0095	.0103	.0111	.0119	.0128
18	.0032	.0035	.0039	.0042	.0046	.0051	.0055	.0060	.0065	.0071
19	.0015	.0017	.0019	.0021	.0023	.0026	.0028	.0031	.0034	.0037

TABLE C *(continued)*

					λ					
x	9.1	9.2	9.3	9.4	9.5	9.6	9.7	9.8	9.9	10.0
20	.0007	.0008	.0009	.0010	.0011	.0012	.0014	.0015	.0017	.0019
21	.0003	.0003	.0004	.0004	.0005	.0006	.0006	.0007	.0008	.0009
22	.0001	.0001	.0002	.0002	.0002	.0002	.0003	.0003	.0004	.0004
23	.0000	.0001	.0001	.0001	.0001	.0001	.0001	.0001	.0002	.0002
24	.0000	.0000	.0000	.0000	.0000	.0000	.0000	.0001	.0001	.0001

					λ					
x	11	12	13	14	15	16	17	18	19	20
0	.0000	.0000	.0000	.0000	.0000	.0000	.0000	.0000	.0000	.0000
1	.0002	.0001	.0000	.0000	.0000	.0000	.0000	.0000	.0000	.0000
2	.0010	.0004	.0002	.0001	.0000	.0000	.0000	.0000	.0000	.0000
3	.0037	.0018	.0008	.0004	.0002	.0001	.0000	.0000	.0000	.0000
4	.0102	.0053	.0027	.0013	.0006	.0003	.0001	.0001	.0000	.0000
5	.0224	.0127	.0070	.0037	.0019	.0010	.0005	.0002	.0001	.0001
6	.0411	.0255	.0152	.0087	.0048	.0026	.0014	.0007	.0004	.0002
7	.0646	.0437	.0281	.0174	.0104	.0060	.0034	.0018	.0010	.0005
8	.0888	.0655	.0457	.0304	.0194	.0120	.0072	.0042	.0024	.0013
9	.1085	.0874	.0661	.0473	.0324	.0213	.0135	.0083	.0050	.0029
10	.1194	.1048	.0859	.0663	.0486	.0341	.0230	.0150	.0095	.0058
11	.1194	.1144	.1015	.0844	.0663	.0496	.0355	.0245	.0164	.0106
12	.1094	.1144	.1099	.0984	.0829	.0661	.0504	.0368	.0259	.0176
13	.0926	.1056	.1099	.1060	.0956	.0814	.0658	.0509	.0378	.0271
14	.0728	.0905	.1021	.1060	.1024	.0930	.0800	.0655	.0514	.0387
15	.0534	.0724	.0885	.0989	.1024	.0992	.0906	.0786	.0650	.0516
16	.0367	.0543	.0719	.0866	.0960	.0992	.0963	.0884	.0772	.0646
17	.0237	.0383	.0550	.0713	.0847	.0934	.0963	.0936	.0863	.0760
18	.0145	.0256	.0397	.0554	.0706	.0830	.0909	.0936	.0911	.0844
19	.0084	.0161	.0272	.0409	.0557	.0699	.0814	.0887	.0911	.0888
20	.0046	.0097	.0177	.0286	.0418	.0559	.0692	.0798	.0866	.0888
21	.0024	.0055	.0109	.0191	.0299	.0426	.0560	.0684	.0783	.0846
22	.0012	.0030	.0065	.0121	.0204	.0310	.0433	.0560	.0676	.0769
23	.0006	.0016	.0037	.0074	.0133	.0216	.0320	.0438	.0559	.0669
24	.0003	.0008	.0020	.0043	.0083	.0144	.0226	.0328	.0442	.0557
25	.0001	.0004	.0010	.0024	.0050	.0092	.0154	.0237	.0336	.0446
26	.0000	.0002	.0005	.0013	.0029	.0057	.0101	.0164	.0246	.0343
27	.0000	.0001	.0002	.0007	.0016	.0034	.0063	.0109	.0173	.0254
28	.0000	.0000	.0001	.0003	.0009	.0019	.0038	.0070	.0117	.0181
29	.0000	.0000	.0001	.0002	.0004	.0011	.0023	.0044	.0077	.0125

TABLE C *(concluded)*

					λ					
x	**11**	**12**	**13**	**14**	**15**	**16**	**17**	**18**	**19**	**20**
30	.0000	.0000	.0000	.0001	.0002	.0006	.0013	.0026	.0049	.0083
31	.0000	.0000	.0000	.0000	.0001	.0003	.0007	.0015	.0030	.0054
32	.0000	.0000	.0000	.0000	.0001	.0001	.0004	.0009	.0018	.0034
33	.0000	.0000	.0000	.0000	.0000	.0001	.0002	.0005	.0010	.0020
34	.0000	.0000	.0000	.0000	.0000	.0000	.0001	.0002	.0006	.0012
35	.0000	.0000	.0000	.0000	.0000	.0000	.0000	.0001	.0003	.0007
36	.0000	.0000	.0000	.0000	.0000	.0000	.0000	.0001	.0002	.0004
37	.0000	.0000	.0000	.0000	.0000	.0000	.0000	.0000	.0001	.0002
38	.0000	.0000	.0000	.0000	.0000	.0000	.0000	.0000	.0000	.0001
39	.0000	.0000	.0000	.0000	.0000	.0000	.0000	.0000	.0000	.0001

Reprinted with permission from W. H. Beyer, *Handbook of Tables for Probability and Statistics,* 2nd ed. Copyright CRC Press, Boca Raton, Fla., 1986.

TABLE D   Random Numbers

10480	15011	01536	02011	81647	91646	67179	14194	62590	36207	20969	99570	91291	90700
22368	46573	25595	85393	30995	89198	27982	53402	93965	34095	52666	19174	39615	99505
24130	48360	22527	97265	76393	64809	15179	24830	49340	32081	30680	19655	63348	58629
42167	93093	06243	61680	07856	16376	39440	53537	71341	57004	00849	74917	97758	16379
37570	39975	81837	16656	06121	91782	60468	81305	49684	60672	14110	06927	01263	54613
77921	06907	11008	42751	27756	53498	18602	70659	90655	15053	21916	81825	44394	42880
99562	72905	56420	69994	98872	31016	71194	18738	44013	48840	63213	21069	10634	12952
96301	91977	05463	07972	18876	20922	94595	56869	69014	60045	18425	84903	42508	32307
89579	14342	63661	10281	17453	18103	57740	84378	25331	12566	58678	44947	05584	56941
85475	36857	43342	53988	53060	59533	38867	62300	08158	17983	16439	11458	18593	64952
28918	69578	88231	33276	70997	79936	56865	05859	90106	31595	01547	85590	91610	78188
63553	40961	48235	03427	49626	69445	18663	72695	52180	20847	12234	90511	33703	90322
09429	93969	52636	92737	88974	33488	36320	17617	30015	08272	84115	27156	30613	74952
10365	61129	87529	85689	48237	52267	67689	93394	01511	26358	85104	20285	29975	89868
07119	97336	71048	08178	77233	13916	47564	81056	97735	85977	29372	74461	28551	90707
51085	12765	51821	51259	77452	16308	60756	92144	49442	53900	70960	63990	75601	40719
02368	21382	52404	60268	89368	19885	55322	44819	01188	65255	64835	44919	05944	55157
01011	54092	33362	94904	31273	04146	18594	29852	71585	85030	51132	01915	92747	64951
52162	53916	46369	58586	23216	14513	83149	98736	23495	64350	94738	17752	35156	35749
07056	97628	33787	09998	42698	06691	76988	13602	51851	46104	88916	19509	25625	58104
48663	91245	85828	14346	09172	30168	90229	04734	59193	22178	30421	61666	99904	32812
54164	58492	22421	74103	47070	25306	76468	26384	58151	06646	21524	15227	96909	44592
32639	32363	05597	24200	13363	38005	94342	28728	35806	06912	17012	64161	18296	22851
29334	27001	87637	87308	58731	00256	45834	15398	46557	41135	10367	07684	36188	18510
02488	33062	28834	07351	19731	92420	60952	61280	50001	67658	32586	86679	50720	94953
81525	72295	04839	96423	24878	82651	66566	14778	76797	14780	13300	87074	79666	95725
29676	20591	68086	26432	46901	20849	89768	81536	86645	12659	92259	57102	80428	25280
00742	57392	39064	66432	84673	40027	32832	61362	98947	96067	64760	64584	96096	98253
05366	04213	25669	26422	44407	44048	37937	63904	45766	66134	75470	66520	34693	90449
91921	26418	64117	94305	26766	25940	39972	22209	71500	64568	91402	42416	07844	69618
00582	04711	87917	77341	42206	35126	74087	99547	81817	42607	43808	76655	62028	76630
00725	69884	62797	56170	86324	88072	76222	36086	84637	93161	76038	65855	77919	88006
69011	65797	95876	55293	18988	27354	26575	08625	40801	59920	29841	80150	12777	48501
25976	57948	29888	88604	67917	48708	18912	82271	65424	69774	33611	54262	85963	03547
09763	83473	73577	12908	30883	18317	28290	35797	05998	41688	34952	37888	38917	88050
91567	42595	27958	30134	04024	86385	29880	99730	55536	84855	29080	09250	79656	73211
17955	56349	90999	49127	20044	59931	06115	20542	18059	02008	73708	83517	36103	42791
46503	18584	18845	49618	02304	51038	20655	58727	28168	15475	56942	53389	20562	87338
92157	89634	94824	78171	84610	82834	09922	25417	44137	48413	25555	21246	35509	20468
14577	62765	35605	81263	39667	47358	56873	56307	61607	49518	89656	20103	77490	18062
98427	07523	33362	64270	01638	92477	66969	98420	04880	45585	46565	04102	46880	45709
34914	63976	88720	82765	34476	17032	87589	40836	32427	70002	70663	88863	77775	69348
70060	28277	39475	46473	23219	53416	94970	25832	69975	94884	19661	72828	00102	66794
53976	54914	06990	67245	68350	82948	11398	42878	80287	88267	47363	46634	06541	97809
76072	29515	40980	07391	58745	25774	22987	80059	39911	96189	41151	14222	60697	59583
90725	52210	83974	29992	65831	38857	50490	83765	55657	14361	31720	57375	56228	41546
64364	67412	33339	31926	14883	24413	59744	92351	97473	89286	35931	04110	23726	51900
08962	00358	31662	25388	61642	34072	81249	35648	56891	69352	48373	45578	78547	81788
95012	68379	93526	70765	10593	04542	76463	54328	02349	17247	28865	14777	62730	92277
15664	10493	20492	38391	91132	21999	59516	81652	27195	48223	46751	22923	32261	85653

TABLE E   The Standard Normal Distribution

Cumulative Standard Normal Distribution

z	.00	.01	.02	.03	.04	.05	.06	.07	.08	.09
−3.4	.0003	.0003	.0003	.0003	.0003	.0003	.0003	.0003	.0003	.0002
−3.3	.0005	.0005	.0005	.0004	.0004	.0004	.0004	.0004	.0004	.0003
−3.2	.0007	.0007	.0006	.0006	.0006	.0006	.0006	.0005	.0005	.0005
−3.1	.0010	.0009	.0009	.0009	.0008	.0008	.0008	.0008	.0007	.0007
−3.0	.0013	.0013	.0013	.0012	.0012	.0011	.0011	.0011	.0010	.0010
−2.9	.0019	.0018	.0018	.0017	.0016	.0016	.0015	.0015	.0014	.0014
−2.8	.0026	.0025	.0024	.0023	.0023	.0022	.0021	.0021	.0020	.0019
−2.7	.0035	.0034	.0033	.0032	.0031	.0030	.0029	.0028	.0027	.0026
−2.6	.0047	.0045	.0044	.0043	.0041	.0040	.0039	.0038	.0037	.0036
−2.5	.0062	.0060	.0059	.0057	.0055	.0054	.0052	.0051	.0049	.0048
−2.4	.0082	.0080	.0078	.0075	.0073	.0071	.0069	.0068	.0066	.0064
−2.3	.0107	.0104	.0102	.0099	.0096	.0094	.0091	.0089	.0087	.0084
−2.2	.0139	.0136	.0132	.0129	.0125	.0122	.0119	.0116	.0113	.0110
−2.1	.0179	.0174	.0170	.0166	.0162	.0158	.0154	.0150	.0146	.0143
−2.0	.0228	.0222	.0217	.0212	.0207	.0202	.0197	.0192	.0188	.0183
−1.9	.0287	.0281	.0274	.0268	.0262	.0256	.0250	.0244	.0239	.0233
−1.8	.0359	.0351	.0344	.0336	.0329	.0322	.0314	.0307	.0301	.0294
−1.7	.0446	.0436	.0427	.0418	.0409	.0401	.0392	.0384	.0375	.0367
−1.6	.0548	.0537	.0526	.0516	.0505	.0495	.0485	.0475	.0465	.0455
−1.5	.0668	.0655	.0643	.0630	.0618	.0606	.0594	.0582	.0571	.0559
−1.4	.0808	.0793	.0778	.0764	.0749	.0735	.0721	.0708	.0694	.0681
−1.3	.0968	.0951	.0934	.0918	.0901	.0885	.0869	.0853	.0838	.0823
−1.2	.1151	.1131	.1112	.1093	.1075	.1056	.1038	.1020	.1003	.0985
−1.1	.1357	.1335	.1314	.1292	.1271	.1251	.1230	.1210	.1190	.1170
−1.0	.1587	.1562	.1539	.1515	.1492	.1469	.1446	.1423	.1401	.1379
−0.9	.1841	.1814	.1788	.1762	.1736	.1711	.1685	.1660	.1635	.1611
−0.8	.2119	.2090	.2061	.2033	.2005	.1977	.1949	.1922	.1894	.1867
−0.7	.2420	.2389	.2358	.2327	.2296	.2266	.2236	.2206	.2177	.2148
−0.6	.2743	.2709	.2676	.2643	.2611	.2578	.2546	.2514	.2483	.2451
−0.5	.3085	.3050	.3015	.2981	.2946	.2912	.2877	.2843	.2810	.2776
−0.4	.3446	.3409	.3372	.3336	.3300	.3264	.3228	.3192	.3156	.3121
−0.3	.3821	.3783	.3745	.3707	.3669	.3632	.3594	.3557	.3520	.3483
−0.2	.4207	.4168	.4129	.4090	.4052	.4013	.3974	.3936	.3897	.3859
−0.1	.4602	.4562	.4522	.4483	.4443	.4404	.4364	.4325	.4286	.4247
−0.0	.5000	.4960	.4920	.4880	.4840	.4801	.4761	.4721	.4681	.4641

For z values less than −3.49, use 0.0001.

Area

z   0

TABLE E   (*continued*)

Cumulative Standard Normal Distribution

z	.00	.01	.02	.03	.04	.05	.06	.07	.08	.09
0.0	.5000	.5040	.5080	.5120	.5160	.5199	.5239	.5279	.5319	.5359
0.1	.5398	.5438	.5478	.5517	.5557	.5596	.5636	.5675	.5714	.5753
0.2	.5793	.5832	.5871	.5910	.5948	.5987	.6026	.6064	.6103	.6141
0.3	.6179	.6217	.6255	.6293	.6331	.6368	.6406	.6443	.6480	.6517
0.4	.6554	.6591	.6628	.6664	.6700	.6736	.6772	.6808	.6844	.6879
0.5	.6915	.6950	.6985	.7019	.7054	.7088	.7123	.7157	.7190	.7224
0.6	.7257	.7291	.7324	.7357	.7389	.7422	.7454	.7486	.7517	.7549
0.7	.7580	.7611	.7642	.7673	.7704	.7734	.7764	.7794	.7823	.7852
0.8	.7881	.7910	.7939	.7967	.7995	.8023	.8051	.8078	.8106	.8133
0.9	.8159	.8186	.8212	.8238	.8264	.8289	.8315	.8340	.8365	.8389
1.0	.8413	.8438	.8461	.8485	.8508	.8531	.8554	.8577	.8599	.8621
1.1	.8643	.8665	.8686	.8708	.8729	.8749	.8770	.8790	.8810	.8830
1.2	.8849	.8869	.8888	.8907	.8925	.8944	.8962	.8980	.8997	.9015
1.3	.9032	.9049	.9066	.9082	.9099	.9115	.9131	.9147	.9162	.9177
1.4	.9192	.9207	.9222	.9236	.9251	.9265	.9279	.9292	.9306	.9319
1.5	.9332	.9345	.9357	.9370	.9382	.9394	.9406	.9418	.9429	.9441
1.6	.9452	.9463	.9474	.9484	.9495	.9505	.9515	.9525	.9535	.9545
1.7	.9554	.9564	.9573	.9582	.9591	.9599	.9608	.9616	.9625	.9633
1.8	.9641	.9649	.9656	.9664	.9671	.9678	.9686	.9693	.9699	.9706
1.9	.9713	.9719	.9726	.9732	.9738	.9744	.9750	.9756	.9761	.9767
2.0	.9772	.9778	.9783	.9788	.9793	.9798	.9803	.9808	.9812	.9817
2.1	.9821	.9826	.9830	.9834	.9838	.9842	.9846	.9850	.9854	.9857
2.2	.9861	.9864	.9868	.9871	.9875	.9878	.9881	.9884	.9887	.9890
2.3	.9893	.9896	.9898	.9901	.9904	.9906	.9909	.9911	.9913	.9916
2.4	.9918	.9920	.9922	.9925	.9927	.9929	.9931	.9932	.9934	.9936
2.5	.9938	.9940	.9941	.9943	.9945	.9946	.9948	.9949	.9951	.9952
2.6	.9953	.9955	.9956	.9957	.9959	.9960	.9961	.9962	.9963	.9964
2.7	.9965	.9966	.9967	.9968	.9969	.9970	.9971	.9972	.9973	.9974
2.8	.9974	.9975	.9976	.9977	.9977	.9978	.9979	.9979	.9980	.9981
2.9	.9981	.9982	.9982	.9983	.9984	.9984	.9985	.9985	.9986	.9986
3.0	.9987	.9987	.9987	.9988	.9988	.9989	.9989	.9989	.9990	.9990
3.1	.9990	.9991	.9991	.9991	.9992	.9992	.9992	.9992	.9993	.9993
3.2	.9993	.9993	.9994	.9994	.9994	.9994	.9994	.9995	.9995	.9995
3.3	.9995	.9995	.9995	.9996	.9996	.9996	.9996	.9996	.9996	.9997
3.4	.9997	.9997	.9997	.9997	.9997	.9997	.9997	.9997	.9997	.9998

For *z* values greater than 3.49, use 0.9999.

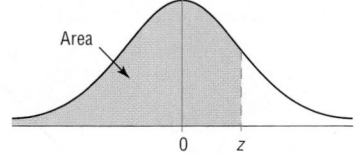

TABLE F   The *t* Distribution

d.f.	Confidence intervals	80%	90%	95%	98%	99%
	One tail, α	0.10	0.05	0.025	0.01	0.005
	Two tails, α	0.20	0.10	0.05	0.02	0.01
1		3.078	6.314	12.706	31.821	63.657
2		1.886	2.920	4.303	6.965	9.925
3		1.638	2.353	3.182	4.541	5.841
4		1.533	2.132	2.776	3.747	4.604
5		1.476	2.015	2.571	3.365	4.032
6		1.440	1.943	2.447	3.143	3.707
7		1.415	1.895	2.365	2.998	3.499
8		1.397	1.860	2.306	2.896	3.355
9		1.383	1.833	2.262	2.821	3.250
10		1.372	1.812	2.228	2.764	3.169
11		1.363	1.796	2.201	2.718	3.106
12		1.356	1.782	2.179	2.681	3.055
13		1.350	1.771	2.160	2.650	3.012
14		1.345	1.761	2.145	2.624	2.977
15		1.341	1.753	2.131	2.602	2.947
16		1.337	1.746	2.120	2.583	2.921
17		1.333	1.740	2.110	2.567	2.898
18		1.330	1.734	2.101	2.552	2.878
19		1.328	1.729	2.093	2.539	2.861
20		1.325	1.725	2.086	2.528	2.845
21		1.323	1.721	2.080	2.518	2.831
22		1.321	1.717	2.074	2.508	2.819
23		1.319	1.714	2.069	2.500	2.807
24		1.318	1.711	2.064	2.492	2.797
25		1.316	1.708	2.060	2.485	2.787
26		1.315	1.706	2.056	2.479	2.779
27		1.314	1.703	2.052	2.473	2.771
28		1.313	1.701	2.048	2.467	2.763
29		1.311	1.699	2.045	2.462	2.756
30		1.310	1.697	2.042	2.457	2.750
32		1.309	1.694	2.037	2.449	2.738
34		1.307	1.691	2.032	2.441	2.728
36		1.306	1.688	2.028	2.434	2.719
38		1.304	1.686	2.024	2.429	2.712
40		1.303	1.684	2.021	2.423	2.704
45		1.301	1.679	2.014	2.412	2.690
50		1.299	1.676	2.009	2.403	2.678
55		1.297	1.673	2.004	2.396	2.668
60		1.296	1.671	2.000	2.390	2.660
65		1.295	1.669	1.997	2.385	2.654
70		1.294	1.667	1.994	2.381	2.648
75		1.293	1.665	1.992	2.377	2.643
80		1.292	1.664	1.990	2.374	2.639
90		1.291	1.662	1.987	2.368	2.632
100		1.290	1.660	1.984	2.364	2.626
500		1.283	1.648	1.965	2.334	2.586
1000		1.282	1.646	1.962	2.330	2.581
(z) ∞		1.282[a]	1.645[b]	1.960	2.326[c]	2.576[d]

[a]This value has been rounded to 1.28 in the textbook.
[b]This value has been rounded to 1.65 in the textbook.
[c]This value has been rounded to 2.33 in the textbook.
[d]This value has been rounded to 2.58 in the textbook.

Source: Adapted from W. H. Beyer, *Handbook of Tables for Probability and Statistics,* 2nd ed., CRC Press, Boca Raton, Fla., 1986. Reprinted with permission.

One tail

Area α

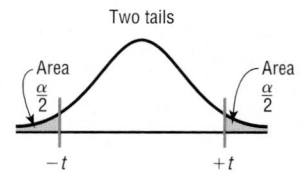

Two tails

Area $\frac{\alpha}{2}$

Area $\frac{\alpha}{2}$

TABLE G   The Chi-Square Distribution

Degrees of freedom	α									
	0.995	0.99	0.975	0.95	0.90	0.10	0.05	0.025	0.01	0.005
1	—	—	0.001	0.004	0.016	2.706	3.841	5.024	6.635	7.879
2	0.010	0.020	0.051	0.103	0.211	4.605	5.991	7.378	9.210	10.597
3	0.072	0.115	0.216	0.352	0.584	6.251	7.815	9.348	11.345	12.838
4	0.207	0.297	0.484	0.711	1.064	7.779	9.488	11.143	13.277	14.860
5	0.412	0.554	0.831	1.145	1.610	9.236	11.071	12.833	15.086	16.750
6	0.676	0.872	1.237	1.635	2.204	10.645	12.592	14.449	16.812	18.548
7	0.989	1.239	1.690	2.167	2.833	12.017	14.067	16.013	18.475	20.278
8	1.344	1.646	2.180	2.733	3.490	13.362	15.507	17.535	20.090	21.955
9	1.735	2.088	2.700	3.325	4.168	14.684	16.919	19.023	21.666	23.589
10	2.156	2.558	3.247	3.940	4.865	15.987	18.307	20.483	23.209	25.188
11	2.603	3.053	3.816	4.575	5.578	17.275	19.675	21.920	24.725	26.757
12	3.074	3.571	4.404	5.226	6.304	18.549	21.026	23.337	26.217	28.299
13	3.565	4.107	5.009	5.892	7.042	19.812	22.362	24.736	27.688	29.819
14	4.075	4.660	5.629	6.571	7.790	21.064	23.685	26.119	29.141	31.319
15	4.601	5.229	6.262	7.261	8.547	22.307	24.996	27.488	30.578	32.801
16	5.142	5.812	6.908	7.962	9.312	23.542	26.296	28.845	32.000	34.267
17	5.697	6.408	7.564	8.672	10.085	24.769	27.587	30.191	33.409	35.718
18	6.265	7.015	8.231	9.390	10.865	25.989	28.869	31.526	34.805	37.156
19	6.844	7.633	8.907	10.117	11.651	27.204	30.144	32.852	36.191	38.582
20	7.434	8.260	9.591	10.851	12.443	28.412	31.410	34.170	37.566	39.997
21	8.034	8.897	10.283	11.591	13.240	29.615	32.671	35.479	38.932	41.401
22	8.643	9.542	10.982	12.338	14.042	30.813	33.924	36.781	40.289	42.796
23	9.262	10.196	11.689	13.091	14.848	32.007	35.172	38.076	41.638	44.181
24	9.886	10.856	12.401	13.848	15.659	33.196	36.415	39.364	42.980	45.559
25	10.520	11.524	13.120	14.611	16.473	34.382	37.652	40.646	44.314	46.928
26	11.160	12.198	13.844	15.379	17.292	35.563	38.885	41.923	45.642	48.290
27	11.808	12.879	14.573	16.151	18.114	36.741	40.113	43.194	46.963	49.645
28	12.461	13.565	15.308	16.928	18.939	37.916	41.337	44.461	48.278	50.993
29	13.121	14.257	16.047	17.708	19.768	39.087	42.557	45.722	49.588	52.336
30	13.787	14.954	16.791	18.493	20.599	40.256	43.773	46.979	50.892	53.672
40	20.707	22.164	24.433	26.509	29.051	51.805	55.758	59.342	63.691	66.766
50	27.991	29.707	32.357	34.764	37.689	63.167	67.505	71.420	76.154	79.490
60	35.534	37.485	40.482	43.188	46.459	74.397	79.082	83.298	88.379	91.952
70	43.275	45.442	48.758	51.739	55.329	85.527	90.531	95.023	100.425	104.215
80	51.172	53.540	57.153	60.391	64.278	96.578	101.879	106.629	112.329	116.321
90	59.196	61.754	65.647	69.126	73.291	107.565	113.145	118.136	124.116	128.299
100	67.328	70.065	74.222	77.929	82.358	118.498	124.342	129.561	135.807	140.169

Source: Owen, *Handbook of Statistical Tables,* Table A–4 "Chi-Square Distribution Table," © 1962 by Addison-Wesley Publishing Company, Inc. Copyright renewal © 1990. Reproduced by permission of Pearson Education, Inc.

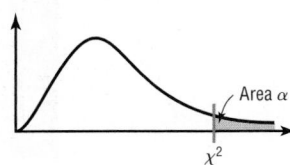

TABLE H   The *F* Distribution

α = 0.005

d.f.D.: degrees of freedom, denominator	d.f.N.: degrees of freedom, numerator																		
	1	2	3	4	5	6	7	8	9	10	12	15	20	24	30	40	60	120	∞
1	16,211	20,000	21,615	22,500	23,056	23,437	23,715	23,925	24,091	24,224	24,426	24,630	24,836	24,940	25,044	25,148	25,253	25,359	25,465
2	198.5	199.0	199.2	199.2	199.3	199.3	199.4	199.4	199.4	199.4	199.4	199.4	199.4	199.5	199.5	199.5	199.5	199.5	199.5
3	55.55	49.80	47.47	46.19	45.39	44.84	44.43	44.13	43.88	43.69	43.39	43.08	42.78	42.62	42.47	42.31	42.15	41.99	41.83
4	31.33	26.28	24.26	23.15	22.46	21.97	21.62	21.35	21.14	20.97	20.70	20.44	20.17	20.03	19.89	19.75	19.61	19.47	19.32
5	22.78	18.31	16.53	15.56	14.94	14.51	14.20	13.96	13.77	13.62	13.38	13.15	12.90	12.78	12.66	12.53	12.40	12.27	12.14
6	18.63	14.54	12.92	12.03	11.46	11.07	10.79	10.57	10.39	10.25	10.03	9.81	9.59	9.47	9.36	9.24	9.12	9.00	8.88
7	16.24	12.40	10.88	10.05	9.52	9.16	8.89	8.68	8.51	8.38	8.18	7.97	7.75	7.65	7.53	7.42	7.31	7.19	7.08
8	14.69	11.04	9.60	8.81	8.30	7.95	7.69	7.50	7.34	7.21	7.01	6.81	6.61	6.50	6.40	6.29	6.18	6.06	5.95
9	13.61	10.11	8.72	7.96	7.47	7.13	6.88	6.69	6.54	6.42	6.23	6.03	5.83	5.73	5.62	5.52	5.41	5.30	5.19
10	12.83	9.43	8.08	7.34	6.87	6.54	6.30	6.12	5.97	5.85	5.66	5.47	5.27	5.17	5.07	4.97	4.86	4.75	4.64
11	12.23	8.91	7.60	6.88	6.42	6.10	5.86	5.68	5.54	5.42	5.24	5.05	4.86	4.76	4.65	4.55	4.44	4.34	4.23
12	11.75	8.51	7.23	6.52	6.07	5.76	5.52	5.35	5.20	5.09	4.91	4.72	4.53	4.43	4.33	4.23	4.12	4.01	3.90
13	11.37	8.19	6.93	6.23	5.79	5.48	5.25	5.08	4.94	4.82	4.64	4.46	4.27	4.17	4.07	3.97	3.87	3.76	3.65
14	11.06	7.92	6.68	6.00	5.56	5.26	5.03	4.86	4.72	4.60	4.43	4.25	4.06	3.96	3.86	3.76	3.66	3.55	3.44
15	10.80	7.70	6.48	5.80	5.37	5.07	4.85	4.67	4.54	4.42	4.25	4.07	3.88	3.79	3.69	3.58	3.48	3.37	3.26
16	10.58	7.51	6.30	5.64	5.21	4.91	4.69	4.52	4.38	4.27	4.10	3.92	3.73	3.64	3.54	3.44	3.33	3.22	3.11
17	10.38	7.35	6.16	5.50	5.07	4.78	4.56	4.39	4.25	4.14	3.97	3.79	3.61	3.51	3.41	3.31	3.21	3.10	2.98
18	10.22	7.21	6.03	5.37	4.96	4.66	4.44	4.28	4.14	4.03	3.86	3.68	3.50	3.40	3.30	3.20	3.10	2.99	2.87
19	10.07	7.09	5.92	5.27	4.85	4.56	4.34	4.18	4.04	3.93	3.76	3.59	3.40	3.31	3.21	3.11	3.00	2.89	2.78
20	9.94	6.99	5.82	5.17	4.76	4.47	4.26	4.09	3.96	3.85	3.68	3.50	3.32	3.22	3.12	3.02	2.92	2.81	2.69
21	9.83	6.89	5.73	5.09	4.68	4.39	4.18	4.01	3.88	3.77	3.60	3.43	3.24	3.15	3.05	2.95	2.84	2.73	2.61
22	9.73	6.81	5.65	5.02	4.61	4.32	4.11	3.94	3.81	3.70	3.54	3.36	3.18	3.08	2.98	2.88	2.77	2.66	2.55
23	9.63	6.73	5.58	4.95	4.54	4.26	4.05	3.88	3.75	3.64	3.47	3.30	3.12	3.02	2.92	2.82	2.71	2.60	2.48
24	9.55	6.66	5.52	4.89	4.49	4.20	3.99	3.83	3.69	3.59	3.42	3.25	3.06	2.97	2.87	2.77	2.66	2.55	2.43
25	9.48	6.60	5.46	4.84	4.43	4.15	3.94	3.78	3.64	3.54	3.37	3.20	3.01	2.92	2.82	2.72	2.61	2.50	2.38
26	9.41	6.54	5.41	4.79	4.38	4.10	3.89	3.73	3.60	3.49	3.33	3.15	2.97	2.87	2.77	2.67	2.56	2.45	2.33
27	9.34	6.49	5.36	4.74	4.34	4.06	3.85	3.69	3.56	3.45	3.28	3.11	2.93	2.83	2.73	2.63	2.52	2.41	2.29
28	9.28	6.44	5.32	4.70	4.30	4.02	3.81	3.65	3.52	3.41	3.25	3.07	2.89	2.79	2.69	2.59	2.48	2.37	2.25
29	9.23	6.40	5.28	4.66	4.26	3.98	3.77	3.61	3.48	3.38	3.21	3.04	2.86	2.76	2.66	2.56	2.45	2.33	2.24
30	9.18	6.35	5.24	4.62	4.23	3.95	3.74	3.58	3.45	3.34	3.18	3.01	2.82	2.73	2.63	2.52	2.42	2.30	2.18
40	8.83	6.07	4.98	4.37	3.99	3.71	3.51	3.35	3.22	3.12	2.95	2.78	2.60	2.50	2.40	2.30	2.18	2.06	1.93
60	8.49	5.79	4.73	4.14	3.76	3.49	3.29	3.13	3.01	2.90	2.74	2.57	2.39	2.29	2.19	2.08	1.96	1.83	1.69
120	8.18	5.54	4.50	3.92	3.55	3.28	3.09	2.93	2.81	2.71	2.54	2.37	2.19	2.09	1.98	1.87	1.75	1.61	1.43
∞	7.88	5.30	4.28	3.72	3.35	3.09	2.90	2.74	2.62	2.52	2.36	2.19	2.00	1.90	1.79	1.67	1.53	1.36	1.00

TABLE H (continued)

$\alpha = 0.01$

d.f.N.: degrees of freedom, numerator

d.f.D.: degrees of freedom, denominator

d.f.D.	1	2	3	4	5	6	7	8	9	10	12	15	20	24	30	40	60	120	∞
1	4052	4999.5	5403	5625	5764	5859	5928	5982	6022	6056	6106	6157	6209	6235	6261	6287	6313	6339	6366
2	98.50	99.00	99.17	99.25	99.30	99.33	99.36	99.37	99.39	99.40	99.42	99.43	99.45	99.46	99.47	99.47	99.48	99.49	99.50
3	34.12	30.82	29.46	28.71	28.24	27.91	27.67	27.49	27.35	27.23	27.05	26.87	26.69	26.60	26.50	26.41	26.32	26.22	26.13
4	21.20	18.00	16.69	15.98	15.52	15.21	14.98	14.80	14.66	14.55	14.37	14.20	14.02	13.93	13.84	13.75	13.65	13.56	13.46
5	16.26	13.27	12.06	11.39	10.97	10.67	10.46	10.29	10.16	10.05	9.89	9.72	9.55	9.47	9.38	9.29	9.20	9.11	9.02
6	13.75	10.92	9.78	9.15	8.75	8.47	8.26	8.10	7.98	7.87	7.72	7.56	7.40	7.31	7.23	7.14	7.06	6.97	6.88
7	12.25	9.55	8.45	7.85	7.46	7.19	6.99	6.84	6.72	6.62	6.47	6.31	6.16	6.07	5.99	5.91	5.82	5.74	5.65
8	11.26	8.65	7.59	7.01	6.63	6.37	6.18	6.03	5.91	5.81	5.67	5.52	5.36	5.28	5.20	5.12	5.03	4.95	4.86
9	10.56	8.02	6.99	6.42	6.06	5.80	5.61	5.47	5.35	5.26	5.11	4.96	4.81	4.73	4.65	4.57	4.48	4.40	4.31
10	10.04	7.56	6.55	5.99	5.64	5.39	5.20	5.06	4.94	4.85	4.71	4.56	4.41	4.33	4.25	4.17	4.08	4.00	3.91
11	9.65	7.21	6.22	5.67	5.32	5.07	4.89	4.74	4.63	4.54	4.40	4.25	4.10	4.02	3.94	3.86	3.78	3.69	3.60
12	9.33	6.93	5.95	5.41	5.06	4.82	4.64	4.50	4.39	4.30	4.16	4.01	3.86	3.78	3.70	3.62	3.54	3.45	3.36
13	9.07	6.70	5.74	5.21	4.86	4.62	4.44	4.30	4.19	4.10	3.96	3.82	3.66	3.59	3.51	3.43	3.34	3.25	3.17
14	8.86	6.51	5.56	5.04	4.69	4.46	4.28	4.14	4.03	3.94	3.80	3.66	3.51	3.43	3.35	3.27	3.18	3.09	3.00
15	8.68	6.36	5.42	4.89	4.56	4.32	4.14	4.00	3.89	3.80	3.67	3.52	3.37	3.29	3.21	3.13	3.05	2.96	2.87
16	8.53	6.23	5.29	4.77	4.44	4.20	4.03	3.89	3.78	3.69	3.55	3.41	3.26	3.18	3.10	3.02	2.93	2.84	2.75
17	8.40	6.11	5.18	4.67	4.34	4.10	3.93	3.79	3.68	3.59	3.46	3.31	3.16	3.08	3.00	2.92	2.83	2.75	2.65
18	8.29	6.01	5.09	4.58	4.25	4.01	3.84	3.71	3.60	3.51	3.37	3.23	3.08	3.00	2.92	2.84	2.75	2.66	2.57
19	8.18	5.93	5.01	4.50	4.17	3.94	3.77	3.63	3.52	3.43	3.30	3.15	3.00	2.92	2.84	2.76	2.67	2.58	2.49
20	8.10	5.85	4.94	4.43	4.10	3.87	3.70	3.56	3.46	3.37	3.23	3.09	2.94	2.86	2.78	2.69	2.61	2.52	2.42
21	8.02	5.78	4.87	4.37	4.04	3.81	3.64	3.51	3.40	3.31	3.17	3.03	2.88	2.80	2.72	2.64	2.55	2.46	2.36
22	7.95	5.72	4.82	4.31	3.99	3.76	3.59	3.45	3.35	3.26	3.12	2.98	2.83	2.75	2.67	2.58	2.50	2.40	2.31
23	7.88	5.66	4.76	4.26	3.94	3.71	3.54	3.41	3.30	3.21	3.07	2.93	2.78	2.70	2.62	2.54	2.45	2.35	2.26
24	7.82	5.61	4.72	4.22	3.90	3.67	3.50	3.36	3.26	3.17	3.03	2.89	2.74	2.66	2.58	2.49	2.40	2.31	2.21
25	7.77	5.57	4.68	4.18	3.85	3.63	3.46	3.32	3.22	3.13	2.99	2.85	2.70	2.62	2.54	2.45	2.36	2.27	2.17
26	7.72	5.53	4.64	4.14	3.82	3.59	3.42	3.29	3.18	3.09	2.96	2.81	2.66	2.58	2.50	2.42	2.33	2.23	2.13
27	7.68	5.49	4.60	4.11	3.78	3.56	3.39	3.26	3.15	3.06	2.93	2.78	2.63	2.55	2.47	2.38	2.29	2.20	2.10
28	7.64	5.45	4.57	4.07	3.75	3.53	3.36	3.23	3.12	3.03	2.90	2.75	2.60	2.52	2.44	2.35	2.26	2.17	2.06
29	7.60	5.42	4.54	4.04	3.73	3.50	3.33	3.20	3.09	3.00	2.87	2.73	2.57	2.49	2.41	2.33	2.23	2.14	2.03
30	7.56	5.39	4.51	4.02	3.70	3.47	3.30	3.17	3.07	2.98	2.84	2.70	2.55	2.47	2.39	2.30	2.21	2.11	2.01
40	7.31	5.18	4.31	3.83	3.51	3.29	3.12	2.99	2.89	2.80	2.66	2.52	2.37	2.29	2.20	2.11	2.02	1.92	1.80
60	7.08	4.98	4.13	3.65	3.34	3.12	2.95	2.82	2.72	2.63	2.50	2.35	2.20	2.12	2.03	1.94	1.84	1.73	1.60
120	6.85	4.79	3.95	3.48	3.17	2.96	2.79	2.66	2.56	2.47	2.34	2.19	2.03	1.95	1.86	1.76	1.66	1.53	1.38
∞	6.63	4.61	3.78	3.32	3.02	2.80	2.64	2.51	2.41	2.32	2.18	2.04	1.88	1.79	1.70	1.59	1.47	1.32	1.00

TABLE H (continued)

α = 0.025

d.f.D.: degrees of freedom, denominator	d.f.N.: degrees of freedom, numerator																		
	1	2	3	4	5	6	7	8	9	10	12	15	20	24	30	40	60	120	∞
1	647.8	799.5	864.2	899.6	921.8	937.1	948.2	956.7	963.3	968.6	976.7	984.9	993.1	997.2	1001	1006	1010	1014	1018
2	38.51	39.00	39.17	39.25	39.30	39.33	39.36	39.37	39.39	39.40	39.41	39.43	39.45	39.46	39.46	39.47	39.48	39.49	39.50
3	17.44	16.04	15.44	15.10	14.88	14.73	14.62	14.54	14.47	14.42	14.34	14.25	14.17	14.12	14.08	14.04	13.99	13.95	13.90
4	12.22	10.65	9.98	9.60	9.36	9.20	9.07	8.98	8.90	8.84	8.75	8.66	8.56	8.51	8.46	8.41	8.36	8.31	8.26
5	10.01	8.43	7.76	7.39	7.15	6.98	6.85	6.76	6.68	6.62	6.52	6.43	6.33	6.28	6.23	6.18	6.12	6.07	6.02
6	8.81	7.26	6.60	6.23	5.99	5.82	5.70	5.60	5.52	5.46	5.37	5.27	5.17	5.12	5.07	5.01	4.96	4.90	4.85
7	8.07	6.54	5.89	5.52	5.29	5.12	4.99	4.90	4.82	4.76	4.67	4.57	4.47	4.42	4.36	4.31	4.25	4.20	4.14
8	7.57	6.06	5.42	5.05	4.82	4.65	4.53	4.43	4.36	4.30	4.20	4.10	4.00	3.95	3.89	3.84	3.78	3.73	3.67
9	7.21	5.71	5.08	4.72	4.48	4.32	4.20	4.10	4.03	3.96	3.87	3.77	3.67	3.61	3.56	3.51	3.45	3.39	3.33
10	6.94	5.46	4.83	4.47	4.24	4.07	3.95	3.85	3.78	3.72	3.62	3.52	3.42	3.37	3.31	3.26	3.20	3.14	3.08
11	6.72	5.26	4.63	4.28	4.04	3.88	3.76	3.66	3.59	3.53	3.43	3.33	3.23	3.17	3.12	3.06	3.00	2.94	2.88
12	6.55	5.10	4.47	4.12	3.89	3.73	3.61	3.51	3.44	3.37	3.28	3.18	3.07	3.02	2.96	2.91	2.85	2.79	2.72
13	6.41	4.97	4.35	4.00	3.77	3.60	3.48	3.39	3.31	3.25	3.15	3.05	2.95	2.89	2.84	2.78	2.72	2.66	2.60
14	6.30	4.86	4.24	3.89	3.66	3.50	3.38	3.29	3.21	3.15	3.05	2.95	2.84	2.79	2.73	2.67	2.61	2.55	2.49
15	6.20	4.77	4.15	3.80	3.58	3.41	3.29	3.20	3.12	3.06	2.96	2.86	2.76	2.70	2.64	2.59	2.52	2.46	2.40
16	6.12	4.69	4.08	3.73	3.50	3.34	3.22	3.12	3.05	2.99	2.89	2.79	2.68	2.63	2.57	2.51	2.45	2.38	2.32
17	6.04	4.62	4.01	3.66	3.44	3.28	3.16	3.06	2.98	2.92	2.82	2.72	2.62	2.56	2.50	2.44	2.38	2.32	2.25
18	5.98	4.56	3.95	3.61	3.38	3.22	3.10	3.01	2.93	2.87	2.77	2.67	2.56	2.50	2.44	2.38	2.32	2.26	2.19
19	5.92	4.51	3.90	3.56	3.33	3.17	3.05	2.96	2.88	2.82	2.72	2.62	2.51	2.45	2.39	2.33	2.27	2.20	2.13
20	5.87	4.46	3.86	3.51	3.29	3.13	3.01	2.91	2.84	2.77	2.68	2.57	2.46	2.41	2.35	2.29	2.22	2.16	2.09
21	5.83	4.42	3.82	3.48	3.25	3.09	2.97	2.87	2.80	2.73	2.64	2.53	2.42	2.37	2.31	2.25	2.18	2.11	2.04
22	5.79	4.38	3.78	3.44	3.22	3.05	2.93	2.84	2.76	2.70	2.60	2.50	2.39	2.33	2.27	2.21	2.14	2.08	2.00
23	5.75	4.35	3.75	3.41	3.18	3.02	2.90	2.81	2.73	2.67	2.57	2.47	2.36	2.30	2.24	2.18	2.11	2.04	1.97
24	5.72	4.32	3.72	3.38	3.15	2.99	2.87	2.78	2.70	2.64	2.54	2.44	2.33	2.27	2.21	2.15	2.08	2.01	1.94
25	5.69	4.29	3.69	3.35	3.13	2.97	2.85	2.75	2.68	2.61	2.51	2.41	2.30	2.24	2.18	2.12	2.05	1.98	1.91
26	5.66	4.27	3.67	3.33	3.10	2.94	2.82	2.73	2.65	2.59	2.49	2.39	2.28	2.22	2.16	2.09	2.03	1.95	1.88
27	5.63	4.24	3.65	3.31	3.08	2.92	2.80	2.71	2.63	2.57	2.47	2.36	2.25	2.19	2.13	2.07	2.00	1.93	1.85
28	5.61	4.22	3.63	3.29	3.06	2.90	2.78	2.69	2.61	2.55	2.45	2.34	2.23	2.17	2.11	2.05	1.98	1.91	1.83
29	5.59	4.20	3.61	3.27	3.04	2.88	2.76	2.67	2.59	2.53	2.43	2.32	2.21	2.15	2.09	2.03	1.96	1.89	1.81
30	5.57	4.18	3.59	3.25	3.03	2.87	2.75	2.65	2.57	2.51	2.41	2.31	2.20	2.14	2.07	2.01	1.94	1.87	1.79
40	5.42	4.05	3.46	3.13	2.90	2.74	2.62	2.53	2.45	2.39	2.29	2.18	2.07	2.01	1.94	1.88	1.80	1.72	1.64
60	5.29	3.93	3.34	3.01	2.79	2.63	2.51	2.41	2.33	2.27	2.17	2.06	1.94	1.88	1.82	1.74	1.67	1.58	1.48
120	5.15	3.80	3.23	2.89	2.67	2.52	2.39	2.30	2.22	2.16	2.05	1.94	1.82	1.76	1.69	1.61	1.53	1.43	1.31
∞	5.02	3.69	3.12	2.79	2.57	2.41	2.29	2.19	2.11	2.05	1.94	1.83	1.71	1.64	1.57	1.48	1.39	1.27	1.00

TABLE H (continued)

$\alpha = 0.05$

d.f.D.: degrees of freedom, denominator	\multicolumn{19}{c}{d.f.N.: degrees of freedom, numerator}
	1	**2**	**3**	**4**	**5**	**6**	**7**	**8**	**9**	**10**	**12**	**15**	**20**	**24**	**30**	**40**	**60**	**120**	**∞**
1	161.4	199.5	215.7	224.6	230.2	234.0	236.8	238.9	240.5	241.9	243.9	245.9	248.0	249.1	250.1	251.1	252.2	253.3	254.3
2	18.51	19.00	19.16	19.25	19.30	19.33	19.35	19.37	19.38	19.40	19.41	19.43	19.45	19.45	19.46	19.47	19.48	19.49	19.50
3	10.13	9.55	9.28	9.12	9.01	8.94	8.89	8.85	8.81	8.79	8.74	8.70	8.66	8.64	8.62	8.59	8.57	8.55	8.53
4	7.71	6.94	6.59	6.39	6.26	6.16	6.09	6.04	6.00	5.96	5.91	5.86	5.80	5.77	5.75	5.72	5.69	5.66	5.63
5	6.61	5.79	5.41	5.19	5.05	4.95	4.88	4.82	4.77	4.74	4.68	4.62	4.56	4.53	4.50	4.46	4.43	4.40	4.36
6	5.99	5.14	4.76	4.53	4.39	4.28	4.21	4.15	4.10	4.06	4.00	3.94	3.87	3.84	3.81	3.77	3.74	3.70	3.67
7	5.59	4.74	4.35	4.12	3.97	3.87	3.79	3.73	3.68	3.64	3.57	3.51	3.44	3.41	3.38	3.34	3.30	3.27	3.23
8	5.32	4.46	4.07	3.84	3.69	3.58	3.50	3.44	3.39	3.35	3.28	3.22	3.15	3.12	3.08	3.04	3.01	2.97	2.93
9	5.12	4.26	3.86	3.63	3.48	3.37	3.29	3.23	3.18	3.14	3.07	3.01	2.94	2.90	2.86	2.83	2.79	2.75	2.71
10	4.96	4.10	3.71	3.48	3.33	3.22	3.14	3.07	3.02	2.98	2.91	2.85	2.77	2.74	2.70	2.66	2.62	2.58	2.54
11	4.84	3.98	3.59	3.36	3.20	3.09	3.01	2.95	2.90	2.85	2.79	2.72	2.65	2.61	2.57	2.53	2.49	2.45	2.40
12	4.75	3.89	3.49	3.26	3.11	3.00	2.91	2.85	2.80	2.75	2.69	2.62	2.54	2.51	2.47	2.43	2.38	2.34	2.30
13	4.67	3.81	3.41	3.18	3.03	2.92	2.83	2.77	2.71	2.67	2.60	2.53	2.46	2.42	2.38	2.34	2.30	2.25	2.21
14	4.60	3.74	3.34	3.11	2.96	2.85	2.76	2.70	2.65	2.60	2.53	2.46	2.39	2.35	2.31	2.27	2.22	2.18	2.13
15	4.54	3.68	3.29	3.06	2.90	2.79	2.71	2.64	2.59	2.54	2.48	2.40	2.33	2.29	2.25	2.20	2.16	2.11	2.07
16	4.49	3.63	3.24	3.01	2.85	2.74	2.66	2.59	2.54	2.49	2.42	2.35	2.28	2.24	2.19	2.15	2.11	2.06	2.01
17	4.45	3.59	3.20	2.96	2.81	2.70	2.61	2.55	2.49	2.45	2.38	2.31	2.23	2.19	2.15	2.10	2.06	2.01	1.96
18	4.41	3.55	3.16	2.93	2.77	2.66	2.58	2.51	2.46	2.41	2.34	2.27	2.19	2.15	2.11	2.06	2.02	1.97	1.92
19	4.38	3.52	3.13	2.90	2.74	2.63	2.54	2.48	2.42	2.38	2.31	2.23	2.16	2.11	2.07	2.03	1.98	1.93	1.88
20	4.35	3.49	3.10	2.87	2.71	2.60	2.51	2.45	2.39	2.35	2.28	2.20	2.12	2.08	2.04	1.99	1.95	1.90	1.84
21	4.32	3.47	3.07	2.84	2.68	2.57	2.49	2.42	2.37	2.32	2.25	2.18	2.10	2.05	2.01	1.96	1.92	1.87	1.81
22	4.30	3.44	3.05	2.82	2.66	2.55	2.46	2.40	2.34	2.30	2.23	2.15	2.07	2.03	1.98	1.94	1.89	1.84	1.78
23	4.28	3.42	3.03	2.80	2.64	2.53	2.44	2.37	2.32	2.27	2.20	2.13	2.05	2.01	1.96	1.91	1.86	1.81	1.76
24	4.26	3.40	3.01	2.78	2.62	2.51	2.42	2.36	2.30	2.25	2.18	2.11	2.03	1.98	1.94	1.89	1.84	1.79	1.73
25	4.24	3.39	2.99	2.76	2.60	2.49	2.40	2.34	2.28	2.24	2.16	2.09	2.01	1.96	1.92	1.87	1.82	1.77	1.71
26	4.23	3.37	2.98	2.74	2.59	2.47	2.39	2.32	2.27	2.22	2.15	2.07	1.99	1.95	1.90	1.85	1.80	1.75	1.69
27	4.21	3.35	2.96	2.73	2.57	2.46	2.37	2.31	2.25	2.20	2.13	2.06	1.97	1.93	1.88	1.84	1.79	1.73	1.67
28	4.20	3.34	2.95	2.71	2.56	2.45	2.36	2.29	2.24	2.19	2.12	2.04	1.96	1.91	1.87	1.82	1.77	1.71	1.65
29	4.18	3.33	2.93	2.70	2.55	2.43	2.35	2.28	2.22	2.18	2.10	2.03	1.94	1.90	1.85	1.81	1.75	1.70	1.64
30	4.17	3.32	2.92	2.69	2.53	2.42	2.33	2.27	2.21	2.16	2.09	2.01	1.93	1.89	1.84	1.79	1.74	1.68	1.62
40	4.08	3.23	2.84	2.61	2.45	2.34	2.25	2.18	2.12	2.08	2.00	1.92	1.84	1.79	1.74	1.69	1.64	1.58	1.51
60	4.00	3.15	2.76	2.53	2.37	2.25	2.17	2.10	2.04	1.99	1.92	1.84	1.75	1.70	1.65	1.59	1.53	1.47	1.39
120	3.92	3.07	2.68	2.45	2.29	2.17	2.09	2.02	1.96	1.91	1.83	1.75	1.66	1.61	1.55	1.50	1.43	1.35	1.25
∞	3.84	3.00	2.60	2.37	2.21	2.10	2.01	1.94	1.88	1.83	1.75	1.67	1.57	1.52	1.46	1.39	1.32	1.22	1.00

TABLE H (concluded)

α = 0.10

d.f.N.: degrees of freedom, numerator

d.f.D.: degrees of freedom, denominator	1	2	3	4	5	6	7	8	9	10	12	15	20	24	30	40	60	120	∞
1	39.86	49.50	53.59	55.83	57.24	58.20	58.91	59.44	59.86	60.19	60.71	61.22	61.74	62.00	62.26	62.53	62.79	63.06	63.33
2	8.53	9.00	9.16	9.24	9.29	9.33	9.35	9.37	9.38	9.39	9.41	9.42	9.44	9.45	9.46	9.47	9.47	9.48	9.49
3	5.54	5.46	5.39	5.34	5.31	5.28	5.27	5.25	5.24	5.23	5.22	5.20	5.18	5.18	5.17	5.16	5.15	5.14	5.13
4	4.54	4.32	4.19	4.11	4.05	4.01	3.98	3.95	3.94	3.92	3.90	3.87	3.84	3.83	3.82	3.80	3.79	3.78	3.76
5	4.06	3.78	3.62	3.52	3.45	3.40	3.37	3.34	3.32	3.30	3.27	3.24	3.21	3.19	3.17	3.16	3.14	3.12	3.10
6	3.78	3.46	3.29	3.18	3.11	3.05	3.01	2.98	2.96	2.94	2.90	2.87	2.84	2.82	2.80	2.78	2.76	2.74	2.72
7	3.59	3.26	3.07	2.96	2.88	2.83	2.78	2.75	2.72	2.70	2.67	2.63	2.59	2.58	2.56	2.54	2.51	2.49	2.47
8	3.46	3.11	2.92	2.81	2.73	2.67	2.62	2.59	2.56	2.54	2.50	2.46	2.42	2.40	2.38	2.36	2.34	2.32	2.29
9	3.36	3.01	2.81	2.69	2.61	2.55	2.51	2.47	2.44	2.42	2.38	2.34	2.30	2.28	2.25	2.23	2.21	2.18	2.16
10	3.29	2.92	2.73	2.61	2.52	2.46	2.41	2.38	2.35	2.32	2.28	2.24	2.20	2.18	2.16	2.13	2.11	2.08	2.06
11	3.23	2.86	2.66	2.54	2.45	2.39	2.34	2.30	2.27	2.25	2.21	2.17	2.12	2.10	2.08	2.05	2.03	2.00	1.97
12	3.18	2.81	2.61	2.48	2.39	2.33	2.28	2.24	2.21	2.19	2.15	2.10	2.06	2.04	2.01	1.99	1.96	1.93	1.90
13	3.14	2.76	2.56	2.43	2.35	2.28	2.23	2.20	2.16	2.14	2.10	2.05	2.01	1.98	1.96	1.93	1.90	1.88	1.85
14	3.10	2.73	2.52	2.39	2.31	2.24	2.19	2.15	2.12	2.10	2.05	2.01	1.96	1.94	1.91	1.89	1.86	1.83	1.80
15	3.07	2.70	2.49	2.36	2.27	2.21	2.16	2.12	2.09	2.06	2.02	1.97	1.92	1.90	1.87	1.85	1.82	1.79	1.76
16	3.05	2.67	2.46	2.33	2.24	2.18	2.13	2.09	2.06	2.03	1.99	1.94	1.89	1.87	1.84	1.81	1.78	1.75	1.72
17	3.03	2.64	2.44	2.31	2.22	2.15	2.10	2.06	2.03	2.00	1.96	1.91	1.86	1.84	1.81	1.78	1.75	1.72	1.69
18	3.01	2.62	2.42	2.29	2.20	2.13	2.08	2.04	2.00	1.98	1.93	1.89	1.84	1.81	1.78	1.75	1.72	1.69	1.66
19	2.99	2.61	2.40	2.27	2.18	2.11	2.06	2.02	1.98	1.96	1.91	1.86	1.81	1.79	1.76	1.73	1.70	1.67	1.63
20	2.97	2.59	2.38	2.25	2.16	2.09	2.04	2.00	1.96	1.94	1.89	1.84	1.79	1.77	1.74	1.71	1.68	1.64	1.61
21	2.96	2.57	2.36	2.23	2.14	2.08	2.02	1.98	1.95	1.92	1.87	1.83	1.78	1.75	1.72	1.69	1.66	1.62	1.59
22	2.95	2.56	2.35	2.22	2.13	2.06	2.01	1.97	1.93	1.90	1.86	1.81	1.76	1.73	1.70	1.67	1.64	1.60	1.57
23	2.94	2.55	2.34	2.21	2.11	2.05	1.99	1.95	1.92	1.89	1.84	1.80	1.74	1.72	1.69	1.66	1.62	1.59	1.55
24	2.93	2.54	2.33	2.19	2.10	2.04	1.98	1.94	1.91	1.88	1.83	1.78	1.73	1.70	1.67	1.64	1.61	1.57	1.53
25	2.92	2.53	2.32	2.18	2.09	2.02	1.97	1.93	1.89	1.87	1.82	1.77	1.72	1.69	1.66	1.63	1.59	1.56	1.52
26	2.91	2.52	2.31	2.17	2.08	2.01	1.96	1.92	1.88	1.86	1.81	1.76	1.71	1.68	1.65	1.61	1.58	1.54	1.50
27	2.90	2.51	2.30	2.17	2.07	2.00	1.95	1.91	1.87	1.85	1.80	1.75	1.70	1.67	1.64	1.60	1.57	1.53	1.49
28	2.89	2.50	2.29	2.16	2.06	2.00	1.94	1.90	1.87	1.84	1.79	1.74	1.69	1.66	1.63	1.59	1.56	1.52	1.48
29	2.89	2.50	2.28	2.15	2.06	1.99	1.93	1.89	1.86	1.83	1.78	1.73	1.68	1.65	1.62	1.58	1.55	1.51	1.47
30	2.88	2.49	2.28	2.14	2.05	1.98	1.93	1.88	1.85	1.82	1.77	1.72	1.67	1.64	1.61	1.57	1.54	1.50	1.46
40	2.84	2.44	2.23	2.09	2.00	1.93	1.87	1.83	1.79	1.76	1.71	1.66	1.61	1.57	1.54	1.51	1.47	1.42	1.38
60	2.79	2.39	2.18	2.04	1.95	1.87	1.82	1.77	1.74	1.71	1.66	1.60	1.54	1.51	1.48	1.44	1.40	1.35	1.29
120	2.75	2.35	2.13	1.99	1.90	1.82	1.77	1.72	1.68	1.65	1.60	1.55	1.48	1.45	1.41	1.37	1.32	1.26	1.19
∞	2.71	2.30	2.08	1.94	1.85	1.77	1.72	1.67	1.63	1.60	1.55	1.49	1.42	1.38	1.34	1.30	1.24	1.17	1.00

From M. Merrington and C. M. Thompson (1943). Table of Percentage Points of the Inverted Beta (*F*) Distribution. *Biometrika 33*, pp. 74–87. Reprinted with permission from Biometrika.

TABLE I Critical Values for the PPMC

Reject H_0: $\rho = 0$ if the absolute value of r is greater than the value given in the table. The values are for a two-tailed test; d.f. $= n - 2$.

d.f.	$\alpha = 0.05$	$\alpha = 0.01$
1	0.999	0.999
2	0.950	0.999
3	0.878	0.959
4	0.811	0.917
5	0.754	0.875
6	0.707	0.834
7	0.666	0.798
8	0.632	0.765
9	0.602	0.735
10	0.576	0.708
11	0.553	0.684
12	0.532	0.661
13	0.514	0.641
14	0.497	0.623
15	0.482	0.606
16	0.468	0.590
17	0.456	0.575
18	0.444	0.561
19	0.433	0.549
20	0.423	0.537
25	0.381	0.487
30	0.349	0.449
35	0.325	0.418
40	0.304	0.393
45	0.288	0.372
50	0.273	0.354
60	0.250	0.325
70	0.232	0.302
80	0.217	0.283
90	0.205	0.267
100	0.195	0.254

Source: From *Biometrika Tables for Statisticians,* vol. 1 (1962), p. 138. Reprinted with permission.

TABLE J Critical Values for the Sign Test

Reject the null hypothesis if the smaller number of positive or negative signs is less than or equal to the value in the table.

	One-tailed, $\alpha = 0.005$	$\alpha = 0.01$	$\alpha = 0.025$	$\alpha = 0.05$
n	Two-tailed, $\alpha = 0.01$	$\alpha = 0.02$	$\alpha = 0.05$	$\alpha = 0.10$
8	0	0	0	1
9	0	0	1	1
10	0	0	1	1
11	0	1	1	2
12	1	1	2	2
13	1	1	2	3
14	1	2	3	3
15	2	2	3	3
16	2	2	3	4
17	2	3	4	4
18	3	3	4	5
19	3	4	4	5
20	3	4	5	5
21	4	4	5	6
22	4	5	5	6
23	4	5	6	7
24	5	5	6	7
25	5	6	6	7

Note: Table J is for one-tailed or two-tailed tests. The term n represents the total number of positive and negative signs. The test value is the number of less frequent signs.

Source: Table 1, p. 560, from "The Statistical Sign Test" by W. J. Dixon and A. M. Mood, vol. 41. no. 236 (Dec. 1946), pp. 557–566.

TABLE K   Critical Values for the Wilcoxon Signed-Rank Test

Reject the null hypothesis if the test value is less than or equal to the value given in the table.

n	One-tailed, $\alpha = 0.05$ / Two-tailed, $\alpha = 0.10$	$\alpha = 0.025$ / $\alpha = 0.05$	$\alpha = 0.01$ / $\alpha = 0.02$	$\alpha = 0.005$ / $\alpha = 0.01$
5	1			
6	2	1		
7	4	2	0	
8	6	4	2	0
9	8	6	3	2
10	11	8	5	3
11	14	11	7	5
12	17	14	10	7
13	21	17	13	10
14	26	21	16	13
15	30	25	20	16
16	36	30	24	19
17	41	35	28	23
18	47	40	33	28
19	54	46	38	32
20	60	52	43	37
21	68	59	49	43
22	75	66	56	49
23	83	73	62	55
24	92	81	69	61
25	101	90	77	68
26	110	98	85	76
27	120	107	93	84
28	130	117	102	92
29	141	127	111	100
30	152	137	120	109

Source: From *Some Rapid Approximate Statistical Procedures,* Copyright 1949, 1964 Lerderle Laboratories, American Cyanamid Co., Wayne, N.J. Reprinted with permission.

TABLE L   Critical Values for the Rank Correlation Coefficient

Reject H_0: $\rho = 0$ if the absolute value of r_S is greater than the value given in the table.

n	$\alpha = 0.10$	$\alpha = 0.05$	$\alpha = 0.02$	$\alpha = 0.01$
5	0.900	—	—	—
6	0.829	0.886	0.943	—
7	0.714	0.786	0.893	0.929
8	0.643	0.738	0.833	0.881
9	0.600	0.700	0.783	0.833
10	0.564	0.648	0.745	0.794
11	0.536	0.618	0.709	0.818
12	0.497	0.591	0.703	0.780
13	0.475	0.566	0.673	0.745
14	0.457	0.545	0.646	0.716
15	0.441	0.525	0.623	0.689
16	0.425	0.507	0.601	0.666
17	0.412	0.490	0.582	0.645
18	0.399	0.476	0.564	0.625
19	0.388	0.462	0.549	0.608
20	0.377	0.450	0.534	0.591
21	0.368	0.438	0.521	0.576
22	0.359	0.428	0.508	0.562
23	0.351	0.418	0.496	0.549
24	0.343	0.409	0.485	0.537
25	0.336	0.400	0.475	0.526
26	0.329	0.392	0.465	0.515
27	0.323	0.385	0.456	0.505
28	0.317	0.377	0.488	0.496
29	0.311	0.370	0.440	0.487
30	0.305	0.364	0.432	0.478

Source: From N. L. Johnson and F. C. Leone, *Statistical and Experimental Design,* vol. I (1964), p. 412. Reprinted with permission from the Institute of Mathematical Statistics.

TABLE M Critical Values for the Number of Runs

This table gives the critical values at $a = 0.05$ for a two-tailed test. Reject the null hypothesis if the number of runs is less than or equal to the smaller value or greater than or equal to the larger value.

Value of n_1	Value of n_2																		
	2	3	4	5	6	7	8	9	10	11	12	13	14	15	16	17	18	19	20
2	1	1	1	1	1	1	1	1	1	1	2	2	2	2	2	2	2	2	2
	6	6	6	6	6	6	6	6	6	6	6	6	6	6	6	6	6	6	6
3	1	1	1	1	2	2	2	2	2	2	2	2	2	3	3	3	3	3	3
	6	8	8	8	8	8	8	8	8	8	8	8	8	8	8	8	8	8	8
4	1	1	1	2	2	2	3	3	3	3	3	3	3	3	4	4	4	4	4
	6	8	9	9	9	10	10	10	10	10	10	10	10	10	10	10	10	10	10
5	1	1	2	2	3	3	3	3	3	4	4	4	4	4	4	4	5	5	5
	6	8	9	10	10	11	11	12	12	12	12	12	12	12	12	12	12	12	12
6	1	2	2	3	3	3	3	4	4	4	4	5	5	5	5	5	5	6	6
	6	8	9	10	11	12	12	13	13	13	13	14	14	14	14	14	14	14	14
7	1	2	2	3	3	3	4	4	5	5	5	5	5	6	6	6	6	6	6
	6	8	10	11	12	13	13	14	14	14	14	15	15	15	16	16	16	16	16
8	1	2	3	3	3	4	4	5	5	5	6	6	6	6	6	7	7	7	7
	6	8	10	11	12	13	14	14	15	15	16	16	16	16	17	17	17	17	17
9	1	2	3	3	4	4	5	5	5	6	6	6	7	7	7	7	8	8	8
	6	8	10	12	13	14	14	15	16	16	16	17	17	18	18	18	18	18	18
10	1	2	3	3	4	5	5	5	6	6	7	7	7	7	8	8	8	8	9
	6	8	10	12	13	14	15	16	16	17	17	18	18	18	19	19	19	20	20
11	1	2	3	4	4	5	5	6	6	7	7	7	8	8	8	9	9	9	9
	6	8	10	12	13	14	15	16	17	17	18	19	19	19	20	20	20	21	21
12	2	2	3	4	4	5	6	6	7	7	7	8	8	8	9	9	9	10	10
	6	8	10	12	13	14	16	16	17	18	19	19	20	20	21	21	21	22	22
13	2	2	3	4	5	5	6	6	7	7	8	8	9	9	9	10	10	10	10
	6	8	10	12	14	15	16	17	18	19	19	20	20	21	21	22	22	23	23
14	2	2	3	4	5	5	6	7	7	8	8	9	9	9	10	10	10	11	11
	6	8	10	12	14	15	16	17	18	19	20	20	21	22	22	23	23	23	24
15	2	3	3	4	5	6	6	7	7	8	8	9	9	10	10	11	11	11	12
	6	8	10	12	14	15	16	18	18	19	20	21	22	22	23	23	24	24	25
16	2	3	4	4	5	6	6	7	8	8	9	9	10	10	11	11	11	12	12
	6	8	10	12	14	16	17	18	19	20	21	21	22	23	23	24	25	25	25
17	2	3	4	4	5	6	7	7	8	9	9	10	10	11	11	11	12	12	13
	6	8	10	12	14	16	17	18	19	20	21	22	23	23	24	25	25	26	26
18	2	3	4	5	5	6	7	8	8	9	9	10	10	11	11	12	12	13	13
	6	8	10	12	14	16	17	18	19	20	21	22	23	24	25	25	26	26	27
19	2	3	4	5	6	6	7	8	8	9	10	10	11	11	12	12	13	13	13
	6	8	10	12	14	16	17	18	20	21	22	23	23	24	25	26	26	27	27
20	2	3	4	5	6	6	7	8	9	9	10	10	11	12	12	13	13	13	14
	6	8	10	12	14	16	17	18	20	21	22	23	24	25	25	26	27	27	28

Source: Adapted from C. Eisenhardt and F. Swed, "Tables for Testing Randomness of Grouping in a Sequence of Alternatives," *The Annals of Statistics,* vol. 14 (1943), pp. 83–86. Reprinted with permission of the Institute of Mathematical Statistics and of the Benjamin/Cummings Publishing Company, in whose publication, *Elementary Statistics,* 3rd ed. (1989), by Mario F. Triola, this table appears.

TABLE N Critical Values for the Tukey Test

$\alpha = 0.01$

k / v	2	3	4	5	6	7	8	9	10	11	12	13	14	15	16	17	18	19	20
1	90.03	135.0	164.3	185.6	202.2	215.8	227.2	237.0	245.6	253.2	260.0	266.2	271.8	277.0	281.8	286.3	290.4	294.3	298.0
2	14.04	19.02	22.29	24.72	26.63	28.20	29.53	30.68	31.69	32.59	33.40	34.13	34.81	35.43	36.00	36.53	37.03	37.50	37.95
3	8.26	10.62	12.17	13.33	14.24	15.00	15.64	16.20	16.69	17.13	17.53	17.89	18.22	18.52	18.81	19.07	19.32	19.55	19.77
4	6.51	8.12	9.17	9.96	10.58	11.10	11.55	11.93	12.27	12.57	12.84	13.09	13.32	13.53	13.73	13.91	14.08	14.24	14.40
5	5.70	6.98	7.80	8.42	8.91	9.32	9.67	9.97	10.24	10.48	10.70	10.89	11.08	11.24	11.40	11.55	11.68	11.81	11.93
6	5.24	6.33	7.03	7.56	7.97	8.32	8.61	8.87	9.10	9.30	9.48	9.65	9.81	9.95	10.08	10.21	10.32	10.43	10.54
7	4.95	5.92	6.54	7.01	7.37	7.68	7.94	8.17	8.37	8.55	8.71	8.86	9.00	9.12	9.24	9.35	9.46	9.55	9.65
8	4.75	5.64	6.20	6.62	6.96	7.24	7.47	7.68	7.86	8.03	8.18	8.31	8.44	8.55	8.66	8.76	8.85	8.94	9.03
9	4.60	5.43	5.96	6.35	6.66	6.91	7.13	7.33	7.49	7.65	7.78	7.91	8.03	8.13	8.23	8.33	8.41	8.49	8.57
10	4.48	5.27	5.77	6.14	6.43	6.67	6.87	7.05	7.21	7.36	7.49	7.60	7.71	7.81	7.91	7.99	8.08	8.15	8.23
11	4.39	5.15	5.62	5.97	6.25	6.48	6.67	6.84	6.99	7.13	7.25	7.36	7.46	7.56	7.65	7.73	7.81	7.88	7.95
12	4.32	5.05	5.50	5.84	6.10	6.32	6.51	6.67	6.81	6.94	7.06	7.17	7.26	7.36	7.44	7.52	7.59	7.66	7.73
13	4.26	4.96	5.40	5.73	5.98	6.19	6.37	6.53	6.67	6.79	6.90	7.01	7.10	7.19	7.27	7.35	7.42	7.48	7.55
14	4.21	4.89	5.32	5.63	5.88	6.08	6.26	6.41	6.54	6.66	6.77	6.87	6.96	7.05	7.13	7.20	7.27	7.33	7.39
15	4.17	4.84	5.25	5.56	5.80	5.99	6.16	6.31	6.44	6.55	6.66	6.76	6.84	6.93	7.00	7.07	7.14	7.20	7.26
16	4.13	4.79	5.19	5.49	5.72	5.92	6.08	6.22	6.35	6.46	6.56	6.66	6.74	6.82	6.90	6.97	7.03	7.09	7.15
17	4.10	4.74	5.14	5.43	5.66	5.85	6.01	6.15	6.27	6.38	6.48	6.57	6.66	6.73	6.81	6.87	6.94	7.00	7.05
18	4.07	4.70	5.09	5.38	5.60	5.79	5.94	6.08	6.20	6.31	6.41	6.50	6.58	6.65	6.73	6.79	6.85	6.91	6.97
19	4.05	4.67	5.05	5.33	5.55	5.73	5.89	6.02	6.14	6.25	6.34	6.43	6.51	6.58	6.65	6.72	6.78	6.84	6.89
20	4.02	4.64	5.02	5.29	5.51	5.69	5.84	5.97	6.09	6.19	6.28	6.37	6.45	6.52	6.59	6.65	6.71	6.77	6.82
24	3.96	4.55	4.91	5.17	5.37	5.54	5.69	5.81	5.92	6.02	6.11	6.19	6.26	6.33	6.39	6.45	6.51	6.56	6.61
30	3.89	4.45	4.80	5.05	5.24	5.40	5.54	5.65	5.76	5.85	5.93	6.01	6.08	6.14	6.20	6.26	6.31	6.36	6.41
40	3.82	4.37	4.70	4.93	5.11	5.26	5.39	5.50	5.60	5.69	5.76	5.83	5.90	5.96	6.02	6.07	6.12	6.16	6.21
60	3.76	4.28	4.59	4.82	4.99	5.13	5.25	5.36	5.45	5.53	5.60	5.67	5.73	5.78	5.84	5.89	5.93	5.97	6.01
120	3.70	4.20	4.50	4.71	4.87	5.01	5.12	5.21	5.30	5.37	5.44	5.50	5.56	5.61	5.66	5.71	5.75	5.79	5.83
∞	3.64	4.12	4.40	4.60	4.76	4.88	4.99	5.08	5.16	5.23	5.29	5.35	5.40	5.45	5.49	5.54	5.57	5.61	5.65

TABLE N (continued)

$\alpha = 0.05$

k / v	2	3	4	5	6	7	8	9	10	11	12	13	14	15	16	17	18	19	20
1	17.97	26.98	32.82	37.08	40.41	43.12	45.40	47.36	49.07	50.59	51.96	53.20	54.33	55.36	56.32	57.22	58.04	58.83	59.56
2	6.08	8.33	9.80	10.88	11.74	12.44	13.03	13.54	13.99	14.39	14.75	15.08	15.38	15.65	15.91	16.14	16.37	16.57	16.77
3	4.50	5.91	6.82	7.50	8.04	8.48	8.85	9.18	9.46	9.72	9.95	10.15	10.35	10.53	10.69	10.84	10.98	11.11	11.24
4	3.93	5.04	5.76	6.29	6.71	7.05	7.35	7.60	7.83	8.03	8.21	8.37	8.52	8.66	8.79	8.91	9.03	9.13	9.23
5	3.64	4.60	5.22	5.67	6.03	6.33	6.58	6.80	6.99	7.17	7.32	7.47	7.60	7.72	7.83	7.93	8.03	8.12	8.21
6	3.46	4.34	4.90	5.30	5.63	5.90	6.12	6.32	6.49	6.65	6.79	6.92	7.03	7.14	7.24	7.34	7.43	7.51	7.59
7	3.34	4.16	4.68	5.06	5.36	5.61	5.82	6.00	6.16	6.30	6.43	6.55	6.66	6.76	6.85	6.94	7.02	7.10	7.17
8	3.26	4.04	4.53	4.89	5.17	5.40	5.60	5.77	5.92	6.05	6.18	6.29	6.39	6.48	6.57	6.65	6.73	6.80	6.87
9	3.20	3.95	4.41	4.76	5.02	5.24	5.43	5.59	5.74	5.87	5.98	6.09	6.19	6.28	6.36	6.44	6.51	6.58	6.64
10	3.15	3.88	4.33	4.65	4.91	5.12	5.30	5.46	5.60	5.72	5.83	5.93	6.03	6.11	6.19	6.27	6.34	6.40	6.47
11	3.11	3.82	4.26	4.57	4.82	5.03	5.20	5.35	5.49	5.61	5.71	5.81	5.90	5.98	6.06	6.13	6.20	6.27	6.33
12	3.08	3.77	4.20	4.51	4.75	4.95	5.12	5.27	5.39	5.51	5.61	5.71	5.80	5.88	5.95	6.02	6.09	6.15	6.21
13	3.06	3.73	4.15	4.45	4.69	4.88	5.05	5.19	5.32	5.43	5.53	5.63	5.71	5.79	5.86	5.93	5.99	6.05	6.11
14	3.03	3.70	4.11	4.41	4.64	4.83	4.99	5.13	5.25	5.36	5.46	5.55	5.64	5.71	5.79	5.85	5.91	5.97	6.03
15	3.01	3.67	4.08	4.37	4.59	4.78	4.94	5.08	5.20	5.31	5.40	5.49	5.57	5.65	5.72	5.78	5.85	5.90	5.96
16	3.00	3.65	4.05	4.33	4.56	4.74	4.90	5.03	5.15	5.26	5.35	5.44	5.52	5.59	5.66	5.73	5.79	5.84	5.90
17	2.98	3.63	4.02	4.30	4.52	4.70	4.86	4.99	5.11	5.21	5.31	5.39	5.47	5.54	5.61	5.67	5.73	5.79	5.84
18	2.97	3.61	4.00	4.28	4.49	4.67	4.82	4.96	5.07	5.17	5.27	5.35	5.43	5.50	5.57	5.63	5.69	5.74	5.79
19	2.96	3.59	3.98	4.25	4.47	4.65	4.79	4.92	5.04	5.14	5.23	5.31	5.39	5.46	5.53	5.59	5.65	5.70	5.75
20	2.95	3.58	3.96	4.23	4.45	4.62	4.77	4.90	5.01	5.11	5.20	5.28	5.36	5.43	5.49	5.55	5.61	5.66	5.71
24	2.92	3.53	3.90	4.17	4.37	4.54	4.68	4.81	4.92	5.01	5.10	5.18	5.25	5.32	5.38	5.44	5.49	5.55	5.59
30	2.89	3.49	3.85	4.10	4.30	4.46	4.60	4.72	4.82	4.92	5.00	5.08	5.15	5.21	5.27	5.33	5.38	5.43	5.47
40	2.86	3.44	3.79	4.04	4.23	4.39	4.52	4.63	4.73	4.82	4.90	4.98	5.04	5.11	5.16	5.22	5.27	5.31	5.36
60	2.83	3.40	3.74	3.98	4.16	4.31	4.44	4.55	4.65	4.73	4.81	4.88	4.94	5.00	5.06	5.11	5.15	5.20	5.24
120	2.80	3.36	3.68	3.92	4.10	4.24	4.36	4.47	4.56	4.64	4.71	4.78	4.84	4.90	4.95	5.00	5.04	5.09	5.13
∞	2.77	3.31	3.63	3.86	4.03	4.17	4.29	4.39	4.47	4.55	4.62	4.68	4.74	4.80	4.85	4.89	4.93	4.97	5.01

TABLE N *(concluded)*

$\alpha = 0.10$

k\v	2	3	4	5	6	7	8	9	10	11	12	13	14	15	16	17	18	19	20
1	8.93	13.44	16.36	18.49	20.15	21.51	22.64	23.62	24.48	25.24	25.92	26.54	27.10	27.62	28.10	28.54	28.96	29.35	29.71
2	4.13	5.73	6.77	7.54	8.14	8.63	9.05	9.41	9.72	10.01	10.26	10.49	10.70	10.89	11.07	11.24	11.39	11.54	11.68
3	3.33	4.47	5.20	5.74	6.16	6.51	6.81	7.06	7.29	7.49	7.67	7.83	7.98	8.12	8.25	8.37	8.48	8.58	8.68
4	3.01	3.98	4.59	5.03	5.39	5.68	5.93	6.14	6.33	6.49	6.65	6.78	6.91	7.02	7.13	7.23	7.33	7.41	7.50
5	2.85	3.72	4.26	4.66	4.98	5.24	5.46	5.65	5.82	5.97	6.10	6.22	6.34	6.44	6.54	6.63	6.71	6.79	6.86
6	2.75	3.56	4.07	4.44	4.73	4.97	5.17	5.34	5.50	5.64	5.76	5.87	5.98	6.07	6.16	6.25	6.32	6.40	6.47
7	2.68	3.45	3.93	4.28	4.55	4.78	4.97	5.14	5.28	5.41	5.53	5.64	5.74	5.83	5.91	5.99	6.06	6.13	6.19
8	2.63	3.37	3.83	4.17	4.43	4.65	4.83	4.99	5.13	5.25	5.36	5.46	5.56	5.64	5.72	5.80	5.87	5.93	6.00
9	2.59	3.32	3.76	4.08	4.34	4.54	4.72	4.87	5.01	5.13	5.23	5.33	5.42	5.51	5.58	5.66	5.72	5.79	5.85
10	2.56	3.27	3.70	4.02	4.26	4.47	4.64	4.78	4.91	5.03	5.13	5.23	5.32	5.40	5.47	5.54	5.61	5.67	5.73
11	2.54	3.23	3.66	3.96	4.20	4.40	4.57	4.71	4.84	4.95	5.05	5.15	5.23	5.31	5.38	5.45	5.51	5.57	5.63
12	2.52	3.20	3.62	3.92	4.16	4.35	4.51	4.65	4.78	4.89	4.99	5.08	5.16	5.24	5.31	5.37	5.44	5.49	5.55
13	2.50	3.18	3.59	3.88	4.12	4.30	4.46	4.60	4.72	4.83	4.93	5.02	5.10	5.18	5.25	5.31	5.37	5.43	5.48
14	2.49	3.16	3.56	3.85	4.08	4.27	4.42	4.56	4.68	4.79	4.88	4.97	5.05	5.12	5.19	5.26	5.32	5.37	5.43
15	2.48	3.14	3.54	3.83	4.05	4.23	4.39	4.52	4.64	4.75	4.84	4.93	5.01	5.08	5.15	5.21	5.27	5.32	5.38
16	2.47	3.12	3.52	3.80	4.03	4.21	4.36	4.49	4.61	4.71	4.81	4.89	4.97	5.04	5.11	5.17	5.23	5.28	5.33
17	2.46	3.11	3.50	3.78	4.00	4.18	4.33	4.46	4.58	4.68	4.77	4.86	4.93	5.01	5.07	5.13	5.19	5.24	5.30
18	2.45	3.10	3.49	3.77	3.98	4.16	4.31	4.44	4.55	4.65	4.75	4.83	4.90	4.98	5.04	5.10	5.16	5.21	5.26
19	2.45	3.09	3.47	3.75	3.97	4.14	4.29	4.42	4.53	4.63	4.72	4.80	4.88	4.95	5.01	5.07	5.13	5.18	5.23
20	2.44	3.08	3.46	3.74	3.95	4.12	4.27	4.40	4.51	4.61	4.70	4.78	4.85	4.92	4.99	5.05	5.10	5.16	5.20
24	2.42	3.05	3.42	3.69	3.90	4.07	4.21	4.34	4.44	4.54	4.63	4.71	4.78	4.85	4.91	4.97	5.02	5.07	5.12
30	2.40	3.02	3.39	3.65	3.85	4.02	4.16	4.28	4.38	4.47	4.56	4.64	4.71	4.77	4.83	4.89	4.94	4.99	5.03
40	2.38	2.99	3.35	3.60	3.80	3.96	4.10	4.21	4.32	4.41	4.49	4.56	4.63	4.69	4.75	4.81	4.86	4.90	4.95
60	2.36	2.96	3.31	3.56	3.75	3.91	4.04	4.16	4.25	4.34	4.42	4.49	4.56	4.62	4.67	4.73	4.78	4.82	4.86
120	2.34	2.93	3.28	3.52	3.71	3.86	3.99	4.10	4.19	4.28	4.35	4.42	4.48	4.54	4.60	4.65	4.69	4.74	4.78
∞	2.33	2.90	3.24	3.48	3.66	3.81	3.93	4.04	4.13	4.21	4.28	4.35	4.41	4.47	4.52	4.57	4.61	4.65	4.69

Source: "Tables of Range and Studentized Range," *Annals of Mathematical Statistics*, vol. 31, no. 4. Reprinted with permission of the Institute of Mathematical Sciences.

APPENDIX B

Data Bank

Data Bank Values

This list explains the values given for the categories in the Data Bank.

1. "Age" is given in years.
2. "Educational level" values are defined as follows:

   0 = no high school degree   2 = college graduate
   1 = high school graduate   3 = graduate degree
3. "Smoking status" values are defined as follows:

   0 = does not smoke
   1 = smokes less than one pack per day
   2 = smokes one or more than one pack per day
4. "Exercise" values are defined as follows:

   0 = none   2 = moderate
   1 = light   3 = heavy

5. "Weight" is given in pounds.
6. "Serum cholesterol" is given in milligram percent (mg%).
7. "Systolic pressure" is given in millimeters of mercury (mm Hg).
8. "IQ" is given in standard IQ test score values.
9. "Sodium" is given in milliequivalents per liter (mEq/1).
10. "Gender" is listed as male (M) or female (F).
11. "Marital status" values are defined as follows:

    M = married   S = single
    W = widowed   D = divorced

Data Bank

ID number	Age	Educational level	Smoking status	Exercise	Weight	Serum cholesterol	Systolic pressure	IQ	Sodium	Gender	Marital status
01	27	2	1	1	120	193	126	118	136	F	M
02	18	1	0	1	145	210	120	105	137	M	S
03	32	2	0	0	118	196	128	115	135	F	M
04	24	2	0	1	162	208	129	108	142	M	M
05	19	1	2	0	106	188	119	106	133	F	S
06	56	1	0	0	143	206	136	111	138	F	W
07	65	1	2	0	160	240	131	99	140	M	W
08	36	2	1	0	215	215	163	106	151	M	D
09	43	1	0	1	127	201	132	111	134	F	M
10	47	1	1	1	132	215	138	109	135	F	D
11	48	3	1	2	196	199	148	115	146	M	D
12	25	2	2	3	109	210	115	114	141	F	S
13	63	0	1	0	170	242	149	101	152	F	D
14	37	2	0	3	187	193	142	109	144	M	M

Data Bank *(continued)*

ID number	Age	Educational level	Smoking status	Exercise	Weight	Serum cholesterol	Systolic pressure	IQ	Sodium	Gender	Marital status
15	40	0	1	1	234	208	156	98	147	M	M
16	25	1	2	1	199	253	135	103	148	M	S
17	72	0	0	0	143	288	156	103	145	F	M
18	56	1	1	0	156	164	153	99	144	F	D
19	37	2	0	2	142	214	122	110	135	M	M
20	41	1	1	1	123	220	142	108	134	F	M
21	33	2	1	1	165	194	122	112	137	M	S
22	52	1	0	1	157	205	119	106	134	M	D
23	44	2	0	1	121	223	135	116	133	F	M
24	53	1	0	0	131	199	133	121	136	F	M
25	19	1	0	3	128	206	118	122	132	M	S
26	25	1	0	0	143	200	118	103	135	M	M
27	31	2	1	1	152	204	120	119	136	M	M
28	28	2	0	0	119	203	118	116	138	F	M
29	23	1	0	0	111	240	120	105	135	F	S
30	47	2	1	0	149	199	132	123	136	F	M
31	47	2	1	0	179	235	131	113	139	M	M
32	59	1	2	0	206	260	151	99	143	M	W
33	36	2	1	0	191	201	148	118	145	M	D
34	59	0	1	1	156	235	142	100	132	F	W
35	35	1	0	0	122	232	131	106	135	F	M
36	29	2	0	2	175	195	129	121	148	M	M
37	43	3	0	3	194	211	138	129	146	M	M
38	44	1	2	0	132	240	130	109	132	F	S
39	63	2	2	1	188	255	156	121	145	M	M
40	36	2	1	1	125	220	126	117	140	F	S
41	21	1	0	1	109	206	114	102	136	F	M
42	31	2	0	2	112	201	116	123	133	F	M
43	57	1	1	1	167	213	141	103	143	M	W
44	20	1	2	3	101	194	110	111	125	F	S
45	24	2	1	3	106	188	113	114	127	F	D
46	42	1	0	1	148	206	136	107	140	M	S
47	55	1	0	0	170	257	152	106	130	F	M
48	23	0	0	1	152	204	116	95	142	M	M
49	32	2	0	0	191	210	132	115	147	M	M
50	28	1	0	1	148	222	135	100	135	M	M
51	67	0	0	0	160	250	141	116	146	F	W
52	22	1	1	1	109	220	121	103	144	F	M
53	19	1	1	1	131	231	117	112	133	M	S
54	25	2	0	2	153	212	121	119	149	M	D
55	41	3	2	2	165	236	130	131	152	M	M
56	24	2	0	3	112	205	118	100	132	F	S
57	32	2	0	1	115	187	115	109	136	F	S

Data Bank *(concluded)*

ID number	Age	Educational level	Smoking status	Exercise	Weight	Serum cholesterol	Systolic pressure	IQ	Sodium	Gender	Marital status
58	50	3	0	1	173	203	136	126	146	M	M
59	32	2	1	0	186	248	119	122	149	M	M
60	26	2	0	1	181	207	123	121	142	M	S
61	36	1	1	0	112	188	117	98	135	F	D
62	40	1	1	0	130	201	121	105	136	F	D
63	19	1	1	1	132	237	115	111	137	M	S
64	37	2	0	2	179	228	141	127	141	F	M
65	65	3	2	1	212	220	158	129	148	M	M
66	21	1	2	2	99	191	117	103	131	F	S
67	25	2	2	1	128	195	120	121	131	F	S
68	68	0	0	0	167	210	142	98	140	M	W
69	18	1	1	2	121	198	123	113	136	F	S
70	26	0	1	1	163	235	128	99	140	M	M
71	45	1	1	1	185	229	125	101	143	M	M
72	44	3	0	0	130	215	128	128	137	F	M
73	50	1	0	0	142	232	135	104	138	F	M
74	63	0	0	0	166	271	143	103	147	F	W
75	48	1	0	3	163	203	131	103	144	M	M
76	27	2	0	3	147	186	118	114	134	M	M
77	31	3	1	1	152	228	116	126	138	M	D
78	28	2	0	2	112	197	120	123	133	F	M
79	36	2	1	2	190	226	123	121	147	M	M
80	43	3	2	0	179	252	127	131	145	M	D
81	21	1	0	1	117	185	116	105	137	F	S
82	32	2	1	0	125	193	123	119	135	F	M
83	29	2	1	0	123	192	131	116	131	F	D
84	49	2	2	1	185	190	129	127	144	M	M
85	24	1	1	1	133	237	121	114	129	M	M
86	36	2	0	2	163	195	115	119	139	M	M
87	34	1	2	0	135	199	133	117	135	F	M
88	36	0	0	1	142	216	138	88	137	F	M
89	29	1	1	1	155	214	120	98	135	M	S
90	42	0	0	2	169	201	123	96	137	M	D
91	41	1	1	1	136	214	133	102	141	F	D
92	29	1	1	0	112	205	120	102	130	F	M
93	43	1	1	0	185	208	127	100	143	M	M
94	61	1	2	0	173	248	142	101	141	M	M
95	21	1	1	3	106	210	111	105	131	F	S
96	56	0	0	0	149	232	142	103	141	F	M
97	63	0	1	0	192	193	163	95	147	M	M
98	74	1	0	0	162	247	151	99	151	F	W
99	35	2	0	1	151	251	147	113	145	F	M
100	28	2	0	3	161	199	129	116	138	M	M

Data Set I   Record Temperatures

Record high temperatures by state in degrees Fahrenheit

112	100	107	122	120
100	118	112	108	113
128	117	115	110	120
120	116	115	121	117
134	118	118	113	107
114	121	117	120	110
106	114	118	119	118
110	114	125	111	112
109	105	106	104	114
112	109	110	111	115

Record low temperatures by state in degrees Fahrenheit

−27	12	−35	−50	−58
−80	−60	−51	−52	−32
−40	−36	−60	−34	−23
−29	−36	−19	−60	−50
−45	−47	−40	−39	−50
−61	−40	−70	−27	−30
−32	−37	−47	−54	−48
−17	−16	−50	−42	−37
−2	−50	−46	−28	−55
−17	−40	−34	−19	−66

Data Set II   Identity Theft Complaints

The data values show the number of complaints of identity theft for 50 selected cities.

2609	1202	2730	483	655
626	393	1268	279	663
817	1165	551	2654	592
128	189	424	585	78
1836	154	248	239	5888
574	75	226	28	205
176	372	84	229	15
148	117	22	211	31
77	41	200	35	30
88	20	84	465	136

Data Set III   Length of Major North American Rivers

729	610	325	392	524
1459	450	465	605	330
950	906	329	290	1000
600	1450	862	532	890
407	525	720	1243	850
649	730	352	390	420
710	340	693	306	250
470	724	332	259	2340
560	1060	774	332	3710

Data Set III   Length of Major North American Rivers   *(continued)*

2315	2540	618	1171	460
431	800	605	410	1310
500	790	531	981	460
926	375	1290	1210	1310
383	380	300	310	411
1900	434	420	545	569
425	800	865	380	445
538	1038	424	350	377
540	659	652	314	360
301	512	500	313	610
360	430	682	886	447
338	485	625	722	525
800	309	435		

Data Set IV   Heights (in Feet) of 80 Tallest Buildings in New York City

1250	861	1046	952	552
915	778	856	850	927
729	745	757	752	814
750	697	743	739	750
700	670	716	707	730
682	648	687	687	705
650	634	664	674	685
640	628	630	653	673
625	620	628	645	650
615	592	620	630	630
595	580	614	618	629
587	575	590	609	615
575	572	580	588	603
574	563	575	577	587
565	555	562	570	576
557	570	555	561	574

Heights (in Feet) of 25 Tallest Buildings in Calgary, Alberta

689	530	460	410
645	525	449	410
645	507	441	408
626	500	435	407
608	469	435	
580	468	432	
530	463	420	

Data Set V School Suspensions

The data values show the number of suspensions and the number of students enrolled in 41 local school districts in southwestern Pennsylvania.

Suspensions	Enrollment	Suspensions	Enrollment
37	1316	63	1588
29	1337	500	6046
106	4904	5	3610
47	5301	117	4329
51	1380	13	1908
46	1670	8	1341
65	3446	71	5582
223	1010	57	1869
10	795	16	1697
60	2094	60	2269
15	926	51	2307
198	1950	48	1564
56	3005	20	4147
72	4575	80	3182
110	4329	43	2982
6	3238	15	3313
37	3064	187	6090
26	2638	182	4874
140	4949	76	8286
39	3354	37	539
42	3547		

Source: U.S. Department of Education, *Pittsburgh Tribune-Review.*

Data Set VI Acreage of U.S. National Parks, in Thousands of Acres

41	66	233	775	169
36	338	223	46	64
183	4724	61	1449	7075
1013	3225	1181	308	77
520	77	27	217	5
539	3575	650	462	1670
2574	106	52	52	236
505	913	94	75	265
402	196	70	13	132
28	7656	2220	760	143

Source: The Universal Almanac.

Data Set VII Acreage Owned by 35 Municipalities in Southwestern Pennsylvania

384	44	62	218	250
198	60	306	105	600
10	38	87	227	340
48	70	58	223	3700
22	78	165	150	160
130	120	100	234	1200
4200	402	180	200	200

Source: Pittsburgh Tribune-Review.

Data Set VIII Oceans of the World

Ocean	Area (thousands of square miles)	Maximum depth (feet)
Arctic	5,400	17,881
Caribbean Sea	1,063	25,197
Mediterranean Sea	967	16,470
Norwegian Sea	597	13,189
Gulf of Mexico	596	14,370
Hudson Bay	475	850
Greenland Sea	465	15,899
North Sea	222	2,170
Black Sea	178	7,360
Baltic Sea	163	1,440
Atlantic Ocean	31,830	30,246
South China Sea	1,331	18,241
Sea of Okhotsk	610	11,063
Bering Sea	876	13,750
Sea of Japan	389	12,280
East China Sea	290	9,126
Yellow Sea	161	300
Pacific Ocean	63,800	36,200
Arabian Sea	1,492	19,029
Bay of Bengal	839	17,251
Red Sea	169	7,370
Indian Ocean	28,360	24,442

Source: The Universal Almanac.

Data Set IX Commuter and Rapid Rail Systems in the United States

System	Stations	Miles	Vehicles operated
Long Island RR	134	638.2	947
N.Y. Metro North	108	535.9	702
New Jersey Transit	158	926.0	582
Chicago RTA	117	417.0	358
Chicago & NW Transit	62	309.4	277
Boston Amtrak/MBTA	101	529.8	291
Chicago, Burlington, Northern	27	75.0	139
NW Indiana CTD	18	134.8	39
New York City TA	469	492.9	4923
Washington Metro Area TA	70	162.1	534
Metro Boston TA	53	76.7	368
Chicago TA	137	191.0	924
Philadelphia SEPTA	76	75.8	300
San Francisco BART	34	142.0	415
Metro Atlantic RTA	29	67.0	136
New York PATH	13	28.6	282
Miami/Dade Co TA	21	42.2	82
Baltimore MTA	12	26.6	48
Philadelphia PATCO	13	31.5	102
Cleveland RTA	18	38.2	30
New York, Staten Island RT	22	28.6	36

Source: The Universal Almanac.

Data Set X   Keystone Jackpot Analysis*

Ball	Times drawn	Ball	Times drawn	Ball	Times drawn
1	11	12	10	23	7
2	5	13	11	24	8
3	10	14	5	25	13
4	11	15	8	26	11
5	7	16	14	27	7
6	13	17	8	28	10
7	8	18	11	29	11
8	10	19	10	30	5
9	16	20	7	31	7
10	12	21	11	32	8
11	10	22	6	33	11

*Times each number has been selected in the regular drawings of the Pennsylvania Lottery.

Source: Copyright *Pittsburgh Post-Gazette,* all rights reserved. Reprinted with permission.

Data Set XI   Pages in Statistics Books

The data values represent the number of pages found in statistics textbooks.

616	578	569	511	468
493	564	801	483	847
525	881	757	272	703
741	556	500	668	967
608	465	739	669	651
495	613	774	274	542
739	488	601	727	556
589	724	731	662	680
589	435	742	567	574
733	576	526	443	478
586	282			

Source: Allan G. Bluman.

Data Set XII   Fifty Top Grossing Movies—2000

The data values represent the gross income in millions of dollars for the 50 top movies for the year 2000.

253.4	123.3	90.2	61.3	57.3
215.4	122.8	90.0	61.3	57.2
186.7	117.6	89.1	60.9	56.9
182.6	115.8	77.1	60.8	56.0
161.3	113.7	73.2	60.6	53.3
157.3	113.3	71.2	60.1	53.3
157.0	109.7	70.3	60.0	51.9
155.4	106.8	69.7	59.1	50.9
137.7	101.6	68.5	58.3	50.8
126.6	90.6	68.4	58.1	50.2

Source: Reprinted with permission from the *World Almanac and Book of Facts.* Copyright © K-III Reference Corporation. All rights reserved.

Data Set XIII   Hospital Data*

Number	Number of beds	Admissions	Payroll ($000)	Personnel
1	235	6,559	18,190	722
2	205	6,237	17,603	692
3	371	8,915	27,278	1,187
4	342	8,659	26,722	1,156
5	61	1,779	5,187	237
6	55	2,261	7,519	247
7	109	2,102	5,817	245
8	74	2,065	5,418	223
9	74	3,204	7,614	326
10	137	2,638	7,862	362
11	428	18,168	70,518	2,461
12	260	12,821	40,780	1,422
13	159	4,176	11,376	465
14	142	3,952	11,057	450
15	45	1,179	3,370	145
16	42	1,402	4,119	211
17	92	1,539	3,520	158
18	28	503	1,172	72
19	56	1,780	4,892	195
20	68	2,072	6,161	243
21	206	9,868	30,995	1,142
22	93	3,642	7,912	305
23	68	1,558	3,929	180
24	330	7,611	33,377	1,116
25	127	4,716	13,966	498
26	87	2,432	6,322	240
27	577	19,973	60,934	1,822
28	310	11,055	31,362	981
29	49	1,775	3,987	180
30	449	17,929	53,240	1,899
31	530	15,423	50,127	1,669
32	498	15,176	49,375	1,549
33	60	565	5,527	251
34	350	11,793	34,133	1,207
35	381	13,133	49,641	1,731
36	585	22,762	71,232	2,608
37	286	8,749	28,645	1,194
38	151	2,607	12,737	377
39	98	2,518	10,731	352
40	53	1,848	4,791	185
41	142	3,658	11,051	421
42	73	3,393	9,712	385
43	624	20,410	72,630	2,326
44	78	1,107	4,946	139
45	85	2,114	4,522	221

(continued)

Data Set XIII   Hospital Data* *(continued)*

Number	Number of beds	Admissions	Payroll ($000)	Personnel
46	120	3,435	11,479	417
47	84	1,768	4,360	184
48	667	22,375	74,810	2,461
49	36	1,008	2,311	131
50	598	21,259	113,972	4,010
51	1,021	40,879	165,917	6,264
52	233	4,467	22,572	558
53	205	4,162	21,766	527
54	80	469	8,254	280
55	350	7,676	58,341	1,525
56	290	7,499	57,298	1,502
57	890	31,812	134,752	3,933
58	880	31,703	133,836	3,914
59	67	2,020	8,533	280
60	317	14,595	68,264	2,772
61	123	4,225	12,161	504
62	285	7,562	25,930	952
63	51	1,932	6,412	472
64	34	1,591	4,393	205
65	194	5,111	19,367	753
66	191	6,729	21,889	946
67	227	5,862	18,285	731
68	172	5,509	17,222	680
69	285	9,855	27,848	1,180
70	230	7,619	29,147	1,216
71	206	7,368	28,592	1,185
72	102	3,255	9,214	359
73	76	1,409	3,302	198
74	540	396	22,327	788
75	110	3,170	9,756	409
76	142	4,984	13,550	552
77	380	335	11,675	543
78	256	8,749	23,132	907
79	235	8,676	22,849	883
80	580	1,967	33,004	1,059
81	86	2,477	7,507	309
82	102	2,200	6,894	225
83	190	6,375	17,283	618
84	85	3,506	8,854	380
85	42	1,516	3,525	166
86	60	1,573	15,608	236
87	485	16,676	51,348	1,559
88	455	16,285	50,786	1,537
89	266	9,134	26,145	939
90	107	3,497	10,255	431
91	122	5,013	17,092	589

Data Set XIII   Hospital Data* *(continued)*

Number	Number of beds	Admissions	Payroll ($000)	Personnel
92	36	519	1,526	80
93	34	615	1,342	74
94	37	1,123	2,712	123
95	100	2,478	6,448	265
96	65	2,252	5,955	237
97	58	1,649	4,144	203
98	55	2,049	3,515	152
99	109	1,816	4,163	194
100	64	1,719	3,696	167
101	73	1,682	5,581	240
102	52	1,644	5,291	222
103	326	10,207	29,031	1,074
104	268	10,182	28,108	1,030
105	49	1,365	4,461	215
106	52	763	2,615	125
107	106	4,629	10,549	456
108	73	2,579	6,533	240
109	163	201	5,015	260
110	32	34	2,880	124
111	385	14,553	52,572	1,724
112	95	3,267	9,928	366
113	339	12,021	54,163	1,607
114	50	1,548	3,278	156
115	55	1,274	2,822	162
116	278	6,323	15,697	722
117	298	11,736	40,610	1,606
118	136	2,099	7,136	255
119	97	1,831	6,448	222
120	369	12,378	35,879	1,312
121	288	10,807	29,972	1,263
122	262	10,394	29,408	1,237
123	94	2,143	7,593	323
124	98	3,465	9,376	371
125	136	2,768	7,412	390
126	70	824	4,741	208
127	35	883	2,505	142
128	52	1,279	3,212	158

*This information was obtained from a sample of hospitals in a selected state. The hospitals are identified by number instead of name.

APPENDIX C

Glossary

adjusted R^2 used in multiple regression when n and k are approximately equal, to provide a more realistic value of R^2

alpha the probability of a type I error, represented by the Greek letter α

alternative hypothesis a statistical hypothesis that states a difference between a parameter and a specific value or states that there is a difference between two parameters

analysis of variance (ANOVA) a statistical technique used to test a hypothesis concerning the means of three or more populations

ANOVA summary table the table used to summarize the results of an ANOVA test

Bayes' theorem a theorem that allows you to compute the revised probability of an event that occurred before another event when the events are dependent

beta the probability of a type II error, represented by the Greek letter β

between-group variance a variance estimate using the means of the groups or between the groups in an F test

biased sample a sample for which some type of systematic error has been made in the selection of subjects for the sample

bimodal a data set with two modes

binomial distribution the outcomes of a binomial experiment and the corresponding probabilities of these outcomes

binomial experiment a probability experiment in which each trial has only two outcomes, there are a fixed number of trials, the outcomes of the trials are independent, and the probability of success remains the same for each trial

blinding subjects of the study do not know whether they are receiving a treatment or a placebo

blocks groups of subjects with similar characteristics in a statistical study that receive different treatments when these characteristics might make a difference in the outcomes of the experiment

boundary a class of numbers in which a data value would be placed before the data value has been rounded

boxplot a graph used to represent a data set when the data set contains a small number of values

categorical frequency distribution a frequency distribution used when the data are categorical (nominal)

census a counting (usually done by government) of all members of the population

central limit theorem a theorem that states that as the sample size increases, the shape of the distribution of the sample means taken from the population with mean μ and standard deviation σ will approach a normal distribution; the distribution will have a mean μ and a standard deviation $\sigma/\sqrt{n}$

Chebyshev's theorem a theorem that states that the proportion of values from a data set that fall within k standard deviations of the mean will be at least $1 - 1/k^2$, where k is a number greater than 1

chi-square distribution a probability distribution obtained from the values of $(n - 1)s^2/\sigma^2$ when random samples are selected from a normally distributed population whose variance is σ^2

class boundaries the upper and lower values of a class for a grouped frequency distribution whose values have one additional decimal place more than the data and end in the digit 5

class midpoint a value for a class in a frequency distribution obtained by adding the lower and upper class boundaries (or the lower and upper class limits) and dividing by 2

class width the difference between the upper class boundary and the lower class boundary for a class in a frequency distribution

classical probability the type of probability that uses sample spaces to determine the numerical probability that an event will happen

cluster sample a sample obtained by selecting a preexisting or natural group, called a cluster, and using the members in the cluster for the sample

coefficient of determination a measure of the variation of the dependent variable that is explained by the regression line and the independent variable; the ratio of the explained variation to the total variation

coefficient of variation the standard deviation divided by the mean with the result expressed as a percentage

combination a selection of objects without regard to order

complement of an event the set of outcomes in the sample space that are not among the outcomes of the event itself

completely randomized design a statistical study where the subjects are assigned to groups by randomization and treatments are assigned to groups by randomization

compound bar graph statistical bar graph which compares data from different groups using vertical or horizontal bars

compound event an event that consists of two or more outcomes or simple events

conditional probability the probability that an event B occurs after an event A has already occurred

confidence interval a specific interval estimate of a parameter determined by using data obtained from a sample and the specific confidence level of the estimate

confidence level the probability that a parameter lies within the specified interval estimate of the parameter

confounding variable a variable that influences the outcome variable but cannot be separated from the other variables that influence the outcome variable

consistent estimator an estimator whose value approaches the value of the parameter estimated as the sample size increases

contingency table data arranged in table form for the chi-square independence test, with R rows and C columns

continuous variable a variable that can assume all values between any two specific values; a variable obtained by measuring

control group a group in an experimental study that is not given any special treatment

convenience sample sample of subjects used because they are convenient and available

correction for continuity a correction employed when a continuous distribution is used to approximate a discrete distribution

correlation a statistical method used to determine whether a linear relationship exists between variables

correlation coefficient a statistic or parameter that measures the strength and direction of a linear relationship between two variables

critical or **rejection region** the range of values of the test value that indicates that there is a significant difference and the null hypothesis should be rejected in a hypothesis test

critical value (C.V.) a value that separates the critical region from the noncritical region in a hypothesis test

cross-sectional study a study in which data are collected at one point in time

cumulative frequency the sum of the frequencies accumulated up to the upper boundary of a class in a frequency distribution

data measurements or observations for a variable

data array a data set that has been ordered

data set a collection of data values

data value or **datum** a value in a data set

decile a location measure of a data value; it divides the distribution into 10 groups

degrees of freedom the number of values that are free to vary after a sample statistic has been computed; used when a distribution (such as the t distribution) consists of a family of curves

dependent events events for which the outcome or occurrence of the first event affects the outcome or occurrence of the second event in such a way that the probability is changed

dependent samples samples in which the subjects are paired or matched in some way; i.e., the samples are related

dependent variable a variable in correlation and regression analysis that cannot be controlled or manipulated

descriptive statistics a branch of statistics that consists of the collection, organization, summarization, and presentation of data

discrete variable a variable that assumes values that can be counted

disjoint sets two or more sets that have no items in common

disordinal interaction an interaction between variables in ANOVA, indicated when the graphs of the lines connecting the mean intersect

distribution-free statistics *see* nonparametric statistics

dotplot statistical graph in which each data value is plotted by using a dot above a horizontal axis

double blinding technique whereby subjects and researchers do not know whether the subjects are receiving a treatment or a placebo

double sampling a sampling method in which a very large population is given a questionnaire to determine those who meet the qualifications for a study; the questionnaire is reviewed, a second smaller population is defined, and a sample is selected from this group

empirical probability the type of probability that uses frequency distributions based on observations to determine numerical probabilities of events

empirical rule a rule that states that when a distribution is bell-shaped (normal), approximately 68% of the data values will fall within 1 standard deviation of the mean; approximately 95% of the data values will fall within 2 standard deviations of the mean; and approximately 99.7% of the data values will fall within 3 standard deviations of the mean

equally likely events the events in the sample space that have the same probability of occurring

estimation the process of estimating the value of a parameter from information obtained from a sample

estimator a statistic used to estimate a parameter

event the outcome of a probability experiment

expected frequency the frequency obtained by calculation (as if the two variables are independent) and used in the chi-square test

expected value the theoretical average of a variable that has a probability distribution

experimental study a study in which the researcher manipulates one of the variables and tries to determine how the manipulation influences other variables

explanatory variable a variable that is being manipulated by the researcher to see if it affects the outcome variable

exploratory data analysis the act of analyzing data to determine what information can be obtained by using stem and leaf plots, medians, interquartile ranges, and boxplots

extrapolation use of the equation for the regression line to predict y' for a value of x that is beyond the range of the data values of x

F distribution the sampling distribution of the variances when two independent samples are selected from two normally distributed populations in which the variances are equal and the variances s_1^2 and s_2^2 are compared as s_1^2/s_2^2

F test a statistical test used to compare two variances or three or more means

factors the independent variables in ANOVA tests

finite population correction factor a correction factor used to correct the standard error of the mean when the sample size is greater than 5% of the population size

five-number summary five specific values for a data set that consist of the lowest and highest values, Q_1 and Q_3, and the median

frequency the number of values in a specific class of a frequency distribution

frequency distribution an organization of raw data in table form, using classes and frequencies

frequency polygon a graph that displays the data by using lines that connect points plotted for the frequencies at the midpoints of the classes

geometric distribution the distribution of a probability experiment that has two outcomes and is repeated until a success outcome is obtained

goodness-of-fit test a chi-square test used to see whether a frequency distribution fits a specific pattern

grouped frequency distribution a distribution used when the range is large and classes of several units in width are needed

Hawthorne effect an effect on an outcome variable caused by the fact that subjects of the study know that they are participating in the study

histogram a graph that displays the data by using vertical bars of various heights to represent the frequencies of a distribution

homogeneity of proportions test a test used to determine the equality of three or more proportions

hypergeometric distribution the distribution of a variable that has two outcomes when sampling is done without replacement

hypothesis testing a decision-making process for evaluating claims about a population

independence test a chi-square test used to test the independence of two variables when data are tabulated in table form in terms of frequencies

independent events events for which the probability of the first occurring does not affect the probability of the second occurring

independent samples samples that are not related

independent variable a variable in correlation and regression analysis that can be controlled or manipulated

inferential statistics a branch of statistics that consists of generalizing from samples to populations, performing hypothesis testing, determining relationships among variables, and making predictions

influential observation an observation that when removed from the data values would markedly change the position of the regression line

interaction effect the effect of two or more variables on each other in a two-way ANOVA study

interquartile range $Q_3 - Q_1$ (i.e. the distance between the first and third quartiles)

interval estimate a range of values used to estimate a parameter

interval level of measurement a measurement level that ranks data and in which precise differences between units of measure exist. *See also* nominal, ordinal, and ratio levels of measurement

Kruskal-Wallis test a nonparametric test used to compare three or more means

law of large numbers a law that says that when a probability experiment is repeated a large number of times, the relative frequency probability of an outcome will approach its theoretical probability

least-squares line another name for the regression line

left-tailed test a test used on a hypothesis when the critical region is on the left side of the distribution

level a treatment in ANOVA for a variable

level of significance the maximum probability of committing a type I error in hypothesis testing

longitudinal study a study conducted over a period of time

lower class limit the lower value of a class in a frequency distribution that has the same decimal place value as the data

lurking variable a variable that influences the relationship between x and y, but was not considered in the study

main effect the effect of the factors or independent variables when there is a nonsignificant interaction effect in a two-way ANOVA study

marginal change the magnitude of the change in the dependent variable when the independent variable changes 1 unit

matched-pairs design a statistical study where subjects are matched and then one subject is assigned to a treatment group and the other subject is assigned to a control group

maximum error of estimate the maximum likely difference between the point estimate of a parameter and the actual value of the parameter

mean the sum of the values, divided by the total number of values

mean square the variance found by dividing the sum of the squares of a variable by the corresponding degrees of freedom; used in ANOVA

measurement scales a type of classification that tells how variables are categorized, counted, or measured; the four types of scales are nominal, ordinal, interval, and ratio

median the midpoint of a data array

midrange the sum of the lowest and highest data values, divided by 2

modal class the class with the largest frequency

mode the value that occurs most often in a data set

Monte Carlo method a simulation technique using random numbers

multimodal a data set with three or more modes

multinomial distribution a probability distribution for an experiment in which each trial has more than two outcomes

multiple correlation coefficient a measure of the strength of the relationship between the independent variables and the dependent variable in a multiple regression study

multiple regression a study that seeks to determine if several independent variables are related to a dependent variable

multiple relationship a relationship in which many variables are under study

multistage sampling a sampling technique that uses a combination of sampling methods

mutually exclusive events probability events that cannot occur at the same time

negative relationship a relationship between variables such that as one variable increases, the other variable decreases, and vice versa

negatively skewed or **left-skewed distribution** a distribution in which the majority of the data values fall to the right of the mean

nominal level of measurement a measurement level that classifies data into mutually exclusive (nonoverlapping) exhaustive categories in which no order or ranking can be imposed on them. *See also* interval, ordinal, and ratio levels of measurement

noncritical or **nonrejection region** the range of values of the test value that indicates that the difference was probably due to chance and the null hypothesis should not be rejected

nonparametric statistics a branch of statistics for use when the population from which the samples are selected is not normally distributed and for use in testing hypotheses that do not involve specific population parameters

nonrejection region *see* noncritical region

nonresistant statistic a statistic that is relatively less affected by outliers

nonsampling error an error that occurs erroneously or from a biased sample

normal distribution a continuous, symmetric, bell-shaped distribution of a variable

normal quantile plot graphical plot used to determine whether a variable is approximately normally distributed

null hypothesis a statistical hypothesis that states that there is no difference between a parameter and a specific value or that there is no difference between two parameters

observational study a study in which the researcher merely observes what is happening or what has happened in the past and draws conclusions based on these observations

observed frequency the actual frequency value obtained from a sample and used in the chi-square test

ogive a graph that represents the cumulative frequencies for the classes in a frequency distribution

one-tailed test a test that indicates that the null hypothesis should be rejected when the test statistic value is in the critical region on one side of the mean

one-way ANOVA a study used to test for differences among means for a single independent variable when there are three or more groups

open-ended distribution a frequency distribution that has no specific beginning value or no specific ending value

ordinal interaction an interaction between variables in ANOVA, indicated when the graphs of the lines connecting the means do not intersect

ordinal level of measurement a measurement level that classifies data into categories that can be ranked; however, precise differences between the ranks do not exist. *See also* interval, nominal, and ratio levels of measurement

outcome the result of a single trial of a probability experiment

outcome variable a variable that is studied to see if it has changed significantly due to the manipulation of the explanatory variable

outlier an extreme value in a data set; it is omitted from a boxplot

parameter a characteristic or measure obtained by using all the data values for a specific population

parametric tests statistical tests for population parameters such as means, variances, and proportions that involve assumptions about the populations from which the samples were selected

Pareto chart chart that uses vertical bars to represent frequencies for a categorical variable

Pearson product moment correlation coefficient (PPMCC) a statistic used to determine the strength of a relationship when the variables are normally distributed

Pearson's index of skewness value used to determine the degree of skewness of a variable

percentile a location measure of a data value; it divides the distribution into 100 groups

permutation an arrangement of n objects in a specific order

pie graph a circle that is divided into sections or wedges according to the percentage of frequencies in each category of the distribution

placebo effect results of a study obtained by subjects who improve but not due to the conditions of the study

point estimate a specific numerical value estimate of a parameter

Poisson distribution a probability distribution used when n is large and p is small and when the independent variables occur over a period of time

pooled estimate of the variance a weighted average of the variance using the two sample variances and their respective degrees of freedom as the weights

population the totality of all subjects possessing certain common characteristics that are being studied

population correlation coefficient the value of the correlation coefficient computed by using all possible pairs of data values (x, y) taken from a population

positive relationship a relationship between two variables such that as one variable increases, the other variable increases or as one variable decreases, the other decreases

positively skewed or **right-skewed distribution** a distribution in which the majority of the data values fall to the left of the mean

power of a test the probability of rejecting the null hypothesis when it is false

prediction interval a confidence interval for a predicted value y

probability the chance of an event occurring

probability distribution the values a random variable can assume and the corresponding probabilities of the values

probability experiment a chance process that leads to well-defined results called outcomes

proportion a part of a whole, represented by a fraction, a decimal, or a percentage

P-value the actual probability of getting the sample mean value if the null hypothesis is true

qualitative variable a variable that can be placed into distinct categories, according to some characteristic or attribute

quantiles values that separate the data set into approximately equal groups

quantitative variable a variable that is numerical in nature and that can be measured or counted

quartile a location measure of a data value; it divides the distribution into four groups

quasi-experimental study a study that uses intact groups rather than random assignment of subjects to groups

random sample a sample obtained by using random or chance methods; a sample for which every member of the population has an equal chance of being selected

random variable a variable whose values are determined by chance

range the highest data value minus the lowest data value

range rule of thumb dividing the range by 4, given an approximation of the standard deviation

ranking the positioning of a data value in a data array according to some rating scale

ratio level of measurement a measurement level that possesses all the characteristics of interval measurement and a true zero; it also has true ratios between different units of measure. *See also* interval, nominal, and ordinal levels of measurement

raw data data collected in original form

regression a statistical method used to describe the nature of the relationship between variables, that is, a positive or negative, linear or nonlinear relationship

regression line the line of best fit of the data

rejection region *see* critical region

relative frequency graph a graph using proportions instead of raw data as frequencies

relatively efficient estimator an estimator that has the smallest variance of all the statistics that can be used to estimate a parameter

replication repetition of the study using different subjects

residual the difference between the actual value of y and the predicted value y' for a specific value of x

residual plot plot of the x values and the residuals to determine how well the regression line can be used to make predictions

resistant statistic a statistic that is not affected by an extremely skewed distribution

retrospective study a study in which data are collected from records obtained from the past

right-tailed test a test used on a hypothesis when the critical region is on the right side of the distribution

run a succession of identical letters preceded by or followed by a different letter or no letter at all, such as the beginning or end of the succession

runs test a nonparametric test used to determine whether data are random

sample a group of subjects selected from the population

sample space the set of all possible outcomes of a probability experiment

sampling distribution of sample means a distribution obtained by using the means computed from random samples taken from a population

sampling error the difference between the sample measure and the corresponding population measure due to the fact that the sample is not a perfect representation of the population

scatter plot a graph of the independent and dependent variables in regression and correlation analysis

Scheffé test a test used after ANOVA, if the null hypothesis is rejected, to locate significant differences in the means

sequence sampling a sampling technique used in quality control in which successive units are taken from production lines and tested to see whether they meet the standards set by the manufacturing company

sign test a nonparametric test used to test the value of the median for a specific sample or to test sample means in a comparison of two dependent samples

simple event an outcome that results from a single trial of a probability experiment

simple relationship a relationship in which only two variables are under study

simulation techniques techniques that use probability experiments to mimic real-life situations

Spearman rank correlation coefficient the nonparametric equivalent to the correlation coefficient, used when the data are ranked

standard deviation the square root of the variance

standard error of the estimate the standard deviation of the observed y values about the predicted y' values in regression and correlation analysis

standard error of the mean the standard deviation of the sample means for samples taken from the same population

standard normal distribution a normal distribution for which the mean is equal to 0 and the standard deviation is equal to 1

standard score the difference between a data value and the mean, divided by the standard deviation

statistic a characteristic or measure obtained by using the data values from a sample

statistical hypothesis a conjecture about a population parameter, which may or may not be true

statistical test a test that uses data obtained from a sample to make a decision about whether the null hypothesis should be rejected

statistics the science of conducting studies to collect, organize, summarize, analyze, and draw conclusions from data

stem and leaf plot a data plot that uses part of a data value as the stem and part of the data value as the leaf to form groups or classes

stratified sample a sample obtained by dividing the population into subgroups, called strata, according to various homogeneous characteristics and then selecting members from each stratum

subjective probability the type of probability that uses a probability value based on an educated guess or estimate, employing opinions and inexact information

sum of squares between groups a statistic computed in the numerator of the fraction used to find the between-group variance in ANOVA

sum of squares within groups a statistic computed in the numerator of the fraction used to find the within-group variance in ANOVA

symmetric distribution a distribution in which the data values are uniformly distributed about the mean

systematic sample a sample obtained by numbering each element in the population and then selecting every kth number from the population to be included in the sample

t **distribution** a family of bell-shaped curves based on degrees of freedom, similar to the standard normal distribution with the exception that the variance is greater than 1; used when you are testing small samples and when the population standard deviation is unknown

t **test** a statistical test for the mean of a population, used when the population is normally distributed and the population standard deviation is unknown

test value the numerical value obtained from a statistical test, computed from (observed value − expected value) ÷ standard error

time series graph a graph that represents data that occur over a specific time

treatment group a group in an experimental study that has received some type of treatment

treatment groups the groups used in an ANOVA study

tree diagram a device used to list all possibilities of a sequence of events in a systematic way

Tukey test a test used to make pairwise comparisons of means in an ANOVA study when samples are the same size

two-tailed test a test that indicates that the null hypothesis should be rejected when the test value is in either of the two critical regions

two-way ANOVA a study used to test the effects of two or more independent variables and the possible interaction between them

type I error the error that occurs if you reject the null hypothesis when it is true

type II error the error that occurs if you do not reject the null hypothesis when it is false

unbiased estimator an estimator whose value approximates the expected value of a population parameter, used for the variance or standard deviation when the sample size is less than 30; an estimator whose expected value or mean must be equal to the mean of the parameter being estimated

unbiased sample a sample chosen at random from the population that is, for the most part, representative of the population

ungrouped frequency distribution a distribution that uses individual data and has a small range of data

uniform distribution a distribution whose values are evenly distributed over its range

upper class limit the upper value of a class in a frequency distribution that has the same decimal place value as the data

variable a characteristic or attribute that can assume different values

variance the average of the squares of the distance that each value is from the mean

Venn diagram a diagram used as a pictorial representative for a probability concept or rule

volunteer sample subjects who decide for themselves to participate in a statistical study

weighted mean the mean found by multiplying each value by its corresponding weight and dividing by the sum of the weights

Wilcoxon rank sum test a nonparametric test used to test independent samples and compare distributions

Wilcoxon signed-rank test a nonparametric test used to test dependent samples and compare distributions

within-group variance a variance estimate using all the sample data for an F test; it is not affected by differences in the means

z **distribution** *see* standard normal distribution

z **score** *see* standard score

z **test** a statistical test for means and proportions of a population, used when the population is normally distributed and the population standard deviation is known

z **value** same as *z* score

Glossary of Symbols

a	y intercept of a line	F_S	Scheffé test value
α	Probability of a type I error	GM	Geometric mean
b	Slope of a line	H	Kruskal-Wallis test value
β	Probability of a type II error	H_0	Null hypothesis
C	Column frequency	H_1	Alternative hypothesis
cf	Cumulative frequency	HM	Harmonic mean
$_nC_r$	Number of combinations of n objects taking r objects at a time	k	Number of samples
		λ	Number of occurrences for the Poisson distribution
C.V.	Critical value	s_D	Standard deviation of the differences
CVar	Coefficient of variation	s_{est}	Standard error of estimate
D	Difference; decile	SS_B	Sum of squares between groups
$\overline{D}$	Mean of the differences	SS_W	Sum of squares within groups
d.f.	Degrees of freedom	s_B^2	Between-group variance
d.f.N.	Degrees of freedom, numerator	s_W^2	Within-group variance
d.f.D.	Degrees of freedom, denominator	t	t test value
E	Event; expected frequency; maximum error of estimate	$t_{\alpha/2}$	Two-tailed t critical value
		μ	Population mean
$\overline{E}$	Complement of an event	μ_D	Mean of the population differences
e	Euler's constant ≈ 2.7183	$\mu_{\overline{X}}$	Mean of the sample means
$E(X)$	Expected value	w	Class width; weight
f	Frequency	r	Sample correlation coefficient
F	F test value; failure	R	Multiple correlation coefficient
F'	Critical value for the Scheffé test	r^2	Coefficient of determination
MD	Median	ρ	Population correlation coefficient
MR	Midrange	r_S	Spearman rank correlation coefficient
MS_B	Mean square between groups	S	Sample space; success
MS_W	Mean square within groups (error)	s	Sample standard deviation
n	Sample size	s^2	Sample variance
N	Population size	σ	Population standard deviation
$n(E)$	Number of ways E can occur	σ^2	Population variance
$n(S)$	Number of outcomes in the sample space	$\sigma_{\overline{X}}$	Standard error of the mean
O	Observed frequency	Σ	Summation notation
P	Percentile; probability	w_s	Smaller sum of signed ranks, Wilcoxon signed-rank test
p	Probability; population proportion		
$\hat{p}$	Sample proportion	X	Data value; number of successes for a binomial distribution
$\overline{p}$	Weighted estimate of p		
$P(B\|A)$	Conditional probability	$\overline{X}$	Sample mean
$P(E)$	Probability of an event E	x	Independent variable in regression
$P(\overline{E})$	Probability of the complement of E	$\overline{X}_{GM}$	Grand mean
$_nP_r$	Number of permutations of n objects taking r objects at a time	X_m	Midpoint of a class
		χ^2	Chi-square
π	Pi ≈ 3.14	y	Dependent variable in regression
Q	Quartile	y'	Predicted y value
q	$1 - p;$ test value for Tukey test	z	z test value or z score
$\hat{q}$	$1 - \hat{p}$	$z_{\alpha/2}$	Two-tailed z critical value
$\overline{q}$	$1 - \overline{p}$	$!$	Factorial
R	Range; rank sum		

APPENDIX D
Photo Credits

Chapter 1

Opener: © Jupiterimages RF; p. 11: © Banana Stock Ltd RF; p. 13: © Jacobs Stock Photography/Digital Vision/Getty RF.

Chapter 2

Opener: © Corbis RF; p. 85: © Getty RF.

Chapter 3

Opener: © Comstock/Jupiter Images RF; p. 110, p. 114: © Getty RF.

Chapter 4

Opener: © Corbis RF; p. 232: © McGraw-Hill Education, Evelyn Jo Hebert, photographer; p. 242, P. 244: © Corbis RF.

Chapter 5

Opener: © Fotosearch RF; p. 262: © Brand X/Punchstock RF; p. 276: © Comstock/SuperStock RF.

Chapter 6

Opener: © Corbis RF; p. 330: © Corbis RF.

Chapter 7

Opener: © Getty RF; p. 394: © Brand X Pictures/Getty RF; p. 399: © Corbis RF.

Chapter 8

Opener: p. 400: © PhotoDisc/Punchstock RF; p. 448: © Jupiterimages/Imagesource RF; p. 474: © Getty RF.

Chapter 9

Opener: © Getty RF; p. 514: © Antonio Reeve/Photo Researchers; p. 523: © Comstcok/PictureQuest RF.

Chapter 10

Opener: © Getty RF; p. 561: © Getty RF; p. 592: © Norma Jean Gargasz/Alamy.

Chapter 11

Opener: © Getty RF; p. 637: © Getty RF.

Chapter 12

Opener: © Aaron Roeth Photography RF; p. 665: Photo by Jeff Vanuga, USDA Natural Resources Conservation Service.

Chapter 13

Opener: © McGraw-Hill Education, Andrew Resek, photographer.

Chapter 14

Opener: © CBS/Getty Images; p. 747: © Getty RF.

APPENDIX E

● Selected Answers*

Chapter 1

Exercises 1–1

1. Statistics is the science of conducting studies to collect, organize, summarize, analyze, and draw conclusions from data.

3. In a census, the researchers collect data from all subjects in the population.

5. Descriptive statistics consists of the collection, organization, summarization, and presentation of data while inferential statistics consists of generalizing from samples to populations, performing estimations and hypothesis testing, determining relationships among variables, and making predictions.

7. Samples are used more than populations both because populations are usually large and because researchers are unable to use every subject in the population.

9. This is inferential because a generalization is being made about the population.

11. This is a descriptive statistic.

13. This is an inferential statistic since a generalization about the population is being made.

15. This is a descriptive statistic since it is based on an online survey of 500 students.

17. This is an inferential statistic since it is a generalization made from data obtained from a sample.

19. Answers will vary.

Exercises 1–2

1. Qualitative variables are variables that can be placed in distinct categories according to some characteristic or attribute and cannot be ranked, while quantitative variables are numerical in nature and can be ordered or counted.

3. Continuous variables need to be rounded because of the limits of the measuring device.

5. Qualitative
7. Quantitative
9. Qualitative
11. Discrete
13. Continuous
15. Discrete
17. 6.5–7.5 feet
19. 142.5–143.5 miles
21. 25.75–25.85 yards
23. Nominal
25. Ratio
27. Ordinal
29. Ratio

Exercises 1–3

1. Data can be collected by using telephone surveys, mail questionnaire surveys, personal interview surveys, by taking a look at records, or by direct observation methods.

3. Random numbers are used in sampling so that every subject in the population has an equal chance of being selected for a sample. Random numbers can be generated by computers or calculators; however, there are other ways of generating random numbers such as using a random number table or rolling dice.

5. The population could be all adults in the United States. A sample could have been selected by a mail survey. Answers will vary.

7. The population could be all pet owners in the United States. A sample could be obtained by looking at veterinarians' records. However, these records would not include pet owners who do not take their pets to veterinarians. Answers will vary.

9. The population could be all adults in the United States who develop diabetes during 2012. The sample could be surveying patient records of these people to see if they have been taking statins. Again, the privacy rights must be considered. Answers will vary.

11. Systematic
13. Random
15. Cluster

Exercises 1–4

1. In an observational study, the researcher observes what is happening and tries to draw conclusions based on the observations. In an experimental study, the researcher manipulates one of the variables and tries to determine how this influences the variables.

3. One advantage of an observational study is that it can occur in a natural setting. In addition, researchers can look at past instances of statistics and draw conclusions from these situations. Another advantage is that the researcher can use variables, such as drugs, that he or she cannot manipulate. One disadvantage is that since the variable cannot be manipulated, a definite cause-and-effect situation cannot be shown. Another disadvantage is that these studies can be expensive and time-consuming. These studies can also be influenced by confounding variables. Finally, in these studies, the researcher sometimes needs to rely on data collected by others.

5. In an experimental study, the researcher has control of the assignment of subjects to the groups, whereas in a quasi-experimental study, the researcher uses intact groups.

7. In research studies, a treatment group subject receives a specific treatment and those in the control group do not receive a treatment or are given a placebo.

9. A confounding variable is one that can influence the results of the research study when no precautions were taken to eliminate it from the study.

11. Blinding is used to help eliminate the placebo effect. Here the subjects are given a sugar pill that looks like the real

*Answers may vary due to rounding or use of technology.

medical pill. The subjects do not know which pill they are getting. When double blinding occurs, neither the subjects nor the researchers are told who gets the real treatment or the placebo.

13. In a completely randomized design, the subjects are assigned to the groups randomly, whereas in a matched-pair design, subjects are matched on some variable. Then one subject is randomly assigned to one group, and the other subject is assigned to the other group. In both types of studies, the treatments can be randomly assigned to the groups.

15. Experimental   17. Observational

19. Independent variable—minutes exercising
Dependent variable—catching a cold

21. Independent variable—time spent in meditation
Dependent variable—rational decisions

23. Age, income, socioeconomic status. Answers will vary.

25. Wealth, age, education. Answers will vary.

27. How is a perfect body defined statistically?

29. How can 24 hours of pain relief be measured?

31. How much weight, if any, will be lost?

33. Only 20 people were used in the study.

35. It is meaningless since there is no definition of "the road less traveled." Also, there is no way to know that for *every* 100 women, 91 would say that they have taken "the road less traveled."

37. There is no mention of how this conclusion was obtained.

39. Since the word *may* is used, there is no guarantee that the product will help fight cancer and heart disease.

41. No. There are many other factors that contribute to criminal behavior.

43. Answers will vary.   45. Answers will vary.

Review Exercises

1. Inferential	3. Descriptive
5. Inferential	7. Descriptive
9. Ratio	11. Interval
13. Ratio	15. Ordinal
17. Ratio	19. Qualitative
21. Quantitative	23. Quantitative
25. Quantitative	27. Discrete
29. Discrete	31. Continuous
33. Continuous	35. 35.5–36.5 inches
37. 72.55–72.65 tons	39. Cluster
41. Random	43. Stratified
45. Experimental	47. Observational

49. Independent variable—types of coffee
Dependent variable—milligrams of caffeine per ounce

51. Independent variable—thyme
Dependent variable—antioxidants

53. A telephone survey won't contact all the types of people who shop online. Answers will vary.

55. People tend not to report their true income. Answers will vary.

57. It depends on how the Internet is used. Answers will vary.

Chapter Quiz

1. True	2. True
3. False	4. False
5. True	6. True
7. False	8. c
9. b	10. d
11. a	12. c
13. a	14. Descriptive, inferential

15. Gambling, insurance. Answers can vary.

16. Population

17. Sample

18. a. Saves time   c. Use when population is infinite
b. Saves money

19. a. Random   c. Cluster
b. Systematic   d. Stratified

20. Quasi-experimental   21. Random

22. a. Descriptive   d. Inferential
b. Inferential   e. Inferential
c. Descriptive

23. a. Nominal   d. Interval
b. Ratio   e. Ratio
c. Ordinal

24. a. Continuous   d. Continuous
b. Discrete   e. Discrete
c. Continuous

25. a. 31.5–32.5 minutes
b. 0.475–0.485 millimeter
c. 6.15–6.25 inches
d. 18.5–19.5 pounds
e. 12.05–12.15 quarts

Chapter 2
Exercises 2–1

1. To organize data in a meaningful way, to determine the shape of the distribution, to facilitate computational procedures for statistics, to make it easier to draw charts and graphs, to make comparisons among different sets of data

3. 5–20; class width should be an odd number so that the midpoints of the classes are in the same place value as the data.

5. 42.5–47.5, 45, 5

7. 8.235–11.365, 9.8, 3.13

9. Class width is not uniform.

11. A class has been omitted.

13.

Class	Tally	Frequency	Percent
F	⫻ ⫻ ⫻ ⫻	19	38
C	⫻ ⫻ ⫻	14	28
B	⫻ ⫻	10	20
A	⫻ //	7	14
		Total 50	100

The class with the most data values is professional football. The class with the least number of data values is auto racing.

15.

Limits	Boundaries	Tally	f
0	−0.5–0.5	//	2
1	0.5–1.5	/////	5
2	1.5–2.5	///// ///// ///// ///// ////	24
3	2.5–3.5	///// ///	8
4	3.5–4.5	///// /	6
5	4.5–5.5	////	4
6	5.5–6.5		0
7	6.5–7.5	/	1
		Total	50

	cf
Less than −0.5	0
Less than 0.5	2
Less than 1.5	7
Less than 2.5	31
Less than 3.5	39
Less than 4.5	45
Less than 5.5	49
Less than 6.5	49
Less than 7.5	50

The category "twice a week" has more values than any other category.

17.

Limits	Boundaries	f
465–473	464.5–473.5	9
474–482	473.5–482.5	7
483–491	482.5–491.5	7
492–500	491.5–500.5	6
501–509	500.5–509.5	7
510–518	509.5–518.5	4
	Total	40

	cf
Less than 464.5	0
Less than 473.5	9
Less than 482.5	16
Less than 491.5	23
Less than 500.5	29
Less than 509.5	36
Less than 518.5	40

19.

Limits	Boundaries	f
27–33	26.5–33.5	7
34–40	33.5–40.5	14
41–47	40.5–47.5	15
48–54	47.5–54.5	11
55–61	54.5–61.5	3
62–68	61.5–68.5	3
69–75	68.5–75.5	2
	Total	55

	cf
Less than 26.5	0
Less than 33.5	7
Less than 40.5	21
Less than 47.5	36
Less than 54.5	47
Less than 61.5	50
Less than 68.5	53
Less than 75.5	55

21.

Limits	Boundaries	f
12–20	11.5–20.5	7
21–29	20.5–29.5	7
30–38	29.5–38.5	3
39–47	38.5–47.5	3
48–56	47.5–56.5	4
57–65	56.5–65.5	3
66–74	65.5–74.5	0
75–83	74.5–83.5	2
84–92	83.5–92.5	1
	Total	30

	cf
Less than 11.5	0
Less than 20.5	7
Less than 29.5	14
Less than 38.5	17
Less than 47.5	20
Less than 56.5	24
Less than 65.5	27
Less than 74.5	27
Less than 83.5	29
Less than 92.5	30

23.

Limits	Boundaries	f
77–83	76.5–83.5	1
84–90	83.5–90.5	1
91–97	90.5–97.5	6
98–104	97.5–104.5	14
105–111	104.5–111.5	8
112–118	111.5–118.5	1
119–125	118.5–125.5	1
	Total	32

	cf
Less than 76.5	0
Less than 83.5	1
Less than 90.5	2
Less than 97.5	8
Less than 104.5	22
Less than 111.5	30
Less than 118.5	31
Less than 125.5	32

25.

Limits	Boundaries	f
6.2–7.0	6.15–7.05	1
7.1–7.9	7.05–7.95	7
8.0–8.8	7.95–8.85	9
8.9–9.7	8.85–9.75	7
9.8–10.6	9.75–10.65	8
10.7–11.5	10.65–11.55	4
11.6–12.4	11.55–12.45	4
	Total	40

	cf
Less than 6.15	0
Less than 7.05	1
Less than 7.95	8
Less than 8.85	17
Less than 9.75	24
Less than 10.65	32
Less than 11.55	36
Less than 12.45	40

27. The percents sum to 101. They should sum to 100% unless rounding was used.

Exercises 2–2

1.

Limits	Boundaries	f	Midpoints
90–98	89.5–98.5	6	94
99–107	98.5–107.5	22	103
108–116	107.5–116.5	43	112
117–125	116.5–125.5	28	121
126–134	125.5–134.5	9	130
		Total 108	

	cf
Less than 89.5	0
Less than 98.5	6
Less than 107.5	28
Less than 116.5	71
Less than 125.5	99
Less than 134.5	108

Eighty applicants do not need to enroll in the developmental programs.

3.

Limits	Boundaries	f	Midpoints
3–44	2.5–45.5	19	24
45–86	45.5–88.5	19	67
89–131	88.5–131.5	10	110
132–174	131.5–174.5	1	153
175–217	174.5–217.5	0	196
218–260	217.5–260.5	1	239
		Total 50	

	cf
Less than 2.5	0
Less than 45.5	19
Less than 88.5	38
Less than 131.5	48
Less than 174.5	49
Less than 217.5	49
Less than 260.5	50

The distribution is positively skewed.

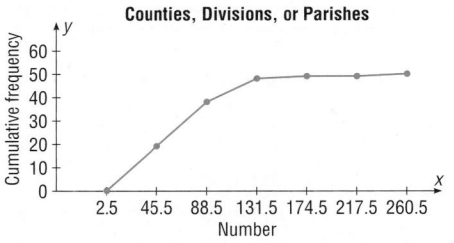

5.

Limits	Boundaries	f	Midpoints
1–43	0.5–43.5	24	22
44–86	43.5–86.5	17	65
87–129	86.5–129.5	3	108
130–172	129.5–172.5	4	151
173–215	172.5–215.5	1	194
216–258	215.5–258.5	0	237
259–301	258.5–301.5	0	280
302–344	301.5–344.5	1	323
		Total 50	

	cf
Less than 0.5	0
Less than 43.5	24
Less than 86.5	41
Less than 129.5	44
Less than 172.5	48
Less than 215.5	49
Less than 258.5	49
Less than 301.5	49
Less than 344.5	50

The distribution is positively skewed.

7.

Limits	Boundaries	f	Midpoints
21–29	20.5–29.5	5	25
30–38	29.5–38.5	10	34
39–47	38.5–47.5	13	43
48–56	47.5–56.5	10	52
57–65	56.5–65.5	4	61
66–74	65.5–74.5	3	70
75–83	74.5–83.5	1	79
		Total 46	

	cf
Less than 20.5	0
Less than 29.5	5
Less than 38.5	15
Less than 47.5	28
Less than 56.5	38
Less than 65.5	42
Less than 74.5	45
Less than 83.5	46

Eight games had more than 56 total points.

9.

Limits	Boundaries	f (now)	f (5 years ago)
10–14	9.5–14.5	6	5
15–19	14.5–19.5	4	4
20–24	19.5–24.5	3	2
25–29	24.5–29.5	2	3
30–34	29.5–34.5	5	6
35–39	34.5–39.5	1	2
40–44	39.5–44.5	2	1
45–49	44.5–49.5	1	1
		Total 24	Total 24

With minor differences, the histograms are fairly similar.

11.

Limits	Boundaries	f	Midpoints
60–64	59.5–64.5	2	62
65–69	64.5–69.5	1	67
70–74	69.5–74.5	5	72
75–79	74.5–79.5	12	77
80–84	79.5–84.5	18	82
85–89	84.5–89.5	6	87
90–94	89.5–94.5	5	92
95–99	94.5–99.5	1	97
		Total 50	

	cf
Less than 59.5	0
Less than 64.5	2
Less than 69.5	3
Less than 74.5	8
Less than 79.5	20
Less than 84.5	38
Less than 89.5	44
Less than 94.5	49
Less than 99.5	50

Most patients fell into the 75–84 range.

13.

Boundaries	rf	Midpoints
89.5–98.5	0.06	94
98.5–107.5	0.20	103
107.5–116.5	0.40	112
116.5–125.5	0.26	121
125.5–134.5	0.08	130
	Total 1.00	

	crf
Less than 89.5	0
Less than 98.5	0.06
Less than 107.5	0.26
Less than 116.5	0.66
Less than 125.5	0.92
Less than 134.5	1.00

The proportion of applicants who do not need to enroll in the developmental program is about 0.74.

15.

Boundaries	rf	Midpoints
0.5–43.5	0.48	22
43.5–86.5	0.34	65
86.5–129.5	0.06	108
129.5–172.5	0.08	151
172.5–215.5	0.02	194
215.5–258.5	0.00	237
258.5–301.5	0.00	280
301.5–344.5	0.02	323
Total	1.00	

	rcf
Less than 0.5	0
Less than 43.5	0.48
Less than 86.5	0.82
Less than 129.5	0.88
Less than 172.5	0.96
Less than 215.5	0.98
Less than 258.5	0.98
Less than 301.5	0.98
Less than 344.5	1.00

17.

Class boundaries	rf	Midpoints
79.5–108.5	0.17	94
108.5–137.5	0.28	123
137.5–166.5	0.04	152
166.5–195.5	0.20	181
195.5–224.5	0.22	210
224.5–253.5	0.04	239
253.5–282.5	0.04	268
Total	0.99	

	crf
Less than 79.5	0.00
Less than 108.5	0.17
Less than 137.5	0.45
Less than 166.5	0.49
Less than 195.5	0.69
Less than 224.5	0.91
Less than 253.5	0.95
Less than 282.5	0.99*

*Due to rounding.

The histogram has two peaks.

19. *a.*

Limits	Boundaries	Midpoints	f
22–24	21.5–24.5	23	1
25–27	24.5–27.5	26	3
28–30	27.5–30.5	29	0
31–33	30.5–33.5	32	6
34–36	33.5–36.5	35	5
37–39	36.5–39.5	38	3
40–42	39.5–42.5	41	2

	cf
Less than 21.5	0
Less than 24.5	1
Less than 27.5	4
Less than 30.5	4
Less than 33.5	10
Less than 36.5	15
Less than 39.5	18
Less than 42.5	20

b.

c.

21.

Boundaries	f	Midpoints
468.5–495.5	6	482
495.5–522.5	15	509
522.5–549.5	10	536
549.5–576.5	7	563
576.5–603.5	6	590
603.5–630.5	6	617
Total	50	

Exercises 2–3

1.

3.

5.

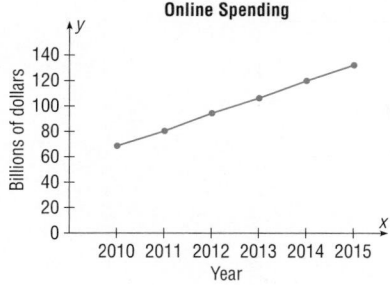

There is an increase over the years.

7.

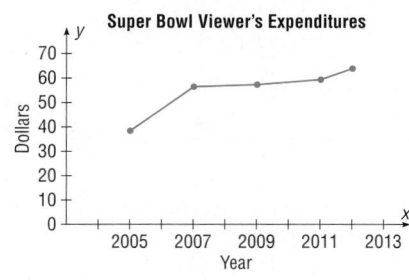

There was a big increase between 2005 and 2007 and slight increases over the next years.

9.

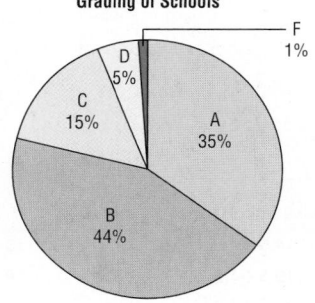

More people graded their child's school as B than any other grade. Very few people graded the schools as D or F.

11.

The fossil fuels accounted for 83% of the total usage.

13.

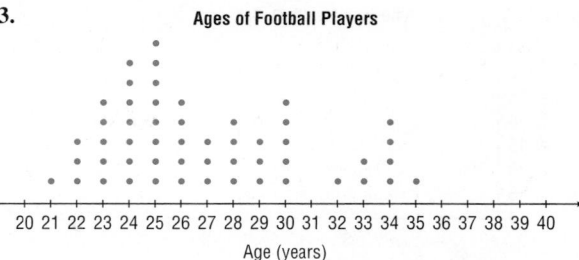

The dotplot is somewhat positively skewed with most players being between the ages of 21 and 30 years old. There are 2 peaks. They are 24 and 25 years with 7 players being 24 years old and 8 players being 25 years old.

15.

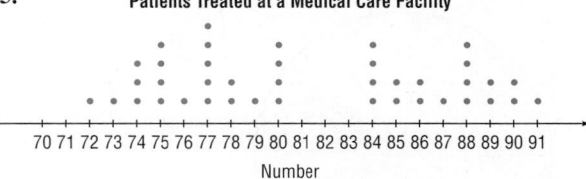

There is a peak in the data at 77 and a gap between 80 and 84. There are two clusters of data values, from 72 to 80 and from 84 to 91.

17. **The 50-Home Run Club**

```
5 | 0 0 0 0 0 0 1 1 1 1 1 2 2 2 2 2 2 4 4 4 4 4 4 4
5 | 6 6 6 7 7 8 8 8 8 8 9
6 | 0 1 3 4
6 | 5 6
7 | 0 3
```

Most players in the club have hit from 50 to 54 home runs in one season. The greatest number of home runs hit is 73.

19. **Lengths of Major Rivers**

South America		Europe
2	0	3 4 4 5 5 5 5 6 6 6 6 6 7 8 8 9
4 2 1 0 0 0 0 0 0 0 0	1	1 2 3 4
7 6 5 5	1	8
1	2	
5	2	
	3	
9	3	

The majority of rivers are longer in South America.

21. *a.* Pareto chart

  b. Pareto chart

  c. Pie graph

  d. Time series graph

  e. Pareto chart

  f. Time series graph

23.

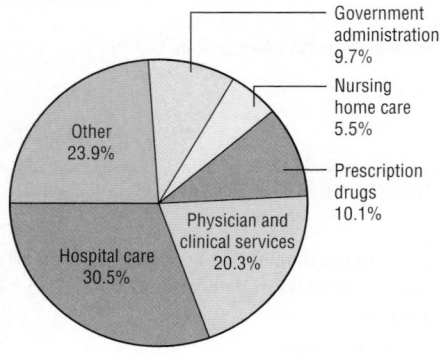

25. The bottle for 2011 is much bigger in area than the bottle for 1988. So your eyes compare areas rather than heights, making the difference appear to be much greater than it is.

27.

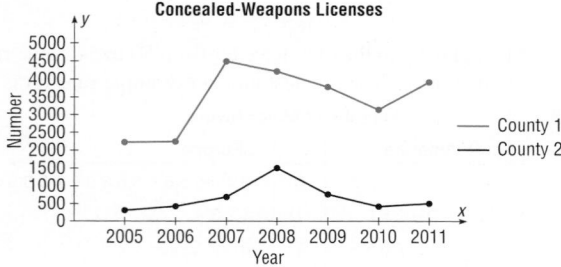

There's no way to tell if the crime rate is decreasing by looking at the graph.

Review Exercises

1.

Class	f	Percent
Newspaper	10	20
Television	16	32
Radio	12	24
Internet	12	24
Total	50	100

3.

Class	f
11	1
12	2
13	2
14	2
15	1
16	2
17	4
18	2
19	2
20	1
21	0
22	1
Total	20

	cf
Less than 10.5	0
Less than 11.5	1
Less than 12.5	3
Less than 13.5	5
Less than 14.5	7
Less than 15.5	8
Less than 16.5	10
Less than 17.5	14
Less than 18.5	16
Less than 19.5	18
Less than 20.5	19
Less than 21.5	19
Less than 22.5	20

5.

Class limits	Class boundaries	f
15–19	14.5–19.5	3
20–24	19.5–24.5	18
25–29	24.5–29.5	18
30–34	29.5–34.5	8
35–39	34.5–39.5	3
	Total	50

	cf
Less than 14.5	0
Less than 19.5	3
Less than 24.5	21
Less than 29.5	39
Less than 34.5	47
Less than 39.5	50

7.

Class limits	Class boundaries	rf
15–19	14.5–19.5	0.06
20–24	19.5–24.5	0.36
25–29	24.5–29.5	0.36
30–34	29.5–34.5	0.16
35–39	34.5–39.5	0.06
	Total	1.00

	crf
Less than 14.5	0.00
Less than 19.5	0.06
Less than 24.5	0.42
Less than 29.5	0.78
Less than 34.5	0.94
Less than 39.5	1.00

9.

11.

13.

15.

17.

Space Launches

The space launches have declined considerably from the decade of the 60s to the decades of the 70s and 80s but increased during the decade of the 90s then decreased in the 2000s.

19.

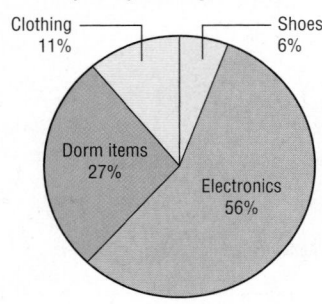

Spending of College Freshmen

Clothing 11% Shoes 6% Dorm items 27% Electronics 56%

21.

Touchdowns

The graph shows almost all but one of the touchdowns per season for Manning's career were between 26 and 33.

23.

2	9 9
3	2 4 5 6 8 8
4	1 2 3 7 7
5	1 3 5 8
6	2 2 2 3 7
7	2 3

25. There are no numbers on the x and y axes. So it is impossible to tell the times of the pain relief.

Chapter Quiz

1. False	**2.** False
3. False	**4.** True
5. True	**6.** False
7. False	**8.** c
9. c	**10.** b
11. b	**12.** Categorical, ungrouped, grouped
13. 5, 20	**14.** Categorical
15. Time series	**16.** Stem and leaf plot
17. Vertical or y	

18.

Class	f	Percent
H	6	24
A	5	20
M	6	24
C	8	32
Total	25	100

19.

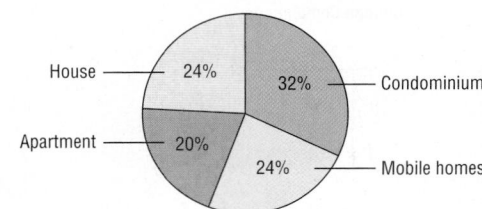

Housing Arrangements

House 24% Condominium 32% Apartment 20% Mobile homes 24%

20.

Class limits	Class boundaries	f
1	0.5–1.5	1
2	1.5–2.5	5
3	2.5–3.5	3
4	3.5–4.5	4
5	4.5–5.5	2
6	5.5–6.5	6
7	6.5–7.5	2
8	7.5–8.5	3
9	8.5–9.5	4
	Total	30

	cf
Less than 0.5	0
Less than 1.5	1
Less than 2.5	6
Less than 3.5	9
Less than 4.5	13
Less than 5.5	15
Less than 6.5	21
Less than 7.5	23
Less than 8.5	26
Less than 9.5	30

21.

22.

Limits	Boundaries	f	rf	Midpoints
0–214	−0.5–214.5	20	0.39	107
215–429	214.5–429.5	15	0.29	322
430–644	429.5–644.5	5	0.10	537
645–859	644.5–859.5	5	0.10	752
860–1074	859.5–1074.5	2	0.04	967
1075–1289	1074.5–1289.5	2	0.04	1182
1290–1504	1289.5–1504.5	2	0.04	1397
	Total	51	1.00	

	cf	crf
Less than 0	0	0
Less than 214.5	20	0.39
Less than 429.5	35	0.69
Less than 644.5	40	0.78
Less than 859.5	45	0.88
Less than 1074.5	47	0.92
Less than 1289.5	49	0.96
Less than 1504.5	51	1.00

23.

Energy Consumption of Coal

24.

25. Identity Thefts

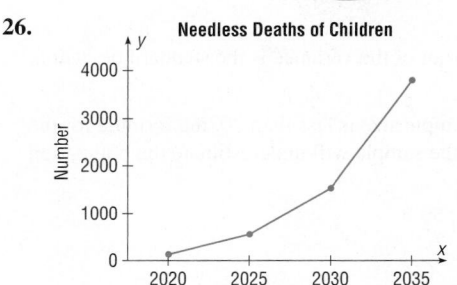

26. Needless Deaths of Children

27.

1	5 9
2	6 8
3	1 5 8 8 9
4	1 7 8
5	3 3 4
6	2 3 7 8
7	6 9
8	6 8 9
9	8

28.

Number of Quarters

29. The bottles have different diameters, so your eyes will compare areas instead of heights.

Chapter 3
Exercises 3–1

1. 994.6; 940; 1180; 1092.5

3. 134.6; 41; 2; 504.5; answers will vary.

5. 113.6; 119.5; 120; 103

7. 4212 km (2617.5 mi); 4232 km (2630 mi); none; 4192 km (2605 mi); the mean, median, and midrange are all very close.

9. 1494.6; 1415.5; none; 1777.5

11. 37.4; 33.7; none; 46.15

13. 5; 3.5–6.5

15. 19.7; 17.5–22.5

17. 26.66; 24.2–28.6

19. 34.1; 0.5–19.5

21. 23.7; 21.5–24.5

23. $9866.67

25. 35.4%

27. 83.2

29. *a.* Mode *c.* Median *e.* Mean
b. Median *d.* Mode *f.* Median

31. Roman letters, $\overline{X}$; Greek letters, μ

33. 320

35. *a.* 40 *b.* 20 *c.* 300 *d.* 3
e. The results will be the same as if you add, subtract, multiply, and divide the mean by 10.

37. *a.* 24.7% *b.* 5.7% *c.* 7.6% *d.* 2.5%

39. 4.31

Exercises 3–2

1. The square root of the variance is the standard deviation.

3. σ^2; σ

5. When the sample size is less than 30, the formula for the variance of the sample will underestimate the population variance.

7. 226; 3577.7; 59.8

9. Men: 71; 446.8; 21.1
Women: 80; 615.8; 24.82
The women's scores are more variable.

11. Triplets: 1233; 198,612.7; 445.7
Quadruplets: 167; 3952.9; 62.9
Quintuplets: 45; 180.8; 13.4
The data for the triplets are the most variable.

13. $s \approx R/4$ so $s \approx 5$ years.

15. 333; 8393.5; 91.6

17. 130; 1156.7; 34.0

19. 133.6; 11.6

21. 27,941.8; 167.2

23. 167.2; 12.9

25. 211.2; 14.5; no, the variability of the lifetimes of the batteries is quite large.

27. 20.9%; 22.5%. The factory workers' data are more variable.

29. 13.1%; 15.2%. The waiting time for people who are discharged is more variable.

31. *a.* 75% *b.* 56%

33. At least 93.75%

35. Between 84 and 276 minutes

37. Between $149,300 and $343,300

39. At least 84%

41. 474–554; 2.5%

43. $\overline{X} = 215.0$ and $s = 20.8$. All the data values fall within 2 standard deviations of the mean.

45. 56%; 75%; 84%; 89%; 92%

47. 4.36

49. It must be an incorrect data value, since it is beyond the range using the formula $s\sqrt{n-1}$.

Exercises 3–3

1. A z score tells how many standard deviations the data value is above or below the mean.

3. A percentile is a relative measurement of position; a percentage is an absolute measure of the part to the total.

5. $Q_1 = P_{25}$; $Q_2 = P_{50}$; $Q_3 = P_{75}$

7. $D_1 = P_{10}$; $D_2 = P_{20}$; $D_3 = P_{30}$; etc.

9. Canada -0.40, Italy 1.47, United States -1.91

11. *a.* 0.6 *b.* -1.2 *c.* 2.4 *d.* -2.2 *e.* 0.2

13. Neither; $z = 1.5$ for each

15. *a.* 0.55 *c.* 19,690; 12,340, 14,090
b. -1.17

17. *a.* 87th; 49th; 20th *c.* 75
b. 79 *d.* 69

19. *a.* 6 *c.* 68 *e.* 94 *g.* 251 *i.* 274
b. 24 *d.* 76 *f.* 234 *h.* 263 *j.* 284

21. 94th; 72nd; 61st; 17th; 83rd; 50th; 39th; 28th; 6th; 597

23. 5th; 15th; 25th; 35th; 45th; 55th; 65th; 75th; 85th; 95th; 2.1

25. $Q_1 = 16$; $Q_3 = 27.1$

27. $Q_1 = 6.2$; $Q_3 = 7.2$

29. *a.* 3   *b.* 54   *c.* None

31. *a.* 12; 20.5; 32; 22; 20   *b.* 62; 94; 99; 80.5; 37

33. Tom, Harry, Dick. Find the z score for Tom, and it is less than Harry's z score; and both z scores are less than the 98th percentile.

Exercises 3–4

1. 6, 8, 19, 32, 54; 24

3. 188, 192, 339, 437, 589; 245

5. 14.6, 15.05, 16.3, 19, 19.8; 3.95

7. 11, 3, 8, 5, 9, 4

9. 95, 55, 70, 65, 90, 25

11.

13. The graph of the data is somewhat positively skewed.

15. The data for the amount of protein in the drinks have a higher median amount of grams of protein and are more variable.

17. Lowest data value = 40; $Q_1 = 59$; median = 62; $Q_3 = 77$; highest data value = 85; IQR = 16

19.

There are no outliers.

Review Exercises

1. $\overline{X} = 27.2$; MD = 19; mode = 17; MR = 38

3. 7.3; 7–9 or 8

5. 1.43 viewers

7. 306; 7242.01; 85.1

9. 566.1; 23.8

11. 6

13. 31.25%; 18.6%; the number of books is more variable

15. $0.26–$0.38

17. 56%

19. 23.7−35.7

21. *a.* 0.86   *b.* −0.87

23. *a.*

b. 50, 53, 55   *c.* 10th; 26th; 78th

25. *a.* 400   *b.* None

27.

Chapter Quiz

1. True   **2.** True

3. False   **4.** False

5. False   **6.** False

7. False   **8.** False

9. False   **10.** *c*

11. *c*   **12.** *a* and *b*

13. *b*   **14.** *d*

15. *b*   **16.** Statistic

17. Parameters, statistics   **18.** Standard deviation

19. σ **20.** Midrange

21. Positively   **22.** Outlier

23. *a.* 15.3   *c.* 15, 16, and 17   *e.* 6   *g.* 1.9
    b. 15.5   *d.* 15   *f.* 3.57

24. *a.* 6.4   *b.* 6–8   *c.* 11.6   *d.* 3.4

25. 4.5

26. The number of newspapers sold in a convenience store is more variable.

27. 88.89%   **28.** 16%; 97.5%

29. 4.5   **30.** −0.75; −1.67; science

31. *a.*

b. 47; 55; 64

c. 56th, 6th, 99th percentiles

32. The cost of prebuy gas is much less than that of the return without filling gas. The variability of the return without filling gas is larger than the variability of the prebuy gas.

Chapter 4

Exercises 4–1

1. A probability experiment is a chance process that leads to well-defined outcomes.

3. An outcome is the result of a single trial of a probability experiment, but an event can consist of more than one outcome.

5. The range of values is 0 to 1 inclusive.

7. 0

9. 0.80 Since the probability that it won't rain is 80%, you could leave your umbrella at home and be fairly safe.

11. *a.* Empirical   *c.* Empirical
    b. Classical   *d.* Classical

13. *a.* $\frac{1}{6}$ *b.* 0   *c.* $\frac{1}{2}$ *d.* 1

15. *a.* $\frac{1}{9}$ *b.* $\frac{2}{9}$ *c.* $\frac{1}{6}$

17. *a.* $\frac{1}{13}$ *c.* $\frac{1}{52}$ *e.* $\frac{4}{13}$
    b. $\frac{1}{4}$ *d.* $\frac{2}{13}$

19. *a.* 0.1   *b.* 0.2   *c.* 0.8

21. *a.* 0.43   *b.* 0.52   *c.* 0.17

23. *a.* 0.04   *b.* 0.52   *c.* 0.4

25. *a.* $\frac{1}{8}$ *c.* $\frac{3}{4}$
    b. $\frac{1}{4}$ *d.* $\frac{3}{4}$

27. $\frac{1}{9}$

29. *a.* 27%   *c.* 67%
    b. 33%   *d.* 14%

31. 0.173; 0.228

33. 0.268; 0.597

35.

37.

39.
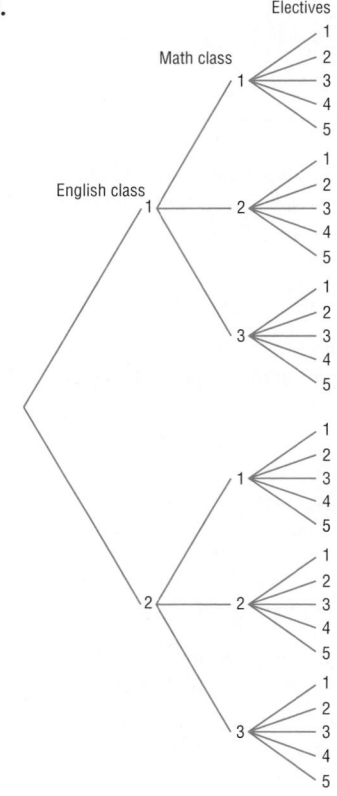

41. *a.* 0.08   *b.* 0.01   *c.* 0.35   *d.* 0.36

43. The statement is probably not based on empirical probability and is probably not true.

45. Answers will vary. However they should be approximately $\frac{1}{8}, \frac{3}{8}, \frac{3}{8}, \frac{1}{8}$.

47. *a.* 1:5, 5:1   *d.* 1:1, 1:1   *g.* 1:1, 1:1
    b. 1:1, 1:1   *e.* 1:12, 12:1
    c. 1:3, 3:1   *f.* 1:3, 3:1

Exercises 4–2

1. Two events are mutually exclusive if they cannot occur at the same time (i.e., they have no outcomes in common). Examples will vary.

3. *a.* No   *b.* No   *c.* Yes   *d.* No

5. *a.* 0.707   *b.* 0.589   *c.* 0.011   *d.* 0.731

7. *a.* $\frac{7}{38} = 0.184$ *b.* $\frac{35}{38} = 0.921$

9. $\frac{11}{19}$

11. *a.* $\frac{6}{7}$ *b.* $\frac{4}{7}$ *c.* 1

13. *a.* 0.058   *b.* 0.942   *c.* 0.335

15. *a.* 0.056   *b.* 0.004   *c.* 0.076

17. *a.* $\frac{7}{58}$ *b.* $\frac{16}{29}$ *c.* $\frac{12}{29}$

19. *a.* $\frac{1}{15}$ *c.* $\frac{5}{6}$ *e.* $\frac{1}{3}$
    b. $\frac{1}{3}$ *d.* $\frac{5}{6}$

21. *a.* $\frac{5}{12}$ *b.* $\frac{1}{8}$ *c.* $\frac{2}{3}$ *d.* $\frac{23}{24}$

23. *a.* $\frac{3}{13}$ *b.* $\frac{3}{4}$ *c.* $\frac{19}{52}$ *d.* $\frac{7}{13}$ *e.* $\frac{15}{26}$

25. 0.318

27. 0.06

29. 0.30

31. $(m + n)/(2m + n)$

Exercises 4–3

1. *a.* Independent   *c.* Dependent
   b. Dependent   *d.* Dependent

3. *a.* 0.009   *b.* 0.227

5. 0.002 The event is highly unlikely since the probability is small.

7. *a.* 0.082   *b.* 0.119   *c.* 0.918

9. 0.179

11. *a.* 0.003   *b.* 0.636   *c.* 0.997

13. *a.* $\frac{1}{270,725}$ *b.* $\frac{11}{4165}$ *c.* $\frac{46}{833}$

15. *a.* $\frac{1}{17}$ *b.* $\frac{4}{17}$ *c.* $\frac{1}{221}$

17. 0.0005; Highly unlikely

19. *a.* 0.167   *b.* 0.406   *c.* 0.691

21. 0.03   23. 0.071

25. 0.656; 0.438   27. 0.2

29. 68.4%

31. *a.* 0.06   *b.* 0.435   *c.* 0.35   *d.* 0.167

33. *a.* 0.198   *b.* 0.188   *c.* 0.498

35. *a.* 0.020   *b.* 0.611

37. *a.* 0.172   *b.* 0.828

39. 0.574

41. 0.987

43. $\frac{14,498}{20,825}$

45. *a.* 0.332   *b.* 0.668

47. $\frac{31}{32}$; the event is likely to occur since the probability is high.

49. 0.665; it will happen almost 67% of the time. It's somewhat likely.

51. $\frac{7}{8}$

53. No, since $P(A \text{ and } B) = 0$ and does not equal $P(A) \cdot P(B)$.

55. Enrollment and meeting with DW and meeting with MH are dependent. Since meeting with MH has a low probability and meeting with LP has no effect, all students, if possible, should meet with DW.

57. No; no; 0.072; 0.721; 0.02

59. 5

Exercises 4–4

1. 100,000; 30,240

3. 720   5. 100,000; 30,240

7. 40,320; 20,160   9. 112

11. 3,991,680; 8064

13. *a.* 40,320   *c.* 1   *e.* 2520   *g.* 60   *i.* 120
    b. 3,628,800   *d.* 1   *f.* 11,880   *h.* 1   *j.* 30

15. 24   17. 7315

19. 840   21. 151,200

23. 5,527,200   25. 495; 11,880

27. 210   29. 1260

31. 18,480

33. *a.* 10   *b.* 56   *c.* 35   *d.* 15   *e.* 15

35. 120   37. 210

39. 1800   41. 6400

43. 495; 210; 420   45. 475

47. 106

49. $_7C_2$ is 21 combinations + 7 double tiles = 28

51. 330   53. 194,040

55. 125,970   57. 1,860,480

59. 136   61. 120

63. 200   65. 336

67. 15

69. *a.* 48   *b.* 60   *c.* 72

71. $(x + 2)(x + 1)/2$

Exercises 4–5

1. $\frac{11}{221}$

3. *a.* $\frac{4}{35}$ *b.* $\frac{1}{35}$ *c.* $\frac{12}{35}$ *d.* $\frac{18}{35}$

5. *a.* 0.192   *b.* 0.269   *c.* 0.538   *d.* 0.013

7. $\frac{1}{1225}$

9. 0.917; 0.594; 0.001

11. *a.* 0.322   *b.* 0.164   *c.* 0.515
    d. It probably got lost in the wash!

13. $\frac{5}{72}$

15. $\frac{1}{60}$

17. 0.727

Review Exercises

1. *a.* 0.167   *b.* 0.667   *c.* 0.5

3. *a.* 0.7   *b.* 0.5

5. 0.265

7. 0.19

9. 0.98

11. *a.* 0.0001   *b.* 0.402   *c.* 0.598

13. *a.* $\frac{2}{17}$ *b.* $\frac{11}{850}$ *c.* $\frac{1}{5525}$

15. *a.* 0.603   *b.* 0.340   *c.* 0.324   *d.* 0.379

17. 0.4

19. 0.507

21. 57.3%

23. *a.* $\frac{19}{44}$ *b.* $\frac{1}{4}$

25. 0.718

27. 175,760,000; 78,624,000; 88,583,040

29. 350

31. 8568

33. 100! (Answers may vary regarding calculator.)

35. 495

37. 60

39. 15,504

41. 175,760,000; 0.00001

43. 0.097

45.

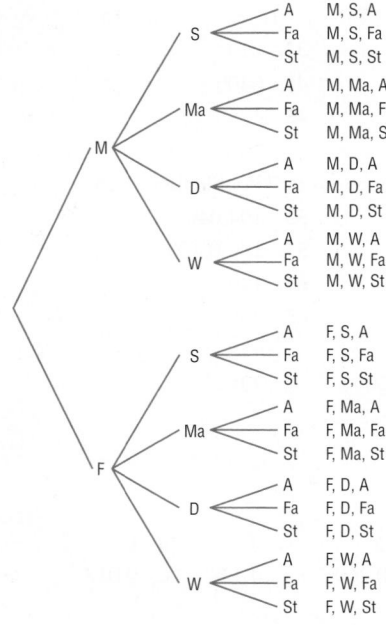

29. *a.* $\frac{253}{9996}$ *b.* $\frac{33}{66,640}$ *c.* 0

30. 0.538   **31.** 0.533

32. 0.814   **33.** 0.056

34. *a.* $\frac{1}{2}$ *b.* $\frac{3}{7}$

35. 0.992   **36.** 0.518

37. 0.9999886   **38.** 2646

39. 40,320   **40.** 1365

41. 1,188,137,600; 710,424,000

42. 720

43. 33,554,432

44. 56

45. $\frac{1}{4}$

46. $\frac{3}{14}$ **47.** $\frac{12}{55}$

48.

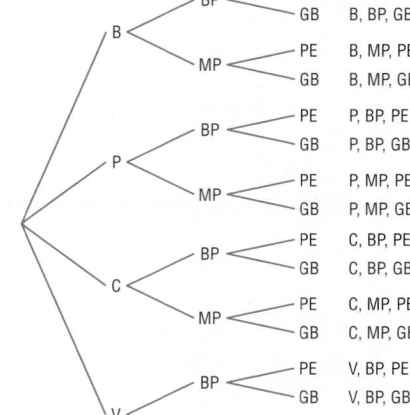

49. 120,120

50. 210

Chapter Quiz

1. False   **2.** False

3. True   **4.** False

5. False   **6.** False

7. True   **8.** False

9. *b*   **10.** *d*

11. *d*   **12.** *b*

13. *c*   **14.** *b*

15. *d*   **16.** *b*

17. *b*   **18.** Sample space

19. 0, 1   **20.** 0

21. 1   **22.** Mutually exclusive

23. *a.* $\frac{1}{13}$ *b.* $\frac{1}{13}$ *c.* $\frac{4}{13}$

24. *a.* $\frac{1}{4}$ *b.* $\frac{4}{13}$ *c.* $\frac{1}{52}$ *d.* $\frac{1}{13}$ *e.* $\frac{1}{2}$

25. *a.* $\frac{12}{31}$ *b.* $\frac{12}{31}$ *c.* $\frac{27}{31}$ *d.* $\frac{24}{31}$

26. *a.* $\frac{11}{36}$ *b.* $\frac{5}{18}$ *c.* $\frac{11}{36}$ *d.* $\frac{1}{3}$ *e.* 0   *f.* $\frac{11}{12}$

27. 0.68

28. 0.002

Chapter 5
Exercises 5–1

1. A random variable is a variable whose values are determined by chance. Examples will vary.

3. The number of commercials a radio station plays during each hour. The number of times a student uses his or her calculator during a mathematics exam. The number of leaves on a specific type of tree. (Answers will vary.)

5. Examples: Continuous variables: length of home run, length of game, temperature at game time, pitcher's ERA, batting average

Discrete variables: number of hits, number of pitches, number of seats in each row, etc.

7. No; probabilities cannot be negative, and the sum of the probabilities is not 1.

9. Yes

11. No. The sum of the probabilities is greater than 1.

13. Discrete

15. Continuous

17. Discrete

19.

X	0	1	2	3
P(X)	$\frac{6}{15}$	$\frac{5}{15}$	$\frac{3}{15}$	$\frac{1}{15}$

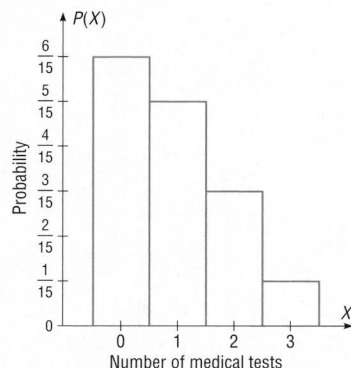

21.

X	2	3	5	7
P(X)	0.35	0.41	0.15	0.09

23.

X	1	2	3	4	5	6
P(X)	$\frac{1}{2}$	$\frac{1}{6}$	$\frac{1}{12}$	$\frac{1}{12}$	$\frac{1}{12}$	$\frac{1}{12}$

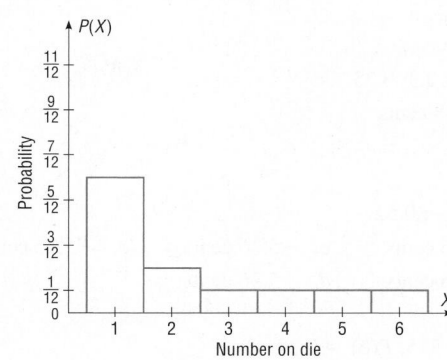

25.

X	2	3	4	5
P(X)	0.01	0.34	0.62	0.03

27.

X	4	7	9	11	13	16	18	21	22	24	25	27	31	36
P(X)	$\frac{1}{15}$	$\frac{1}{15}$	$\frac{1}{15}$	$\frac{1}{15}$	$\frac{1}{15}$	$\frac{2}{15}$	$\frac{1}{15}$	$\frac{1}{15}$	$\frac{1}{15}$	$\frac{1}{15}$	$\frac{1}{15}$	$\frac{1}{15}$	$\frac{1}{15}$	$\frac{1}{15}$

29.

X	1	2	3	4	5
P(X)	0.124	0.297	0.402	0.094	0.083

31.

X	1	2	3
P(X)	$\frac{1}{6}$	$\frac{1}{3}$	$\frac{1}{2}$

Yes

33.

X	3	4	7
P(X)	$\frac{3}{6}$	$\frac{4}{6}$	$\frac{7}{6}$

No, the sum of the probabilities is greater than 1.

35.

X	1	2	4
P(X)	$\frac{1}{7}$	$\frac{2}{7}$	$\frac{4}{7}$

Yes

37.

X	1	2	3	4
P(X)	$\frac{3}{28}$	$\frac{6}{28}$	$\frac{12}{28}$	$\frac{7}{28}$

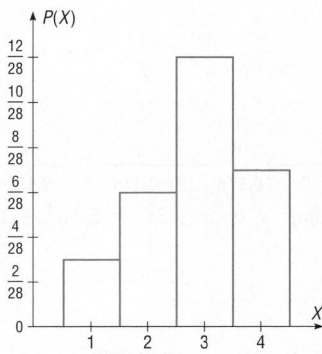

Exercises 5–2

1. 0.17; 0.321; 0.567

3. 1.3; 0.9; 1. No, on average, each person has about 1 credit card.

5. 5.4; 2.9; 1.7; 0.027

7.

X	1	2	3	4	5	6	7	8	9
P(X)	0.111	0.111	0.111	0.111	0.111	0.111	0.111	0.111	0.111

5; 6.7; 2.6

9. 9.4; 5.24; 2.3; 0.25

11. $E(X) = 88$ cents

13. $0.83

15. −$1.00

17. −$0.50; −$0.52

19. *a.* −5.26 cents   *c.* −5.26 cents   *e.* −5.26 cents
     b. −5.26 cents   *d.* −5.26 cents

21. 10.5

23. $P(4) = 0.345; P(6) = 0.23$
     $\overline{X} = 3.485; \sigma^2 = 3.819; \sigma = 1.954$

25. Answers will vary.

27.

X	2	3	4	5	6	8	9	11	14
P(X)	0.1	0.1	0.1	0.1	0.1	0.2	0.1	0.1	0.1

$\mu = 7; \sigma^2 = 12.6; \sigma = 3.55$

Exercises 5–3

1. *a.* Yes   *b.* Yes   *c.* Yes   *d.* No   *e.* No

3. *a.* 0.420   *b.* 0.346   *c.* 0.590   *d.* 0.251   *e.* 0.000

5. *a.* 0.0005   *b.* 0.131   *c.* 0.342

7. *a.* 0.832   *b.* 0.441   *c.* 0.336

9. *a.* 0.124   *b.* 0.912   *c.* 0.016

11. 0.071

13. *a.* 0.346   *b.* 0.913   *c.* 0.663   *d.* 0.683

15. *a.* 0.242   *b.* 0.547   *c.* 0.306

17. *a.* 75; 18.8; 4.3   *c.* 10; 5; 2.2
     b. 90; 63; 7.9   *d.* 8; 1.6; 1.3

19. 8; 7.9; 2.8

21. 52.7; 6.4; 2.5

23. 210; 165.9; 12.9

25. 0.199

27. 0.559

29. 0.177

31. 0.246

33.

X	0	1	2	3
P(X)	0.125	0.375	0.375	0.125

35. $\mu = 0(q^3) + 3pq^2 + 6p^2q + 3p^3 = 3p(q^2 + 2pq + p^2)$
     $= 3p(1) = 3p$

Exercises 5–4

1. *a.* 0.135   *b.* 0.324   *c.* 0.0096

3. 0.0025

5. 0.0385

7. *a.* 0.1563   *b.* 0.1465   *c.* 0.0504

9. *a.* 0.0183   *b.* 0.0733   *c.* 0.1465   *d.* 0.7619

11. 0.0521

13. 0.0498

15. 0.1563

17. 0.117

19. 0.2

21. 0.597

23. 0.068

25. 0.144

27. 12

29. 17.33 or 18

31. 1.25; 0.559

33. 5; 4.472

Review Exercises

1. Yes

3. No. The sum of the probabilities is greater than 1.

5. *a.* 0.35   *b.* 1.55; 1.808; 1.344

7.

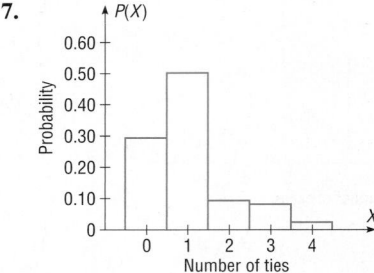

9. 7.2; 2.2; 1.5

11. 24.2; 1.5; 1.2

13. $2.15

15. *a.* 0.008   *b.* 0.724   *c.* 0.0002   *d.* 0.275

17. 120; 24; 4.9

19. 0.886

21. 0.190

23. 0.026

25. 0.050

27. *a.* 0.5543   *b.* 0.8488   *c.* 0.4457

29. 0.274

31. 0.086

33. $\frac{27}{256}$

Chapter Quiz

1. True   **2.** False

3. False   **4.** True

5. Chance   **6.** $n \cdot p$

7. 1   **8.** *c*

9. *c*   **10.** *d*

11. No, since $\Sigma P(X) > 1$ **12.** Yes

13. Yes   **14.** Yes

15.

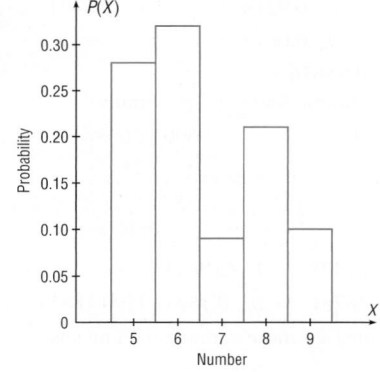

16.

X	0	1	2	3	4
P(X)	0.02	0.3	0.48	0.13	0.07

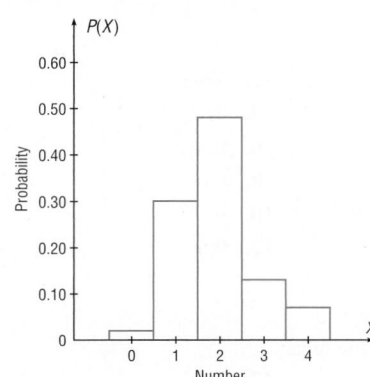

17. 2.0; 1.3; 1.1 **18.** 32.2; 1.1; 1.0

19. 5.2 **20.** $9.65

21. 0.124

22. *a.* 0.075 *b.* 0.872 *c.* 0.126

23. 240; 48; 6.9 **24.** 9; 7.9; 2.8

25. 0.008 **26.** 0.0003

27. 0.061 **28.** 0.122

29. *a.* 0.5470 *b.* 0.9862 *c.* 0.453

30. 0.128

31. *a.* 0.160 *b.* 0.42 *c.* 0.07

32. 0.033 **33.** 0.007

Chapter 6
Exercises 6–1

1. The characteristics of the normal distribution are as follows:
  a. It is bell-shaped.
  b. It is symmetric about the mean.
  c. Its mean, median, and mode are equal.
  d. It is continuous.
  e. It never touches the *x* axis.
  f. The area under the curve is equal to 1.
  g. It is unimodal.
  h. About 68% of the area lies within 1 standard deviation of the mean, about 95% within 2 standard deviations, and about 99.7% within 3 standard deviations of the mean.

3. 1 or 100%

5. 68%; 95%; 99.7% **7.** 0.3365

9. 0.4838 **11.** 0.3859

13. 0.0823 **15.** 0.1043

17. 0.0258 **19.** 0.0482

21. 0.9868 **23.** 0.5478

25. 0.3574 **27.** 0.3212

29. 0.4236 **31.** 0.0060

33. 0.0721 **35.** 0.9507

37. 0.0505 **39.** 0.9222

41. −1.39 (TI: −1.3885) **43.** −2.08 (TI: −2.0792)

45. −1.26 (TI: −1.2602)

47. *a.* −2.28 (TI: −2.2801)
  b. −0.92 (TI: −0.91995)
  c. −0.27 (TI: −0.26995)

49. *a.* $z = +1.96$ and $z = -1.96$ (TI: ±1.95996)
  b. $z = +1.65$ and $z = -1.65$, approximately (TI: ±1.64485)
  c. $z = +2.58$ and $z = -2.58$, approximately (TI: ±2.57583)

51. 0.6827; 0.9545; 0.9973; they are very close.

53. 2.10

55. −1.45 and 0.11

57. $y = \dfrac{e^{-X^2/2}}{\sqrt{2\pi}}$

59. 1.00

Exercises 6–2

1. 0.0022

3. *a.* 0.2005 (TI: 0.2007) *b.* 0.4315 (TI: 0.4316)

5. *a.* 0.3023 *b.* 0.0062

7. *a.* 0.3557 (TI: 0.3547)
  b. 0.8389 (TI: 0.8391)

9. 0.0262; 0.0001; would want to know why it had only been driven less than 6000 miles (TI: 0.0260; 0.0002)

11. *a.* 0.9803 (TI: 0.9801)
  b. 0.2514 (TI: 0.2511)
  c. 0.3434 (TI: 0.3430)

13. *a.* 0.1635 *b.* 0.0516 *c.* 0.4658

15. *a.* 0.6879 *b.* 0.1320 *c.* 110,734

17. 0.0838

19. The maximum size is 1927.76 square feet; the minimum size is 1692.24 square feet.
(TI: 1927.90 maximum, 1692.10 minimum)

21. 0.006; $821

23. The maximum price is $9222, and the minimum price is $7290. (TI: $7288.14 minimum, $9223.86 maximum)

25. 6.7; 4.05 (TI: for 10%, 6.657; for 30%, 4.040)

27. $18,840.48 (TI: $18,869.48)

29. 18.6 months

31. *a.* $\mu = 120, \sigma = 20$ *c.* $\mu = 30, \sigma = 5$
  b. $\mu = 15, \sigma = 2.5$

33. 11.7 degrees

35. $1175.54

37. 0.1075

39. Not normal

41. Not normal

43. Answers will vary.

Exercises 6–3

1. The distribution is called the sampling distribution of sample means.

3. The mean of the sample means is equal to the population mean.

5. The distribution will be approximately normal when the sample size is large.

7. 0.0075; Yes. The distribution of benefits is normal.

9. *a.* 0.0026 (TI: 0.0026)
   b. 0.8212 (TI: 0.8201)
   c. 0.1787 (TI: 0.1799)

11. 0.2673 (TI: 0.2660)

13. 0.2877

15. 0.2358; less than 0.0001

17. 0.4176 (TI: 0.4199)

19. 0.1254 (TI: 0.12769)

21. *a.* 0.4052 or 40.52% (TI: 0.4067)
   b. 0.0901 or 9.01% (TI: 0.0908)
   c. Yes, the probability is slightly more than 40%.
   d. It's possible since the probability is about 9%.

23. *a.* 0.3707 (TI: 0.3694)   *b.* 0.0475 (TI: 0.04779)

25. Approximately 60

27. 0.0143

29. $\sigma_{\bar{X}} = 1.5, n = 25$

Exercises 6–4

1. When *p* is approximately 0.5, as *n* increases, the shape of the binomial distribution becomes similar to that of the normal distribution.

3. The correction is necessary because the normal distribution is continuous and the binomial distribution is discrete.

5. *a.* 0.0811   *b.* 0.0516   *c.* 0.1052

7. *a.* Yes   *b.* No   *c.* No

9. 0.2578

11. 0.8900

13. 0.1003

15. 0.8577

17. 0.9875; very likely

19. 0.3936

21. 0.0087

23. *a.* $n \geq 50$ *c.* $n \geq 10$ *e.* $n \geq 50$
   b. $n \geq 17$ *d.* $n \geq 25$

Review Exercises

1. *a.* 0.4744   *c.* 0.0590   *e.* 0.2139
   b. 0.1443   *d.* 0.8329

3. *a.* 0.4808   *c.* 0.9219   *e.* 0.6391
   b. 0.4664   *d.* 0.0617

5. 0.1131; $4872 and $5676
   (TI: $4869.31 minimum, $5678.69 maximum)

7. *a.* 0.3621 or 36.21%   *c.* 0.0606 or 6.06%
   b. 0.1190 or 11.9%

9. $130.92

11. Not normal

13. *a.* 0.0143 (TI: 0.0142)   *b.* 0.9641

15. *a.* 0.3859 (TI: 0.3875)   *b.* 0.1841 (TI: 0.1831)
   c. Individual values are more variable than means.

17. 0.5234

19. 0.7123; 0.9999 (TI: 0.7139)

21. 0.0465

Chapter Quiz

1. False   **2.** True

3. True   **4.** True

5. False   **6.** False

7. *a*   **8.** *a*

9. *b*   **10.** *b*

11. *c*   **12.** 0.5

13. sampling error

14. the population mean

15. standard error of the mean

16. 5   **17.** 5%

18. *a.* 0.4332   *d.* 0.1029   *g.* 0.0401   *j.* 0.9131
   b. 0.3944   *e.* 0.2912   *h.* 0.8997
   c. 0.0344   *f.* 0.8284   *i.* 0.017

19. *a.* 0.4846   *d.* 0.0188   *g.* 0.0089   *j.* 0.8461
   b. 0.4693   *e.* 0.7461   *h.* 0.9582
   c. 0.9334   *f.* 0.0384   *i.* 0.9788

20. *a.* 0.7734   *b.* 0.0516   *c.* 0.3837
   d. Any rainfall above 65 inches could be considered an extremely wet year since this value is 2 standard deviations above the mean.

21. *a.* 0.0668   *b.* 0.0228   *c.* 0.4649   *d.* 0.0934

22. *a.* 0.4525   *b.* 0.3707   *c.* 0.3707   *d.* 0.019

23. *a.* 0.0013   *b.* 0.5   *c.* 0.0081   *d.* 0.5511

24. *a.* 0.0037   *b.* 0.0228   *c.* 0.5   *d.* 0.3232

25. 8.804 centimeters

26. 121.24 is the lowest acceptable score.

27. 0.015   **28.** 0.9738

29. 0.0495; no   **30.** 0.0455 or 4.55%

31. 0.8577   **32.** 0.0495

33. Not normal   **34.** Approximately normal

Chapter 7

Exercises 7–1

1. A point estimate of a parameter specifies a particular value, such as $\mu = 87$; an interval estimate specifies a range of values for the parameter, such as $84 < \mu < 90$. The advantage of an interval estimate is that a specific confidence level (say 95%) can be selected, and one can be 95% confident that the interval contains the parameter that is being estimated.

3. The margin of error is the likely range of values to the right or left of the statistic that may contain the parameter.

5. A good estimator should be unbiased, consistent, and relatively efficient.

7. *a.* 2.58   *c.* 1.96   *e.* 1.88
    b. 2.33   *d.* 1.65

9. $26.6 < \mu < 29.6$

11. *a.* 16.6 hours
    b. $15.7 < \mu < 17.5$
    c. $15.4 < \mu < 17.8$
    d. The 99% confidence interval is larger since you want to be 99% confident that the mean is contained in the interval rather than 95% confident.

13. $295.2 < \mu < 397.3$

15. $56.1 < \mu < 60.3$

17. $4913 < \mu < 5087$; 4000 hours does not seem reasonable since it is outside the interval.

19. $59.5 < \mu < 62.9$

21. 137

23. 44 subjects

25. 240 exams

Exercises 7–2

1. The characteristics of the *t* distribution are as follows: It is bell-shaped, it is symmetric about the mean, and it approaches, but never touches the *x* axis. The mean, median, and mode are equal to 0 and are located at the center of the distribution. The variance is greater than 1. The *t* distribution is a family of curves based on degrees of freedom. As a sample size increases, the *t* distribution approaches the standard normal distribution.

3. *a.* 2.898   *c.* 2.624   *e.* 2.093
    b. 2.074   *d.* 1.833

5. $74.6 < \mu < 86.8$

7. $\overline{X} = 33.4$; $s = 28.7$; $21.2 < \mu < 45.6$; the point estimate is 33.4, and it is close to 32. Also, the interval does indeed contain $\mu = 32$. The data value 132 is unusually large (an outlier). The mean may not be the best point estimate in this case.

9. $226.3 < \mu < 260.1$

11. $13.5 < \mu < 15.1$; about 30 minutes

13. $17.87 < \mu < 20.53$; It's higher.

15. $28.4 < \mu < 38.0$

17. $32.0 < \mu < 71.0$

19. $22.827 < \mu < 58.161$

21. $\overline{X} = 2.175$; $s = 0.585$; $\mu > \$1.95$ means one can be 95% confident that the mean revenue is greater than $1.95; $\mu < \$2.40$ means one can be 95% confident that the mean revenue is less than $2.40.

Exercises 7–3

1. *a.* 0.5, 0.5   *c.* 0.46, 0.54   *e.* 0.42, 0.58
    b. 0.45, 0.55   *d.* 0.25, 0.75

3. $0.529 < p < 0.591$

5. $0.092 < p < 0.152$; 11% is contained in the confidence interval.

7. $0.797 < p < 0.883$

9. $0.596 < p < 0.704$

11. $0.125 < p < 0.375$. No, since 0.28 is contained in the interval.

13. $0.184 < p < 0.346$

15. 385; 601

17. 801 homes; 1068 homes

19. 1089

21. 95%

Exercises 7–4

1. Chi-square

3. *a.* 3.816; 21.920   *d.* 0.412; 16.750
    b. 10.117; 30.144   *e.* 26.509; 55.758
    c. 13.844; 41.923

5. $56.6 < \sigma^2 < 236.3$; $7.5 < \sigma < 15.4$

7. Use $s = r \div 4$.
$1,593,755.84 < \sigma^2 < 16,537,507.73$;
$1262.44 < \sigma < 4066.63$;
$8,469,845.02 < \sigma^2 < 87,886,811.42$;
$2910.30 < \sigma < 9374.80$

9. $603.72 < \sigma^2 < 5836.83$; $24.57 < \sigma < 76.40$

11. $130,136 < \sigma^2 < 413,084$
$361 < \sigma < 643$

13. $17.3 < \sigma < 38.4$

15. $31.5 < \sigma < 67.9$

Review Exercises

1. $13.99 < \mu < 25.27$ (or $14 < \mu < 25$)
(TI: $14.005 < \mu < 25.255$)

3. 28

5. $76.9 < \mu < 88.3$

7. $0.409 < p < 0.471$

9. $0.467 < p < 0.573$

11. 1634

13. $0.22 < \sigma < 0.44$. Yes. It seems that there is a large standard deviation.

15. $5.1 < \sigma^2 < 18.3$

Chapter Quiz

1. True   **2.** True

3. False   **4.** True

5. *b*   **6.** *a*

7. *b*

8. Unbiased, consistent, relatively efficient

9. Margin of error

10. Point

11. 90; 95; 99

12. $121.60; $119.85 < \mu <$ $123.35

13. $44.80; $43.15 < \mu <$ $46.45

14. 4150; 3954 $< \mu <$ 4346

15. 45.7 $< \mu <$ 51.5

16. 418 $< \mu <$ 458

17. 26 $< \mu <$ 36

18. 180

19. 25

20. 0.374 $< p <$ 0.486

21. 0.295 $< p <$ 0.425

22. 0.342 $< p <$ 0.547

23. 545

24. 7 $< \sigma <$ 13

25. 30.9 $< \sigma^2 <$ 78.2
 5.6 $< \sigma <$ 8.8

26. 1.8 $< \sigma <$ 3.2

Chapter 8

Note: For Chapters 8–13, specific *P*-values are given in parentheses after the *P*-value intervals. When the specific *P*-value is extremely small, it is not given.

Exercises 8–1

1. The null hypothesis states that there is no difference between a parameter and a specific value or that there is no difference between two parameters. The alternative hypothesis states that there is a specific difference between a parameter and a specific value or that there is a difference between two parameters. Examples will vary.

3. A statistical test uses the data obtained from a sample to make a decision about whether the null hypothesis should be rejected.

5. The critical region is the range of values of the test statistic that indicates that there is a significant difference and the null hypothesis should be rejected. The noncritical region is the range of values of the test statistic that indicates that the difference was probably due to chance and the null hypothesis should not be rejected.

7. α, β

9. A one-tailed test should be used when a specific direction, such as greater than or less than, is being hypothesized; when no direction is specified, a two-tailed test should be used.

11. *a.* ±1.96 *c.* +2.58 *e.* −1.65
  b. −2.33 *d.* +2.33

13. *a.* $H_0: \mu = 24.6$ and $H_1: \mu \neq 24.6$
  b. $H_0: \mu = $51,497$ and $H_1: \mu \neq $51,497$
  c. $H_0: \mu = 25.4$ and $H_1: \mu > 25.4$
  d. $H_0: \mu = 88$ and $H_1: \mu < 88$
  e. $H_0: \mu = 70$ and $H_1: \mu < 70$

Exercises 8–2

1. $H_0: \mu = 305$; $H_1: \mu > 305$ (claim); C.V. = 1.65; $z = 4.69$; reject. There is enough evidence to support the claim that the mean depth is greater than 305 feet. It might be due to warmer temperatures or more rainfall.

3. $H_0: \mu = 24 billion and $H_1: \mu > 24 billion (claim); C.V. = 1.65; $z = 1.85$; reject. There is enough evidence to support the claim that the average revenue is greater than $24 billion.

5. $H_0: \mu = 30.9$; $H_1: \mu \neq 30.9$ (claim); C.V. = ±2.58; $z = 1.89$; do not reject. There is not enough evidence to support the claim that the mean has changed.

7. $H_0: \mu = 29$ and $H_1: \mu \neq 29$ (claim); C.V. = ±1.96; $z = 0.944$; do not reject. There is not enough evidence to say that the average height differs from 29 inches.

9. $H_0: \mu = 8121; $H_1: \mu > 8121 (claim); C.V. = 2.33; $z = 1.93$; do not reject. There is not enough evidence to support the claim that the mean is greater than $8121.

11. $H_0: \mu = 150$, $H_1: \mu > 150$ (claim); C.V. = 2.33; $z = 1.48$; do not reject. There is not enough evidence to support the claim that the mean cost of a speeding ticket is greater than $150.

13. $H_0: \mu = 60.35$; $H_1: \mu < 60.35$ (claim); C.V. = −1.65; $z = -4.82$; reject H_0. There is sufficient evidence to conclude that the state senators are younger.

15. *a.* Do not reject. *d.* Reject.
  b. Reject. *e.* Reject.
  c. Do not reject.

17. $H_0: \mu = 264$ and $H_1: \mu < 264$ (claim); $z = -2.53$; *P*-value = 0.0057; reject. There is enough evidence to support the claim that the average stopping distance is less than 264 ft. (TI: *P*-value = 0.0056)

19. $H_0: \mu = 546$ and $H_1: \mu < 546$ (claim); $z = -2.40$; *P*-value = 0.0082. Yes, it can be concluded that the number of calories burned is less than originally thought. (TI: *P*-value = 0.0082)

21. $H_0: \mu = 444$; $H_1: \mu \neq 444$; $z = -1.70$; *P*-value = 0.0892; do not reject H_0. There is insufficient evidence at $\alpha = 0.05$ to conclude that the average size differs from 444 acres. (TI: *P*-value = 0.0886)

23. $H_0: \mu = 30{,}000$ (claim) and $H_1: \mu \neq 30{,}000$; $z = 1.71$; *P*-value = 0.0872; reject. There is enough evidence to reject the claim that the customers are adhering to the recommendation. Yes, the 0.10 level is appropriate. (TI: *P*-value = 0.0868)

25. $H_0: \mu = 10$ and $H_1: \mu < 10$ (claim); $z = -8.67$; *P*-value < 0.0001; since *P*-value < 0.05, reject. Yes, there is enough evidence to support the claim that the average number of days missed per year is less than 10. (TI: *P*-value = 0)

27. $H_0: \mu = 8.65$ (claim) and $H_1: \mu \neq 8.65$; C.V. = ±1.96; $z = -1.35$; do not reject. Yes; there is not enough evidence to reject the claim that the average hourly wage of the employees is $8.65.

Exercises 8–3

1. It is bell-shaped, it is symmetric about the mean, and it approaches, but never touches the *x* axis. The mean, median, and mode are all equal to 0, and they are located at the center of the distribution. The *t* distribution differs from the standard normal distribution in that it is a family of curves and the variance is greater than 1; and as the degrees of freedom increase, the *t* distribution approaches the standard normal distribution.

3. *a.* +1.833 *c.* −3.365
   b. ±1.740 *d.* +2.306

5. Specific *P*-values are in parentheses.
   a. $0.01 < P\text{-value} < 0.025$ (0.018)
   b. $0.05 < P\text{-value} < 0.10$ (0.062)
   c. $0.10 < P\text{-value} < 0.25$ (0.123)
   d. $0.10 < P\text{-value} < 0.20$ (0.138)

7. H_0: $\mu = 200$, H_1: $\mu < 200$ (claim); C.V. = −1.833; d.f. = 9; $t = -4.680$; reject. There is enough evidence to support the claim that the mean number of seeds in strawberries is less than 200.

9. H_0: $\mu = 700$ (claim) and H_1: $\mu < 700$; C.V. = −2.262; d.f. = 9; $t = -2.710$; reject. There is enough evidence to reject the claim that the average height of the buildings is at least 700 feet.

11. H_0: $\mu = 73$; H_1: $\mu > 73$ (claim); C.V. = 2.821; d.f. = 9; $t = 4.063$; reject. There is enough evidence to support the claim that the average is greater than the national average.

13. H_0: $\mu = \$54.8$ million and H_1: $\mu > \$54.8$ million (claim); C.V. = 1.761; d.f. = 14; $t = 3.058$; reject. Yes. There is enough evidence to support the claim that the average cost of an action movie is greater than $54.8 million.

15. H_0: $\mu = \$50.07$; H_1: $\mu > \$50.07$ (claim); C.V. = 1.833; d.f. = 9; $t = 2.741$; reject. There is enough evidence to support the claim that the average phone bill has increased.

17. H_0: $\mu = \$7.89$, H_1: $\mu > \$7.89$ (claim); C.V. = 2.624; d.f. = 14; $t = 2.550$; do not reject. There is not enough evidence to support the claim that the mean cost of movie tickets is greater than $7.89.

19. H_0: $\mu = 25.4$ and H_1: $\mu < 25.4$ (claim); C.V. = −1.318; d.f. = 24; $t = -3.11$; reject. Yes. There is enough evidence to support the claim that the average commuting time is less than 25.4 minutes.

21. H_0: $\mu = 5.8$ and H_1: $\mu \neq 5.8$ (claim); d.f. = 19; $t = -3.462$; $P\text{-value} < 0.01$; reject. There is enough evidence to support the claim that the mean number of times has changed. (TI: $P\text{-value} = 0.0026$)

23. H_0: $\mu = 123$ and H_1: $\mu \neq 123$ (claim); d.f. = 15; $t = -3.019$; $P\text{-value} < 0.01$ (0.0086); reject. There is enough evidence to support the hypothesis that the mean has changed. The *Old Farmer's Almanac* figure may have changed.

Exercises 8–4

1. Answers will vary.

3. $np \geq 5$ and $nq \geq 5$

5. H_0: $p = 0.456$, H_1: $p \neq 0.456$ (claim); C.V. = ±1.65; $z = 1.87$; reject. There is enough evidence to support the claim that the proportion of accidents involving improper driving differs from 45.6%.

7. H_0: $p = 0.36$, H_1: $p > 0.36$ (claim); C.V. = 2.05; $z = 2.36$; reject. There is enough evidence to support the claim that the proportion of baseball fans in southwestern Pennsylvania is greater than 36%.

9. H_0: $p = 0.30$, H_1: $p \neq 0.30$ (claim); C.V. = ±1.96; $z = 1.14$; do not reject. There is not enough evidence to support the claim that the proportion of open or unlocked door or window burglaries is different from 30%.

11. H_0: $p = 0.32$; H_1: $p \neq 0.32$ (claim); C.V. = ±2.58; $z = 3.61$; reject. There is enough evidence to support the claim that the proportion is different than 32%.

13. H_0: $p = 0.54$ (claim) and H_1: $p \neq 0.54$; $z = 0.93$; $P\text{-value} = 0.3524$; do not reject. There is not enough evidence to reject the claim that the proportion is 0.54. Yes, a healthy snack should be made available for children to eat after school. (TI: $P\text{-value} = 0.3511$)

15. H_0: $p = 0.18$ (claim) and H_1: $p < 0.18$; $z = -0.60$; $P\text{-value} = 0.2743$; since $P\text{-value} > 0.05$, do not reject. There is not enough evidence to reject the claim that 18% of all high school students smoke at least a pack of cigarettes a day. (TI: $P\text{-value} = 0.2739$)

17. H_0: $p = 0.67$ and H_1: $p \neq 0.67$ (claim); C.V. = ±1.96; $z = 3.19$; reject. Yes. There is enough evidence to support the claim that the percentage is not 67%.

19. H_0: $p = 0.576$ and H_1: $p < 0.576$ (claim); C.V. = −1.65; $z = -1.26$; do not reject. There is not enough evidence to support the claim that the proportion is less than 0.576.

21. No, since $p = 0.508$.

23. $z = \dfrac{X - \mu}{\sigma}$

$z = \dfrac{X - np}{\sqrt{npq}}$ since $\mu = np$ and $\sigma = \sqrt{npq}$

$z = \dfrac{X/n - np/n}{\sqrt{npq}/n}$

$z = \dfrac{X/n - np/n}{\sqrt{npq/n^2}}$

$z = \dfrac{\hat{p} - p}{\sqrt{pq/n}}$ since $\hat{p} = X/n$

Exercises 8–5

1. *a.* H_0: $\sigma^2 = 225$ and H_1: $\sigma^2 > 225$; C.V. = 27.587; d.f. = 17
   b. H_0: $\sigma^2 = 225$ and H_1: $\sigma^2 < 225$; C.V. = 14.042; d.f. = 22
   c. H_0: $\sigma^2 = 225$ and H_1: $\sigma^2 \neq 225$; C.V. = 5.629; 26.119; d.f. = 14
   d. H_0: $\sigma^2 = 225$ and H_1: $\sigma^2 \neq 225$; C.V. = 2.167; 14.067; d.f. = 7

3. *a.* $0.01 < P\text{-value} < 0.025$ (0.015)
   b. $0.005 < P\text{-value} < 0.01$ (0.006)
   c. $0.01 < P\text{-value} < 0.02$ (0.012)
   d. $P\text{-value} < 0.005$ (0.003)

5. H_0: $\sigma = 15$ and H_1: $\sigma < 15$ (claim); C.V. $= 4.575$; d.f. $= 11$; $\chi^2 = 9.0425$; do not reject. There is not enough evidence to support the claim that the standard deviation is less than 15.

7. H_0: $\sigma = 1.2$ (claim) and H_1: $\sigma > 1.2$; $\alpha = 0.01$; d.f. $= 14$; $\chi^2 = 31.5$; P-value < 0.005 (0.0047); since P-value < 0.01, reject. There is enough evidence to reject the claim that the standard deviation is less than or equal to 1.2 minutes.

9. H_0: $\sigma = 100$; H_1: $\sigma > 100$ (claim); C.V. $= 12.017$; d.f. $= 7$; $\chi^2 = 11.241$; do not reject. There is not enough evidence to support the claim that the standard deviation is greater than 100 mg.

11. H_0: $\sigma = 35$ and H_1: $\sigma < 35$ (claim); C.V. $= 3.940$; d.f. $= 10$; $\chi^2 = 8.359$; do not reject. There is not enough evidence to support the claim that the standard deviation is less than 35.

13. H_0: $\sigma = 150$, H_1: $\sigma > 150$ (claim); C.V. $= 21.026$; d.f. $= 12$; $\chi^2 = 14.012$; do not reject. There is not enough evidence to support the claim that the standard deviation is greater than 150 mg.

15. H_0: $\sigma = 0.52$; H_1: $\sigma > 0.52$ (claim); C.V. $= 30.144$; d.f. $= 19$; $\chi^2 = 22.670$; do not reject H_0. There is insufficient evidence to conclude that the standard deviation is outside the guidelines.

17. H_0: $\sigma = 60$ (claim) and H_1: $\sigma \neq 60$; C.V. $= 8.672$; 27.587; d.f. $= 17$; $\chi^2 = 19.707$; do not reject. There is not enough evidence to reject the claim that the standard deviation is 60.

19. H_0: $\sigma = 679.5$; H_1: $\sigma \neq 679.5$ (claim); C.V. $= 5.009$; 24.736; d.f. $= 13$; $\chi^2 = 16.723$; do not reject. There is not enough evidence to support the claim that the sample standard deviation differs from the estimated standard deviation.

Exercises 8–6

1. H_0: $\mu = 25.2$; H_1: $\mu \neq 25.2$ (claim); C.V. $= \pm2.032$; $t = 4.50$; $27.2 < \mu < 30.2$; reject. There is enough evidence to support the claim that the average age is not 25.2 years. The confidence interval does not contain 25.2.

3. H_0: $\mu = \$19,150$; H_1: $\mu \neq \$19,150$ (claim); C.V. $= \pm1.96$; $z = -3.69$; $15,889 < \mu < 18,151$; reject. There is enough evidence to support the claim that the mean differs from $19,150. Yes, the interval supports the results because it does not contain the hypothesized mean $19,150.

5. H_0: $\mu = 19$; H_1: $\mu \neq 19$ (claim); C.V. $= \pm2.145$; d.f. $= 14$; $t = 1.37$; do not reject H_0. There is insufficient evidence to conclude that the mean number of hours differs from 19. 95% C.I.: $17.7 < \mu < 24.9$. Because the mean ($\mu = 19$) is in the interval, there is no evidence to support the idea that a difference exists.

7. The power of a statistical test is the probability of rejecting the null hypothesis when it is false.

9. The power of a test can be increased by increasing α or selecting a larger sample size.

Review Exercises

1. H_0: $\mu = 18.3$, H_1: $\mu \neq 18.3$ (claim); C.V. $= \pm2.33$; $z = 3.16$; reject. There is enough evidence to support the claim that the mean time Internet users spend online is not 18.3 hours.

3. H_0: $\mu = 18,000$; H_1: $\mu < 18,000$ (claim); C.V. $= -2.33$; test statistic $z = -3.58$; reject H_0. There is sufficient evidence to conclude that the mean debt is less than $18,000.

5. H_0: $\mu = 1229$; H_1: $\mu \neq 1229$ (claim); C.V. $= \pm1.96$; $z = 1.875$; do not reject H_0. There is insufficient evidence to conclude that the rent differs.

7. H_0: $\mu = 10$; H_1: $\mu < 10$ (claim); C.V. $= -1.782$; d.f. $= 12$; $t = -2.230$; reject. There is enough evidence to support the claim that the mean weight is less than 10 ounces.

9. H_0: $p = 0.17$, H_1: $p > 0.17$ (claim); C.V. $= 1.65$; $z = 4.34$; reject. There is enough evidence to support the claim that the proportion of homes protected by a security system is greater than 17%.

11. H_0: $p = 0.593$; H_1: $p < 0.593$ (claim); C.V. $= -2.33$; $z = -2.57$; reject H_0. There is sufficient evidence to conclude that the proportion of free and reduced-cost lunches is less than 59.3%.

13. H_0: $p = 0.204$; H_1: $p \neq 0.204$ (claim); C.V. $= \pm1.96$; $z = -1.03$; do not reject. There is not enough evidence to support the claim that the proportion is different from the national proportion.

15. H_0: $\sigma = 4.3$ (claim) and H_1: $\sigma < 4.3$; d.f. $= 19$; $\chi^2 = 6.95$; $0.005 < P$-value < 0.01 (0.006); since P-value < 0.05, reject. Yes, there is enough evidence to reject the claim that the standard deviation is greater than or equal to 4.3 miles per gallon.

17. H_0: $\sigma^2 = 40$; H_1: $\sigma^2 \neq 40$ (claim); C.V. $= 2.700$ and 19.023; test statistic $\chi^2 = 9.801$; do not reject H_0. There is insufficient evidence to conclude that the variance in the number of games played differs from 40.

19. H_0: $\mu = 4$ and H_1: $\mu \neq 4$ (claim); C.V. $= \pm2.58$; $z = 1.49$; $3.85 < \mu < 4.55$; do not reject. There is not enough evidence to support the claim that the growth has changed. Yes, the results agree. The hypothesized mean is contained in the interval.

Chapter Quiz

1. True
2. True
3. False
4. True
5. False
6. b
7. d
8. c
9. b
10. Type I
11. β
12. Statistical hypothesis
13. Right
14. $n - 1$

15. H_0: $\mu = 28.6$ (claim) and H_1: $\mu \neq 28.6$; $z = 2.15$; C.V. $= \pm1.96$; reject. There is enough evidence to reject the claim that the average age of the mothers is 28.6 years.

16. H_0: $\mu = \$6500$ (claim) and H_1: $\mu \neq \$6500$; $z = 5.27$; C.V. $= \pm1.96$; reject. There is enough evidence to reject the agent's claim.

17. H_0: $\mu = 8$ and H_1: $\mu > 8$ (claim); $z = 6$; C.V. $= 1.65$; reject. There is enough evidence to support the claim that the average is greater than 8.

18. H_0: $\mu = 500$ (claim) and H_1: $\mu \neq 500$; d.f. $= 6$; $t = -0.571$; C.V. $= \pm3.707$; do not reject. There is not enough evidence to reject the claim that the mean is 500.

19. H_0: $\mu = 67$ and H_1: $\mu < 67$ (claim); $t = -3.1568$; P-value < 0.005 (0.003); since P-value < 0.05, reject. There is enough evidence to support the claim that the average height is less than 67 inches.

20. H_0: $\mu = 12.4$ and H_1: $\mu < 12.4$ (claim); $t = -2.324$; C.V. $= -1.345$; reject. There is enough evidence to support the claim that the average is less than the company claimed.

21. H_0: $\mu = 63.5$ and H_1: $\mu > 63.5$ (claim); $t = 0.47075$; P-value > 0.25 (0.322); since P-value > 0.05, do not reject. There is not enough evidence to support the claim that the average is greater than 63.5.

22. H_0: $\mu = 26$ (claim) and H_1: $\mu \neq 26$; $t = -1.5$; C.V. $= \pm2.492$; do not reject. There is not enough evidence to reject the claim that the average is 26.

23. H_0: $p = 0.39$ (claim) and H_1: $p \neq 0.39$; C.V. $= \pm1.96$; $z = -0.62$; do not reject. There is not enough evidence to reject the claim that 39% took supplements.

24. H_0: $p = 0.55$ (claim) and H_1: $p < 0.55$; $z = -0.8989$; C.V. $= -1.28$; do not reject. There is not enough evidence to reject the survey's claim.

25. H_0: $p = 0.35$ (claim) and H_1: $p \neq 0.35$; C.V. $= \pm2.33$; $z = 0.668$; do not reject. There is not enough evidence to reject the claim that the proportion is 35%.

26. H_0: $p = 0.75$ (claim) and H_1: $p \neq 0.75$; $z = 2.6833$; C.V. $= \pm2.58$; reject. There is enough evidence to reject the claim.

27. P-value $= 0.0316$

28. P-value < 0.0001

29. H_0: $\sigma = 6$ and H_1: $\sigma > 6$ (claim); $\chi^2 = 54$; C.V. $= 36.415$; reject. There is enough evidence to support the claim.

30. H_0: $\sigma = 8$ (claim) and H_1: $\sigma \neq 8$; $\chi^2 = 33.2$; C.V. $= 27.991, 79.490$; do not reject. There is not enough evidence to reject the claim that $\sigma = 8$.

31. H_0: $\sigma = 2.3$ and H_1: $\sigma < 2.3$ (claim); $\chi^2 = 13$; C.V. $= 10.117$; do not reject. There is not enough evidence to support the claim that the standard deviation is less than 2.3.

32. H_0: $\sigma = 9$ (claim) and H_1: $\sigma \neq 9$; $\chi^2 = 13.4$; P-value > 0.20 (0.291); since P-value > 0.05, do not reject. There is not enough evidence to reject the claim that $\sigma = 9$.

33. $28.9 < \mu < 31.2$; no

34. $\$6562.81 < \mu < \$6637.19$; no

Chapter 9
Exercises 9–1

1. Testing a single mean involves comparing a population mean to a specific value such as $\mu = 100$; testing the difference between two means involves comparing the means of two populations, such as $\mu_1 = \mu_2$.

3. Both samples are random samples. The populations must be independent of each other, and they must be normally or approximately normally distributed.

5. H_0: $\mu_1 = \mu_2$ (claim) and H_1: $\mu_1 \neq \mu_2$; C.V. $= \pm2.58$; $z = -0.88$; do not reject. There is not enough evidence to reject the claim that the average lengths of the major rivers are the same. (TI: $z = -0.856$)

7. H_0: $\mu_1 = \mu_2$; H_1: $\mu_1 \neq \mu_2$ (claim); C.V. $= \pm1.96$; $z = -3.65$; reject. There is sufficient evidence at $\alpha = 0.05$ to conclude that the commuting times differ in the winter.

9. H_0: $\mu_1 = \mu_2$; H_1: $\mu_1 > \mu_2$ (claim); C.V. $= 2.33$; $z = 3.75$; reject. There is sufficient evidence at $\alpha = 0.01$ to conclude that the average hospital stay for men is longer.

11. H_0: $\mu_1 = \mu_2$ and H_1: $\mu_1 < \mu_2$ (claim); C.V. $= -1.65$; $z = -2.01$; reject. There is enough evidence to support the claim that the stayers had a higher grade point average.

13. H_0: $\mu_1 = \mu_2$; H_1: $\mu_1 \neq \mu_2$ (claim); C.V. $= \pm1.96$; $z = 0.66$; do not reject. There is not enough evidence to support the claim that there is a difference in the means.

15. H_0: $\mu_1 = \mu_2$ and H_1: $\mu_1 \neq \mu_2$ (claim); $z = 1.01$; P-value $= 0.3124$; do not reject. There is not enough evidence to support the claim that there is a difference in self-esteem scores. (TI: P-value $= 0.3131$)

17. $2.8 < \mu_1 - \mu_2 < 6.0$

19. $10.5 < \mu_1 - \mu_2 < 59.5$. The interval provides evidence to reject the claim that there is no difference in mean scores because the interval for the difference is entirely positive. That is, 0 is not in the interval.

21. H_0: $\mu_1 = \mu_2$, H_1: $\mu_1 > \mu_2$ (claim); C.V. $= 2.33$; $z = 3.43$; reject. There is enough evidence to support the claim that women watch more television than men.

23. H_0: $\mu_1 = \mu_2$, H_1: $\mu_1 \neq \mu_2$ (claim); $z = -2.47$; P-value $= 0.0136$; do not reject. There is not enough evidence to support the claim that there is a significant difference in the mean daily sales of the two stores.

25. H_0: $\mu_1 - \mu_2 = 8$ (claim) and H_1: $\mu_1 - \mu_2 > 8$; C.V. $= +1.65$; $z = -0.73$; do not reject. There is not enough evidence to reject the claim that private school students have exam scores that are at most 8 points higher than those of students in public schools.

27. H_0: $\mu_1 - \mu_2 = \$30,000$; H_1: $\mu_1 - \mu_2 \neq \$30,000$ (claim); C.V. $= \pm2.58$; $z = 1.22$; do not reject. There is not enough evidence to support the claim that the difference in income is not $30,000.

Exercises 9–2

1. H_0: $\mu_1 = \mu_2$; H_1: $\mu_1 \neq \mu_2$ (claim); C.V. $= \pm1.761$; d.f. $= 14$; $t = -1.595$; do not reject. There is not enough evidence to support the claim that the means are different.

3. H_0: $\mu_1 = \mu_2$; H_1: $\mu_1 \neq \mu_2$ (claim); C.V. $= \pm 2.093$; d.f. $= 19$; $t = 3.811$; reject. There is enough evidence to support the claim that the mean noise levels are different.

5. H_0: $\mu_1 = \mu_2$; H_1: $\mu_1 \neq \mu_2$ (claim); C.V. $= \pm 1.812$; d.f. $= 10$; $t = -1.220$; do not reject. There is not enough evidence to support the claim that the means are not equal.

7. H_0: $\mu_1 = \mu_2$; H_1: $\mu_1 \neq \mu_2$ (claim); d.f. $= 9$; $t = 5.103$; the P-value for the t test is P-value < 0.001; reject. There is enough evidence to support the claim that the means are different.

9. $3.07 < \mu_1 - \mu_2 < 10.53$
   (TI: Interval $3.18 < \mu_1 - \mu_2 < 10.42$)

11. H_0: $\mu_1 = \mu_2$; H_1: $\mu_1 \neq \mu_2$ (claim); C.V. $= \pm 2.977$; d.f. $= 14$; $t = 2.601$; do not reject. There is insufficient evidence to conclude a difference in viewing times.

13. H_0: $\mu_1 = \mu_2$ and H_1: $\mu_1 > \mu_2$ (claim); C.V. $= 3.365$; d.f. $= 5$; $t = 1.057$; do not reject. There is not enough evidence to support the claim that the average number of students attending cyber charter schools in Allegheny County is greater that the average number of students attending cyber charter schools in surrounding counties. One reason why caution should be used is that cyber charter schools are a relatively new concept.

15. H_0: $\mu_1 = \mu_2$ (claim) and H_1: $\mu_1 \neq \mu_2$; d.f. $= 15$; $t = 2.385$. The P-value for the t test is $0.02 < P$-value < 0.05 (0.026). Do not reject since P-value > 0.01. There is not enough evidence to reject the claim that the means are equal. $-0.1 < \mu_1 - \mu_2 < 0.9$
   (TI: Interval $-0.07 < \mu_1 - \mu_2 < 0.87$)

17. $9.9 < \mu_1 - \mu_2 < 219.6$
   (TI: Interval $13.23 < \mu_1 - \mu_2 < 216.24$)

19. H_0: $\mu_1 = \mu_2$, H_1: $\mu_1 < \mu_2$ (claim); $t = -6.222$; P-value < 0.01; reject. There is enough evidence to support the claim that the mean of the monthly gasoline prices in 2005 was less than the mean of the monthly gasoline prices in 2011.

21. H_0: $\mu_1 = \mu_2$, H_1: $\mu_1 \neq \mu_2$ (claim); C.V. $= \pm 1.761$; $t = -1.782$; reject. There is enough evidence to support the claim that the means of the two groups of numbers differ.

Exercises 9–3

1. *a.* Dependent   *d.* Dependent
   b. Dependent   *e.* Independent
   c. Independent

3. H_0: $\mu_D = 0$ and H_1: $\mu_D < 0$ (claim); C.V. $= -1.397$; d.f. $= 8$; $t = -2.818$; reject. There is enough evidence to support the claim that the seminar increased the number of hours students studied.

5. H_0: $\mu_D = 0$ and H_1: $\mu_D \neq 0$ (claim); C.V. $= \pm 2.365$; d.f. $= 7$; $t = -1.658$; do not reject. There is not enough evidence to support the claim that the means are different.

7. H_0: $\mu_D = 0$ and H_1: $\mu_D > 0$ (claim); C.V. $= 2.571$; d.f. $= 5$; $t = 2.236$; do not reject. There is not enough evidence to support the claim that the errors have been reduced.

9. H_0: $\mu_D = 0$ and H_1: $\mu_D \neq 0$ (claim); d.f. $= 7$; $t = 0.978$; P-value > 0.20 (0.361). Do not reject since P-value > 0.01. There is not enough evidence to support the claim that there is a difference in the pulse rates. $-3.2 < \mu_D < 5.7$

11. H_0: $\mu_D = 0$, H_1: $\mu_D \neq 0$ (claim); C.V. $= \pm 2.365$; $t = -1.967$; do not reject. There is not enough evidence to support the claim that the means of the scores of the two rounds are different.

13. $\overline{X_1 - X_2} = \sum \dfrac{X_1 - X_2}{n} = \sum \left(\dfrac{X_1}{n} - \dfrac{X_2}{n} \right)$
    $= \sum \dfrac{X_1}{n} - \sum \dfrac{X_2}{n} = \overline{X}_1 - \overline{X}_2$

Exercises 9–4

1. *a.* $\hat{p} = \frac{34}{48}, \hat{q} = \frac{14}{48}$ *d.* $\hat{p} = \frac{6}{24}, \hat{q} = \frac{18}{24}$
   b. $\hat{p} = \frac{28}{75}, \hat{q} = \frac{47}{75}$ *e.* $\hat{p} = \frac{12}{144}, \hat{q} = \frac{132}{144}$
   c. $\hat{p} = \frac{50}{100}, \hat{q} = \frac{50}{100}$

3. *a.* 16   *c.* 48   *e.* 30
   b. 4   *d.* 104

5. *a.* $\bar{p} = 0.5$; $\bar{q} = 0.5$
   b. $\bar{p} = 0.5$; $\bar{q} = 0.5$
   c. $\bar{p} = 0.27$; $\bar{q} = 0.73$
   d. $\bar{p} = 0.2125$; $\bar{q} = 0.7875$
   e. $\bar{p} = 0.216$; $\bar{q} = 0.784$

7. $\hat{p}_1 = 0.83$; $\hat{p}_2 = 0.75$; $\bar{p} = 0.79$; $\bar{q} = 0.21$; H_0: $p_1 = p_2$ (claim) and H_1: $p_1 \neq p_2$; C.V. $= \pm 1.96$; $z = 1.39$; do not reject. There is not enough evidence to reject the claim that the proportions are equal. $-0.032 < p_1 - p_2 < 0.192$

9. $\hat{p}_1 = 0.55$; $\hat{p}_2 = 0.46$; $\bar{p} = 0.5$; $\bar{q} = 0.5$; H_0: $p_1 = p_2$ and H_1: $p_1 \neq p_2$ (claim); C.V. $= \pm 2.58$; $z = 1.23$; do not reject. There is not enough evidence to support the claim that the proportions are different. ($-0.104 < p_1 - p_2 < 0.293$)

11. $\hat{p}_1 = 0.347$; $\hat{p}_2 = 0.433$; $\bar{p} = 0.385$; $\bar{q} = 0.615$; H_0: $p_1 = p_2$ and H_1: $p_1 \neq p_2$ (claim); C.V. $= \pm 1.96$; $z = -1.03$; do not reject. There is not enough evidence to say that the proportion of dog owners has changed.

13. $\hat{p}_1 = 0.25$; $\hat{p}_2 = 0.31$; $\bar{p} = 0.286$; $\bar{q} = 0.714$; H_0: $p_1 = p_2$ and H_1: $p_1 \neq p_2$ (claim); C.V. $= \pm 2.58$; $z = -1.45$; do not reject. There is not enough evidence to support the claim that the proportions are different. $-0.165 < p_1 - p_2 < 0.045$

15. $0.077 < p_1 - p_2 < 0.323$

17. $\hat{p}_1 = 0.4$; $\hat{p}_2 = 0.295$; $\bar{p} = 0.3475$; $\bar{q} = 0.6525$; H_0: $p_1 = p_2$; H_1: $p_1 \neq p_2$ (claim); C.V. $= \pm 2.58$; $z = 2.21$; do not reject. There is not enough evidence to support the claim that the proportions are different.

19. $-0.0667 < p_1 - p_2 < 0.0631$. It does agree with the *Almanac* statistics stating a difference of -0.042 since -0.042 is contained in the interval.

21. $\hat{p}_1 = 0.80$; $\hat{p}_2 = 0.60$; $\bar{p} = 0.69$; $\bar{q} = 0.31$; H_0: $p_1 = p_2$ and H_1: $p_1 \neq p_2$ (claim); C.V. $= \pm 2.58$; $z = 5.05$; reject. There is enough evidence to support the claim that the proportions are different.

23. $\hat{p}_1 = 0.6$, $\hat{p}_2 = 0.533$; $\bar{p} = 0.563$, $\bar{q} = 0.437$. H_0: $p_1 = p_2$ and H_1: $p_1 \neq p_2$ (claim); C.V. $= \pm 2.58$;

$z = 1.10$; do not reject. There is not enough evidence to support the claim that the proportion of males who commit interview errors is different from the proportion of females who commit interview errors.

25. $\hat{p}_1 = 0.733$, $\hat{p}_2 = 0.56$; $\overline{p} = 0.671$, $\overline{q} = 0.329$; $H_0: p_1 = p_2$ and $H_1: p_1 > p_2$ (claim); $z = 2.96$; P-value < 0.002; reject. There is enough evidence to support the claim that the proportion of couponing women is greater than the couponing men. (Note: TI says P-value $= 0.00154$.)

27. $\hat{p}_1 = 0.065$; $\hat{p}_2 = 0.08$; $\overline{p} = 0.0725$; $\overline{q} = 0.9275$; $H_0: p_1 = p_2$; $H_1: p_1 \neq p_2$ (claim); C.V. $= \pm 1.96$; $z = -0.58$; do not reject. There is insufficient evidence to conclude a difference.

Exercises 9–5

1. The variance in the numerator should be the larger of the two variances.

3. One degree of freedom is used for the variance associated with the numerator, and one is used for the variance associated with the denominator.

5. a. d.f.N. $= 15$; d.f.D. $= 22$; C.V. $= 3.36$

   b. d.f.N. $= 24$; d.f.D. $= 13$; C.V. $= 3.59$

   c. d.f.N. $= 45$; d.f.D. $= 29$; C.V. $= 2.03$

7. Specific P-values are in parentheses.

   a. $0.025 < P$-value < 0.05 (0.033)

   b. $0.05 < P$-value < 0.10 (0.072)

   c. P-value $= 0.05$

   d. $0.005 < P$-value < 0.01 (0.006)

9. $H_0: \sigma_1^2 = \sigma_2^2$; $H_1: \sigma_1^2 \neq \sigma_2^2$ (claim); C.V. $= 3.43$; d.f.N. $= 12$; d.f.D. $= 11$; $F = 2.08$; do not reject. There is not enough evidence to support the claim that the variances are different.

11. $H_0: \sigma_1^2 = \sigma_2^2$ and $H_1: \sigma_1^2 \neq \sigma_2^2$ (claim); C.V. $= 4.99$; d.f.N. $= 7$; d.f.D. $= 7$; $F = 1.00$; do not reject. There is not enough evidence to support the claim that there is a difference in the variances.

13. $H_0: \sigma_1^2 = \sigma_2^2$; $H_1: \sigma_1^2 > \sigma_2^2$ (claim); C.V. $= 4.950$; d.f.N. $= 6$; d.f.D. $= 5$; $F = 9.80$; reject. There is sufficient evidence at $\alpha = 0.05$ to conclude that the variance in area is greater for Eastern cities. C.V. $= 10.67$; do not reject. There is insufficient evidence to conclude the variance is greater at $\alpha = 0.01$.

15. $H_0: \sigma_1^2 = \sigma_2^2$ and $H_1: \sigma_1^2 \neq \sigma_2^2$ (claim); C.V. $= 4.03$; d.f.N. $= 9$; d.f.D. $= 9$; $F = 1.10$; do not reject. There is not enough evidence to support the claim that the variances are not equal.

17. $H_0: \sigma_1^2 = \sigma_2^2$ (claim) and $H_1: \sigma_1^2 \neq \sigma_2^2$; C.V. $= 3.87$; d.f.N. $= 6$; d.f.D. $= 7$; $F = 3.18$; do not reject. There is not enough evidence to reject the claim that the variances of the heights are equal.

19. $H_0: \sigma_1^2 = \sigma_2^2$ (claim) and $H_1: \sigma_1^2 \neq \sigma_2^2$; $F = 5.32$; d.f.N. $= 14$; d.f.D. $= 14$; P-value < 0.01 (0.004); reject. There is enough evidence to reject the claim that the variances of the weights are equal. The variance for men is 2.363 and the variance for women is 0.444.

21. $H_0: \sigma_1^2 = \sigma_2^2$ and $H_1: \sigma_1^2 \neq \sigma_2^2$ (claim); $F = 3.67$; d.f.N. $= 8$; d.f.D. $= 13$; C.V. $= 3.39$; reject. There is enough evidence to support the claim that the variances are different.

23. $H_0: \sigma_1^2 = \sigma_2^2$; $H_1: \sigma_1^2 \neq \sigma_2^2$ (claim); C.V. $= 1.88$; d.f.N. $= 59$; d.f.D. $= 59$; $F = 1.98$; reject. There is enough evidence to support the claim that the variances are not equal.

Review Exercises

1. $H_0: \mu_1 = \mu_2$ and $H_1: \mu_1 > \mu_2$ (claim); C.V. $= 2.33$; $z = 0.59$; do not reject. There is not enough evidence to support the claim that single drivers do more pleasure driving than married drivers.

3. $H_0: \mu_1 = \mu_2$, $H_1: \mu_1 \neq \mu_2$ (claim); C.V. $= \pm 2.861$; $t = -3.238$; reject. There is enough evidence to support the claim that the means are different.

5. $H_0: \mu_1 = \mu_2$ and $H_1: \mu_1 \neq \mu_2$ (claim); C.V. $= \pm 2.624$; d.f. $= 14$; $t = 6.540$; reject. Yes, there is enough evidence to support the claim that there is a difference in the teachers' salaries. $\$3494.80 < \mu_1 - \mu_2 < \$8021.20$

7. $H_0: \mu_D = 10$; $H_1: \mu_D > 10$ (claim); C.V. $= 2.821$; d.f. $= 9$; $t = 3.249$; reject. There is sufficient evidence to conclude that the difference in temperature is greater than 10 degrees.

9. $\hat{p}_1 = 0.245$, $\hat{p}_2 = 0.31$, $\overline{p} = 0.2775$, $\overline{q} = 0.7225$; $H_0: p_1 = p_2$; $H_1: p_1 \neq p_2$ (claim); C.V. $= \pm 1.96$; $z = -1.45$; do not reject. There is not enough evidence to support the claim that the proportions are different.

11. $H_0: \sigma_1 = \sigma_2$ and $H_1: \sigma_1 \neq \sigma_2$ (claim); C.V. $= 2.77$; $\alpha = 0.10$; d.f.N. $= 23$; d.f.D. $= 10$; $F = 10.37$; reject. There is enough evidence to support the claim that there is a difference in the standard deviations.

13. $H_0: \sigma_1^2 = \sigma_2^2$; $H_1: \sigma_1^2 \neq \sigma_2^2$ (claim); C.V. $= 2.45$; d.f.N. $= 24$; d.f.D. $= 19$; $F = 1.63$; do not reject. There is not enough evidence to support the claim that the standard deviations are different. Store Z's paint would have to have a standard deviation of $\$3.33$.

Chapter Quiz

1. False

2. False

3. True

4. False

5. d

6. a

7. c

8. a

9. $\mu_1 = \mu_2$

10. t

11. Normal

12. Negative

13. $F = \dfrac{s_1^2}{s_2^2}$

14. $H_0: \mu_1 = \mu_2$ and $H_1: \mu \neq \mu_2$ (claim); $z = -3.69$; C.V. $= \pm 2.58$; reject. There is enough evidence to support the claim that there is a difference in the cholesterol levels of the two groups. $-10 < \mu_1 - \mu_2 < -2$

15. $H_0: \mu_1 = \mu_2$ and $H_1: \mu_1 > \mu_2$ (claim); C.V. $= 1.28$; $z = 1.61$; reject. There is enough evidence to support the

claim that the average rental fees for the apartments in the East are greater than the average rental fees for the apartments in the West.

16. $H_0: \mu_1 = \mu_2$ and $H_1: \mu_1 \neq \mu_2$ (claim); $t = 11.094$; d.f. $= 11$; C.V. $= \pm 3.106$; reject. There is enough evidence to support the claim that the average prices are different. $0.29 < \mu_1 - \mu_2 < 0.51$
(TI: Interval $0.2995 < \mu_1 - \mu_2 < 0.5005$)

17. $H_0: \mu_1 = \mu_2$ and $H_1: \mu_1 < \mu_2$ (claim); C.V. $= -2.132$; d.f. $= 4$; $t = -4.046$; reject. There is enough evidence to support the claim that accidents have increased.

18. $H_0: \mu_1 = \mu_2$ and $H_1: \mu_1 \neq \mu_2$ (claim); $t = 9.807$; d.f. $= 11$; C.V. $= \pm 2.718$; reject. There is enough evidence to support the claim that the salaries are different. $\$6653 < \mu_1 - \mu_2 < \$11,757$
(TI: Interval $\$6619 < \mu_1 - \mu_2 < \$11,491$)

19. $H_0: \mu_1 = \mu_2$ and $H_1: \mu_1 > \mu_2$ (claim); d.f. $= 10$; $t = 0.874$; $0.10 < P\text{-value} < 0.25$ (0.198); do not reject since $P\text{-value} > 0.05$. There is not enough evidence to support the claim that the incomes of city residents are greater than the incomes of rural residents.

20. $H_0: \mu_D = 0$ and $H_1: \mu_D < 0$ (claim); $t = -4.172$; d.f. $= 9$; C.V. $= -2.821$; reject. There is enough evidence to support the claim that the sessions improved math skills.

21. $H_0: \mu_D = 0$ and $H_1: \mu_D < 0$ (claim); $t = -1.714$; d.f. $= 9$; C.V. $= -1.833$; do not reject. There is not enough evidence to support the claim that egg production was increased.

22. $\hat{p}_1 = 0.05$, $\hat{p}_2 = 0.08$, $\bar{p} = 0.0615$, $\bar{q} = 0.9385$; $H_0: p_1 = p_2$ and $H_1: p_1 \neq p_2$ (claim); $z = -0.69$; C.V. $= \pm 1.65$; do not reject. There is not enough evidence to support the claim that the proportions are different. $-0.105 < p_1 - p_2 < 0.045$

23. $\hat{p}_1 = 0.04$, $\hat{p}_2 = 0.03$, $\bar{p} = 0.035$, $\bar{q} = 0.965$; $H_0: p_1 = p_2$ and $H_1: p_1 \neq p_2$ (claim); C.V. $= \pm 1.96$; $z = 0.54$; do not reject. There is not enough evidence to support the claim that the proportions have changed. $-0.026 < p_1 - p_2 < 0.046$. Yes, the confidence interval contains 0; hence, the null hypothesis is not rejected.

24. $H_0: \sigma_1^2 = \sigma_2^2$ and $H_1: \sigma_1^2 \neq \sigma_2^2$ (claim); $F = 1.64$; d.f.N. $= 17$; d.f.D. $= 14$; $P\text{-value} > 0.20$ (0.357). Do not reject since $P\text{-value} > 0.05$. There is not enough evidence to support the claim that the variances are different.

25. $H_0: \sigma_1^2 = \sigma_2^2$ and $H_1: \sigma_1^2 \neq \sigma_2^2$ (claim); $F = 1.30$; C.V. $= 1.90$; do not reject. There is not enough evidence to support the claim that the variances are different.

Chapter 10

Exercises 10–1

1. Two variables are related when a discernible pattern exists between them.

3. r, ρ (rho)

5. A positive relationship means that as x increases, y increases. A negative relationship means that as x increases, y decreases.

7. The diagram is called a scatter plot. It shows the nature of the relationship.

9. t test

11. $H_0: \rho = 0$; $H_1: \rho \neq 0$; $r = 0.804$; C.V. $= \pm 0.707$; reject. There is sufficient evidence to say that there is a linear relationship between the number of murders and the number of robberies per 100,000 people for a random selection of states in the United States.

13. $H_0: \rho = 0$; $H_1: \rho \neq 0$; $r = 0.880$; C.V. $= \pm 0.666$; reject. There is sufficient evidence to conclude that a significant linear relationship exists between the number of releases and gross receipts.

15. $H_0: \rho = 0$; $H_1: \rho \neq 0$; $r = -0.883$; C.V. $= \pm 0.811$; reject. There is a significant linear relationship between the number of years a person has been out of school and his or her contribution.

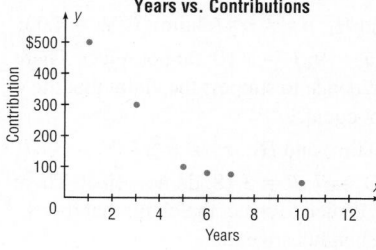

17. $H_0: \rho = 0$; $H_1: \rho \neq 0$; $r = 0.800$; C.V. $= \pm 0.811$; do not reject. There is not enough evidence to conclude that there is a significant linear relationship between the energy consumption for gas and the energy consumption for oil.

19. H_0: $\rho = 0$; H_1: $\rho \neq 0$; $r = 0.950$; C.V. $= \pm 0.811$; reject. There is a significant linear relationship between the number of grams of carbohydrates and the number of kilocalories in 100-gram servings of fruits and vegetables.

21. H_0: $\rho = 0$; H_1: $\rho \neq 0$; $r = 0.812$; C.V. $= \pm 0.754$; reject. There is a significant linear relationship between the number of faculty and the number of students at small colleges. When the values for x and y are switched, the results are identical. The independent variable is most likely the number of students.

23. H_0: $\rho = 0$; H_1: $\rho \neq 0$; $r = 0.908$; C.V. $= \pm 0.811$; reject. There is a significant linear relationship between the literacy rates of men and women for various countries.

25. H_0: $\rho = 0$; H_1: $\rho \neq 0$; $r = -0.190$; C.V. $= \pm 0.811$; do not reject. There is not enough evidence to conclude that there is a significant linear relationship between the national bowling championship scores of men and women.

27. H_0: $\rho = 0$; H_1: $\rho \neq 0$; $r = -0.673$; C.V. $= \pm 0.811$; do not reject. There is not enough evidence to say that there is a significant linear relationship between class size and average grades for students.

29. $r = 1.00$: All points fall in a straight line. $r = 1.00$: The value of r between x and y is the same when x and y are interchanged.

Exercises 10–2

1. A scatter plot should be drawn, and the value of the correlation coefficient should be tested to see whether it is significant.

3. $y' = a + bx$

5. It is the line that is drawn on a scatter plot such that the sum of the squares of the vertical distances from each point to the line is a minimum.

7. When r is positive, b will be positive. When r is negative, b will be negative.

9. The closer r is to $+1$ or -1, the more accurate the predicted value will be.

11. $y' = -13.151 + 25.333x$; $y' = 100.848$ robberies

13. $y' = 181.661 + 7.319x$; $y' = 1645.5$ (million \$)

15. $y' = 453.176 - 50.439x$; \$251.42

17. Since r is not significant, no regression should be done.

19. $y' = -7.957 + 4.601x$; $y' = 47.255$ kcal

21. $y' = -14.974 + 0.111x$

23. $y' = -33.261 + 1.367x$; $y' = 76.1\%$

25. Since r is not significant, no linear regression should be done.

27. Since r is not significant, no regression should be done.

29. H_0: $\rho = 0$; H_1: $\rho \neq 0$; $r = 0.429$; C.V. $= \pm 0.811$; do not reject. There is insufficient evidence to conclude a relationship exists between number of farms and acreage.

31. H_0: $\rho = 0$; H_1: $\rho \neq 0$; $r = 0.970$; C.V. $= \pm 0.707$; reject; $y' = -33.358 + 6.703x$; when $x = 500$, $y' = 3318.142$, or about 3318 tons. There is a significant relationship between number of employees and tons of coal produced.

33. H_0: $\rho = 0$; H_1: $\rho \neq 0$; $r = -0.981$; C.V. $= \pm 0.811$; reject. There is a significant linear relationship between the number of absences and the final grade; $y' = 96.784 - 2.668x$.

35. H_0: $\rho = 0$; H_1: $\rho \neq 0$; $r = -0.265$; d.f. $= 8$; $t = -0.777$; P-value > 0.05 (0.459); do not reject. There is no significant linear relationship between the ages of billionaires and their net worth. No regression should be done.

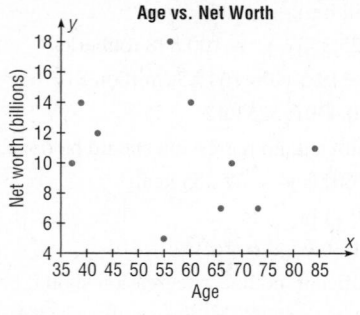

37. 453.173; regression should not be done.

Exercises 10–3

1. Explained variation is the variation due to the relationship. It is computed by $\Sigma(y' - \bar{y})^2$.

3. Total variation is the sum of the squares of the vertical distances of the points from the mean. It is computed by $\Sigma(y - \bar{y})^2$.

5. The coefficient of determination is found by squaring the value of the correlation coefficient.

7. The coefficient of nondetermination is found by subtracting r^2 from 1.

9. $r^2 = 0.5625$; 56.25% of the variation of y is due to the variation of x; 43.75% is due to chance.

11. $r^2 = 0.1764$; 17.64% of the variation of y is due to the variation of x; 82.36% is due to chance.

13. $r^2 = 0.8281$; 82.81% of the variation of y is due to the variation of x; 17.19% is due to chance.

15. 629.49

17. 94.22*

19. $365.88 < y' < 2925.04$*

21. $\$30.46 < y < \$472.38$*

*Answers may vary due to rounding.

Exercises 10–4

1. Simple regression has one dependent variable and one independent variable. Multiple regression has one dependent variable and two or more independent variables.

3. The relationship would include all variables in one equation.

5. They will all be smaller.

7. 98.569 kcal

9. 85.75 (grade) or 86

11. R is the strength of the relationship between the dependent variable and all the independent variables.

13. R^2 is the coefficient of multiple determination. R^2_{adj} is adjusted for sample size and number of predictors.

15. F test

Review Exercises

1. H_0: $\rho = 0$; H_1: $\rho \neq 0$; $r = -0.686$; C.V. $= \pm 0.917$; d.f. $= 4$; do not reject. There is insufficient evidence to conclude that a relationship exists between number of passengers and one-way fare cost. No regression should be done.

3. H_0: $\rho = 0$; H_1: $\rho \neq 0$; $r = 0.873$; d.f. $= 5$; C.V. $= \pm 0.875$; do not reject. There is not a significant linear relationship between the number of touchdowns and the quarterback's rating. No regression should be done.

5. H_0: $\rho = 0$; H_1: $\rho \neq 0$; $r = -0.974$; C.V. $= \pm 0.708$; d.f. $= 10$; reject. There is a significant linear relationship between speed and time; $y' = 14.086 - 0.137x$; $y' = 4.2$ hours.

7. H_0: $\rho = 0$; H_1: $\rho \neq 0$; $r = 0.907$; d.f. $= 5$; C.V. $= \pm 0.875$; reject. There is sufficient evidence to conclude a linear relationship exists between the numbers of female physicians and male physicians in a given field. $y' = 102.846 + 3.408x$; $y' = 6919$

9. $0.468*$ (TI value 0.513)   11. $3.34 < y < 5.10*$
13. $22.01*$ 15. $R_{adj}^2 = 0.643*$

*Answers may vary due to rounding.

Chapter Quiz

1. False   2. True
3. True   4. False
5. False   6. False
7. a 8. a
9. d 10. c
11. b 12. Scatter plot
13. Independent   14. -1, $+1$
15. b (slope)   16. Line of best fit
17. $+1$, -1
18. H_0: $\rho = 0$; H_1: $\rho \neq 0$; d.f. $= 5$; $r = 0.600$; C.V. $= \pm 0.754$; do not reject. There is no significant linear relationship

between the price of the same drugs in the United States and in Australia. No regression should be done.

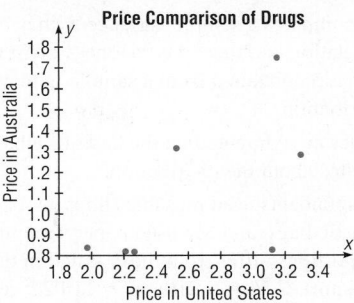

19. H_0: $\rho = 0$; H_1: $\rho \neq 0$; d.f. $= 5$; $r = -0.078$; C.V. $= \pm 0.754$; do not reject. No regression should be done.

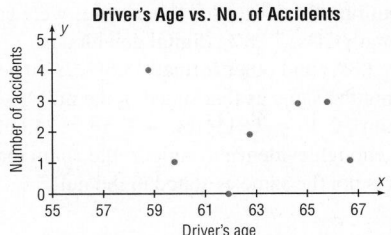

20. H_0: $\rho = 0$; H_1: $\rho \neq 0$; $r = 0.842$; d.f. $= 4$; C.V. $= \pm 0.811$; reject. $y' = -1.918 + 0.551x$; 4.14 or 4

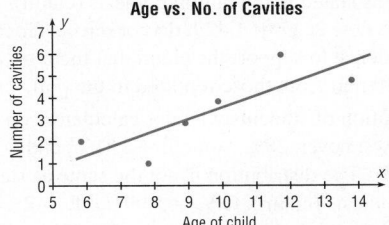

21. H_0: $\rho = 0$; H_1: $\rho \neq 0$; $r = 0.602$; d.f. $= 6$; C.V. $= \pm 0.707$; do not reject. No regression should be done.

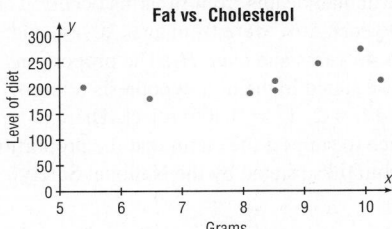

22. $1.129*$
23. $29.5*$ For calculation purposes only. No regression should be done.
24. $0 < y < 5*$
25. 217.5 (average of y' values is used since there is no significant relationship)
26. $119.9*$
27. $R = 0.729*$
28. $R_{adj}^2 = 0.439*$

*These answers may vary due to the method of calculation or rounding.

Chapter 11

Exercises 11–1

1. The variance test compares a sample variance with a hypothesized population variance; the goodness-of-fit test compares a distribution obtained from a sample with a hypothesized distribution.

3. The expected values are computed on the basis of what the null hypothesis states about the distribution.

5. H_0: 60% of the respondents used reusable shopping bags, 32% asked for plastic bags, and 8% used paper shopping bags. H_1: The proportions differ from those stated in the null hypothesis (claim). C.V. = 9.210; $\chi^2 = 11.022$; reject. There is sufficient evidence to conclude that the proportions differ from those stated in the magazine survey.

7. H_0: The distribution of the recorded music sales were as follows: full-length CDs, 77.8%; digital downloads, 12.8%; singles, 3.8%; and other formats, 5.6%. H_1: The distribution is not the same as that stated in the null hypothesis (claim). C.V. = 7.815; d.f. = 3; $\chi^2 = 24.660$; reject. There is enough evidence to support the claim that the distribution is not the same as stated in the null hypothesis.

9. H_0: 35% feel that genetically modified food is safe to eat, 52% feel that genetically modified food is not safe to eat, and 13% have no opinion. H_1: The distribution is not the same as stated in the null hypothesis (claim). C.V. = 9.210; d.f. = 2; $\chi^2 = 1.429$; do not reject. There is not enough evidence to support the claim that the proportions are different from those reported in the poll.

11. H_0: The distribution of students who use calculators on tests is as follows: never, 28%; sometimes, 51%; and always, 21%. H_1: The distribution is not the same as stated in the null hypothesis (claim). C.V. = 5.991; d.f. = 2; $\chi^2 = 2.999$; do not reject. There is not enough evidence to support the claim that the distribution is different from the one stated in the null hypothesis.

13. H_0: 10% of the annual deaths from firearms occurred at birth to age 19 years, 50% were from ages 20–44, and 40% were ages 45 years and over. H_1: The proportions differ from those stated in the null hypothesis (claim). C.V. = 5.991; d.f. = 2; $\chi^2 = 9.405$; reject. There is enough evidence to support the claim that the proportions are different from those stated by the National Safety Council.

15. H_0: The proportion of Internet users is the same for the groups. H_1: The proportion of Internet users is not the same for the groups (claim). C.V. = 5.991; d.f. = 2; $\chi^2 = 0.208$; do not reject. There is insufficient evidence to conclude that the proportions differ.

17. H_0: The distribution of the ways people pay for their prescriptions is as follows: 60% use personal funds, 25% use insurance, and 15% use Medicare (claim). H_1: The distribution is not the same as stated in the null hypothesis. The d.f. = 2; $\alpha = 0.05$; $\chi^2 = 0.667$; do not reject since P-value > 0.10. There is not enough evidence to reject the claim that the distribution is the same as stated

in the null hypothesis. An implication of the results is that the majority of people are using their own money to pay for medications. Maybe the medication should be less expensive to help out these people. (TI: P-value = 0.716)

19. H_0: The coins are balanced and randomly tossed (claim). H_1: The coins are not balanced or are not randomly tossed. C.V. = 7.815; d.f. = 3; $\chi^2 = 139.407$; reject the null hypothesis. There is enough evidence to reject the claim that the coins are balanced and randomly tossed.

Exercises 11–2

1. The independence test and the goodness-of-fit test both use the same formula for computing the test value. However, the independence test uses a contingency table, whereas the goodness-of-fit test does not.

3. H_0: The variables are independent (or not related). H_1: The variables are dependent (or related).

5. The expected values are computed as (row total × column total) ÷ grand total.

7. H_0: The choice of restaurants is independent of the type of meal selected (breakfast, lunch, or dinner) by the patron. H_1: The choice of restaurant is dependent upon the type of meal selected (claim). C.V. = 13.277; d.f. = 4; $\chi^2 = 25.421$; reject. There is enough evidence to support the claim that the choice of restaurant is dependent on the type of meal ordered.

9. H_0: The number of endangered species is independent of the number of threatened species. H_1: The number of endangered species is dependent upon the number of threatened species (claim). C.V. = 9.488; d.f. = 4; $\chi^2 = 45.315$; reject. There is sufficient evidence to conclude a relationship. The result is not different at $\alpha = 0.01$.

11. H_0: The types of violent crimes committed are independent of the cities where they are committed. H_1: The types of violent crimes committed are dependent upon the cities where they are committed (claim). C.V. = 12.592; d.f. = 6; $\chi^2 = 43.890$; reject. There is enough evidence to support the claim that the types of violent crimes are dependent upon the cities where they are committed.

13. H_0: The length of unemployment time is independent of the type of industry where the worker is employed. H_1: The length of unemployment time is dependent upon the type of industry where the worker is employed (claim). C.V. = 9.488; d.f. = 4; $\chi^2 = 4.974$; do not reject. There is not enough evidence to support the claim that the length of unemployment time is dependent upon the type of industry where the worker is employed.

15. H_0: The program of study of a student is independent of the type of institution. H_1: The program of study of a student is dependent upon the type of institution (claim). C.V. = 7.815; d.f. = 3; $\chi^2 = 13.702$; reject. There is sufficient evidence to conclude that there is a relationship between program of study and type of institution.

17. H_0: The study group a student selects is independent of his or her statistics professor. H_1: The study group a student

selects is dependent upon his or her statistics professor (claim). C.V. = 9.488; d.f. = 4; χ^2 = 5.483; do not reject. There is not enough evidence to support the claim that the study group selection is dependent upon the statistics professor.

19. H_0: The type of book purchased by an individual is independent of the gender of the individual (claim). H_1: The type of book purchased by an individual is dependent on the gender of the individual. The d.f. = 2; α = 0.05; χ^2 = 19.429; P-value < 0.005; reject since P-value < 0.05. There is enough evidence to reject the claim that the type of book purchased by an individual is independent of the gender of the individual. (TI: P-value = 0.00006)

21. H_0: $p_1 = p_2 = p_3$ (claim). H_1: At least one proportion is different from the others. C.V. = 4.605; d.f. = 2; χ^2 = 5.749; reject. There is enough evidence to reject the claim that the proportions are equal.

23. H_0: $p_1 = p_2 = p_3 = p_4$ (claim). H_1: At least one proportion is different. C.V. = 7.815; d.f. = 3; χ^2 = 5.317; do not reject. There is not enough evidence to reject the claim that the proportions are equal.

25. H_0: $p_1 = p_2 = p_3 = p_4$ (claim). H_1: At least one of the proportions is different from the others. C.V. = 7.815; d.f. = 3; χ^2 = 1.447; do not reject. There is not enough evidence to reject the claim that the proportions are equal. Since the survey was done in Pennsylvania, it is doubtful that it can be generalized to the population of the United States.

27. H_0: $p_1 = p_2 = p_3 = p_4 = p_5$. H_1: At least one proportion is different. C.V. = 9.488; d.f. = 4; χ^2 = 12.028; reject. There is sufficient evidence to conclude that the proportions differ.

29. H_0: $p_1 = p_2 = p_3 = p_4$ (claim). H_1: At least one proportion is different. The d.f. = 3; χ^2 = 1.735; α = 0.05; P-value > 0.10; do not reject since P-value > 0.05. There is not enough evidence to reject the claim that the proportions are equal. (TI: P-value = 0.6291)

31. H_0: $p_1 = p_2 = p_3$ (claim). H_1: At least one proportion is different. C.V. = 4.605; d.f. = 2; χ^2 = 2.401; do not reject. There is not enough evidence to reject the claim that the proportions are equal.

33. χ^2 = 1.064

Review Exercises

1. H_0: The distribution of traffic fatalities was as follows: used seat belt, 31.58%; did not use seat belt, 59.83%; status unknown, 8.59%. H_1: The distribution is not as stated in the null hypothesis (claim). C.V. = 5.991; d.f. = 2; χ^2 = 1.819; do not reject. There is not enough evidence to support the claim that the distribution differs from the one stated in the null hypothesis.

3. H_0: The distribution of denials for gun permits is as follows: 75% for criminal history, 11% for domestic violence, and 14% for other reasons. H_1: The distribution is not the same as stated in the null hypothesis. C.V. = 4.605; d.f. = 2; χ^2 = 27.753; reject. There is

enough evidence to reject the claim that the distribution is as stated in the null hypothesis. Yes, the distribution may vary in different geographic locations.

5. H_0: The type of investment is independent of the age of the investor. H_1: The type of investment is dependent on the age of the investor (claim). C.V. = 9.488; d.f. = 4; χ^2 = 27.998; reject. There is enough evidence to support the claim that the type of investment is dependent on the age of the investor.

7. H_0: $p_1 = p_2 = p_3$ (claim). H_1: At least one proportion is different. χ^2 = 4.912; d.f. = 2; 0.05 < P-value < 0.10 (0.086); do not reject since P-value > 0.01. There is not enough evidence to reject the claim that the proportions are equal.

9. H_0: Health care coverage is independent of the state of residence of the individual. H_1: Health care coverage is related to the state of residence of the individual (claim). C.V. = 11.345; d.f. = 3; χ^2 = 18.993; reject. There is sufficient evidence to say that health care coverage is related to the state of residence of the individual.

Chapter Quiz

1. False
2. True
3. False
4. c
5. b
6. d
7. 6
8. Independent
9. Right
10. At least 5

11. H_0: The reasons why people lost their jobs are equally distributed (claim). H_1: The reasons why people lost their jobs are not equally distributed. C.V. = 5.991; d.f. = 2; χ^2 = 2.333; do not reject. There is not enough evidence to reject the claim that the reasons why people lost their jobs are equally distributed. The results could have been different 10 years ago since different factors of the economy existed then.

12. H_0: Takeout food is consumed according to the following distribution: 53% at home, 19% in the car, 14% at work, and 14% at other places (claim). H_1: The distribution is different from that stated in the null hypothesis. C.V. = 11.345; d.f. = 3; χ^2 = 5.271; do not reject. There is not enough evidence to reject the claim that the distribution is as stated. Fast-food restaurants may want to make their advertisements appeal to those who like to take their food home to eat.

13. H_0: College students show the same preference for shopping channels as those surveyed. H_1: College students show a different preference for shopping channels (claim). C.V. = 7.815; d.f. = 3; α = 0.05; χ^2 = 21.789; reject. There is enough evidence to support the claim that college students show a different preference for shopping channels.

14. H_0: The number of commuters is distributed as follows: 75.7%, alone; 12.2%, carpooling; 4.7%, public transportation; 2.9%, walking; 1.2%, other; and 3.3%, working at home. H_1: The proportion of workers using each type of transportation differs from the stated proportions. C.V. = 11.071; d.f. = 5; χ^2 = 68.988; reject. There is enough

evidence to support the claim that the distribution is different from the one stated in the null hypothesis.

15. H_0: Ice cream flavor is independent of the gender of the purchaser (claim). H_1: Ice cream flavor is dependent upon the gender of the purchaser. C.V. = 7.815; d.f. = 3; $\chi^2 = 7.198$; do not reject. There is not enough evidence to reject the claim that ice cream flavor is independent of the gender of the purchaser.

16. H_0: The type of pizza ordered is independent of the age of the individual who purchases it. H_1: The type of pizza ordered is dependent on the age of the individual who purchases it (claim). $\chi^2 = 107.3$; d.f. = 9; $\alpha = 0.10$; P-value < 0.005; reject since P-value < 0.10. There is enough evidence to support the claim that the pizza purchased is related to the age of the purchaser.

17. H_0: The color of the pennant purchased is independent of the gender of the purchaser (claim). H_1: The color of the pennant purchased is dependent on the gender of the purchaser. $\chi^2 = 5.632$; d.f. = 2; C.V. = 4.605; reject. There is enough evidence to reject the claim that the color of the pennant purchased is independent of the gender of the purchaser.

18. H_0: The opinion of the children on the use of the tax credit is independent of the gender of the children. H_1: The opinion of the children on the use of the tax credit is dependent upon the gender of the children (claim). C.V. = 4.605; d.f. = 2; $\chi^2 = 1.534$; do not reject. There is not enough evidence to support the claim that the opinion of the children on the use of the tax credit is dependent on their gender.

19. H_0: $p_1 = p_2 = p_3$ (claim). H_1: At least one proportion is different from the others. C.V. = 4.605; d.f. = 2; $\chi^2 = 6.711$; reject. There is enough evidence to reject the claim that the proportions are equal. It seems that more women are undecided about their jobs. Perhaps they want better income or greater chances of advancement.

Chapter 12
Exercises 12–1

1. The analysis of variance using the F test can be employed to compare three or more means.

3. The populations from which the samples were obtained must be normally distributed. The samples must be independent of one another. The variances of the populations must be equal, and the samples should be random.

5. H_0: $\mu_1 = \mu_2 = \cdots = \mu_k$. H_1: At least one mean is different from the others.

7. H_0: $\mu_1 = \mu_2 = \mu_3$. H_1: At least one mean is different from the others (claim). C.V. = 3.55; d.f.N. = 2; d.f.D. = 18; $F = 6.69$; reject. There is enough evidence to conclude that at least one mean is different from the others.

9. H_0: $\mu_1 = \mu_2 = \mu_3$. H_1: At least one of the means differs from the others. C.V. = 4.26; d.f.N. = 2; d.f.D. = 9; $F = 14.15$; reject. There is sufficient evidence to conclude at least one mean is different from the others.

11. H_0: $\mu_1 = \mu_2 = \mu_3$. H_1: At least one mean is different from the others (claim). C.V. = 3.74; d.f.N. = 2; d.f.D. = 14; $F = 2.91$; do not reject. There is not enough evidence to support the claim that at least one mean is different from the others.

13. H_0: $\mu_1 = \mu_2 = \mu_3$. H_1: At least one mean is different from the others (claim). C.V. = 3.68; d.f.N. = 2; d.f.D. = 15; $F = 8.14$; reject. There is enough evidence to support the claim that at least one mean is different from the others.

15. H_0: $\mu_1 = \mu_2 = \mu_3$. H_1: At least one mean is different from the others (claim). C.V. = 3.81; d.f.N. = 2; d.f.D. = 13; $F = 5.59$; reject. There is enough evidence to support the claim that at least one mean is different from the others.

17. H_0: $\mu_1 = \mu_2 = \mu_3$. H_1: At least one mean is different from the others (claim). $F = 10.12$; P-value = 0.00102; reject. There is enough evidence to conclude that at least one mean is different from the others.

19. H_0: $\mu_1 = \mu_2 = \mu_3$. H_1: At least one mean is different from the others (claim). C.V. = 3.01; d.f.N. = 2; d.f.D. = 9; $F = 3.62$; reject. There is enough evidence to support the claim that at least one mean is different from the others.

Exercises 12–2

1. The Scheffé and Tukey tests are used.

3. $F_{1\times2} = 2.10$; $F_{2\times3} = 17.64$; $F_{1\times3} = 27.923$. Scheffé test: C.V. = 8.52. There is sufficient evidence to conclude a difference in mean cost to drive 25 miles between hybrid cars and hybrid trucks and between hybrid SUVs and hybrid trucks.

5. Tukey test: C.V. = 3.67; $\overline{X}_1 = 7.0$; $\overline{X}_2 = 8.12$; $\overline{X}_3 = 5.23$; $\overline{X}_1$ versus $\overline{X}_2$, $q = -2.20$; $\overline{X}_1$ versus $\overline{X}_3$, $q = 3.47$; $\overline{X}_2$ versus $\overline{X}_3$, $q = 5.67$. There is a significant difference between $\overline{X}_1$ and $\overline{X}_3$ and between $\overline{X}_2$ and $\overline{X}_3$. One reason for the difference might be that the students are enrolled in cyber schools with different fees.

7. Scheffé test: C.V. = 8.20; $\overline{X}_1$ versus $\overline{X}_2$, $F_3 = 0.94$; $\overline{X}_1$ versus $\overline{X}_3$, $F = 15.56$; $\overline{X}_2$ versus $\overline{X}_3$, $F = 26.27$. There is a significant difference between $\overline{X}_1$ and $\overline{X}_3$ and between $\overline{X}_2$ and $\overline{X}_3$.

9. H_0: $\mu_1 = \mu_2 = \mu_3$. H_1: At least one mean is different from the others (claim). C.V. = 3.68; d.f.N. = 2; d.f.D. = 15; $F = 3.76$; Tukey test: C.V. = 3.67; $\overline{X}_1 = 32.33$; $\overline{X}_2 = 27.83$; $\overline{X}_3 = 22.5$; $\overline{X}_1$ versus $\overline{X}_2$, $q = 1.77$; $\overline{X}_2$ versus $\overline{X}_3$, $q = 2.10$; $\overline{X}_1$ versus $\overline{X}_3$, $q = 3.87$. There is a significant difference between $\overline{X}_1$ and $\overline{X}_3$.

11. H_0: $\mu_1 = \mu_2 = \mu_3$. H_1: At least one mean is different from the others (claim). C.V. = 3.47; $\alpha = 0.05$; d.f.N. = 2; d.f.D. = 21; $F = 1.99$; do not reject. There is not enough evidence to support the claim that at least one mean is different from the others.

13. H_0: $\mu_1 = \mu_2 = \mu_3$. H_1: At least one mean differs from the others (claim). C.V. = 3.68; d.f.N. = 2; d.f.D. = 15; $F = 17.17$; reject. There is enough evidence to support the claim that at least one mean differs from the others. Tukey test: C.V. = 3.67; $\overline{X}_1$ versus $\overline{X}_2$, $q = -8.17$; $\overline{X}_1$ versus $\overline{X}_3$, $q = -2.91$; $\overline{X}_2$ versus $\overline{X}_3$, $q = 5.27$. There is a significant difference between $\overline{X}_1$ and $\overline{X}_2$ and between $\overline{X}_2$ and $\overline{X}_3$.

Exercises 12–3

1. The two-way ANOVA allows the researcher to test the effects of two independent variables and a possible interaction effect. The one-way ANOVA can test the effects of only one independent variable.

3. The mean square values are computed by dividing the sum of squares by the corresponding degrees of freedom.

5. *a.* For factor A, $\text{d.f.}_A = 2$ *c.* $\text{d.f.}_{A \times B} = 2$
   b. For factor B, $\text{d.f.}_B = 1$ *d.* $\text{d.f.}_{\text{within}} = 24$

7. The two types of interactions that can occur are ordinal and disordinal.

9. *Interaction:* H_0: There is no interaction between the amount of glycerin additive and the soap concentration. H_1: There is an interaction between the amount of glycerin additives.
   Glycerin additives: H_0: There is no difference in the means of the glycerin additives. H_1: There is a difference in the means of the glycerin additives.
   Soap concentrations: H_0: There is no difference in the means of the soap concentrations. H_1: There is a difference in the means of the soap concentrations.

ANOVA Summary Table

Source of variation	SS	d.f.	MS	F
Soap additive	100.00	1	100.00	5.39
Glycerin concentration	182.25	1	182.25	9.83
Interaction	272.25	1	272.25	14.68
Within	222.5	12	18.54	
Total	777.0	15		

The critical value at $\alpha = 0.05$ with $\text{d.f.N.} = 1$ and $\text{d.f.D.} = 12$ is 4.75. There is a significant difference at $\alpha = 0.05$ for the interaction and a significant difference for the soap additive and the glycerin concentration.

11. *Interaction:* H_0: There is no interaction effect between the temperature and the level of humidity. H_1: There is an interactive effect between the temperature and the level of humidity. *Humidity:* H_0: There is no difference in mean length of effectiveness with respect to humidity. H_1: There is a difference in mean length of effectiveness with respect to humidity. *Temperature:* H_0: There is no difference in the mean length of effectiveness based on temperature. H_1: There is a difference in mean length of effectiveness based on temperature.

C.V. = 5.32; $\text{d.f.N.} = 1$; $\text{d.f.D.} = 8$; $F = 18.38$ for humidity. There is sufficient evidence to conclude a difference in mean length of effectiveness based on the humidity level. The temperature and interaction effects are not significant.

ANOVA Summary Table for Exercise 11

Source of variation	SS	d.f.	MS	F	P-value
Humidity	280.3333	1	280.3333	18.383	0.003
Temperature	3	1	3	0.197	0.669
Interaction	65.33333	1	65.33333	4.284	0.0722
Within	122	8	15.25		
Total	470.6667	11			

13. *Interaction:* H_0: There is no interaction effect on the durability rating between the dry additives and the solution-based additives. H_1: There is an interaction effect on the durability rating between the dry additives and the solution-based additives. *Solution-based additive:* H_0: There is no difference in the mean durability rating with respect to the solution-based additives. H_1: There is a difference in the mean durability rating with respect to the solution-based additives. *Dry additive:* H_0: There is no difference in the mean durability rating with respect to the dry additive. H_1: There is a difference in the mean durability rating with respect to the dry additive. C.V. = 4.75; $\text{d.f.N.} = 1$; $\text{d.f.D.} = 12$. There is not a significant interaction effect. Neither the solution additive nor the dry additive has a significant effect on mean durability.

ANOVA Summary Table for Exercise 13

Source	SS	d.f.	MS	F	P-value
Solution additive	1.563	1	1.563	0.50	0.494
Dry additive	0.063	1	0.063	0.020	0.890
Interaction	1.563	1	1.563	0.50	0.494
Within	37.750	12	3.146		
Total	40.939	15			

15. H_0: There is no interaction effect between the ages of the salespeople and the products they sell on the monthly sales. H_1: There is an interaction effect between the ages of the salespeople and the products they sell on the monthly sales.

H_0: There is no difference in the means of the monthly sales of the two age groups. H_1: There is a difference in the means of the monthly sales of the two age groups.

H_0: There is no difference among the means of the sales for the different products. H_1: There is a difference among the means of the sales for the different products.

ANOVA Summary Table

Source	SS	d.f.	MS	F
Age	168.033	1	168.033	1.57
Product	1,762.067	2	881.034	8.22
Interaction	7,955.267	2	3,977.634	37.09
Within	2,574.000	24	107.250	
Total	12,459.367	29		

At $\alpha = 0.05$, the critical values are as follows: for age, $\text{d.f.N.} = 1$, $\text{d.f.D.} = 24$, C.V. = 4.26; for product and interaction, $\text{d.f.N.} = 2$, $\text{d.f.D.} = 24$, C.V. = 3.40. There is a significant interaction between the age of the salesperson and the type of product sold, so no main effects should be interpreted without further study.

Age \ Product	Pools	Spas	Saunas
Over 30	38.8	28.6	55.4
30 and under	21.2	68.6	18.8

Since the lines cross, there is a disordinal interaction; hence, there is an interaction effect between the ages of salespeople and the type of products sold.

Review Exercises

1. $H_0: \mu_1 = \mu_2 = \mu_3$ (claim). H_1: At least one mean is different from the others. C.V. = 5.39; d.f.N. = 2; d.f.D. = 33; α = 0.01; F = 6.94; reject. Tukey test: C.V. = 4.45; $\overline{X}_1$ versus $\overline{X}_2$: q = 0.34; $\overline{X}_1$ versus $\overline{X}_3$: q = 4.72; $\overline{X}_2$ versus $\overline{X}_3$: q = 4.38. There is a significant difference between $\overline{X}_1$ and $\overline{X}_3$.

3. $H_0: \mu_1 = \mu_2 = \mu_3$. H_1: At least one mean is different from the others (claim). C.V. = 3.55; α = 0.05; d.f.N. = 2; d.f.D. = 18; F = 0.04; do not reject. There is not enough evidence to support the claim that at least one mean is different from the others.

5. $H_0: \mu_1 = \mu_2 = \mu_3$. H_1: At least one mean is different from the others (claim). C.V. = 2.61; α = 0.10; d.f.N. = 2; d.f.D. = 19; F = 0.49; do not reject. There is not enough evidence to support the claim that at least one mean is different from the others.

7. $H_0: \mu_1 = \mu_2 = \mu_3 = \mu_4$. H_1: At least one mean is different from the others (claim). C.V. = 3.59; α = 0.05; d.f.N. = 3; d.f.D. = 11; F = 0.18; do not reject. There is not enough evidence to support the claim that at least one mean is different from the others.

9. *Interaction:* H_0: There is no interaction effect between type of formula delivery system and review organization. H_1: There is an interaction effect between type of formula delivery system and review organization. *Review:* H_0: There is no difference in mean scores based on who leads the review. H_1: There is a difference in mean scores based on who leads the review. *Formulas:* H_0: There is no difference in mean scores based on who provides the formulas. H_1: There is a difference in mean scores based on who provides the formulas.

C.V. = 4.49; d.f.N. = 1; d.f.D. = 16; F = 5.244 for review organization. There is sufficient evidence to conclude a difference in mean scores based on who leads the review. The formula and interaction effects are not significant.

ANOVA Summary Table for Exercise 9

Source of variation	SS	d.f.	MS	F	P-value
Sample	288.8	1	288.8	5.24	0.036
Columns	51.2	1	51.2	0.93	0.349
Interaction	5	1	5	0.09	0.767
Within	881.2	16	55.075		
Total	1226.2	19			

Chapter Quiz

1. False
2. False
3. False
4. True
5. *d*
6. *a*
7. *a*
8. *c*
9. ANOVA
10. Tukey

11. $H_0: \mu_1 = \mu_2 = \mu_3$. H_1: At least one mean is different from the others (claim). C.V. = 8.02; d.f.N. = 2; d.f.D. = 9; F = 77.69; reject. There is enough evidence to support the claim that at least one mean is different from the others. Tukey test: C.V. = 5.43; $\overline{X}_1$ = 3.195; $\overline{X}_2$ = 3.633; $\overline{X}_3$ = 3.705; $\overline{X}_1$ versus $\overline{X}_2$, q = -13.99; $\overline{X}_1$ versus $\overline{X}_3$, q = -16.29; $\overline{X}_2$ versus $\overline{X}_3$, q = -2.30. There is a significant difference between $\overline{X}_1$ and $\overline{X}_2$ and between $\overline{X}_1$ and $\overline{X}_3$.

12. $H_0: \mu_1 = \mu_2 = \mu_3 = \mu_4$. H_1: At least one mean is different from the others (claim). C.V. = 3.49; α = 0.05; d.f.N. = 3; d.f.D. = 12; F = 3.23; do not reject. There is not enough evidence to support the claim that there is a difference in the means.

13. $H_0: \mu_1 = \mu_2 = \mu_3$. H_1: At least one mean is different from the others (claim). C.V. = 6.93; α = 0.01; d.f.N. = 2; d.f.D. = 12; F = 3.49; do not reject. There is not enough evidence to support the claim that at least one mean is different from the others. Writers would want to target their material to the age group of the viewers.

14. $H_0: \mu_1 = \mu_2 = \mu_3$. H_1: At least one mean differs from the others (claim). C.V. = 4.26; d.f.N. = 2; d.f.D. = 9; F = 10.03; reject. There is enough evidence to conclude that at least one mean differs from the others. Tukey test: C.V. = 3.95; $\overline{X}_1$ versus $\overline{X}_2$, q = -1.28; $\overline{X}_1$ versus $\overline{X}_3$, q = 4.74; $\overline{X}_2$ versus $\overline{X}_3$, q = 6.02. There is a significant difference between $\overline{X}_1$ and $\overline{X}_3$ and between $\overline{X}_2$ and $\overline{X}_3$.

15. $H_0: \mu_1 = \mu_2 = \mu_3$. H_1: At least one mean differs from the others (claim). C.V. = 4.46; d.f.N. = 2; d.f.D. = 8; F = 6.65; reject. Scheffé test: C.V. = 8.90; $\overline{X}_1$ versus $\overline{X}_2$, F_s = 9.32; $\overline{X}_1$ versus $\overline{X}_3$, F_s = 10.13; $\overline{X}_2$ versus $\overline{X}_3$, F_s = 0.13. There is a significant difference between $\overline{X}_1$ and $\overline{X}_2$ and between $\overline{X}_1$ and $\overline{X}_3$.

16. $H_0: \mu_1 = \mu_2 = \mu_3 = \mu_4$. H_1: At least one mean is different from the others (claim). C.V. = 3.07; α = 0.05; d.f.N. = 3; d.f.D. = 21; F = 0.46; do not reject. There is not enough evidence to support the claim that at least one mean is different from the others.

17. *a.* Two-way ANOVA

 b. Diet and exercise program

 c. 2

 d. H_0: There is no interaction effect between the type of exercise program and the type of diet on a person's weight loss. H_1: There is an interaction effect between the type of exercise program and the type of diet on a person's weight loss.

 H_0: There is no difference in the means of the weight losses of people in the exercise programs. H_1: There is a difference in the means of the weight losses of people in the exercise programs.

H_0: There is no difference in the means of the weight losses of people in the diet programs. H_1: There is a difference in the means of the weight losses of people in the diet programs.

e. Diet: $F = 21.0$, significant; exercise program: $F = 0.429$, not significant; interaction: $F = 0.429$, not significant.

f. Reject the null hypothesis for the diets.

Chapter 13
Exercises 13–1

1. *Nonparametric* means hypotheses other than those using population parameters can be tested; *distribution-free* means no assumptions about the population distributions have to be satisfied.

3. Nonparametric methods have the following advantages:
   a. They can be used to test population parameters when the variable is not normally distributed.
   b. They can be used when data are nominal or ordinal.
   c. They can be used to test hypotheses other than those involving population parameters.
   d. The computations are easier in some cases than the computations of the parametric counterparts.
   e. They are easier to understand.
   f. There are fewer assumptions that have to be met, and the assumptions are easier to verify.

5. Distribution-free means the samples can be selected from populations that are not normally distributed.

7.
Data	22	32	34	43	43	65	66	71
Rank	1	2	3	4.5	4.5	6	7	8

9.
Data	3.2	5.9	10.3	11.1	19.4	21.8	23.1
Rank	1	2	3	4	5	6	7

11.
Data	11	28	36	41	47	50	50	50	52	71	71	88
Rank	1	2	3	4	5	7	7	7	9	10.5	10.5	12

Exercises 13–2

1. The sign test uses only positive or negative signs.

3. The smaller number of positive or negative signs

5. H_0: median = 26.1 and H_1: median ≠ 26.1 (claim); test value = 4; C.V. = 3; do not reject. There is not enough evidence to support the claim that the median age is not 26.1 years.

7. H_0: median = $32,137 and H_1: median > $32,137 (claim); test value = 3; C.V. = 3; reject. There is enough evidence to support the claim that the median is greater than $32,137.

9. H_0: median = $10.86 (claim) and H_1: median ≠ $10.86; C.V. = ±1.96; $z = -0.77$; do not reject. There is not enough evidence to reject the claim that the median is $10.86. Home buyers could estimate the yearly cost of their gas bills.

11. H_0: median number of faculty = 150 (claim) and H_1: median ≠ 150; C.V. = ±1.96; $z = -2.70$; reject. There is sufficient evidence at the 0.05 level of significance to reject the claim that the median number of faculty is 150.

13. H_0: median = 49 (claim) and H_1: median ≠ 49; $z = -2.53$; P-value = 0.0114; reject. There is enough evidence to reject the claim that 50% of the students are against extending the school year.

15. H_0: The medication has no effect on weight loss and H_1: The medication affects weight loss (claim); C.V. = 0; test value = 1; do not reject. There is not enough evidence to support the claim that the medication affects weight loss.

17. H_0: There is no difference in the number of cookies that are made using two different methods of getting a teaspoonful of dough. H_1: There is a difference in the number of cookies baked using two different methods of getting a teaspoonful of dough (claim). Test value = 3; C.V. = 1; do not reject. There is not enough evidence that there is a difference in the number of cookies baked.

19. H_0: The number of viewers is the same as last year (claim) and H_1: The number of viewers is not the same as last year; C.V. = 0; test value = 2; do not reject. There is not enough evidence to reject the claim that the number of viewers is the same as last year.

21. $6 ≤$ median $≤ 22$

23. $4.7 ≤$ median $≤ 9.3$

25. $17 ≤$ median $≤ 33$

Exercises 13–3

1. n_1 and n_2 are each greater than or equal to 10.

3. H_0: There is no difference in the speed skating times of the students at the two universities (claim) and H_1: There is a difference in the speed skating times of the students at the two universities; C.V. = ±1.96; $z = -0.26$; do not reject. There is not enough evidence to reject the claim that there is no difference in the times.

5. H_0: There is no difference in the test scores and H_1: There is a difference in the test scores (claim); C.V. = ±1.96; $z = -1.22$; do not reject. There is not enough evidence to support the claim that there is a difference in the test scores.

7. H_0: There is no difference between the stopping distances of the two types of automobiles (claim) and H_1: There is a difference between the stopping distances of the two types of automobiles; C.V. = ±1.65; $z = -2.72$; reject. There is enough evidence to reject the claim that there is no difference in the stopping distances of the automobiles. In this case, midsize cars have a smaller stopping distance.

9. H_0: There is no difference in the number of hunting accidents in the two geographic areas and H_1: There is a difference in the number of hunting accidents (claim); C.V. = ±1.96; $z = -2.57$; reject. There is enough evidence to support the claim that there is a difference in the number of accidents in the two areas. The number of accidents may be related to the number of hunters in the areas.

11. H_0: There is no difference in the pain relief times of the drugs and H_1: There is a difference in the pain relief times of the drugs (claim); C.V. = ± 1.96; $z = 2.91$; reject. There is enough evidence to support the claim that there is a difference in the pain relief times of the drugs.

Exercises 13–4

1. The t test for dependent samples

3. Sum of minus ranks is -6; sum of plus ranks is $+15$. The test value is 6.

5. C.V. = 20; reject

7. C.V. = 102; reject

9. H_0: The human dose is equal to the animal dose and H_1: The human dose is more than the animal dose (claim); C.V. = 6; $w_s = 2$; reject. There is enough evidence to support the claim that the human dose costs more than the equivalent animal dose. One reason is that some people might not be inclined to pay a lot of money for their pets' medication.

11. H_0: There is no difference in the weights of the subjects and H_1: There is a difference in the weights of the subjects (claim); C.V. = 4; $w_s = 5$; do not reject. There is insufficient evidence to support the claim that the weights have changed.

13. H_0: The prices of prescription drugs in the United States are equal to the prices in Canada and H_1: The drugs sold in Canada are cheaper (claim); C.V. = 11; $w_s = 3$; reject. There is enough evidence to support the claim that the drugs are less expensive in Canada.

Exercises 13–5

1. H_0: There is no difference in the number of calories and H_1: There is a difference in the number of calories (claim); C.V. = 7.815; $H = 2.842$; do not reject. There is not enough evidence to support the claim that there is a difference in the number of calories.

3. H_0: There is no difference in the number of crimes committed in each of the towns and H_1: There is a difference in the number of crimes committed in each of the towns (claim); C.V. = 9.210; $H = 1.582$; do not reject. There is not enough evidence to support the claim that there is a difference in the number of crimes committed in each of the three towns.

5. H_0: There is no difference in the amounts of the benefits for the areas and H_1: There is a difference in the amount of the benefits for the areas (claim); C.V. = 5.991; $H = 12.430$; reject. There is significant evidence to support the claim that there is a difference in the amount of the benefits for the areas. The benefits are probably not normally distributed.

7. H_0: There is no difference in spending between regions and H_1: There is a difference in spending between regions (claim); $H = 0.740$; C.V. = 5.991; do not reject. There is insufficient evidence to conclude a difference in spending.

9. H_0: There is no difference in the number of crimes in the five precincts and H_1: There is a difference in the number of crimes in the five precincts (claim); C.V. = 13.277; $H = 20.753$; reject. There is enough evidence to support the claim that there is a difference in the number of crimes in the five precincts.

11. H_0: There is no difference in speeds and H_1: There is a difference in speeds (claim); $H = 3.815$; C.V. = 5.991; do not reject. There is insufficient evidence to conclude a difference in speeds.

Exercises 13–6

1. 0.716

3. 0.648

5. $r_s = 0.929$; H_0: $\rho = 0$ and H_1: $\rho \neq 0$; C.V. = ± 0.786; reject. There is enough evidence to say that there is a relationship between the grade 4 achievement tests and the grade 8 achievement tests.

7. $r_s = 0.817$; H_0: $\rho = 0$ and H_1: $\rho \neq 0$; C.V. = ± 0.700; reject. There is a significant relationship between the number of new releases and the gross receipts.

9. $r_s = 0.048$; H_0: $\rho = 0$ and H_1: $\rho \neq 0$; C.V. = ± 0.738; do not reject. There is not enough evidence to say that a significant correlation exists between calories and the cholesterol amounts in fast-food sandwiches.

11. $r_s = -0.657$; H_0: $\rho = 0$ and H_1: $\rho \neq 0$; C.V. = 0.886; do not reject. There is not enough evidence to say that there is a relationship between class size and grades.

13. $r_s = -0.100$; H_0: $\rho = 0$ and H_1: $\rho \neq 0$; C.V. = ± 0.900; do not reject. There is no significant relationship between the number of cyber school students and the cost per pupil. In this case, the cost per pupil is different in each district.

15. H_0: The number of cavities in a person occurs at random (claim) and H_1: The number of cavities in a person does not occur at random. There are 21 runs; the expected number of runs is between 10 and 22. Therefore, do not reject the null hypothesis; the number of cavities in a person occurs at random.

17. H_0: The types of admissions occur at random (claim) and H_1: The types of admissions do not occur at random. There are 23 runs. Do not reject the null hypothesis since the expected number of runs is between 13 and 27. The admissions occur at random.

19. H_0: The seating occurs at random (claim), and H_1: The seating does not occur at random. There are 14 runs. Since the expected number of runs is between 10 and 23, do not reject. The seating occurs at random.

21. H_0: The number of absences of employees occurs at random over a 30-day period (claim) and H_1: The number of absences of employees does not occur at random. There are only 6 runs, and this value does not fall within the 9-to-21 range. Hence, the null hypothesis is rejected; the absences do not occur at random.

23. H_0: The number of on-demand movie rentals occurs at random (claim) and H_1: The number of on-demand movie rentals does not occur at random. The number of runs is 10. Do not reject the null hypothesis since the number of runs is between 6 and 16. It can be concluded that the number of rentals occurs at random.

25. H_0: The gender of the patients at a medical center occurs at random (claim) and H_1: The gender of patients does not occur at random; C.V. $= \pm 1.96$; $z = -1.64$; do not reject. There is not enough evidence to reject the claim that the sequence is random.

27. H_0: The patients who were treated for an accident or illness occur at random (claim) and H_1: The patients who were treated for an accident or illness do not occur at random; C.V. $= \pm 1.96$; $z = 1.14$; do not reject. There is not enough evidence to reject the claim that the sequence occurs at random.

29. ± 0.28

31. ± 0.400

33. ± 0.413

Review Exercises

1. H_0: median $=$ \$9.00 (claim) and H_1: median $\neq$ \$9.00; $z = -2.01$; C.V. $= \pm 1.96$; reject. There is enough evidence to reject the claim that the median price is \$9.00.

3. H_0: There is no difference in prices and H_1: There is a difference in prices (claim); test value $= 1$; C.V. $= 0$; do not reject. There is insufficient evidence to conclude a difference in prices. Comments: Examine what affects the result of this test.

5. H_0: There is no difference in the hours worked and H_1: There is a difference in the hours worked (claim); $z = -1.76$; C.V. $= \pm 1.645$; reject. There is sufficient evidence to conclude a difference in the hours worked. C.V. $= \pm 1.96$; do not reject.

7. H_0: There is no difference in the amount spent and H_1: There is a difference in the amount spent (claim); $w_s = 1$; C.V. $= 2$; reject. There is sufficient evidence of a difference in amount spent at the 0.05 level of significance.

9. H_0: There is no difference in beach temperatures and H_1: There is a difference in temperatures (claim); $H = 15.524$; C.V. $= 7.815$; reject. There is sufficient evidence to conclude a difference in beach temperatures. (Without the Southern Pacific: $H = 3.661$; C.V. $= 5.991$; do not reject.)

11. $r_s = 0.7054$; H_0: $\rho = 0$ and H_1: $\rho \neq 0$; C.V. $= \pm 0.786$; do not reject. There is not a significant relationship between the number of pages and the number of references.

13. H_0: The grades of students who finish the exam occur at random (claim) and H_1: The grades do not occur at random. Since there are 8 runs and this value does not fall in the 9-to-21 interval, the null hypothesis is rejected. The grades do not occur at random.

Chapter Quiz

1. False   **2.** False

3. True   **4.** True

5. a **6.** c

7. d **8.** b

9. Nonparametric   **10.** Nominal, ordinal

11. Sign   **12.** Sensitive

13. H_0: median $=$ \$177,500; H_1: median $\neq$ \$177,500 (claim); C.V. $= 2$; test value $= 3$; do not reject. There is not enough evidence to say that the median is not \$177,500.

14. H_0: median $= 1200$ (claim) and H_1: median $\neq 1200$. There are 10 minus signs. Do not reject since 10 is greater than the critical value 6. There is not enough evidence to reject the claim that the median is 1200.

15. H_0: There will be no change in the weight of the turkeys after the special diet and H_1: The turkeys will weigh more after the special diet (claim). There is 1 plus sign; hence, the null hypothesis is rejected, since the critical value is zero. There is enough evidence to support the claim that the turkeys gained weight on the special diet.

16. H_0: There is no difference in the amounts of money received by the teams and H_1: There is a difference in the amounts of money each team received (claim); C.V. $= \pm 1.96$; $z = -0.79$; do not reject. There is not enough evidence to say that the amounts differ.

17. H_0: The distributions are the same and H_1: The distributions are different (claim); $z = -0.14$; C.V. $= \pm 1.65$; do not reject the null hypothesis. There is not enough evidence to support the claim that the distributions are different.

18. H_0: There is no difference in the GPA of the students before and after the workshop and H_1: There is a difference in the GPA of the students before and after the workshop (claim); test statistic $= 0$; C.V. $= 2$; reject the null hypothesis. There is enough evidence to support the claim that there is a difference in the GPAs of the students.

19. H_0: There is no difference in the amounts of sodium in the three sandwiches and H_1: There is a difference in the amounts of sodium in the sandwiches (claim); C.V. $= 5.991$; $H = 11.795$; reject. There is enough evidence to conclude that there is a difference in the amounts of sodium in the sandwiches.

20. H_0: There is no difference in the reaction times of the monkeys and H_1: There is a difference in the reaction times of the monkeys (claim); $H = 6.91$; $0.025 < P$-value < 0.05 (0.032); reject the null hypothesis. There is enough evidence to support the claim that there is a difference in the reaction times of the monkeys.

21. $r_s = 0.683$; H_0: $\rho = 0$ and H_1: $\rho \neq 0$; C.V. $= \pm 0.600$; reject. There is enough evidence to say that there is a significant relationship between the drug prices.

22. $r_s = 0.943$; H_0: $\rho = 0$ and H_1: $\rho \neq 0$; C.V. $= \pm 0.829$; reject. There is a significant relationship between the amount of money spent on Head Start and the number of students enrolled in the program.

23. H_0: The births of babies occur at random according to gender (claim) and H_1: The births according to gender do not occur at random. There are 10 runs, and since this is between 8 and 19, the null hypothesis is not rejected. There is not enough evidence to reject the null hypothesis that gender occurs at random.

24. H_0: There is no difference in the rpm of the motors before and after the reconditioning and H_1: There is a difference in the rpm of the motors before and after the reconditioning (claim); test statistic = 0; C.V. = 6; do not reject the null hypothesis. There is not enough evidence to support the claim that there is a difference in the rpm of the motors before and after reconditioning.

25. H_0: The numbers occur at random (claim) and H_1: The numbers do not occur at random. There are 20 runs, and since this is between 9 and 21, the null hypothesis is not rejected. There is not enough evidence to reject the null hypothesis that the numbers occur at random.

26. H_0: The showing of the type of movie (black and white or color) occurs at random (claim). H_1: The showing of the type of movie does not occur at random. C.V. = ± 1.96; $z = -5.54$; reject. There is enough evidence to reject the claim that the showing of the type of movie occurs at random.

Chapter 14
Exercises 14–1

1. Random, systematic, stratified, cluster

3. A sample must be randomly selected.

5. Talking to people on the street, calling people on the phone, and asking your friends are three incorrect ways of obtaining a sample.

7. Random sampling has the advantage that each unit of the population has an equal chance of being selected. One disadvantage is that the units of the population must be numbered; if the population is large, this could be somewhat time-consuming.

9. An advantage of stratified sampling is that it ensures representation for the groups used in stratification; however, it is virtually impossible to stratify the population so that all groups are represented.

11, 13, 15, 17, and 19. Answers will vary.

Exercises 14–2

1. Flaw—biased; it's confusing.

3. Flaw—the question is too broad.

5. Flaw—confusing words. How many hours did you study for this exam?

7. Flaw—confusing words. If a plane were to crash on the border of New York and New Jersey, where should the victims be buried?

9. Flaw—The word *vaguely* is too general.

11. Answers will vary.

Exercises 14–3

1. Simulation involves setting up probability experiments that mimic the behavior of real-life events.

3. John Von Neumann and Stanislaw Ulam

5. The steps are as follows:
   a. List all possible outcomes.
   b. Determine the probability of each outcome.
   c. Set up a correspondence between the outcomes and the random numbers.
   d. Conduct the experiment by using random numbers.
   e. Repeat the experiment and tally the outcomes.
   f. Compute any statistics and state the conclusions.

7. When the repetitions increase, there is a higher probability that the simulation will yield more precise answers.

9. Use three-digit random numbers; numbers 001 through 681 mean that the mother is in the labor force.

11. Select 100 two-digit random numbers. Numbers 00 to 34 mean the household has at least one set with premium cable service. Numbers 35 to 99 mean the household does not have the service.

13. Let an odd number represent heads and an even number represent tails. Then each person selects a digit at random.

15, 17, 19, 21, 23, and 25. Answers will vary.

Review Exercises

1, 3, 5, and 7. Answers will vary.

9. Flaw—asking a biased question. Have you ever driven through a red light?

11. Flaw—asking a double-barreled question. Do you think all automobiles should have heavy-duty bumpers?

13. Use one-digit random numbers 1 through 4 for a strikeout, and 5 through 9 and 0 represent anything other than a strikeout.

15. The first person selects a two-digit random number. Any two-digit random number that has a 7, 8, 9, or 0 is ignored, and another random number is selected. Player 1 selects a one-digit random number; any random number that is not 1 through 6 is ignored, and another one is selected.

17, 19, and 21. Answers will vary.

Chapter Quiz

1. True	2. True
3. False	4. True
5. *a*	6. *c*
7. *c*	8. Larger
9. Biased	10. Cluster

11–14. Answers will vary.

15. Use two-digit random numbers: 01 through 45 means the player wins. Any other two-digit random number means the player loses.

16. Use two-digit random numbers: 01 through 05 means a cancellation. Any other two-digit random number means the person shows up.

17. The random numbers 01 through 10 represent the 10 cards in hearts. The random numbers 11 through 20 represent the 10 cards in diamonds. The random numbers 21 through 30 represent the 10 spades, and 31 through 40 represent the 10 clubs. Any number over 40 is ignored.

18. Use two-digit random numbers to represent the spots on the face of the dice. Ignore any two-digit random numbers with 7, 8, 9, or 0. For cards, use two-digit random numbers between 01 and 13.

19. Use two-digit random numbers. The first digit represents the first player, and the second digit represents the second player. If both numbers are odd or even, player 1 wins. If a digit is odd and the other digit is even, player 2 wins.

20–24. Answers will vary.

INDEX

A

Addition rules, 201–206
Adjusted R^2, 597
Alpha, 419
Alternative hypotheses, 414
Analysis of variance (ANOVA), 648–655
    assumptions, 651
    between-group variance, 649
    degrees of freedom, 650, 688
    F-test, 650
    hypotheses, 648, 667
    one-way, 648
    summary table, 650
    two-way, 665–673
    within-group variance, 649
Assumption for the use of the chi-square test, 464, 611
Assumptions, 370
Assumptions for valid predictions in regression, 570
Averages, 111–121
    properties and uses, 120–121

B

Bar graph, 75–76
Bell curve, 312
Beta, 419
Between-group variance, 649
Biased sample, 3, 742
Bimodal, 64, 116
Binomial distribution, 276–282
    characteristics, 276
    mean for, 281–282
    normal approximation, 354–359
    notation, 277
    standard deviation, 281–282
    variance, 281–282
Binomial experiment, 276
Binomial probability formula, 277
Blinding, 20
Blocks, 20
Boundaries, 7
Boundary, 7
Boundaries, class, 45
Boxplot, 168–171

C

Categorical frequency distribution, 43–44
Census, 3

Central limit theorem, 344–357
Chebyshev's theorem, 139–141
Chi-square
    assumptions, 464, 611
    contingency table, 624
    degrees of freedom, 400
    distribution, 399–401, 610
    goodness-of-fit test, 610–616
    independence test, 624–630
    use in H-test, 713
    variance test, 461–468
    Yates correction for, 632
Class, 42
    boundaries, 7, 45
    limits, 45
    midpoint, 45
    width, 45
Classical probability, 189–193
Cluster sample, 14, 749–750
Coefficient of determination, 585–586
Coefficient of nondetermination, 586
Coefficient of variation, 138–139
Combination, 232–234
Combination rule, 233
Complementary events, 192–193
Complement of an event, 192
Compound bar graph, 76–77
Completely randomized designs, 20
Compound event, 189
Conditional probability, 215, 217–220
Confidence interval, 371
    hypothesis testing, 474–476
    mean, 372–377, 383–386
    means, differences of, 493, 501, 514
    median, 700
    proportion, 391–393
    proportions, differences, 523–524
    variances and standard deviations, 399–403
Confidence level, 371
Confounding variable, 19
Consistent estimator, 371
Contingency coefficient, 637
Contingency table, 624
Continuous variable, 6, 212, 258, 312
Control group, 19
Convenience sample, 14, 751
Correction for continuity, 354
Correlation, 554–562

Correlation coefficient, 554
   multiple, 595–596
    Pearson's product moment, 554
    population, 554
    Spearman's rank, 719–722
Critical region, 420
Critical value, 420, 422–424
Cross-sectional study, 18
Cumulative frequency, 59
Cumulative frequency distribution,
    48–49
Cumulative frequency graph, 59
Cumulative relative frequency, 62

D

Data, 3
Data array, 115
Data set, 3
Data value (datum), 3
Deciles, 157
Degrees of freedom, 383, 442
Dependent events, 215
Dependent samples, 488, 507
Dependent variable, 19, 488, 507, 508,
    550, 665
Descriptive statistics, 3
Difference between two means, 488–493,
    499–502, 507–513
   assumptions for the test to determine,
    489, 500, 509
   proportions, 519–523
Discrete probability distributions, 259
Discrete variable, 6, 258
Disjoint events, 202
Disordinal interaction, 671
Distribution-free statistics
    (nonparametric), 690
Distributions
   bell-shaped, 63, 312
   bimodal, 64, 116
   binomial, 276–282
   chi-square, 399–401
   F, 529
   frequency, 42
   geometric, 295–297
   hypergeometric, 293–295
   multinomial, 290–291
   negatively skewed, 64, 122
   normal, 312–321
   Poisson, 291–293
   positively skewed, 63–64, 121, 315
   probability, 258, 263
   sampling, 344
   standard normal, 315–318
   symmetrical, 63, 122, 314
Dot plot, 83

Double blinding, 20
Double sampling, 750

E

Empirical probability, 194–196
Empirical rule, 142, 314
Equally likely events, 189
Estimation, 370
Estimator, properties of a good, 371
Event, 188
Event, simple, 189
Events
   complementary, 192–193
   compound, 189
   dependent, 215
   disjoint, 202
   equally likely, 189
   independent, 213
   mutually exclusive, 202
Expectation, 269–272
Expected frequency, 610
Expected value, 269
Experimental study, 18
Explained variation, 19, 582
Explanatory variable, 19, 550
Exploratory data analysis (EDA), 168–171
Extrapolation, 571

F

Factorial notation, 229
Factors, 665
F-distribution, characteristics of, 529,
    648–649
Finite population correction factor,
    350–351
Five-number summary, 168
Frequency, 42
Frequency distribution, 42
   categorical, 43–44
   grouped, 44–48
   reasons for, 50–51
   rules for constructing, 45–46
   ungrouped, 49–50
Frequency polygon, 58–59
F-test, 528–531, 650
   comparing three or four means, 648
   comparing two variances, 531–534
   notes for the use of, 531
Fundamental counting rule, 226–229

G

Gallup poll, 742
Gaussian distribution, 312
Geometric distribution, 295–297

Geometric experiment, 295
Geometric mean, 126
Goodness-of-fit test, 610–616
Grand mean, 649
Grouped frequency distribution, 44–48

H

Harmonic mean, 126
Hawthorne effect, 19
Hinges, 171
Histogram, 57–58
Homogeneity or proportions, 630–632
Homoscedasticity assumption, 585
Hypergeometric distribution, 293–295
Hyperexperiment, 294
Hypothesis, 4, 414
Hypothesis testing, 4, 414–425
    alternative, 414
    common phrases, 416
    critical region, 420
    critical value, 420
    definitions, 414
    level of significance, 419
    noncritical region, 420
    null, 414
    one-tailed test, 420
    P-value method, 430–434
    research, 415
    statistical, 414
    statistical test, 417
    test value 417, 426
    traditional method, steps in, 424
    two-tailed test, 421, 422
    types of errors, 418–419

I

Independence test (chi-square), 624–630
Independent events, 213
Independent samples, 4, 488, 499
Independent variables, 19, 550, 665
Inferential statistics, 4
Influential observation or point, 571
Interaction effect, 666
Intercept (y), 567–570
Interquartile range (IQR), 156
Interval estimate, 371
Interval level of measurement, 8

K

Kruskal-Wallis test, 712–715

L

Law of large numbers, 196
Left-tailed test, 420–422

Level of significance. 419
Levels of measurement, 8
    interval, 8
    nominal, 8
    ordinal, 8
    ration, 8
Limits, class, 45
Line of best fit, 566
Longitudinal study, 18
Lower class boundary, 45
Lower class limit, 44
Lurking variable, 19, 562

M

Main effects, 666
Marginal change, 571
Margin of error, 372
Matched pair design, 20
Mean, 111–114
    binomial variable, 281–282
    definition, 112
    population, 112
    probability distribution, 265–267
    sample, 112
Mean deviation, 146–147
Mean square, 650
Measurement, levels of, 8
Measurement scales, 8
Measures of average, uses of,
        120–121
Measures of dispersion, 128–138
Measures of position, 148–157
Measures of variation, 130–138
Measures of variation and standard
        deviation, uses of, 138
Median, 115–116
    confidence interval for, 700
    defined, 115
    for grouped data, 127
Midquartile, 161
Midrange, 118–119
Misleading graphs, 23, 86–89
Modal class, 117
Mode, 116–118
Modified box plot, 171, 173
Monte Carlo method, 760–764
Multimodal, 116
Multinomial distribution, 290–291
Multinomial experiment, 290
Multiple correlation coefficient,
        595–596
Multiple regression, 592–598
Multiplication rules probability,
        213–217
Multistage sampling, 751
Mutually exclusive events, 202

N

Negatively skewed distribution, 122, 315
Negative linear relationship, 551, 554
Nielson television ratings, 742
Nominal level of measurement, 8
Noncritical region, 420
Nonparametric statistics, 690–733
    advantages, 690–691
    disadvantages, 690–691
Nonrejection region, 420
Nonresistant statistic, 157
Nonsampling error, 16
Normal approximation to binomial
        distribution, 354–359
Normal distribution, 312–321
    applications of, 328–334
    approximation to the binomial
        distribution, 354–359
    areas under, 314–315
    formula for, 313
    probability distribution as a, 318–320
    properties of, 314
    standard, 315–318
Normal quantile plot, 337, 342, 343
Normally distributed variables, 312–315
Notation for the binomial
        distribution, 277
Null hypothesis, 414

O

Observational study, 18
Observed frequency, 610
Odds, 201
Ogive, 59–61
One-tailed test, 420
    left, 420
    right, 420
One-way analysis of variance, 648
Open-ended distribution, 46
Ordinal interaction, 671
Ordinal level of measurement, 8
Outcome, 186
Outcome variable, 19
Outliers, 64, 118, 157–158, 335

P

Paired-sample sign test, 695–697
Parameter, 111
Parametric tests, 690
Pareto chart, 77–78
Pearson coefficient of skewness, 147,
    334–335
Pearson product moment correlation
    coefficient, 554

Percentiles, 149–155
Permutation, 229–231
Permutation rule 1, 230
Permutation rule 2, 231
Pie graph, 80–83
Placebo effect, 20
Point estimate, 370
Poisson distribution, 291–293
Poisson experiment, 291
Pooled estimate of variance, 502
Population, 3, 742
Population correlation coefficient, 554
Positively skewed distribution, 121, 315
Positive linear relationship, 551, 554
Power of a test, 476
Practical significance, 434
Prediction interval, 586, 589–591
Probability, 4, 186
    addition rules, 201–206
    at least, 220–221
    binomial, 276–281
    classical, 189–193
    complimentary rules, 193
    conditional, 215, 217–220
    counting rules, 242–243
    distribution, 258–263
    empirical, 194–196
    experiment, 186
    multiplication rules, 213–217
    subjective, 196
Properties of the distribution of sample
        means, 344
Proportion, 61, 390–394
P-value, 431
    for F test, 533
    method for hypothesis testing,
        452–456
    for t test, 445–447
    for X^2 test, 466–468

Q

Quadratic mean, 127
Qualitative variables, 6
Quantitative variables, 6
Quantile plot, 337, 342–343
Quartiles, 155–157
Quasi-experimental study, 19
Questionnaire design, 757–758

R

Random numbers, 12
Random samples, 12, 742
Random sampling, 12, 743–746
Random variable, 3, 258
Range, 47, 129

Range rule of thumb, 139
Rank correlation, Spearman's, 719–722
Ranking, 691–692
Ratio level of measurement, 8
Raw data, 42
Regression, 566–572
    assumptions for valid prediction, 570
    multiple, 592–598
Regression line, 566
    equation, 567
    intercept, 567
    line of best fit, 566
    prediction, 571
    slope, 567
Rejection region, 420
Relationships, 4, 550
Relative frequency graphs, 61–63
Relatively efficient estimator, 371
Replication, 20
Requirements for a probability
    distribution, 261
Research hypothesis, 415
Residual, 567
Residual plot, 584–585
Resistant statistic, 157
Retrospective study, 18
Response variable, 550
Right-tailed test, 420, 422
Robust statistical technique, 373
Run, 722
Runs test, 722–727

S

Sample, 3, 742
    biased, 742
    cluster, 14, 749–750
    convenience, 14
    random, 12, 742
    size for estimating means, 377–378
    size for estimating proportions,
        393–395
    stratified, 14, 748–749
    systematic, 3
    unbiased, 742
    volunteer, 14
Sample space, 186–187
Sampling, 3, 12–14, 742–751
    distribution of sample means, 344
    double, 750
    error, 14, 16, 344
    multistage, 751
    random, 12, 742
    sequence, 750
Scatter plot, 551–554
Scheffe' test, 660–662
Sequence sampling, 750

Short-cut formula for variance and
    standard deviation, 134–135
Significance, level of, 419
Sign test, 693
    test value, 693–695
Simple event, 189
Simulation technique, 739, 759–764
Single sample sign test, 693–695
Skewness, 63–64
Slope, 567
Spearman rank correlation coefficient,
    719–722
Standard deviation, 130–138
    binomial distribution, 281–282
    definition, 130, 133
    formula, 130, 133
    population, 130
    probability distribution, 267–269
    sample, 133
    uses of, 138
Standard error of difference between
    means, 490
Standard error of difference between
    proportions, 520
Standard error of the estimate, 586–589
Standard error of the mean, 346
Standard normal distribution, 315–318
Standard score, 148–149
Statistic, 111
Statistical hypothesis, 414
Statistical test, 417
Statistics, 2
    descriptive, 3
    inferential, 4
    misuses of, 21–23
Stem and leaf plot, 83–86
Stratified sample, 13, 748–749
Student's t distribution, 383
Subjective probability, 196
Sum of squares, 650
Surveys, 11, 757–758
    mail, 11
    personal interviews, 11
    telephone, 11
Symmetric distribution, 63, 122, 314
Systematic sampling, 12, 746–748

T

t-distribution, characteristics of, 383, 442
Test of normality, 334–337, 342, 343,
    616–618
Test value, 417, 426
Time series graph, 78–79
Total variation, 582
Treatment groups, 19, 666
Tree diagram, 188, 217, 227, 228

t-test, 442
   coefficient for correlation, 554
   for difference of means, 499–502,
      507–513
   for mean, 442–448
Tukey test, 662, 663
Two-tailed test, 421, 422
Two-way analysis of variance, 665–673
Type I error, 418, 476–478
Type II error, 418, 476–478

U

Unbiased estimate of population
      variance, 133
Unbiased estimator, 371
Unbiased sample, 742
Unexplained variation, 582
Ungrouped frequency distribution, 49–50
Uniform distribution, 63, 321
Unimodal, 64, 116
Upper class boundary, 45
Upper class limit, 44–45

V

Variable, 3, 258, 550
   confounding, 19
   continuous, 6, 212, 258, 312
   dependent, 19, 488, 507, 508, 550
   discrete, 6, 258
   explanatory, 19, 550
   independent, 19, 550
   qualitative, 6
   quantitative, 6
   outcome, 19
   random, 3, 258
   response, 550

Variance, 130–138
   binomial distribution, 281–282
   definition of, 130, 133
   formula, 130, 133
population, 130
   probability distribution, 267–269
   sample, 133
   short-cut formula, 134
   unbiased estimate, 133
   uses of, 138
Variances
   equal, 528–529
   unequal, 528–529
Venn diagram, 193, 203, 204, 218
Volunteer sample, 14

W

Weighted estimate of p, 520
Weighted mean, 119–120
Wilcoxon rank sum test, 702–704
Wilcoxon signed-rank test, 707–710
Within-group variance, 649

Y

Yates correction for continuity, 632
y-intercept, 567–570

Z

z-score, 148–149, 316
z-test, 427
z-test for means, 427–430, 488–493
z-test for proportions, 452–456,
      519–523
z-values (scores) 316

Glossary of Symbols

a	y intercept of a line		MR	Midrange
α	Probability of a type I error		MS_B	Mean square between groups
b	Slope of a line		MS_W	Mean square within groups (error)
β	Probability of a type II error		n	Sample size
C	Column frequency		N	Population size
cf	Cumulative frequency		$n(E)$	Number of ways E can occur
$_nC_r$	Number of combinations of n objects taking r objects at a time		$n(S)$	Number of outcomes in the sample space
C.V.	Critical value		O	Observed frequency
CVar	Coefficient of variation		P	Percentile; probability
D	Difference; decile		p	Probability; population proportion
$\overline{D}$	Mean of the differences		$\hat{p}$	Sample proportion
d.f.	Degrees of freedom		$\overline{p}$	Weighted estimate of p
d.f.N.	Degrees of freedom, numerator		$P(B|A)$	Conditional probability
d.f.D.	Degrees of freedom, denominator		$P(E)$	Probability of an event E
E	Event; expected frequency; maximum error of estimate		$P(\overline{E})$	Probability of the complement of E
$\overline{E}$	Complement of an event		$_nP_r$	Number of permutations of n objects taking r objects at a time
e	Euler's constant ≈ 2.7183		π	Pi ≈ 3.14
$E(X)$	Expected value		Q	Quartile
f	Frequency		q	$1 - p$; test value for Tukey test
F	F test value; failure		$\hat{q}$	$1 - \hat{p}$
F'	Critical value for the Scheffé test		$\overline{q}$	$1 - \overline{p}$
MD	Median		R	Range; rank sum
			F_S	Scheffé test value
			GM	Geometric mean

H	Kruskal-Wallis test value
H_0	Null hypothesis
H_1	Alternative hypothesis
HM	Harmonic mean
k	Number of samples
λ	Number of occurrences for the Poisson distribution
s_D	Standard deviation of the differences
s_{est}	Standard error of estimate
SS_B	Sum of squares between groups
SS_W	Sum of squares within groups
s_B^2	Between-group variance
s_W^2	Within-group variance
t	t test value
$t_{\alpha/2}$	Two-tailed t critical value
μ	Population mean
μ_D	Mean of the population differences
$\mu_{\bar{X}}$	Mean of the sample means
w	Class width; weight
r	Sample correlation coefficient
R	Multiple correlation coefficient
r^2	Coefficient of determination
ρ	Population correlation coefficient

r_S	Spearman rank correlation coefficient
S	Sample space; success
s	Sample standard deviation
s^2	Sample variance
σ	Population standard deviation
σ^2	Population variance
$\sigma_{\bar{X}}$	Standard error of the mean
Σ	Summation notation
w_s	Smaller sum of signed ranks, Wilcoxon signed-rank test
X	Data value; number of successes for a binomial distribution
$\bar{X}$	Sample mean
x	Independent variable in regression
$\bar{X}_{\text{GM}}$	Grand mean
X_m	Midpoint of a class
χ^2	Chi-square
y	Dependent variable in regression
y'	Predicted y value
z	z test value or z score
$z_{\alpha/2}$	Two-tailed critical z value
$!$	Factorial

McGraw Hill Education

SPICELAND • SEPE • NELSON • THOMAS

McGraw Hill Education

INTERMEDIATE ACCOUNTING

Eighth Edition

Special Binder-Ready Version

- This loose-leaf alternative will save you money

- Offers a flexible format

- Nonrefundable if shrink-wrap is removed